MODERN POWER ELECTRONICS

IEEE PRESS
445 Hoes Lane, PO Box 1331
Piscataway, NJ 08855-1331

IEEE Industrial Electronics Society, *Sponsor*

IE-S Liaison for the IEEE PRESS
Richard C. Born
Milwaukee School of Engineering

Technical Reviewer for the IE-S
Fred A. Stich
Director, Research and Development
Best Power Technology, Inc., Necedah, WI

MODERN POWER ELECTRONICS

Evolution, Technology, and Applications

Edited by

B. K. Bose

Condra Chair of Excellence in Power Electronics

University of Tennessee, Knoxville

A Selected Reprint Volume

IEEE Industrial Electronics Society, *Sponsor*

The Institute of Electrical and Electronics Engineers, Inc., New York

Printed in the United States of America

10 9 8 7 6 5 4 3 2

ISBN 0-87942-282-3

IEEE Order Number: PC0276-6

Library of Congress Cataloging-in-Publication Data

Modern power electronics : evolution, technology, and applications / edited by B. K. Bose.
p. cm.
"A Selected reprint volume."
Includes bibliographical references and index.
ISBN 0-87942-282-3
1. Power electronics. I. Bose, Bimal K.
TK7881.15.M63 1992
621.31'7—dc20 91-39029

Contents

Preface

POWER electronics has gone through intense technological evolution during the last three decades. Recently, it has been finding wide application in industrial, commercial, residential, and aerospace environments. At present, power electronics seems to have been polarized in two directions: low-power high-frequency electronics, which essentially caters to the need of switching-mode power supplies, and moderate-to-high power electronics, which essentially covers motor drives, uninterruptible power supplies, lighting and heating control, etc. Circuit miniaturization seems to be the principal focus in the former category, whereas cost, efficiency, size, and other performance improvements are the main criteria in the latter category.

It is important to note that saving energy is an important aspect of power electronics applications. For example, it is estimated that in this country roughly 60 percent of generated electrical energy is consumed in electrical machine drives and 20 percent is consumed in lighting. Adjustable speed drives and high-frequency fluorescent lighting can significantly contribute to energy saving in these areas.

Other aspects of power electronics applications are productivity and product quality improvements in process control industries, and reduction of urban pollution and the earth's "greenhouse" effect. Power electronics is a complex subject and, in general, a modern power electronics engineer should have good knowledge of power semiconductor devices, converter circuits, electrical machines, power systems, control electronics, control theory, microprocessors, CAD techniques, and VLSI circuits. The subject is becoming very challenging because of evolution in each of the component disciplines.

The power semiconductor device is the most important component in a power electronic system. In fact, the evolution of power electronics has followed the evolution of devices. Starting with the conventional thyristor-type devices in the early days, the recent availability of high-frequency, high-power, MOS-gated self-controlled devices is opening new frontiers in power electronics. It is interesting to note that both power semiconductor devices and modern microchips operate in the switching mode. The integration of these end-of-the-spectrum solid-state elements is providing tremendous capability in size and cost reduction, as well as performance improvement in modern power electronics equipment.

The aim of this book is to integrate both low-power and high-power electronics so that members of each community find the opportunity to expand their horizons. The book starts with "Introduction to Power Electronics," an original contribution by the editor. The section is written in a very comprehensive manner as a state-of-the-art tutorial review of power semiconductor devices, converter topologies, PWM techniques, and power electronics applications. A special feature of this section is a summary comparison of power semiconductor devices and converters, with particular emphasis on ac-drive applications. Although discussion of modern power electronics is the principal aim of this book, the conventional phase-controlled converters have been included in this part for completeness. By far, the majority of power electronics applications still use phase-controlled converters.

The main body of the book consists of 49 carefully selected papers from the ocean of published literature. The selection process has been extremely difficult because of so many excellent publications in this area. I have taken a novel approach. I have taken into consideration the input from a number of top specialists in the power electronics area who were requested to make their recommendations. In a book like this, papers that have considerable tutorial value and are well written, with a wide breadth of contents and lucidity of expression, found high preference. Often, quality papers with narrow and deep technical content have been intentionally avoided. Each section ends with a selected bibliography. A list of key reference books has also been included. Part 2 provides a general review of power electronics that includes its historical aspect, general technology trends, and applications. This part demonstrates the truly interdisciplinary nature of power electronics. Part 3 describes power semiconductor devices, with emphasis on power MOSFETs, GTOs, IGBTs, and MCTs. Note that our interests are device applications, not their design aspects. A very comprehensive paper on power integrated circuits is included at the end of this part. Part 4 describes the modern ac–dc and ac–ac converters where the conventional phase-controlled converters and cycloconverters have been excluded. The tutorial discussion in Part 1 should be used to supplement this section. Part 5 deals with dc–dc converters that include PWM converters and resonant/quasiresonant link converters. The publications in this area are so vast that selection of only nine papers represents a reluctant injustice. Part 6 deals with dc–ac converters that include essentially current-fed and resonant-link inverters. The conventional hard-switched voltage-fed inverters that are so common in industry applications are omitted. Again, readers are directed to Part 1 for discussion of this topic. Part 7 discusses the key PWM methods that are also reviewed in Part 1. Finally, Part 8 considers general power electronics applications. To be sure, most of the papers in the book discuss applications.

I have authored/edited three books in power electronics, i.e., *Adjustable Speed AC Drive Systems* (IEEE Press, 1981), *Power Electronics and AC Drives* (Prentice Hall, 1986), and *Microcomputer Control of Power Electronics and Drives* (IEEE Press, 1987). It is my hope that this book will complement the others.

Before concluding, I must express sincere thanks to several of my professional colleagues for their valuable input. They are Mr. F. G. Turnbull, Dr. R. L. Steigerwald, and Dr. T. M. Jahns, who are my former colleagues at the General Electric Research and Development Center, Schenectady, NY; Prof. J. Holtz of the Wuppertal University, West Germany; Prof. F. Lee of the Virginia Polytechnic and State University, Blacksburg; Prof. R. D. Middlebrook of the California Institute of Technology, Pasadena; Dr. K. Shenai of General Electric Company, Schenectady; Dr. A. K. Chattopadhyay of the Indian Institute of Technology, Kharagpur; Prof. G. K. Dubey of the Indian Institute of Technology, Kanpur; Prof. J. D. Van Wyk of the Rand Afrikaans University, South Africa; Prof. A. Nabae of the Tokyo Institute of Polytechnics (formerly of the Technical University of Nagaoka), Japan; Prof. P. D. Ziogas of the Concordia University, Canada; Dr. J. S. Lai of the Tennessee Center for Research and Development, Knoxville; and Prof. K. Harada of the Kyushu University, Japan. I also must thank my wife, who is always so patient during my intellectual ventures.

B. K. Bose

Part 1
Introduction to Power Electronics

Introduction to Power Electronics

BIMAL K. BOSE
THE UNIVERSITY OF TENNESSEE

POWER electronics is a branch of electrical engineering that is concerned with the conversion and control of electrical power for various applications, such as heating and lighting control, electrochemical processes, dc and ac regulated power supplies, induction heating, dc and ac electrical machine drives, electrical welding, active power line filtering, static var compensation, and many more. The utility systems usually generate, transmit, and distribute power at a fixed frequency (50 or 60 Hz), and a fixed voltage is maintained at the consumer's terminal. A consumer, however, may need power at dc or ac at the same, higher, lower, or variable frequency. Frequently, this power needs to be controlled with precision. A power electronics system interfaces between the utility system and consumer's load to satisfy this need. Sometimes, power is generated in dc form by battery, photovoltaic, fuel cell or magnetohydrodynamic (MHD) method, or in variable/fixed-frequency ac form in a windmill, gas turbine, or diesel generator. Again, a power electronic system permits the generator to be coupled with the utility system or process the power directly for customer load. Often, the interaction between the power electronics, customer load, and supply system is of crucial importance.

The core of a power electronic apparatus consists of a converter built on a matrix of power semiconductor switching devices that works under the guidance of control electronics. The converters can be classified as rectifier (ac-to-dc converter), inverter (dc-to-ac converter), chopper (dc-to-dc converter), ac power controller (at same frequency), and cycloconverter (direct frequency changer). Often, a conversion system is a hybrid type that mixes more than one basic conversion process. The motivation for using switching devices in a converter is to increase conversion efficiency to a high value. An ideal power semiconductor switch has zero conduction drop, zero leakage current at OFF condition, and turns on and off instantaneously. Such a device is lossless, and therefore, the converter efficiency tends to be 100%. Practical devices have losses that will be discussed later. The harmful effect of a switching-mode operation (instead of linear-mode operation) is the generation of harmonics on the load and source lines. A converter with the control electronics can be looked upon as a power amplifier in a control system. However, due to discrete on and off operation of the switches, it is a complex amplifier with nonlinearity and time lag.

The present state of power electronics has evolved technologically over a considerable period of time. In the late nineteenth to early twentieth century, the use of rotating machines for power control and conversion was well known. Popular examples are the Ward–Leonard speed control of dc motor, and Kramer and Scherbius drives of wound rotor induction motors. The history of power electronics began with the introduction of the glass bulb mercury arc rectifier in 1900. Then, gradually, the metal tank rectifier, grid-controlled rectifier, ignitron, phanotron, and thyratron were introduced. During World War II, magnetic amplifiers based on saturable core reactors and selenium rectifiers became especially attractive due to their ruggedness, reliability, and radiation-hardened characteristics. Possibly the greatest revolution in the history of electrical engineering occurred in 1948 with the invention of the transistor by Bardeen, Brattain, and Shockley of Bell Telephone Laboratory. In 1956, the same laboratory invented the PNPN triggering transistor, which was later defined as a thyristor, or silicon-controlled rectifier (SCR). In 1958, General Electric Company introduced a commercial thyristor to the market. It was the beginning of the modern era of power electronics. Many different types of power semiconductor devices have been introduced since then, and these will be described later.

It is interesting to note that in modern power electronics apparatus, there are essentially two types of semiconductor elements: the power semiconductors that can be defined as the muscle of the equipment, and microelectronic control chips, which have the power and intelligence of the brain. Both are digital in nature, except that one manipulates large power up to gigawatts, and the other handles power only on the order of milliwatts. Today's power electronics apparatus integrates both of these end-of-the-spectrum electronics, providing large size and cost advantages, and sophisticated system performance.

In this section, we review power semiconductor devices, various converter types and their topologies, pulsewidth modulation methods, and, finally, some power electronics applications. For completeness, phase-control-type converters, which are so common in industrial applications, have also been included. Summary comparison charts for devices and converter systems have also been included. The background knowledge gained in this part will help the reader to successfully explore the other parts of the book that describe the topics in considerable detail.

1. Power Semiconductor Devices

Power semiconductor devices are the most important elements in a power electronics apparatus. Although basically these are on and off switches, practical devices are far more complex, delicate, and "fragile" elements. A power electronics engineer needs to understand the devices thoroughly for efficient, reliable, and cost-effective design of the equipment. Historically, the evolution of power electronics has generally followed the evolution of power devices. In turn, power semiconductor devices have followed the evolution of solid-state electronics. The researchers in solid-state electronics have worked relentlessly to improve semiconductor processing, device fabrication, and packaging and, as a result, today's high-density, high-performance, high-reliability, and high-yield microelectronic chips are available at an economical price. Every piece of these efforts has contributed to the successful evolution of today's power semiconductor devices. In this section, operation principles and the salient features of different types of power semiconductor devices will be reviewed.

1.1. Thyristor

The thyristor, or silicon-controlled rectifier (SCR), is the main workhorse in today's power electronics. Figure 1(a) shows the device symbol and (b) indicates its volt-ampere characteristics. Basically, it is a trigger-into-conduction device that can be turned on by a positive gate current pulse, but once the device is on, a negative gate pulse cannot turn it off. The commutation, or turn-off, is possible by ac line or load voltage wave, or by an auxiliary transient circuit. A thyristor has a P-N-P-N structure, and its triggering action can be explained by the regenerative feedback configuration of the component PNP and NPN transistors, which show increasing current gain (α) at higher emitter current. A thyristor can also turn on by excessive anode voltage or its rate of rise (dv/dt), high temperature, or light shining on the junctions. The device turns on very fast and the time is limited by the rate of rise (di/dt) of anode current. The turn-off process is slow because the minority carriers are to be cleared from the inner junctions by "recovery" and "recombination" processes. The recovery is enhanced by voltage reversal across the device, but the recombination effect is influenced by the lifetime of minority carriers.

Like other power semiconductor devices, a thyristor needs a snubber 1) to protect the device from voltage transients, 2) to limit anode di/dt effect, 3) to reduce off-state and reapplied anode dv/dt, and 4) to reduce switching loss within the device. A thyristor can tolerate a large transient fault current and can be protected by a fast fuse. Within a specified junction temperature limit (125°C), the device can carry larger current on a smaller duty cycle basis that can be further enhanced by improved cooling.

Commercial thyristors can be classified as phase-control and inverter types. The latter can be further classified as a reverse-conducting thyristor (RCT) and asymmetrical thyristor (ASCR). The inverter grade thyristors have faster turn-off time, but block voltage in the forward direction (asymmetrical blocking) only. Thyristors have been widely used in dc and ac drives, power supplies in electrochemical processes, lighting and heating control, welding control, high-voltage dc (HVDC) conversion, static var compensation, and solid-state circuit breakers.

1.2. Triac

A triac has a complex multiple junction structure, but functionally it is an integrated pair of phase-controlled thyristors connected in antiparallel. Figure 2(a) shows the triac symbol and (b) shows its volt-ampere characteristics. In the I^+ mode, the terminal T_2 is positive and can be switched on by a positive gate current pulse. In the III^- mode, the terminal T_1 is positive and is switched on by negative gate-current pulse. A triac is more economical than a pair of thyristors in antiparallel and its control is simpler, but the integrated construction has limitations of poor reapplied dv/dt, poor gate-current sensitivity for firing, and longer turn-off time. Triac is popularly used in 60-Hz phase-control resistive loads, such as heating and lighting control and in solid-state ac relays.

1.3. Gate Turn-off Thyristor (GTO)

A GTO is a thyristor-like PNPN device that can be triggered into conduction by a small positive gate-current pulse, but also has the capability of being turned off by a negative gate-current pulse. However, the turn-off current gain is low (typically 4 or 5). For example, a 4000-V, 3000-A device may need -750 A gate current to turn it off. A GTO is fabricated with a highly sensitive NPN transistor component and interdigitated gate–cathode boundary so that negative gate current completely diverts the PNP collector current, and thus helps turn off the device. Minority carrier lifetime control and shorted anode construction are frequently used to reduce the turn-off time.

GTOs are available with symmetric or asymmetric voltage blocking capabilities. A symmetric blocking device cannot have anode shorting, and, therefore, is somewhat slower. The turn-on behavior of a GTO is almost similar to a thyristor, but its turn-off characteristics are somewhat complex. Figure 3 shows the device symbol and the turn-off characteristics. During the steep fall time of the anode current, even a very small leakage inductance in the snubber will create an anode spike voltage that will tend to cause a second breakdown failure. Besides, a large anode tail current during device voltage build-up causes excessive power dissipation. Therefore, GTO circuits should be designed with large snubbers to avoid these problems. Because of high snubber loss, the switching frequency is usually restricted to 1 or 2 kHz. Recently, regenerative snubbers have been suggested to improve the converter efficiency.

GTOs are used in dc and ac machine drives, uninterruptible power supply systems (UPS), static var compensators, induction heating, and photovoltaic and fuel cell converters from a few hundred kilowatts to several megawatts, and this boundary is continuously increasing.

1.4. Power Transistor

A power bipolar junction transistor (BJT) is a two-junction self-controlled device where the collector current is under the

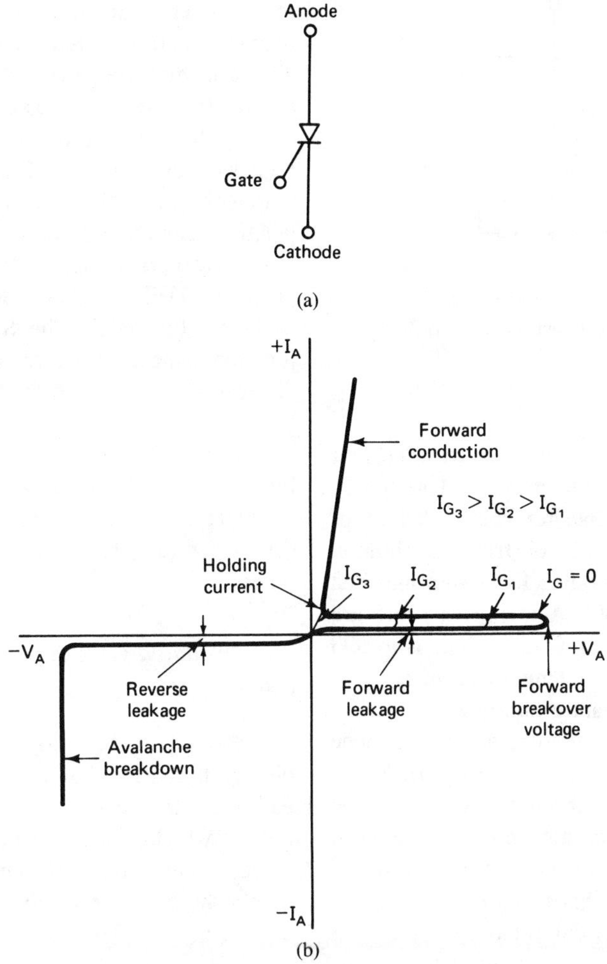

Fig. 1. (a) Thyristor symbol and (b) volt-ampere characteristics. Reprinted with permission from *Power Electronics and AC Drives*, B. K. Bose. © 1986 Prentice Hall.

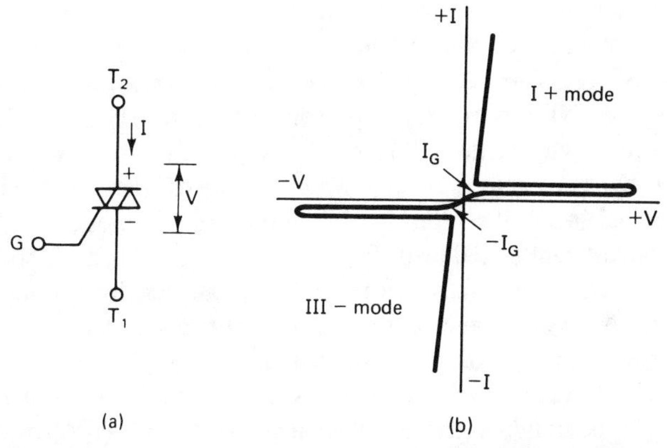

Fig. 2. (a) Triac symbol and (b) volt-ampere characteristics. Reprinted with permission from *Power Electronics and AC Drives*, B. K. Bose. © 1986 Prentice Hall.

control of base drive current. Basically, it is a linear device that is operated in the switching mode, and fault overcurrent can be suppressed by base drive control. The current gain (α) of a power transistor is low, but is increased to a high value in the Darlington transistor, shown in Fig. 4. The

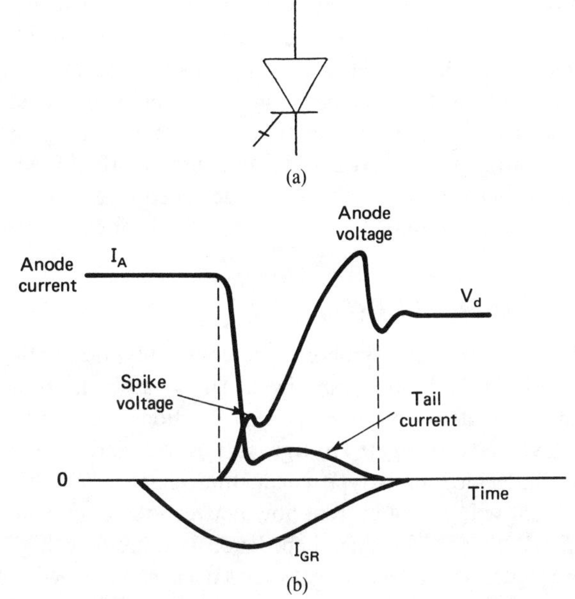

Fig. 3. (a) GTO symbol and (b) turn-off characteristics. Reprinted with permission from *Power Electronics and AC Drives*, B. K. Bose. © 1986 Prentice Hall.

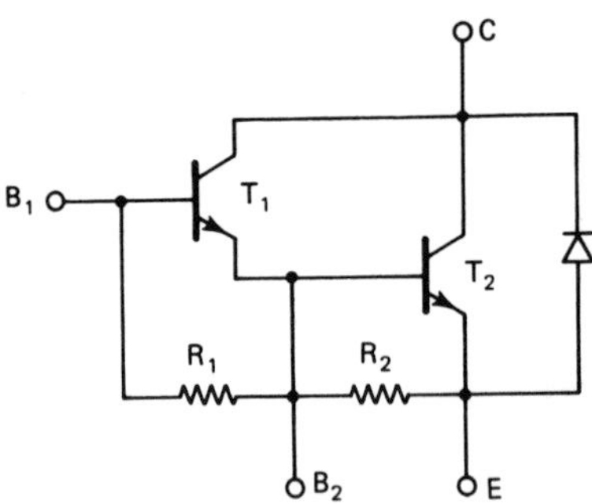

Fig. 4. A two-stage Darlington transistor with bypass diode. Reprinted with permission from *Power Electronics and AC Drives*, B. K. Bose. © 1986 Prentice Hall.

transistor current gain varies widely with collector current and temperature. The device has asymmetrical voltage blocking capability and is therefore suitable for voltage-fed chopper and inverter applications. Double or triple Darlington power transistors are available in module form with matched parallel devices (up to 1200 V, 800 A at present) and are popularly used in converters from a few kilovoltamps to 500 kilovoltamps with several kilohertz switching frequency.

Power transistors have an important property known as the second-breakdown effect. This is in contrast to avalanche breakdown of a junction (known as first breakdown). When the collector current is switched on, it tends to crowd on the base-emitter junction periphery (emitter crowding effect), thus constricting the collector current in a narrow area of the reverse-biased collector junction. This tends to create a hot spot and the junction fails by thermal runaway (known as second breakdown). The rise in junction temperature at the hot spot accentuates the current concentration due to the negative temperature coefficient of the drop, and this regeneration effect causes collapse of the collector voltage, destroying the device. A similar problem arises when an inductive load is turned off. As the base-emitter junction becomes reverse-biased, the collector current tends to concentrate in a narrow area of the collector junction. The manufacturers provide specifications in the form of safe operating areas (SOA) during turn on (FBSOA) and turn off (RBSOA), as shown in Fig. 5. Obviously, a well-designed polarized snubber is an indispensable component of a transistor converter.

1.5. Power MOSFET (Paper 3.2)

The structure and symbol of a commonly used N-type power MOSFET is shown in Fig. 6. Unlike a bipolar transistor, it is a voltage-controlled, "zero-junction" majority carrier device. If the gate voltage is positive and beyond a threshold value, an N-type conducting channel will be induced that will permit current flow between the drain and the source. Although the gate impedance is extremely high at steady state, the effective gate-source capacitance will demand a pulse current during fast turn-on and turn-off. The device is basically linear with asymmetrical blocking capability, and has an integral body diode that can carry full current in the reverse direction. The diode is characterized by slow recovery and is often bypassed by external fast recovery diodes in high-frequency applications. Being a majority carrier device, the turn-on and turn-off times are extremely fast, causing low switching loss, but it has the disadvantage of higher conduction drop. For a high-voltage power MOSFET, a longer conduction channel makes this drop larger. The positive temperature coefficient of conduction resistance permits easy paralleling of devices. An important property of power MOSFET is that it does not have a second breakdown problem, like BJT. The SOA is solely determined by the junction temperature limit and, therefore, the device power dissipation can be high on a short duty cycle basis, as shown in Fig. 7.

Power MOSFETs are extremely popular in low-voltage, low-power, and high-frequency switching applications, such as switching mode power supply, brushless dc motor (BLDM) drives, solid-state dc relay, automobile applications, and others.

1.6. Insulated Gate Bipolar Transistor (IGBT) (Paper 3.4)

An IGBT is basically a hybrid MOS-gated turn on/off bipolar transistor that combines the attributes of MOSFET, BJT, and thyristor. Figure 8 shows the basic structure of IGBT, which also indicates its equivalent circuit and the device symbol. Its architecture is similar to that of MOSFET, except the N^+ layer at the drain is substituted by a P^+ layer at the collector. The device has the high input impedance of a MOSFET, but BJT-like conduction characteristics. If the gate is positive with respect to the emitter, an N-channel is induced in the P region. This forward-biases the base-emitter junction of the PNP transistor, turning it on and causing conductivity modulation of the N^- region, which gives significant improvement of the conduction drop over that of a MOSFET. The thyristor-like latching action because of the parasitic NPN transistor is prevented by properly controlling the resistivity of the P^+ layer. The device is normally turned off by zero-gate voltage, which removes the conducting channel in the P region. The "tail current" in modern IGBT is significantly reduced by the proton-irradiated minority carrier lifetime control in the N^- region, and by adding an extra N^+ buffer layer at the emitter. The device has a higher current density compared to BJT and MOSFET, and needs 30% of the die size of a MOSFET. Its input capacitance (C_{iss}) is significantly less than that of MOSFET. Also, the ratio of gate-collector capacitance to gate-emitter capacitance is lower, giving improved Miller feedback effect during dv/dt turn-on and turn-off. The FBSOA and RBSOA of IGBT are thermally limited by T_j, and the device does not show any second breakdown phenomena. The present IGBTs have a power handling capability comparable to that of BJT, but can operate at higher switching frequency. Acoustic noise-free ac drives using IGBTs are available in the marketplace. The simplicity of gate drives, ease of protection,

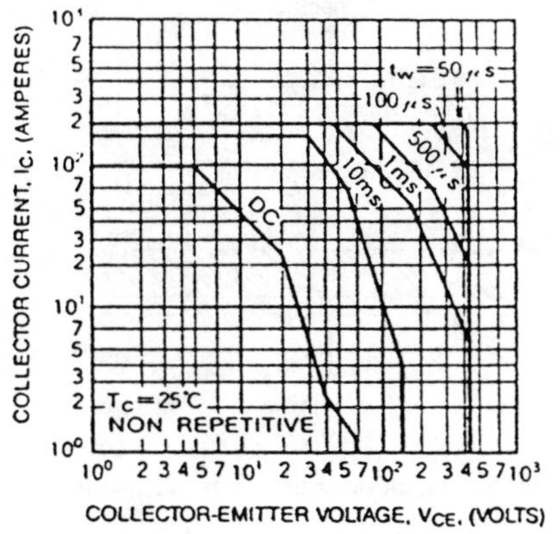

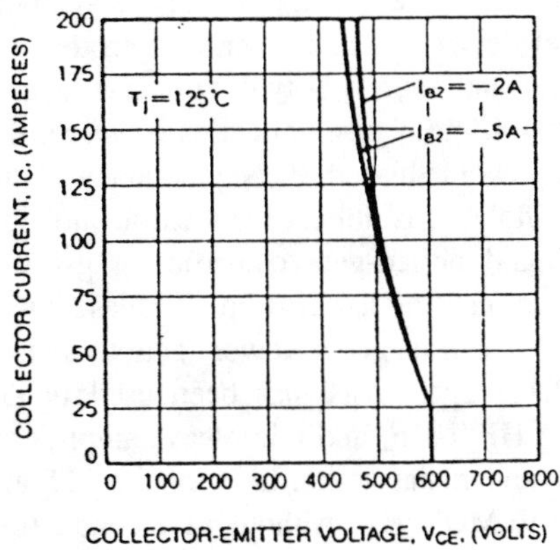

Fig. 5. Safe operating areas (FBSOA and RBSOA) of a Darlington transistor (Powerex-KS224510).

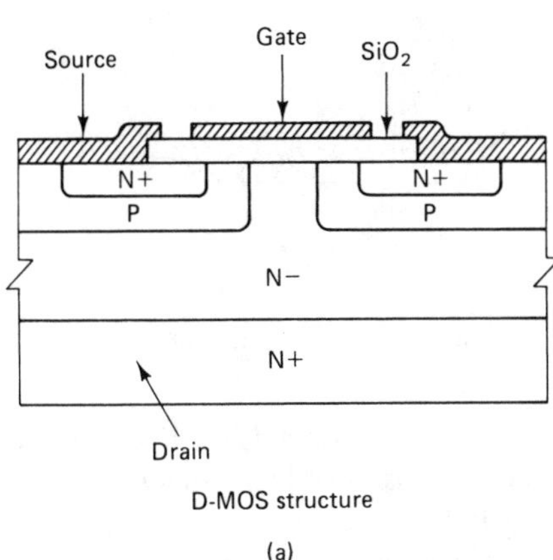

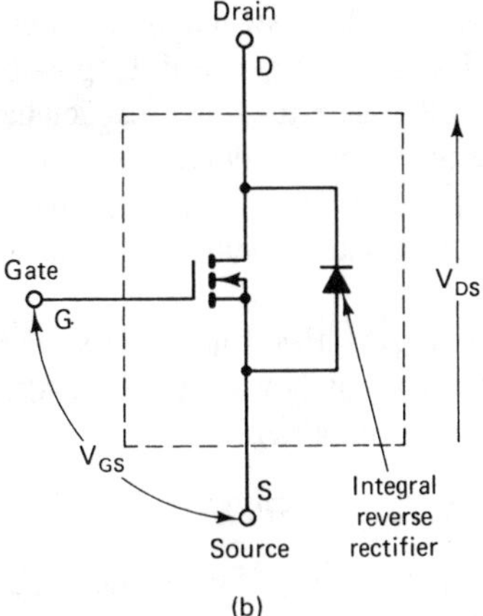

Fig. 6. (a) Power MOSFET structure and (b) circuit symbol (NMOS-type). Courtesy of International Rectifier Corporation.

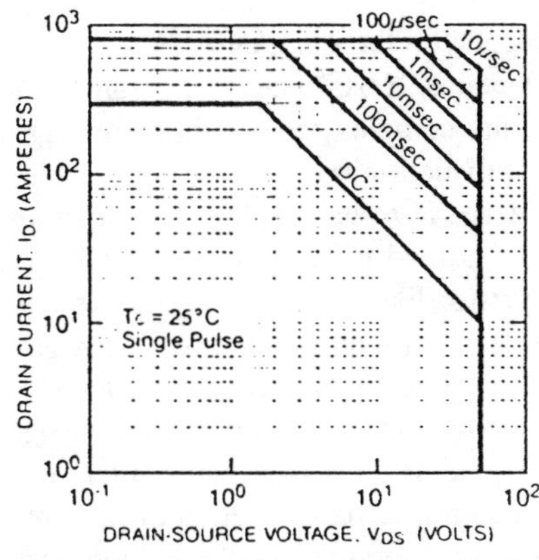

Fig. 7. Safe operating areas of power MOSFET (Powerex-J936).

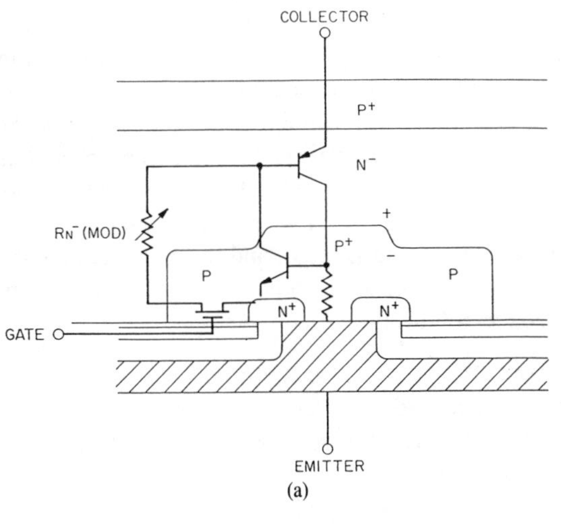

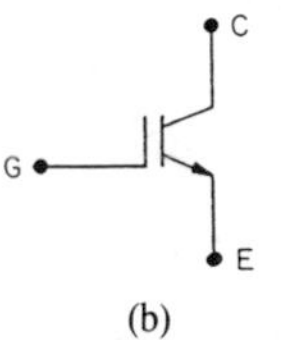

Fig. 8. (a) Basic structure of IGBT with equivalent circuit and (b) device symbol.

power circuit integration capability, snubberless operation, and high switching speed make IGBT converters more attractive than BJT converters.

1.7. Static Induction Transistor (SIT)

An SIT is a high-power high-frequency device and can be considered essentially as the solid-state version of the triode vacuum tube, which has been known for a long time. Figure

9 shows the basic structure of the SIT and the device symbol. It is a short N-channel device where the gate electrodes are buried within the drain and source N-type epitaxial layers. The device is normally on, but if gate voltage is negative, the depletion layer of the reverse-biased P^+N junction will inhibit the drain current flow. It is almost identical to junction FET, except vertical and buried-gate construction gives a lower channel resistance, causing lower drop. Besides, lower gate-source channel resistance gives lower gate-to-source negative feedback effect. The device has been used in the linear mode in audio, VHF/UHF, and microwave amplifiers. The reliability, noise, and radiation hardness of the SIT are claimed to be superior to MOSFET. Although the conduction drop is lower than that of an equivalent series-parallel combination of MOSFETs, the excessively large drop makes it unsuitable for general power electronics applications, unless justified by the need of FET-like switching frequency. In fact, faster-than-MOSFET switching speed is possible because of the lower equivalent gate-to-source capacitance and resistance. Being a majority carrier device, the SOAs are limited by junction temperature. Device paralleling is easy because of the positive temperature coefficient characteristics of channel resistance.

SITs have been used in AM/FM transmitters, induction heating, high-voltage low-current power supplies, ultrasonic generators, and linear power amplifiers.

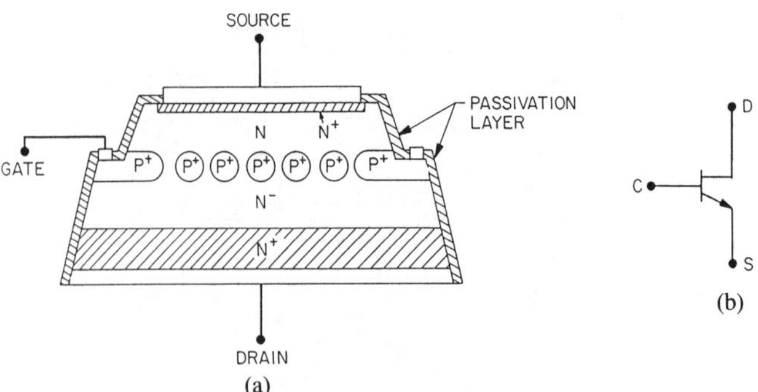

Fig. 9. (a) Basic structure of SIT and (b) circuit symbol.

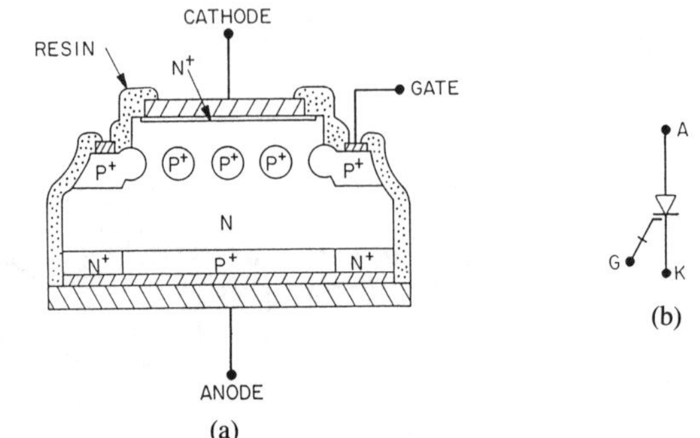

Fig. 10. (a) Basic structure of SITH and (b) circuit symbol.

1.8. Static Induction Thyristors (SITH)

A SITH, or SI-thyristor, is a self-controlled GTO-like on–off device. Figure 10 shows the basic structure of SITH and the device symbol. It is basically a P^+NN^+ diode (*not* a thyristor, as the name indicates) with a buried P^+ grid-like gate structure. The structure is analogous to SIT except that a P^+ layer is added to the anode side. Similar to SIT, it is a normally-on device with the N region saturated with a minority carrier. If the gate is reverse-biased with respect to the cathode, a depletion layer will block the anode current flow. The device does not have reverse blocking capability, due to the emitter shorting that is needed for high-speed operation. The turn-off behavior of SITH is similar to that of GTO, i.e., the negative gate current is large, and the anode circuit shows a tail current. The general comparison with GTO can be summarized as follows:

- Unlike GTO, it is a normally-on device
- The conduction drop is slightly higher
- The turn-off current gain is lower (below 3) compared to 4 to 5 for GTO
- Both devices show long tail current
- The switching frequency is higher
- The dv/dt and di/dt ratings are higher
- The SOA is improved

1.9. MOS-Controlled Thyristor (MCT) (Paper 3.5)

An MCT is a thyristor-like trigger-into-conduction device that can be turned on or off by a small pulse on the MOS gate. It is more of a GTO-like device, except the turn-off current gain is very high. In switching speed, it is comparable to IGBT, but has a lower conduction drop. At present, the device is not available commercially*, but developmental devices have been released by General Electric Co. (500 V/1000 V, 50 A/100 A) and Harris Semiconductor.

An MCT is basically a parallel connection of thousands of identical microcells on the same chip. For example, a 500-V, 50-A device contains 100 000 cells in parallel. The structure of the cell is quite complex, and is shown in Fig. 11. Figure 12 gives the equivalent circuit with the device symbol. It is turned on by a negative gate voltage pulse (with respect to anode), and it is turned off by a positive voltage pulse. The device has thyristor-like P-N-P-N layers, and a PNP-NPN regenerative effect turns on the device. If the gate voltage is negative, the P-FET turns on, and causes forward-biasing of the NPN transistor, and this in turn causes triggering of the device. If the gate is positive, the N-FET turns on, and short-circuits the emitter-base junction of the PNP transistor. This breaks the regenerative feedback loop and the device turns off. The turn-off process occurs purely by recombination of minority carriers in N and P layers. The tailing effect is carefully controlled by proton irradiation so that the conduction drop remains small.

The device has asymmetric voltage blocking capability, and its SOA is junction-temperature-limited. Unlike MOS-

*At the time of this writing, it is known that Harris will commercially release 600/1200 V, 30 A (rms) and 600/1200 V, 60 A (rms) devices in the near future.

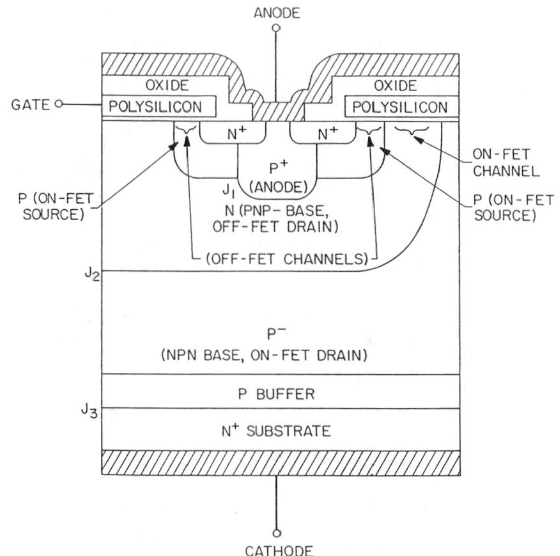

Fig. 11. Basic structure of MCT.

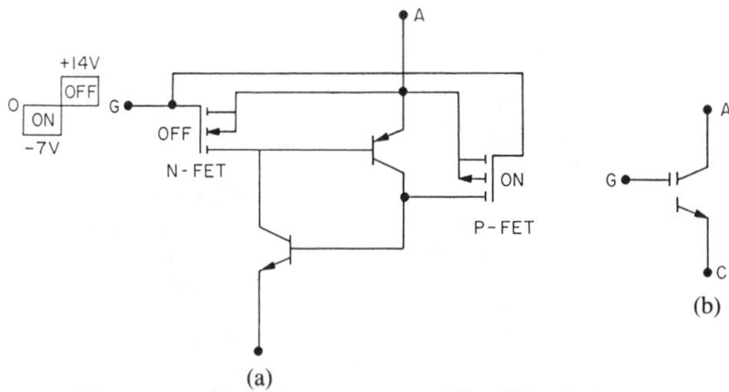

Fig. 12. (a) MCT equivalent circuit and (b) circuit symbol.

FET, its input capacitance is fixed because of the absence of the Miller effect. With the N-FET normally on, the device is extremely insensitive to dv/dt and T_j triggering effects. Although MCT is rated for $T_{j\,\max} = 150°\mathrm{C}$, it can successfully operate in a higher temperature range. The MCTs can be easily connected in a series-parallel combination for higher power requirements. In the next-generation power electronics, MCTs are expected to offer a serious challenge to other high-power devices.

1.10. Power Semiconductor Materials

The power semiconductor devices of today invariably use silicon as the basic material. Silicon has enjoyed a monopoly over a long period of time in both power and microelectronic devices, and this will very likely remain so in the near future. However, new types of materials, such as gallium arsenide, silicon carbide, and diamond, show tremendous promise for future generations of devices. Silicon carbide and diamond are particularly interesting because of the large band gap, high carrier mobility, and high electrical and thermal conductivities. These materials can be used to build power MOSFET-like devices that have high power capability, high frequency, low conduction drop, good radiation hardness, and high junction temperature. Diamonds (in synthetic thin-film form) look to be the most promising among all of the materials. For example, a diamond power MOSFET can have sixth-order magnitude of power, fifty times higher frequency, an order of magnitude less conduction drop, and 600°C junction temperature, compared to a silicon power device. In addition, a superconductive power control device based on the Josephson effect also shows future promise.

1.11. Summary Comparison of Devices

It is difficult to compare devices, especially their numerical ratings, because the ratings not only vary widely from one device type to another, but there may be a wide variation of ratings within one type of device. Manufacturers' specification sheets show a considerable amount of parameter tolerance for a particular device. However, test conditions for parameter evaluation can vary widely. The following comparison chart (Table I) is intended to give a general idea of commonalities and differences among the devices. All of the numerical parameters shown are approximate and do not necessarily hold for the sample device selected for comparison.

1.12. Power Integrated Circuits (Paper 3.7)

This section would remain incomplete without some review of the recent power integrated circuits (PIC). In a PIC, the control and power electronics are integrated on the same chip. Loosely, a PIC is defined as "smart power." The motivation for power circuit integration is reduction of cost and improvement of reliability. The main problems in PIC synthesis are isolation between high-voltage and low-voltage devices and cooling. A PIC is often differentiated from a high-voltage integrated circuit (HVIC) where the voltage is high but the current is small. Low-voltage NMOS, CMOS, and bipolar devices can be conveniently integrated with MOS-gated power devices. Recently, a large family of PICs that includes a power MOSFET smart switch, half-bridge inverter driver, H-bridge inverter, two-phase step motor driver, one-quadrant chopper for dc motor drive, three-phase brushless dc motor driver, three-phase diode rectifier-PWM inverter, has become available. Evidently, the majority of PICs is being targeted for motion control applications. Recently, application-specific PICs (ASPIC) are also available in the marketplace. Figure 13 shows a half-bridge power MOSFET driver manufactured by Harris (GS6000/1). It can be defined more as an HVIC. The diode-capacitor charge pump permits the gate drive command of switch S1 to be level-shifted. The driver uses 500-V junction isolation, and provides logic lock-out protection between the power devices. Other protection features include overcurrent (using integrated current sensors, if desired), logic supply undervoltage detection, and an output state monitor when V_{out} does not follow the logic command. The detected faults are reported to the central controller, which is then given as a logic output.

TABLE I

	Thyristor	Triac	GTO	Darlington BJT
1. Voltage and current ratings (sample device selected for comparison)	1800 V, 300 A (rms) Phase-control type*	600 V, 40 A (rms)*	1200 V, 300 A (peak)*	700 V, 100 A (dc)*
2. Present power capability	6000 V, 3500 A	800 V, 40 A	4500 V, 3000 A	1200 V, 800 A (paralleled module)
3. Linear/trigger	Trigger	Trigger	Trigger	Linear
4. Voltage blocking	Symmetric or asymmetric	Symmetric	Asymmetric or symmetric	Asymmetric
5. Gating	Current	Current	Current	Current
6. T_j range (°C)	−40 to 125	−40 to 115	−40 to 125	−40 to 150
7. Safe operating area	Does not apply	Does not apply	Second breakdown at turn-off	Second breakdown and T_j limit
8. Conduction drop (V) at rated current	1.9	1.4	4	1.9
9. Drop sensitivity with °C	Negative	Negative	Negative	Negative
10. Switching frequency (Hz)	Up to 400	Up to 400	Up to 2000	Up to 10 000
11. Turn-off current gain	—	—	4 to 5	200
12. Reapplied dv/dt (V/μs)	30	5	Limit for device loss	Limit for device loss and SOA
13. Turn-on di/dt (A/μs)	200	21 A/ms	300	100
14. Turn-on time (μs)	1.1	1.7	4	1.7
15. Turn-off time (μs)	220	Comparable to thyristor	10	5
16. Leakage current (mA)	3	1	30	2.5
17. Snubber	Unpolarized	Unpolarized	Polarized or unpolarized	Polarized
18. Protection	Gate inhibit or fast fuse	Gate inhibit or fast fuse	Gate inhibit or fast fuse	Base control
19. Applications	DC motor drives Large power supplies Lighting and heating Static var compensators Electronic circuit breakers	Lamp dimming Heating control Zero voltage switched ac relay AC motor starting and control	Motor drives UPS systems Static var compensators Induction heating	Motor drives UPS systems Static var and harmonic compensators Switching-mode power supplies
20. Comments	Large surge current capability	Large surge current capability	High uncontrollable surge current Large snubber to limit device loss Low switching frequency at high power	Current gain varies with °C and collector current
	* POWEREX FT300DM	* GE SC265/SC266	* POWEREX GDM2—30	* POWEREX D67DE

2. Phase-Controlled Converters

This class of converters converts ac-to-dc, dc-to-ac, and ac-to-ac at the same frequency (ac voltage controller) or at a different frequency (cycloconverter). They belong to the first generation of converters, and exclusively use devices such as diodes, thyristors, and triacs. The devices are commutated by a segment of inverse line voltage. In this section, we will review all of the aforementioned types of phase-controlled converters.

2.1. AC–DC/DC–AC Converter

This type of converter is used in electrochemical processes (electroplating, anodizing, chemical gas production, aluminum reduction, metal refining, etc.), dc motor speed control, HVDC converters for power transmission systems, magnet dc supply, dc supply for ac drive inverters, battery chargers, and more. A single-phase-type converter may have half-wave, transformer-coupled center-tapped, semi-bridge, or full-bridge (H-bridge) topology. The general topologies of the three-phase converter are half-wave, six-pulse center-tapped, semi-bridge, and full-bridge. With the help of phase-shifting transformers, the number of phases or pulses can be increased to 12, 24, etc. Such multipulse converters produce waves with low harmonic content in both the ac and dc sides, and are popular for high-power applications. A three-phase, six-pulse bridge converter (also known as a Graetz bridge), shown in Fig. 14, is a very popular configuration. Figure 15 shows its idealized voltage and current waveforms for a highly inductive load. All the thyristors conduct for 120° intervals, except that the lower group of thyristors have a phase skew of 60° with respect to the upper group. At firing angle $\alpha = 0$, the circuit behaves as a diode rectifier. By delaying α, the output dc voltage v_d can be controlled. At $\alpha = 90°$, the dc voltage, or the power delivered to the load, is zero. It can be shown that by varying the angle in the range

TABLE I (*Continued*)

Power MOSFET	IGBT	SIT	SITH	MCT
200 V, 18 A (dc)*	600 V, 50 A (dc)*	800 V, 18 A (dc)*	1200 V, 300 A (rms)*	600 V, 60 A (rms)*
500 V, 50 A	1200 V, 400 A	1200 V, 300 A	1200 V, 300 A	—
Linear	Linear	Linear	Linear	Trigger
Asymmetric	Asymmetric	Asymmetric	Asymmetric	Asymmetric
Voltage	Voltage	Voltage	Current	Voltage
−55 to 150	−20 to 150	−50 to 150	−40 to 125	−55 to 150
T_j limited	T_j limited	T_j limited	T_j limited	T_j limited
3.2†	3.2	18	4	1.1
Positive	Negative (positive at high current)	Positive	Negative	Negative
Up to 100 000	Up to 20 000	Up to 70 000	Several kHz‡	Up to 20 000
—	—	—	Below 3	—
Limited by Miller effect	Limit for device loss	Very high	2000	5000
Very high	Very high	Very high	900	1000
90 ns	0.9	0.25	2	1.0
0.14	1.4	0.3	9	2.1
0.2	1	0.1	25	1.0
Polarized (snubberless operation possible)	Polarized (snubberless operation possible)	Polarized (snubberless operation possible)	Polarized	Polarized (snubberless operation possible)
Gate control	Gate control	Gate control	Fast fuse or gate inhibit	Fast fuse or gate inhibit
Switching-mode power supply Brushless dc motor drive Electronic dc relay	AC motor drives UPS systems Static var and harmonic compensators Switching-mode power supplies	Induction heating Ultrasonic generators AM/FM generators	Induction heating Static var compensation	AC motor drives UPS systems Static var and harmonic compensators
Built-in body diode can carry full current, but slow recovery † Becomes high with higher voltage and current ratings		Available from Tokin America Inc.	Available from Toyo Elec. Co. ‡ Selected devices can operate at higher frequency	−196 to +250 T_j range possible Characteristics comparable to IGBT except lower drop Device not yet available commercially
* MOTOROLA IRF240	* POWEREX ID226005 (high speed type)	* TOKIN 2SK182	* TOYO DENKI—only device	* HARRIS MCTA60P60 (developmental device)

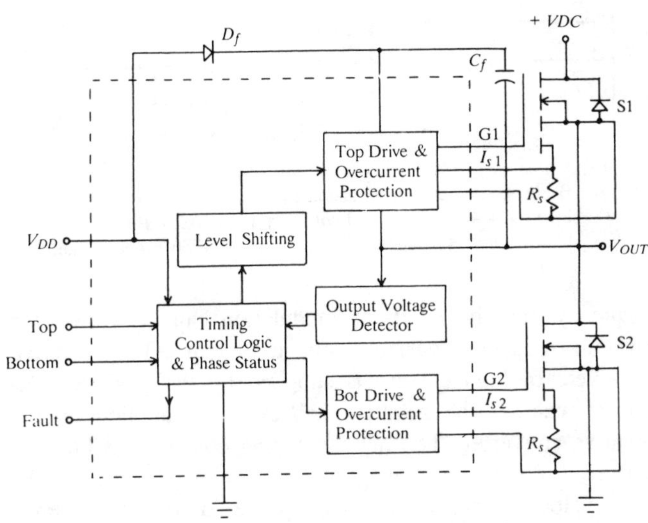

Fig. 13. Half-bridge integrated power MOSFET driver (Harris GS6000/1).

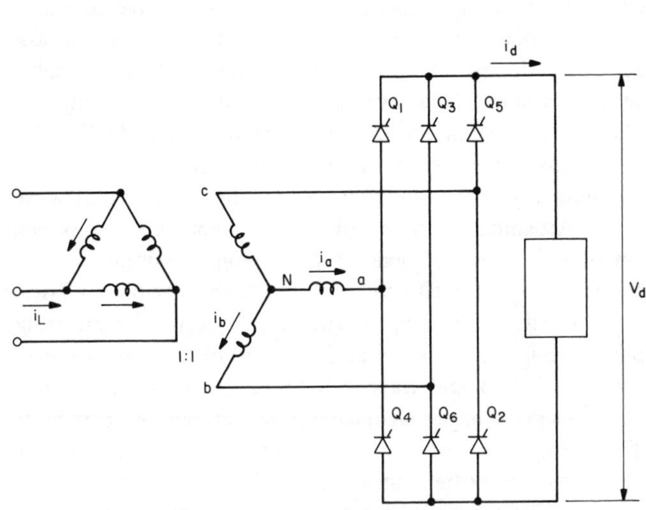

Fig. 14. A three-phase six-pulse thyristor bridge converter.

$90° < \alpha < 180°$, the circuit can function as an inverter, and dc power from a battery (inversely connected) or energy trapped in the load inductance can be pumped to the ac line with the dc current direction remaining the same. An inverter of this type is defined as a current-fed line-commutated inverter. The converter operation may be continuous, as shown in Fig. 15, or it may be discontinuous at light load, especially if the load contains a counter electromagnetic force (EMF). Even in continuous conduction, a practical load current wave will be wavy, unlike that shown in Fig. 15.

The basic characteristics of a phase-controlled converter are that the load voltage and line current waves are rich in harmonics, and the line fundamental current lags the line voltage wave. The distorted line current tends to distort the line voltage wave, which often creates problems in the reliable operation of sensitive equipment operating on the same bus. It also loads the line equipment, creates interference with the communication lines, and may create harmful resonance problems with the line parameters. The recent growth of this type of power electronic equipment on utility systems is creating power quality problems that are of serious concern. The harmonics in line current and load voltage can be improved by increasing the pulse number of the converter, as mentioned before. For example, a 12-pulse converter consisting of two series bridges that are supplied respectively by delta–delta and delta–wye transformers are used in the HVDC system. Passive filters and active power line conditioners can combat the harmonic distortion and lagging var problems. These problems can also be solved by PWM-type rectifiers or a diode rectifier cascaded with boost chopper, which will be described later.

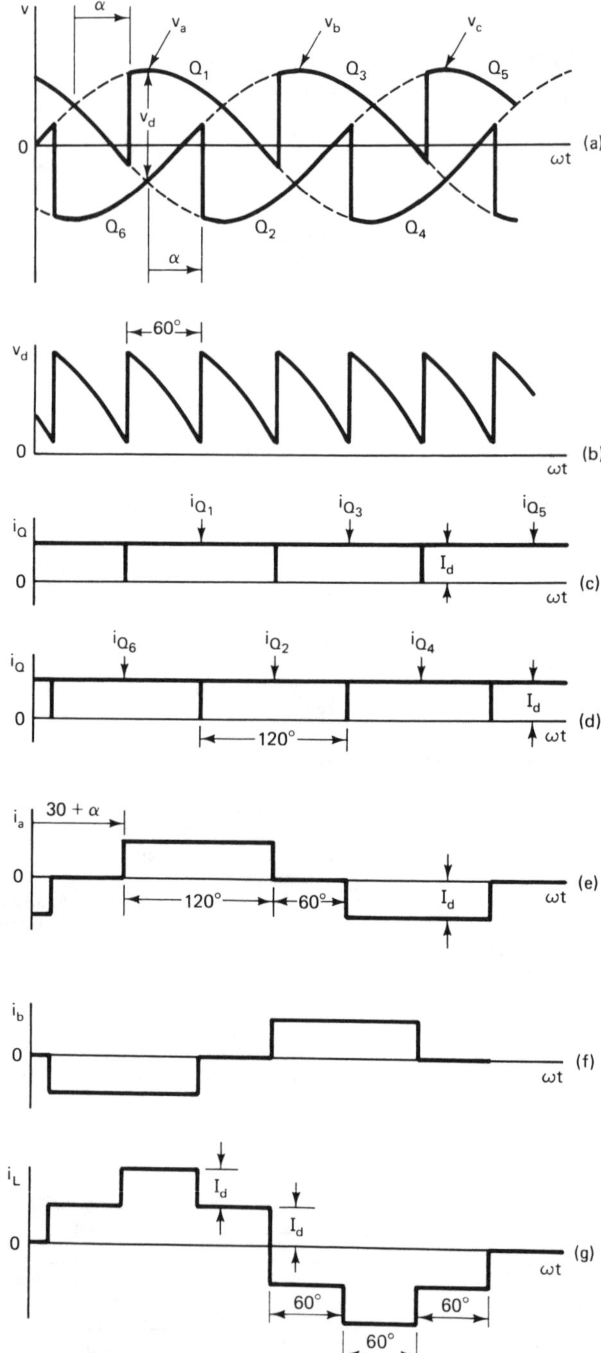

Fig. 15. Bridge converter voltage and current waves at highly inductive load ($\alpha = 45°$). Reprinted with permission from *Power Electronics and AC Drives*, B. K. Bose. © 1986 Prentice Hall.

2.2. Cycloconverter

A cycloconverter is a frequency changer that converts ac input power at one frequency to output power at a different frequency with one-stage conversion. The output may be dc (zero frequency) or at higher-than-the-input frequency. The cycloconverters operating on the phase-control line commutation principle will be reviewed here. They are used in large ac motor drives, static Scherbius drives, VSCF (variable-speed constant-frequency) systems, induction heating, etc. The PWM-type direct frequency changer and dc link frequency conversion systems will be described later.

Figure 16 shows an 18-thyristor, three-phase half-wave-type cycloconverter where the 60-Hz input voltage is converted to variable-frequency variable-voltage output for speed control of an isolated neutral ac machine. For higher power applications, a 36-thyristor circuit consisting of dual-bridge phase groups can also be used. In Fig. 16, each phase group consists of two half-wave converters connected in inverse-parallel, providing four-quadrant power control capability. The firing angle of each phase group is modulated sinusoidally to fabricate a mean sinusoidal voltage, as shown in Fig. 17. The other phase groups are identical, except that the modulating waves are phase-shifted by 120°. The output frequency and the depth of modulation can be varied for variable-frequency variable-voltage output. The positive half-cycle of load current is supplied by the positive converter, whereas the negative half-cycle is supplied by the negative converter. The nonconducting converter is blocked to prevent short circuit.

A cycloconverter is basically a phase-controlled converter and, therefore, the basic characteristics such as distortion of load voltage and line current and lagging input displacement

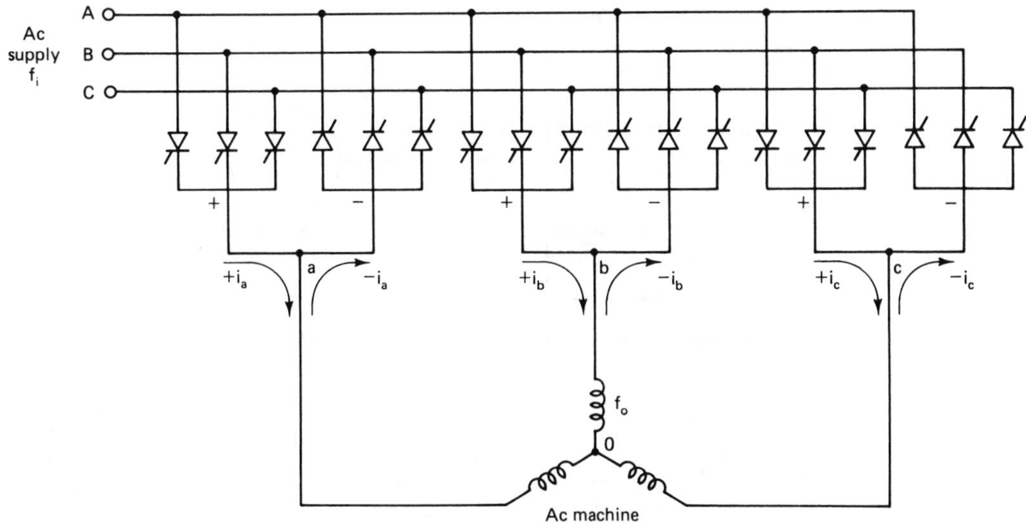

Fig. 16. An 18-thyristor, three-phase half-wave cycloconverter. Reprinted with permission from *Power Electronics and AC Drives*, B. K. Bose. © 1986 Prentice Hall.

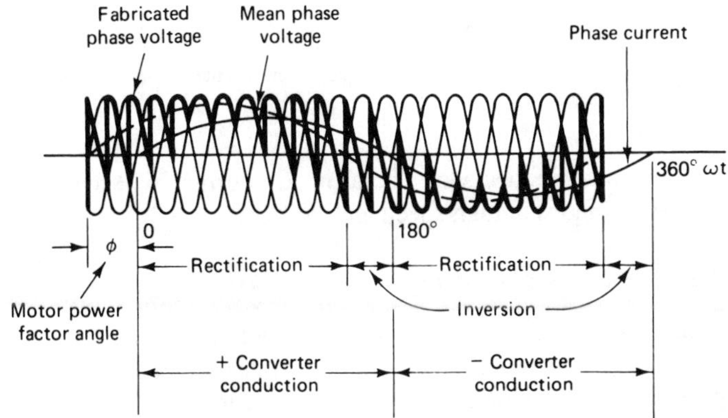

Fig. 17. Fabricated phase voltage and current waves of 18-thyristor half-wave cycloconverter. Reprinted with permission from *Power Electronics and AC Drives*, B. K. Bose. © 1986 Prentice Hall.

factors are retained. However, because of modulation of the firing angle, the harmonic pattern is very complex. Due to harmonic constraint, the typical output frequency range is from zero to one-third of the input frequency. A cycloconverter can also be operated in the circulating current mode. In this case, a reactor is connected between the component converters to prevent short circuit, and to limit the circulating current due to harmonics. Although the intergroup reactor adds weight and the cycloconverter needs current derating, the advantages are that control becomes simple and harmonic distortion is less, thus permitting a higher output frequency range. It can be shown that by controlling the circulating current, the input var loading can be regulated irrespective of the load power factor, so that a fixed capacitor bank can compensate the displacement factor to unity. Such a scheme has been used in commercial equipment. An active harmonic and var compensator (to be discussed later) on the input ac line is an ideal solution to improve the power factor to unity.

2.3. AC Voltage Controller

An ac voltage controller controls rms voltage at the output, but the frequency remains the same. Functionally, it can be viewed as a solid-state auto-transformer. Thyristors in antiparallel, or triacs in single- or three-phase configuration, are normally used in the converters. One popular application of a single-phase triac controller is incandescent lamp dimming. Other applications include heating control, electronic circuit breaker, induction motor starter, speed control of single- and three-phase induction motors, transformer tap changing, induction heating, and static var generator. Figure 18 shows a commonly used three-phase controller configuration used here as the starter of an induction motor. The switches can be turned on very fast at any desired point on the cycle and turned off in a subcycle period, or, by controlling the firing angle, the output voltage can be regulated between zero to the full value. At full ON-condition, there is power loss due to the conduction drop of the devices, which can be eliminated by a bypass mechanical contactor. Due to phase control, both the load and line sides have heavy distortion, and the line-side displacement factor (lagging) becomes poor.

The converter can be used as a simple and economical speed controller for induction motors (NEMA Class D type, which has high rotor resistance) used for pump- or blower-type applications. However, poor efficiency and line power and distortion factor problems hardly make them popular except for low-power single-phase applications. The so-called Nola power factor controller for an induction motor drive uses this type of converter to cut down the machine voltage at light load so that the reactive current is low. However, the additional cost, efficiency, and harmonic penalties do not make these schemes very attractive.

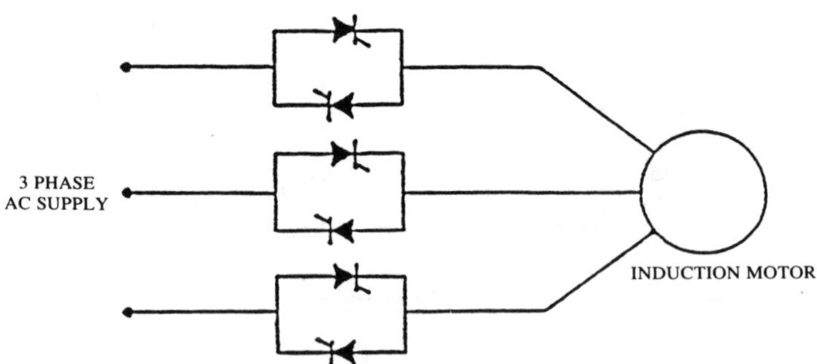

Fig. 18. Three-phase ac voltage controller using antiparallel thyristors.

3. PWM DC–DC Converters (Paper 5.1)

DC–DC converters of this type (PWM) convert unregulated dc voltage to regulated or variable dc voltage at the output, for applications such as dc motor motion control and switching-mode power supplies (SMPS). The input dc is usually a battery, or can be derived from single-phase or three-phase ac by a diode rectifier and capacitor filter. It can also be obtained from a photovoltaic- or fuel-cell-type dc generator. This class of converters can be PWM- or resonant-link type. Resonant-link converters will be described later. Traditionally, PWM-type dc–dc converters have been known as choppers. Of course, the term is synonymous with high-power dc–dc converter. Choppers were initially introduced in the early 1960s using force-commutated thyristors that were constrained to operate at low PWM frequency. The switching frequency could be raised when power BJTs became available, and then to a very high frequency by the advent of power MOSFETs. High-frequency switching regulators found acceptance over the traditional linear regulators because of improved efficiency and the reduced size of the heat sink.

At present, GTOs are popular in high-power subway dc traction drives, while BJTs or IGBTs are used in low-to-medium power applications such as power supplies and electric vehicle drives, and power MOSFETs are almost exclusively used in high-frequency low-power SMPS. DC–DC converters can have many possible topologies, but in this section we review only a few commonly used types.

3.1. Buck Converter

Figure 19 shows an IGBT buck converter for one-quadrant speed control of a dc motor. The IGBT switches on and off on a duty-cycle basis to impress a variable average voltage (which is always less than the input) across the motor armature. The freewheeling diode provides a close path for the inductive armature current and clamps zero voltage across the armature when the switch is off. High PWM frequency is desirable so that the harmonic current in the load can be easily filtered by the armature-leakage inductance. The one-quadrant converter can only permit power flow from the source to the load. To get a larger range of duty cycle, the frequency can be reduced, maintaining constant ON-time or OFF-time. The converter can operate in continuous or discontinuous conduction mode. The armature current will tend to be discontinuous at high speed and/or light load.

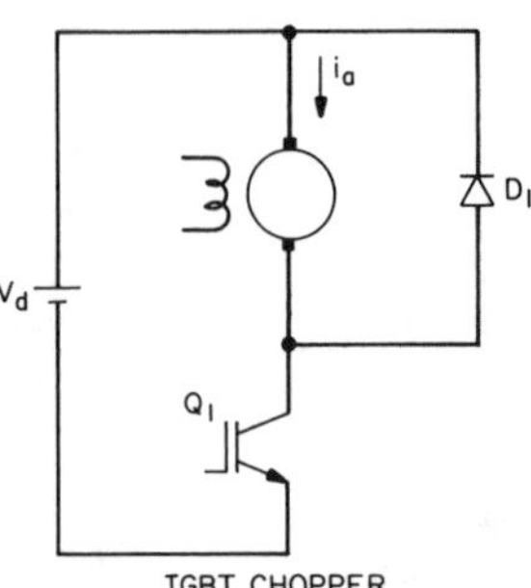

Fig. 19. PWM buck converter for one-quadrant speed control of dc motor.

3.2. Buck–Boost Converter

In machine control applications, often two-quadrant or regenerative operation of the chopper is desirable, and this is possible by the hybrid buck–boost converter shown in Fig. 20 (Paper 5.3). The IGBT Q_1 with diode D_2 operates in the buck mode to provide controllable motoring torque on the machine. The devices Q_2 and D_1 operate to provide regenerative braking torque on the machine. This segment constitutes a boost converter, and its function can be explained as follows: When Q_2 turns on, the machine counter EMF helps build up armature current in the reverse direction, transferring mechanical energy into electrical form. When the device turns off, the inductor energy is pumped back to the source, which is at higher voltage. The boost converter can, of course, be constructed independently.

A four-quadrant buck–boost converter for reversible and regenerative speed control of a dc machine using an H-bridge is shown in Fig. 21. Here, the four quadrants of operation can be summarized as follows.

Quadrant 1: Buck converter (forward motoring)
Q_1 = on
Q_2 = chopping
D_3, Q_1 = freewheeling
Quadrant 2: Boost converter (forward regeneration)
Q_4 = chopping
D_2, D_1 = freewheeling

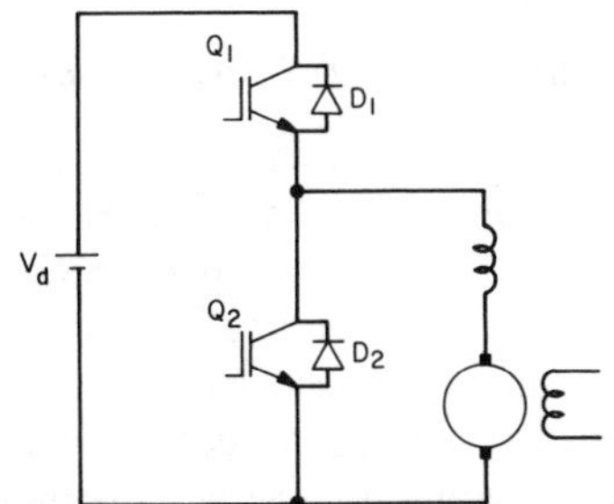

Fig. 20. PWM buck–boost converter for two-quadrant speed control of dc motor.

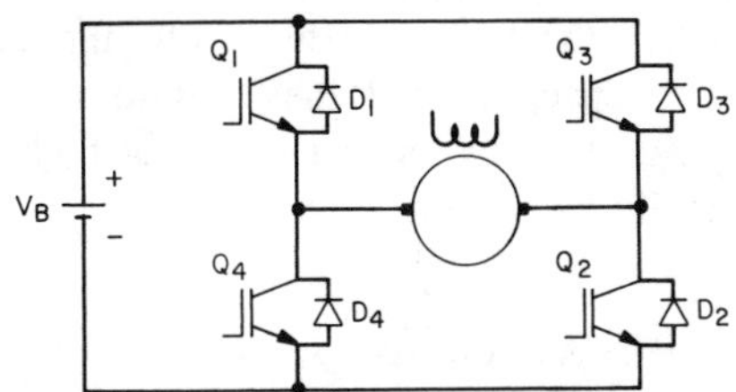

Fig. 21. Four-quadrant dc machine drive using H-bridge converter.

Quadrant 3: Buck converter (reverse motoring)
Q_3 = on
Q_4 = chopping
D_1, Q_3 = freewheeling

Quadrant 4: Boost converter (reverse regeneration)
Q_2 = chopping
Q_3, D_4 = freewheeling

An economical buck–boost converter, where buck or boost function is controlled by the duty cycle, is shown in Fig. 22. The circuit uses only one switch, but does not permit any power feedback to the source. It is not a drawback for switching-mode power supply. When the switch closes, the source energizes the inductance L, but when it is opened, the energy is transferred to the output. The voltage relation can easily be derived as

$$V_o / V_d = D/(1 - D)$$

where D = duty cycle of the switch. Note that if $D < 0.5$, the circuit operates as a buck converter, whereas for $D > 0.5$ it operates as a boost converter. The output polarity reversal is a disadvantage in this type of converter. Another popular converter in this class is known as the Ćuk converter (Fig. 23), which works somewhat on the duality principle of Fig. 22.

3.3. *Transformer-Coupled Converters*

In a switching-mode power supply, a transformer is often needed to provide input-to-output electrical isolation and voltage level change. Besides, coupled transformer windings permit multiple output power supplies with one-stage conversion. A primitive type of power supply system employed a 60-Hz line transformer, which was followed by a diode

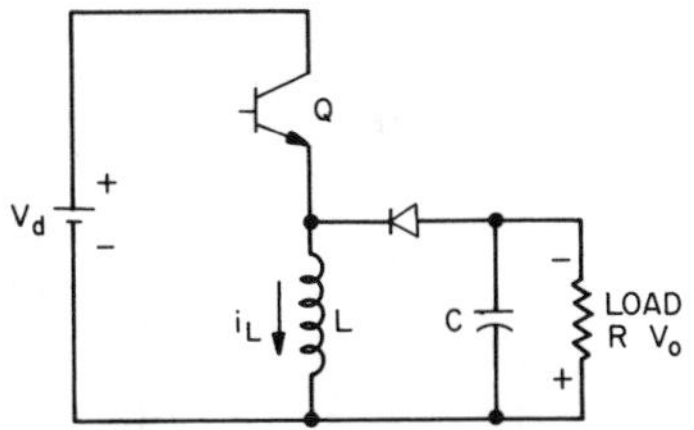

Fig. 22. Duty-cycle-modulated buck–boost converter.

rectifier, filter, dc–dc converter, and an output filter to get the regulated output. The transformer, in this case, was large and bulky. The size of the transformer can be significantly decreased if it transfers power in a high-frequency link. Gradually, with the advent of power transistors, the scheme that found acceptance uses a diode rectifier in the front end and is followed by a filter, a transformer-coupled push–pull-type PWM inverter, a diode rectifier, and a filter. If the primary power supply is dc, the input rectifier and filter are not needed.

A simple and popular flyback converter topology using only one switching device is shown in Fig. 24. When the switch is on, the energy is transferred to the self-inductance of the transformer. When the switch turns off, the stored energy is released to the output through the diode rectifier. The output voltage regulation is done by the duty cycle of the switch. Figure 25 uses a forward-type converter that needs a three-winding transformer. When the power MOSFET is on, the induced output voltage is applied to the load circuit, and, at the same time, a magnetizing current is built up linearly in the transformer self-inductance. When the switch turns off, the middle winding returns the magnetic energy, and thus resets the core flux. This biases the diode D_2 off and the filter current freewheels through the diode D_3. Again, the output voltage is controlled by the duty cycle of the switch. Because of the clamping action of D_1, the power MOSFET uses twice the supply voltage. It can be shown that for proper core flux resetting, the switch duty cycle cannot exceed 50%.

4. Diode Rectifier with Active Line Current Shaping

It has been stated that a phase-controlled rectifier generates a harmonic-rich line current with poor lagging displacement factor. More stringent power quality standards on utility systems are discouraging this type of converter. One method to improve the line displacement factor is to replace this converter by a cascaded connection of diode rectifier, LC filter, and chopper. The ideal six-step line-current wave will be practically in phase, providing near-unity displacement factor. If the filter inductance is eliminated, the line current will flow in pulses, giving poor spectral performance. This, in addition, will stress the diodes and reduce the outlet power capability (because of poor form factor of line current). The so-called active power factor correction techniques have been developed to solve these problems.

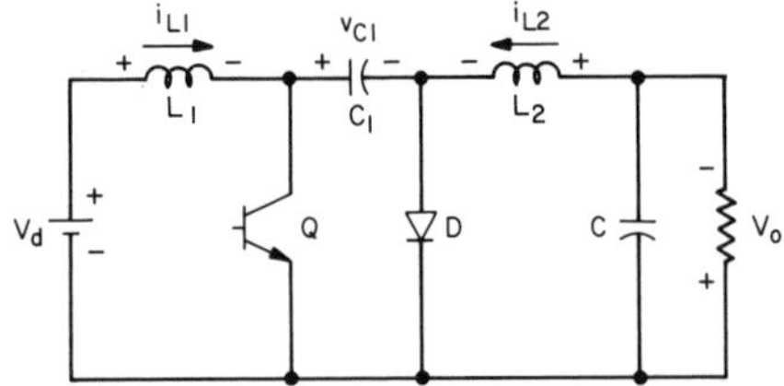

Fig. 23. Ćuk converter.

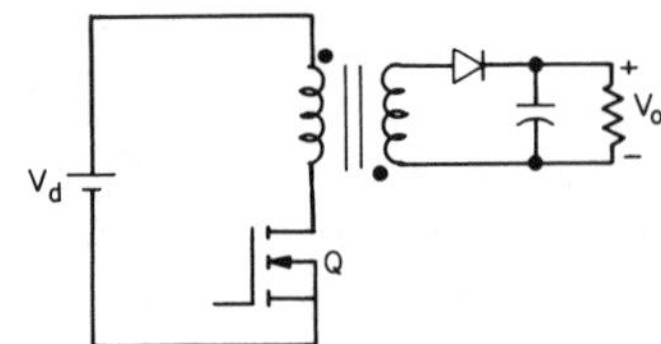

Fig. 24. Flyback dc–dc converter.

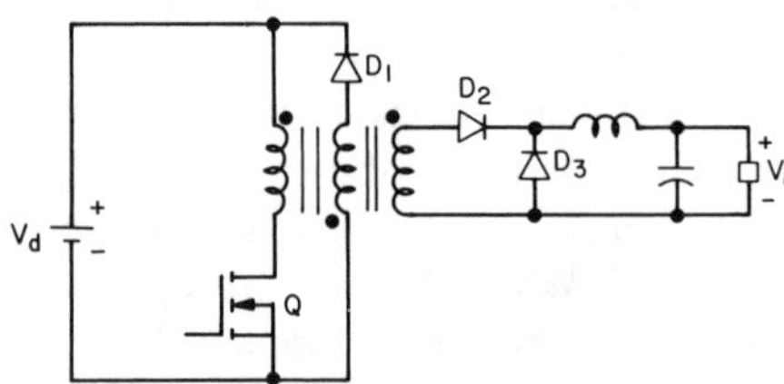

Fig. 25. Forward dc–dc converter.

4.1. Single-Phase Rectifier–Boost Chopper (Paper 4.1)

This class of converters consists of a diode rectifier cascaded with a PWM boost chopper, as shown in Fig. 26. The boost chopper basically serves two functions: 1) it regulates the capacitor voltage, which should always be higher than the peak line voltage, and 2) it controls the inductor current to be of sinusoidal full-wave rectified form, so that the line current is sinusoidal at unity power factor. The dc output can be reduced by a buck converter, if desirable, or it can supply a PWM inverter for ac machine speed control, as shown. For servo motor drives, the extended PWM range with better PWM wave fabrication due to higher and regulated dc voltage may be very useful. Instead of a boost converter, a buck–boost chopper (shown in Fig. 22) can be used to permit the output dc voltage at any desired level. However, it can be shown that in this scheme the line current will be discontinuous, giving high-frequency distortion and an electromagnetic interference (EMI) problem. This type of converter is used at low power (below 100 W), whereas the former type is built up to several kilowatts. The power can flow only in one direction, i.e., ac to dc, and therefore the regenerative braking of the drive is not possible.

The control of the converter is reasonably simple. The dc output voltage is controlled in the outer loop. The voltage loop error is multiplied with the absolute line voltage signal to generate the inductor command current wave. The measured current is controlled to track the command current within a hysteresis band.

4.2. Three-Phase Rectifier–Boost Chopper (Paper 4.2)

Three single-phase units, as previously described, can be combined into a three-phase system. However, the scheme shown in Fig. 27 is simpler and more economical. Note that the boost chopper inductance has been transferred to the line side and distributed as phase inductances, as shown. The chopper operates at constant frequency, but with pulsewidth modulation, to fabricate the average in-phase sinusoidal current in each phase. When the transistor is on, a symmetrical short circuit is created at the rectifier input and, therefore, phase currents build up proportional to the respective voltage magnitude. When the transistor turns off, the currents are pumped to the capacitor until they fall to zero value, as shown. The discontinuous current pulses at high PWM frequency can be filtered with a small LC filter.

5. DC–AC and AC–AC Converters

Converters that convert dc to ac are known as inverters. Inverters can be classified into voltage-fed and current-fed types. A voltage-fed inverter is fed by a stiff dc voltage, whereas a current-fed inverter is fed by a stiff current source. Phase-controlled line-commutated current-fed inverters were introduced in Section 2. A voltage source can be converted to a current source by connecting a series inductance and then varying the voltage to generate the desired current by a feedback loop. A voltage-fed inverter can be operated in the current control mode. Similarly, a current-fed inverter can be controlled to operate in the voltage control mode. A generic single-phase-voltage or current-fed inverter can have half-bridge, full-, or H-bridge, and push–pull transformer center-tap configurations. The H-bridge was described in the previous section. The single-phase units can be combined to have three-phase or other multiphase topologies. The inverters are used in ac machine drives, regulated-voltage and frequency-power supplies, uninterruptible power supplies (UPS), induction heating, ultrasonic wave generation, static var generators, active power line filters, and so on.

In this section, both voltage-fed and current-fed inverters will be reviewed. The discussion, in fact, will include ac–dc–ac and ac–ac–ac schemes, and the class of direct ac–ac PWM frequency changers. Finally, a summary comparison chart of various ac-to-ac conversion schemes will be presented.

5.1. Voltage-Fed Inverters

5.1.1. Square-Wave Inverter. Three single-phase half-bridge legs can be combined to have a three-phase full-bridge configuration, shown in Fig. 28. A phase-controlled thyristor bridge rectifier with an LC filter supplies dc at the input. The upper and lower transistors of a phase leg conduct for 180°, and the three-phase groups are mutually phase-shifted by 120° to generate the six-step line voltage wave at the output. The addition of a bypass diode with each transistor permits

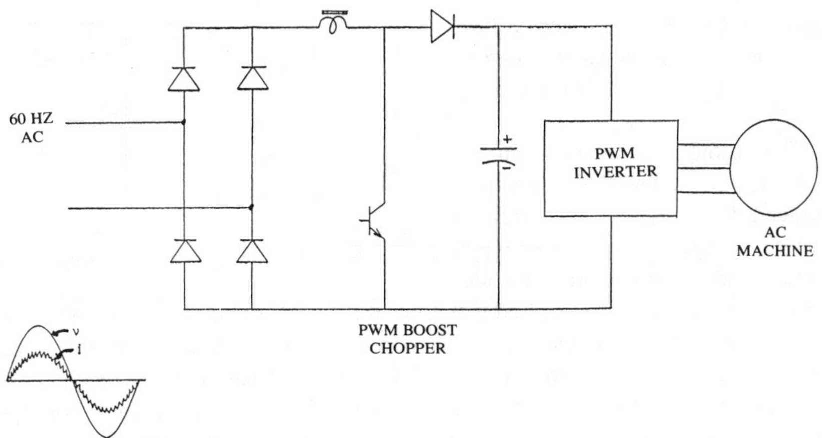

Fig. 26. Single-phase diode rectifier with boost chopper for active line-current wave shaping.

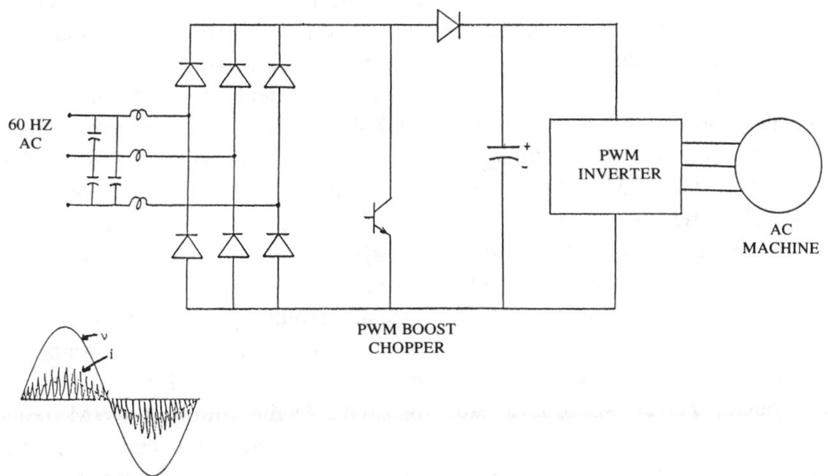

Fig. 27. Three-phase diode rectifier with boost chopper for active line-current wave shaping.

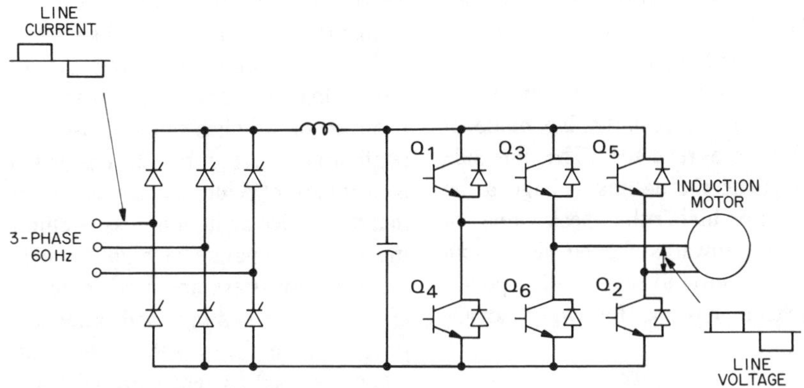

Fig. 28. Three-phase square-wave inverter with phase-controlled rectifier.

reactive power circulation and active power flow in either direction. They also clamp the load voltage wave that remains independent of the load parameters. The output frequency is controlled within the inverter, but the voltage is controlled by the firing angle of the rectifier. Many industrial installations use thyristor force-commutated inverters (such as McMurray, McMurray–Bedford, Verhoeff, and ac-switched), but these are becoming obsolete. The six-step output voltage is rich in harmonics, and therefore needs heavy filtering. Harmonic current heating and torque pulsation may be problems if the wave is directly applied across an ac machine. Multiple bridges can be combined through phase shifting transformers to generate 12-step or 24-step voltage waves. The output then becomes low in harmonic content, but the high inverter cost can only be justified for large power applications (Paper 8.3).

5.1.2. PWM Inverter. The problems associated with the square-wave inverter can be solved in the PWM inverter, shown in Fig. 29. The front-end diode rectifier and capacitor filter generates uncontrolled dc voltage at the inverter input. The output fundamental voltage and frequency are controlled within the inverter by the pulsewidth modulation method that is described in the next section. The harmonic components in a PWM wave are easily filtered because they are shifted to a high-frequency region. A PWM inverter can be viewed as a four-quadrant buck chopper in a small angular interval where the output voltage and current can be of any polarity. This function becomes evident if the inverter operates at zero frequency. The inverter can have active power flow in either direction. In the rectification mode, it can be viewed as a four-quadrant boost chopper. Of course, the recovered dc power cannot flow to the ac line, and only boosts the capacitor voltage. A buck chopper on the dc bus with resistive load can absorb this energy (defined as dynamic brake in ac drive). For an ac machine drive, the PWM voltage wave will generate a nearly sinusoidal current wave because the machine leakage inductance is enough to filter the output. Voltage-fed inverters are normally operated in the current control mode for high-performance drive applications. Modern high-power inverters invariably use GTOs. In the medium power range, IGBTs or BJTs can be used, whereas in the low-voltage and low-power range, power MOSFETs are preferred.

5.1.3. PWM Double Converter (Paper 8.2). Because a PWM inverter can have active power flow in either direction, it makes sense to connect a similar unit on the line side that will act as a rectifier. Such a PWM rectifier–PWM inverter configuration is shown in Fig. 30. In the motoring mode, the machine demands active power and, therefore, the line-side converter acts as the rectifier, whereas the machine-side converter acts as the inverter. In the regenerative mode of operation, the converter roles are reversed. The line-side converter is controlled to regulate the dc-link voltage to be constant. The dc voltage has to be higher than peak values of line and load voltages because towards the ac sides both appear as buck converters. In addition to regenerative power feedback capability, the scheme has the following advantages:

- The harmonic ripple in the line current will be very small. A small inductance is enough to make the line current nearly sinusoidal.
- The line displacement factor can be controlled to be unity. In fact, the displacement factor can be controlled to be leading or lagging as well.

5.1.4. Static var and Harmonic Compensator (Paper 8.5). The programmability of input var (leading or lagging) by the PWM rectifier in Fig. 30 is an extremely important concept, and application of this circuit as static var and harmonic compensator has recently received wide attention. To amplify the var generation concept only, let us consider the inverter section supplying an ac machine load. An ac machine may demand lagging or leading var of variable magnitude and, in an extreme case, the power factor may be zero. At zero lagging power factor load, for example, the inverter output power is zero, and, in such a case, the input rectifier can be disconnected; the inverter can be represented by an equivalent circuit of three-phase variable capacitor bank that is exchanging reactive power with the load. Using the same basic concept, a PWM rectifier with capacitor load on the dc side can be controlled to operate as lagging or leading var generator, as shown in Fig. 31. The capacitor voltage, V_d, is used to fabricate three-phase sinusoidal ac voltages at an appropriate phase angle such that the fundamental current is leading or lagging. Considering instantaneous power balance, the capacitor carries only ripple current and, therefore, with high PWM frequency, its value can be small. Again, with high PWM frequency, the inverter can fabricate input harmonic current wave to be in antiphase with that generated by a nonlinear load, i.e., the PWM rectifier can also work as an harmonic current compensator. In Fig. 31, the lagging var and harmonic currents due to thyristor converter are absorbed by the var and harmonic compensator so that the line current is sinusoidal at unity power factor.

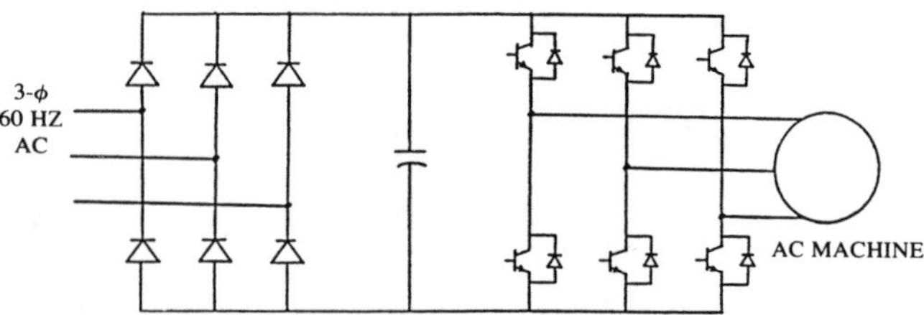

Fig. 29. Three-phase PWM inverter with diode rectifier.

5.1.5. Resonant Inverter. An inverter with a resonant circuit load is known as a resonant inverter. This class of inverters usually has single-phase, half-bridge, and full-bridge configurations. Figure 32(a) shows a full-bridge GTO resonant inverter. A unique advantage of this type of inverter is that the device switching loss is eliminated and, therefore, the inverter can operate at high frequency with high efficiency. Resonant inverters are used in resonant-link dc–dc converters, induction heating, and other high-frequency power supplies. Figure 32(b) shows the voltage and current waves where the load current harmonics are neglected. The inverter is operated at higher-than-resonance frequency so that the load current lags the output voltage, as shown. This has the advantage that the incoming pair of devices is turned on when the respective bypass diodes are conducting, reducing the turn-on loss to zero. The snubber of the inverter is a pure capacitor that charges to the supply dc voltage when the device pair is turned off. In an ordinary inverter, the capacitor energy is dumped into the snubber resistor at turn-on of the device, but here, the energy is absorbed in the main

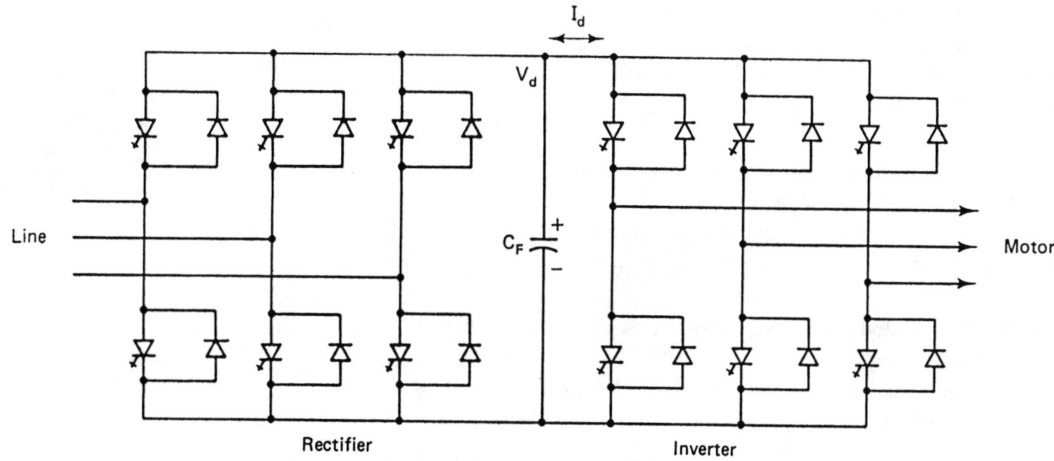

Fig. 30. PWM rectifier–PWM inverter configuration. Reprinted with permission from *Power Electronics and AC Drives*, B. K. Bose. © 1986 Prentice Hall.

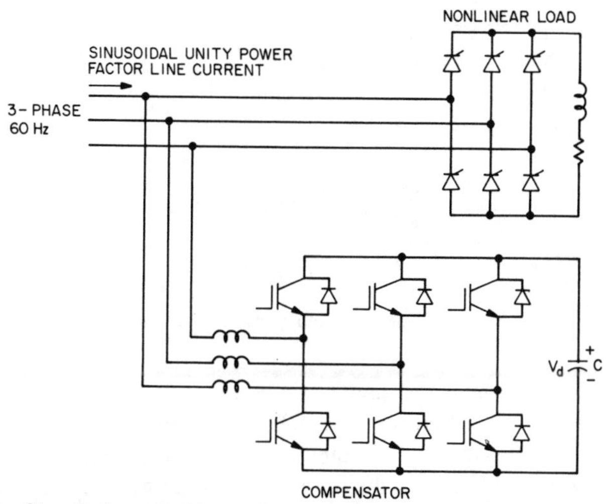

Fig. 31. Static var and harmonic compensator using PWM voltage-fed inverter principle.

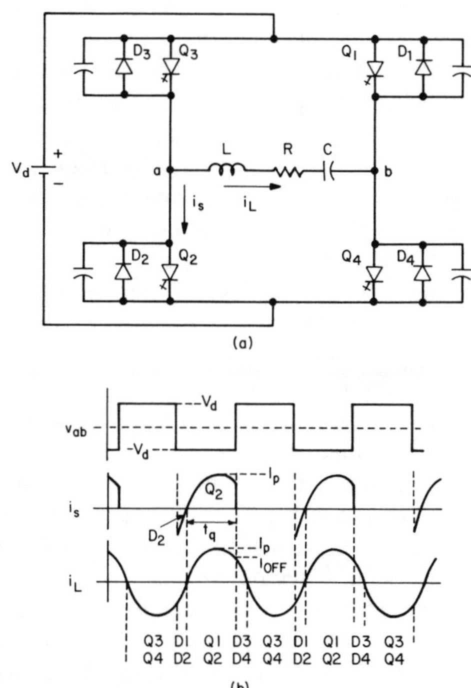

Fig. 32. (a) GTO bridge inverter with series resonant load; (b) inverter voltage and current waves.

circuit. This type of snubber is often called a lossless snubber. If the load parameters vary, the natural resonance frequency will also vary. However, the inverter frequency can easily track this variation in order to maintain the desired load power factor. The load power dissipation, or voltage, across the inductive element can be controlled either by varying the inverter frequency or by phase skewing one leg with respect to the other. GTO induction heaters of this type have been built up to 20-kHz frequency. The high-frequency output voltage can also be converted to variable-voltage variable-frequency output for the motor drive, which will be discussed later.

5.1.6. Resonant DC-Link Inverter (Paper 6.4). Conventional dc-link inverters use so-called "hard" or "stressed" switching, i.e., the devices turn on and turn off at full dc voltage, causing large switching loss. In the resonant dc-link inverter, a resonant circuit is added at the inverter input to convert fixed dc to a pulsating dc form. The purpose is to turn on and turn off the inverter devices during the zero-voltage interval. Zero-voltage, or zero-current, switching (ZVS or ZCS) is often defined as "soft," or "relaxed," switching. The resonant frequency may be in the tens of kilohertz range, so that the inverter output fundamental voltage can be fabricated at a desirable magnitude and frequency with reasonable precision, integrating these discrete pulses. An inverter operating on this principle has the following advantages:

- The device switching loss at both turn-on and turn-off disappears, thus giving high inverter efficiency.
- The device heating is low due to conduction loss only; therefore, the heat sinking or cooling requirement is low.

- The inverter can be operated without snubbers.
- All of the preceding factors make the inverter size small and at reduced cost. Lower size and smaller heat dissipation open up the possibility of inverter integration at a higher power level.
- The device reliability is improved because there is no stress due to excursion in the active area.
- The EMI problem is less severe because resonant voltage pulses have less dv/dt compared to those of a stress-switched inverter.
- For a machine drive system, the acoustic noise will be very small because of high frequency.
- The machine insulation is less stressed because of lower dv/dt resonant voltage pulses.

Because of these merits, resonant-link inverters show great promise in the future. A resonant-link inverter for induction motor drive is shown in Fig. 33 (Paper 6.5), and Fig. 34 shows the link voltage and current waves. The circuit is shown with a diode rectifier and filter to establish the dc voltage V_s. The elements L_r and C_r constitute the resonant circuit that establishes the pulsating V_d wave, shown in Fig. 34. The inverter switches operate during zero-crossing intervals to fabricate the output voltage wave by integrating these pulses (integral PWM). A desired current wave can also be fabricated by the hysteresis-band (normally with zero bandwidth) method, which will be discussed later. The lack of PWM resolution as that of a stress-switched inverter causes the harmonic ripple current to become somewhat higher. The shunt switch S_r establishes (through the ON device S_A) the desired initial current in the inductor L_r before releasing the resonant voltage swing. The initial current controls the peak dc voltage and the zero-crossing intervals. It should track the inverter input current, which can be of either polarity. The current initialization circuit can make the polarity of I_m negative with the help of an auxiliary dc source. This bidirectional current tracking, based on the predictive estimation of inverter input current, restricts the dc peak voltage near $2V_s$ and assures reliable inverter operation. The over-voltage penalty is another demerit of the inverter. Note that the negative current initialization occurs by stressed switching at reasonably low frequency (at motoring mode). This slightly offsets the efficiency advantage of the inverter.

Instead of initial inductor current control, as previously described, constant control can be maintained on a conservative basis and the dc-link peak voltage can be controlled by a passive or active clamping technique. In the passive clamping method, a transformer with a series diode in the secondary is connected across the inductor L_r and, as the voltage tends to exceed a threshold value, the diode conducts pumping the inductor trapped energy to the source. In this method, the dc-link voltage can be limited typically to 2.5 V_s. Using active clamping, the voltage can typically be reduced to 1.3 V_s. A resonant inverter with active clamping is shown in Fig. 35. Note that here the shunt switch S_r is eliminated, and, instead, all the inverter switches turn on simultaneously

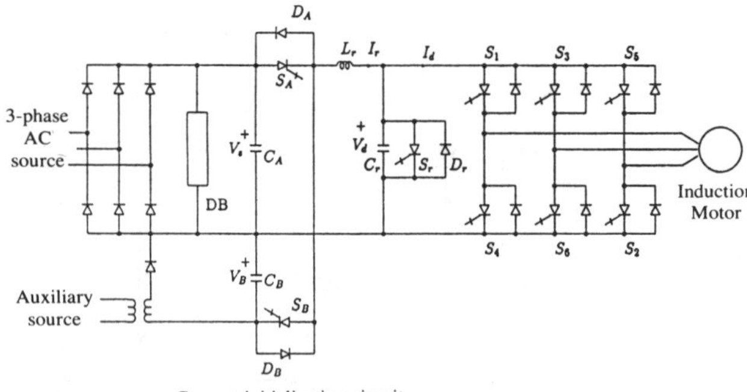

Fig. 33. Resonant dc-link inverter system with current initialization scheme.

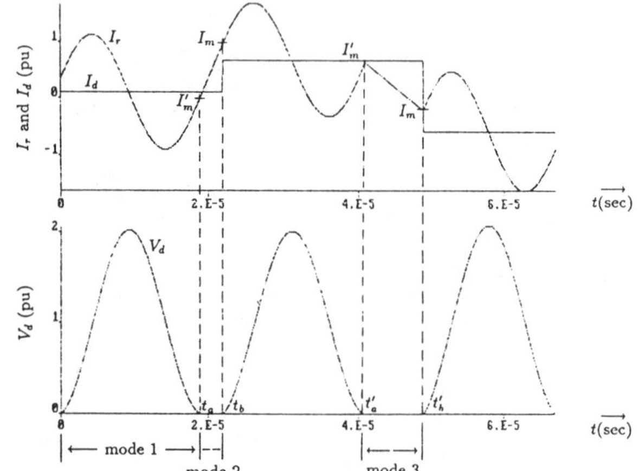

Fig. 34. Resonant-link voltage and current waves.

to establish the fixed and positive inductor initial current. When the desired current is reached, the selected devices are opened to establish the output voltages as dictated by the PWM algorithm. At the end of the resonant cycle, the inverter diodes provide a path for negative current in the zero-crossing interval. The active clamping circuit consists of a precharged capacitor in series with a transistor–diode pair as shown, and its operation can be explained as follows: On releasing the dc bus short, the link voltage swings toward its natural peak. However, on reaching the voltage level KV_s, the diode D conducts and clamps the bus voltage. With D conducting, the transistor Q is turned on in a lossless manner. The trapped inductor current linearly decays to zero (assume large C) and then becomes negative through Q. The charge transferred to C by the diode is recovered by the transistor conduction. When the net charge transfer is zero, Q is turned off to initiate resonance again until the bus voltage falls to zero. The active voltage clamping is definitely superior because of reduced voltage penalty. But there are disadvantages: 1) The effective resonant time period is lengthened due to linear decay of inductor current during clamping. This constrains the maximum frequency; 2) the volt-second interval of each resonant pulse will vary due to the interaction of the inverter input current. Both of these effects will cause harmonic deterioration of inverter output current.

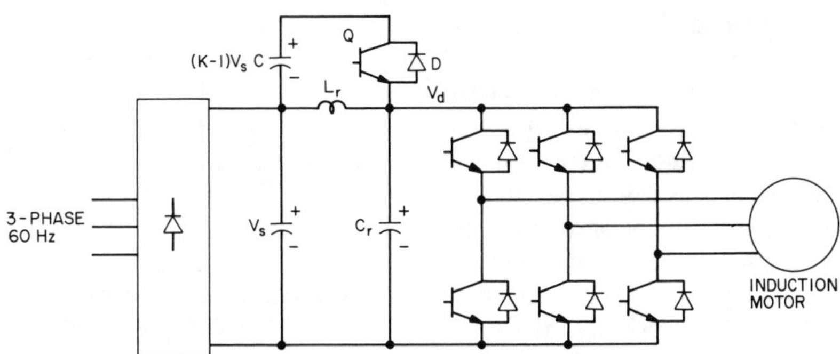

Fig. 35. Resonant dc-link inverter system with active voltage clamping.

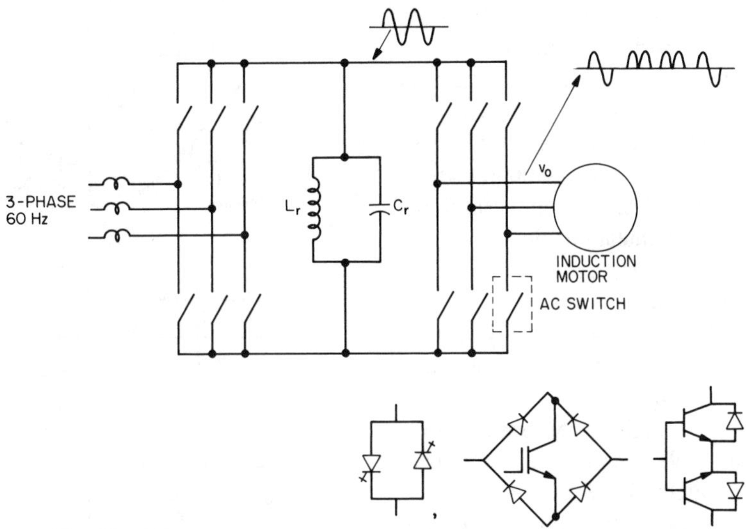

Fig. 36. Resonant ac-link converter system showing configuration of ac switches.

5.1.7. Resonant AC-Link Converter. The concept of resonant ac-link power conversion using thyristor phase-controlled cycloconverters was known in the early 1970s. In a typical scheme, three-phase 60-Hz ac is converted to high-frequency ac (several kilohertz) by three single-phase-to-single-phase cycloconverter units. The high-frequency ac (single-phase) is then cycloconverted to three-phase variable-voltage variable-frequency ac for ac motor drive. The link frequency is maintained nearly constant by a parallel resonant circuit. Such a scheme can have bidirectional power flow, and the input displacement factor can be programmed to be unity, leading or lagging. A recently proposed topology of a resonant ac-link converter using self-controlled ac switches is shown in Fig. 36 (Paper 4.6). The 60-Hz power is first converted to high-frequency ac (typically 20 kHz), which is then converted to variable-voltage variable-frequency ac for ac machine drive. Since the link voltage is ac, the devices should have symmetric voltage blocking capability and must carry current in either direction. Possible configurations of the ac switch are shown in the figure. Both the input and output converters switch at zero voltage to synthesize the low-frequency voltage waves by the integral half-cycle PWM method. The line currents are nearly sinusoidal, and power can be controlled to flow in either direction. The line-side converter regulates the resonant tank voltage, and, in addition, controls the input power factor near unity (leading or lagging power factor is possible). The need for high-frequency ac switches is the principal drawback of the scheme. High-frequency devices do not have reverse voltage-blocking capability. Therefore, antiparallel high-speed switches need series-blocking diodes. Since the tank capacity is small, a small mismatch between input and output instantaneous power will tend to modulate the link voltage. Besides, the link frequency will drift because of the loading effect. This will cause harmonic deterioration of input and output currents, and possible system instability during fast transient.

5.2. Current-Fed Inverters

5.2.1. Load-Commutated Inverter. It has been previously stated that a phase-controlled line-commutated converter demands lagging var at the input in both rectification and inversion modes. A synchronous machine can be controlled to operate at leading power factor, i.e., it can deliver lagging var at the output. Therefore, the ac source can be replaced by a synchronous machine that can run in the motoring or regenerative braking mode. This type of commutation by a leading power factor load is known as load commutation. Figure 37 shows a general load-commutated inverter synchronous machine drive system, and Fig. 38 shows the waveforms at motoring condition. In the motoring mode, the line-side converter operates as the rectifier ($0 < \alpha < 90°$) and the machine-side converter operates as the inverter ($90° < \alpha < 180°$), whereas in the regenerative mode, their roles are reversed. The simple and economical converter topology and the simplicity of control make the scheme attractive for large power wound-field synchronous machine drives. The inverter commutation depends on machine counter EMF and, therefore, the scheme cannot be used at low speed. Besides, there are other disadvantages of line-side poor power factor and harmonic distortion of current.

5.2.2. Force-Commutated Auto-Sequential Inverter. A current-fed inverter supplying a lagging power factor load, such as an induction motor, needs forced commutation. Figure 39 shows an auto-sequential-type force-commutated inverter for induction motor drive. The capacitors and the diodes in the inverter are the commutation elements. The diodes tend to isolate the commutating capacitors from the machine terminal. Each thyristor conducts for 120°, as in a phase-controlled converter. When an incoming thyristor is fired, capacitor voltage with inverse polarity is impressed across the outgoing thyristor to turn it off. This type of inverter is used in medium- to high-power applications. Four-quadrant operation of the drive system is easy and there is no shoot-through failure problem. However, the inverter frequency range is low due to a large commutation angle, and the commutation voltage spikes require voltage derating of the devices. Again, harmonic current heating and torque pulsation (especially at low speed) are additional problems. Now, this type of inverter is becoming obsolete.

5.2.3. PWM Inverter (Paper 6.2). If the thyristor inverter in Fig. 39 is replaced by self-controlled reverse blocking devices such as GTOs or IGBTs with series diodes, the commutating diodes can be removed and then the inverter can be operated in a six-step waveform mode at any load power factor. Such an inverter configuration is shown in Fig. 40. In fact, with self-controlled switches, the PWM current wave can be synthesized at the output. The shunt capacitor bank, as shown, has the following functions: 1) it provides a bypass path for the load inductive current so that the GTOs can be switched without causing undue voltage overshoot, and 2) it acts as a low-pass filter so that the machine voltage and current waves are nearly sinusoidal. The distinct advantages of this type of inverter are, the machine harmonic copper loss is substantially low, giving better efficiency; there is no pulsating torque problem at any machine speed; and the annoying acoustic noise practically disappears. However, if an harmonic current component falls near the resonant frequency (due to machine leakage inductance and capacitor bank), the corresponding voltage component will be boosted.

Note that the capacitor size is small, and the major amount

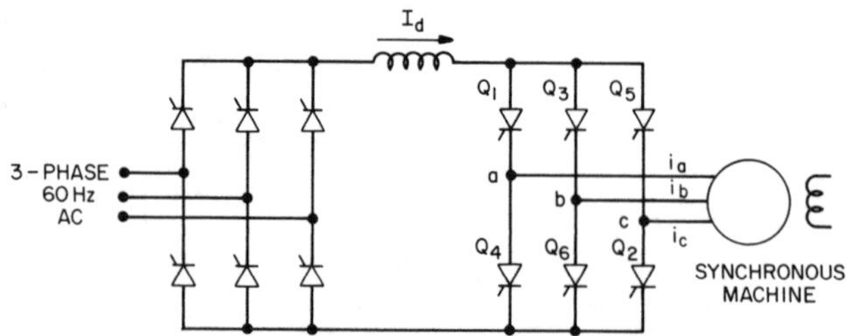

Fig. 37. Load-commutated thyristor inverter with wound-field synchronous machine load.

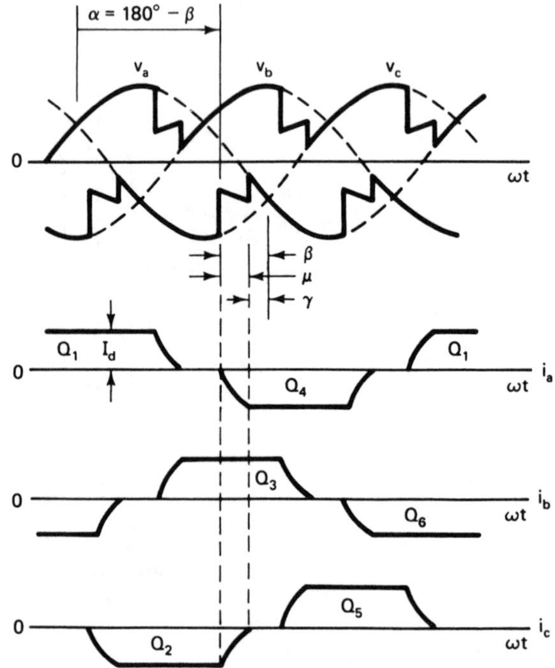

Fig. 38. Load-commutated inverter voltage and current waves in motoring mode. Reprinted with permission from *Power Electronics and AC Drives*, B. K. Bose. © 1986 Prentice Hall.

of load lagging var is supplied by the inverter. The PWM principle is explained in Fig. 41, where the middle 60° interval is unmodulated, as indicated. For example, unmodulated phase a positive current is modulated in phase b and phase c negative currents. The modulation factor (A/B) is normally fixed to generate an harmonically optimum current wave, but the modulation frequency is varied so that the GTO switching frequency is nearly constant. Intentional leg shoot-through is permitted in the unmodulated 60° interval to reduce the capacitor overshoot voltage. The output fundamental current is varied by the dc-link current, which in turn is varied by the front-end converter. The power can easily flow in either direction. This type of drive is becoming popular in large (several thousand horsepower) ratings, especially for retrofit applications.

5.2.4. PWM Double Converter (Paper 6.3). The line-side power factor in Fig. 40 can be improved by replacing the phase-controlled converter with a PWM rectifier as shown in Fig. 42. The system has duality in configuration with the

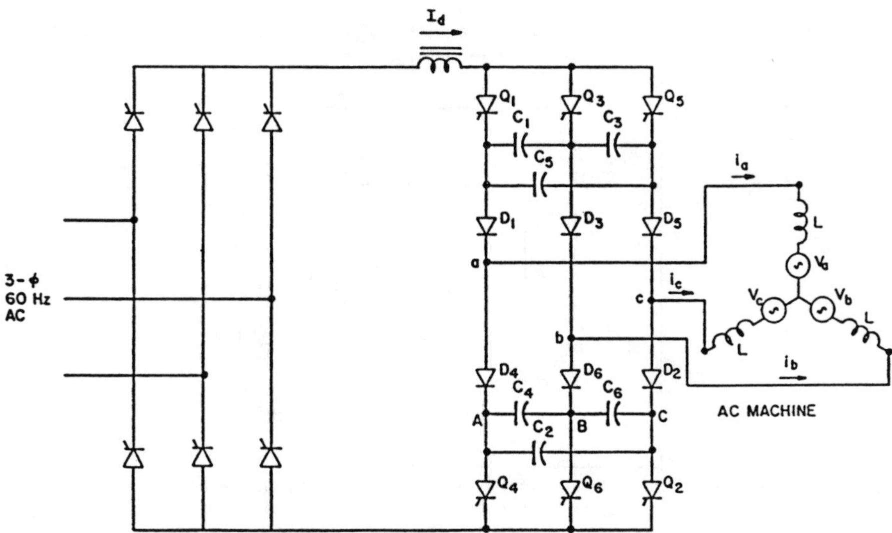

Fig. 39. Force-commutated auto-sequential-type thyristor inverter.

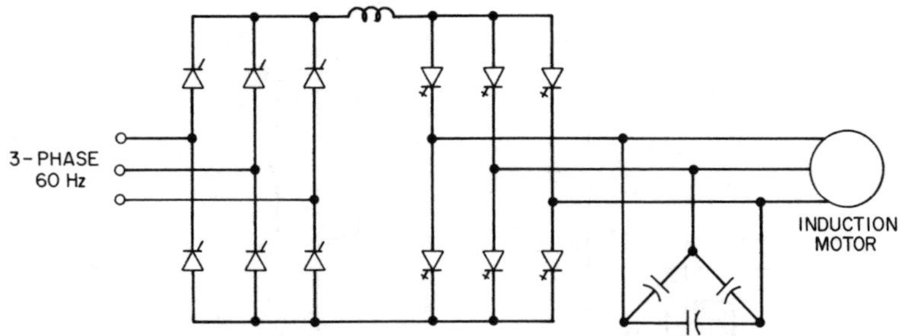

Fig. 40. GTO PWM current-fed inverter system for induction motor drive.

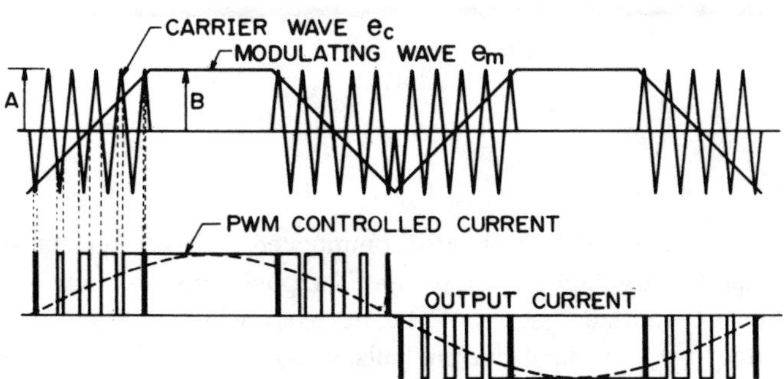

Fig. 41. Pulsewidth modulation principle of GTO current-fed inverter.

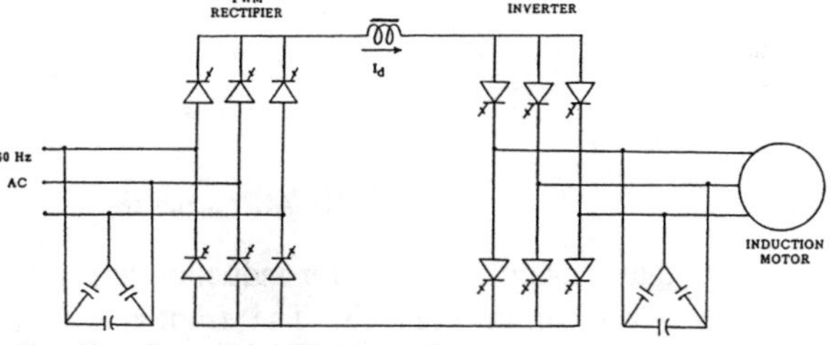

Fig. 42. Current-fed PWM rectifier–PWM inverter configuration.

PWM voltage-fed converter system shown in Fig. 30. The rectifier can also function as an inverter for bidirectional power flow. It controls the dc-link current by modulating the dc voltage, and the phase position of the input PWM-fabricated current wave is controlled such that the displacement factor is unity (leading or lagging possible). The line current wave is nearly sinusoidal to that of the machine current due to the input capacitor filter. Since the dc link inductor sees reduced voltage ripple compared to that in Fig. 39, its value is substantially reduced.

5.2.5. Static var and Harmonic Compensator (Papers 8.5, 8.8). In Fig. 42, the inverter section with the machine load can be removed and the dc-link output can be shorted. Such a converter configuration can be used as a static var and harmonic compensator. The scheme can be considered as dual to the voltage-fed scheme shown in Fig. 31. The dc current, I_d, is used to fabricate the PWM current wave such that the reactive and harmonic currents are totally absorbed in the converter. The losses in the inductor and the switches are supplied from the ac side, which consumes a small active current.

Both the voltage-fed and current-fed schemes can be designed for single-phase circuit operation, but the capacitor or inductor size will be larger due to a large second harmonic component. The current-fed compensator scheme is not popular because of higher losses and the need for high-frequency self-controlled symmetric blocking PWM switches (which are usually not available).

5.2.6. Resonant Inverter. A single-phase parallel reso-

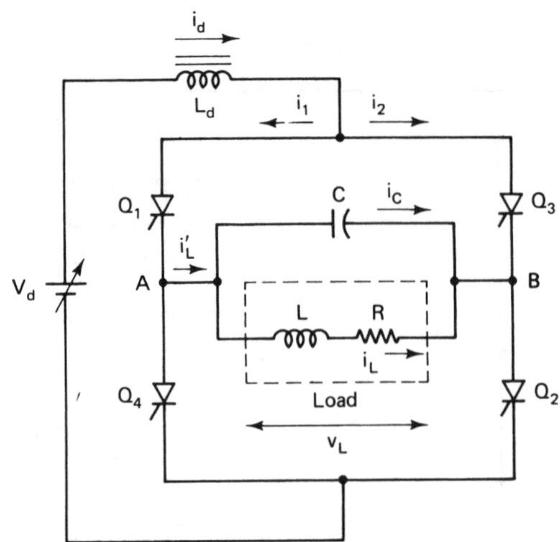

Fig. 43. Single-phase current-fed parallel resonant inverter. Reprinted with permission from *Power Electronics and AC Drives*, B. K. Bose. © 1986 Prentice Hall.

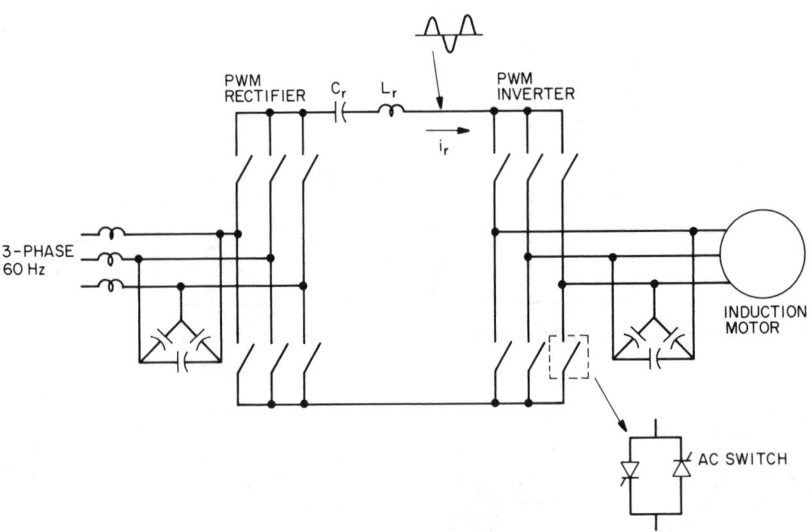

Fig. 44. Series resonant ac-link rectifier–inverter system.

nant inverter that is popularly used for induction-heating-type applications is shown in Fig. 43. The front-end rectifier generates the dc-link current, which is converted to a square wave by the inverter. The inverter always operates at higher-than-resonance frequency so that the load power factor is leading and the thyristors are commutated by the load voltage (load commutation). If load parameters vary, causing variation of resonance frequency, the inverter frequency tracks it so that the load-leading power factor angle remains constant. Forward-blocking (self-commutating) GTOs can be substituted for thyristors, and zero-voltage switching permits a higher frequency range.

Again, the high-frequency voltage can be used to synthesize three-phase variable-voltage variable-frequency output for an ac machine drive with the help of a zero-voltage-switched ac switch converter, shown in Fig. 36.

5.2.7. Series Resonant AC-Link Inverter. The series resonant ac-current-link converter system shown in Fig. 44 can be considered as dual to the voltage-fed scheme given in Fig. 36. Normally, antiparallel thyristors have been used as ac switches and these are commutated at zero current of discrete resonant current pulses. The power flow is controlled by appropriate gating of the devices, which set up high-frequency resonant current pulses. At the end of a current pulse, the outgoing thyristors become reverse-biased and turn off. The magnitude, polarity, and duration of resonant current pulses are dependent on the tank elements L_r and C_r, and the line-to-line dc voltage segment (positive or negative) selected on the input- and output-side converters. The PWM current wave consists of a train of discontinuous resonant current pulses that are filtered by the capacitor banks to constitute near-sinusoidal current waves at both input and output. Again, the active power flow can be in either direction, and the line-side power factor can be controlled to be near unity, leading or lagging.

5.3. PWM Direct Frequency Changer (Papers 4.4, 4.5)

The standard nine-switch PWM direct frequency changer, often called a Venturini or matrix converter, is shown in Fig. 45. The circuit topology can be considered analogous to that

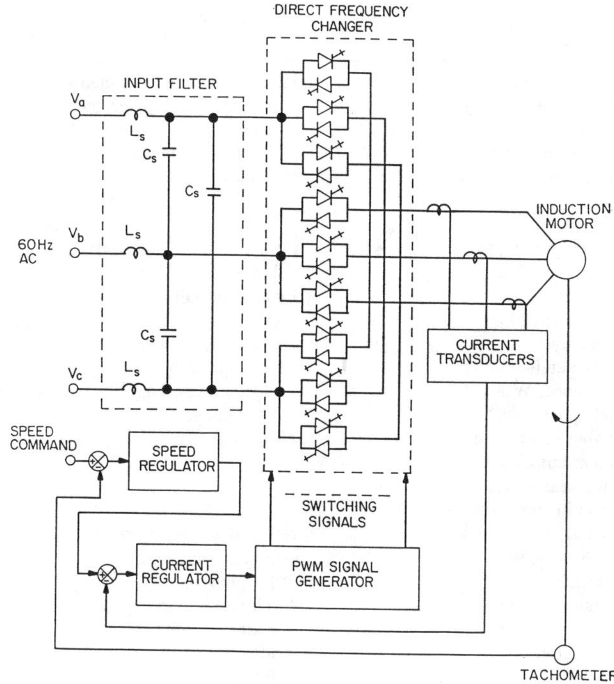

Fig. 45. Nine-switch PWM direct frequency changer.

of the 18-thyristor cycloconverter shown in Fig. 16, where the antiparallel thyristors constitute the nine ac switches. The exception here is that the ac switches are self-controlled and are operated at high-frequency PWM mode to synthesize variable sinusoidal voltage at variable frequency. The PWM operation of the switches requires that at least one side should appear as the voltage source (with capacitance connection) to provide a bypass path for the inductive current. The capacitor size is determined by the voltage transient overshoot and filtering requirement. The general features of the converter can be summarized as follows:

- The sinusoidal output fundamental voltage can be controlled from zero up to 95% of the input. The output fundamental frequency can be controlled from zero (dc) typically up to 200 Hz.
- The harmonic spectrum of the output voltage and input current is such that nominal load inductance and input capacitance will filter it.
- There is no need for dc- or ac-link passive components.
- The input power factor can be controlled to be near unity, leading or lagging.

In spite of these advantages, the lack of availability of integrated high-frequency ac switches has not made the converter attractive. The use of multiple devices to constitute an ac switch is uneconomical, more lossy, and introduces control complexity.

5.4. Summary Comparison of AC–AC Converters

In previous sections, the principles and characteristics of various converter systems that can convert fixed-frequency utility power to variable-voltage variable-frequency output power have been described. In this section (Table II), we will make a summary comparison of the general features of the main converter types with emphasis on ac drive applications. For topology identification, figure numbers are given in the chart.

6. PWM Methods

Although PWM converters have been introduced in previous sections, here we describe the important PWM techniques that are applicable to voltage-fed inverters. By this time, it is evident that the object of pulsewidth modulation is to generate harmonically optimum voltage or current wave at the inverter output so that the magnitude and frequency of the fundamental component can be smoothly varied. The PWM methods can be classified as voltage-control PWM and current-control PWM. In the latter category, the recent predictive space vector method is described in some detail.

6.1. Voltage-Control PWM

6.1.1. Sinusoidal PWM. The sinusoidal PWM method, also known as the triangulation, subharmonic, or suboscillation method, is very popular in industrial applications and is extensively reviewed in the literature. The sinusoidal PWM principle for a half-bridge inverter is explained in Fig. 46. The sine modulating wave is compared with a triangle carrier wave, and the natural points of intersection determine the switching points of the inverter power devices. A common carrier can be used for all three phases. The frequency and amplitude of the modulating wave can be varied to get variable-frequency variable-voltage output. For an isolated neutral three-phase load, such as the ac machine, it can be shown that the phase-voltage wave has the steps of 0, $+1/3\ V_d$, and $+2/3\ V_d$, whereas the line voltage steps are 0, $+V_d$. The carrier may be free-running (asynchronous) or can be tracked with the modulating frequency (synchronous) with a fixed ratio. This ratio is programmed so that the inverter switching frequency remains within a small band. The modulation index $m(V_p/V_T)$ can be varied between zero and 1 to get a linear relationship between the modulating and output voltages. But, as m approaches 1, the notch widths near the center of the modulating wave tend to vanish, causing a "voltage jump" problem. By increasing m to a large value, gradual transition to a square wave is possible. In the linear range, the output harmonics are carrier-frequency-related with modulating-frequency sidebands. However, overmodulation will introduce modulating-frequency-related harmonics.

6.1.2. Selected Harmonic Elimination. The undesirable lower order harmonics (5th, 7th, 11th, 13th, etc.) of a square wave can be selectively eliminated, and the fundamental output voltage can be controlled by this method. Here, the notches are created at predetermined angles of the square wave, as shown in Fig. 47. The half-cycle output shown has quarter-wave symmetry. With the four notch angles ($\alpha 1$, $\alpha 2$,

TABLE II

	Square-wave VFI (Fig. 28)	PWM VFI (Fig. 29)	Boost chopper PWM VFI (Fig. 26)
1. Power devices	Symmetric thyristors in rectifier. Asymmetric devices and fast recovery diodes in inverter.	High-frequency asymmetric devices and fast recovery and fast recovery diodes in inverter.	High-frequency asymmetric devices for chopper and inverter and fast recovery diodes for inverter.
2. Converter rating	Up to tens of kWs. Very high with larger number of steps.	Up to hundreds of kWs to MWs.	Up to a few kWs.
3. Power flow	Only to output. Dynamic braking possible.	Only to output. Dynamic braking possible.	Only to output. Dynamic braking possible.
4. Load harmonics	High. May have torque pulsation problem at low frequency.	Low, especially with higher switching frequency.	Low, especially with higher switching frequency.
5. Line harmonics	High with lower order harmonics. EMI problem.	High. Depends on line inductance. Worse in single phase.	Low, especially with higher switching frequency.
6. Line power factor	Low lagging, mainly due to phase control.	Somewhat low due to current pulses but disp. factor near unity. Worse in single phase.	Near unity.
7. Machine acoustic noise	Moderate. Lower with larger number of steps.	Somewhat high. Low at higher switching frequency.	Somewhat high. Low at higher switching frequency.
8. Efficiency	High.	High, but additional switching losses.	Moderately high. Extra chopper loss.
9. Cost	Low to medium.	Low to medium.	Additional chopper cost. Somewhat larger capacitor.
10. Control complexity	Simple for rectifier and inverter.	Somewhat complex.	Additional complexity due to chopper control.
11. Comments	Becoming obsolete except with larger number of steps for higher power.	Very popular. Direct dc input may be from battery.	Popular with single-phase input. Buck/boost chopping and dc voltage level control possible.

TABLE II (*Continued*)

	Double PWM CFI (Fig. 42)	Res. DC-link VFI (Fig. 33 or 35)	Res. AC-link VFI (Fig. 36)
1. Power Devices	High-frequency symmetric devices.	High-frequency asymmetric devices and fast recovery diodes in inverter.	High-frequency symmetric ac switches.
2. Converter rating	Up to hundreds of kWs to MWs.	May be tens of kWs.	May be tens of kWs.
3. Power flow	Bidirectional power flow.	Only to output*. Dynamic braking possible.	Bidirectional power flow.
4. Load harmonics	Very low. Selected harmonic component may cause resonance.	Medium. Low at higher resonance frequency.	Medium. Low at higher resonance frequency.
5. Line harmonics	Very low. Selected harmonic component may cause resonance.	High. Depends on line inductance. Worse in single phase.	Medium. Low at higher resonance frequency.
6. Line power factor	Near unity. Leading or lagging possible.	Somewhat low due to current pulses but disp. factor near unity. Worse in single phase.	Near unity. Leading or lagging possible.
7. Machine acoustic noise	Low.	Very low.	Very low.
8. Efficiency	Moderately high. High switching loss, but less inductor loss.	High. No switching loss.	Somewhat high. No switching loss but extra conduction loss.
9. Cost	High, but dc-link inductance is small.	Medium.	High.
10. Control complexity	Very complex.	Complex.	Very complex.
11. Comments	Very attractive in high power, but expensive.	Technology under development. High future potential. * Bidirectional power flow may be possible.	Technology under development. AC-link modulation problem. Problem of high-frequency ac switches.

TABLE II (*Continued*)

Double PWM VFI (Fig. 30)	Auto-sequential CFI (Fig. 39)	PWM CFI (Fig. 40)
High-frequency asymmetric devices and fast recovery diodes.	Symmetric thyristors in rectifier and inverter.	Symmetric thyristors in rectifier. High-frequency symmetric devices in inverter.
Up to hundreds of kWs to MWs.	Hundreds of kWs.	Hundreds of kWs to MWs.
Bidirectional power flow.	Bidirectional power flow.	Bidirectional power flow.
Low, especially with higher switching frequency.	High. May have torque pulsation problem at low frequency.	Very low. Selected harmonic component may cause resonance.
Low, especially with higher switching frequency.	High with low-order harmonics. EMI problem.	High with low-order harmonics. EMI problem.
Near unity. Leading or lagging possible.	Low lagging mainly due to phase control.	Low lagging mainly due to phase control.
Somewhat high. Low at higher switching frequency.	Moderate. Lower with larger number of steps.	Low.
Moderately high. High switching loss.	High, but additional inductor loss.	High, but extra switching and inductor loss.
High.	Somewhat high.	Somewhat high.
Very complex.	Simple for rectifier and inverter.	Somewhat complex.
Very attractive, but expensive. Single-phase input popular in locomotive.	Commutation transient problem. Becoming obsolete.	Presently popular in multi-MW drive especially for retrofit applications.

TABLE II (*Continued*)

Res. AC-link CFI (Fig. 44)	Phase-Control Cyclo (Fig. 16)	PWM Cyclo (Fig. 45)
High-frequency symmetric ac switches.*	Symmetric thyristors.	High-frequency symmetric ac switches.
May be tens of kWs.	Hundreds of kWs to MWs.	Up to tens of kWs.
Bidirectional power flow.	Bidirectional power flow.	Bidirectional power flow.
Low. Selected harmonic component can cause resonance.	High. Somewhat high. May have subharmonic problem.	Low to medium. Low at higher switching frequency.
Low. Selected harmonic component can cause resonance.	High. May have subharmonic problem.	Low. Lower at high switching frequency. Selected harmonic component can cause resonance.
Near unity. Leading or lagging possible.	Low lagging (lower than phase-controlled converter).	Near unity. Leading or lagging possible.
Very low.	Low with 60-Hz input.	Somewhat high. Low at higher switching frequency.
Somewhat high. No switching loss but extra conduction loss.	Very high.	Moderately high. High switching and conduction losses.
High.	Somewhat low.	Somewhat high.
Very complex.	Somewhat complex.	Complex.
Technology under development. Problem of high-frequency ac switches.	Common in multi-MW drive. Likely to be replaced by PWM converter in future.	Attractive, but problem of high-frequency ac switches.

* Anti-parallel thyristors can be used if frequency is not high.

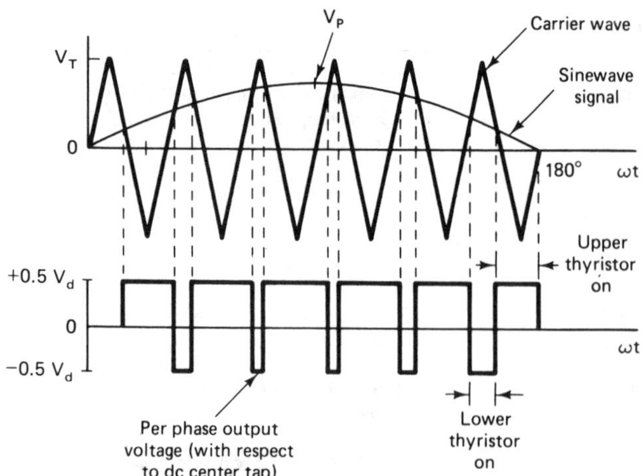

Fig. 46. Principle of sinusoidal pulsewidth modulation. Reprinted with permission from *Power Electronics and AC Drives*, B. K. Bose. © 1986 Prentice Hall.

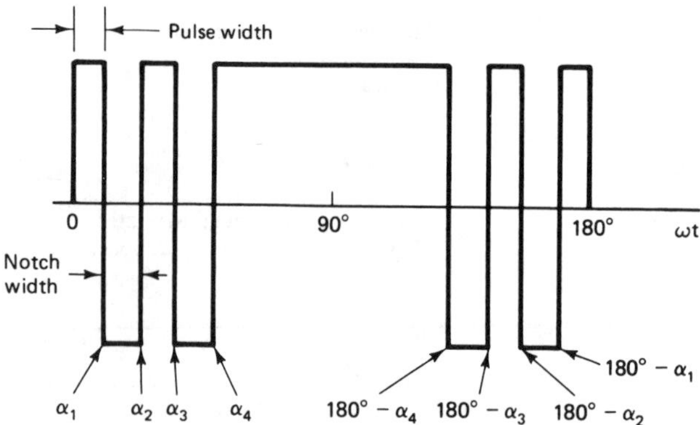

Fig. 47. PWM voltage wave with selected harmonic elimination (for half-bridge with respect to dc center tap). Reprinted with permission from *Power Electronics and AC Drives*, B. K. Bose. © 1986 Prentice Hall.

$\alpha 3$, and $\alpha 4$) shown, for example, the 5th, 7th, and 11th harmonics can be eliminated, and the fundamental component can be controlled to a desirable value. At low fundamental frequency, the number of notch angles may be large for elimination of a large number of lower order harmonics. This method is normally implemented by microcomputer, using a large look-up table of notch angles. At high frequency, the transition to the square wave may be smooth because the last two notches can be gradually shifted to the edges of the half-cycle before dropping them.

6.1.3. Minimum Ripple Current. One disadvantage of the harmonic elimination method discussed is that the elimination of lower order harmonics considerably boosts the other lower order significant harmonics. Since the harmonic loss in a machine is essentially dictated by the rms ripple current, it is this parameter that should be minimized instead of harmonic elimination on an individual basis. The notch angles shown in Fig. 47 can be iterated in a computer program in order to minimize the calculated rms ripple current for a particular machine. This modified look-up table of α-angles, based on harmonic copper loss minimization, is more desirable than that of the harmonic elimination method. However, one problem is that the parameters of a machine are not strictly constant and can vary with saturation and temperature. The look-up table of angles can be refined to some extent by incorporating this variation.

6.1.4. Delta Modulation. This is a simple and idealized PWM scheme especially suitable for ac machine drive where a constant flux, i.e., volts/Hz is desired. The operation principle is somewhat analogous to the hysteresis-band current control scheme described later. Figure 48 explains the delta-modulation principle. The circuit consists of a Schmitt trigger in series with an integrator, and the integrator output is fed back to the Schmitt trigger through a comparator. The sinusoidal reference signal V_R is fed at the input, as shown. The output signal V_A is the desired PWM wave. With V_R of positive polarity, V_A will also tend to be positive until the feedback voltage, V_B, generated by the integrator and comparator exceeds V_R by the preset hysteresis-band $V_A R_2/R_3$. Then, V_A becomes negative and the slope of the integrator is reversed, thus forcing V_F to oscillate around the reference wave V_R, as shown. The fundamental component of V_F is equal to that of V_R, but because of integration, the following relations are valid:

$$V_R = V_{RM} \sin \omega t = V_F = V_{AF} \cos \omega t = V_{AF}/\omega \sin \omega t \quad (1)$$

or,

$$V_{RM} = V_{AF}/\omega = \psi_s \quad (2)$$

where V_R = fundamental stator-phase voltage, ω = fundamental frequency, and ψ_s = machine stator flux per phase. This means that delta modulation is essentially an open-loop volts/Hz, or flux control, scheme. As the frequency is gradually increased, the voltage saturates and the machine smoothly transitions into the square-wave mode. The performance of the delta-modulated inverter is crude, because stator drop compensation is not possible at low speed, and dc-link fluctuation (average or ripple voltage) cannot be compensated. Besides, independent frequency control for the high-performance drive is not possible. The scheme is rarely used in practice.

6.2. Current-Control PWM (Paper 7.2)

6.2.1. Hysteresis-Band Method (Paper 7.1). The voltage PWM methods discussed so far assume that the dc voltage is constant and ripple-free, which is practically far from true. Of course, for regulated voltage output, the feedback control loop will provide the necessary correction. If current control is desired, a feedback current-control loop is necessary, and then the loop error generates the voltage command such that dc link–voltage-variation is compensated. High-performance ac machine drives invariably use current-control PWM because machine torque and flux are directly related to current. The hysteresis-band current-control method

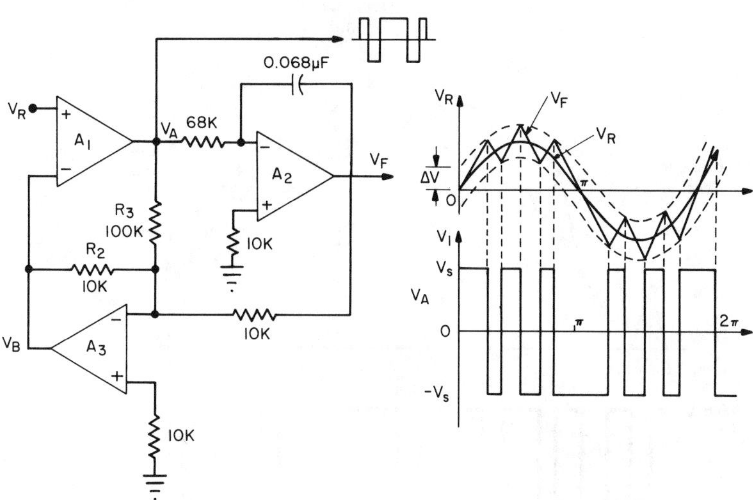

Fig. 48. Delta-modulation principle.

is very popular in such applications. Figure 49 explains this PWM method. The magnitude and frequency of the desired current wave are determined by the outer control loop. The reference current wave is compared with the actual current wave, and, as the current exceeds a prescribed H-band, the upper transistor of the half-bridge is turned off and the lower transistor is turned on. The current starts to decay, and, as the lower band is crossed, the switching of the transistors is reversed. Thus, the actual current wave is forced to track the reference wave within the H-band by back-and-forth switching of upper and lower transistors, irrespective of dc voltage fluctuation and the ripple. The scheme is simple to implement by hardware. The peak-to-peak current ripple is directly controlled and the response time of the current controller is very fast. It does not need any system parameter information except the actual current wave. However, it can be shown that the PWM frequency varies within a band and the load current harmonic ripple is not optimum. In addition, there is a phase lag of the fundamental current that increases with fundamental frequency.

6.2.2. Adaptive Hysteresis-Band Method (Paper 7.3). The shortcomings of the constant H-band current-control method can be compensated by using a programmable H-band scheme, as shown in Fig. 50. The band is modulated with a phase angle, and the mean bandwidth is varied such that the PWM frequency remains constant, irrespective of system parameter variations. Such a current wave can be made harmonically optimal. If, for example, the dc voltage decreases, the PWM frequency will decrease with a fixed H-band, causing an increased ripple current. This is compensated by reduction of the band so that the original PWM frequency and the corresponding ripple content is restored. The implementation of the scheme needs a microcomputer for calculation of the band from system parameter information. The phase interaction of the three-phase isolated neutral load can also be compensated in this method.

6.2.3. Instantaneous Current-Control with Voltage PWM. This method is essentially based on the sinusoidal-voltage PWM technique, as described before, but uses an instantaneous current control in the outer loop. The desired reference current wave is compared with the actual current and the error generates the sinusoidal modulating voltage wave through a high-gain PI (proportional-integral) compensator. The voltage wave then usually generates the PWM signal by asynchronous sinusoidal PWM method. The carrier frequency is normally high compared to modulating frequency so that the subharmonic beating effect is minimal. The phase lag of the actual current wave with respect to the reference wave is a problem that can be improved with high loop gain (within a stability limit). This lag angle increases as the frequency increases. The modulating voltage wave contains a high-frequency ripple, and there may be a problem due to multiple zero crossings with the triangular ramp if the voltage slope exceeds the ramp slope.

6.2.4. Predictive Space Vector Method (Paper 7.4). This is a computation-intensive indirect current tracking control method that is based on the concept of machine-voltage and current space vectors. The space vector PWM technique essentially eliminates the interaction between the phases of a three-phase isolated neutral load and, therefore, the tracking current wave has reduced harmonic content compared to that of a fixed H-band method. The principle of this method is explained in Fig. 51(a). The three-phase voltage-fed inverter shown in Fig. 29 has basically eight switching states, and, corresponding to each state, there is a machine space vector, as summarized in Table III.

A space vector is derived by the combination of instantaneous phase voltages as follows:

$$V = 2/3\,[\,V_A + \alpha V_B + \alpha_2 V_C] \tag{3}$$

where $\alpha = 120°$.

A sinusoidal machine with three-phase sine-wave-applied voltages generates a space vector of magnitude V_m (peak phase voltage) that rotates synchronously in the airgap. In a

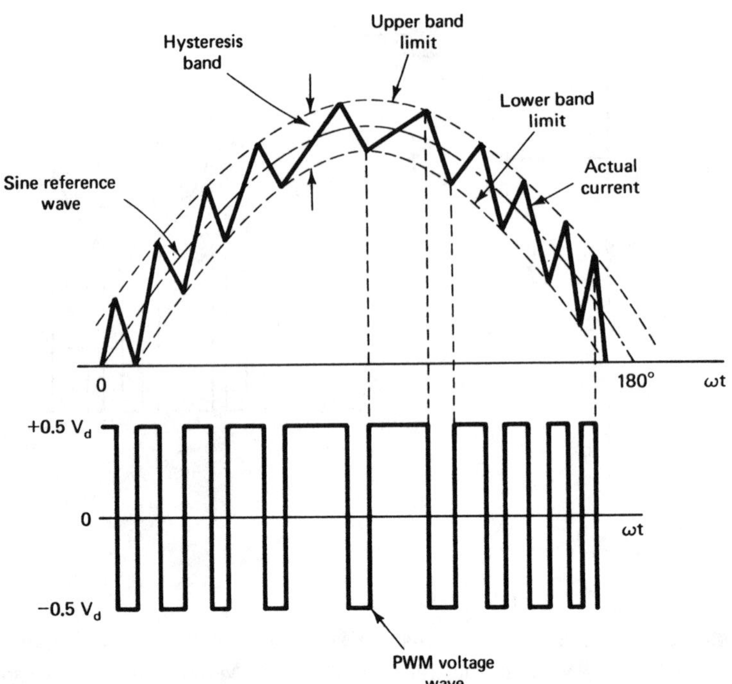

Fig. 49. Hysteresis-band current control PWM principle. Reprinted with permission from *Power Electronics and AC Drives*, B. K. Bose. © 1986 Prentice Hall.

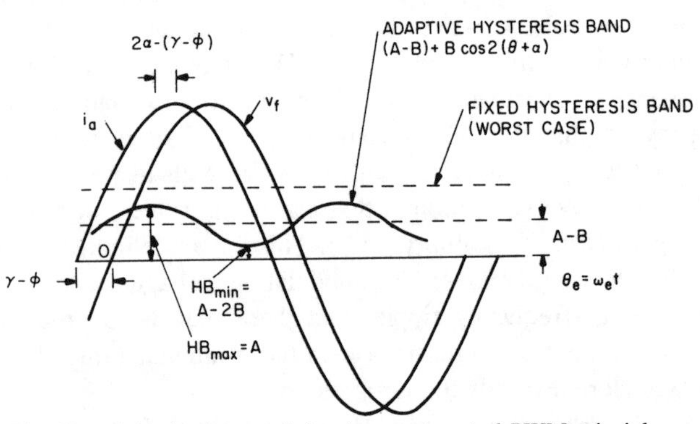

Fig. 50. Adaptive hysteresis-band current control PWM principle.

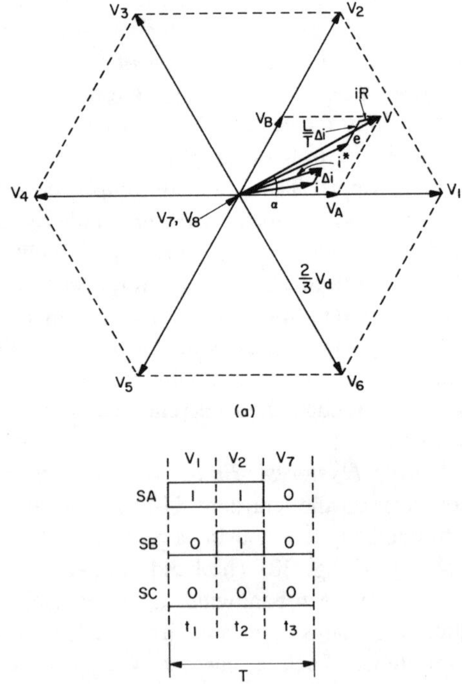

Fig. 51. (a) Inverter voltage space vectors showing synthesis of desired voltage to minimize current error; (b) corresponding PWM wave in the interval T.

dc-switched inverter of voltage V_d, the space vectors are of length $2/3V_d$ and their locus forms the hexagon shown in Fig. 51(a). The machine current space vector is given by an equation similar to (4). The different steps of computation of the space-vector PWM method can be summarized as follows:

1) Sample the machine phase currents i_a, i_b, and i_c at every PWM sampling period T.

2) Calculate the space vector $i(k)$ by (3).

3) Calculate the current error $i = i^*(k+1) - i(k)$, where $i^*(k+1)$ = predicted command current space vector in $(k+1)$th interval.

4) Calculate the desired inverter voltage space vector by using the following difference equation:

$$V(k) = e(k) + \frac{i^*(k+1) - i(k)}{T} \cdot L + Ri(k) \quad (4)$$

where $e(k)$ = machine counter EMF, R = machine equivalent resistance, L = machine equivalent inductance, and T = sampling period.

5) Compute V_A and V_B components that align with the

TABLE III
INVERTER SWITCHING STATES AND THE CORRESPONDING SPACE VECTORS (SEE FIG. 28)

State	ON-Device	Voltage Space Vector
1	Q1 Q6 Q2	V1
2	Q1 Q3 Q2	V2
3	Q4 Q3 Q2	V3
4	Q4 Q3 Q5	V4
5	Q4 Q6 Q5	V5
6	Q1 Q6 Q5	V6
7	Q4 Q6 Q2	V7 (free wheeling)
8	Q1 Q3 Q5	V8 (free wheeling)

nearest voltage vectors as follows:

$$V_A = V\cos\alpha - 0.5\, V_B \tag{5}$$

$$V_B = 2/3\, V\sin\alpha. \tag{6}$$

6) Generate the corresponding inverter switching intervals as shown in Fig. 51(b) (from Table III) as follows:

$$t_1 = \frac{V_A}{2/3\, V_d}\cdot T \tag{7}$$

$$t_2 = \frac{V_B}{2/3\, V_d}\cdot T \tag{8}$$

$$t_3 = T - (t_1 + t_2). \tag{9}$$

The scheme is predictive because computations are done in the kth interval to compensate the current error for the $(k+1)$th interval. The inverter switching frequency $(1/T)$ is always constant. The complex computations are to be done every T interval by a high-speed digital signal processor. The variation of machine parameters and error of computation may be problems, resulting in a significant current tracking error. The transient performance of the control is poor due to computational delay. Besides, there is no direct current-limiting feature as in H-band control.

7. RESONANT-LINK DC–DC CONVERTERS (PAPERS 5.4, 5.5)

7.1. Resonant Converter

The PWM type dc–dc converters using the stressed switching principle have already been discussed. If the switching frequency is raised too high for a reduction of size of the passive components, the switching loss will be excessive, which will not only adversely affect the converter efficiency, but the additional heatsinking need will increase its size and weight. The designers of power supplies that are used in computer, telecommunication, and instrumentation applications are under tremendous pressure to reduce the size of power supply units so that they become compatible with that of miniature IC chips. The class of high-frequency resonant-link dc–dc converters tends to fulfill this need. There are wide varieties of this type of converter, but here only a typical but popular topology given in Fig. 52 will be described.

In the circuit, the primary dc source may be a battery, or a rectified dc supply. The supply is split with the help of capacitors and then inverted to high-frequency (several MHz) ac by a MOSFET half-bridge inverter. The resonant capacitor voltage is transformer-coupled, diode-rectified, and then filtered to get the output dc voltage. The inverter is operated at higher-than-resonance frequency, as discussed in Section 5.1.5, to eliminate the switching loss. Therefore, the efficiency is improved as well as the size of the transformer, and the filter parameters are reduced. The transformer helps buck/boost operation and isolation of the output. The output voltage is regulated by control of the inverter frequency. For a higher power inverter, the half-bridge can be replaced by a full-bridge. Again, instead of parallel loading, as shown in Fig. 52, the resonant circuit can be series-loaded, i.e., the transformer with the output circuit can be placed in series with the tuned circuit. The series loading has the inherent short-circuit current-limiting feature that is not possible with parallel loading. However, no-load regulation is not possible with series load; it is easy with parallel load. It can be shown that hybrid operation (part of C_r in series with the resonant circuit) overcomes both of the shortcomings. The voltage-fed series resonant inverter can be replaced by the current-fed parallel resonant inverter shown in Fig. 43.

7.2. Quasi-Resonant Converter (Paper 5.8)

This class of converters, as the name indicates, is a hybrid between the PWM and the resonant-link types and, therefore, combines the good features of both. In a PWM converter, the transformer leakage inductance, or stray inductance, in series with the switch and parallel capacitance contributed by the switching device are both harmful. However, in a quasi-resonant converter, both elements are gainfully utilized to get zero voltage and/or zero-current-switching to eliminate the switching losses.

Although varieties of circuit topologies are possible, we will discuss here only the zero-voltage-switched flyback-type converter, as shown in Fig. 53(a). The regulated dc voltage V_o is derived from an unregulated dc input V_d. The waveforms of the converter are shown in Fig. 53(b). The converter operates at several MHz frequency. The resonant inductance L_r consists of the transformer leakage inductance (referred to the primary) in series with stray lead inductance. The MOSFET body diode D and the junction capacitance C_1 are shown by dotted lines. The additional capacitance C_2 is connected in parallel to constitute the total resonant capacitance C_r. The resonant frequency is higher than the switching frequency. The MOSFET is switched on at zero voltage when its bypass diode is conducting, as shown in Fig. 53(b). At ON-condition, the current wave is nearly rectangular in shape, as in a PWM converter. The switch turns off at zero voltage, initiating the resonant pulse. A minimum load current must be maintained in order to prevent

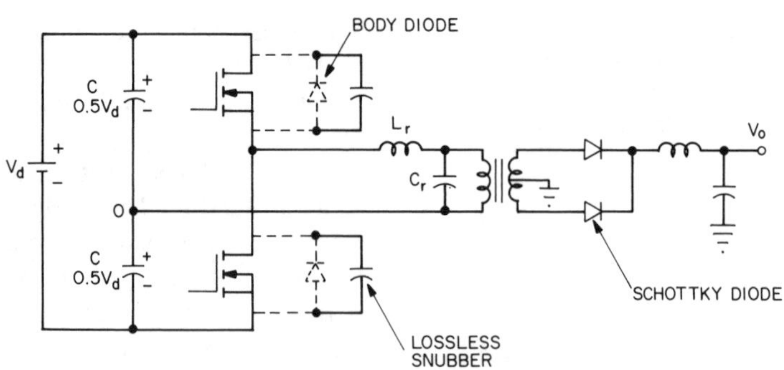

Fig. 52. Resonant-link dc–dc converter.

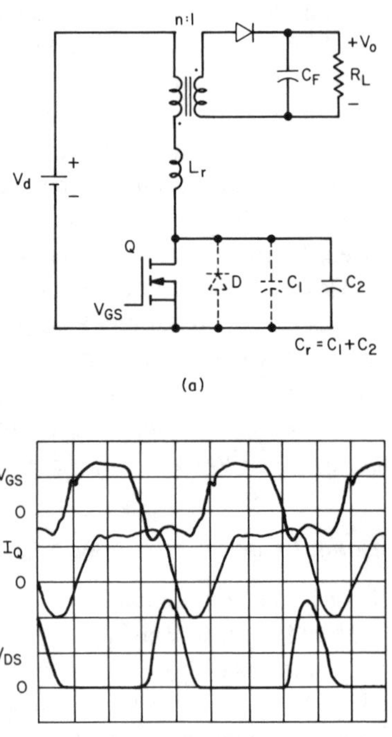

Fig. 53. (a) Quasi-resonant flyback converter with zero-voltage switching; (b) voltage and current waves.

the loss of oscillation. The output voltage is regulated by the control of switching frequency. Although the switching device has voltage penalty, there is practically no current penalty due to its flat-topped waveshape. The resonant frequency may vary widely due to tolerance of the circuit parameters.

8. Power Electronics Applications

Power electronics is widely used in industrial, commercial, residential, and aerospace systems, as was discussed at the beginning of this Introduction. Many other applications have been reviewed in the previous sections. A few more selected applications will be described here.

8.1. High-Frequency Fluorescent Lighting

Although fluorescent lamps are expensive, they are popular because of their longer life and higher energy efficiency (3 to 4 times) compared to incandescent lamps. The efficiency can be improved further, typically 20% to 30%, by using high-frequency electronic ballast. A typical high-frequency ballast system is shown in Fig. 54. A single-phase 60-Hz supply is rectified to dc and then inverted to 30-kHz ac by a standard half-bridge PWM voltage-fed inverter. Alternatively, a resonant-type inverter can also be used. The lamp cathodes of the two fluorescent lamps are continually heated by the three secondary windings, as shown. The inverter output is boosted by an autotransformer and applied across the two lamps in series. The transformer winding leakage inductances provide the series ballast needed for stable operation at lamp conduction when its resistance is low. A filter is normally used at the input of the rectifier (not shown) to suppress conducted EMI. High-frequency ballast not only is smaller in size, gives better efficiency, and reduces the harmful low-frequency stroboscopic effect, but also makes light-dimming control possible.

8.2. Uninterruptible Power Supply (UPS) (Paper 8.7)

Utility power supplies have inherent blackout, brownout, overvoltage, distortion, and transient problems. A reliable and high-quality power supply is of vital importance for critical loads, such as computers, communication equipment, and medical systems. In such applications, battery-backed uninterruptible power supplies are often used. The power supply may be dc or ac, and the system topology varies widely, depending on the application. Figure 55 shows a typical three-phase UPS system where the load can be supplied either from the utility line or from the battery-fed inverter. An electronic circuit breaker consisting of antiparallel thyristor switches helps in the fast transfer of the source. In Fig. 55, the utility line normally supplies the load, and the floating inverter is considered as standby. The inverter system consists of a diode rectifier, battery charger, storage battery, LC filter in the dc link, PWM inverter, and output LC filter. The inverter generates sinusoidal-regulated voltage at 60 Hz at the output from the unregulated dc input. Under normal conditions, the rectifier directly supplies the inverter input when thyristor Q remains off. At utility power interruption, Q is switched on and then the battery takes over to supply the inverter input. When the inverter is a standby, the battery is charged by the single-phase thyristor rectifier. The

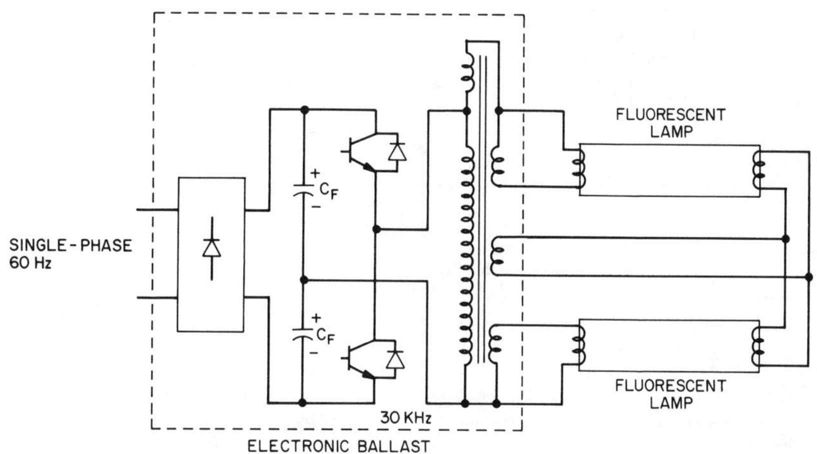

Fig. 54. High-frequency electronic ballast for fluorescent lamps.

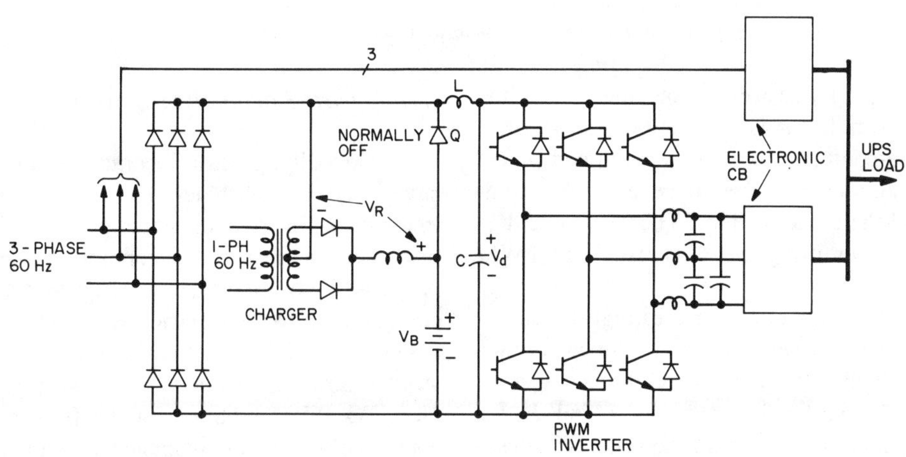

Fig. 55. Three-phase UPS system with standby inverter.

rectifier boost voltage $+V_R$ acts in series with the voltage V_d to charge the battery. At the partially discharged condition, the battery is charged with full rated current, and then a trickle charging current is maintained at the fully charged condition. In case the utility power is lost or its quality deteriorates, the line-side breaker is opened and the inverter breaker is closed to transfer the load to the inverter. The transfer causes power interruption for a subcycle period while load-storage elements maintain the continuity. When utility power is restored, the load is transferred back to the line. Parallel loads are normally connected through properly coordinated fuses so that the faulty load is quickly isolated without affecting the source and other loads. It is also possible to keep the line as standby and supply the load from the inverter.

The same principle is also applicable to a single-phase UPS system. Transformer isolation can be provided between the load and the source, if desired. Highly critical loads can always be supplied from a parallel redundant inverter system, where the inverter outputs are synchronized on the same bus. If an inverter component becomes faulty, it can be quickly isolated by opening its electronic circuit breaker. A more versatile UPS system with an engine generator is shown in Fig. 56. The normal loads that can withstand interruption are supplied from the utility bus, but the supply for essential and critical loads can be transferred to the engine generator, as shown. The engine generator start-up time is assumed to be less than 1/2 minute. During this time, the critical loads are supplied by a low-capacity battery-backed UPS.

8.3. *High-Frequency Induction Heating*

In induction heating, high-frequency current passing through a coil causes iron loss (hysteresis and eddy current losses) in a workpiece that raises its temperature. It was mentioned in Section 5 that a high-frequency induction heating system can use either a voltage-fed series resonant inverter or a current-fed parallel resonant inverter. Figure 57 shows a typical 100-kHz 5-kW induction heating system that uses the voltage-fed inverter principle. The dc supply for the inverter is obtained from a diode rectifier-boost chopper unit, which was explained in Section 4.1. This scheme permits

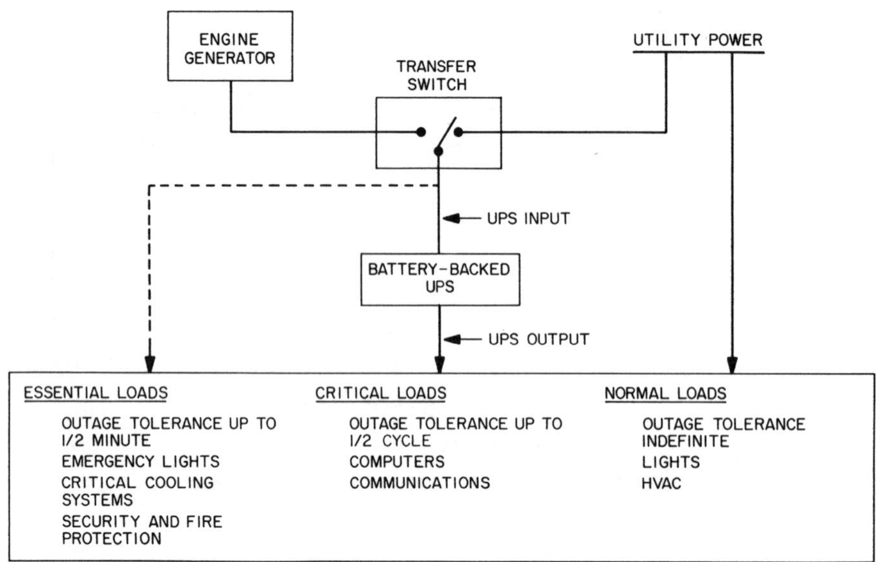

Fig. 56. A versatile UPS system with engine generator.

control of the dc voltage V_d as well as shaping the ac line current so that the power factor is near unity. As shown in the figure, the voltage-control loop error is multiplied by the full-wave–rectified-line-voltage wave to generate the command current wave of the diode rectifier. This current is then controlled by the chopper using the hysteresis-band PWM principle.

The inverter is a full-bridge type that uses high-frequency static induction transistors (SITs). Its output is stepped down by a transformer and applied to the work coil through a series tuning capacitor C. The work coil parameters L and R, the transformer leakage inductance, and the capacitor C constitute the resonance circuit. The resonance frequency varies with the variation of parameters L and R. The inverter is controlled such that its frequency f tracks the resonance frequency f_r, but $f > f_r$, so that the load power factor is always lagging. This permits lossless inverter switching, which was explained in Section 5.1.5. As the workpiece gets heated and its temperature rises, the inductance L will decrease, causing a rise of both the f and f_r frequencies. This will correspondingly raise the power output of the inverter. However, the voltage V_d can be regulated to control this power flow. The inverter is self-controlled and the basic control elements are indicated in the figure. The capacitor voltage that lags the coil current by 90° and the load voltage V_L by an additional lag angle is phase-shifted for control of the inverter. The signal is converted to high frequency by the phase-locked loop (PLL) circuit and then used to synthesize a triangular wave by an UP–DOWN counter. The triangular wave is phase-split and compared with a bias voltage V_B to generate the logic drive signals for the SITs. The bias signal generates the appropriate lock-out time to prevent a shoot-through fault. Note that the SITs are normally ON devices. Therefore, they are biased OFF outside the desired conduction intervals.

8.4. Electric Locomotive Drive with Induction Motors

Traditionally, electric locomotives and subway transit cars have used dc machine drives. Recently, there has been tremendous interest in induction motor drives because the machine is more robust, economical, lightweight, and needs practically no maintenance. Figure 58 shows the typical configuration for an electric locomotive induction motor drive system. The 25-kV 60-Hz single-phase catenary supply is stepped down and isolated by transformers to feed the multiple GTO PWM rectifiers in the front end. Each drive unit consists of two parallel-connected rectifiers, a capacitor filter, a GTO PWM inverter, and a pair of induction motors connected in parallel. Each of the four motors drives an axle of the locomotive. The scheme permits bidirectional power flow for four-quadrant drive operation. The parallel rectifier units permit better current sharing than that with direct paralleling of devices. The rectifier operates in the PWM mode to regulate the dc-link voltage as well as to fabricate sinusoidal ac line current at unity power factor. The built-in leakage inductance of the line transformer absorbs the PWM wave voltage harmonics. The inverters operate in the PWM mode at low speed, but go to the square-wave mode at high speed. It is desirable that the machines should have matched parameters for parallel operation. Again, it is desirable that the parallel machines should run at identical speed.

A practical problem arises in traction drive because the wheel diameters cannot be identical. A larger wheel, for example, will have a slower speed (i.e., larger slip), and this will cause larger torque sharing for the machine in the motoring mode. However, in the braking mode, the same machine will share a smaller torque. This sensitivity with wheel diameter tolerance is serious because the machines have low slip characteristics. Finite mismatch of machine parameters may compound the problem of torque sharing. It

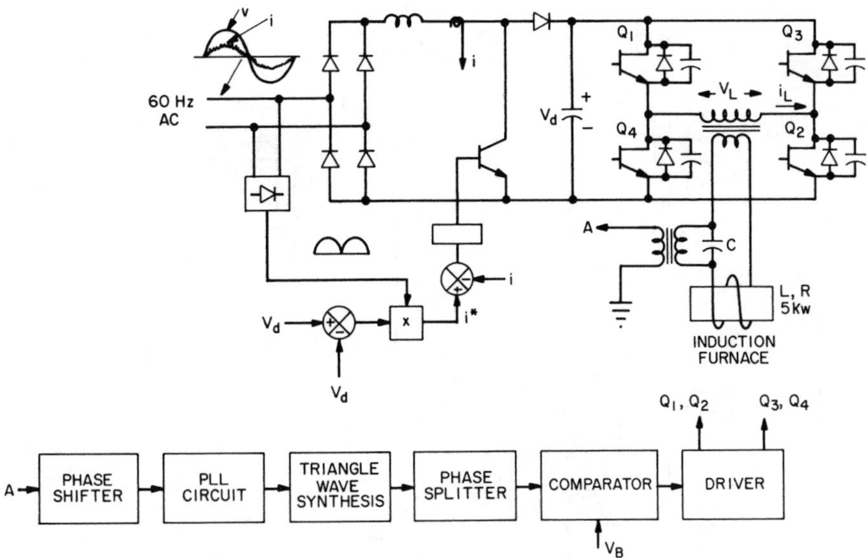

Fig. 57. High-frequency induction heating system using SITs.

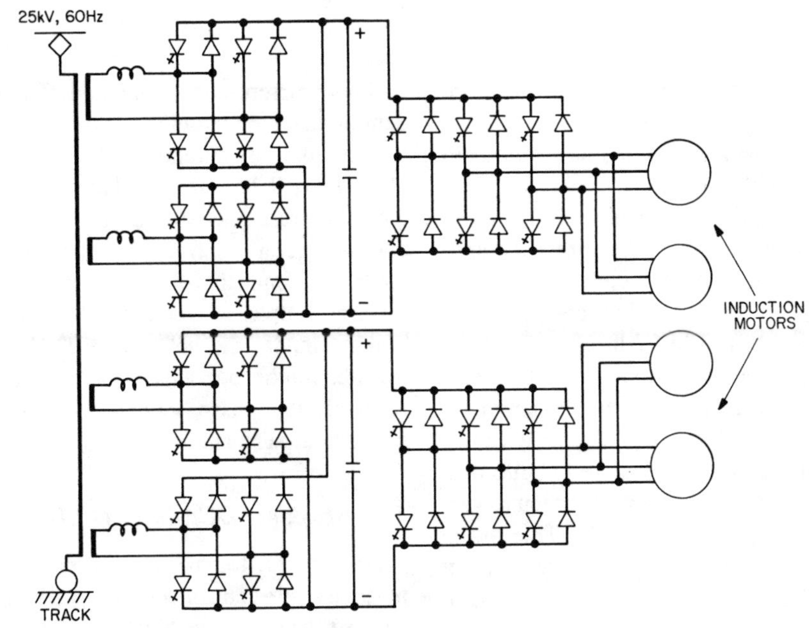

Fig. 58. Electric locomotive induction motor drive system.

is convenient to control the parallel-connected machines in the voltage-control mode; therefore, volts/Hz control with slip-command (proportional to torque) control is normally preferred. The subway transit drive system is essentially the same, except the dc input supply is directly obtained from the third rail. In a diesel electric locomotive, the regulated synchronous generator ac voltage is diode-rectified to get the dc voltage for the inverter.

8.5. Induction Motor Servo Drive with Indirect Vector Control

The transient response of an induction motor drive is somewhat sluggish with the conventional volts/Hz control method, because both torque and flux are functions of stator voltage and frequency. By using the vector- or field-oriented-control method, the performance of the induction motor drive can be made almost identical to that of a separately excited dc motor. This means that the transient response is dc-machine-like, the conventional instability problem does not exist, and flux and torque can be controlled in a decoupled manner. Between the direct (or feedback) method and indirect (or feedforward) method, the latter is preferred because of less interference of harmonics in feedback signal processing. Figure 59 shows a block diagram of an induction motor servo drive using the indirect vector-control method. The power circuit consists of a diode bridge rectifier, capacitor filter, and three-phase IGBT PWM inverter that drives an induction motor. A dynamic brake is

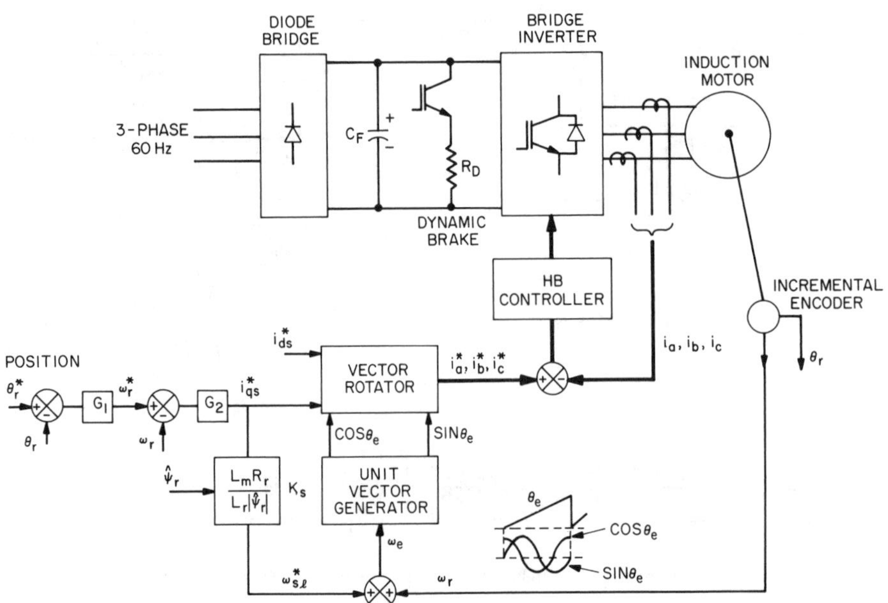

Fig. 59. Induction motor servo drive using indirect vector-control method.

included in the dc link, which is essentially a one-quadrant buck chopper that limits the dc-link voltage in case it tends to exceed a threshold value. The servo drive operates from zero speed with four-quadrant capability.

In Fig. 59, the position-control loop generates the speed command, and the speed loop generates the torque component of current i_{qs}^*, as shown. The machine is operated at constant rotor flux $\hat{\psi}_r$; therefore, the flux component of current i_{ds}^* is maintained constant. The feedback position and speed signals are usually generated from an optical-type encoder. The speed signal ω_r is added with the slip command (ω_{sl}^*) to generate the stator frequency (ω_e) signal. It can be shown by derivation from the d–q equivalent circuits that, for decoupling control, the slip frequency ω_{sl}^* should vary with i_{qs}^* by the gain factor $K_s = L_m R_r / L_r \hat{\psi}_r$. This means that i_{ds}^* controls only $\hat{\psi}_r$ and i_{qs}^* controls torque by the dc-machine-like relation $T_e = K_t \, i_{ds} \, i_{qs}$. The signal ω_e is processed by a voltage-controlled oscillator, up-counter, and look-up table $\sin\theta_e$ and $\cos\theta_e$ generator. The unit vector signals $\sin\theta_e$ and $\cos\theta_e$ are then used in the vector rotator to generate the phase-current commands by the following equations:

$$i_{qs}^{*s} = i_{qs}^* \cos\theta_e + i_{ds}^* \sin\theta_e \tag{10}$$

$$i_{ds}^{*s} = -i_{qs}^* \sin\theta_e + i_{ds}^* \cos\theta_e \tag{11}$$

$$i_a^* = i_{qs}^{*s} \tag{12}$$

$$i_b^* = -1/2\, i_{qs}^{*s} - \frac{\sqrt{3}}{2} i_{ds}^{*s} \tag{13}$$

$$i_c^* = -1/2\, i_{qs}^{*s} + \frac{\sqrt{3}}{2} i_{ds}^{*s}. \tag{14}$$

Then, the inverter PWM signals are generated by the hysteresis-band current-control method. The slip gain K_s is dependent on machine parameters; therefore, to achieve decoupling between the flux component (i_{ds}) and torque component (i_{qs}) of current, it is desirable that these parameters should track the actual machine parameters, which may vary widely. Note that in vector control, the current (instead of voltage) is controlled and the frequency and phase positions of the inverter output are controlled by the unit vectors. In the braking mode, the polarity of i_{qs}^* becomes negative and the inverter-motor operates as a rectifier-generator. For speed reversal, the phase sequence of the inverter automatically reverses at zero speed.

8.6. Brushless DC Motor (BLDM) Drive

An inverter-fed permanent-magnet synchronous motor is normally self-controlled, i.e., the inverter control signals are derived from an absolute position sensor mounted on the motor shaft. It can be shown that the performance of such a drive is somewhat analogous to that of a separately excited dc motor. The so-called "dc machine" can be considered as inverse to a conventional dc machine, i.e., the magnetic field is rotating and armature is stationary, and the mechanical commutators and brushes are replaced by an electronic commutator. The inverter with the position sensor can be viewed as an electronic commutator. In standard terminology, a BLDM uses a surface-magnet-type synchronous machine with trapezoidal stator winding (in contrast to sinusoidal winding) such that the induced phase voltages have trapezoidal waveshapes. Figure 60 shows the BLDM power circuit, and Fig. 61 shows the normal 120° switch-on mode of the devices. The line–line machine-induced dc voltage always appears at the inverter input. Instead of a battery supply, if a dc current source I_d is impressed, the machine stator current will have a

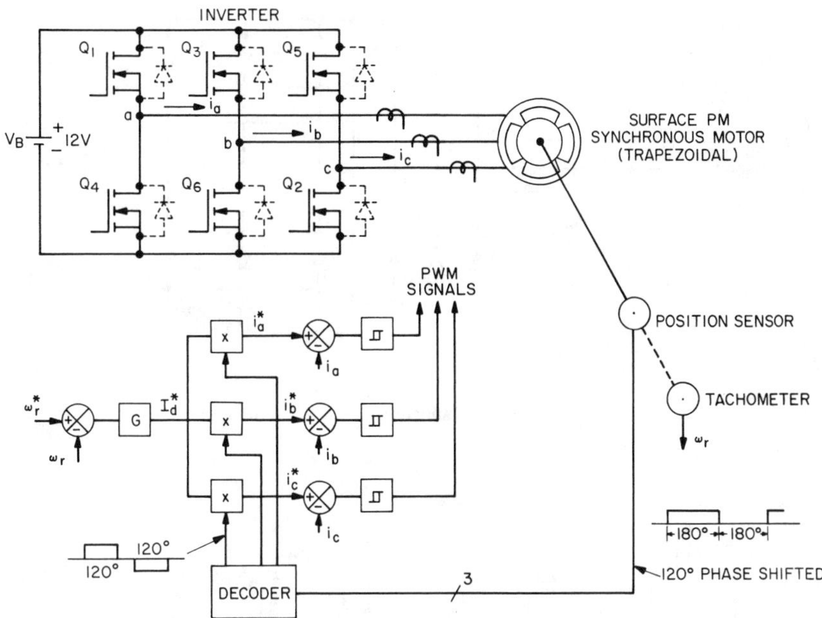

Fig. 60. Speed-control system with brushless dc motor drive.

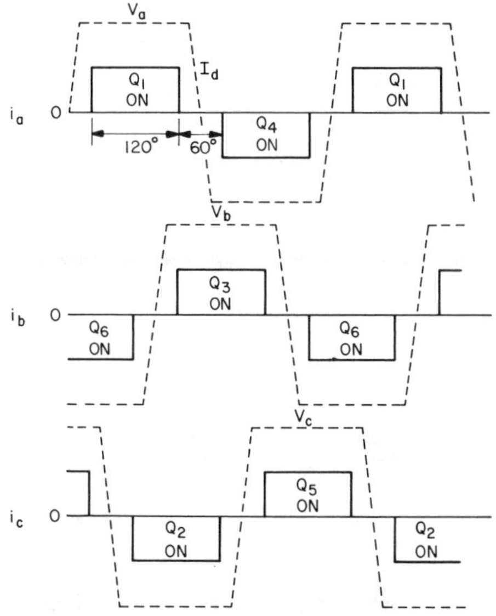

Fig. 61. BLDM phase voltage and current waves.

six-stepped wave with amplitude I_d. With a battery voltage supply, the inverter has the capability of limiting start-up or transient overload current by PWM control. In a typical speed-control system, shown in Fig. 60, the machine stator current can be controlled continuously by the hysteresis-band method. The speed-loop error generates the current command I_d^*, which is positive in the motoring mode and negative in the regeneration mode. The Hall position sensor generates three-phase square logic waves coincident with the magnet flux waves. These signals are decoded to generate the 120° switching logic waves shown in the figure. With the ideal six-step current wave, the machine-developed torque is very smooth. However, at high speed, the current will deviate from the rectangular waveshape, giving rise to some pulsating torque. The inverter shown uses power MOSFETs because the supply voltage is low. Recently, inverters with the controller have become available in the form of a single-chip power integrated circuit (PIC) in the low-power range. The BLDM drive is very popular because of the simplicity of the machine, controller, and position encoder.

8.7. Sinusoidal PM Synchronous Machine Drive with Vector Control

In a sinusoidal PM machine, the stator windings are sinusoidally distributed (similar to an induction machine), and therefore, the induced voltages are sine waves. This is in contrast to a trapezoidal machine, which has been described in the previous section. A sinusoidal machine can have two classes: a) a surface-magnet machine, where the magnets are mounted on the rotor surface. The effective airgap in this machine is large, and therefore, the armature reaction effect is weak; and b) an interior, or buried-magnet, machine, where the armature reaction effect is strong due to a smaller effective airgap. The vector-control method is easily applicable to both types of machine. Let us consider the surface-magnet machine only because it is popularly used in industry. The induction-motor vector control described in Fig. 53 can also be used for the PM machine, except with the following modifications:

- For a PM machine, the airgap flux ψ_g is constant and, therefore, $i_{ds} = 0$.
- The slip ω_{sl} of a synchronous machine is zero; therefore, $\omega_r = \omega_e$; i.e., the slip path remains open.
- In a synchronous machine, the θ_e angle that relates to magnet position must be absolute instead of incremental. The

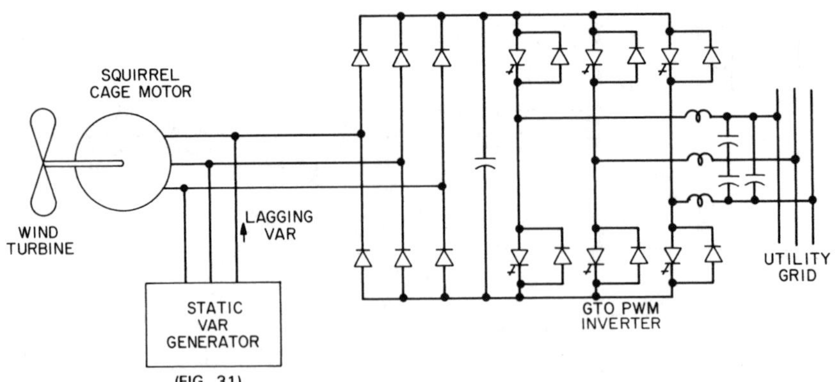

Fig. 62. Wind-power induction generator system.

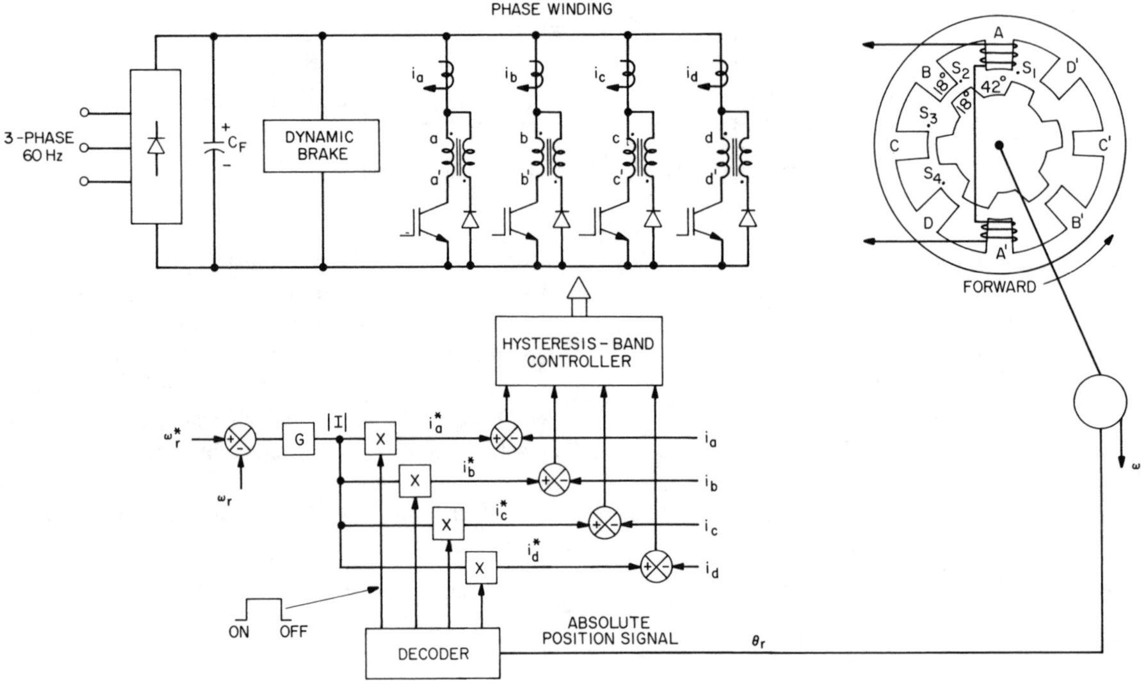

Fig. 63. Switched-reluctance motor drive.

absolute rotor angle θ_e signal should be used to generate the unit vector signals $\cos\theta_e$ and $\sin\theta_e$.

8.8. *Wind-Power Induction Generator System*

A wind turbine operates at variable speed, and the problem here is to convert the mechanical power into electrical power and pump it into a utility grid. Many alternative schemes are possible, but a viable system using an induction generator is shown in Fig. 62. Here, the turbine drives a squirrel-cage-type induction generator. The machine excitation is supplied from the stator side by a static var generator (see Fig. 31). Basically, it acts as a three-phase variable capacitor bank that supplies lagging reactive current to the machine to regulate its airgap flux. The machine operates at supersynchronous speed to function as a generator. The shaft torque determines the slip frequency, and it subtracts from the rotor speed to determine the stator frequency (variable). The regulated induced voltage at the stator is diode-rectified, filtered, and then inverted to 60-Hz supply for the utility grid. The scheme can also operate as a stand-alone power generator. For the machine to act as a generator, the var generator has to supply initial excitation. The PWM inverter also permits unity-power-factor operation at the grid terminal. It can also function as a static var compensator when the active power loading is low or does not exist. The whole power circuit can also be replaced by a PWM double-converter system. Here, the PWM rectifier can supply the variable var demand of the machine and maintain a smooth sinusoidal current in the machine winding as well.

8.9. *Switched-Reluctance Machine Drive*

The switched-reluctance motor (SRM) is a member in the class of variable-reluctance machines (VRM), but it is some-

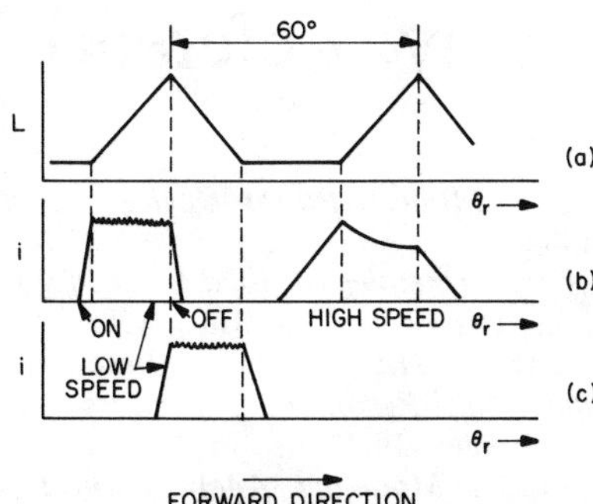

Fig. 64. Typical phase current waves of SRM in relation to inductance profile. (a) Stator-pole pair inductance profile; (b) motoring-phase current waves at low and high speeds; (c) braking-phase current pulse at low speed.

what different from the commonly known stepping motors. This type of motor has double saliency (see Fig. 63), i.e., both stator and rotor have projecting poles. The machine rotor construction is the same as that of a synchronous reluctance motor, i.e., it does not have permanent magnets or any winding, but the stator poles have a concentrated winding (instead of the sinusoidal winding in a synchronous reluctance motor). Figure 63 shows an SRM drive system. The machine, as indicated, has eight stator poles and six rotor poles, where an opposite stator-pole pair has one winding that is excited by a converter phase. A stator-phase winding is energized by switching on the particular IGBT when the rotor-pole pair approaches the corresponding stator-pole pair, but is switched off when the pole alignment occurs. All four machine phases are excited sequentially in synchronism with the rotor position to get unidirectional torque. When a phase is switched on, energy is absorbed by the winding, but at turn-off, the bifilar secondary winding returns the stored energy through the series diode. The converter is unipolar because the winding current is unipolar. The inductance profile of a stator-pole pair with respect to rotor angular position and the corresponding phase-current waves are shown in Fig. 64. The stator-current pulse is established at the positive inductance slope for forward-motoring torque, whereas for braking torque the current pulse is at the negative slope. At high speed, the machine counter EMF is high, which makes the current wave as indicated. A simplified block diagram for four-quadrant control of the drive is indicated in Fig. 63. The machine must have an absolute position sensor that helps the controller to establish the phase-current pulses. The phase-current magnitude $|I|$ that relates to the developed torque is controlled by the hysteresis-band technique. At high speed, however, current control is lost, leaving only angle control. The bifilar energy feedback scheme, as indicated above, can be replaced by 2-IGBT, 2-diode phase legs, or many alternate configurations.

The proponents of the SRM drive claim the following principal merits:

- The machine has a simple construction, making it a potentially cheaper alternative.
- Its robust rotor construction makes it more reliable and suitable for high-speed operation.
- It has simple converter topology with fewer devices, although the device voltage rating is higher.
- There is no possibility of converter shoot-through fault because the winding is always in series with the devices. Also, no short-circuit fault current is possible in the stator due to rotor-induced EMF.
- There is independent and uncoupled operation of motor phases so that the machine will continue to operate (with higher pulsating torque) if a phase fails.

The principal demerits of the drive are that the machine-pulsating torque is high, giving high acoustic noise, and the machine is somewhat bulky (comparable to the synchronous-reluctance machine). An absolute position sensor is a definite need for this drive. The response of the drive is very slow in the high-speed field-weakening region.

9. Conclusion

A broad but comprehensive review of power electronics has been given in this Introduction. The discussion included power semiconductor devices, topologies of different classes of converters, PWM methods, and, finally, some selected power electronics applications. In the device section, the modern power devices that appeared in the 1980s, i.e., IGBT, SIT, SITH, and MCT, have been emphasized. A general comparison chart of different devices with sample numerical parameter ratings has been included. Although modern converter circuits have been emphasized, the phase-controlled converters and cycloconverters have been included for completeness. In fact, this class of converters is by far the most commonly used in general industrial applications. The features of different types of converters, particularly for ac motor drive applications, have been highlighted in the comparison chart. A few selected power electronics applications indicate in general the complexity of total power electronic systems.

Industrial power conversion technology and its applications have recently grown at such a phenomenal rate that the discussion of the subject can easily fill several large volumes. The intention here has been to broadly review the mainstream technology in simple, descriptive language, giving the reader a comprehensive background in the subject. This background will help the motivated reader to successfully launch into the other sections of the book, and dig into the bibliography for further details. The author believes that a thorough understanding of this section, with subsequent reading of the papers, will bring the readers to the leading edge of the technology.

Selected Bibliography: Reference Books

[1] B. K. Bose, *Power Electronics and AC Drives.* Englewood Cliffs, NJ: Prentice Hall, 1986.

[2] B. K. Bose (Ed.), *Adjustable Speed AC Drive Systems.* New York: IEEE Press, 1982.

[3] B. K. Bose (Ed.), *Microcomputer Control of Power Electronics and Drives.* New York: IEEE Press, 1987.

[4] M. H. Rashid, *Power Electronics.* Englewood Cliffs, NJ: Prentice Hall, 1988.

[5] P. Wood, *Switching Power Converters.* New York: Van Nostrand, 1981.

[6] J. M. D. Murphy and F. G. Turnbull, *Power Electronic Control of AC Motors.* New York: Pergamon Press, 1988.

[7] B. J. Baliga and D. Y. Chen (Eds.), *Power Transistors: Device Design and Applications.* New York: IEEE Press, 1984.

[8] B. W. Williams, *Power Electronics.* New York: John Wiley, 1987.

[9] P. Wood, *Fundamentals and Applications of Gate Turn-Off Thyristors.* Palo Alto, CA: Electric Power Research Institute, 1988.

[10] D. C. Griffith, *Uninterruptible Power Supplies.* New York: Marcel Dekker, 1989.

[11] N. Mohan, T. M. Undeland, and P. Robbins, *Power Electronics.* New York: John Wiley, 1989.

[12] R. G. Hoft, *Semiconductor Power Electronics.* New York: Van Nostrand, 1986.

[13] G. K. Dubey, *Power Semiconductor Controlled Drives.* Englewood Cliffs, NJ: Prentice Hall, 1985.

[14] B. J. Baliga, *Modern Power Devices.* New York: John Wiley, 1987.

[15] R. E. Tarter, *Principles of Solid State Power Conversion.* Indianapolis, IN: Howard W. Sams, 1985.

*[16] F. C. Lee (Ed.), *High-Frequency Resonant, Quasi-Resonant, and Multi-Resonant Converters.* Virginia Power Electronics Center, 1989.

*[17] F. C. Lee (Ed.), *Modeling, Analysis, and Design of PWM Converters.* Virginia Power Electronics Center, 1990.

*[18] F. C. Lee and D. Y. Chen (Ed.), *Power Devices and Their Applications.* Virginia Power Electronics Center, 1990.

*[19] R. D. Middlebrook and S. Ćuk (Eds.), *Advances in Switching Mode Power Conversion, Vol. I & II.* TESLA Co., 1983.

[20] R. P. Severns and G. E. Bloom, *Modern DC-to-DC Switch Mode Power Converter Circuits.* New York: Van Nostrand, 1985.

[21] R. E. Hnatek, *Design of Solid State Power Supplies.* New York: Van Nostrand, 1981.

[22] G. Chryssis, *High Frequency Switching Power Supplies: Theory and Design.* New York: McGraw-Hill, 1984.

[23] K. Kit Sum, *Switch Mode Power Conversion: Basic Theory and Design.* New York: Marcel Dekker, 1984.

[24] V. Rajagopalan, *Computer Aided Analysis of Power Electronic Systems.* New York: Marcel Dekker, 1987.

* These papers are from the parent institution only.

Part 2
General Overview

Power electronics, control of the electromechanical energy conversion process and some applications

Prof. J.D. Van Wyk, Dr.sc.tech., Prof. H.-Ch. Skudelny, Dr.Ing., and A. Müller-Hellmann, Dr.Ing.

Indexing terms: *Power electronics, Energy conversion and storage, Electrical machines and drives, Convertors, Traction*

Abstract: Some fundamental considerations regarding power electronics and machine electronics are discussed. The historical development of ideas in this field is examined, the applications in the field of electric traction for rail vehicles are summarised and possible future developments are outlined. A systematic approach to power electronics, based upon the control of energy flow in switching convertors, is presented. This approach takes into consideration the different possible switching functions, the modulation functions, the realisation of these switching and modulation functions, the realisation of these switching and modulation functions by practical power semiconductor switches and the different classes of forced turn-off and commutation in power electronic circuits. Subsequently the concepts of topology and structure are defined, leading to different generic topologies for singular convertors. The structure of the five different families of composite convertors are examined, and practical examples are given.

The systematic approach to machine electronics presented in the paper is based on a power flow model, using the unifying concept of rotating field theory. In combination with previously defined systematics for power electronics, this enables a systematic approach to the different classes of variable speed drives, based on power flow considerations.

The historical developments of some power electronic and machine electronic ideas are traced, starting at the beginning of this century. Since the introduction of power semiconductor switches, applications of the older ideas have increased exponentially in all fields, making it impossible to cover all of them. As a consequence the development of power electronics and control of machines by electronic convertors in the field of electric traction is discussed in some detail, because this represents a record of important engineering achievements in this field.

In conclusion, the present state and future trends of power and machine electronics are examined. This evaluation covers the development in the field of switching devices regarding the improvement of interfacing between signal and power electronics, the decrease of switching transition times, the reduction of device losses during conduction, and device developments for decreasing energy storage devices in convertors.

The development of power electronic convertors for the reduction of the number of components in the topology and the development of convertors with a high frequency link are then covered, related to the expected development of switching devices.

New directions of development regarding the electronic conditioning of the electromechanical energy conversion process concerning the elimination of undesirable effects and losses are important. The implementation of these trends by utilising the improved switching characteristics of power electronic switches and the information processing capability of microprocessors is discussed. This is then extended toward control aspects, where both these characteristics enable solutions not possible hitherto. Field control of AC machines imparts control characteristics equal to, or better than, those obtainable with DC machines to the systems, while the processing capability of microprocessors allows the configuration of adaptive machine electronic systems. Finally attention is given to the interfacing of power electronic and machine electronic systems to the power supply network. If the exponential growth of the installed capacity of equipment in the future is to be handled, active compensation of the distorted currents drawn from the supply by this equipment will have to be considered seriously.

1 Electronic processing of power

The distribution of electric power has become one of the accepted forms of energy infrastructure in the modern world. Whether it is a small-scale power system supplied by solar photovoltaic panels, medium-scale system supplied by diesel-electric generators or large scale system supplied by larger nuclear and thermal power stations, the fundamental problems remain the same. Power generation and distribution characteristics of a given nature have to be adapted to electrical load characteristics of a totally different nature. This requires some form of controlling energy flow between source and load, and introduces the concept of the processing of power in its electrical form. In modern technology the electronic processing of power is the alternative that offers the benefits of low losses, long equipment life, low maintenance and maximum adaptability and controllability. However, as the accent is on power processing, the equipment must of necessity be switching convertors, as any linear control device would have an efficiency that is too low and a dissipation that is too high to handle power at any appreciable level. The consequence of this is the concern of power electronics with convertors operating in the switching mode, with the associated problems of devices having two stable states (conducting and nonconducting), and of having to switch stably at low loss from one state to the other as well as with the associated problems of control by devices and subsystems inherently discrete in their control characteristics.

It has to be realised, however, that the development of modern power electronics did not start only after the present power switches based on semiconductor technology appeared, but that the subject already has a long history dating back to the turn of this century [1, 2] when the first power switching devices appeared, based on con-

Paper 4752B received in final form 2nd April 1986. Commissioned IEE Review

Prof. van Wyk is with the Faculty of Engineering, Rand Afrikaans University, Johannesburg, Republic of South Africa. Prof. Skudelny is with the Institute for Power Electronics and Electrical Drives, Technical University of Aachen, Aachen, West Germany. Dr. Müller-Hellman is with the Public Transport Association, Cologne, West Germany

Reprinted with permission from *IEE Proc.*, vol. 133, Pt. B, no. 6, pp. 369–399, November 1986.

duction in gases and in vacuum. These concepts were applied to the control of the electromechanical energy conversion process in electrical machines at an early stage, and a variety of methods became established in this field. This field will be referred to as machine electronics, i.e. where the study of the system involves both the switching convertor and the electrical machine as opposed to power electronics where the study concentrates on the technology of the power switches and convertor itself. In machine electronics, the switching power electronic convertor is mostly represented merely by a series of periodically operated switches, because the aim is to determine the energy conversion characteristics under the switched excitation applied to the machine in steady state and dynamic conditions. The problems of machine electronics are a subset of the problems involving the control of electrical drives and leads to the determination of the transfer function of the switching convertor-machine part of the system for this control process.

Power electronics covers a much wider field encompassing the application of switching power to all types of loads. Electric machines form but a small fraction of the loads found for power electronic convertors. The study of power electronics consequently covers the systematic topological investigation of switching power convertors in particular, as well as the technology of all the different power switches and their applications. From this viewpoint the problems of machine electronics also form a subset to the wider field of power electronics, as well as to the field of electric machines, as shown schematically in Fig. 1.

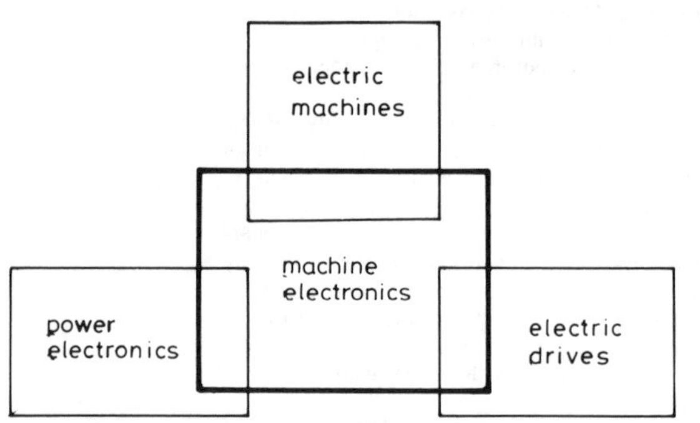

Fig. 1 *Relationship of different fields to power and machine electronics*

As it is impossible to cover all these fields in this discussion, some selected aspects of a systematic approach and of the development and applications of power and machine electronics will be covered. This process of selection is inevitably influenced by the authors' interests and points of view. Furthermore, this Review also attempts to establish a certain systematic structure for this particular field of knowledge. It is appreciated that this is unconventional in many aspects, yet experience over many years has indicated that it is a valuable approach to bring some order into the multitude of ideas, circuits and systems found in this field. Although it is impossible not to refer to electric machines and drives in this process, the accent will be on power electronics and machine electronics. The thoughts on the systematics of power electronics and machine electronics are followed by the historical development of the fundamental ideas in this field. This will cover the history of power switching devices, of circuit ideas for switching convertors, of the control of DC machines and of AC machines. As an example of the historical development of the application of these ideas, occurring in parallel to the development of devices and circuit ideas, the application of power electronics to drives for railway vehicles will be reviewed. The state of the art in power electronics and machine electronics is then reviewed, and some possible future developments are discussed in conclusion.

In conclusion to this introductory section, it is now in order to comment on the nature and organisation of the present paper. Many excellent reviews and expository contributions on the subject have been published in the literature [1–32]. Studying and absorbing all this material is a formidable task to the reader — at the end of it he still has to construct his own systematic approach to the subject, as well as evaluate all the historical details. Consequently, the present contribution does not attempt to be encyclopaedic, nor present a detailed literature referenced narrative of the field. The already cited works are adequate, for instance Reference 1 contains more than 1000 references to important works up to 1966. Rather, it is hoped that the brief systematic introduction to power electronics and machine electronics, supported by the historical introduction and the review of traction applications, may lead up to an appreciation of the direction of development of the subject, as treated in the final section and supported with adequate references for further reading.

Finally, the choice of applications in the traction field should be commented on. This is an attempt to stress the important motivation for development in electric traction that has resulted from developments in power electronic convertors, starting early in this century. Although industrial applications have often been discussed in reviews, the treatment of traction in this context is very rare. It is hoped that the present treatment adds to the appreciation of the exacting demands this field of application places on power electronics and machine electronics.

2 Power electronics: a proposed systematic approach

It has already been noted that efficiency and loss requirements dictate the control of power in a switching mode in power electronics. For a systematic approach the technology of the specific types of power switches, as well as particular peculiarities of behaviour should be omitted. These characteristics — such as switching speed, switching

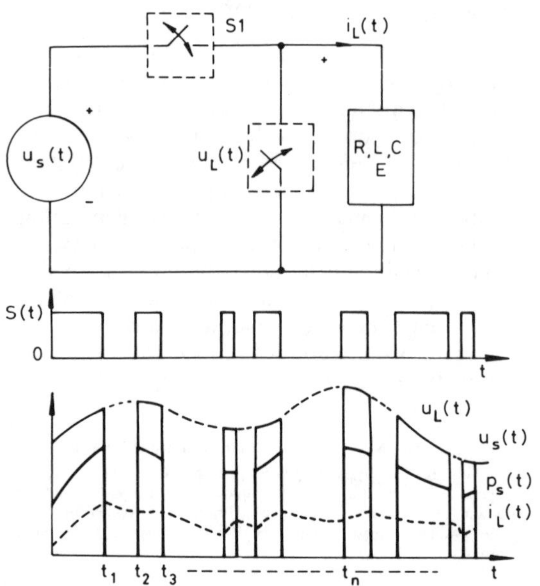

Fig. 2 *Fundamental possibilities for control of power flow by means of switching functions*

losses, conduction losses, surge capacity, overvoltage capacity, temperature dependence and power gain — are extremely important when considering a specific application and type of switching device in practice. For the present systematic approach, however, the power switch will be considered to change instantaneously from the non-conducting state to the conducting state or back at any chosen instant. This leads to the fundamental possibility to control power flow as shown in Fig. 2. By operation of the switches S_1 and S_2, the switching function $s(t)$ is generated, so that the load voltage becomes

$$u_L(t) = s(t)u_s(t)$$

As the load may contain inductance and/or sources of EMF, the function $s(t)$ is generated by operating S_2 inverse to S_1, allowing circulating or 'free wheeling' load current if necessary. The average power flow between source and load $P_s(t)$ therefore becomes a function of the switching function $s(t)$. Ideally this power transfer is now being controlled by S_1 and S_2 with no losses involved in S_1 and S_2, as either the voltage across them or the current conducted by them is always zero.

2.1 *Switching function*

The generation of the switching function may be done in many different ways, and a large body of knowledge has grown around the different techniques and technologies for achieving this. It is normally required that the applied load voltage obey some externally prescribed modulation function through which control is effected, but that the load voltage should be affected as little as possible by the switching function. By switching at a sufficiently high frequency with respect to the modulation function, the ripple due to the switching frequency in the load current is reduced. At the same time the wide separation between modulation frequency and switching frequency facilitates elimination of the latter in the output voltage by filtering. From this it would seem that the only requirement for the switching function would be that it should be many times the frequency of the modulation function. Limitations in practical switching devices, however, severely limit the upper switching frequencies in power electronic convertors in many instances, so that the switching function is in these cases usually related to the modulation function in such a way that the elimination of certain harmonic frequencies in the load voltage is obtained. The previous considerations therefore result in two large families of control techniques for switching control, i.e. modulation synchronous techniques and modulation asynchronous techniques, some of which are indicated in Fig. 3. Although fundamentally the source voltage could be any function of time, the two desired types almost exclusively encountered in power electronics are perfect direct voltage and perfect sinusoidal voltage, so that the latter has been selected for the illustrations in Figs. 3*a–d*. Fig. 3*a* represents the possibilities of pulse-width modulation (PWM, the switching frequency f_s being constant) where the synchronous relationship holds:

$$f_s = n/t \qquad n = 2, 3, 4, \ldots$$

The special case where $n = 2$, as illustrated in Fig. 3*c* constitutes a very important class of modulation synchronous power electronic switching functions. For all the other values of n, the relationship obeyed by t_p and n is determined by the desired harmonic component elimination in u_L, with n normally larger than unity.

Pulse-frequency modulation (PFM), as in Fig. 3*b*, is an asynchronous technique, although the range of frequency sweep for f_s is known. Harmonic elimination in this case could only be effective if the switching frequency f_s is always much larger than the modulation frequency, implying a very short pulse width t_p. The high maximum switching frequency, short t_p and extremely large sweep in f_s imparts many drawbacks to this technique, so it is not often found in practice.

In the examples discussed for Figs. 3*a*, *b* and *c* the nature of the function $s(t)$ is determined beforehand, and dependent on the value $u_r(t)$ to which it is referenced. This value may be derived from a load feedback, but will only change f_s and t_p in a previously determined fashion, this being one of the system characteristics. When the load related band-bang mechanism of Fig. 3*d* is used to derive the switching function, a fully arbitrary switching function results, as shown. Under given load conditions the value of the current swing Δi will determine the shortest time between two consecutive switching cycles of S_1 and S_2, but the technique is modulation asynchronous. Owing to the current-source characteristics of the output, and the good correspondence between i_r and i_m, the technique has found widespread acceptance in practice.

It will be obvious that the characteristics of equipment using modulation synchronous or asynchronous techniques by derivation of $s(t)$ are very different regarding high-frequency electromagnetic radiation, supply reaction and harmonics in the entire frequency spectrum and output filtering. In practice, it is often found that these boundary conditions dictate the technique selected for obtaining $s(t)$.

It should be noted that the frequency of the modulation function is not always synchronised with that of the source voltage as shown in Fig. 3. If the modulation frequency and source frequency are not synchronised, the output contains components resulting from all these frequencies, and beats between them, i.e. that of the source, the modulation and $s(t)$. For the case of a direct voltage source only the modulation and the switching function affect the output components, with only $s(t)$ appearing when the modulation function also becomes a constant, as in the many instances when a direct voltage load is driven (battery chargers, DC machines etc.). When this type of load is supplied by a system with specific AC source voltage, the output again contains these components, those of $s(t)$ and their cross modulation.

The above systematic discussion of the switching function used voltage fed systems and the resulting output voltage as an illustration. Perfect duality exists regarding all the techniques discussed with respect to current fed systems. The asynchronous technique of Fig. 3*d* could, for instance, also be applied by sensing the load voltage and deriving a switching function for the current into the load, as drawn from a current source $i_s(t)$.

2.2 *Realisation of switching functions*

The switching functions discussed previously have to be realised by using practical power electronic devices. These devices allow different types of functions to be realised by being used alone or in combination with each other. The possible configurations of the power switches S_1, S_2 are shown systematically in Fig. 4 as follows:

(i) *Unidirectional conduction function or diode function*: as the diode conducts when the voltage across the device is positive, the current has to be turned off by an external voltage across the device, developed by some other part of the system. This voltage could be derived from either the supply or the load or both.

(ii) *Unidirectional delayable conduction function*: while the current turn-off through the switch is still subject to an external voltage developed by the supply or load, control via a switching function may delay the conduction process in the switch. The switching function $s(t)$ as in Fig. 3c, with

using antiparallel grid controlled mercury-arc rectifiers, ignitrons excitrons, and thyristors, the triac has been added to this range of devices.

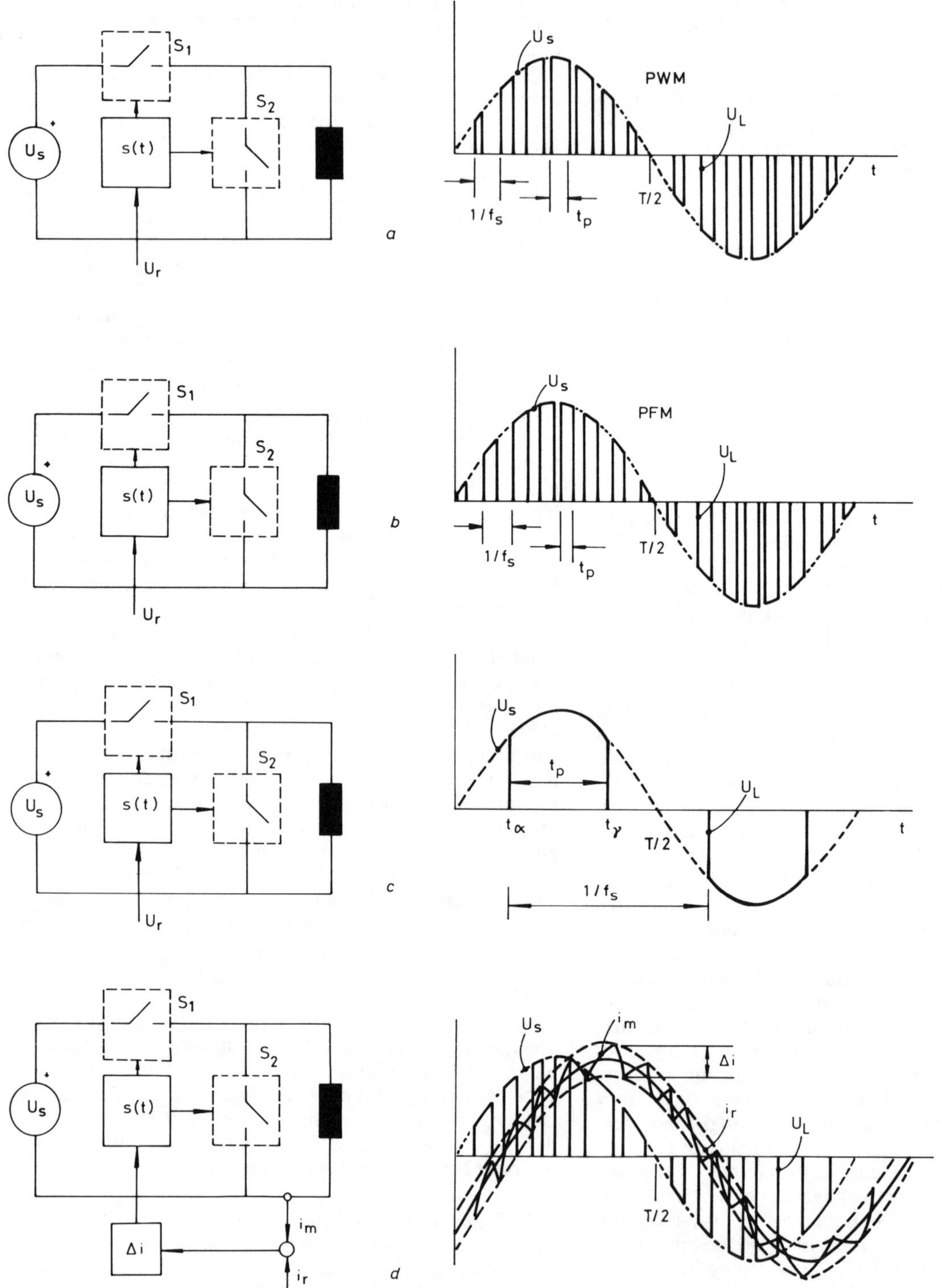

Fig. 3 *Fundamental relationships between some modulation and switching functions*

$t = T/2$ may be realised in this case, for unilateral conduction and this represents the large family of naturally commutated (load or supply) systems with thyristors, grid controlled mercury-arc devices, ignitrons, excitrons, magnetic amplifiers etc.

(iii) *Bidirectional delayable conduction function or antiparallel function*: this adds the generation of symmetric AC outputs, to the previous possibilities but it is subject to the same limitations with $t_\gamma = T/2$. Apart from the circuits

(iv) *Unidirectional on-off conduction function or force commutated switch*: the realisation of PWM, PFM, bang-bang control for unidirectional conduction by using this function in S_1 and S_2 as in Figs. 3a–d is possible. Both the current turn-on and turn-off are under control, and the switch turns off current independently of load or supply voltage. The turn-off is achieved either by inherent device characteristics, or by using an externally derived voltage for turning the delayable conduction function off, unrelated to the natural behaviour of the circuit. The former refers to switches based upon devices such as bipolar power transistors, field effect thyristors and gate turn-off thyristors, while the latter refers to the few force commutated grid controlled mercury arc rectifier circuits and the large number of force commutated thyristor circuits.

(v) Bidirectional on-off conduction function or bidirectional force commutated switch. This is the most general power electronic switch realisable, and may either be obtained by arranging the function or devices discussed under (iv) in antiparallel, or by employing forced commutation on triac switches. The latter has severe limitations and it is not often found.

Space limitations do not allow a full discussion of past and present devices used in power electronic switches. Although the first realisation of power electronic switches of the diode type started with mercury-vapour devices, vacuum rectifiers were used for many years. The first bidirectional delayable conduction functions and force commutated switches used vacuum triode tubes, but until the invention of the modern range of power semiconductor devices, the work horse of the power electronics field was the family of controllable mercury arc devices and mercury vapour devices, with a short span given to the magnetic amplifier family. The mercury devices, however, allowed functions of types (ii) and (iii), and forced commutation as in type (iv) was not generally implemented.

The smaller and much faster power semiconductor diodes and thyristors gave rise to a very large number of schemes for obtaining forced commutation and current turn-off, which have been studied systematically in the past to some extent [5, 6, 9, 10]. A full discussion of all the schemes developed would be very extensive and therefore, Fig. 5 indicates four classes of forced turn-off and commutation that may be found, if the power electronic circuits are reduced to the most simple 'singular' circuits (see Section 2.3.1) as shown in Fig. 5.

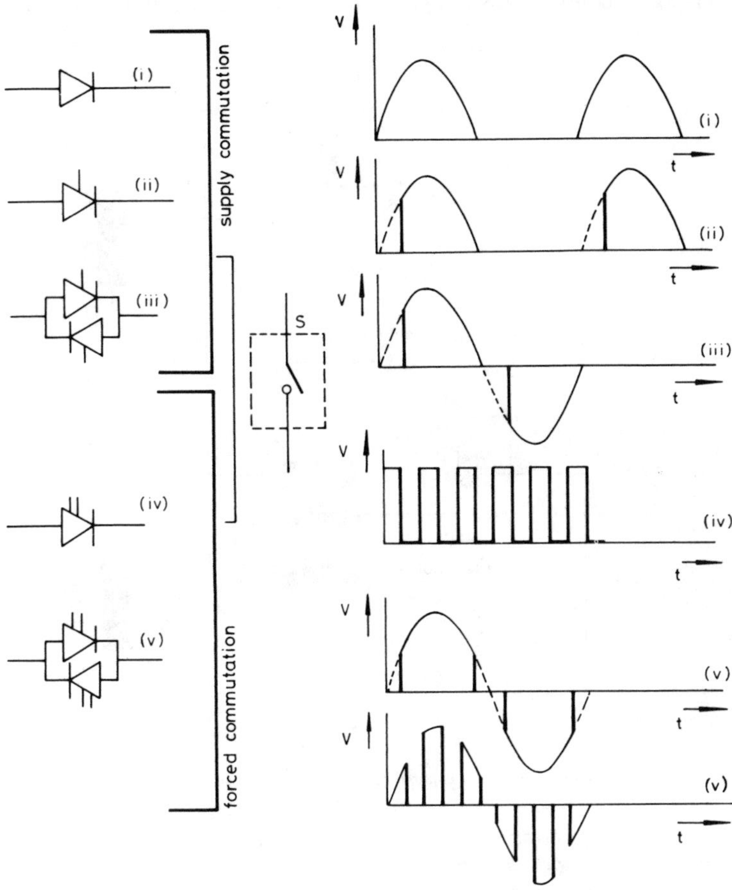

Fig. 4 *Different switching functions to consider in relation to realisable possibilities with electronic switches*
(i) Diode function, supply commutated AC supply
(ii) Supply commutated switching function, control by switch-on delay, AC supply
(iii) Bidirectional switching function, supply commutated, control by switch on delay, AC supply
(iv) Electronic switching function, force commutated, control by pulse width modulation, DC supply
(v) Bidirectional electronic switching function, force commutated, control by switch on and switch off, AC supply or the same with control by pulse width modulation

Parallel forced turn-off and commutation as shown in Fig. 5*a* has become widely used in power electronics. The conducted current through Th is reduced to zero by closing S_k, the impedance Z being dimensioned to style the turn-off and commutation process. The switch S_2 comprises simply the diode D_F, which will turn on with any appreciable inductance in the load, realising the switching function $s(t)$ as previously discussed. The turn-off problem has now been transferred from Th to S_k. The device used for realising S_k is required to have comparable current capability with Th (although only for a short time), and this has favoured the use of a second thyristor to realise S_k, so that turn-off in the auxiliary circuit is mostly achieved by supply or load commutation in the turn-off circuit itself. The large variety of methods of obtaining u_k, of turning off the commutation circuit and of the elimination of drawbacks associated with a specific circuit have given rise to a multitude of schemes to achieve this in practice. The class of forced commutation schemes falling into this group is called 'parallel commutation'.

On the other hand, a large variety of convertors have the peculiarity that a diode is in antiparallel to Th during the turn-off and commutation process. This may be reduced to the equivalent circuit shown in Fig. 5*c*. The presence of the diode eliminates the possibility of a high reverse voltage across the main thyristor Th during turnoff and commutation, so that the class comprising the family of topologies reducible to this scheme may be called 'reverse voltage free parallel commutation'.

The turn-off and commutation scheme of Fig. 5*b* operates differently, because the turn-off voltage is introduced in series with the conducting thyristor Th. Usually this is achieved by using a commutating transformer Tr as the resetting time. The resetting time in turn determines the shortest time between consecutive switching cycles and consequently the maximum switching repetition frequency.

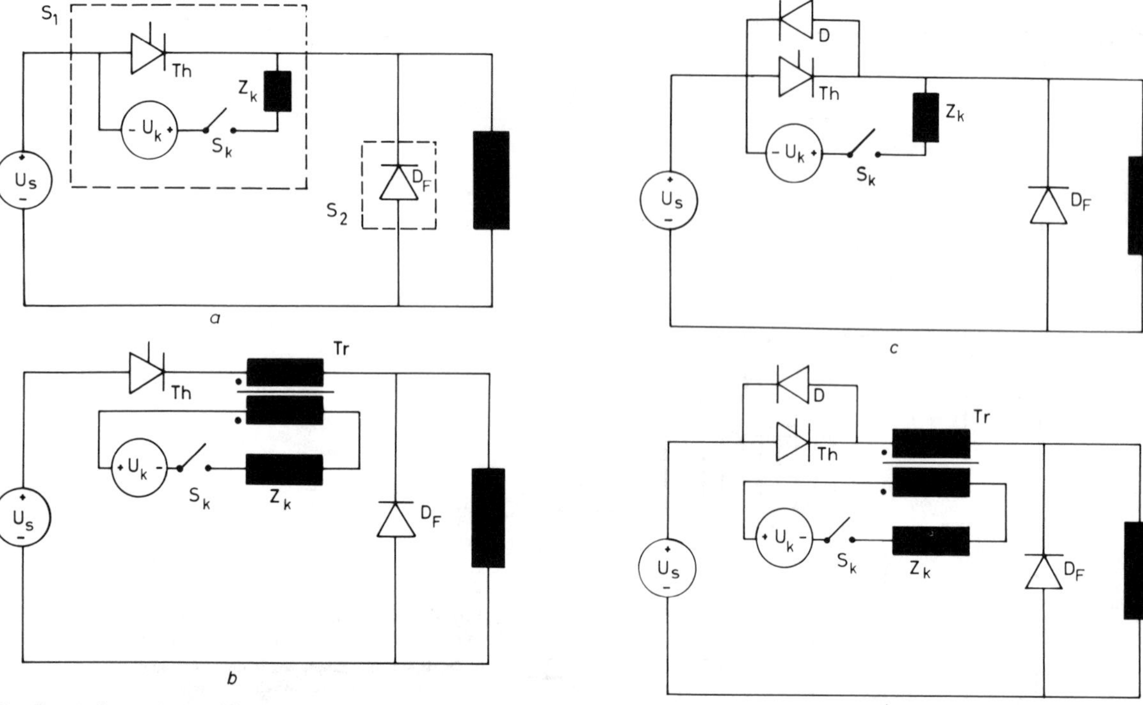

Fig. 5 *Different classes of forced turn-off commutation*
a Parallel turn off and commutation *b* Series turn off and commutation *c* Reverse voltage free parallel commutation *d* Reverse voltage free series commutation

shown, the diode D_F again taking over the function of switch S_2. Again the methods of obtaining u_k, and further detailed arrangements result in a large number of circuits using this 'series commutation'. In some instances it may also be applied to the situation where the turn-off and commutation process may be called 'reverse voltage free series commutation'. In this class of systems, the turn-off of S_k may again be done through device selection or through supply or load commutation of a thyristor.

In all the classes of forced turn-off and commutation circuits the turnoff circuit uses a finite time to commutate to its original condition to be able to turn the main device off again. The turnoff source u_k contains inductive and capacitive energy storage, and the natural frequencies of this arrangement become the limiting factor in determining

2.3 Topology and structure of power electronic convertors

Up to now the discussion has concerned topologically the simplest convertor configuration: that of a single source, single load and single or double switch arrangement, as in Fig. 2. The following discussion will now attempt a systematic approach to the large number of configurations in which power electronic convertors are found in practice. When convertors with different or the same topologies are cascaded in series, the configuration will be termed a 'composite' convertor, whereas the convertors used as building blocks for these composite convertors will be called 'singular' convertors. Singular convertors will be said to have 'topology', determined by the way in which the switches are connected to each other and between load and supply.

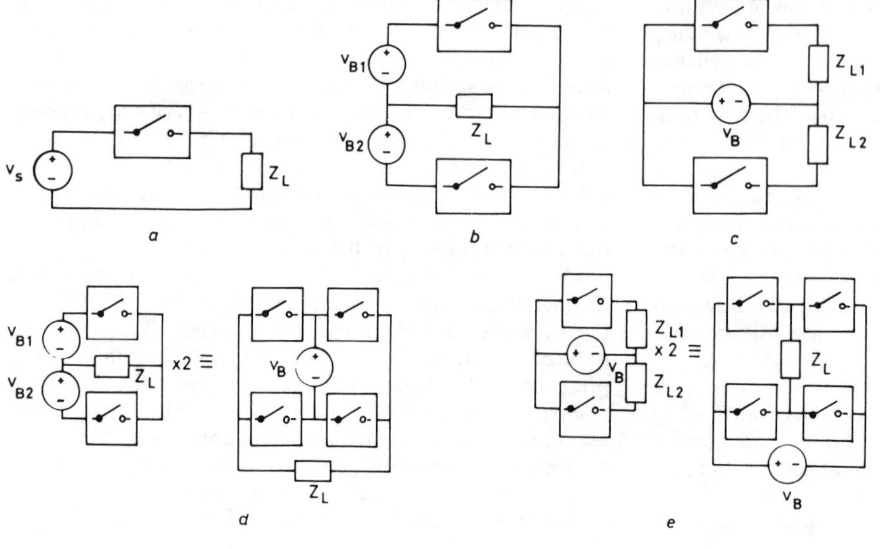

Fig. 6 *Evolution of the simplest bridge convertor*
a Simple single-switch singular convertor
b Split-source double convertor
c Split-load double convertor
d Combination of two split-source convertors into a bridge convertor with source in the bridge
e Combination of two split-load convertors into a bridge convertor with load in the bridge

Composite convertors have 'structure', determined by the way in which the singular convertors are connected together to form the composite convertor.

2.3.1 Topology of singular power electronic convertors: Those topologies where a source and a load are connected by a single power switch or a set of power switches will be considered as singular power electronic convertors. Fig. 6*a* represents the simple singular convertor, while two of these topologies may be combined to give either the split source double convertor, or the split-load double convertor as shown in Figs. 6*b* and *c*, respectively. Although the first topology is invariant to the position of the source and the load, the latter two are derived by an interchange of load and source positions. Extending these combinations leads to the bridge topologies shown in Figs. 6*d* and *e*. A combination of two split-source double convertor topologies leads to a bridge topology with the source in the bridge, whereas a combination of two split-load double convertor topologies leads to a bridge convertor with the load in the bridge. Upon close inspection, these topologies are seen to be identical. A systematic study of the many possible characteristics obtainable from this so-called single-phase bridge topology is available in the Reference 15.

The topologies of Fig. 6 may be termed the generic topologies in the switching convertor field, as all known variations may be derived from them. This process is illustrated in Fig. 7. A combination of n of the simple topologies can result in two families of n-phase topologies, with either n sources and a single load or n loads and a single source. This is illustrated for $n = 3$ in Fig. 7. For any one of these two families of multiphase topologies, the combination of two will lead to two families of multiphase bridge topologies, again either having n sources and a single load or n loads and a single source. Fig. 8 illustrates this again for $n = 3$. Some further consideration of the 'twin' topologies of Figs. 6*d*, *e*; 7*a*, *b*; 8*a*, *b*, indicate that they may be represented as in Fig. 9. An interchange of load and source positions from state 1 to state 2 yields the well known single-phase bridge, 3-phase 3-pulse and 3-phase 6-pulse topologies for rectification or inversion, well known from the literature. From the previous considerations it will also be clear that the procedure for obtaining the topologies of Fig. 8 may be extended to any multiphase convertor. The topology of Fig. 9*b* shows a 'star' configuration and the bridge of Fig. 9*c* shows a 'delta' connection. In fact, for any multiphase topology,

Fig. 7 *Multiphase topologies generated from the simple singular convertor of Fig. 6a*

a Triple source combination of simple singular convertor
b Triple load combination of simple singular convertor

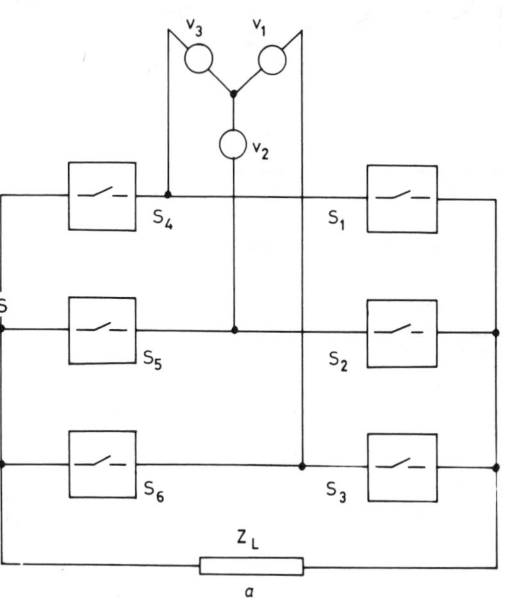

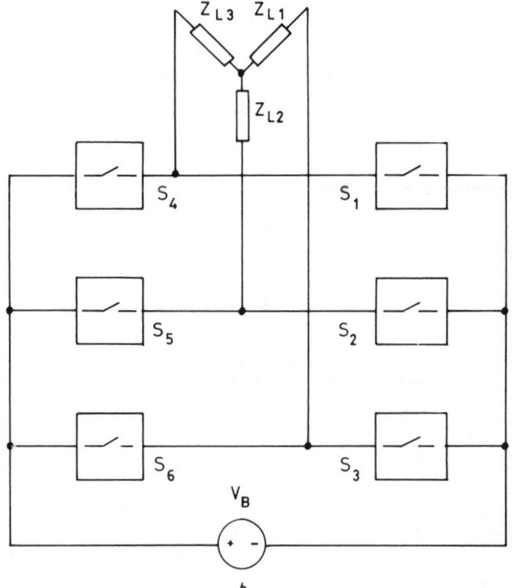

Fig. 8 *Generation of multiphase topologies*

a Combination of two of the convertors of Fig. 7*a* into a 3-phase bridge
b Combination of two of the convertors of Fig. 7*b* into a 3-phase bridge

either the centre-connected ('star') or ring ('delta') configuration may be used.

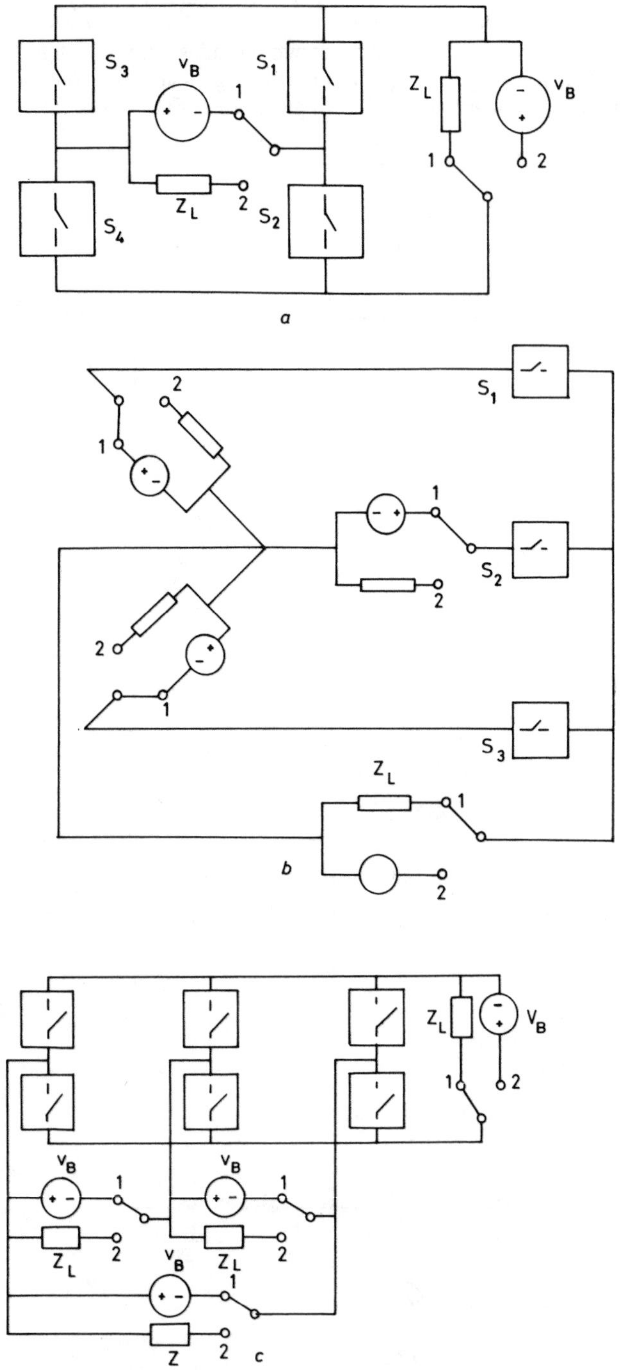

Fig. 9 *Unification of topologies*

2.3.2 Examples of singular convertors: In the topologies of Figs. 6–9, the type of switching function to be inserted into each switch position in the topology had not been given any consideration. In singular convertors, the types of functions introduced in Fig. 4 are found as they are shown there, or they are found in combination with each other, as shown in Fig. 10*a*. Fig. 10*b* represents the well known split-source single-phase inverter, while Fig. 10*c* illustrates a transformer fed 3-phase cycloconvertor for single-phase output at a lower frequency, as had been used in the past for coupling 50 Hz 3-phase systems to $16\frac{2}{3}$ Hz single-phase rail systems. Further examples may be found in Fig. 12, where these switch combinations have been used in the topologies discussed in the preceding Section to obtain the singular convertors that are joined together

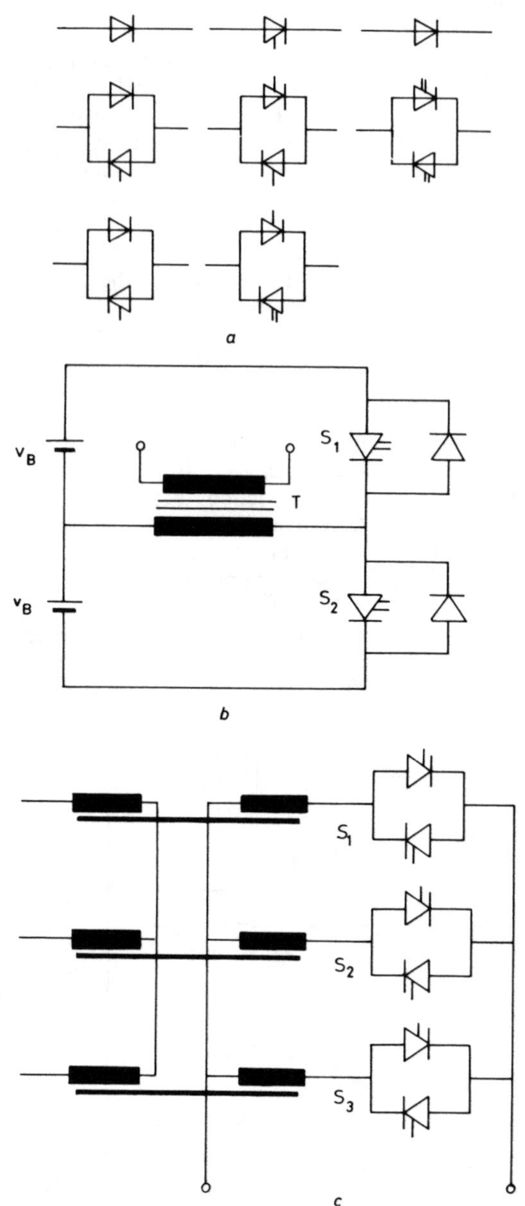

Fig. 10 *Examples of singular convertors*
a Switches and combinations of switches that may be inserted in each position of a topology
b Split-source single-phase inverter, according to Fig. 6*b*
c Star connected 3-phase cycloconvertor, according to Fig. 7*b*

in the structures for composite convertors. The switches of Fig. 10*a* have been extended a step nearer their practical realisation in Fig. 12, by indicating power field-effect transistors and bipolar transistors for the forced commutation function of Fig. 4(iv) for instance. It will be evident from the discussion in section 2.3.1 that a large number of topologies may be synthesised by implementing all the different combinations of switches. In principle, all the different switch combinations of Fig. 10*a* may also be used in different variations within each topology, so that a vast collection of these convertors exist, as is evident from the review literature [1–32].

2.3.3 Structure of composite power electronic convertors: Different topologies of singular switching convertors may be used together in a structure comprising a composite switching convertor. As shown in Fig. 11, several fundamentally different structures are possible. To avoid

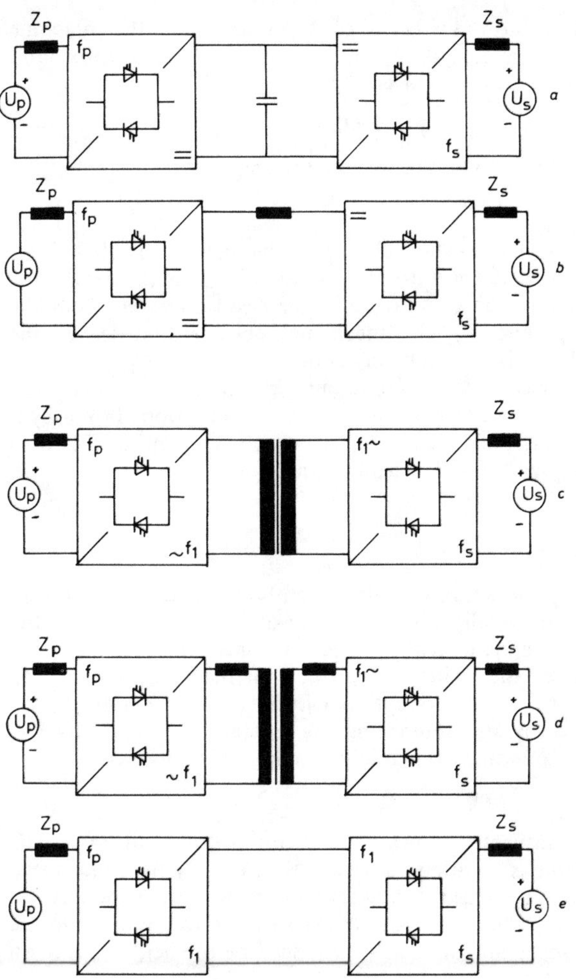

Fig. 11 *Structure of composite switching convertors*
a Direct voltage link convertor
b Direct current link convertor
c Alternating voltage link convertor
d Alternating current link convertor
e Directly linked composite convertor

discussing the detailed topology of the singular convertors, each has been indicated symbolically as a *p*-pulse convertor using the bidirectional on-off switching function from Fig. 4. By definition, the left-hand singular convertor is the primary convertor and the right-hand convertor the secondary convertor of each composite convertor. The use of the bidirectional on-off switching function in the convertors has the following consequences:

(i) No restrictions are placed on the primary and secondary sources (loads)

(ii) All convertors can pass current in two directions at both input and output

(iii) All convertors can pass power in both directions.

Fundamentally, the primary and secondary convertors may be joined by a link circuit — Fig. 11*a–d* or the two convertors may be coupled directly as in Fig. 11*e*. A direct voltage link or a direct current link as in Fig. 11*a* and *b* may be found, and an alternating voltage link and alternating current link via a coupling transformer as in *c* and *d* is also possible. In composite convertors with a transformer link it is usually found that the link frequency $f_1 \gg f_p, f_s$, to use the advantages of a smaller transformer. In principle, the direct voltage link composite convertor of Fig. 11*a* has a steady link voltage, but alternating components of link current. For the direct current link convertor of Fig. 11*b*, the converse is true. The alternating link of Fig. 11*c* is an alternating voltage link and that of Fig. 11*d* an alternating current link, so that, for both these types of composite convertors, only alternating voltages and currents are found in the (high-frequency) link circuit. Any directly linked composite structure as in Fig. 11*e* will exhibit steady and alternating components of current and voltage in the link circuit as a matter of principle.

When taking into account that the singular convertors shown, used as elements in the composite convertors of Fig. 11, may have any of the hundreds of topologies for singular convertors, as well as use any of the device switching functions indicated in Fig. 4, it becomes evident that the number of detailed structures is so vast that a systematic discussion is not possible in the confines of the present review. This number is even further increased when considering the much larger family of compound convertors. In compound convertors the primary and secondary convertors may consist of direct composite convertors or link composite convertors, again with the numerous device

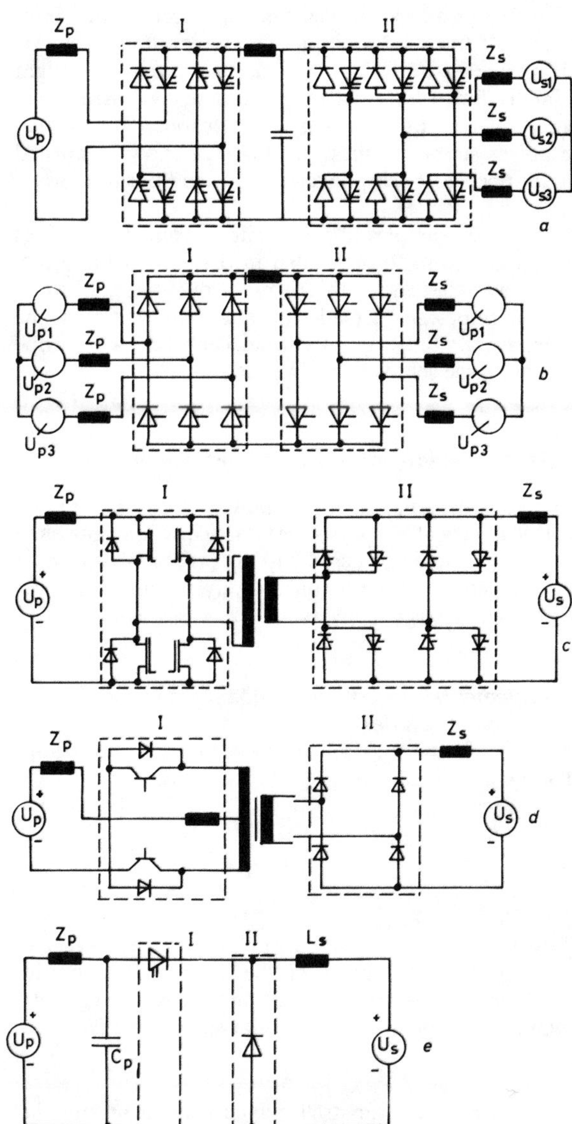

Fig. 12 *Examples of composite switching convertors corresponding to the different classes defined in Fig. 11*
The convertors numbered I and II refer to the primary and secondary convertors as in Fig. 11

switching functions determined by each specific application.

Finally it should be noted that although the schematic representations in Fig. 11 are given for single-phase structures, the number of input and output phases form another variable, with the pulse number p of singular convertors as used in the topologies and structures being a further variable.

2.3.4 Examples of composite power electronic convertors: Examples selected at random from among the structures of composite convertors known from the literature are shown in Fig. 12, each corresponding to the respective part of Fig. 11. Fig. 12*a* shows a voltage fed inverter supplied by a so-called four quadrant controller from a single-phase supply as has been applied for traction drives in locomotives (see Section 6.6), and Fig. 12*b* represents a machine commutated variable frequency 3-phase inverter system supplied from the 3-phase network, as has been applied for the acceleration of large gas turbines used for peak demand generation. When the switching function in singular convertor II of this example is replaced by a unidirectional on-off conduction function (force commutated thyristor for instance), the well known current fed inverter is found. AC from a DC input via a high-frequency AC link is shown in Fig. 12*c*. This leads to ultra-lightweight and small dimensions. The high-frequency current fed system shown in Fig. 12*d* has been proposed for switch mode power supply application. Fig. 12*e* shows a normal down chopper or buck converter as a composite convertor.

Many more examples of composite convertor structures can be chosen from those known in the subject literature. Again, as was the case with examples of singular convertors, no attempt can be made to be comprehensive in the examples given: those given should each be seen as one from a very large set available in practice.

3 Machine electronics: a systematic approach

To approach the application of power electronics to the control of electrical machines systematically, an approach of electrical machines based upon the revolving field theory is taken, and an attempt to unify the different electromechanical energy conversion processes is presented [23].

3.1 Fundamental frequency relationships in rotating electrical machines

In any multiphase electrical machine the stator windings build a magnetic field revolving at an angular speed

$$\Omega_s = \omega_s/q$$

where

$$\omega_s = \pi 2 f_s$$

and f_s is the stator supply frequency and $2q$ the number of magnetic poles. If the rotor of the machine also carries some multiphase electrical excitation, the rotor magnetic field would be revolving at an angular speed

$$\Omega_r = \omega_r/q$$

with respect to the rotor itself, which runs at an angular speed Ω_m with respect to the stator. As continuous conversion of electrical into mechanical energy will only occur when the rotor and the stator magnetic fields rotate at the same angular speed, i.e. when the two 'magnets' will line up, the following relationship may be written:

$$\omega_s/q - \omega_r/q = \Omega_m$$

If it is now furthermore supposed that the machine develops a torque T_g in its airgap between rotor and stator, it may be written that

$$T_g\,\omega_s/q - T_g\,\omega_r/q = T_g\,\Omega_m$$

or in the form of a power relationship

$$P_g - P_r = P_m$$

In this relationship, P_g represents the power that flows from the stator into the airgap of the machine, P_r the power that flows into the rotor electric circuits from the airgap, and P_m the mechanical power that leaves the machine via its mechanical port.

Now consider the different types of electrical machines in terms of this angular frequency condition. For a synchronous machine the rotor is excited by either DC or a permanent magnetic field, so that

$$\omega_r = 0$$

$$\Omega_m = \omega_s/q$$

For an induction machine, the above frequency condition is automatically obeyed, as the difference in speed of the stator magnetic field and the rotor mechanical speed is the cause of the induced frequency on the rotor. For a DC machine in its conventional form, the application of this relation is also interesting. As its stator is excited by DC (field excitation), the following relation is obtained:

$$-\omega_r/q = \Omega_m$$

This naturally indicates that the rotor field of a DC machine is rotating backward with exactly the same speed that the rotor is rotating forward, so that the net effect is a rotor magnetic field stationary in space to line up with the stationary magnetic field produced by the field winding on the stator.

Thus a general law for electrical machines has been illustrated, i.e. that in any rotating electrical machine at least one of either the rotor or the stator must carry an alternating current. In induction and synchronous machines the multiphase alternating current is applied to the stator windings, whereas in a DC machine the multiphase alternating current is supplied to the rotor by means of the commutator — an ingenious mechanical frequency convertor — and the exact mechanical counterpart of the electronic switching inverter. This is also the reason why, as will be shown subsequently, the DC machine remains such an attractive drive machine in variable speed electrical drives. It is only necessary to control the applied DC

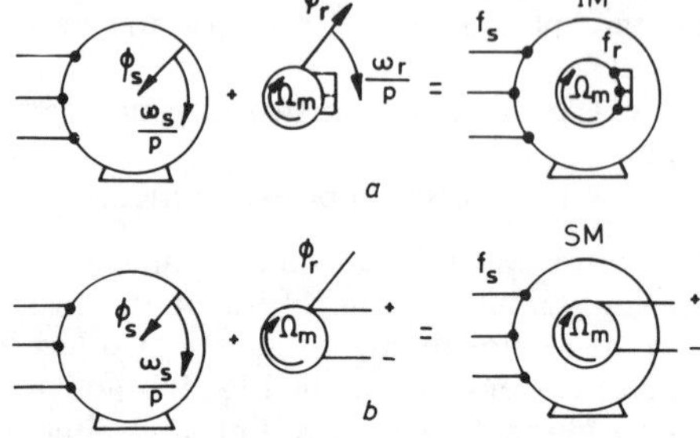

Fig. 13 *Schematic representation of conventional AC machines*

a Induction machine
b Synchronous machine
ϕ_s = magnetic field rotating with respect to the stator
ϕ_r = magnetic field of the rotor, rotating at Ω_r with respect to the rotor in *a* and stationary with respect to the rotor in *b*

voltage — the machine automatically adapts its own frequency via the commutator. Figs. 13 and 14 illustrate these

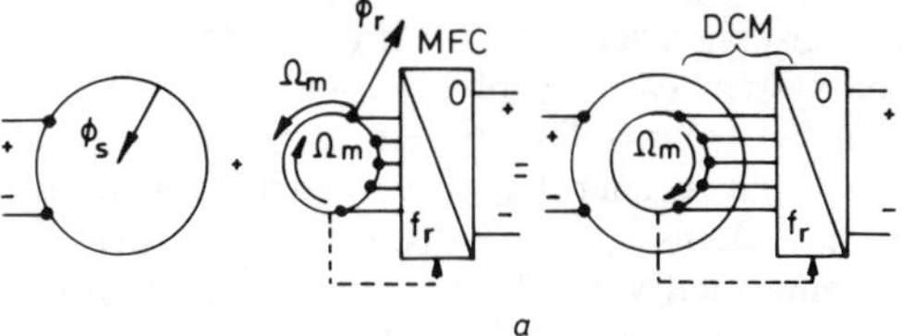

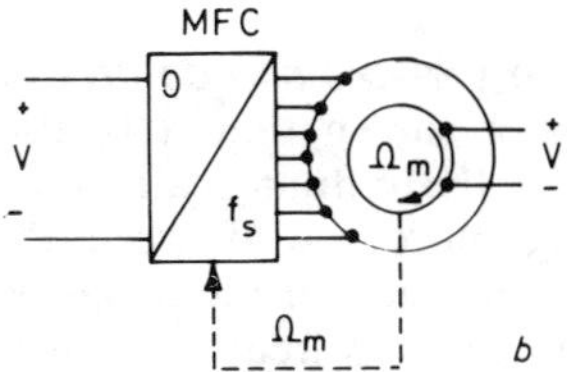

Fig. 14 *Schematic representation of conventional DC machine and inverted DC machine*

a DC machine
b inverted DC machine
ϕ_s = stationary stator field
ϕ_r = revolving field with respect to the rotor
MFC = mechanical frequency changer
DCM = DC machine with mechanical commutator

concepts, from which it follows why induction and synchronous machines are essentially constant-speed machines, whereas the DC machine is directly suited to variable speed drives. Fig. 14*b* shows an inverted DC machine, where the stator carries the commutator. In the past some of these types of variable speed drives have in fact been built, but have not met with success, owing to the intricacies of the mechanical commutator and brush arrangement. It will be shown, however, that what the most modern electrical variable speed drives with electronic switching convertors attempt, is just to emulate this old idea by replacing the mechanical commutator with an electronic invertor. A close investigation indicates, in fact, that this inverted DC machine is a multiphase synchronous machine; with variable frequency supplied to its stator windings via the mechanical commutator (MFC). The feedback of Ω_m from the rotor shaft to the stationary mechanical commutator sees to the observance of the frequency condition as previously discussed.

3.2 Different types of electrical variable-speed drives

Modern electrical variable-speed drives with electronic control form a small part of all the solutions that have been suggested for this problem in the past. Systems to be discussed are those that are of the most practical interest today, these systems being:

(i) Variable-speed drives with armature voltage control of DC machines by controlled rectifiers

(ii) Variable-speed drives with variable stator frequency control of synchronous and induction machines by inverters

(iii) Variable-speed drives with variable slip control of induction machines by switching amplitude convertors.

3.2.1 Variable-speed drives with armature voltage control of DC machines: The two types of armature voltage control systems most widely found at present are shown in Fig. 15. Although it has not been shown, both of these systems may also operate with field control. As a controlled rectifier is able to allow power flow in two directions, while maintaining current flow in one direction, the system as shown in Fig. 15*a* will be able to operate in the first two quadrants of the torque-speed plane. If operation in quadrants III and IV is desired, the field connec-

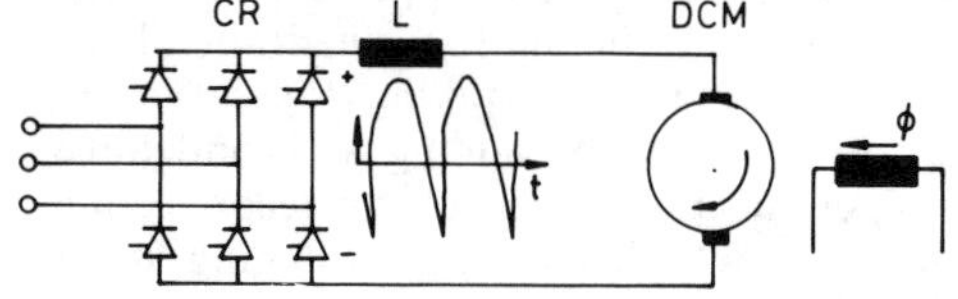

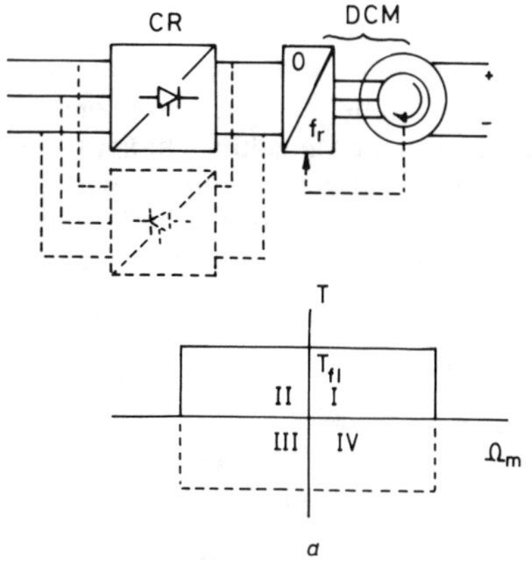

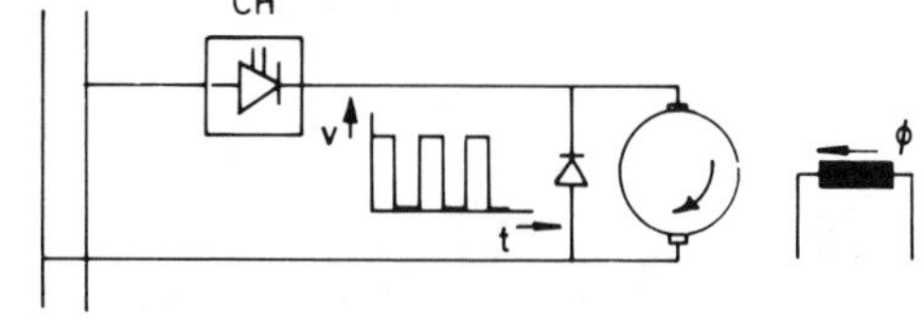

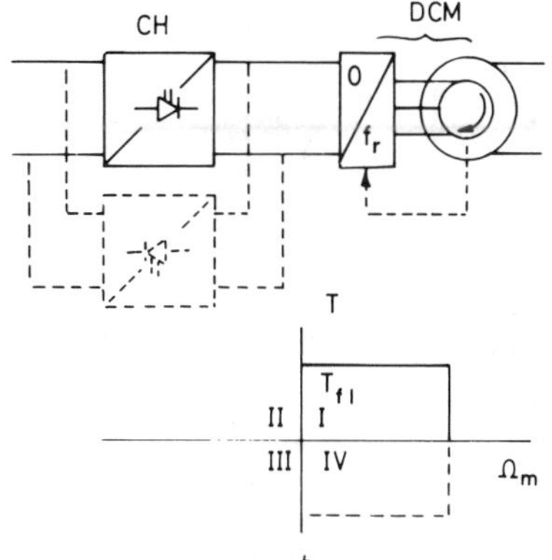

Fig. 15 *Variable speed drives*

a Armature voltage control by rectification from the 3-phase supply
b Armature voltage control by force commutated chopper, fed from AC supply
CR = controlled rectifier
CH = chopper
DCM = DC machine
T_{fl} = full-load torque
Ω_m = mechanical speed

tions should be reversed, the armature connections should be reversed, or a second antiparallel controlled rectifier should be provided, as shown in the Figure. Although these solutions differ very much in their operational characteristics, it would carry beyond the limits of the present investigation to discuss them at length.

Low-loss control of variable-speed drives fed from DC busbars, such as traction equipment with overhead wire systems and battery fed drives, may be achieved by means of force commutated chopper controllers. As shown in Fig. 15*b*, these units operate on a pulse modulation principle, the drive being capable of operating in the first quadrant of the torque-speed plane. As both the direction of power flow and current flow through the chopper are fixed, the drive is able to operate only in the first quadrant of the torque-speed plane. Regenerative braking (operation in quadrant IV) can be obtained by adding a second force commutated chopper in antiparallel, or by reconnecting the existing chopper by multiple contactor switching. If the DC busbar cannot accept regenerative energy, resistors should be brought in by contactor across the input to limit the voltage rise.

3.2.2 Variable-speed drives with variable stator frequency: Variation of stator frequency of a synchronous machine or a squirrel cage induction machine changes the speed of rotation of the magnetic airgap field and therefore also the output mechanical speed of the drive shaft. Some particulars of these types of systems are shown in Fig. 16.

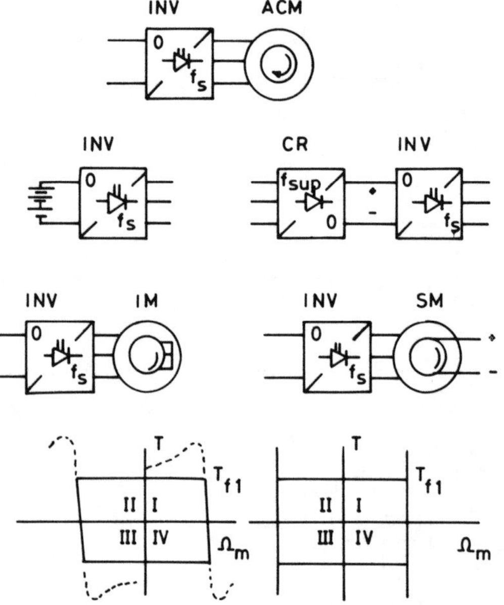

Fig. 16 *Variable speed drive with variable frequency inverter and AC machines*

INV = inverter (force commutated or machine commutated)
CR = controlled rectifier
IM = induction machine
SM = synchronous machine
T_{fl} = full-load torque
Ω_m = mechanical speed

The inverter converts the DC input to variable frequency 3-phase output. This means that the system may be fed from a DC busbar, such as in overhead DC traction systems or battery vehicles (as also indicated for force commutated chopper circuits). Using either a controlled or uncontrolled rectifier, the intermediary DC voltage may also be obtained from a 3-phase supply system. The amplitude control of the multiphase AC output of the inverter may either be done by pulse width modulation in the inverter itself, or by controlling the rectifier to control the intermediary DC voltage. Choosing between these two methods affects the behaviour and characteristics of the drive fundamentally.

Both the induction machine drive and the synchronous machine drive are automatically regenerative, because inverter circuits allow current and power flow in two directions. Reversing the rotation of the drive also presents no problem, because this means changing the phase rotation of the output of the inverter. This change in phase rotation is simply accomplished by changing the switching sequence of the semiconductor switches in the inverter circuit. Regenerative operation presents no problem in inverter variable-speed drives fed from a 3-phase system, as long as the rectifier can reverse its direction of power flow, because the AC system can accept this power. When the inverter is being fed from a DC system, it is not always possible to absorb the regenerated power, such as in some overhead traction systems. In these cases the same precautions as with chopper fed variable-speed drives have to be taken, i.e. resistors switched in across the supply to limit system voltage.

3.2.3 Variable speed drives with variable slip control of induction machines: It has been shown that it is also possible to change the speed of the output shaft of an induction machine by allowing more slip between the rotor and the constant speed of rotation of the magnetic field (fixed by the constant 3-phase supply frequency). This is possible by including an amplitude convertor in either stator or rotor circuits, as shown in Fig. 17.

Controlling the amplitude of the applied stator voltage reduces the torque-speed characteristic, so that the machine runs at lower speed. The power passed from the stator to the rotor via the airgap, is fixed by two quantities: the supply frequency and the torque. As the former is fixed, the power passed to the rotor would also remain fixed if the load torque is constant. If the mechanical output power (again at constant torque) is reduced by reducing the output speed, the difference between these two powers has to increase, all being dissipated in the rotor. Consequently, provision has to be made for handling this power.

Using a squirrel-cage drive motor, such as in Fig. 17*a*, only square-law loads such as fans and some pumps can be driven. With these drives the load torque decreases drastically as the speed falls, leading to much less power being passed from stator to rotor, and consequently to a reduction of the power being dissipated in the rotor. Even so, the squirrel-cage drive motor should be derated properly to compensate for the additional dissipation at reduced speeds where the motor's own cooling is also strongly reduced.

Constant-load torques can only be handled by this type of variable-speed drive by using a slip-ring induction motor with rotor resistors in which to dissipate the additional rotor power at low speeds. These applications require derating of the machine and/or additional forced ventilation. As the systems shown in Fig. 17*a* and in the first illustration of Fig. 17*b* all operate in the first and fourth quadrant of the torque speed plane only, phase reversal and consequent operation in quadrant III can be made available by adding additional switches in the convertor. Referring to Fig. 17*a*, the phase rotation can be changed by inhibiting the use of pairs 1 and 3, and using pairs 4 and 5. This effectively means the addition of a second parallel amplitude convertor with two thirds the component cost of the original convertor.

Variable slip control can also be achieved by the addition of an amplitude convertor in the rotor of the slip-ring induction motor. Although more similar in efficiency, losses and torque-speed operation than the stator controlled system with rotor resistors, the arrangement has the advantage of the convertor operating at lower voltage, lower harmonic supply interference and shielding of the convertor from electric supply transients by the induction machine. Various other arrangements for this type of system are known, and all have some specific advantages.

The last system for using a slip-ring induction machine

as a variable-speed drive at constant load torque shown in Fig. 17*b* is the recovery of the rotor power to the supply system. The function of the amplitude convertor is taken over by the supply-commutated inverter. This inverter presents a variable DC voltage to the output of the rotor rectifier, setting the rotor current. Although this system eliminates the dissipation of large powers in the rotor circuits, it suffers again in system complication and cost. In comparison to variable-speed drives using variable frequency inverters and squirrel-cage induction machines, the rotor recovery drive uses a more expensive wound rotor machine, but on the other hand uses a much simpler, constant-frequency, supply commutated, inverter and one extremely simple and reliable uncontrolled rectifier, all the other parameters being more or less equal. Whereas the inverters in the former handles the maximum power input to the variable-speed drive, the inverter in the rotor recovery system handles only the difference between constant stator power input and the mechanical power output.

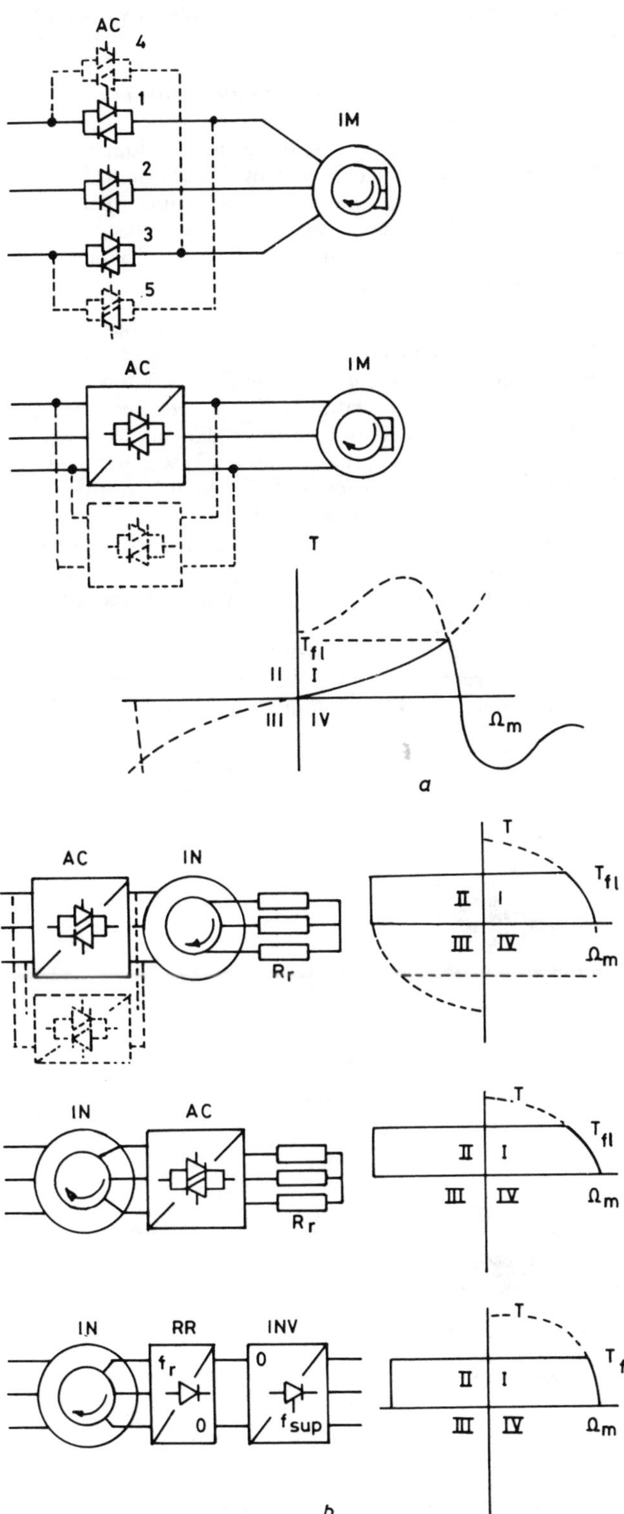

Fig. 17 *Variable speed drives*

a constant stator supply frequency and amplitude convertor for variable slip control of squirrel-cage machine
b With slip ring induction machines and rotor and stator control
AC = amplitude convertor
IM = squirrel-cage induction machine
1, ..., 5 = antiparallel pairs of thyristors
IN = slip ring induction machine
INV = supply commutated inverter
R_r = rotor resistors
RR = rotor commutated rectifier
T_{fl} = full-load torque
Ω_m = mechanical speed

This means a rotor inverter rating directly proportional to the fractional speed range. For a 3 : 1 speed range, it handles only two thirds of the maximum drive power — a decided advantage.

As eddy-current couplings operate on the principle of variable slip, they are analogous in their loss characteristics to the variable-slip induction machine systems, and will not be discussed separately.

4 Development of the subject of machine electronics

The oldest known switch used in the control of electrical machines is the mechanical commutator. This was followed by a mechanical switching arrangement to control the field of generators, the Tirrill controller. Subsequently the gaseous valves showed promise for generating the switching functions necessary to control machines. These devices had some disadvantages and at a time it appeared that the mechanical metallic rectifier (a modified commutator!) was the future promise. Almost simultaneously it was succeeded by a device developing in parallel, the transductor or magnetic amplifier. The era of semiconductor switches then dawned, an era from which we, being still concerned in its development, are able to derive but limited historical perspective.

Numerous works have been published and circuit configurations and methods of controlling electrical machines electronically worked out or suggested in the past. It has therefore become extremely difficult to ascertain the origin of most of the circuits and methods of control employed at present in machine electronics. The aim of this historical introduction is to present the knowledge acquired on these matters in an attempt to clear up some of these aspects.

4.1 Development of the different switching devices

Although the practical application of these devices did not come into being before nearly a quarter of the 20th century was past, it is interesting to note that the physical principles underlying the behaviour of mercury-arc rectifiers had apparently been recognised in 1882 by Jemin and Meneuvrier [33]. They gave an account of the property of an electric arc established between mercury and carbon electrodes, mentioning that the current will flow in one direction only. In 1889, Fleming investigated the property of unilateral conductivity of the electric arc in air, while between 1894 and 1898 Sahulka described the results of identical investigations pertaining to atmospheric arcs between mercury and iron or carbon electrodes.

All these experiments were conducted under atmospheric conditions. In the years 1890–1892 Arons made the first vapour lamps by enclosing the arc in an evacuated vessel. Apparently a rectifier based on the unidirectional conduction principle of the mercury-arc emerged around 1900, when Cooper-Hewitt took up the manufacture of these lamps on a commercial scale for lighting purposes. During further investigations of his lamps the idea of building a convertor for alternating current to direct current came up. This conversion equipment was apparently first demonstrated at the end of 1902, beginning of 1903 [34, 35] in public, and aroused considerable interest. The mercury-arc rectifier family developed from this beginning, and Table 1 gives an impression of this development

Table 1: Development of some switching devices used in the control of electrical machines

Mercury-arc rectifier (glass envolope)	Cooper-Hewitt	1900 [33]
Mercury-arc rectifier (metal envelope)	Cooper-Hewitt	1908 [36]
	Schäfer	1910 [37]
Controlled mercury-arc rectifier (ignition by high voltage impulse on auxiliary electrodes)	Cooper-Hewitt	1903 [38]
Hot-cathode mercury vapour tube: without grid: phanotron, with grid: thyratron	Langmuir	1914 [39]
Mechanical field regulator	Tirrill	1902 [40]
Contact rectifier, high current metal contacts	Koch	1901 [41]
	Kesselring	1923 [42]
	Koppelman	1941 [43]
Selenium rectifier	Presser	1925 [44]
Copper-oxide rectifier	Grondahl	1926 [45]
Junction thyristor, *pnpn* configuration	Shockley	1951 [46]
	Moll/York	1956 [47]
		1957 [48]
Bidirectional triode switch *pnpnp* configuration	Gentry, Scace, Flowers	1964 [49]

and of related devices. It may be said that the development of the mercury-arc rectifier family did not reach a stage where much practical development of circuits was inspired before 1930.

4.2 Development of circuits for the electronic control of electrical power

It is, of course, impossible to describe the development of all the power electronic techniques in a few words, therefore only the most important ideas concerning (i) power electronic frequency changers (ii) DC to DC transforming circuits (electronic choppers) and (iii) phase control circuits for adjusting output voltage will be discussed

Although in the preceding paragraph it has been indicated that the efficient controlled power switches had a gradual development, static frequency conversion dates from 1903, as far as rectification is concerned. Performing the inverse of this process proved more difficult, as a suitable method of controlling the arc discharge was not available. Before 1906, Steinmetz actually built an inverter circuit by using a single-cathode, 4-anode unit in which the discharge spontaneously switched from anode to anode in predictable order (Fig. 18*a*). Switching characteristics of the tube were found to be mostly dependent on the inter-electrode distance of the electrodes [50]. It appears reasonable to assume that this characteristic was necessary to start up the circuit, and once AC loads had been connected to the output, natural commutation would aid the process of inversion. This process for the circuit shown depends on the cyclic transfer of the arc in the order 1–2–3–4–1. Prince developed the later well known parallel

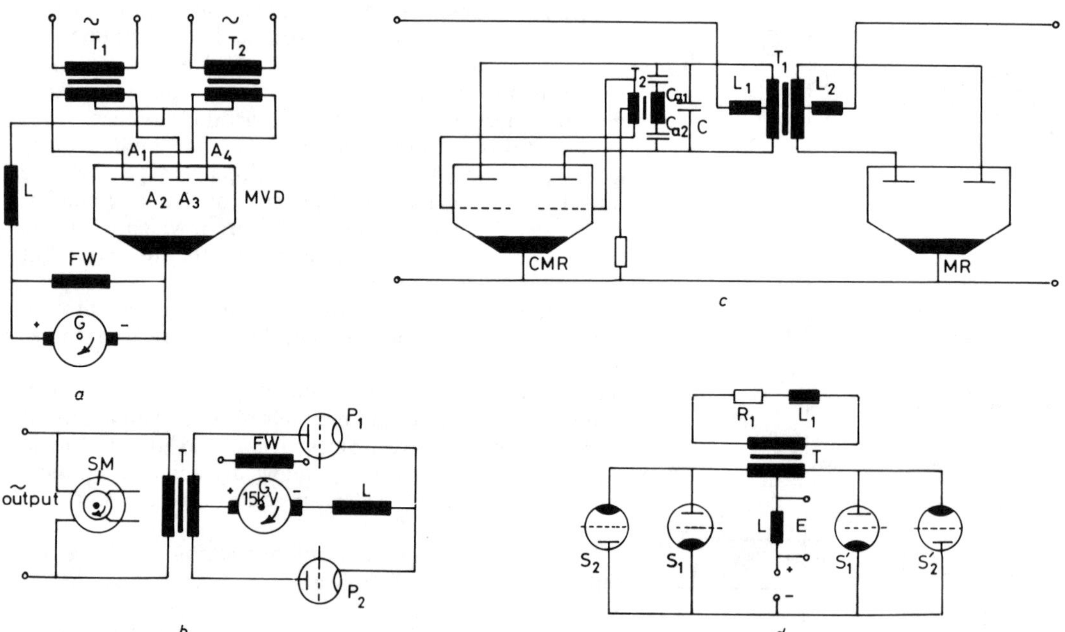

Fig. 18 *Initial development of some fundamental ideas in power electronics*

a Steinmetz inverter
MVD = mercury-vapour device
A_1–A_4 = anodes
T_1, T_2 = output transformers
L = smoothing inductor
G = DV generator
FW = field winding
b Inverter circuit of Prince
SM = synchronous machine
G = high-voltage DV generator
T = inverter transformer
FW = field winding
P_1, P_2 = 'pliotron' tubes
L = smoothing inductor
c DV transforming circuit of Prince with forced commutation
T_1 = inverter transformer
T_2 = grid transformer
CMR = controlled mercury-arc rectifier
MR = mercury-arc rectifier
C = commutation capacitor
C_{a1}, C_{a2} = auxiliary capacitors
L_1, L_2 = smoothing inductors
d Proposed inverter circuit of Petersen with 'Petersen' tubes
R_L = load resistance
L_l = load inductance
T = inverter transformer
L = commutation inductor
E = commutation EMF
S_1, S_2, S'_1, S'_2 = gas tubes

inverter in 1925, adding forced commutation to the scheme in 1928. As indicated in Fig. 18*b* the first inverter circuit used natural commutation, assisted by the grids of the thermionic vacuum tubes. It was unable to handle any reactive power, and therefore the synchronous machine in the output circuit was a necessity. The use of 15 kV to overcome the disadvantage of the high voltage drop in the vacuum switching elements is interesting. The force commutated circuit of Fig. 18*c* was still unable to handle reactive power, but represented a major advance in the characteristic that it was able to work independently of an already existing supply. After the possibility of handling reactive power with these circuits was introduced by Steenbeck and then by Petersen (Fig. 18*d*) and the cycloconvertor family of circuits had been developed, the development of power-electronic frequency changers advanced significantly. Table 2 again presents some aspects of this development.

Table 2: Development of some important power-electronic circuit techniques

'Switching tube' inverter circuit	Steinmetz	pre-1906 [50]
'Parallel'-inverter circuit with natural commutation	Prince	1925 [51]
Parallel-inverter circuit with forced commutation	Prince	1928 [52]
Inverter circuit with series configuration	Fitzgerald, Henderson, Sabbah	1929 [53]
Feedback diodes to handle reactive power in inverter circuits	Steenbeck	1931 [54]
Decoupling diodes for commutation circuits	Umarov	1956 [55]
Cycloconvertor circuits	Rissik	1930 [33]
Synchronous envelope cyclonconvertor	Löbl	1932 [56]
Asynchronous envelope cyclonconvertor	Krämer	pre-1935 [33]
Continuously variable cyclonconvertor	Schenkel, von Issendorf	1932 [58]
Direct-voltage chopper circuit	Prince, Hull	1929 [53]
	Tompkins	1932 [57]
Phase control DV circuits	Dunoyer, Toulon	1924 [59]
Phase control AV circuits (antiparallel configuration)	Lenz	1933 [60]

A direct voltage chopper circuit, or DC to DC transformer, necessitates the forced commutation of direct current through the electronic switch. Although this art was well understood before 1930, as introduced by Prince [52] and Hull [53], and treated explicitly by Tompkins [57] it was apparently not applied to the control of electromechanical transducers until recently.

On the other hand efficient phase control circuits were developed much earlier and applied with success to the control of DC machines and other DC loads, and to the control of AC loads. Using the idea of control of the discharge of Cooper-Hewitt, Dunoyer and Toulon [59] effectively demonstrated how to obtain regulation at the output of an electronic convertor in 1924. Modifying this idea for current flow in both directions, Lenz [60] proposed and tested the antiparallel naturally commutated switch configuration in 1933. This configuration and the previous one were used extensively in the control of welding equipment [61].

5 Development of ideas to control electrical machines

Ideas to use electronic elements to control, regulate or augment electrical machines appear to have been put into practice for the first time around 1920. It is possible that these contributions may not be characterised as machine electronics as it is known today, yet may be considered as the very beginning of the subject.

5.1 *Initial attempts*

In 1917, Bolliger came upon the idea of a 'high-voltage' DV machine (published 1921) in which the substantial part of the commutator action is executed by a mercury-arc rectifier [62].

From the preceding paragraph and from figure 19*a* it may be gathered that by connecting the discharge tube in series with a mechanical switch he was able to obtain the characteristic of a controlled rectifier. This is the more remarkable, because at that stage the controlled mercury-arc rectifier still belonged to the future. The high voltages in the reverse direction and the actual commutation were the responsibilities of the rectifier. This indicates that Bolliger had already fully realised the necessity for a static electronic commutator but did not yet have the necessary circuit elements.

Van der Bijl described control systems for DC generator current and voltage in 1920 [63], attributing the origin of the ideas to Wold. In these systems a vacuum triode ('audion') was connected either in series or in parallel with the field winding of the generator, the essential control element (Fig. 19*b*).

Before 1930 Voorhoeve in the Netherlands investigated the possibilities of controlling generator voltages by electronic means. Contrary to the work reported by Van der Bijl, he employed vacuum diodes, the heating current being the variable (Fig. 19*c*). This was done in the conviction that gas discharge tubes did not yet have the constant characteristics essential for achieving accurate control. Later work by the same group included the use of vacuum triodes, but was overshadowed by the fast developing control schemes with grid controlled mercury-arc rectifiers [64, 65].

5.2 *Machines with electronic commutators*

Reference has already been made to the fact that electronic switches may be used to perform the same function as mechanical switches in conjunction with an electrical machine.

One of the initial ideas that sprung from the availability of the controlled mercury-arc rectifier was to build an electronic commutator. This idea grew gradually. It is worth mentioning that in 1913 two steel tank mercury-arc rectifiers were installed in a traction unit of the Pennsylvania Railroad in the USA. This unit, with four 200 HP 600 V motors completed approximately 20 000 km in normal traction service by 1920 [38]. In this case two frequency conversion processes are to be observed, one of which is still mechanical. The first machine to use a true electronic commutator was the machine of Kern — a now famous example [66]. In fact, Kern suggested various configurations, one being shown in Fig. 20. The first locomotive with this system was built by Brown Boveri around 1930.

Before 1940, these types of machines were studied by many workers, and were originally primarily intended for traction purposes [67]. Although it was applied in Europe and in the USA to a certain extent [68], the thyratron or controlled mercury-arc commutator motor never attained true widespread practical application, despite considerable enthusiasm (see, for instance, discussion of Alexanderson to Marti [67]).

One of the ideas being applied at present is the use of thyristor frequency changers in conjunction with squirrel-cage induction machines for electric traction purposes [69, 70]. This idea is not new, it has been considered in the

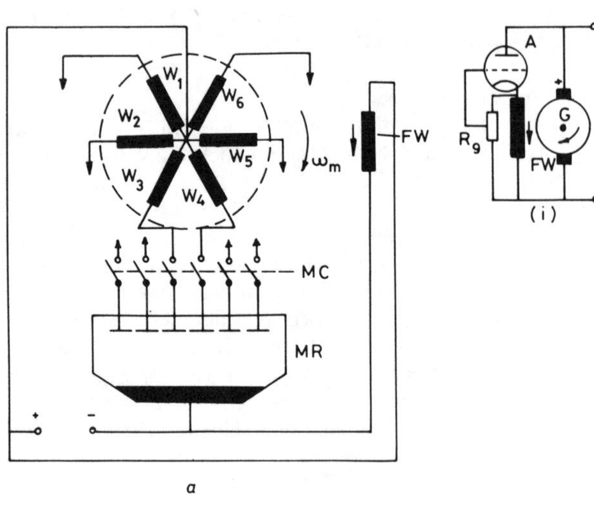

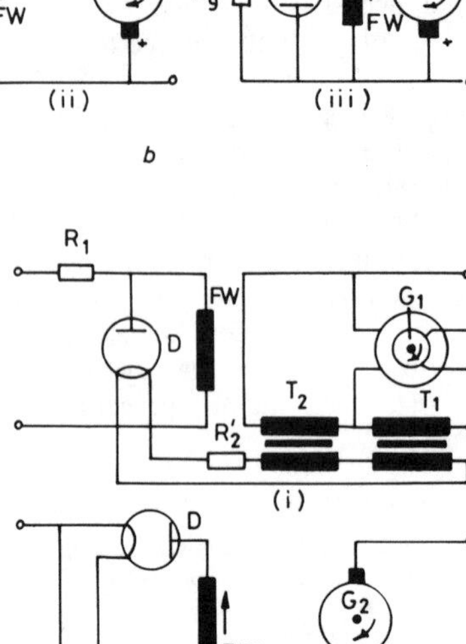

Fig. 19 *Some initial attempts at controlling electrical machines by electronic methods*

a Illustration of the principle of the 'high-voltage' DV machine of Bolliger
MC = mechanical commutator
MR = mercury-arc rectifier
W_1–W_6 = machine armature windings
FW = field winding
b Schemes presented by van der Bijl
A = 'audion'
G = DV generator
R_s = grid resistor
R_i = current resistor

c Original schemes of Voorhoeve for controlling generator voltage
G_1 = AV generator
G_2 = DV generator
D = vacuum diode
T_1 = current transformer
T_2 = voltage transformer

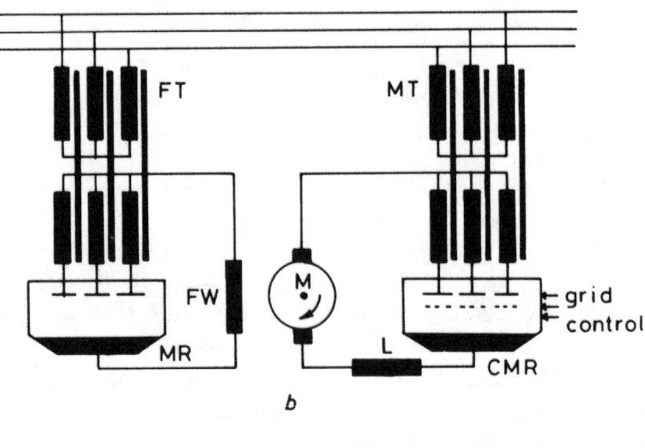

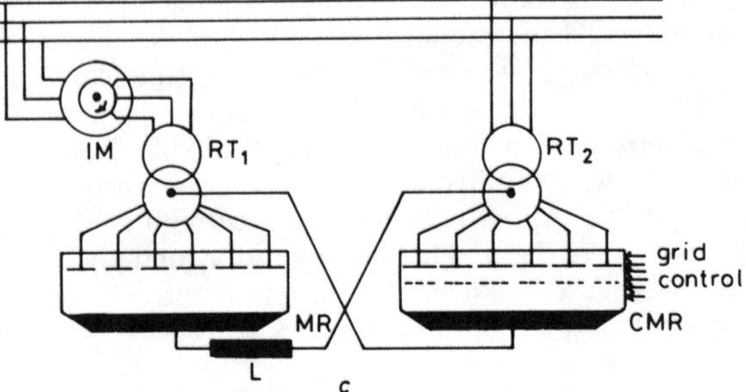

Fig. 20 *Important machine electronic developments*

a Thyratron-commutator machine proposed by Kern
W_1–W_{12} = machine stator windings
R = rotor and field winding
T = transformer
CMR = controlled mercury-arc rectifier
b Original scheme for AV fed DV motor investigated by Schilling
FT = field transformer
MT = main transformer
MR = mercury-arc rectifier
CMR = controlled mercury-arc rectifier
L = smoothing inductor
M = direct voltage motor
FW = field winding

c Electronic Scherbius cascade of Stöhr
IM = induction motor
RT_1, RT_2 = rectifier transformers
CMR = controller mercury-arc rectifier
MR = mercury-arc rectifier
L = smoothing inductor

past, but rejected [71]. The reason for the rejection of this proposal in 1940 was the enormous volume of equipment needed, as it was impossible to transport it aboard an ordinary locomotive. Thyristors are relatively small in size and eliminated this problem, as has been illustrated by the present developments (see discussion in Section 6).

The interest in electronic commutators, stimulated anew by the thyristor, has apparently stimulated the use of transistors for the same function in small machines. This is the inevitable conclusion, as it was not until 1962 that this type of electronically commutated machine received serious attention [72, 73], although switching transistors were available years before.

5.3 Schemes for control of induction machines without changing the supply frequency

The first work on electronic rotor control of induction machines concerned electronic Scherbius cascades. The consideration that mercury-arc controlled rectifiers are expensive and have a voltage drop of 15–25 V during forward conduction confined these investigations to larger machines. Alexanderson proposed an electronic Scherbius cascade in 1938 [74]. Working independently, Stöhr reported investigations comparing machines with an electronic commutator to the mentioned cascade in 1939 [75]. Later the operation of the electronic Scherbius cascade was extended to the oversynchronous region of operation [76]. Subsequently Hölters [77] also investigated this type of system.

The development of silicon rectifiers renewed the interest in systems consisting of wound-rotor induction machines and frequency convertors in the rotor [78], while thyristors held the promise of making this drive economic and compact — also for smaller machines.

The magnetic amplifier was applied with good results to stator and rotor control [79], but it is only after the development of the thyristor that this type of control has received increasing attention in the form of electronic switching of the rotor current, notably in Germany (see, for instance, Reference 80). Although the idea of using antiparallel switches to regulate voltage had been around for a long time, it does not seem to have been worked out for the stator control of induction machines. About 1950, the idea of applying phase control to the rotor and stator circuits of induction machines by magnetic amplifiers found wide application [79, 81]. Only after 1960 did interest arise in employing this type of control to advantage on the stator of squirrel-cage motors by using electronic switches [82].

5.4 Voltage conditioning of commutator machines

Control of DC machines fed by 3-phase or single-phase AC systems drew attention after the introduction of the controlled mercury-arc rectifier in 1928. It was realised that this offers the possibility to regulate the main current in the motor [83], and was apparently first extensively investigated by Schilling [84], (see Fig. 20). Later, attention was devoted to constructing static Ward-Leonard drives in this way (see for instance Reference 64). Semiconductor switches increased the possibilities, and it may be expected that the present popularity of this type of semiconductor controlled drive will still continue for some time. In the same way that the thyristor revived the interest in convertor locomotives in countries with AC traction systems, the controlled mercury-arc rectifier originally initiated the design of the convertor locomotive, one of the first examples being that of Reichel [85].

5.5 Electronic chopper control of direct voltage machines

Apparently the inventor of armature voltage control of DC machines by pulse modulation, the so-called series chopper, was Blaufuss in 1940 [86]. The problem was to obtain a mechanical or electronic switch that could be operated reliably and fast enough to achieve this control. Many years elapsed before the idea of Blaufuss was taken up again. The first practical realisation of this scheme by electronic means appears to be due to Jones [87] in the USA and to Abraham, Heumann and Koppelmann [88] in Germany, the two groups working independently, and employing thyristors as switches. It is interesting to note that the electronic chopper as employed by these groups was discussed in 1929 by Hull in relation to the parallel inverter [53]. These types of power-electronic systems have since developed rapidly, especially with respect to the circuit improvements possible. Electronic choppers regulating series, parallel and separately excited direct voltage machines are one of the most successful machine-electronics systems at present, finding widespread applications in low-loss control in traction circuits.

Some of the important developments in machine electronics are summarised in Table 3.

Table 3: Some important developments in machine electronics

Semi-electronic commutator machine	Bolliger	1917 [62]
Field-regulation of generators by vacuum triodes	Van der Bijl, Wold	1920 [63]
Field-regulation of generators by vacuum diodes	Voorhoeve	1928 [65]
All-electronic commutator machine	Kern	1930 [66]
Electronic Scherbius cascade	Alexanderson	1938 [74]
Electronic Ward-Leonard Control	Schilling Bayha	1933 [84]
Electronic chopper control	Jones	1961 [87]
	Abraham, Heumann, Koppelman	1962 [88]

6 Growth of power electronics in rail drives as an example of application in the control of electric machines

From the early attempts outlined in the preceding sections, a tremendous growth has resulted in all fields where power electronics have been applied to condition power flow. As only one example of this, the applications to the field of electric traction will be traced in some detail in the subsequent paragraphs.

With power electronic convertors it is possible to achieve appreciable technical improvements in drives for electric rail vehicles. In this part of the paper the following developments will be discussed:

(i) Replacement of the unfavourable single-phase series commutator motor with DC or pulsating current commutator machines in conjunction with rectifiers

(ii) The control of tractive effort with controlled rectifiers instead of transformer tap changing or with DC choppers instead of resistance variation

(iii) Favourable control of electric braking both for resistive braking and regenerative braking

(iv) Replacement of commutator machines with lighter multiphase AC machines with more favourable maintenance characteristics

(v) Reduction of supply reaction caused by traction drives with line side power electronic convertors.

6.1 Traction drives for rail vehicles with uncontrolled rectifiers and DC machines

At present, approximately half of all the electrified long-distance railway lines in the world are supplied with single-phase alternating current [89–91]. This solved the problem of energy supply to railways. The price that had to be paid for this was the use of the single-phase AC commutator machine which was unfavourable from the viewpoint of machine construction. It is consequently not surprising that with the development of mercury-arc rectifiers, attempts were made to install these elements in traction vehicles to convert the AC to DC, so that normal DC machines with more favourable construction characteristics could be employed.

In 1906 there were attempts in the USA at using mercury-arc rectifiers in a traction vehicle [92]. In the following years, General Electric and Westinghouse built experimental railway equipment with mercury-arc rectifiers [92, 93].

Five series E 80 locomotives of the German Federal Railways were put into service in 1930. These locomotives used two parallel 6-anode mercury-arc rectifiers in glass enclosures in single-way connection. The control was obtained by means of transformer tap changing and resistors.

The Westinghouse Corporation in the USA developed mercury-arc rectifiers in steel tanks with igniters called ignitrons. These robust elements without vacuum pumps were well suited for use in traction vehicles. The first experimental vehicle consisted of a multiple unit changed to this system for the Pennsylvania Railroad by the Westinghouse Corporation in 1949 [93, 95]. The ignitrons were used in a single-phase bridge connection and the tractive effort was controlled with series resistors. Once this technology proved itself, several American railroad companies ordered series of units using this method. [96–98].

Between 1960 and 1963, 66 rectifier locomotives of the Series 44 are also an example of this technology. The last locomotives of this series were not supplied with ignitrons but with silicon diodes, as these were at that stage already available with a sufficient power capability [99]. In this case a smooth transition from convertor technology with mercury-arc rectifier systems to convertor technology with the much simpler and more robust semiconductor diodes may be observed.

The new development was extensively used all over the world. In France, the Societé Nationale des Chemin de Fers (SNCF) used ignitron-type rectifier locomotives [100, 101], as well as excitron type rectifier locomotives [102, 103]. With the arrival of semiconductor diodes in 1959, the SNCF also used these devices.

Multisystem locomotives is a particular problem of the European Railway System. After the Second World War, railway traffic across the borders increased continuously, causing a demand for 2-, 3- and 4-system locomotives. Several electric circuits were used for these locomotives. Most often the locomotives used circuits with resistive control and motor rearangement in the DC drive mode, where the motor rearrangement was also used as a means of transferring between the DC voltage systems for 1.5 kV and 3 kV. When the locomotives were fed from AC systems, the supply was via a transformer and a rectifier to supply the DC busbar in the locomotive. These locomotives were used by the SNCF [104, 105], by the Belgian National Railways (SNCB) [106, 107] and by the Deutsche Bundesbahn (DB) [108, 109]. Japanese National Railways (JNR) started, in 1955, to use AC locomotives with ignitrons or excitrons. From 1960 onwards, the mercury-arc rectifiers were replaced with silicon diodes [110].

A similar development occurred with British Railways (BR). After experiments with mercury-arc rectifiers, the first locomotives with multi-anode mercury-arc rectifiers were equipped in 1957. In a short time several hundred locomotives and multiple units of the series AL 1–AL 4 and AM 2–AM 5 were equipped with excitrons or ignitrons [111]. With British Rail the transition to semiconductor technology took place by using germanium diodes. After 1960, silicon diodes were used instead. Also in this case, several hundreds of multiple units were equipped with these diodes and tractive control with transformer tap changing [111, 112].

Many more examples of the transition from mercury-arc rectifiers to silicon-diode rectifiers on railway drives are described in the literature. As examples papers about the Swiss [107, 112], the Swedish [114], the German [115], the Indian [116], and the USSR [117] development can be found in our Reference list.

6.2 Traction drives on rail vehicles using controlled rectifiers

From 1920 onwards the principle of grid control with mercury arc rectifiers was known. Soon after the construction of the first mercury-arc rectifier locomotive, suggestions were made to obtain tractive effort control with grid control of the mercury-arc rectifier [118]. In 1936, a locomotive with a grid controlled mercury-arc rectifier for experimental use on a 50 Hz system by the German Federal Railways on the Höllental part of the network was equipped [89]. During these experiments a locomotive with single phase series field commutator machines, a machine-convertor locomotive with uncontrolled rectifiers [119], as well as a locomotive with grid controlled mercury arc rectifier [120] were tested.

This last locomotive, representing a very important state in the development, was equipped by the AEG Company. The convertor was built in a particularly interesting circuit arrangement (refer to Fig. 21). Four groups of four anodes worked on different taps of the main transformer. Additionally a zero anode was also available. The 18 anodes of a mercury-arc rectifier in a steel tank were connected as shown in the Figure.

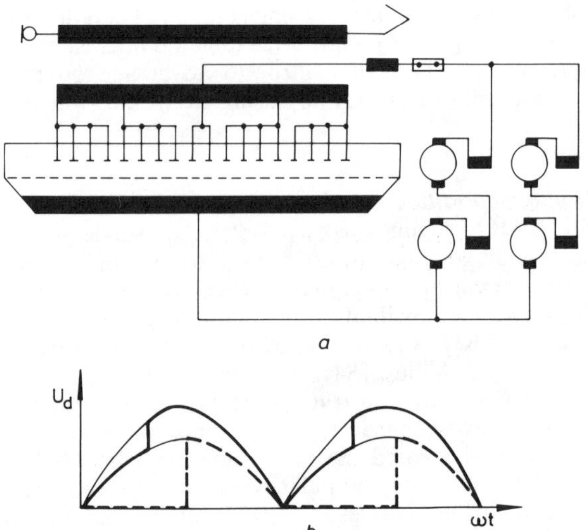

Fig. 21 *Principle of first locomotive systems using controlled rectifiers*
a Simplified main circuit diagram of the AEG-Höllental locomotive
b Idealised time dependence of the output voltage
partly controlled, 1st stage
partly controlled, 2nd stage

In the USA, the change to controlled convertors was actually made surprisingly late. In so far as we were able to determine, it was the Pennsylvania Railroad who pioneered this change. In 1963, 38 railcars with silicon-diode rectifiers and ignitron control were put into serive [121–123]. The circuit diagram in Fig. 22 indicates three silicon-diode bridges in series on the DC side, which are connected on the AC side to the transformer windings. One of these bridges was fed by a bidirectional AC controller using ignitrons, enabling a continuous voltage adjustment over the entire working range. This apparently unusual arrangement is a possible explanation for the late change to the use of controlled rectifiers.

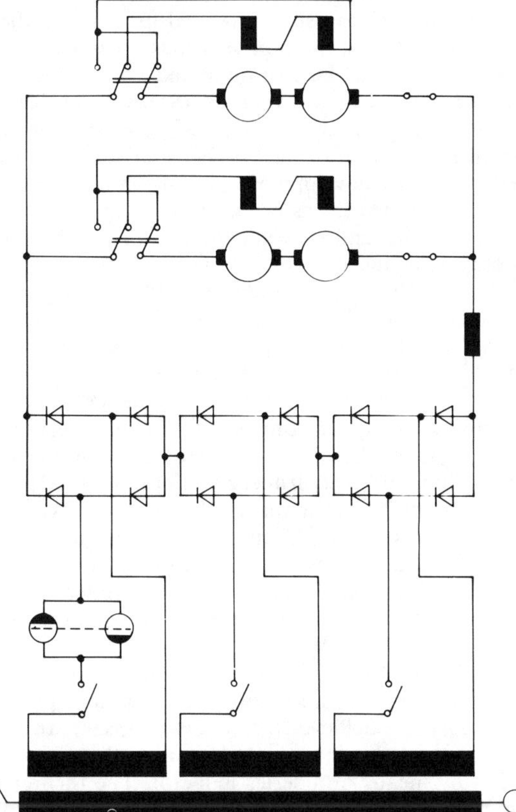

Fig. 22 *Diagram of ignitron locomotive drive system*

In a convertor with centre tap or bridge arrangement the blocking voltage after the conducting phase increases with the angle of ignition. In the same way the danger of backfiring also increases [124]. In the arrangement shown in Fig. 22 with bidirectional AC controller, no rise of blocking voltage is found, because the ignitrons always switch off when the voltage passes through zero. In this way the danger of backfiring is appreciably smaller in this circuit.

In Europe there was practically no further development in this area during the Second World War. The work that started again after the Second World War led to some notable results.

In Germany between 1950 and 1955, the Rheinischen Braunkohlenwerke AG started to increase the power of their railway, and in this programme also started modernising the coal trains. The electrical supply was changed from 1200 V DC to 6 kV, 50 Hz AC [125]. For this they acquired rotating convertor locomotives and static convertor locomotives. In 1956 and 1957 AEG, BBC and Siemens equipped, in total, 36 locomotives with static convertor drives [126–128]. The tractive effort control on these locomotives was achieved with the grid control in the starting region and in the subsequent ranges with the aid of tap changing. The static convertors used single-anode tanks without pumps. These locomotives were used with success for approximately ten years and were re-equipped with thyristor control from 1965 onwards.

In France, several series of locomotives were equipped, from 1954 onwards, with controlled static convertors [129, 130], using ignitrons and excitrons. These series will be discussed further regarding regenerative braking.

Between 1955 and 1965 two solutions were developed for AC fed traction drives: these solutions were rectifier drives with silicon-diode rectifiers and tractive effort control via transformer tap changing or series resistors and stepless control with controlled static rectifiers using ignitrons or excitrons. Both these solutions were used alongside each other and were implemented in many locomotive series all over the world. As an example, the supply list of the 50 Hz group formed by several European companies may be consulted [131].

Between 1960 and 1965 thyristors with reverse voltages over 1 kV and current capabilities over 100 A were developed. The time was ripe to combine the advantages of controlled rectifiers and static semiconductor devices in traction drives. In several countries companies developed thyristor based static convertors for locomotives. As far as we know, the first thyristor locomotive in Europe was developed by Siemens and equipped as an industrial locomotive for a coal mine in 1964 [132]. The static convertor in this locomotive consisted of two half-controlled single phase bridges connected in series on the DC side. Further thyristor locomotives were supplied in the following years [132–134].

In the USA, General Electric supplied two mine locomotives with thyristor control for the Muskingum Electric Rail Road (MERR). These locomotives had five diode bridges connected in series on the DC side and connected mechanically to taps on the transformer windings. On the AC side of one of these bridges a bidirectional AC controller was rated at only one-fifth of the total power. By alternately connecting different bridges to the transformer windings, it was possible to have continuous control over the entire voltage range with a limited power rating of the AC controller [135].

In the field of public rail transport, several railway companies equipped experimental vehicles with thyristor convertors. The first series of motor coaches with thyristor control was taken into service in Sweden and in Japan. In Sweden, railcars were taken into service in 1964 by the Swedish State Railways, supplied on an experimental basis with thyristor convertors by ASEA [114]. In the following year a locomotive Rb 1 was equipped with thyristor control. [114]. As a consequence of the good results of these experiments, a series of thyristor locomotives Rc 1 were put into service from 1967 onwards. The convertors on these locomotives consisted of three half-controlled single-phase bridges in series on the DC side [136]. In the following years these locomotives were developed further, so that, from 1969 onwards, the series Rc 2 only had two bridges in series.

This design was used in all subsequent models with a reduction of the number of devices used per leg until the series Rc 5 was developed, and is in use today [137].

The Japanese National Railways (JNR) implemented the first series of thyristor locomotives in the ED76S, in 1966 [138]. In the following years further series of locomotives and motor coaches with thyristor convertors were put into service. It is worthwhile to note that in the convertors up to six bridges are used in series [139]. Today trains in Japan — also the world famous Shinkansen — are equipped with thyristor convertors [140].

In the last decade, thyristor controlled traction vehicles were put into service in many countries with AC traction systems. Instead of listing all these, the reader is referred to the review literature in this field [139, 141, 142]

Further development of devices in the direction of higher power ratings has led to convertors with a continuously decreasing number of devices. As an example, the already discussed Swedish locomotive Rc 1 used 72 devices per motor. The Rc 2 and Rc 3 used only 36 devices, the Rc 4, 16 devices and the Rc 5 only one device per leg, that is eight per motor [137]. Therefore it becomes less attractive to use circuit schemes with multiple series devices during operation. Today the series connection of two half controlled bridges has become widely accepted. In this regard a variation that was developed in Switzerland is worth noting. In this case the multistep control range was not obtained by connecting bridges in series, but by connecting them in parallel [143]. This solution makes the use of semiconductor devices with very high blocking voltages possible, without increasing the machine voltage unduly.

6.3 Regenerative braking

In the classical drives with single-phase series field commutator machine and transformer tap changing, the use of regenerative braking is not fully possible and can only be achieved with the aid of additional switching arrangements [141, 144]. In contrast, drives with a fully-controlled convertor offer the advantage of regenerative braking. Soon after the implementation of controlled static convertors on traction vehicles, the use of regenerative braking was investigated. Possibly the first static convertor locomotive suited to regenerative control was the Rhein-Braun locomotive discussed earlier and put into service in 1956–1957 [126–128]. The SNCF were possibly first among the public railway systems to have static convertor locomotives with regenerative braking in service. In 1958, the locomotive BB 10 001 with an excitron convertor was equipped for regenerative braking [130]. By 1961, approximately 100 locomotives with regenerative braking had been put into service by the SNCF [130, 144].

For static convertor locomotives with regenerative braking, a problem is posed by the danger of inverting instability in the convertor. When, for example, there is a voltage dip caused by a jump of the pantograph, the AC voltage necessary for commutation falls away, and the traction machine, working as a generator, can supply a sharply increasing short-circuit current via the conducting devices in the controllable bridge, with possible destruction of the equipment. To counteract this, very fast DC switches [93] and fast de-excitation have been tried [145]. An elegant solution is to use the traction machine as a separately excited generator with an additional series winding when braking [133]. When instability in the inverter occurs, the fast increasing short-circuit current of the machine de-energises the generator and limits the current.

In locomotives with thyristor convertors, the problems discussed have for a time prevented the application of regenerative braking, because the semiconductor devices are more sensitive to excessive currents (also for very short times). It was, however, possible to solve these problems. In 1965, AEG equipped a locomotive with thyristor convertors for the Rhein-Braun AG, using regenerative braking, [133].

At present, regenerative control of traction vehicles is already widely accepted. It is particularly advantageous on railways with very steep gradients. In Section 6.6, pulse-type convertors will be discussed which enable regenerative braking with no reactive current and almost no harmonic injection into the supply.

6.4 DC drives with chopper controllers

In the convertor arrangements described so far, the AC voltage from the traction supply is used for commutation. When the supply to the traction vehicle is a DC voltage, it is necessary to use self-commutated convertors or choppers for control of the vehicles. (See Section 2). The idea of controlling the speed of a DC machine through pulse-width modulation of the voltage source had already appeared before the development of semiconductor power technology [1]. When thyristors with blocking and reverse voltages of several hundred volts and currents higher than 10 A became available, several researchers suggested chopper control for traction vehicles [88, 146–148]. For practical applications, battery traction vehicles were selected because they did not have the overvoltage problems that one could expect when selecting a vehicle with an overhead supply. As far as we know, the first railway vehicle with DC chopper control was put into service in 1963. This was a shunting locomotive in the Siemens Transformer Factory in Nürnberg in Germany [149]. For a power rating of 30 kW it was at that stage necessary to use four thyristors in parallel in the armature circuit. The same firm built a battery shunting locomotive of some 200 kW power rating with DC chopper controller in 1964, with change over for regenerative braking already implemented in the vehicle [150].

The next stage of development was to construct DC chopper vehicles that could be operated from an overhead traction supply. To achieve this, it was necessary to use a filter capacitor on the vehicle itself, limiting the resonance frequencies by means of a series inductor. The theoretical solution to the problem was published in 1966 with a report on a locomotive of this type that was put into service in 1965 [151].

This enabled the introduction of DC chopper controllers in tramways and underground railways [152, 153]. The literature reports on a series of chopper controlled drives, introduced into service from 1971 onwards [154]. Thus from about 1970 chopper control in the armature circuit of traction vehicles for urban use have been in common use. Many of these series of vehicles are in service worldwide [155–157].

With increasing power, a conflict appears in the design of the system when choosing the switching frequency. On the grounds of dimensioning the chopper circuit itself, the frequency must be as low as possible, preferably in the range 100–300 Hz. When taking the filter design into account, the chopping frequency should be as high as possible. This problem was solved through a phase shift between several parallel chopper circuits. As an example, the RATP (Régie Autonome des Transport Parisiens) put several Metro vehicles into service with power ratings of over 400 kW between 1969 and 1971. These vehicles were supplied with chopper controllers by several firms [158]. In these systems the parallel operation of 2, 3 and 4 phase-displaced choppers was investigated systematically. Fig. 23 represents the principle of a 3-pulse chopper.

To apply chopper controllers also for large railway vehicles, the problem of series connection of several thyristors and the surge voltages in traction networks had to be overcome. At first, auxiliary drives with powers below 100 kW, such as battery chargers or fan motors, were supplied by choppers operating from the normal traction supply [159]. In 1968, the SNCF installed chopper controllers for 1500 V 350 kW and 600 kW on two motor

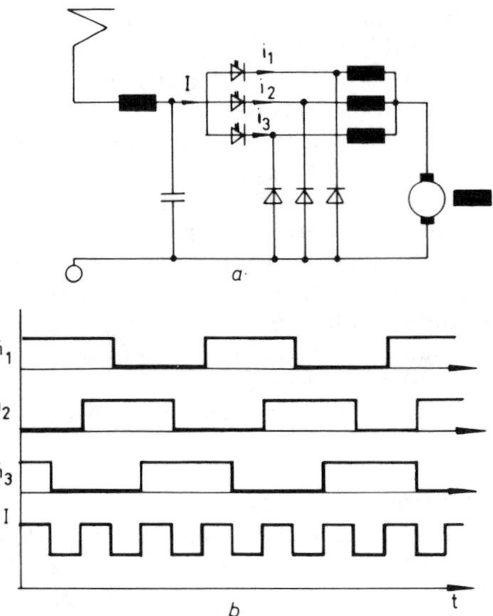

Fig. 23 *Three-pulse DC chopper controllers for traction drive*
a Simplified schematic diagram
b Idealised current waveforms with duty cycle of 50%

coaches [160]. After a full-scale experimental run on a re-equipped locomotive CC20002, with phase shifted parallel operation of six choppers [161], the SNCF ordered several series of vehicles with chopper controllers, for example, the series BB 7200 [162].

The Belgian National Railways (SNCB) implemented chopper controllers early on their 3 kV DC system. After initial experimentation a motor coach equipped by ACEC (Ateliers de Constructions Electriques de Charleroi) was put into service in 1968 [163]. Information on the series using chopper technology in the SNCB is found in the literature [164] and the same development in the Italian State Railways is reported in Reference 165.

6.5 Power electronics for multiphase AC traction drives

With the aid of power electronic convertors, it is possible to convert the power from the single-phase overhead supply in such a way that multiphase AC traction machines can be driven. The fundamental circuits for inverters and convertors have been known from the thirties, as already discussed previously. The use of these circuits in the age of the ignitron for traction vehicles was not possible, due to various technical considerations. It had to wait for the invention of controllable semiconductor devices for power applications to make the construction of sufficiently fast and large convertors for multiphase AC on traction vehicles possible.

The first traction vehicle with multiphase convertor drive was an experimental diesel electric locomotive of British Railways called 'Hawk' This locomotive was supplied in 1965 by the British firm Brush with a thyristor convertor and multiphase AC traction machines [166, 167]. The convertor consisted of a controlled rectifier for feeding the direct voltage link circuit and of three force commutated inverters for feeding the traction motors from this direct voltage link circuit. The power rating of the inverter was 670 kW and for this it contained 208 thyristors. Owing to technical problems, this locomotive was not taken into normal service.

In the USSR, early experiments with convertor locomotives of these types were undertaken. In 1968, half the drives of a locomotive of the type WL 80 were converted to multiphase AC drive with induction traction motors and the other half with synchronous traction motors. The induction motor drives had variable voltage in the DC link circuits and four force commutated inverters. The synchronous traction motor drive employed machine commutated inverters [168]. In 1971, another developed version of the synchronous machine drive was also tested [169]. In 1975, a further locomotive with induction traction machines was put into service [170].

In West Germany, a very successful line of development started with the diesel-electric locomotive series DE 2500 that was first completed in 1971 as a joint effort between Henschel and BBC. These 80-tonne locomotives had a power of 1840 kW. The six squirrel cage traction machines were fed from four parallel force commutated inverters, feeding onto a busbar. Adjustment of voltage and frequency was obtained by way of the subsynchronous PWM control technology. The technology employed in these locomotives was transferred with success to locomotives fed from the overhead power supply. The first application was six industrial locomotives of Ruhrkohle AG in 1976. These locomotives could be fed from 15 kV, 16 2/3 Hz or 15 kV, 50 Hz for operation and had a power rating of 1.5 MW [171]. Apart from further electric and diesel-electric industrial locomotives, this technology was also applied in locomotives of the Swiss [172–174], German [175], Norwegian [176], Danish [177] and Austrian [178] Railways. It is worth noting that the semiconductor convertors of the locomotive series E 120 DB as well as the EL 17 NSB have been equipped with indirect oil cooling.

By using an experimental locomotive the Netherlands Railways (NS) demonstrated that the same technology could also be applied for power supply by an overhead line at 1.5 kV [179]. Fig. 24 represents the fundamental circuit

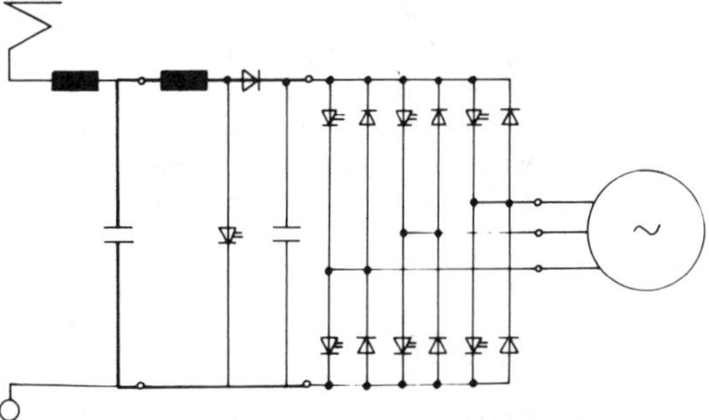

Fig. 24 *Schematic diagram of main circuit diagram of locomotive with multiphase AC traction motor, fed from DC overhead supply*

arrangement used. Apart from the locomotives mentioned above, many experiments have recently been reported with multiphase AC traction vehicles by, for example the SNCF, BR, FS and JNR [180].

An interesting development by the SNCF with synchronous traction motors should be mentioned [181, 182]. In this case machine commutated inverters are supplied by a direct current link.

It is necessary to devote some specific attention to the newer developments in the application of power electronics to tramways and underground railways with multiphase AC traction drives. In this field, current fed inverters have been widely used for multiphase AC traction machine supply.

In current fed inverters, a DC chopper is used to feed

the DC link from the overhead traction wire. The disadvantage of causing torque pulsation by feeding the traction machine with current blocks via the force commutated inverter can be prevented by pulsing the phase currents in such a way that specific current harmonics are supressed [183]. The first tramway with an inverter in current fed technology was implemented in 1975 by Siemens in Nürnberg, West Germany [184]. Series of vehicles with these types of drives were put into service in the underground railway systems of Nürnberg and Berlin.

Series of variable frequency AC vehicles are in operation or have been ordered for city transport in various countries, e.g. in Germany, Finland, France, Italy, the Netherlands, Japan and Austria [185].

The motivations for introducing AC multiphase traction technology in railway applications is different for different applications. Naturally, induction traction machines with squirrel-cage rotors are cheaper to construct than DC machines or AC commutator machines. This advantage is neutralised by the much higher cost of the inverter to generate the multiphase AC current. It is to be expected that AC traction drives would need less maintenance than DC drives, as there is no commutator in the system. An important argument for multiphase AC traction is the possibility to operate the squirrel-cage machines at a much higher speed than DC machines, and in this way open up the possibility of building much lighter and smaller traction machines. This could be of important influence on the dynamic behaviour of traction vehicles due to the much lower unsprung weight.

6.6 Supply reaction

With the application of power electronics to railway vehicles, there were some drawbacks. Static convertors draw current from the supply system which contains many harmonics and also has a fundamental that is shifted with regard to the supply voltage waveform. This is a disadvantage especially in railway supply systems. This resulted in early attempts to reduce the supply reaction of static convertors. In 1954, Kübler already proposed to equip the M2-circuit normally used at that time with a zero anode and to operate it with a constant phase angle of 60° to eliminate all triplen harmonics from the supply current [186].

With the advent of thyristor convertors, and the use of the half controlled circuit as well as the series connection on the DC side, the supply reaction was automatically somewhat reduced.

An important development was the suggestion by Förster that the thyristors in the half controlled single-phase bridge circuit should be equipped with a means of forced commutation [187]. With this so called LUB-circuit it is, in principle, possible to eliminate all fundamental reactive power due to the shift between the fundamental of the current and the voltage. This circuit was first tested in 1972 on a multiple unit of type 420 used by the German Federal Railways (DB) [188]. This is actually the first use of a force commutated static convertor in the main circuit of a traction drive. After this, the LUB-circuit was implemented in many locomotives, for example in the locomotive type 7E of the South African Railways (SAR) as well as in multiple units of type 4020 of the Austrian State Railways (OBB). Derivatives of this circuit, especially also for regenerative braking, have been suggested [189].

While the LUB-circuit can in principle only eliminate the fundamental reactive power, it is possible to eliminate harmonic powers also, by using high-frequency pulse operation in static convertors. In this way, the supply current of the E120 locomotive of the DB, which has already been discussed, has been made harmonic free to a very high degree by using this 4-quadrant force commutated single-phase bridge arrangement with high-frequency switching [190]. With the aid of this circuit, it is not only possible to reduce the total reactive power so far that the power factor is above 0.99, but it is also possible to draw capacitive currents from the supply, and in this way aid the elimination of voltage drops in the system [191].

The 4-quadrant controller is only suitable for applications where the force commutated convertor for the multiphase AC traction drive needs a direct voltage link for operation. In applications with a direct current link and also for applications with AC commutator traction motors, the use of static convertors that also operate in a pulsed mode have been suggested [192]. As far as we know, such circuits have not yet been tested in railway drives.

6.7 Possible future developments

Applications in railway systems have often been important engineering achievements. It is to be expected that the further development of power electronics on traction vehicles will continue in the future. At present, diodes and thyristors are being replaced by newer semiconductor power switches. Asymmetrical thyristors and reverse conducting thyristors [193] bring advantages regarding the dimensions of components in force commutated convertors using the circuit with antiparallel diode. In drives for urban applications, these devices are already being applied [194]. The commutating circuit becomes unnecessary when gate-turnoff thyristors (GTOs) are applied to the convertors [195]. The first applications of GTOs in traction vehicle drives have already been put into service in Japan [196]. Significant progress has been made with development of power transistors in the last few years and it is not yet clear whether these switching elements would be advantageous for applications in the traction field [197].

With the development of devices with better dynamic properties, higher switching frequencies also became possible. This enabled the reduction of electric and magnetic energy storage in the DC chopper technology and AC inverter technology. There is already a proposition to reduce the large and heavy supply transformer necessary at $16\frac{2}{3}$ Hz in the locomotive by increasing the frequency of the voltage obtained from the overhead cables before transforming it for traction purposes in the locomotive [198].

With the saving in space and weight of traction drives, one also has to acknowledge the specific contribution of the cooling system. So-called heatpipe cooling, water cooling and freon cooling, are, at present, being investigated and applied [199–203]. Freon cooling, especially, is reported to have important advantages over the other methods. Naturally, the developments regarding information processing also reflect in the power electronic applications for traction drives. Integrated control systems and microprocessors, at present, allow more and sophisticated functions when compared to earlier designs, and, at the same time, also allowing an important reduction in volume and an increase in reliability. In this regard, the automatic fault tracing and diagnosis on the vehicle will become important in the future [204–207]. In conclusion, it should be pointed out that in the field of auxiliary drives and supplies, such as for battery charging, or for the use of 50 Hz systems on the vehicle, power electronics are replacing the conventional rotating convertors, to a large extent. For these, see References 204–207.

The extensive research and development work in the field of magnetically levitated vehicles driven by linear motors have not been covered in this review. If these futuristic traffic systems become economically viable in the future, they will open up new fields for the application of power electronics.

It should be kept in mind that this review has been compiled in a field that has many new developments and the scene could change dramatically very quickly.

7 State of the art and future trends in power and machine electronics

Although the art and science of electrical machines have for some time been considered well known, the future possibilities for power conditioning and conditioning and control of the electromechanical energy conversion process is being affected profoundly by the present and future developments in semiconductor technology, especially with regard to power semiconductor devices and control electronics, which have been aided by the developments in the field of microelectronics. The discussion in the following sections will centre on the different switching devices, the present and future power convertor topologies, the present and future situation regarding the use of convertors as machine actuators in control systems, the present and future situation regarding control of DC and AC machine drives, including adaptive control ideas, and, finally, the interface between power and machine electronics and power system technology.

7.1 Development in the field of switching devices

The present range of power semiconductor devices available for application in power conversion equipment has developed from the original range of diodes and thyristors into a large family including asymmetric thyristors [208], gate-turnoff thyristors [209, 210], power field-effect transistors [211] (MOSFETs and JFETs), field controlled thyristors [21, 212], static induction transistors [213], bipolar power transistors [214]. As the switching times for these devices range from some 10 ns for MOSFETs, to the turn-off time of a few hundred microseconds for the largest and slowest thyristors, the circuit technologies for their application differ so much that it cannot be discussed at length in this Review. The difference in circuit technology is also accentuated by the voltage range and current range covered, i.e. from below 100 V to over 4000 V, and from 1 A to 5000 A, as well as the fact that each device does not cover the entire range of application but only part of it. The decrease in switching times achieved, particularly with MOSFETs, bipolar power transistors and asymmetric thyristors, has extended the frequency range of power electronics from the traditional power frequencies up to 1 MHz [215].

In particular, the short switching times have accentuated the thermal shock and dissipation problems caused by the concentration of the switching losses in such short times (smaller than 1 μs), so that there has been considerable development in snubbing technology as a means of eliminating the adverse effects of these ultra-fast thermal transients [216]. As snubbing implies storing reactive energy at turn-on and turn-off, these capacitive and inductive reactances have to be discharged. Although a certain amount of snubbing also occurred in thyristor circuits [217] (di/dt and dv/dt limitation) the increase in frequency soon made the dissipation of the reactive energy impractical, so that the technology of regenerative snubbing was developed [218–221]. This has enabled the development of power conditioners and convertors operating at up to 100 kHz [222] and above with such low switching losses that the efficiency is being determined by the conduction losses in the power semiconductors [223, 224].

The higher-frequency developments have been confined to the lower voltage and current ranges (200 V, 20 A) chiefly due to the power diode technology lagging behind the other power devices in turn-on and turn-off times at high-voltage capability. At present, the power diodes available are a limiting factor in many power electronic convertors above 5 kHz, although efforts to improve these devices are in evidence, as it has become clear that turn-off and turn-on time in power diodes should be of the same order to achieve the lowest possible switching losses.

Further developments in the field of power switching devices may be expected to attempt to improve the following characteristics:

(i) Decrease the complication (power level) of the interface between signal electronics and power electronics

(ii) Decrease of the switching transition times, as this determines switching losses and maximum repetition frequencies

(iii) Decrease of conduction voltage drop (losses) as this determines current rating, device cost, process yield, efficiency and cost of cooling requirements

(iv) Eliminate the necessity for bulky forced commutation components by improving turn-off characteristics of power switching devices.

Some comments on these considerations are now in order.

7.1.1 Improvement of interfacing: A number of device improvements recently announced and currently under development fall into this category. This concerns work on light-activated power devices with the most notable advances having been made in the field of light activated thyristors [225–229]. In view of the enormous charge removal problems associated with gate-turnoff thyristors, there is, at present, not much promise of achieving this optoelectronic simplification with these devices, as well.

The family of field-effect devices (MOSFETs, field controlled thyristors and static induction transistors) has also tended to reduce the interface complication [230]. Owing to the gate structure of the devices, the charge establishment and removal requirements for turning on and off, respectively, are less severe than in particular, with bipolar transistors and gate-turnoff thyristors when operating at comparable switching speeds and repetition frequencies.

7.1.2 Decrease of switching transition times: Improvement of the mechanism to establish and remove the required charge distribution has been, and will be, the key to decrease the switching transition times in semiconductor power devices, and therefore the key to achieving the corresponding reduction in switching losses [28, 219, 231]. As these mechanisms are related to both the structure of the device and the semiconducting properties of the material (doping, defects, traps) the optimisation of one aspect always affects a range of others. The history of device development up to the present has indicated that the trade-offs between device structure, production processing parameters and semiconducting properties have allowed a steady improvement.

In the area of turn-on times of diodes this is, at present, leading to the same improvement in turn-on times as had been observed a few years ago in turn-off times. It is therefore reasonable to expect that the present limitation of the voltage rating of high power semiconductor diodes with fast turn-on and turn-off times may yet disappear in the near future [232, 233]. In the area of the high-power bipolar power transistors and gate-turnoff thyristors, the devices have already derived much benefit from the more accurate semiconductor processing requirements related to power MOSFET technology. It may be expected that the charge transport and gain improvements in these devices will still benefit considerably from the new steps and technology at present being realised for IC-technology and power MOSFET.

7.1.3 Decrease of device losses during conduction: One of the results of the different trade-offs between internal semiconductor parameters and device structure options is inevitably the voltage drop across the conducting device. In principle, the voltage drop across all minority carrier junction devices is fixed to a certain range of values which cannot be reduced below a certain point (Schottky diode, pn and pvn diodes, bipolar power transistors, GTOs, triacs, ASCRs, bipolar Darlington pairs). The field-effect devices, being majority carrier devices along the main current path, do not have this limitation [234]. In principle, the conduction drop (on-resistance) may be decreased indefinitely by simply increasing device area. In terms of device processing yields, device layout and eventually cost, this is soon limited, however. This leads to a higher voltage drop, especially for higher device voltage ratings which has to be accepted for field-effect devices [234].

As a voltage drop of 1.5–2.5 V leads to unacceptable efficiency reduction in power electronic convertors for voltages below 100 V, as well as unacceptable cooling loads at larger currents (100 A to 1000 A) in the entire medium voltage range (up to 500 V) which, in turn, leads to unacceptable convertor volume, weight and cost, especially for mobile applications, it has recently been suggested that compensated bipolar Darlington power switches could be used [235, 236]. In this scheme, a compensating voltage is injected into the Darlington loop to reduce conduction losses to that of a singular bipolar transistor (800 mV and below). As it has been shown that this method combines the conduction loss advantages of directly driven bipolar transistor power switches, as well as the low drive power advantages of bipolar Darlingtons [231, 237], it will have important applications in convertors in the medium voltage range. It has subsequently been shown to have no deterioration in dynamic performance [231, 237], and a successful prototype demonstration has also been reported [223, 224, 237, 238].

7.1.4 Device developments for decreasing energy storage devices in convertors: With the successful development of high power gate-turnoff thyristors, an important advance in the reduction of forced commutation energy storage elements in power convertors has been made. Asymmetric thyristors and reverse conducting thyristors, taking advantage of advances in semiconductor processing, reduced turn-off times, leading to the simplification of commutation. Although attempts are made to eliminate energy storage components completely from power convertors ('snubberless operation') [239] this should be viewed with some reserve, especially in larger convertors. Energy storage devices (inductors in series and capacitance in parallel) limit dI/dt and dV/dt stresses on devices, as well as reducing dissipation, thermal shock and thermal stresses in devices. It has not yet been cleared up decisively where the limits of these effects in large devices are [240], and it should be kept in mind that with the continuous reduction in switching transition times the thermal shocks and their localisation becomes increasingly more severe [241]. From this viewpoint it might be expected that although device development will lead to smaller forced commutation components and to larger power switches with a turn-off capability (GTOs, bipolars and FETs), it will not be possible to eliminate snubbing components completely by device development in large converters [242, 243].

7.2 Development of power convertor topologies

At present, AC to DC supply commutated convertors and quasi-square-wave DC to AC convertors may be considered to have become an industry standard in the power range from the order of a few kilowatts up to the megawatt level [20, 29]. In the low power range, new switching convertor topologies and ideas have also made the switched mode power supply an industrial standard, and large bulky supply transformers, filters and regulators are being eliminated from new designs [30]. In the highest power ranges (up to the gigawatt level) and highest voltage ranges, supply commutated thyristor power convertors have also become accepted in high voltage DC transmission [11].

Pulse-width modulated DC to AC convertors, especially for 3-phase variable frequency output, have only found limited acceptance owing to the large cost penalties involved up until now for the forced commutated inverters. The development of GTOs will increase the possibilities for these convertors [244, 245], while the applications of bipolar power transistors are increasing in the medium power range [197, 231]. MOSFETs are enabling the PWM-inverter technology to reach down to very low power levels, due to the low interfacing costs. The suggestions for the simplification of topologies for 3-phase application in recent years [246, 247] may reduce the cost penalty for PWM inverters even further, although it appears as if the 3-phase bridge with four switches shows the most promise [248]. It has been shown to have characteristics equivalent to 6-pulse topologies, provided that the switching frequency is high enough. It is exactly this characteristic that will still be improving the most for modern power switches in the future.

Power electronic convertors with a high frequency link [70] have been investigated extensively in recent years [249–252], but only found limited application, chiefly due to a more complicated topology. As the present development of faster thyristors and diodes are improving the operating link frequencies for the naturally commutated type, and the faster transistor and GTOs favour the forced commutated type [253, 254], the application for these convertors will certainly increase. As many interesting and advantageous applications have already been demonstrated for these convertors [255, 256], further topological development is also taking place.

7.3 On some prospects for electronic conditioning of the electromechanical energy conversion process

Power electronic convertors may be seen as the adaptable interface between electrical machine and power source. The function of the convertor as it reflects into the power supply will be discussed in a subsequent section, so that, at present, attention will be focused on the convertor-machine interface.

As the primary function of the electrical machine is to deliver a constant energy flow, and hence constant torque at any specific speed at its mechanical port, the function of the electronic power conditioning in the convertor should attempt to approach this ideal as close as possible. When DC machines are being used, at present, with supply commutated AC-DC convertors, the output ripple frequency is fixed by the supply frequency and the equivalent number of phases of the convertor in AC supplied systems, while the amplitude of the current ripple is determined by the DC inductor included and the DC machine constants. The torque ripple, being proportional to the current fluctuations, is of a known frequency and left to the discretion of the system designer. For forced commutation DC systems, the switching frequency in the convertor is an additional degree of freedom, so that the torque ripple may be decreased by increasing the switching frequency.

In systems with variable frequency multiphase AC machines, the expected drive systems of the future, the torque ripple caused by a variable frequency supply with quasi-square-wave excitation has been much more troublesome. This problem is being solved by two different approaches, i.e.

(i) Increasing the switching frequency in the convertor enables the output waveform to approach a given function of time, in this case a sinusoidal output [222], closely, eliminating all but the highest harmonics

(ii) Determination of the switching function in such a way that certain harmonics are eliminated, while still using a limited switching frequency [257–259].

7.3.1 Increasing the switching frequency: This approach allows freedom in choosing the excitation waveform for the electromechanical energy convertor on an instantaneous basis, without reference to a predetermined function and its harmonics. Particularly under dynamic conditions, this would be very attractive, especially when it is attempted to maintain electromagnetic conditions in the electromechanical convertor in a specific state (see the section on control). Although the necessary increase in switching frequency could not be attained in forced commutated thyristor convertors due to the limited switching repetition frequencies, the present and future developments in bipolar and field-effect transistors in the lower power range has already established this to be viable, while the expected increase in the frequency response of gate-turnoff thyristors in the higher power range will certainly increase the attractiveness of this approach in the future.

7.3.2 Harmonic elimination by predetermination of the switching function: Although this approach was originally developed when the switching repetition frequencies of power convertors appeared to be limited appreciably below 1 kHz indefinitely, it is still attractive due to the modest requirements in convertor switching technology for voltage fed invertor systems, while it is the only answer to the problem of torque pulsation at uncomfortable frequencies with current fed inverter systems [260]. In the latter the predetermination of the convertor switching frequency is either determined according to a specific required current waveform for amplitude modulation as determined by the control electronics [261, 262], or it is determined according to a previously calculated and stored pulse modulated waveform of the current [183, 263]. For voltage fed inverter systems it has also been suggested that the optimal pulse modulation routine be determined online and instantaneously by the use of information processing algorithms allowed by present microcomputers [264], according to the operating condition of the electromechanical energy convertor. In future, attention will have to be focused on observing this optimality criterion, while still taking the limited frequency characteristics of the convertor into account.

7.4 Control developments regarding power electronics and machines

As the attainable switching frequency in power conditioners increased, the dynamic response also increased to a point where the response is being determined by the load, as the speed of response of the switches in the conditioners is several orders of magnitude faster. As the control functions of DC machines for the field (i.e. electromagnetic condition of the convertors) and armature (i.e. corresponding to output torque) are, in principle, orthogonal, the control of DC machines as loads has not presented severe problems in position and speed control systems. AC machines have presented another set of problems, however. Owing to their different electromagnetic structure, the field and output torque are not so easily separated [265, 266], so that control schemes for variable-speed drives with AC machines originally had a severe penalty regarding dynamic response when compared to DC machine variable-speed drives and servo systems. Although the first implementation of the control of AC machines by using transformed variables for field and torque control separation was proposed relatively early [267, 268], the associated information processing was comprehensive. It is only the advances in microelectronic technology in the last few years that have allowed both digital [269–271], (microprocessor based) and analogue realisation of the so-called field-oriented control [272, 273], (or control by transformed variables) of induction and synchronous machines by power electronic convertors in such a way that the excellent dynamic response of DC machines could be equalled.

As the field-oriented control of AC machines may at present be considered to be state of the art [274, 275], it is to be expected that AC machines with variable frequency excitation will, in the coming decades, become the mainstay of controlled drives in servo systems, heavy industrial applications (mills, cranes) and traction (electric trains, suburban railcars, locomotives, ships), with dynamic characteristics equal to and better than previous systems based on DC machines. Robustness of machines and reduced maintenance are expected advantages of this new technology.

The advent of appreciable processing capability in dedicated functions such as control has also brought the application of adaptive control schemes to variable speed and servo applications. As the characteristics of the load varies, the control system structure and criteria may be varied [276, 277]. In the next decade, it may be expected that the implementation of microprocessors and the increased switching frequency of power conditioners may also lead to optimal control of the electromagnetic energy conversion process under widely varying conditions, taking both dynamic performance and maximum output from a given structure into account.

7.5 Prospects for interfacing power conditioning and conversion to power supply systems

By and large, energy for supplying systems for power conditioning and conversion are being derived from public utility supplies. These supplies are at either 50 Hz or 60 Hz, with the voltage being a simple harmonic function of time. From these networks, active power can consequently only be supplied at this frequency, although the utility systems are normally tolerant to supply current as an arbitrary function of time (arc furnace loads, power convertors for mills etc.) These currents departing from the exact waveform and phase of the voltage all represent an unnecessary processing of power. Although this has been known and quantified long ago, the modest load on the power system presented by power electronic convertors has not warranted serious attention to this problem, the only exception probably being the coupling between 50 Hz power networks and the $16\frac{2}{3}$ Hz railway networks in Europe after 1930.

The increasing installed total rating of power electronic equipment has drawn more and more attention to the problem of absorption of harmonic currents and nonspecific harmonic currents from the power system. The attempts to compensate for these effects have been based on the use of variable (switchable) banks of capacitors or inductors, and the elimination of specific harmonic currents from utility networks by the installation of tuned circuits for these harmonics in the system [278–282].

The best solution would be, however, that the current drawn from the supply would be in phase with the supply and only of the fundamental frequency. If, however, the power electronic convertor is drawing an arbitrary current as a function of time, this ideal can only be realised by a force commutated convertor switching energy storage elements at a frequency much higher than the supply frequency. The first practical system of this nature to achieve a power factor approaching unity was the so-called 4-quadrant convertor [190] developed for inverter locomotives fed from the $16\frac{2}{3}$ Hz supply system, as shown in Fig. 12*a*, and a number of subsequent suggestions have been made to compensate current of an arbitrary nature both by force commutated convertors and supply commutated convertors, operating in parallel with the supply network and supplying the instantaneous current necessary to compensate the load current to an in-phase sinusoidal value [191, 282–289].

As the total installed rating of power electronic convertors rises, in the future, and the dynamic response of the equipment is being improved simultaneously, these classes of ultra-fast active compensators will have to be developed to very large ratings to be able to maintain the supply integrity as well as to observe the restrictions placed on the consumers of power by the utilities.

8 References

1 VAN WYK, J.D.: 'Power and machine electronics, 1914–1966: a selected bibliography and review on the electronic control of electrical machines'. Monograph, South African Institute of Electrical Engineers, Johannesburg, 1971

2 OWEN, E.L., MORACK, M.M., HERSKIND, C.C., and GRIMES, A.S.: 'AC adjustable-speed drives with electronic power convertors — the early days', *IEEE Trans.*, 1984, **IA-20,** (2), pp. 298–308

3 WILLIS, C.D.: 'Harmonic commutation for thyratron inverters and rectifiers', *General Electric Rev.*, 1932, **35,** (12), pp. 632–638

4 DEPENBROCK, M.: 'Ruhende Frequenzumformer in der Energietechnik', *Elektrotech. Z. ETZ A*, 1962, **26,** pp. 868–876

5 MAPHAM, N.W.: 'The classification of SCR-inverter circuits'. IEEE International Convention Record, Pt. 4, 1964, pp. 99–105

6 ABRAHAM, L., KOPPELMANN, F.: 'Die Zwangskommutierung, ein neuer Zweig der Stromrichtertechnik', *Elektrotech. Z. ETZ A*, 1966, **87,** (18), pp. 649–658

7 GERECKE, E.: 'New methods of power control with thyristors'. Survey paper, Third Congress of the International Federation of Automatic Control, London, 20th–25th June 1966

8 GERECKE, E.: 'Die moderne Elektronik und Ihre Anwendungen in der elektronischen Zugförderung', *Elektrotech. Z. ETZ A*, 1967, **88,** (15), pp. 358–363

9 HEUMANN, K.: 'Elektrotechnische Grundlagen der Zwangskommutierung — neue Möglichkeiten der Stromrichtechnik', *Elektrotechnik & Maschinenbau*, 1967, **84,** (3), pp. 99–112

10 HUMPHREY, A.J.: 'Inverter commutation circuits'. *IEEE Trans.*, 1968, **IGA-4,** (1), pp. 104–110

11 JÖTTEN, R.: 'Hochspannung — Gleichstrom-Übertragung', *Elektrotech. Z. ETZ A*, 1968, **89,** (19–20), pp. 514–518

12 DEPENBROCK, M.: 'Stand und Entwicklungsrichtung der Leistungselektronik', *ibid.*, 1968, **89,** (19–20), pp. 526–530

13 SPENKE, E., and VOS, P.: 'Current status of power thyristors and rectifiers'. Proceedings of 2nd IFAC Symposium on Control in Power Electronics and Electrical Drives, Düsseldorf, West Germany, 1977, pp. 355–368

14 WEBER, H.H.: 'The application of controlled static converters in tractive units'. Proceedings of 2nd IFAC Symposium on Control in Power Electronics and Electrical Drives, Düsseldorf, West Germany, 1977, pp. 651–698

15 MÜLLER-HELLMANN, A., and SKUDELNY, H.-Ch.: 'Beitrag zur Systematik der Einphasen Brückenschaltungen', *Elektrotech. Z. ETZ A*, 1977, **98,** (12), pp. 803–807

16 ZWICKY, R.: 'Systematik regelbarer Antriebe mit Induktionsmaschinen', *Bull, Schweiz. Electrotech. Ver.*, 1979, **70,** (11), pp. 555–559

17 MÜLLER-HELLMANN, A.: 'Entwicklung der stufenlos steuerbaren Netzstromrichter für Wehselstromtriebfahrzeuge', *Elektr. Bahnen*, 1979, **50,** (3), pp. 72–77

18 MÜLLER-HELLMANN, A., and SKUDELNY, H.Ch.: 'Weltweite Entwicklung von Thyristorstromrichtern auf Triebfahrzeugen am Wechselspannungsfahrdraht', *Z. Eisenbahnwes & Verkehrstech. (Glasers Ann.)*, 1980, **104,** (8/9), pp. 266–274

19 VOSZ, H.: 'Ein Beitrag zur Systematisierung der selbstgeführten Stromrichterschaltungen', *ETZ Arch.*, 1980, **2,** (2), pp. 49–54

20 BOSE, B.K.: 'Introduction to AC drives', *in* BOSE, B.K., (Ed.): Adjustable speed AC drive systems (IEEE Press, 1981) pp. 1–21

21 SKUDELNY, H.-Ch.: 'Stand und Entwicklungstendenzen drehzahlgeregelter Drehstromantriebe', *Elektrotech. Z. ETZ*, 1981, **102,** (22), pp. 1150–1154

22 MAGGETTO, G.: 'Snelheidsregeling van motoren'. *Bull., SRBE-KBVE* (Belgium), 1981, **97,** (2), pp. 111–130

23 VAN WYK, J.D.: 'On some characteristics of electrical variable speed drives with electronic switching control', *Trans. S. Afr. Inst. Electr. Eng.*, 1981, **72,** pp. 126–139

24 MÜLLER-HELLMANN, A., and SKUDELNY, H-Ch.: 'Ubersicht über den Stand der Drehstromantriebstechnik bei Bahnverwaltungen in der Bundesrepublik Deutschland und weltweit, *Elektr. Bahnen*, 1981, **79,** (11), pp. 374–422

25 PELLY, B.R.: 'Power semiconductor devices — a status review.' Proceedings of IEEE/IAS, International Semiconductor Power Converter Conference, Orlando, FL, USA, May 1982, pp. 1–19

26 CHAUPRADE, R., and ABBONDANTI, A.: 'Variable speed drives: Modern concepts and approaches'. Proceedings of IEEE/IAS International Semiconductor Power Converter Conference, Orlando, FL, USA, May 1982, pp. 20–37

27 SATPATI, H., DUBEY, G.K., and SINGH, L.P.: 'A comparative study of some chopper commutation circuits', *Int. J. Electron.* 1982, **53,** (1), pp. 47–56

28 ADLER, M.S., and WESTBROOK, S.R.: 'Power semiconductor switching devices — a comparison based on inductive switching'. *IEEE Trans.*, 1982, **ED-29,** (6), pp.947–952

29 STEFANOVIC, V.R.: 'Present trends in variable speed AC drives'. Proceedings of International Power Electronics Conference (IPEC), Tokyo, 1983, pp. 438–449

30 CUK, S., and MIDDLEBROOK, R.D.: 'Advances in switched-mode power conversion, Pts. I and II', *IEEE Trans.*, 1983, **IE-30,** pp. 10–29

31 LEONHARD, W.: 'Control of AC-machines with the help of microelectronics'. Preprints, 3rd IFAC Symposium on Control in Power Electronics and Electrical Drives, Lausanne, Switzerland, Sept. 1983, Pt I Tutorial and Survey Papers, pp. 35–47

32 MURPHY, J.M.D., and EGAN, M.G.: 'A comparison of PWM-strategies for inverter-fed induction motors', *IEEE Trans.*, 1983, **IA-19,** (3), pp. 363–369

33 RISSIK, H.: 'Mercury-arc current converters' (Pitman, London, 1935)

34 Editorial in *ETZ*, 1903, **24,** (10), pp. 187–188

35 VON RECKLINGHAUSEN, M.: 'Die Quecksilberlampe und sonstige Quecksilber-Vakuumapparate', *ETZ*, 1904, **25,** (51), pp. 1102–1107

36 COOPER-HEWITT, P.: USA Patent application 1,007,694, 20th March, 1908

37 SCHÄFER, B.: 'Ein neuer Quecksilberdampfgleichrichter für grosse Leistungen', *ETZ*, 1911, **32,** (1), p. 2

38 MARTI, O.K., and WINOGRAD, H.: 'Stromrichter (Unter besonderer Berücksichtigung der Quecksilberdampf-Grossgleichrichter)'. Deutsche Bearbeitung von O. Gramisch, Oldenbourg, München, Germany, 1933

39 HULL, A.W.: 'Gas-filled thermionic tubes', *Trans. Amer. Inst. Electr. Eng.*, 1928, **47,** pp. 753–763

40 TIRRILL, A.A.: 'Regulators for alternating current work', *Electr. J.*, 1980, **8,** pp. 502–509

41 KOCH, F.: 'Über ein neues System der Entnahme von Gleichstrom aus Wechselstromnetzen', *ETZ*, 1901, **22**, pp. 853–854

42 KESSELRING, F.: 'Theoretische und experimentelle Untersuchung über den rotierenden Gleichrichter'. Dissertation, ETH, Zürich, Switzerland, 1923

43 KOPPELMANN, F.: 'Der Kontaktumformer'. *ETZ*, 1941, **62**, pp. 3–16

44 PRESSER, E.: 'Der Selengleichrichter', *ibid.*, 1932, **53**, pp. 339–341

45 GRONDAHL, L.O.: 'Theories of a new solid junction rectifier', *Science*, 1926, **64**, pp. 306–308

46 SCHOCKLEY, W., SPARKS, M., and TEAL, G.K.: '*pn* Junction transistors', *Phys. Rev.*, 1951, **83**, (1), pp. 151–162

47 MOLL, J.L., TANNENBAUM, M., GOLDEY, I.M., and HOLONYAK, N.: "*p–n–p–n* transistor switches', *Proc. Inst. Radio Eng.*, 1956, **44**, (9), pp. 1174–1182

48 GENTRY, F.E., HOLONYAK, N., VON ZASTROW, E.E., and GUTZWILLER, F.W.: 'Semiconductor controlled rectifiers', (Prentice-Hall, New Jersey, 1964)

49 GENTRY, E.E., SCACE, R.I., FLOWERS, J.A.: 'A three terminal AC switch'. IEEE Electron Device Conference, Washington, 31st Oct. 1983

50 LIBESNY, A.: 'Stromwandlung durch Quecksilber-Vakuum-Apparate', *Elektrotechnik & Maschinenbau*, 1906, **24**, pp. 799–802

51 PRINCE, D.C.: 'The inverter', *General Electric Rev.*, 1925, **28**, pp. 676–681

52 PRINCE, D.C.: 'The direct current transformer utilizing thyratron tubes', *ibid.*, 1928, **31**, pp. 347–350

53 HULL, A.W.: 'Hot-cathode thyratons', *ibid.*, 1929, **32**, (7), pp. 390–399

54 STEENBECK, M.: 'Einrichtung zur Speisung eines elektrischen Verbrauchers über ein gesteuertes Ventil'. DRP 655 484, 7 Aug. 1931

55 HAMUDHANOV, M.Z.: 'Variable frequency operation of asynchronous motors using electronic frequency changers' *in* 'Technical Problems of electric drives'. Academy of Science, Moscow, USSR, 1957

56 LÖBL, O.: 'Bahnumrichtersystem Löbl/RWE', *Elektr. Bahnen*, 1932, **8**, pp. 65–69

57 TOMPKINS, F.N.: 'The parallel type inverter', *Trans. Amer. Inst. Electr. Eng.*, 1932, **51**, pp. 707–714

58 SCHENKEL, M.: 'Eine unmittelbare asynchrone Umrichtung für niederfrequente Bahnnetze', *Elektr. Bahnen*, 1932, **8**, pp. 69–73

59 DUNOYER, L., and TOULON, P.: 'Sur une propriété remarquable de la colonne positive de l'arc au mercurer relais a arc de grande puissance', *J. Phys. Radium*, 1924, **5**, pp. 257–266, pp. 289–303

60 LENZ, O.: 'Gittergesteuerte Gasentladung als regelbarer Wechselstromwiderstand'. *Arch. Elektrotech.* 1933, **27**, pp. 497–504

61 GRIFFITH, R.C.: 'Thyratron control equipment for high speed resistance welding', *General Electric Rev.*, 1930, **33**, p. 511

62 BOLLIGER, A.: 'Die Hochspannungs-Gleichstrommaschine' (Springer, Berlin, 1921)

63 VAN DER BIJL, H.J.: 'The thermionic vacuum tube and its applications' (McGraw-Hill, New York, 1920)

64 SEQUENZ, H.: 'Die Verwendung von Entladungsgefässen bei elektrischen Maschinen', *Elektrotechnik & Maschinenbau*, 1937, **55**, pp. 274–280

65 VOORHOEVE, N.A.J.: 'Ein für praktische Verwendung geeignetes Verfahren für Spannungsregelung an Generatoren mit Hilfen von Hochvakuumröhren', *Arch. Elektrotech.*, 1929, **21**, pp. 228–243

66 KERN, E.: 'Der kommutatorlose Einphasen-Lokomotivmotor 40 bis 60 Hz', *Elektr. Bahnen*, 1931, **7**, pp. 313–321

67 MARTI, O.K.: 'The mercury-arc rectifier applied to AC railway electrification', *Trans. Amer. Inst. Electr. Eng.*, 1932, **51**, pp. 659–668

68 BEILER, A.H.: 'Thyratron motor at the Logan plant', *ibid.*, 1938, **57**, pp. 19–24

69 DAVIS, R.M., and BARWELL, F.T.: 'The commutatorless diesel-electric locomotive'. *IEE. Conf. Publ.* 10th–11th Nov. 1965, pp. 126–133

70 DOLABERIDZE, G.P.: 'The conversion of DC into AC at variable frequency for electric traction', *Elektrotechnika*, April 1965, (4), pp. 58–62

71 STÖHR, M.: 'Lokomotivsysteme für hochgespannten Gleichstrom', *Elektrotechnik & Maschinenbau*, 1940, **58**, pp. 381–389

72 KROST, H., and MOCZALA, H.: 'Elektronische Drehzahlregelung bürstenloser Gleichstrom-Kleinstmotoren', *Elektrotech. Z. ETZ A*, 1965, **86**, (19), pp. 628–632

73 BAUERLEIN, G.: 'Brushless DC motor uses Hall-effect devices', *Electronics*, 6th April 1962, p. 58

74 ALEXANDERSON, E.F.W., EDWARDS, M.A., and WILLIS, C.H.: 'Electronic speed control of motors. Discussions of the paper by Alexanderson', *Trans. Amer. Inst. Electr. Eng.*, 1938, **57**, pp. 343–352

75 STÖHR, M.: 'Vergleich zwischen Stromrichtermotor und untersynchroner Stromrichterkaskade', *Elektrotechnik & Maschinenbau*, 1939, **57**, pp. 581–591

76 STÖHR, M.: 'Stromrichterkaskade für Doppelzonenregelung', *ibid.*, 1949, **58**, pp. 177–186

77 HÖLTERS, F.: 'Schaltung und Steuerung von Stromrichtermotoren', *ibid.*, 1943, **61**, pp. 221–228

78 MEYER, M.: 'Über die asynchrone Stromrichterkaskade', *Elektrotech. Z. ETZ A*, 1961, **82**, pp. 589–596

79 LAITHWAITE, E.R.: 'Electrical variable speed drives', *Eng. Dig.*, 1964, **25**, pp. 115–165

80 ABRAHAM, L., and PATZCHKE, U.: 'Pulstechnik für die Drehzahlsteuerung von Asynchronmotoren', *AEG-Mitt.*, 1964, **54**, pp. 133–140

81 IVAKHENKO, A.G.: 'Regulation of the speed of a three phase asynchronous motor with the aid of thyratrons and series transformers', *Elektrichestvo*, Sept. 1948, **9**, pp. 57–59

82 GERECKE, E., and BADR, H.: 'Asynchronmaschinen mit primärseitig eingebauten steuerbaren Ventilen', *Neue Tech.*, 1962, **4**, pp. 125–143

83 BAYHA, H.: 'Regelantriebe mit Stromrichtern', *Siemens Z.*, 1933, **13**, p. 303

84 SCHILLING, W.: 'Zur Regelung von Gleichstrommotoren über gittergesteuerte Gleichrichter', *Arch. Elektrotech.*, 1935, **29**, pp. 622–631

85 REICHEL, W.: 'Diskussionsbeitrag', *ETZ*, 1932, **53**, pp. 778–779

86 BLAUFUSS, K.: 'Drehzahlregelung von Gleichstrommotoren durch Stromstösse', *Arch. Elektrotech.*, 1940, **34**, pp. 581–590

87 JONES, D.: 'Variable pulse width inverter', *Electron. Equip. Eng.*, Nov. 1961, pp. 29–30

88 ABRAHAM, L., HEUMANN, K., and KOPPELMANN, F.: 'Anfahren, Regeln und Nutzbremsen von Gleichstromfahrzeugen mit steuerbaren Siliziumzellen'. *VDE Fachber.*, 1962, **22**, pp. 89–100

89 BENZENBERG, M. *et al.*: '1879–1979: 100 Jahre Elektrische Eisenbahn' (Josef Keller Verlag, Starnberg, 1979)

89 BENZENBERG, M., VON WEIHER, S., GOETZELER, H., JOACHIMSTHALER, A., TROCHE, H., TIETZE, C., VOSS, U., SCHOLTIS, G., SCHMITT-MANDERBACH, D., BADSTIEBER, J., RÖHLK, J., GAMMERT, R., SCHAMBACH, H.G., FORK, K., KESTE, M., and DUFFERT, H.: '1879–1979: 100 Jahre Elektrische Eisenbahn' (Josef Keller Verlag, Starnberg, 1979)

91 'Gegenwärtig werden auf der Erde rund 165 000 Streckenkilometer elektrisch betrieben', *Elektr. Bahnen*, 1980, **78**, pp. 244 & 246

92 MIDDLETON, W.D.: 'When the steam Railroads electrified' (Kalmbach Publishing Co., Milwaukee, WI, USA, 1974)

93 EBELING, H.: 'Elektrische Zugförderung mit Ignitrongleichrichtern', *Elektr. Bahnen*, 1955, **26**, pp. 74–79

94 MICHEL, O., and HEGELMANN, M.: 'Die Verschiebelokomotive Bauart A1A-A1A Reihe E80 der Deutschen Reichsbahn', *ibid.*, 1933, **4**, pp. 280–288

95 KELLEY, W.E., and FOLEY, E.P.: 'Leistungshalbleiter, für Gleichrichter-Triebfahrzeuge der Penn Central Transportation Co.', *Bull. Schweiz. Elektrotech. Ver.*, 1971, **62**, pp. 35–43

96 AMES, E.W., and DOWDEN, V.F.: 'Ignitron multiple-unit cars for the New Haven railroad', *Trans. Amer. Inst. Electr. Eng.* , 1955, **74**, Pt. II, pp. 147–152

97 GOWANS, F.D.: 'Rectifier Locomotives for the New York, New Haven and Hartford railroad', *ibid.*, 1955, **74**, Pt. II, pp. 183–189

98 BROWN, J.C.: 'The electric system of the rectifier-type locomotives for the Virginian Railways', *ibid.*, 1957, **76**, Pt. II, pp. 68–73

99 'Pennsylvanian Silicon Rectifier Locomotives', *Railw. Gaz.*, 1964, **120**, pp. 20–21

100 ROSSIGNOL, M., and MACHEFERT-TASSIN, M.: 'Les locomotives BB a redresseurs ignitrons', *Rev. Gen. Chemins de Fer*, 1955, **74**, pp. 126–147

101 TESSIER, M.M.: 'Le materiel moteur a redresseurs', *ibid.*, 1955, **74**, pp. 595–618

102 NOUVION, M.F.: 'L'evolution prochaine des locomotives monophasee a 50 Hz', *ibid.*, 1955, **74**, pp. 582–594

103 HENRY, X., and STEGELITZ, H.: 'Les exitrons pour locomotives monophasees', *Rev. Jeumont*, 1957, pp. 19–28

104 GARREAU, M.: 'Les locomotives poly-courants', *Rev. Gen. Chemins de Fer*, 1963, **82**, pp. 585–602

105 NOUVION, M., LE BERRIGAUD, M., and COSSIÉ, M.: 'Les locomotives tricourant et quadricourant de la SNCF', *ibid.*, 1954, **73**, pp. 593–624

106 NERUEZ, J.: 'Die elektrische Viersystemlokomotive der SNCB, Bauart 160', *Elektr. Bahnen*, 1967, **38**, pp. 128–136

107 JÄGER, A.: 'Thyristorsteuerung einer Zweifrequenz-Rangierlokomotive der Schweizerischen Bundesbahnen'. *Brown Boveri Mitt.*, 1970, pp. 410–418

108 STÖTZER, K.S.: 'Die elektrische Ausrüstung der Mehrsystemlokomotive E 320.01 der Deutschen Bundesbahn'. *Elektr. Bahnen*, 1962, **33**, pp. 97–118

109 GIERTH, E.: 'Die Mehrsystemlokomotiven E 410 uns E 310 der Deutschen Bundesbahn', *ibid.*, 1966, **37**, pp. 250–259

110 KAWAZOE, T.: 'Essentials of AC Electric Rolling Stocks', (Denkisha Kenkyukai, Tokyo, 1971)

111 SOMMERSCHIELD, J.G.: ' Applications of rectifiers to British Railways AC motive power'. *Proc. IEE*, 1969, **116**, pp. 247–260.

112 SOMMERSCHIELD, J.G.: 'Moderne Wechelstrom-Triebfahrzeuge der Britischen Eisenbahnen', *Elektrotech. Z. ETZ A*, 1967, **88**, pp. 375–380

113 WEBER, H.H.: 'Stromrichter-Traktionstechnik bei den Schweizerischen Bundesbahnen und ihr prognostizierter Nutzen', *Elektr. Bahnen*, 1980, **78**, pp. 312–319 and 1981, **79**, pp. 23–32

114 NORDIN, T.: 'Der Weg zu serienmäszigen Thyristorschienenfahrzeugen in Schweden', *Glasers Ann.*, 1968, **92**, pp. 198–208

115 RAMBOLD, W.: 'Die lokomotive E 80 der Deutschen Bundesbahn mit Siliziumgleichrichter', Elektr. Bahnen, 1958, **29**, pp. 9–11

116 LUDWIG, E.: 'Neue elektrische Triebfahrzeuge und der bei ihnen erzielte Fortschritt', *Eisenbahntech. Rundschau*, 1961, pp. 297–309

117 RAMBOLD, W.: 'Die elektrische, Ausrüstung von 50 Hz-Lokomotiven mit Siliziumgleichrichtern für die UdSSR', *Elektr. Bahnen*, 1961, **32**, pp. 169–180

118 SCHENKEL, M., and VON ISSENDORF, J.: 'Die Stromrichterlokomotive.' *Siemens-Z.*, 1933, pp. 289–294

119 HUTT, H.: 'Elektrische Ausrüstung der BBC Gleichrichterlokomotive, Reihe E 244 Nr. 11', *Elektr. Bahnen*, 1937, **13**, pp. 68–76

120 HERMLE, H., and PARTZSCH, R.: 'Die elektrische Ausrüstung der AEG-Stromrichter-Lokomotive für die Höllentalbahn, Reihe 244 Nr. 01', *ibid.*, 1937, **13**, pp. 59–68

121 SMITH, S.V.: 'Modern efficient silicon, rectifier-type multiple-unit cars for Philadelphia Area Commuter Service', *Trans. Amer. Inst. Electr. Eng.*, 1964, **83**, Pt. II, pp. 343–352

122 OGDEN, H.S.: 'A unique propulsion system for electric multiple-unit cars for Philadelphia Area Commuter Service', *ibid.*, 1964, **83**, Pt. II, pp. 329–336

123 'AC commuter coaches with ignitron speed control', *Railw. Gaz.*, 1964, pp. 400–402

124 WASSERAB, Th.: 'Die Belastbarkeit der Mutatoren', *Brown Boveri Mitt.*, 1955, **42**, pp. 133–143

125 FALKE, H.: 'Einphasenwechselstrom-Lokomotiven 50 Hz, 6 kV im rheinischen Braunkohlerevier', *Energ. & Tech.*, 1969, **21**, pp. 131–139

126 SANDNER, F.: 'Die Stromrichterlokomotiven für Einphasenwechselstrom 50 Hz, 6 kV für den rheinischen Braunkohlentagebau (Bauart AEG)', *Elektr. Bahnen*, 1956, **27**, (56), pp. 221–230

127 LÄPPLE, K.: 'Die BBC Stromrichterlokomotive 6 kV, 50 Hz für den rheinischen Braunkohlentagebau', *Brown Boveri Mitt.*, 1957, **44**, pp. 39–63

128 SCHADOW, W.: 'Die 50 Hz Stromrichterlokomotive für den rheinischen Braunkohlentagebau Bauart SSW', *Elektr. Bahnen*, 1956, **27**, pp. 269–277

129 DUFFNER, M., and GERMANIER, M.: 'Les locomotives bifrequence C20151 à C20159 de la SNCF', *Rev. Gen. Chemins de Fer*, 1964, **83**, p. 685

130 COSSIE, M., and THAUVIN, M.: 'Les locomotives BB 16500 a récupération', *ibid.*, 1966, **85**, pp. 253–273

131 '50 c/s GROUP'. Druckschrift E-41/1674-101 c/s GROUP, POB 433, CH 8021 Zürich 1, Switzerland

132 MAISZ, K.J.: 'Mehrkraft-Thyristor-Lokomotiven für Fahrdraht-, Batterie- und Dieselhilfsbetrieb auf Zechen- und Hüttenbahnen', *Z. Eisenbahnwes. & Verkehrstech.* (*Glasers Ann.*), 1972, **96**, pp. 107–125

133 BEZOLD, K.H., and KARAMOUSAS, N.: 'Schwere Industrielokomotive mit Thyristorstromrichtern, *Elektr. Bahnen*, 1967, **38**, pp. 230–237

134 STOLZE, W., and MAISZ, K.H.: 'Elektrifizierung der Bahnanlagen der Hibernia AG', *Elektr. Bahnen*, 1970, **41**, pp. 15–20

135 WEFERS, H.J., and ETTLINGER, L.E.: 'Modern Railwoad Electrification at Muskingum'. ASME-IEEE Joint Railroad Conference, Philadelphia, PA, USA, 1970

136 BJÖRKLUND, B.: 'Thyristorlokomotive Typ Rcl der Schwedischen Staatsbahnen', *Elektr. Bahnen*, 1970, **41**, pp. 76–84 and 112–115

137 MAGNUSSON, A.: 'Thyristorlokomotiven für schweren Dienst', *Z. Eisenbahnwes. & Verkehrstech.* (*Glasers Ann.*), 1979, **103**, pp. 98–103

138 SATO, T.: 'Recent Application on Thyristors to JNR Rolling stock', *Jpn. Railw. Eng.*, 1970, **10**, pp. 4–8

139 MÜLLER-HELLMANN, A., and SKUDELNY, H.Ch.: 'Weltweite Entwicklung von Thyristorstromrichtern auf Triebfahrzeugen am Wechselspannungsfahrdraht', *Z. Eisenbahnwes. & Verkehrstech.* (*Glasers Ann.*), 1980, **104**, pp. 266–274

140 'The 200-series Shinkansen Train for the Tohoko and Joetsu Shinkansen', *Jpn. Railw. Eng.*, 1981, **20**, (4), pp. 23–24

141 SACHS, K.: 'Elektrische Triebfahrzeuge' (Springer-Verlag, 1973)

142 'First Series-built 50 kV locos delivered', *Rail. Gaz. Int.*, 1978, pp. 301–305

143 WINTER, P.: 'Netzverhalten von Wechelstrom-Triebfahrzeugen mit Mehrfachfolgesteuerungen in Stromrichtersparschaltung', *Elektr. Bahnen*, 1973, **44**, pp. 279–284 and 1974, **45**, pp. 15–18

144 COSSIÉ, A.: 'Les engins moteurs á thyristors á la SNCF', *Bull. Schweiz. Elektrotech. Ver.*, 1974, **65**, pp. 341–356

145 KAWAZOE, T.: 'ED 78 a.c. locomotive of thyristor control with regenerative brake', *Jpn. Railw. Eng.*, 1968, **8**, pp. 25–26

146 BLAUFUSS, K.: 'Impulssteuerung von Gleichstrom-Fahrmotoren', *Elektr. Bahnen*, 1962, **33**, pp. 135–136

147 'Loss-free control of traction motors', *Engineer*, 1961, **212**, pp. 480–481

148 MCMURRAY, W.: 'SCR DC to DC Power Converters'. *IEEE Trans.*, 1964, **83**, pp. 168–203

149 WAGNER, R.: 'Elektronischer Gleichstromsteller für die Geschwindigkeitssteuerung Elektrischer Triebfahrzeuge', *Siemens Z.*, 1964, **38**, pp. 14–19

150 WAGNER, R., and WOLSKI, A.: 'Batterie-Triebfahrzeuge mit Gleichstromsteuerung über Silizium-Stromtore, *Elektr. Bahnen*, 1964, **35**, pp. 294–301

151 HEINTZE, K., and MARTEN, F.: 'Gleichstromlokomotive für Fahrleitungsbetrieb mit Thyristorgleichstromsteller', *ibid.*, 1966, **37**, pp. 129–137

152 FORSTBAUER, W., OTZDORF, H., and PROTTENGEIER, E.: 'Über den Einsatz von Gleichstromstellern zur Geschwindichkeitssteuerung von Nahverkehrsfahrzeugen', *ibid.*, 1969, **40**, pp. 148–155

153 LÖCKER, H.: 'Der Gleichstromsteller und seine Anwendung auf vollelektronisch gesteuerten Trolleybussen', *Brown Boveri Mitt.*, 1970, pp. 419–428

154 WAGNER, R.: 'Gleichstromsteller für elektrische Triebfahrzeuge', *Siemens Z*, 1971, *Beiheft Bahntechnik*, pp. 143–147

155 SONE, S., and HORI, Y.: 'Seventeen years experience of power electronics traction systems of Japanese railways with special emphasis on interference problems', *IEE Conf. Publ.*, *203*, 1981

156 BROCKMAN, J.J., KUSKO, A., and KING, J.H.: 'Rapid transit experience with chopper controlled DC motor propulsion'. Proceedings of IAS/IEEE Annual Meeting, 1979, pp. 338–346

157 KÖVESSI, F.: 'Stromrichteranwendungen beim Zugbetrieb Teil II'. IFAC Symposium Control in Power Electronics and Electrical Drives, Düsseldorf, West Germany, 1974, Survey papers, pp. 147–180

158 LEROY, J., and GUIBERAU, S.: 'Experimentations d'équipments a hacheurs (Késar), *Rev. Gen. Chemins de Fer*, 1973, **92**, pp. 23–28

159 LEROY, L.: 'Application aux engins de traction des régleurs de courant continu du type Hacheurs', *Rev.-Jeumont-Schneider*, 1971, **20**, pp. 57–62

160 COSSIÉ, A.: 'Les haheurs à la SNCF', *Rev. Gen. Chemins de Fer*, 1973, **92**, pp. 13–22

161 DEMOULIN, J., and JONARD, F.: 'Equipement de la locomotive électrique CC20 002 avec un prototype de hacheur de 4400 kW'. *Rev. Jeumont-Schneider*, 1972, **21**, pp. 21–42

162 COGET, G.: 'La construction et la mise en service des locomotives à hacheurs de courant BB 7000 et BB 22200', *Rev. Gen. Chemin de Fer*, 1978, **97**, pp. 239–355

163 GOUTHIERE, J., GREGOIRE, J., and HOLOGNE, H.: 'Verwendung der Thyristor-Chopper in der elektrischen Zugförderung', *ACEC Z.*, 1970, **2**, pp. 45–68

164 SQUILBEN, M.: 'Eine Weiterentwicklung der Benutzung von Thyristoren bei der Elektrischen Zugförderung: die neuen Lokomotiven der Baureihe 20 der SNCB', *Schienen der Welt*, 1976, pp. 28–40

165 COGLIATI, A., and FRAMBA, B.: 'Die Versuchslokomotive der Italienischen Staatsbahnen mit elektronischem Gleichstromsteller für 3000 V Gleichstrom', *Brown Boveri Mitt*, 1976, pp. 737–743

166 CORNWELL, E.L.: 'The Brush Hawk', *Mod. Railw.*, June 1965

167 TEICH, W.: 'Drehstromantriebstechnik in Schienenfahrzeugen-Versuchseinheiten, Prototypen, Serien', *Z. Eisenbahnwes. & Verkehrstech.* (*Glasers Ann.*), 1977, **101**, pp. 371–382

168 BARANOV, B.K., STROMIN, B.A., and SOKUT, L.D.: 'Kollektorlose Elektrolokomotive mit Ventilmotoren', *Električeskaja i Teplovoznaja Tjaga*, 1968, **12**, pp. 13–15

169 BONDARENKO, B.R.: 'Die Achtachsige Wechselstrom-Güterzuglokomotive der BauartVL 83 mit einmotorigen Drehgestellen', *Schienen der Welt*, 1979, pp. 965–972

170 GORIN, N.N., and KUCUMOV, V.A.: 'Elektrische Lokomotive mit Asynchronmotoren', *Električeskaja i Teplovoznaja Tjaga*, 1979, **23**, pp. 42–44

171 MAISZ, K.J., and TEICH, W.: 'Elektrische Lokomotiven für 15 kV $16\frac{2}{3}$ und 50 Hz mit BBC-Drehstromantriebstechnik für schweren Industrieeinsatz', *Elektr. Bahnen*, 1977, **48**, pp. 95–103

172 GERBER, M., MÜLLER, M., WINTER, P.: 'Die dieselelektrischen Lokomotiven Am 6/6 der Schweizerischen Bundesbahnen', Schweiz. Bauzeitung, 1977, **95**, pp. 193–202 and pp. 217–226

173 ROFFLER, M.: 'Die Umrichterlokomotiven Serie Ee 6/6 II der Schweizerischen Bundesbahnen'. *Brown Boveri Mitt.*, 1979, pp. 764–777

174 TEICH, W.: 'Leisstungsstarke DE-Lokomotiven mit BBC-

Drekstromantriebstechnik für die Norwegische und Dänische Staatsbahn', *Elektr. Bahnen*, 1981, **79**, pp. 388–393

175 KÖRBER, J.: 'Die elektrischen Austrüstung der Hochleistungslokomotive Baureihe E 120 der Deutschen Bundesbahn mit Drehstromfahrmotoren. Planung-Bau-Betriebserprobung', *Z. Eisenbahnwes. & Verkehrstech. (Glasers Ann.)*, 1980, **104**, pp. 299–308

176 REICHELT, E.: 'Leichte Universallokomotive E117 der Norwegischen Staatsbahn mit Drehstromantriebstechnik', *Elektr. Bahnen*, 1982, **80**, pp. 207–214

177 BONDESEN, A., BECKER, E., and KÖRBER, J.: 'EA 3000 — Entwicklung und Bau elektrischer Lokomotiven für die Dänischen Staatsbahnen', *ibid.*, 1985, **83**, pp. 116–123

178 KRAMER, W., and SOMMEREGGER, K.: 'Die Vorschub- und Nebenbahnlokomotive Baureihe 1063 der Österreichischen Bundeshahnen', *Eisenbahnen*, 1983, pp. 10–25

179 KITZEN, J., DAUMANN, W., DRAGANOV, B., and NILL, R.: 'Drehstromversuchsfahrzeug der Niederländschen Eisenbahn — Elektrische Verhalten am 1,5 kV Gleichspannungsnetz', *Elektr. Bahnen*, 1979, **77**, pp. 320–328

180 MÜLLER-HELLMANN, A., and SKUDELNY, H.Ch.: 'Übersicht über den Stand der Drehstromantriebstechnik bei Bahnverwaltungen in der Bundesrepublik Deutschland und weltweit', *ibid.*, 1981, **79**, pp. 374–380 and pp. 418–422

181 COSSIÉ, A.: 'L'application à la traction du moteur synchrone autopilote', *Rev. Gen. Chemins de Fer*, 1983, **102**, pp. 250–270

182 KUNNES, W., and MÜLLER-HELLMANN, A.: 'Fahrdrahtgespeiste Triebfahrzeuge in Drehstromtechnik mit Asynchronoder Synchronfahrmotoren', *ETR*, 1984, **33**, pp. 761–772

183 LIENAU, W., and MÜLLER-HELLMANN, A.: 'Möglichkeiten zum Betrieb von stromeinprägenden Wechselrichtern ohne niederfrequente Oberschwingungen', *ETZ Arch.*, 1976, **97**, pp. 97–105

184 'Versuchswagen mit Drehstromantrieb bei der VAG Nürberg'. Sonderdruck Ref. E4–75/86, Siemens

185 MÜLLER-HELLMANN, A.: 'Drehstromantriebe auf Fahrzeugen des Schienen-Nahverkehrs', *Nahverkerhr*, 1984, **2**, (4), pp. 15–26

186 KÜBLER, E.: 'Einphasen, Gleichrichter für Bahnfahrzeuge mit nahezu sechsphasiger Rückwirkung auf die Fahrleitung', *Elektrotech. Z. ETZ*, 1954, **75**, pp. 789–790

187 FÖRSTER, J.: 'Löschbare Fahrzeugstromrichter zur Netzentlastung und — stützung'. *Elektr. Bahnen*, 1972, **43**, pp. 13–17

188 DREIMANN, K., and FALK, P.: 'Stand der Betriebserprobung der löschbaren unsymmetrischen Brückenschaltung LUB', *ibid.*, 1976, **47**, pp. 132–136

189 MÜLLER-HELLMANN, A., and SKUDELNY, H.Ch.: 'Ein Beitrag zur Systematik der Einphasen-Brückenschaltung', *Elektrotech. Z. ETZ A*, 1977, **98**, pp. 803–807

190 KEHRMANN, H., LIENAU, W., and NILL, R.: 'Vierquadrantensteller — eine netzfreundliche Einspeisung für Triebfahrzeuge mit Drehstromantrieb', *Elektr. Bahnen*, 1974, **45**, pp. 135–142

191 APPUN, P., and LIENAU, W.: 'Der Vierquadrantensteller bei induktivem und kapazitivem Betrieb', *ETZ Arch.*, 1984, **6**, (1), pp. 3–8

192 MÜLLER-HELLMANN, A.: 'Pulsstromrichter am Einphasen-Wechselstromnetz', *ETZ Arch.*, 1979, **1**, pp. 73–78

193 GAMO, H., FUNAKAWA, S., and SHIMIZU, J.: 'The present status and application of power reverse conducting thyristors'. IEEE/IAS International Semiconductor Power Converter Conference, 1977, pp. 50–60

194 TSUBOI, T., IZAWA, S., WAJIMA, K., OGAWA, T., and KATTA, T.: 'Newly developed thyristor chopper equipment for electric railcars', *IEEE Trans.*, 1973, **IA-9**, pp. 29–301

195 OKAMURA, M., NAGANO, R., and OGAWA, T.: 'The current status of the power gate turn-off switch (GTO)'. IEEE/IAS International Semiconductor Power Converter Conference 1977, pp. 39–49

196 KANZAKI, T., YASUOKA, J., YAMAMOTO, G., JINZENJI, T.: 'Direct digital controlled PWM GTO inverter for DC 1500 V electric cars'. International Power Electronics Conference, Tokyo, 1983, pp. 1587–1598

197 SMITH, G.B.: 'An overdriven transistor inverter'. International Power Electronics Conference, Tokyo, 1983, pp. 1532–1543

198 MENNICKEN, H.: 'Stromrichtersystem mit Wechselspannungswischenkreis und seine Anwendung in der Traktionstechnik', Dissertation, TH Aachen, West Germany, 1978

199 LAUGHLIN, M.H., and VON ZASTROW, E.E.: 'Power semiconductor equipment cooling methods and application criteria, *IEEE Trans.*, 1975, **IA-11**, pp. 546–555

200 KOBAYASHI, G., TANAKA, O., and MITSOMOTO, S.: 'Boiling and condensing heat transfer for cooling of high-power semiconductor rectification equipment', *Mitsubishi Electr. Eng.*, 1974, **41**, pp. 24–33

201 VOGEL, X.: 'Ölgekühlte Traktions-Stromrichter', *Brown Boveri Mitt.*, 1973, pp. 551–558

202 HEINEMEYER, P., LUKANZ, W., STEINWEG, M., and OSWALD, D.: 'Siede-Kühlung für Leistungshalbleiter', *Wiss. Ber. AEG-Telefunken*, 1978, **52**, pp. 30–39

203 KIMMEL, H., ROSE, W., and MEURER, Ch.: 'Physikalische Grundlagen der Siedekühlung', *Siemens Forsch. & Entwicklungsber.*, 1977, **6**, pp. 22–28

204 WEIGEL, W.D.: 'Eine neue Generation von elektronischen Triebfahrzeug-Steuerungen mit Mikro-computern', *Z. Eisenbahnwes. & Verkehrstech. (Glasers Ann.)*, 1983, **107**, pp. 305–312

205 BANGE, G.: 'Die Störungsdiagnose leittechnischer Einrichtungen auf Schienenfahrzeugen', *Eisenbahntech. Rundschau*, 1958, **34**, pp. 741–746

206 'Dash 8 prototypes start to roll off GE's production line', *Railw. Gaz. Int.*, 1984, **140**, pp. 965–966

207 HARRIS, W.J.: 'The shape of tomorrow's freight trains, *ibid.*, 1985, **141**, pp. 499–501

208 VITINS, J.: 'Improved AC and DC motor drives with purpose-designed, integrated asymmetric SCRs'. IEEE/IAS International Semiconductor Power Converter Conference Orlando FL., USA, May 1982, pp. 75–83

209 AZUMA, M., KURATA, M., and TAKIGAMI, K.: '2500 V, 600 A gate turn-off thyristor', *IEEE Trans.*, 1981, **ED-28**, (3), pp. 270–274

210 TOKUNOH, F., HAGINO, H., and MIYAJIMA, T.: 'Electrical characteristics of high-voltage, high-current gate turn-off thyristor'. *IEE Conf. Publ. 234*, 1984, pp. 11–14

211 PELLY, BR.: 'Power semiconductor devices — a status review'. IEEE/IAS International Semiconductor Power Converter Conference, Orlando FL., USA, May 1982, pp. 1–19

212 BALIGA, B.J.: 'The asymmetrical field controlled thyristor'. *IEEE Trans.*, 1980, **ED-27**, (7), pp. 1262–1268

213 NISHIZAWA, J.I., TERASAKI, T., and SHIBATA, J.: 'Field effect transistor versus analog transistor (static induction transistor)', *ibid.*, 1975, **ED-22**, (4), pp. 185–197

214 KNÖLL, H.: 'Power converters for Maglev-systems'. Proc. Motorcon, Geneva, Switzerland, Sept. 1982, pp. 37–49

215 GUTMANN, R.J.: 'Application of RF circuit design principles to distributed power converters', *IEEE Trans.*, 1980, **IECI-27**, (3), pp. 156–164

216 MCMURRAY, W.: 'Selection of snubbers and clamps to optimize the design of transistor switching converters', *ibid.*, 1980, **IA–16**, pp. 513–523.

217 SKUDELNY, H.-C.: 'Verluste in R-C-Beschaltungen von Stromrichterelementen'. *BBC-Nachr.*, 1968, **50**, pp. 21–29

218 KNÖLL, H.: 'High current transistor choppers'. Proceedings of 2nd IFAC Symposium on Control in Power Electronics and Electrical Drives, 1977, pp. 307–315

219 BOEHRINGER, A.F., and KNÖLL, H.: 'Transistorschalter im Bereich hoher Leistungen und Frequenzen', *Elektrotech. Z. ETZ*, 1979, **100**, (13), pp. 664–670

220 WILLIAMS, B.W., and PALMER, P.R.: 'Drive and snubber techniques for GTOs and power transistors — particularly for inverter bridges'. *IEE Conf. Publ. 234*, 1984, pp. 42–45

221 FERRARO, A.: 'An overview of low loss snubber technology for transistor converters'. IEEE PESC-82 Record, pp. 466–477

222 BOEHRINGER, A., and BRUGGER, F.: 'Transformatorlose Transistor-Pulsumrichter mit Ausgangsleistungen bis 50 kVA', *Elektrotech. & Maschinenbau*, 1979, **96**, pp. 538–545

223 SCHOEMAN, J.J., and WYK, J.D.: 'A simplified maximal power controller for terrestrial photovoltaic panel arrays'. IEEE PESC-82 Record, pp. 361–367

224 VAN WYK, J.D., and SCHOEMAN, J.J.: 'A study of a class of low loss power conditioners'. Proceedings of International Power Electronics Conference, Tokyo, Japan, 1983, Pt. II, pp. 1061–1071

225 SCHLEGEL, E.S., and PAGE, D.J.: 'A high power light activated thyristor'. IEEE Electron Devices Meeting Conference Record, 1976, pp. 483–486

226 SILBER, D., FÜLLMANN, M., and LUKANZ, W.: 'Recent developments in light activated power thyristors'. *IEE Conf. Publ. 154*, 1977, pp. 14–17

227 TEMPLE, V.A.K.: 'Development of a 2.6 kV light triggered thyristor for electric power systems', *IEEE Trans.*, 1980, **ED-27**, (3), pp. 583–591

228 NIWAYAMA, K., KIYOHARA, T., NAKAGAWA, T., and KAWAKAMI, A.: 'A high voltage high power light triggered thyristor'. *IEE Conf. Publ. 234*, 1984, pp. 15–18

229 KANO, T., KOBAYASHI, S., HORIUCHI, T., NISHIKAWA, H., GOTO, K., and SENDA, T.: 'Development of light-triggered thyristor valve for HVDC transmission'. International Power Electronics Conference, Tokyo, Japan, 1983, Pt. I, pp. 87–92

230 KAESEN, K., and TIHANYI, J.: 'MOS-Leistungstransistoren', *Elektrotech. Z. ETZ*, 1983, **104**, (24), pp. 1260–1263

231 VAN DER BROECK, H.W., FERREIRA, J.A., and VAN WYK, J.D.: 'DC to AC converter for controlled drives, based on a high efficiency, high current transistor switch. 3rd IFAC Symposium on

Control in Power Electronics and Electrical Drives, Lausanne, Switzerland, Sept. 1983, pp. 217–224

232 CORDINGLEY, B.V.: 'PIN fast power diodes'. *IEE Conf. Publ. 234*, 1984, pp. 19–21

233 WOODWORTH, F.A.: 'High voltage epitaxial rectifiers'. *IEE Conf. Publ. 234*, 1984, pp. 38–41.

234 ADLER, M.S.: 'A comparison between BIMOS device types'. IEEE PESC-82 Record, pp. 371–377

235 VAN WYK, J.D., and SCHOEMAN, J.J.: 'n Nuwe metode vir die kompensasie van verliese in elektroniese drywingskakelaars met bipolêre drywingstransistors', *S. Afr. Tydskrif vir Natuurwetenskap & Tegnologie*, 1982, **1**, (4), pp. 175–178

236 VAN DER BROECK, H.W., VAN WYK, J.D., and SCHOEMAN, J.J.: 'Neuartige Darlingtonschaltung met sehr niedriger Durchlassspannung durch Verwendung einer Kompensationsspannungsquelle', *ETZ-Arch.*, 1983, **5**, (6), pp. 183–188

237 VAN WYK, J.D., VAN DER BROECK, H.W., and SCHOEMAN, J.J.: 'Characteristics and technology of novel high efficiency compensated Darlington power switches with application to high current bipolar transistor inverters with output transformers'. *IEE Conf. Publ. 234*, 1984, pp. 50–53

238 VAN WYK, J.D., and FERREIRA, J.A.: 'Transistor inverter design optimization in the frequency range above 5 kHz up to 50 kVA', *IEEE Trans.*, 1983, **IA-19**, pp. 296–302

239 NAGANO, T., FUKUI, H., YATSUO, T., and OKAMURA, M.: 'A snubberless GTO'. IEEE PESC-82 Record, pp. 383–387

240 GAUR, S.P., and LOWE, G.: 'Power transistor crystal damage in inductive load switching, *Solid-State Electron.*, 1977, **20**, pp. 1026–1027

241 WEBB, P.W.: 'Measurement of thermal transients in semiconductor power devices and circuits'. *IEE Proc. I, Solid-State & Electron Dev.*, 1983, **130**, (4), pp. 153–159

242 SMIT, W.B., PONTIUS, D.H., and BUDENSTEIN, P.B.: 'Second breakdown and damage in junction devices', *IEEE Trans.*, 1973, **ED-20,** pp. 731–743

243 GAUR, S.P., NAVON, D.H., and TEERLINCK, R.W.: 'Transistor design and thermal stability', *ibid.*, 1973, **ED-20,** pp. 527–534

244 JINZENJI, T., MORIYA, F., KANZAKI, T., and AZUMA, M.: 'Three-phase static power supplies for air-conditioned electric coaches using high power GTO', *ibid.*, 1981, **IA-17**, (2), pp. 179–188

245 HONBU, M., MATSUDO, Y., MIYAZAKI, K., and JIFUKU, Y.: 'Parallel operation techniques of GTO-inverter sets for large AC motor drives', *ibid.*, 1983, **IA-19,** (2), pp. 198–205

246 EASTHAM, J.F., DANIELS, A.R., and LIPCYNSKI, R.T.: 'A novel power inverter configuration'. IEEE/IAS Annual Meeting Conference Record, 1980, pp. 748–751

247 EVANS, P.D., DODSON, R.C., and EASTHAM, J.F.: 'Delta inverter', *IEE Proc. B, Electr. Power Appl.*, 1980, **127**, (6), pp. 333–340

248 VAN DER BROECK, H.W., and VAN WYK, J.D.: 'A comparative investigation of a three-phase induction machine drive with a component minimized voltage-fed inverter under different control options', *IEEE Trans.*, 1984, **IA-20,** (2), pp. 309–320

249 SCHWARZ, F.C., and KLAASSENS, J.B.: 'A controllable secondary multikilowatt DC current source with constant maximum power factor in its three phase supply line', *ibid.*, 1976, **IECI-23,** (2), pp. 142–150

250 SCHWARZ, F.C., and KLAASSENS, J.B.: 'A 95-percent efficient 1 kW DC converter with internal frequency of 50 kHz', *ibid.*, 1978, **IECI-25,** (4), pp. 326–333

251 SCHWARZ, F.C.: 'A double sided cycloconverter', *ibid.*, 1981, **IECI-28,** (4), pp. 282-291

252 RANGANATHAN, V.T., ZIOGAS, P.D., and STEFANOVIC, V.R.: 'A DC-AC power conversion technique using twin resonant high frequency links', *ibid.*, 1983, **IA-19**, (3), pp. 393–400

253 VAN WYK, J.D.: 'Control of DC and AC machines by converters with high frequency AC link'. Proceedings of International Conference on Electrical Machines, Athens, Greece, Sept. 1980, Pt. 2, pp. 1072–1079

254 VAN WYK, J.D., and SNYMAN, D.B.: 'High frequency link systems for specialised power control applications'. IEEE/IAS Annual Meeting, Oct. 1982, pp. 793–801

255 BREDENKAMP, G.L., and VAN RHYN, P.: 'High-frequency transistor inverters for low mass welders'. *IEE Conf. Publ. 234*, 1984, pp. 107–110

256 BENDIEN, J.C., FREGIEN, G., and VAN WYK, J.D.: 'A low-cost high-efficiency battery charger with special self-oscillating DC-DC convertor'. *IEE Conf. Publ. 234*, 1984, pp. 95–98

257 PATEL, H.S., and HOFT, R.G.: 'Generalized techniques of harmonic elimination and voltage control in thyristor inverters. Part I — harmonic elimination', *IEEE Trans.*, 1973, **IA-9**, pp. 310–317

258 BUJA, G.S., and INDRI, G.B.: 'Optimal pulse width modulation for feeding AC motors', *ibid.*, 1977, **IA-13**, pp. 38–44

259 MURPHY, J.M.D., and EGAN, M.G.: 'A comparison of pwm strategies for inverter-fed induction motors', *ibid.*, 1983, **IA-19,** (3), pp. 363–369

260 ANDRESEN, E.C., and BIENEK, K.: 'On the torques and losses of voltage and current-source inverter drives', *ibid.*, 1984, **IA-20,** (2), pp. 321–327

261 CHIN, T.H.: 'A new controlled current type inverter with improved performance', *ibid.*, 1979, **IA-15,** (5), pp. 532–537

262 CHIN, T.H., and TOMITA, H.: 'The principles of eliminating pulsating torque in current source inverter induction motor systems', *ibid.*, 1981, **IA-17**, (2), pp. 160–166

263 CASE, M.J., and VAN WYK, J.D.: 'EPROM-techniques for selected harmonic reduction in current source inverters', *Trans. S. Afr. Inst. Electr. Eng.*, 1983, **74**, (4), pp. 98–103

264 ZACH, F.C., BERTHOLD, R.J., and KAISER, K.H.: 'General purpose microprocessor modulator for a wide range of PWM techniques for AC motor control'. IEEE-IAS Annual Conference Record, 1982, pp. 446–451

265 GARCES, L.J.: 'Parameter adaption for the speed-controlled static AC drive with a squirrel cage induction motor', *IEEE Trans.*, 1980, **IA-16,** (2), pp. 173–178

266 JÖTTEN, R., and MAEDER, G.: 'Control methods for good dynamic performance induction motor drives based on current and voltage as measured quantities'. IEEE/IAS International Semiconductor Power Converter Conference, Orlando, FL., USA, May 1982, pp. 385–396

267 HASSE, K.: 'Zur Dynamik drehzahlgeregelter Antriebe mit stromrichtergespeisten Asynchronkurzschlussläufermaschinen'. Dissertation, TH Darmstadt, West Germany, 1969

268 BLASCHKE, F.: 'Das Prinzip der Feldorientierung, die Grundlage für die Transvektor-Regelung van Asynchronmaschinen', *Siemens Z.*, 1971, **45,** pp. 757–760

269 SCHAUDER, C.D., CHOO, F.H., and ROBERTS, M.T.: 'High performance torque-controlled induction motor drives'. *IEEE Trans.*, 1983, **IA-19,** (3), pp. 349–355

270 GABRIEL, R., LEONARD, W., and NORDBY, C.: 'Microprocessor control of the converter-fed induction motor', *Process Autom.*, 1980, **1**, pp. 35–41

271 GABRIEL, R., and LEONARD, W.: 'Microprocessor control of induction motor'. IEEE/IAS International Semiconductor Power Converter Conference, Orlando, FL., USA, May 1982, pp. 385–396

272 KAZMIERKOWSKI, M.P., and KÖPCKE, H-J.: 'Vergleich dynamischer Eigenschaften verschiedener Steuer-und Regelverfahren für Umrichtergespeiste Asynchronmaschinen', *ETZ Arch.*, 1982, **4**, (9), pp. 269–277

273 KAZMIERKOWSKI, M.P., and KÖPCKE, H.J.: 'Ein analoger Echtzeitrechner zur Untersuchung and Regelung von umrichtergespeisten Drehstromantrieben', *ibid.*, 1982, **4,** (6), pp. 171–176

274 LEONARD, W.: 'Control of AC machines with the help of microelectronics'. 3rd IFAC Symposium on Control in Power Electronics and Electrical Drives, Lausanne, Switzerland, Sept. 1983, Pt. 1, pp. 35–58

275 SCHUMACHER, W., LEFAS, H-H., and LEONARD, W.: 'Microprocessor-controlled AC servo drives with synchronous and asynchronous motors'. *IEE Conf. Publ. 234*, 1984, pp. 233–236

276 HARASHIMA, F., HASHIMOTO, H., and KONDO, S.: 'MOSFET converter-fed servo system with sliding mode control'. IEEE PESC-83, pp. 1–7

277 EVANS, R.J., COOK, B.J., and BETZ, R.E.: 'Nonlinear adaptive control of an inverter fed induction motor linear load case'. *IEEE Trans.*, 1983, **IA-19,** (1), pp. 74–83

278 GYUGYI, L., and TAYLOR, E.R.: 'Characteristics of static, thyristor-controlled shunt compensators for power transmission system applications', *ibid.*, 1980, **PAS-99,** (5), pp. 1795–1804

279 HOSONO, I., YANO, M., TAKEDA, M., and YUYA, S.: 'Suppression and measurement of arc furnace flicker with a large static VAR-compensator', *ibid.*, 1979, **PAS-98,** (6), pp. 2276–2284

280 STEEPER, D.E., and STRATFORD, R.P.: 'Reactive compensation and harmonic suppression for industrial power systems using thyristor converters', *ibid.*, 1976, **IA-12,** (3), pp. 232–254

281 STRATFORD, R.P.: 'Analysis and control of harmonic current systems with static power converters', *ibid.*, 1981, **IA-19,** (1), pp. 71–81

282 MÄRZ, G.: 'Die ZDB-Schaltung, ihre Eigenschaften und ihre Anwendung in der Leistungselektronik', *Elektrotech. Z. ETZ A*, 1972, **93,** (10), pp. 571–576

283 DEPENBROCK, M.: 'Kompensation schnell veränderlicher Blindströme', *ibid.*, 1977, **98,** (6), pp. 408–411

284 FISCHER, H.D.: 'Blindleistungskompensation bei nicht periodischen Strömen und Spannungen', *ETZ Archiv.*, 1982, **4,** (4), pp. 127–131

285 KLINGER, G.: 'Steuer- und Regeleinrichtung einer selbstgeführten

Kompensations — Stromrichterschaltung', *Elektrotech. Z. ETZ A*, 1977, **98,** (6), pp. 411–414
286 EPSTEIN, E., YAIR, A., and ALEXANDROVITZ, A.: 'Analysis of a reactive current source used to improve current drawn by static inverters', *IEEE Trans.*, 1979, **IECI-26,** (3), pp. 172–177
287 HARASHIMA, F., INABA, H., and TSUBOI, K.: 'A closed loop control system for reduction of reactive power required by electronic converters', *ibid.*, 1976, **IECI-23,** (2), pp. 162–166
288 FUKAO, T., MATSUI, M., and HIEDA, I.: 'A novel static var-generator using cycloconverter operating in circulating current mode'. International Power Electronics Conference, Tokyo, Japan, 1983, Pt. 2, pp. 1643–1652
289 ALEXANDROVITZ, A., YAIR, A., and EPSTEIN, E.: 'Analysis of a static var-compensator with optimal energy storage element', *IEEE Trans.*, 1984, **IE-31,** (1), pp. 28–33
290 RISSIK, H.: 'Fundamental theory of the arc convertor' (Chapman and Hall, London, 1939)
291 WASSERAB, Th.: 'Schaltungslehre der Stromrichtertechnik' (Springer, Berlin, 1962)
292 BEDFORD, B.D., and HOFT, R.G.: 'Principles of inverter circuits' (Wiley, New York, 1964)
293 HOFFMANN, A., and STOCKER, K.: 'Thyristor Handbuch: Der Thyristor als Bauelement der Leistungselektronik' (Siemens, Berlin, 1965)
294 SCHAEFER, J.: 'Rectifier circuits' (Wiley, New York, 1965)
295 'Silicon rectifier handbook' (Motorola Inc., Phoenix, AZ., USA, 1966)
296 MEYER, M.: 'Stromrichter mit erzwungener Kommutierung' (Siemens, Erlangen, 1967) Thyristoren in der technischen Anwendung Band 1
297 MÖLTGEN, G.: 'Netzgeführte Stromrichter' (Siemens, Erlangen, 1967) Thyristoren in der technischen Anwendung Band 2
298 SCHILLING, W.: 'Thyristortechnik' (Oldenbourg, München/Wien, 1968)
299 TAKEUCHI, T.J.: 'Theory of SCR circuit and application to motor control' (Electrical Engineering College Press, Tokyo, 1968)
300 KUSKO, A.: 'Solid state DC motor drives' (MIT Press, 1968)
301 'Power engineering using thyristors, volume 1' (Mullard Limited, London, 1970)
302 PELLY, B.R.: 'Thyristor phase-controlled convertors and cycloconvertors' (Wiley-Interscience, Toronto, 1971)
303 DAVIS, R.M.: 'Power diode and thyristor circuits' (Peter Peregrinus, London, 1971)
304 MAGGETTO, G.: 'Le Thyristor; definitions- protections- commandes' (Presses Universitaires de Bruxelles, 1971)
305 MCMURRAY, W.: 'The theory and design of cycloconverters', (MIT Press, 1972)
306 MURPHY, J.M.D.: 'Thyristor control of AC motors', (Pergamon Press, London, 1973)
307 KOSOW, I.L.: 'Control of electric machines' (Prentice-Hall, New Jersey, 1973)
308 RAMSHAW, R.: 'Power electronics'. (Chapman and Hall, London, 1973)
309 'Solid-state devices manual, SC-16' (RCA, Somerville, 1975)
310 DEWAN, S.B., and STRAUGHEN, A.: 'Power semiconductor circuits' (Wiley, New York, 1975)
311 HEUMANN, K.: 'Grundlagen der Leistungselektronik' (BG Teubner, Stuttgart, 1975)
312 SHEPHERD, W.: 'Thyristor control of AC circuits' (Bradford University Press, London, 1975)
313 BLICHER, A.: 'Thyristor physics' (Springer, New York, 1976)
314 GYUGYI, L., and PELLEY, B.R.: 'Static power frequency changers: theory, performance and application' (Wiley-Interscience, New York, 1976)
315 JÖTTEN, R.: 'Leistungselektronik, Band 1: Stromrichter Schaltungstechnik' (Vieweg, Braunschweig, 1977)
316 RAMAMOORTY, M.: 'An introduction to thyristors and their application' (Macmillan, London, 1978)
317 BÜHLER, H.: 'Einführung in die Theorie geregelter Drehstromantriebe'. Band 1 Grundlagen and Band 2 Anwendungen, (Birkhäuser, Basel/Stuttgart, 1977)
318 LAPPE, R.: 'Leistungselektronik' (VEB-Verlag, Berlin, 1978)
319 GERLACH, W.: 'Thyristoren' (Springer, Berlin, 1979)
320 'SCR Manual' (General Electric, Auburn, 1979, 6th edn.)
321 GOTTLIEB, I.M.: 'Solid-state power electronics' (Howard W. Sams & Co, Indiana, 1979)
322 JÄGER, R.: 'Leistungselektronik: Grundlagen und Anwendungen' (VDE-Verlag, Berlin, 1979)
323 ZACH, F.: 'Leistungselektronik' (Springer-Verlag, New York, 1979)
324 SCHRAGE, J.J., and DE ZEEUW, W.J.: 'Vermogenselektronica' (The Netherlands, Culemborg, Educaboek, 1980)
325 FINNEY, D.: 'The power thyristor and its applications' (McGraw-Hill, London, 1980)
326 HEMPEL, H.-P.: 'Power semiconductor handbook' (Semikron International, Nuremberg, 1980)
327 KLOSS, A.: 'Leistungselektronik ohne Ballast' (Franzis Verlag, München, 1980)
328 CSÁKI, F., GANSZKY, K., IPSITS, I., and MARTI, S.: 'Power electronics' (Akadémiai Kiadó, Budapest, 1980)
329 KLEINRATH, H.: 'Stromrichtergespeiste Drehfeldmaschinen' (Springer, Wien, 1980)
330 WOOD, P.: 'Switching power convertors' (Van Nostrand Reinhold, New York, 1981)
331 LANDER, C.W.: 'Power electronics' (McGraw-Hill, Maidenhead, 1981)
332 BOSE, B.K. (Ed.): 'Adjustable speed AC drive systems' (IEEE Press, New York, 1981)
333 SEN, P.C.: 'Thyristor DC drives' (Wiley, New York, 1981)
334 WELLS, R.: 'Solid-state power rectifiers' (Granada, London, 1982)
335 BIRD, B.M., and KING, K.G.: 'An introduction to power electronics' (John Wiley & Sons, Chichester, 1983)
336 LARSON, L.: 'Power control electronics' (Prentice-Hall, Englewood Cliffs, 1983)
337 LEONHARD, W.: 'Control of electrical drives' (Springer, Berlin, 1985)
338 MEYER, M.: 'Elektrische antriebstechnik' (Springer, Berlin, 1985)
339 COSSIE, A.: 'Evolution de la locomotive à thyristors à la SNCF' *Elektr. Bahnen*, 1981, **79,** pp. 18–22 and 52–60.
340 FORRAY, M.: 'Les locomotives se la Series BB 12000 a redresseurs au silicium', *Rev. Gen. Chemins de Fer*, 1965, **84,** pp. 95–102
341 NETHERSALE, H.J.H., and LESTER, F.D.: 'Thyristor-controlled locomotives', *Rail. Gaz.*, 1969
342 HACKSTEIN, M.: 'Stromrichter-Traktionstechnik bei der Deutschen Bundesbahn; Stand und Ausblick', *Elektr. Bahnen*, 1980, **78,** pp. 319–325 and p. 328
343 TIETZE, Ch.: 'Modern Wechelstrom-Triebfahrzeuge mit kontaktloser Antriebstechnik', *ibid.*, 1981, **79,** pp. 117–126.
344 NOUVION, M.F., and AUTRUFFE, M.H.: 'L'utilisation des thyristors sur les engines de traction', *Rev. Gen. Chemins de Fer*, 1966, **85,** pp. 733–744
345 STÖTZER, K.S.: 'Elektrische Bremsen moderner Wechelstrom-Triebfahrzeuge', *Glasers Ann.*, 1971, **95,** pp. 384–393, and 1972, **96,** pp. 23–29
346 FISCHER, R., and SCHOLTIS, G.: 'Die thyristorgesteuerte Nutzbremse im Triebwagen ET 4501 der DB', *Elektr. Bahnen*, 1968, **39,** pp. 136–141 and 154–161
347 NOUVION, F., COSSIÉ, A., and DUPONT, R.: 'Les locomotives monophasees BB 15000', *Rev. Gen. Chemins de Fer*, 1971, **90,** pp. 407–437
348 LOZANOVSKIJ, A.J., KOPANEV, A.S., and NAJNOV, B.M.: 'Fahrstromrichter der Thyristorlokomotive des Type 80R', *Elektrotechnika*, 1970, pp. 55–56
349 ELKIN, S.N., JANOV, W.P., and CHERRJAVSKIN, S.N.: 'Der Elektrolokomotivbau in der UdSSR', *Elektr. & Teplovoznaja Tjaga*, 1973, **17,** pp. 4–7
350 KATTA, T.: 'Thyristor chopper-controlled electric cars in Japan', *Jpn. Rail. Eng.*, 1980, **20,** pp. 3–13
351 MOURY, P.: 'Développement et utilisation des hacheurs en traction électrique', *Revue Jeumont-Schneider*, 1976, **25,** pp. 3–13
352 GOUTHIERE, J., and HOLOGNE, H.: 'Die Thyristor-Chopper bei der elektrischen Zugförderung', *ACEC-Z.*, 1976, (1–2), pp. 3–22
353 KNAPP, P.: '10 Jahre BBC-Gleichstromsteller für Nahverkehrsfahrzeuge', *Brown Boveri Mitt.*, 1978, **60,** pp. 77–785
354 'Microprocessors boost EMD's 60 series', *Railw. Gaz. Int.*, Dec. 1984, pp. 963–965

Power Electronic Circuit Topology

WILLIAM MCMURRAY, FELLOW, IEEE

Invited Paper

A generalized concept of "sources" embracing both power generators and power consumers simplifies the basic topological aspects of power electronic converter circuits, which are reduced to an array of switches for selectively interconnecting two source systems. Capacitive and inductive filters can modify the nature of the systems, because they act as short-time sources and effectively determine whether the converter sees a voltage source or a current source at its terminals. These differing source qualities require different types of switching devices and have extensive ramifications in the mode of operation of the equipment. This paper presents some basic configurations and describes their significant properties, with emphasis on the most widely used circuits in high-power equipment, particularly ac/dc converters.

INTRODUCTION

Electrical loads often require, or would prefer, a power supply having characteristics different from the available source. The function of power electronic converters is to perform this desired transformation with minimum losses and acceptable cost. Low loss demands a switching mode of operation, and many types of semiconductor devices have been optimized for this purpose. However, switching results in discontinuous power flow through the devices, and temporary energy storage or filtering is necessary to render the overall power flow smooth enough to be acceptable to the source and to the load, and not to impose undue stress on the switches.

The interconnection of switching devices with inductive and capacitive filter elements between the source and load terminals forms the topology of the converter circuit. Certain basic rules must be observed in making the interconnections, depending on the type of power conversion desired but not on the power level. Switching changes the effective topology of the circuit, so the operation of a power converter can be regarded as a sequence of different topological states or modes which are repeated cyclically. There are usually restrictions on the allowable state of the circuit (polarity of voltages and currents of the sources and reactive elements) at the instants of switching, depending on the characteristics of the switching devices. Control of the converter, fundamentally, reduces to controlling the on/off state of the switches in the proper sequence to perform the desired conversion function while observing these restrictions. The normal control may need to be modified for protection against overloads and faults.

The selection of topology for a converter must consider the following factors:

- The basic conversion function required.
- The properties of the switching devices that are available in the necessary size.
- The number, size, and cost of filter elements and other accessories.
- The losses and stresses involved in switching.
- Ease of control and protection.

As in any other field of engineering, there are many tradeoffs. Certain circuit arrangements have a combination of characteristics that meet the needs of many applications and are widely used. Other arrangements have special characteristics that are needed in a more limited range of applications. Some topologies are not yet practical, but have desirable features that may be realized with future development of components.

BASIC PRINCIPLES

This section discusses the various classifications and operating mechanisms of converter power circuits. A generalized concept of "source" is introduced, including both power generators and power consumers, regarding the latter as negative sources. Capacitance and inductance, often added as filters to suppress unwanted frequency components or for temporary energy storage, are considered to be short-time sources. This viewpoint simplifies the basic topological aspects of converter circuits, which are reduced to an array of switches for selectively interconnecting two source systems. The inherent regenerative capability of many converters is stressed by avoiding restrictive terms such as input/output or supply/load when referencing to the two sources. Brief discussions of semiconductor power devices and the principles of switching-mode conversion are presented. Finally, the effects of minor topological elements such as snubbers and parasitic impedances are mentioned.

Manuscript received November 10, 1987; revised February 22, 1988. Portions of this paper are based on work performed for Electric Power Research Institute Research Project 2443-5, "Feasibility of GTOs in a Valve System."

The author is with Corporate Research and Development, General Electric Company, Schenectady, NY 12301, USA.

IEEE Log Number 8820936.

Reprinted from *Proc. IEEE*, vol. 76, no. 4, pp. 428–437, April 1988.

Voltage and Current Sources (Supplies) or Sinks (Loads)

The links between a power converter and the outside world are its power supply or source and its load or power sink, which may be perceived as a negative source. In some systems, the direction of power flow can reverse, so the roles of "source" and "sink" are interchanged. It is, therefore, convenient to regard both as "sources." Obviously, the nature of these sources and the desired interchange of power between them specifies the duty of the converter and imposes certain topological conditions on the circuit. An electrical source implies a conversion of energy from some other form to electromagnetic. Examples of dc sources are batteries, solar cells, and dc machines, while ac sources are rotating machines or oscillating tuned circuits. Resistive sources (sinks) are heaters or loads where most of the energy is ultimately converted to heat.

It is important to clearly define the terms "voltage source" and "current source" as applied to converters, since these differing modes of operation have extensive ramifications in the operation of the equipment. These terms derive from mathematical circuit analysis, as follows:

- A voltage source maintains a prescribed voltage across its terminals, irrespective of the magnitude or polarity of the current flowing through the source. The prescribed voltage may be constant dc, sinusoidal ac, a series of pulses, etc. The current depends on the impedance connected across the terminals.
- A current source maintains a prescribed current flowing between its terminals, irrespective of the magnitude or polarity of the voltage applied across these terminals. The prescribed current may be constant dc, sinusoidal ac, a series of pulses, etc. The voltage depends on the impedance connected across the terminals.

While no practical source has these ideal properties, approximate voltage sources are familiar: a battery approximates a dc voltage source, and the EMF induced in conductors by rotation of a magnetic field is an approximate ac voltage source. For many applications, the source imperfections are reduced by feedback regulation: a utility system endeavors to maintain the appearance of an ac voltage source, as seen by its customers. One of the major applications of power converters is to provide an "artificial" source for other equipment. DC power supplies and ac uninterruptible power supplies are familiar examples, and tight regulation to mimic a voltage source is usually specified. There seem to be no natural current sources, but a large superconducting coil approaches this ideal. Approximate current sources can be obtained from voltage-source supplies by appropriately regulated conversion equipment. For example, electrochemical power supplies and field exciters for machines are usually current-regulated.

Capacitance and Inductance as Short-Time Sources (Filters)

For short-time transients, a capacitor can be regulated as a voltage source, and an inductor can be regarded as a current source. This makes these components useful as filters for artificial sources, maintaining the desired source properties for times shorter than the response time of the controlling equipment. For example, a voltage-source dc power supply can be regarded as capacitor provided with a controller to replenish its charge at the same rate as it is withdrawn by the load, as closely as possible. Similarly, a current-source dc supply can be regarded as an inductor with controlled means to match the average voltage of its input terminal to the voltage of its output terminal as closely as possible. Most conversion equipment employs filters of both types and often includes both types of control loop. For example, a dc motor drive usually has an inner current/torque control loop and an outer voltage/speed regulator.

Converters are often classified to distinguish between "voltage-source" and "current-source" inverters (or converters), abbreviated as "VSI" and "CSI," respectively. *Note that the "source" classification of an ac/dc converter depends on the type of filter and control that is most immediate to the dc terminals of the network of switching devices.* In general, a voltage-source ac/dc or dc/ac converter has a capacitor connected directly across the dc terminals, with no intervening impedance apart from snubbers and wiring. Conversely, a current-source converter has an inductance in series with the dc terminals, preceded by no shunt impedance apart from snubbers and stray capacitance. The switching devices are controlled to interconnect the dc and ac terminals in a time sequence such that an ac source of the same type as the dc source is produced. Thus, one type of voltage-source converter produces a quasi-square-wave ac voltage and the corresponding dual type of current-source converter generates a quasi-square-wave ac current.

For ease of explanation and elementary analysis, it is often assumed that the dc inductance or capacitance is "infinite," equivalent to an ideal current or voltage source, respectively. However, a major objective of the designer is to minimize these filter components. Often, this is accomplished by employing more complex topologies, such as multiphase transformer connections [1]. Another method of reducing filter size is to raise the operating frequency, particularly favored in the case of low power dc/dc converters.

Classification of Converter Circuits

Besides their "source" nature, there are many other criteria by which power converter circuits can be classified. For example, the type of conversion performed: ac/dc (rectifier), dc/ac (inverter), dc/dc (chopper), or ac/ac (voltage controller or frequency changer). Some circuits can transmit power in only the one direction implied by this source/load ordering, while others are capable of transmitting power in both directions, that is, they can operate in a regenerative mode. The difference is not critical if the application requires only one direction of conversion.

Often, conversion systems employ two stages, where a pair of converters are cascaded via an intermediate link. AC motor drives from a utility supply usually consist of a rectifier, dc link, and adjustable-frequency inverter [2], [3]. For isolation or shifting voltage level through a wide range, dc/dc converters frequently include an inverter-rectifier cascade with an ac transformer link. If system regeneration is required, both converters in the chain must be reversible.

Another classification is according to the type of switching or "commutation" employed by the circuit. While commutation is generally synonymous with switching, referring to either turn-on or turn-off of a switching device, it is more often employed when turn-off is under discussion, since this is generally more difficult for the device, and is impossible for diode and ordinary thyristor devices without external assistance. Such external assistance may be the cyclic voltage reversal of an ac source or an ac load (including the counter EMF of a motor or an oscillating tuned circuit). The terms "natural commutation," "line commutation," "load commutation," or "external commutation" are often used to describe this mode of circuit operation [1], [4].

A converter in which turn-off commutation of the switching devices is provided by means internal to the equipment is termed "self-commutated" or "force-commutated" [5]. Current extinction or turn-off may be accomplished by base/gate control of the devices themselves, or by auxiliary circuit means in the case of ordinary thyristors [6]. The mode of commutation of converter may depend on the "quadrant" of operation, as determined by the four possible combinations of voltage and current polarities where these can vary. A circuit that is self-commutated in one quadrant may be externally-commutated in another quadrant. However, since self-commutation is a necessary feature, the equipment will be classified as a "self-commutated converter."

In some converters, the action of a resonant L-C circuit provides relatively low-stress on- and off-commutation for the switching devices. This mode of commutation could be regarded as a particular case of self-commutation if the resonant circuit is contained within the converter or a particular case of external-commutation if the resonant circuit is located outside of the converter. However, the operational behavior is sufficiently different to justify a special category. In essence, forced oscillations are maintained by switching, and the oscillations return the circuit state to conditions favorable for operation of the switches. Control is obtained by adjusting the frequency below or above resonance. Various topologies employing series or parallel resonance have been developed [7]–[9] but, for brevity, further discussion will be omitted.

Power Electronic Switching Devices

Switching devices are the essential components of a power converter and their properties are reflected in the properties of the equipment. The ideal switch would be a fully controllable impedance of infinite range in both directions of voltage and current. Practical devices have limited range, of course, and are restricted to some combination of the following alternative capabilities:

- unidirectional/bidirectional current,
- unidirectional/bidirectional voltage,
- controlled/uncontrolled turn-on,
- controlled/uncontrolled turn-off,
- proportionally controllable/latching.

Diodes, for example, are limited to unidirectional current and voltage, uncontrolled turn-on and turn-off, and are latching. Ordinary thyristors can withstand bidirectional voltage but are limited to unidirectional current (TRIAC types excepted), have controlled turn-on but uncontrolled turn-off, and are latching. Gate turn-off thyristors (GTOs) add the capability of controlled turn-off, but some types are asymmetrical and cannot withstand reverse voltage. Reverse-conducting thyristors cannot withstand reverse voltage but, instead, are designed to conduct reverse current without controllability.

Transistors are generally limited to unidirectional current and voltage, but can control both turn-on and turn-off, and are proportionally controllable. Proportional control is useful in limiting the rate of switching and the resulting transients generated by parasitic impedances, particularly if no snubbers are employed. However, switching transistors are driven into or near saturation during the on-state, so they operate in a fashion similar to latching devices at normal current levels. There is an advantage over latching devices in that, above a certain current level, they come out of saturation and proportional control is regained, allowing faults to be more easily limited. This description of transistors applies to bipolar junction devices (BJTs) and field effect devices such as MOSFETs, as well as many specialized variations that have been developed.

Viewed from the power circuit topology and type of conversion required, the quadrants of operation and controllability of the switches are the critical factors, and not the particular internal construction of the devices. Sometimes, composite switches of two or more devices are employed where a single device having the desired characteristics may not be available. For example, inverse diodes are often connected across transistors or thyristors to provide reverse conduction capability. However, the availability and cost of suitable devices largely determines what types of converter are practical. Integrated packages of multiple power devices and associated drivers are being intensively developed, primarily to reduce cost and size.

Switching-Mode Conversion: Time-Average Voltage Control

Fundamentally, a power converter is a device for interconnecting two sources. In performing this function, the converter should consume a minimum of power, so the connection should not intentionally be resistive. This goal is achieved by employing a switching mode of operation. The great majority of converters operate upon the following basic principle: *A current-source terminal is selectively connected or switched between two or more voltage-source terminals.*

This is illustrated in Fig. 1, which also serves to define the

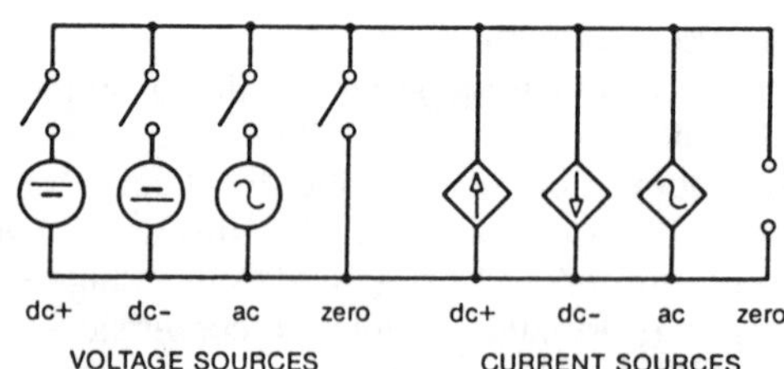

Fig. 1. Switching-mode converter: basic topology.

source symbols that will be used here. The voltage sources may be dc of either polarity, ac of any amplitude, phase or frequency, and one switch terminal may be a zero-voltage source, or ground. Similarly, the current source may be dc of either polarity or ac of any amplitude, phase or frequency. While it is unusual, several current sources may be connected together, as indicated in Fig. 1. However, at any time, one and only one of the switches must be closed to connect a single voltage source to the current-source terminal. (Except that, in most converter circuits, there is a discontinuous-current mode of operation where all switches are open; the prevailing topology includes an inductance carrying no current, equivalent to a zero-current source or open circuit.)

In a diode rectifier, the switch selection is automatic: the diode switches "on" whenever the voltage across its terminals becomes positive and turns "off" when the current attempts to go negative. In this case, the power flow is entirely determined by the state of the two sources, and is restricted to one direction.

To obtain control over the power flow, the switching devices must be able to control their time of turn-on or their time of turn-off, or both. With control of the switching times between terminals, the average voltage at the current-source terminal is determined by the fraction of time it dwells at each voltage-source terminal and the average source voltage during the dwell time. This time-average voltage control is the major means of adjusting the power to achieve the desired performance. Note that the voltage at the current-source terminal cannot exceed the maximum of the voltage sources. That is, power from the voltage sources is "stepped down" in voltage level, or power from the current source is "stepped up" in voltage level. With multiple voltage sources and a given desired voltage at the current-source terminal, the switches should be operated to time-share its connection between the "closest higher" and "closet lower" of the available voltage sources.

The voltage and current polarities at the instant of switching determine the mode of commutation and the type of devices required. Suppose, in Fig. 2, that the switches *S*1

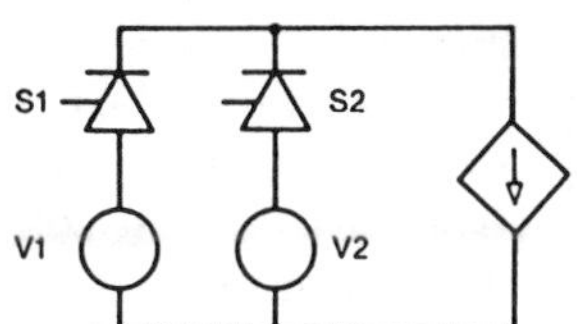

Fig. 2. Commutation between voltage sources.

and *S*2 are unidirectional current devices, as indicated, and *S*1 is initially conducting to connect voltage source *V*1 to the dc current source. When it is desired to reconnect the current source to voltage source *V*2 by turning *S*1 off and *S*2 on, the required sequence of switching depends on the voltage difference between *V*1 and *V*2. If *V*2 is instantaneously more positive than *V*1, then switch *S*2 is forward biased and can be turned on, which will cause the current to commutate "naturally" from *S*1 to *S*2, driven by the external voltage (*V*2-*V*1) which will now appear as reverse voltage across *S*1.

However, if *V*1 is more positive than *V*2, switch *S*2 will be reverse biased and cannot turn on. Or, if *S*2 were a bidirectional current switch, turning *S*2 on would short circuit the voltage *V*2 to *V*1. Therefore, switch *S*1 must be turned off first by self-commutation, forcing its voltage to rise. This will bring *S*2 into forward bias, so it can now be turned on and limit the forward voltage on *S*1 to (*V*1-*V*2).

For a return commutation from *S*2 back to *S*1 again, the situation has now reversed, unless and until the difference voltage (*V*2-*V*1) changes polarity. That is, an external commutation from *S*1 to *S*2 must be followed by self-commutation of *S*2 to *S*1, and vice versa. With dc sources, the voltage never changes polarity, so at least one of the switches must be self-commutated. A converter employing only externally-commutated switches must rely on ac sources to provide cyclic voltage reversals, and the switching frequency is limited to the ac source frequency.

Commutation Aids: Snubbers

Snubbers are relatively small auxiliary circuit elements that are added to the basic circuit topology in order to reduce the transient voltage or current stresses on the semiconductor switching devices. Shunt snubber capacitors are connected across the devices to limit the rate of rise of voltage (*dv*/*dt*) or the peak voltage (or both) during turn-off [10], [11]. They also may serve to limit the effects of externally imposed voltage transients. Series snubber inductances are connected in series with the devices to limit the rate of rise or fall of current (*di*/*dt*) through the device when turning on or off, respectively. A typical arrangement is illustrated in Fig. 3 [12]. In the various converter topologies to be presented, it should be understood that snubbers may be included in the location of the switching devices.

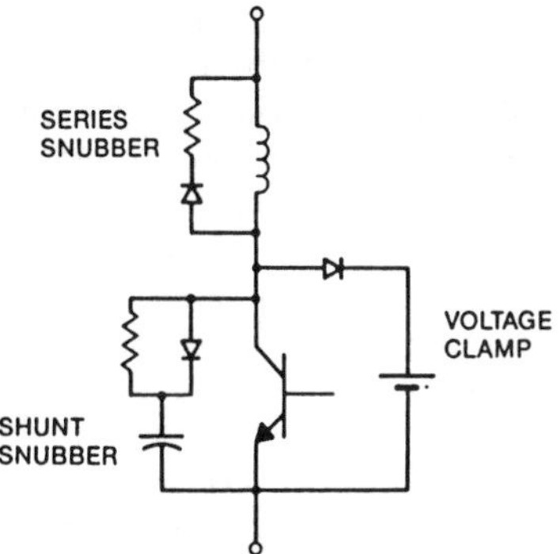

Fig. 3. Typical snubber and clamp arrangement for a switching transistor.

The action of a series snubber tends to interfere with the action of a shunt snubber and vice versa, so diodes are often used to polarize the action and limit the interference. In both types of snubber, energy is stored in the reactive elements and is usually "trapped," that is, not easily recoverable and must be dissipated by discharge through a resistor. This offsets the reduction of switching losses in the semiconductor devices. A great many different arrangements have been developed to reduce or avoid snubber losses, but at the expense of complexity [13]. It is desirable to extend the safe operating area of the devices and increase their switching speed to reduce the energy absorbed, so that they can be operated without snubbers. This has been accomplished with low and medium power devices.

Clamps are auxiliary circuit elements similar to snubbers except that they do not limit the rate of change, but only the peak value, of voltage or current. They are often needed to absorb the energy trapped in parasitic impedances, particularly when high *di*/*dt* switching generates inductive spikes. To avoid this, in snubberless operation the switching rate should be carefully controlled, if the devices allow it.

Parasitic Impedances

Parasitic impedances appear in locations where they are not desired, and are usually neglected in idealized analysis and omitted from circuit diagrams. The series resistance of windings, wiring, and on-state switches is the major cause of losses, but otherwise has little effect. Since inductance and capacitance have a dimension of length, they cannot be eliminated from physical equipment. Both can be important, because they impose ultimate limits on switching speed. The most significant stray element in many converters is series inductance, in the form of transformer or machine winding leakage inductance. While it is often desirable to minimize parasitic impedances, they may provide some "free" benefits.

The ac system or load connected to a converter should appear to be a source of the opposite type, at least transiently, since it is not permissible to connect voltage sources in parallel or current sources in series. Thus, a quasi-square-wave voltage-source converter must be connected to a sine-wave voltage-source utility (or motor) via series inductance, which might be simply the leakage reactance of windings. This reactance represents an imperfection of the ideal utility source which is advantageous in the above instance and acceptable for an ordinary thyristor current-source converter, where it assists natural commutation by acting as a large series snubber. Furthermore, ac system reactance is of prime importance in limiting fault currents. However, inductance hinders self-commutation in a current-source converter, and filter capacitors must be connected across the ac terminals to improve the voltage-source quality.

In high-voltage equipment, the shunt capacitance of transformer windings and stray capacitance to ground become significant, because the capacitance is reflected to the low-voltage side by the square of the turns ratio. In a self-commutated current-source converter, the stray capacitances can be regarded as a small addition to the ac filter and snubber capacitors. In an ordinary thyristor converter, the stray capacitances must be discharged when the devices turn on, and leg reactors (series snubbers) are required to limit *di/dt*. While these reactors are relatively small and can be allowed to saturate, they are not necessary in low-voltage systems where stray capacitance is negligible.

For a self-commutated voltage-source converter, the stray capacitances are an impediment to generation of the "ideal" waveform. However, the switching devices require snubbers which affect this waveform in a similar manner; stray capacitance has an effect akin to shunt snubber capacitance, for which *di/dt* limiting inductance is provided in any case. If the energy stored in stray capacitance were as large as the energy stored in leakage inductance, then the effect on voltage-source converters would be more serious.

AC/DC Converters

This class includes both rectifiers and inverters; since the equipment is inherently regenerative when controlled switches are employed, the generic term "converter" will be used. In the general description of topologies, the use of self-commutated switches is assumed; the restrictions of external commutation are discussed later.

Voltage-Source Converter Topologies

The basic single-phase arrangements are presented in Figs. 4–6. In a voltage-source converter, the switching devices do not have to block reverse voltage, as indicated by omission of the "blocking bar" from the device symbols

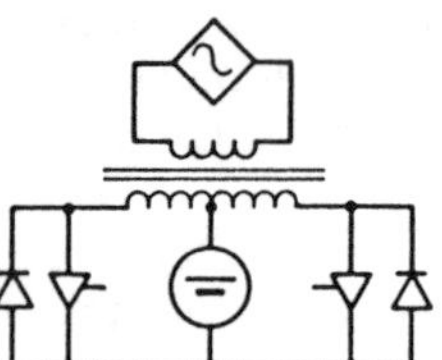

Fig. 4. Single-phase voltage-source converter: center-tapped ac source.

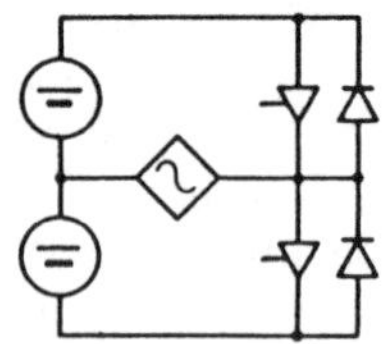

Fig. 5. Single-phase voltage-source converter: center-tapped dc source.

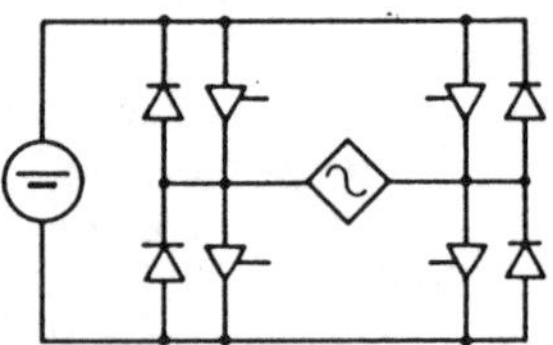

Fig. 6. Single-phase bridge voltage-source converter.

in the figures. Instead, the switches must be reverse conducting or employ antiparallel diodes. Devices of this type can be better optimized for fast switching. The full bridge, Fig. 6, is more common because the half-bridge, Fig. 5, requires a center-tapped dc source that must carry large ac currents and Fig. 4 requires a center-tapped transformer. The leakage inductance between the center-tapped windings impairs the switching performance. However, there is only one device in the loop through the dc source, giving the advantage of lower forward conduction drop, which is significant when the dc voltage is low.

In its simplest form, a voltage-source converter switches at the ac fundamental frequency and generates a square wave of voltage. With alternate conduction of the pair of switches in Figs. 4 and 5, a square-wave voltage is impressed across the ac current source. The same waveform is produced by Fig. 6 if the two legs are switched simultaneously. However, by introducing a phase displacement in the switching times, the quasi-square waveform in Fig. 7 can be generated. This is one common method of adjusting the ac/dc voltage ratio, and can also reduce the harmonic content of voltage on the ac side and ripple current on the dc side. Note that when the voltage in Fig. 7 is zero, the ac current

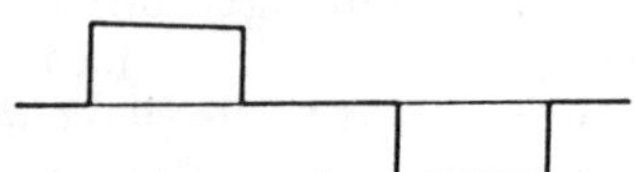

Fig. 7. Quasi-square waveform.

coasts through the pair of switches connected to the same dc rail (positive or negative), so there is no current in the dc source.

For three-phase ac systems, the bridge circuit in Fig. 8 is widely employed. When the three component half-bridge

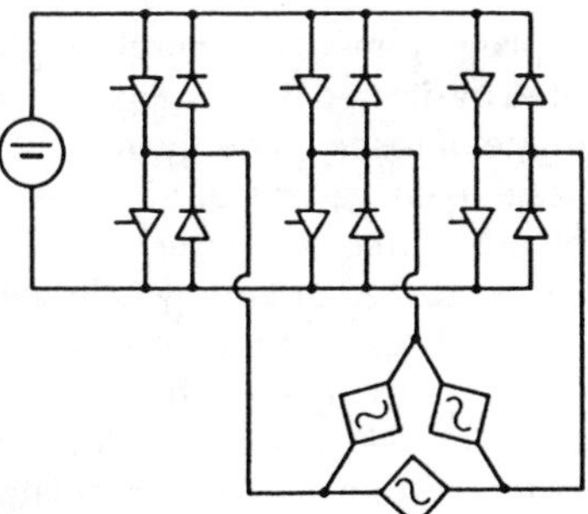

Fig. 8. Three-phase bridge voltage-source converter.

phase legs in Fig. 8 have symmetrical 120° phase displacement, the square waves at each ac terminal combine to produce the so-called "six-step" waveform seen in Fig. 9. A better waveform can be obtained with a multi-phase converter

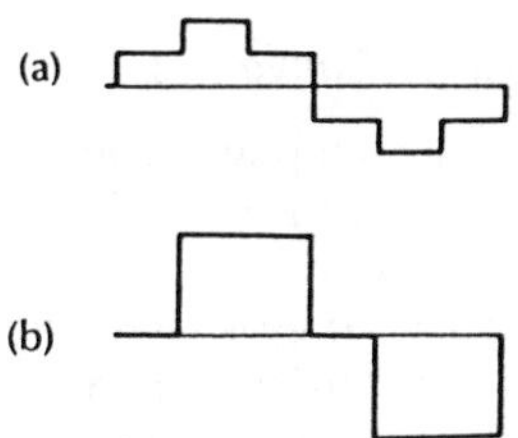

Fig. 9. Six-step voltage waveform produced by three-phase bridge circuit. (a) Line to neutral. (b) Line to line.

composed of two or more three-phase bridges in parallel across the dc source. The ac outputs are combined in special transformer connections to produce a stepped wave having low harmonic content, such as depicted in Fig. 10.

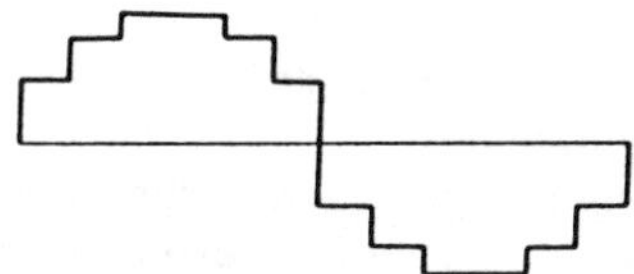

Fig. 10. Stepped waveform.

This is a popular arrangement for uninterruptible power supplies, but not for applications such as motor drives where an output transformer is generally not necessary.

In any of these circuits, one may exercise the option of operating the pair of switching elements in each phase leg many times during each fundamental ac cycle. A switching pattern of pulse-width modulation (PWM) can be chosen to reduce objectionable ac harmonics or otherwise shape the voltage waveform, at the same time adjusting the ac/dc voltage ratio. Many different patterns of PWM have been proposed, frequently with claims of "optimum" in respect of some criterion; a typical example is shown in Fig. 11. The

Fig. 11. AC voltage waveform produced by pulse-width modulation (PWM).

high-frequency harmonics can be suppressed with a relatively small series inductance and shunt capacitance. PWM control is favored because it does not require complex topology. The major design tradeoff involves the PWM switching frequency, with corresponding losses, and the size of the filters, both dc and ac. The disadvantage of higher switching losses is being overcome by the development of faster high-power semiconductor devices. A small electrolytic dc capacitor can be used, except where the application requires high voltage, high or low operating temperatures, or very high reliability.

Another method of adjusting the ac voltage is regulation of the dc voltage by means of another converter, such as a rectifier or dc chopper. For regeneration in dc-linked systems, it is desirable that both converters be of the same type; in this case, a second voltage-source converter should be used. Optimum system performance might be obtained with a combined system, in which the amplitude of the ac voltage is regulated by adjusting the dc link voltage, while a PWM control is devoted to harmonic suppression.

Current-Source Converter Topologies

A current-source converter is, essentially, the dual of a voltage-source converter. The switching devices must block reverse voltage, or else have series diodes instead of antiparallel diodes. Instead of a shunt capacitor, the dc side is filtered by a series inductance. Generally, a set of ac filter capacitors must be connected directly across the ac terminals of the converter if self-commutation is to be employed. For example, by interchanging the ac and dc nature of the sources in Fig. 5 and replacing the reverse-conducting switches with reverse-blocking devices, the arrangement of Fig. 12 is obtained. The center-tapped ac

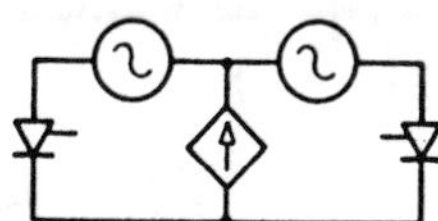

Fig. 12. Single-phase current-source converter: center-tapped ac source.

voltage source is usually a transformer, as in Fig. 4. The leakage inductance between the windings is not critical for external commutation, but addition of capacitors is necessary for self-commutation. With alternate conduction of the pair of switches in Fig. 12, a square-wave current is forced through the ac voltage source.

The single-phase full bridge circuit in Fig. 13 is obtained

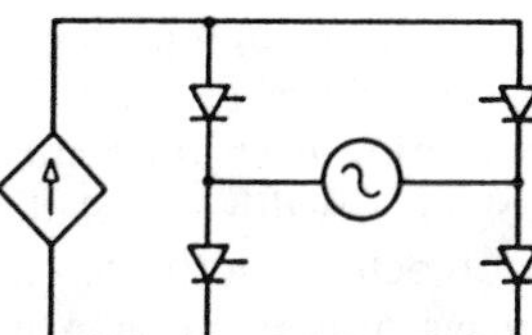

Fig. 13. Single-phase bridge current-source converter.

from Fig. 6 by interchanging the voltage/current nature of the sources and substituting appropriate switches. Again, a square waveform is produced by Fig. 13 if the two legs are switched simultaneously but a quasi-square current waveform like Fig. 7 is obtained by introducing a phase displacement in the switching times. This provides a method of adjusting the ac/dc current ratio, and can also reduce the harmonic content of current on the ac side and ripple voltage on the dc side. Note that when the ac current in Fig. 13 is zero, the dc current is bypassed through a pair of switches that short-circuit the dc current source, while the switches in the other leg are both open.

For three-phase ac systems, the arrangement in Fig. 14 is a basic building block, forming what is called a 3-pulse commutating group. The zero-voltage bypass arm, indicated by dashed lines, is an optional addition. When the three main switches are operated in sequence with symmetrical 120° phase displacement, the direct current is chopped into 120° blocks (pulses), forced through each ac voltage source in turn. This scheme was popular for mercury-arc rectifiers having a common cathode, but has lost favor today because a dc component of current flows through the ac sources (usually, polyphase transformer windings). However, two 3-pulse groups can be combined to form the 6-pulse three-phase bridge circuit in Fig. 15 (dual of Fig. 8), which is the most common converter circuit for high-power equipment. When the six switches in Fig. 15 are operated with symmetrical 60° phase displacement, quasi-square waves of current are forced into each ac terminal, producing a "six-step" current waveform like the voltage waveform seen in Fig. 10. The main method of adjusting the ac current is usually regulation of the dc current by means of another current-source converter.

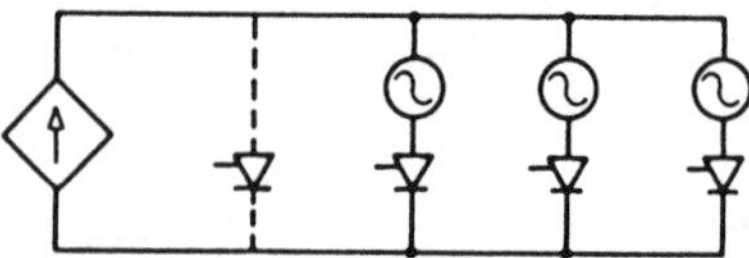
Fig. 14. Three-phase current-source converter.

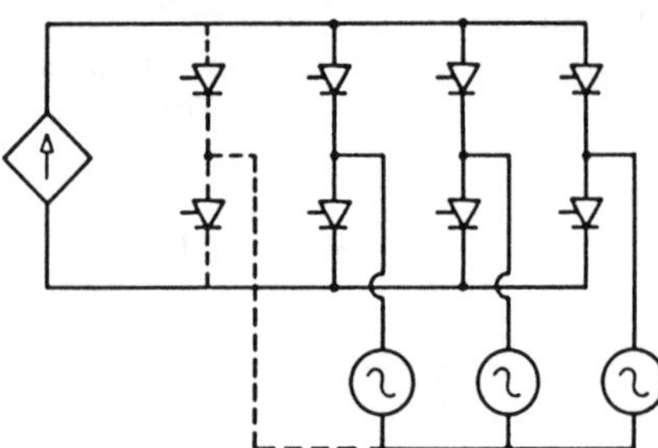
Fig. 15. Three-phase bridge current-source converter.

As in the case of voltage-source converters, with self-commutation it is possible to operate the switching elements many times during each fundamental ac cycle. A switching pattern of pulse-width modulation (PWM) can be chosen to reduce objectionable harmonics or otherwise shape the current waveform, at the same time adjusting the ac/dc current ratio [14]. Just as the dc voltage must exceed the peak ac voltage in a voltage-source converter, the dc current must exceed the peak value of the ac current envelope for the three phase in a current-source converter. The margin of dc current excess must be bypassed through the converter, that is, the PWM pattern must include modes that short-circuit the dc link for certain intervals. These modes may be programmed to occur through a neutral leg, such as indicated by dashed lines in Fig. 15. This can be considered as storage of reserve energy in the dc filter inductance, just as reserve energy is stored in the dc filter capacitance of a voltage-source converter.

Since inductive storage of energy is lossier than capacitive storage, the current-source converter is at a disadvantage. To minimize the losses, the dc link current must be modulated to closely match the load demand. This requires a very fast response current regulator for the controlling converter. One advantage of current-source converters pertains to the regenerative mode of operation. In a current-linked two-stage ac/ac converter system, reversal of power flow is obtained by reversing the dc voltage instead of the dc current. This allows an ordinary thyristor rectifier to operate as a load-commutated inverter, where external commutation of the thyristors is provided by the counter-EMF of a synchronous machine or ac system.

Externally-Commutated Converters

Historically, the first high-power electronic switches were mercury-arc rectifiers and similar devices having characteristics much like thyristors, with which they were replaced. In particular, they shared the requirement of external commutation. Ordinary thyristors are turned on by application of forward gate current, but cannot be turned off by reverse gate current. Instead, the anode current must be extinguished by external means. In the classical natural- or line-commutated phase-controlled rectifier, which may be classified as a current-source ac/dc converter, this is accomplished by turning on the thyristor in the next phase of the commutating group, which connects the line voltage to produce the desired switching. However, this mode of operation is restricted to the half-cycle in which the line voltage has the proper polarity. The only method of control is to delay the time (or phase angle) of turn-on in this half-cycle. As a result, the converter always draws lagging current from the supply.

The displacement angle between the source voltage and the fundamental component of current is proportional to the turn-on delay angle, so the reactive power is greatest when operating near 90° to produce a low dc voltage. By including a switched connection to a source of zero voltage (ground) in the topology of the circuit, such as indicated by dashed lines in Figs. 14 and 15, a level closer to the desired dc voltage may be selected. When the freewheeling switch in Fig. 14 is closed, the dc current bypasses the ac sources, reducing the reactive power. A freewheeling diode rectifier is often employed, but a thyristor is needed if regeneration is required. The fourth leg in the bridge circuit of Fig. 15, connected to the neutral point of the ac voltage sources, operates in similar fashion [15]. The power factor can also be improved by methods that do not require a change in topology, such as by asymmetrical control of commutating groups, or by sequential control of groups in converters where two or more commutating groups are connected in series (as in Fig. 15) [16].

The ordinary thyristors employed in externally-commutated converters need only simple pulse turn-on control and can withstand high surge currents. Because a relatively large ac source reactance is permissible, overloads and faults, including the effects of miscommutation, can be limited by relatively simple control techniques. Rapid recovery is possible, so the equipment is rugged and reliable. These features are difficult to duplicate with self-commutated converters, where the switching devices must be able to turn off the peak fault current or special, complex arrangements are necessary to limit the current and the normal performance of the converter may be compromised.

Most high-power externally-commutated converters are of the current-source type. However, some externally-commutated voltage-source converters have been developed [17], [18]. Also, rectifiers with capacitor-input filters, including voltage multiplier circuits, can be regarded as a special category within the class of voltage-source converters. A large number of such topologies have been used [19].

Self-Commutated Converters

Self-commutated power converters of many types have been developed extensively since the introduction of power semiconductors. While controllable turn-off semiconductor devices have always been preferred for this type of equipment, they have only recently (within the past ten years) become available in large sizes. A self-commutated converter using ordinary thyristors must be provided with an auxiliary commutating circuit including capacitors, inductors and, often, additional thyristors. This results in a quite complex and expensive arrangement, and the large number of different topological configurations that were developed for commutating circuits indicates that no one was entirely satisfactory.

As power transistors have increased in size, they have taken over applications at power levels originally restricted to ordinary thyristors with commutating circuits. As their name implies, gate turn-off thyristors (GTOs) can be turned off by reverse gate current and, as in the case of power transistors, major accessory components are not required. From the viewpoint of the power circuit, a GTO can be regarded as a very large power transistor with, perhaps, reverse blocking capability. The very high power GTOs now available are supplanting the remaining applications of ordinary thyristors in all self-commutated power converter equipment. The elimination of commutating circuits greatly enhances the practicality of high-power self-commutated converters and extends their range of application.

The controls required by a self-commutated converter are more complex and critical than for an externally-commutated converter, because turn-on of the incoming arm must be properly timed with respect to turn-off of the outgoing arm. Multiple switching within each cycle (PWM) may be used to adjust voltage or reduce harmonics, but requires careful timing to be effective. For protection, it is necessary to continuously monitor the current in each phase arm and override the normal control signals within a few microseconds after overcurrent is detected. Signals to produce appropriate action in the other phase arms should simultaneously be generated. With due care, these needs can be met reliably with integrated circuit and other techniques, and the generated signals can be transmitted from ground to each gate (or base) driver via optical links.

AC/AC Converters

Systems in which a pair of ac/dc converters (rectifier and inverter) are operated in cascade have been mentioned previously. These systems may be described as "dc link converters" or "indirect frequency changers." They have major applications as adjustable-speed ac motor drives and UPS systems, including a battery charger and inverter. Interaction between the input and output frequencies is buffered by the dc link filter. Cascaded voltage-source converters need only a common dc filter capacitor. Similarly, a pair of current-source converters can share a common dc filter inductor, and the rectifier can be an inexpensive circuit using externally-commutated thyristors. However, cascaded converters of the opposite type require both inductance and capacitance in the dc filter, and problems arise if regeneration is necessary. If regeneration is not required, then a diode rectifier followed by a voltage-source PWM inverter is an attractive system, because it operates close to unity power factor.

Cascaded systems involve two stages of power conversion, rectification and inversion, in which the load current must pass through at least two power switching devices in series. This increases the conduction losses. Direct frequency changers or cycloconverters have the advantage of only one stage of power conversion: current can flow from input to output through only one switching device so that conduction losses are minimized. However, reverse-blocking thyristor-type devices are required. If the only available devices having the desired high-frequency switching characteristics are of the forward-blocking transistor-type, then series diodes must be employed and the advantage is lost. Cycloconverters are inherently capable of reverse power flow without additional components, so that regenerative systems need only the appropriate control functions.

Externally-Commutated Cycloconverter

In concept, this type of frequency changer can be regarded as an inverse-parallel pair of phase-controlled rectifiers, one for each polarity of current, which are modulated to produce ac output [20], [21]. Commonly, a polyphase set of voltage sources feeds a single-phase current source at a lower frequency, as in the bridge arrangement of Fig. 16. This same configuration is popular for reversing

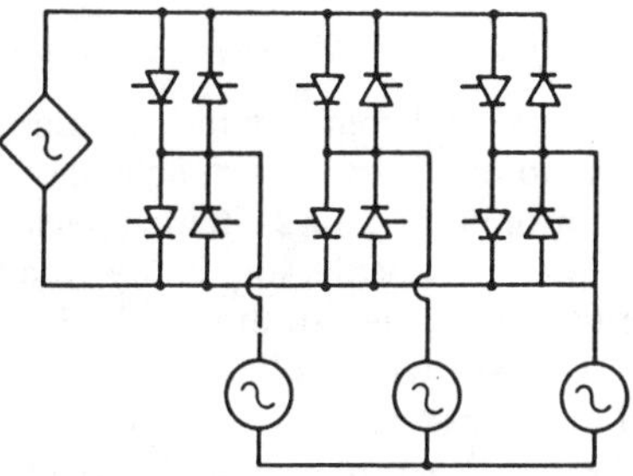

Fig. 16. Direct frequency changer: three-phase voltage source, one-phase current source.

dc motor drives, where it is known as a "dual converter." For three-phase output, three such converters are required. Externally-commutated cycloconverters can employ ordinary thyristors, but are limited to switching at the supply frequency. Ideally, the supply should act as a voltage source with only a small amount of series inductance to act as a "series snubber," limiting the *di/dt* in the devices.

The frequency at the current-source, inductively filtered

output side can, theoretically, approach and possibly exceed the input frequency. However, the interaction between the asynchronous sources becomes excessive and the quality of the waveform deteriorates rapidly. For practical utilization, a relatively high ratio between the supply frequency and the output frequency must be maintained, often in combination with many input phases. That is, a high pulse number is beneficial, but the penalty is that a large number of thyristors is required. Another serious disadvantage of externally-commutated cycloconverters is the poor power factor imposed upon the supply, because of the phase control delay required for voltage regulation and waveshaping of the output. Various techniques for improving the power factor of externally-commutated cycloconverters have been proposed, but all provide only marginal improvement for greater complexity and introduce other problems.

Self-Commutated Cycloconverters

The basic concept and circuit configuration of a self-commutated cycloconverter is the same as the externally-commutated type, except that gate turn-off thyristors (GTOs) or similar devices are substituted for the ordinary thyristors [22]. As before, each device may switch at the supply frequency, but the option of operating in a PWM mode is added. While self-commutation, with suitable control, allows operation near unity power factor or with a leading power factor on the supply, there is generally no reduction in the number of switching devices or the output filter size.

Ideally, the supply should act as a voltage source with zero series inductance because self-commutation abruptly interrupts the source current into the converter. Many theoretical treatments assume an ideal ac voltage source and neglect the effect of source reactance. In practice, a capacitive input filter is necessary to prevent loss of energy stored in the supply system reactance, particularly with transformer input, and to limit the overvoltages that must be produced in order to transfer the current with this associated stored energy from one supply phase to another. The capacitance itself may compensate for a substantial part of the poor power factor that the converter is intended to improve.

Pulse-Width-Modulated (PWM) Frequency Changer

This is a type of self-commutated frequency changer which attempts to overcome the deficiencies of the conventional type by operating the switching devices in a PWM mode at a frequency considerably higher than either the input or output frequencies. In the ideal minimum circuit topology, each phase of a polyphase set of voltage sources is connected directly to each phase of a polyphase set of current sources via a pair of antiparallel reverse-blocking devices such as GTOs, for a total of 18 devices in a three-phase system, as illustrated in Fig. 17. The switches are controlled in the manner proposed by Venturini, or some similar mode [23]–[25]. If the supply system inductance is sufficient to provide a current-source quality for voltage-averaging at the input and a set of small filter capacitors can provide a voltage-source quality for current-averaging at the output, the number of filters is reduced to a minimum.

While this "universal frequency changer" or "generalized transformer" is attractive in concept, there are many obstacles to its practical development. To maintain a reasonable efficiency, the switching loss must be reduced to a very low value. Conventional snubbers effective for both turn-on and turn-off of bidirectional device arrangements are inefficient, while "lossless" snubbers introduce considerable complexity. Alternatively, devices that can switch at very high frequencies without snubbers would have to be developed. Many analyses of this type of converter have been published, but most assume balanced load and do not address the problems of current limiting and protection. Because of strong interactions between phases at both input and output, the circuit behavior becomes very complicated. It is concluded that PWM changers are impractical at present, but may become important in the future.

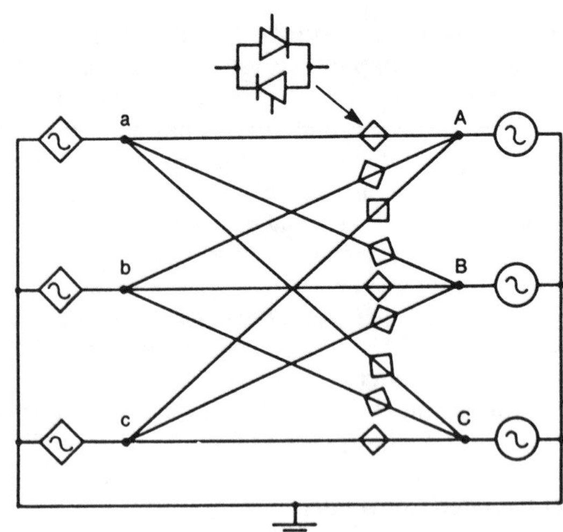

Fig. 17. Direct frequency changer: three-phase to three-phase using bidirectional self-commutated switches.

DC/DC Converters

Just as many ac/ac converters employ a dc link between a rectifier and an inverter, many dc/dc converters employ an ac link between an inverter and a rectifier, especially when a transformer is required to provide a large shift in voltage level. When a transformer is not needed, the single-phase bridge topology of Fig. 6, employing self-commutated switches, can be used to produce a reversible dc current source capable of regeneration. If only unidirectional current is needed, the topology can be simplified by eliminating certain of the switching devices. The reduced form in Fig. 18(a) is known as a voltage step-down chopper or buck converter, while the variant shown in Fig. 18(b) is called a step-up chopper or boost converter. From another viewpoint, the dc converters in Fig. 18 can be regarded as basic building blocks for reversible dc converters and inverters, which may be obtained by adding switching elements in suitable locations.

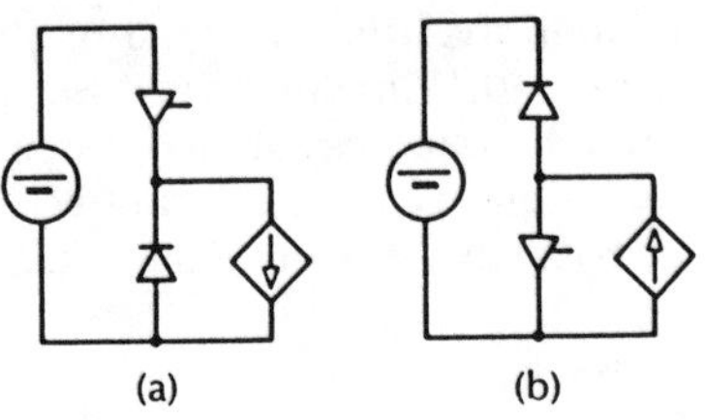

Fig. 18. Basic dc chopper circuits. (a) Voltage step-down (buck). (b) Voltage step-up (boost).

In both buck and boost types of direct dc converter, a dc form of pulse-width modulation or duty-ratio control produces a voltage waveform of the type shown in Fig. 19 at the current-source terminal. The current in the dc voltage source has a similar pulsed form. Many topological variations for dc switchmode converters have been developed, such as the "buck-boost" circuit, mainly in the low-power range of application. The thrust of development is towards topologies that are effective at very high frequencies and integration of accessory components with the switching devices, to achieve power supplies of very small size.

Fig. 19. DC waveform produced by pulse-width modulation (PWM).

Conclusion

Historically, the field of power electronics has been divided into a high power range mainly concerned with externally-commutated ac/dc converters for industrial applications and a low power range where the main interest began with self-commutated dc/dc switchmode converters for aerospace applications. Previous studies of high-power self-commutated converters contained extensive discussions of the many topologies devised as auxiliary commutating circuits for ordinary thyristors [26], [27]. Development of high-power self-commutated switching devices has made the latter obsolete, allowing the circuit topologist to concentrate on the more basic aspects common to all types of converters. An approach based on a generalized concept of sources has been presented here. Also, an expanded concept of switchmode conversion encompasses external commutation, regarded as a switching mode limited to the ac source frequency. In these ways, the inherent common ground of power electronics is revealed.

References

[1] J. Schaefer, *Rectifier Circuits.* New York, NY: Wiley, 1965.

[2] B. K. Bose, Ed., *Adjustable Speed AC Drive Systems.* New York, NY: IEEE Press, 1980.

[3] B. K. Bose, *Power Electronics and AC Drives.* Englewood Cliffs, NJ: Prentice-Hall, 1986.

[4] G. Moltgen, *Line Commutated Thyristor Converters.* London, England: Siemens/Pitman, 1972.

[5] ANSI/IEEE Standard 936, "Guide for Self-Commutated Converters," 1987.

[6] B. D. Bedford and R. G. Hoft, *Principles of Inverter Circuits.* New York, NY: Wiley, 1964.

[7] V. Vorperian and S. Cuk, "A complete dc analysis of the series resonant converter," in *Conf. Rec. IEEE-PESC*, pp. 85-100, 1982.

[8] R. L. Steigerwald, "High-frequency resonant transistor dc-dc converters," *IEEE Trans. Indust. Electron.*, vol. IE-31, no. 2, pp. 181-191, 1984.

[9] R. Oruganti and F. C. Lee, "Resonant power processors," *IEEE Trans. Ind. Appl.*, vol. IA-21, no. 6, 1985; "Part I—State plane analysis," pp. 1453-1460; "Part II—Methods of control," pp. 1461-1471.

[10] J. B. Rice and L. E. Nickels, "Commutation *dv/dt* effects in thyristor three-phase bridge converters," *IEEE Trans. Ind. Gen. Appl.*, vol. IGA-4, pp. 665-672, 1968.

[11] W. McMurray, "Optimum snubbers for power semiconductors," *IEEE Trans. Ind. Appl.*, vol. IA-8, no. 5, pp. 593-600, 1972.

[12] —, "Selection of snubbers and clamps to optimize the design of transistor switching converters," *IEEE Trans. Ind. Appl.*, vol. IA-16, no. 4, pp. 513-523, 1980.

[13] A. Ferraro, "An overview of low loss snubber technology for transistor converters," in *Conf. Rec. IEEE-PESC*, pp. 466-477, 1982.

[14] M. Hombu, S. Ueda, A. Ueda, and Y. Matsuda, "A new current source GTO inverter with sinusoidal output voltage and current," *IEEE Trans. Ind. Appl.*, vol. IA-21, no. 5, pp. 1192-1198, 1985.

[15] V. R. Stefanovic, "Power factor improvement with a modified phase-controlled converter," *IEEE Trans. Ind. Appl.*, vol. IA-15, no. 2, pp. 193-201, 1979.

[16] W. McMurray, "A study of asymmetrical gating for phase-controlled converters," *IEEE Trans. Ind. Appl.*, vol. IA-8, no. 3, pp. 289-295, 1972.

[17] M. Michel, "Converter using external commutation on the dc side," in *Conf. Rec. IEEE-PESC*, pp. 143-148, 1982.

[18] F. W. Kelley, Jr., (to General Electric Co.), "Line-commutated converter circuit," U.S. Patent 4 517 635, May 14, 1985.

[19] G. J. Scoles, *Handbook of Rectifier Circuits.* Chichester, England: Ellis Horwood Ltd., 1980.

[20] B. R. Pelly, *Thyristor Phase-Controlled Converters and Cycloconverters.* New York, NY: Wiley, 1971.

[21] W. McMurray, *The Theory and Design of Cycloconverters.* Cambridge, MA: MIT Press, 1972.

[22] L. Gyugyi and B. R. Pelly, *Static Power Frequency Changers.* New York, NY: Wiley, 1976.

[23] M. G. B. Venturini and A. Alesina, "The generalized transformer: A new bidirectional sinusoidal waveform frequency converter with continuously adjustable input power factor," in *Conf. Rec. IEEE-PESC*, pp. 242-252, 1980.

[24] A. Alesina and M. G. B. Venturini, "Solid-state power conversion: A Fourier analysis approach to generalized transformer synthesis," *IEEE Trans. Circuits Syst.*, vol. CAS-28, no. 4, pp. 319-330, 1981.

[25] X. Ma, "High-performance frequency changers," *IEEE Trans. Ind. Appl.*, vol. IA-22, no. 2, pp. 267-280, 1986.

[26] W. McMurray, "Survey of controlled electronic power converters," in *1st IFAC Symp. Control in Power Electronics and Electrical Drives*, Survey Papers, pp. 39-62, 1974.

[27] —, "Frequency converter technology for aircraft power systems," *J. Energy*, vol. 6, no. 5, pp. 328-333, 1982.

Paper 2.3

Power Electronics Diversity

MOTOHISA NISHIHARA

Hitachi Research Laboratory, Hitachi, Ltd.
4026 Kuji-cho, Hitachi-shi, Ibaraki-ken 319-12 JAPAN

Abstract - Power electronics are being employed in a broad range of areas, e.g. electric power utilities, manufacturing industries, transportation, automobiles, home appliances, information, aerospace, etc. The historical progress leading to this diversity is described from the viewpoints of fundamental technologies and applications. Then, a general review of future prospects for power electronics is presented and the indispensability of the technology is emphasized .

I. INTRODUCTION

The origin of power electronics is commonly given as the development and introduction of thyristors by General Electric Company in 1957. However, its roots, in fact, date back to the invention of the single-phased bridge circuit by Graetz at the end of the 19th century.

Fig. 1 shows the historical and predicted trends of needs for power electronics and their application areas. Before the invention of thyristors, motor generators or mercury-arc rectifiers were employed. However, a number of problems were associated with them including difficulties and complications in servicing and maintenance, short lifetime and large equipment size. Thyristors were developed then to fulfill demands for labor and size reductions, and extension of lifetime.

Many products using thyristors such as static Leonard devices for steel industry, chopper controlled rolling stocks for transportation and HVDC converters for electric power system have been put into practical use.

Demands in the 1970's after twice experiencing oil crises prompted energy-saving efforts and the development of inverter technology to provide higher performance, lower energy consumption and more efficient operations of the equipment. The inverter technology has enabled wide range variable-speed control of AC motors, and has been widely applied from home appliances to industrial applications including air conditioners, rolling stocks, elevators, rolling mills and so on.

In conjunction with the development of power devices such as power transistors, MOS FETs and GTOs, VLSIs, as typified by microcomputers, have made remarkable progress, allowing control technology to shift from analog to digital. Multi-variable control techniques have also been introduced in addition to PID control, to provide quicker response and higher accuracy. Technical progress in power devices, power converters and VLSIs for their control moved along the lines of providing compact and miniaturized products. Consequently, application areas of power electronics rapidly expanded to many fields including power utilities, transportation, home appliances, information, aircraft/aerospace, and automobile industries. Truly, today is an era of power electronics diversity.

II. PROGRESS IN POWER ELECTRONICS TECHNOLOGY

Technology generically referred to as power electronics is a merger of three fundamental technologies comprising (i) power semiconductor device technology, (ii) power conversion technology and (iii) control technology. This section describes progress in these fundamental technologies.

Reprinted with permission from *Int. Power Electron. Conf. (IPEC) Rec.*, vol. 1, pp. 21-28, April 1990.

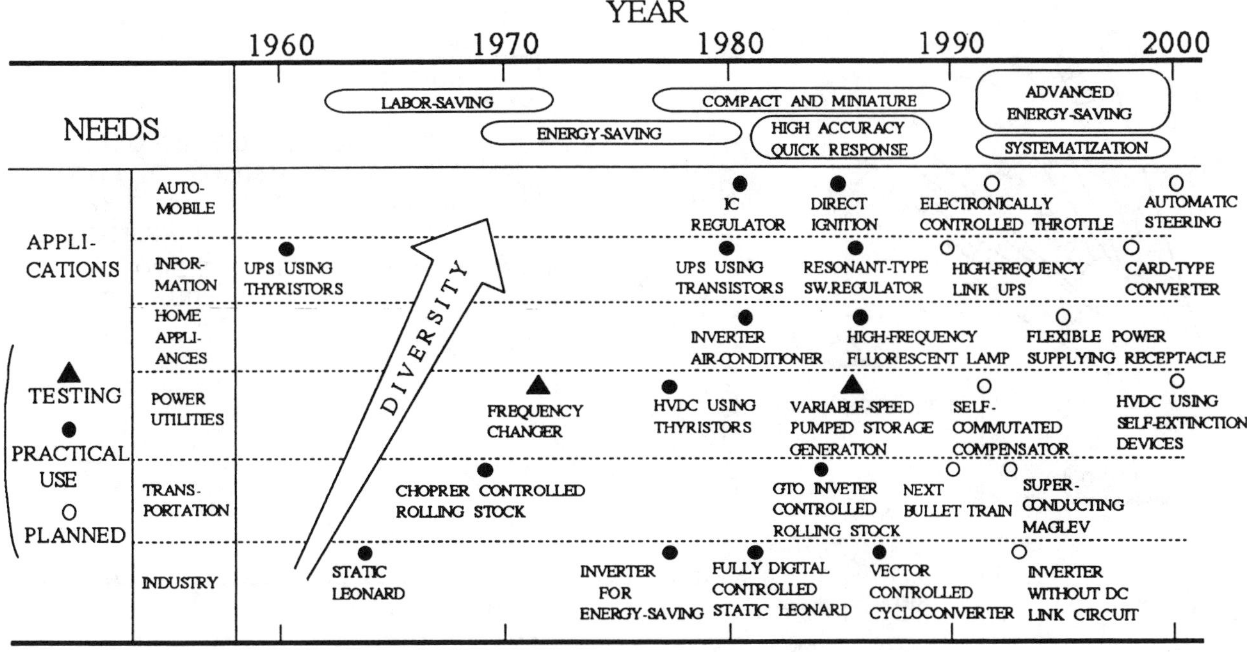

Fig. 1. Historical and predicted trends of power electronics applications.

Power Semiconductor Devices

Progress in power semiconductor devices accelerated progress in power electronics, which in turn, is facilitating further advancements in power semiconductor devices. Fig. 2 shows the transition in handling power, operation frequency and types of power semiconductor devices. During the 1970's, thyristors, GTO thyristors and bipolar transistors constituted the primary power semiconductor devices, while MOSFETs were still too new to enjoy wide applications. Thyristors with increased capacity were employed in HVDC transmission power converters. As regards improvement in capability of switching frequency, power converters with switching frequency of 1 to 2kHz using bipolar transistors played a main role. During the 1980's major advances deserving special mention here include (i) reduction of on -resistance of power MOSFETs, and increase in handling power, (ii) higher voltage and larger current of GTO thyristors, (iii) development of bipolar-MOS hybrid devices such as IGBTs, and (iv) increase in capacity of power ICs and expansion of their applications.

MOSFETs with high speed, large safety operation area and easy drive, are employed for a broad range of uses such as high frequency switching regulators and high precision control of motors. In addition, progress in fine patterning process and in device design technologies have allowed the production of GTO thyristors with high voltage and large current. Consequently, GTO thyristors are versatilely employed for high power converters for rolling stocks or rolling mills. GTO thyristors, as compared with thyristors, provide reduced size and improved efficiency of power converters.

IGBTs comprised of bipolar and MOS devices are much more suited to higher voltage and larger current than MOSFETs, and they are also capable of switching at higher speeds than bipolar transistors. IGBTs can operate above audible frequencies, which facilitates the reduction of noise and offers better output control for power converters. In addition, recently, MCTs(MOS controlled thyristors) comprised of a MOSFET and a thyristor have been developed. These are expected to be yet another device with higher voltage and larger current capacity.

In the future, GTO thyristors may supersede thyristors in the large power converters. More power semiconductor devices having easy

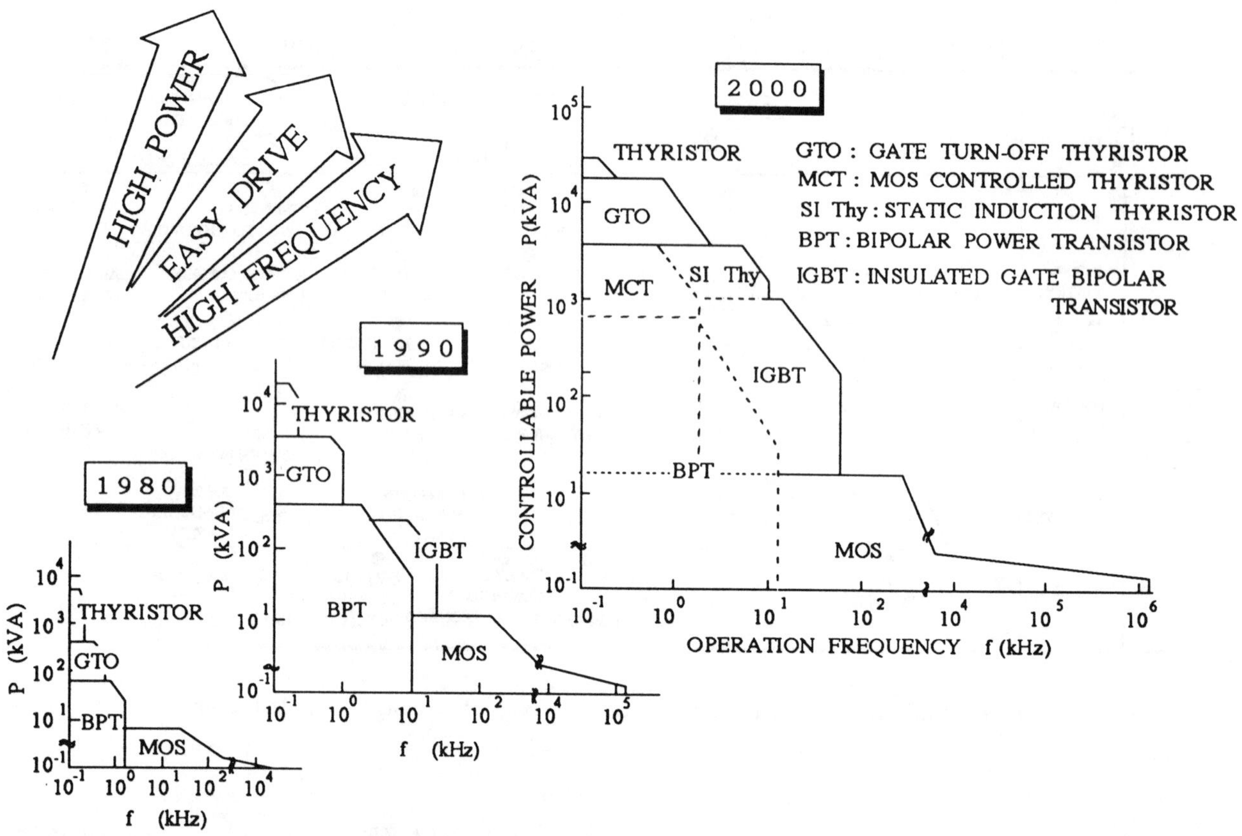

Fig. 2. Territory in power semiconductor devices.

driving ability like MCTs and SI thyristors will be put into practical use. IGBTs and MOSFETs are also expected to have increased capacity and high frequency switching capability, while bipolar transistors will be gradually replaced by these power semiconductor devices in the future.

The IGBTs and MCTs may tend to increase in capacity; both are expected to attain further technological progress, the former with increases in higher frequency switching capability, and the latter with higher voltage and larger current aided by easy driving ability equivalent to that of MOSFET devices.

Power ICs, differing from the former discrete devices, integrate a system on the chip and have a potential to influence various areas of power electronics. Static induction thyristors are also expected to carve their applicational niche in larger capacity and higher frequency switching uses.

Power Converters

Power converters are broadly classified into motor drive and power supply uses. Topics to be studied concerning power converters are the reduction of their sizes and weight, improvement of their efficiency, and in particular, high accuracy, quick response and wide range controls of output voltage, current or frequency. The size and performance of power converters are closely related to the performance of power semiconductor devices. For example, the volume of general-purpose inverters was reduced to one-third of the original volume simply by substituting bipolar transistors for thyristors. The maximum output frequency increased from 60Hz for thyristors to 360Hz for bipolar transistors. It will be possible to increase the output frequency above 1 kHz by using IGBTs or MOSFETs.

So far, many kinds of power converters have been developed and put into practical use.

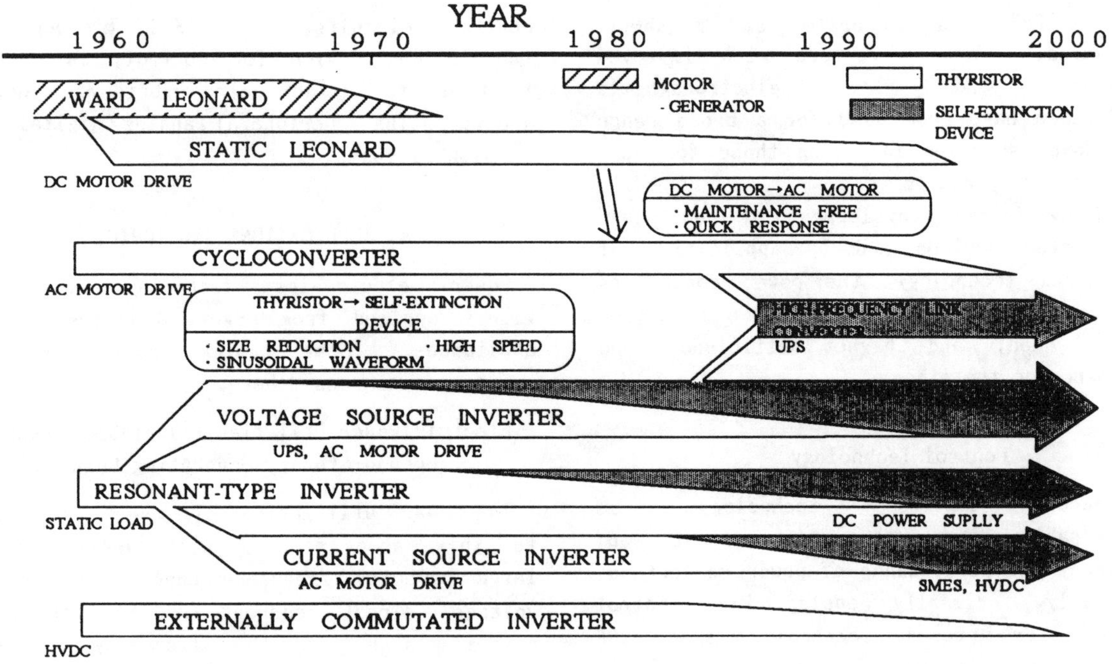

Fig. 3. Historical and predicted trends of power converters.

Fig. 3 shows the historical and predicted trends of power converters. With reference to the area of motor control, DC motors were primarily used for rolling mills or rolling stocks which would require variable-speed drives. Speeds of DC motors can be simply controlled by varying the voltages applied to them. For that purpose, static Leonard equipment, i.e. a thyristor phase-controlled rectifier, or chopper is widely utilized as a power converter. DC motors, however, are nowadays often being substituted by AC motors in that commutators and brushes on the former require regular maintenance and inspection, and the former have manufacturing limits, especially for high-speed and large-capacity machines.

In the speed control of AC motors, on the other hand, not only voltage but also frequency and phase-angle must be adjusted. Therefore, AC motor control is more complicated as compared with DC motors. Cycloconverters and inverters are used as power converters for AC motors.

Cycloconverters have been recently employed for rolling mill drives in addition to applications to fan and cement kiln drives, thanks to the quicker response in speed control realized by the introduction of vector control. In cycloconverters, however, the power factor of the utility line is low and the line currents have many harmonics. Therefore, they may gradually be replaced by inverters in the future.

There are two types of inverters; voltage source type and current source type. Both types now employ self-extinction devices such as bipolar power transistors, IGBTs or GTO thyristors providing input/output sinusoidal waveforms for versatile applications. The voltage source inverter, which has been so far employed for an uninterruptible power supply (UPS) and AC motor drives, is today's leader in power converters. The current source inverter, capable of regenerating power into the utility lines, has been primarily used for AC motor drives for table rollers in steel making lines and elevators where frequent variable-speed operation has been required from the viewpoint of energy saving. This current source inverter will also be employed for superconducting magnetic energy storage systems in the future.

There is also a resonant type inverter which uses the resonant phenomenon for commutation. This inverter, at first, was used for static loads such as induction heating. Compact new resonant type inverters using MOSFETs can operate at megahertz frequencies. These inverters with improved efficiency and low electromagnetic interference have been used for a broad range of DC power supplies including those for host computers and OA equipment.

Aided by further development of new power semiconductor devices and by application of new control technology, the power converters are expected to attain further size reduction on one hand, and higher efficiency and performance on the other.

Control Technology

Advanced control technology is indispensable to the improvement of efficiency and performance of power converters.

Initially, primarily analog PID control employed for process control played the leading role. It was desired, however, that the PID system, which had several drawbacks including a large temperature drift and necessity of making adjustments in many parts, be switched over to the digital control system. The introduction of microcomputers immediately saw their employment for control circuits of power converters. Next came ASIC microcomputers which are more suited to customers' specific demands.

The first microcomputers lacked adequate computation speeds and were barely able to perform PID control digitally. Later, multi-variable control employing state variable formulation, aided by the advanced technology to operate microcomputers at high speed, led to a highly accurate control system of power converters. Since the multi-variable control centralizes control functions in a system, its response time tends to increase in proportion to system complexity. This is where the distributed control has been conceived. In addition, recently, an intelligent AI control has been developed, which, instead of solving equations arithmatically, interprets the state value as knowledge and information. An example of such an application is typified by a fuzzy control system developed for rolling mills to produce extra high quality plates or subways to improve riding comfort in rolling stocks.

Through efforts extended to reduce the size and improve the efficiency and performance of control circuits, the ASIC microcomputer, today's key device for control, is expected to lead to large-scaled hybrid ASIC devices incorporating peripheral analog/digital conversion circuits.

II. APPLICATIONS AND TOPICS

Power electronics technology has been widely applied from power utilities to home appliances. Some typical applications and topics are discussed here.

Electric Power Utilities - Variable Speed Pumped-Storage Generating Unit

In Japan utilization of power electronics to this area started with application to large capacity frequency converters and high voltage direct current (HVDC) transmission systems such as the frequency converter stations in Sakuma and Shin Shinano and the HVDC links between Hokkaido and Honshu.

At present, variable speed pumped-storage generating units are drawing interest as a means of load leveling of electric power systems. The pumped-storage generating units utilize surplus power at midnight to operate turbines as pumps and store water in a reservoir at an elevated location. Then, during daytime heavy loads, water thus stored is used for power generation.

In conventional pumped-storage generating units, pump turbines would only operate at a constant speed, consequently making power adjustments almost impossible. Here, if only the turbines' rotating speeds can be changed freely, input power also can be changed accordingly, facilitating power adjustments. In fact, in variable speed pumped-storage generating units, pump turbines' rotating speed is controlled by AC excitation over their rotors. Cycloconverters are used for the AC excitation and their output frequency is adjusted according to the desired turbines' speed. Cycloconverters have many advantages, as they can change turbines' speeds flexibly responding to load demands, and can generate electricity at the most efficient speed.

Transportation - Superconducting Magnetic Levitated Railway System

The history of technical development of

rolling stock has been the pursuit of high speed and energy-saving. Power electronics technology has again played an important role in the realization of the Bullet trains. The primary technical innovation to realize extra high speed propulsion has been the development of large capacity converters. The first Bullet trains adopted the DC motor drive system using converters with diode bridges of 1.7MVA. The Tohoku and Joetsu Bullet trains have adopted phase control bridges employing 2.5-kV, 1-kA thyristors. In addition, new Bullet trains, scheduled for operation at much higher speed, are expected to employ inverter-controlled induction motors instead of DC motors. The AC motor system is expected to adopt the voltage source PWM inverter employing 4.5-kV, 3-kA GTO thyristors.

Recently, the superconducting magnetic levitated railway system is arousing wide interest. This system, when completed, will enable trains to run with speeds up to 500km/h maximum, to travel the distance between Tokyo and Osaka in an hour and transport 100,000 passengers daily. This super high speed railway is expected to employ linear synchronous motors. A number of propulsion coils will be placed on the ground, while superconducting magnets will be placed on board. The train is driven by applying voltage to the propulsion coils from the power converters on the ground. The frequency of the applied voltage will be adjusted in proportion to the travelling speed. In order to apply the voltage only to the propulsion coils at the train position, the coils to be energized must be switched on and off one after another. For that reason, power converters should be placed at intervals of every few tens of kilometers. The train thus travels across the power energized regions.

The power converter for this particular purpose should be a large capacity inverter of 50 to 100MVA, comprised of several unit inverters in which a number of large capacity GTO thyristors are connected in series.

Computer - Power Supply Unit

In recent year, the power supply unit occupies almost one-half of the space inside main frame computers. Therefore, miniaturizing the power supply unit is very important. Primary requirements for the power supply unit in addition to the more compact and efficient unit are that it must be capable of supplying power non-stop during any period of service. Such a reliable power supply has already been realized by an uninterruptible power supply (UPS). The UPS consists of a redundant system for emergency back up, and essentially is comprised of voltage source type inverters. In the efforts to reduce the size of the UPS, a high frequency link between the primary and secondary sides has been developed, whereby feeding 20kHz at the primary side, 50 or 60Hz waveforms are generated through a cycloconverter in the secondary side.

The CPU power supply unit formerly employed a motor-generator as its power source because of the specific requirements for the low voltage and large current output (3V, 500A for example). Recently, however, thanks to the advancement of power electronics, highly reliable DC-DC converters have been developed to replace the motor-generator, though they still need to be made more compact. Increasing switching frequencies may be a solution to make them smaller. For example, with the switching frequency increased to 1MHz, the volume of the DC-DC converter can be reduced to one-seventh of the volume at 20kHz.

It is predicted that a card-type power source will be much in demand for use in future personal computers and OA equipment, as these products become thinner and lighter weight. Further miniaturization of passive parts and the development of more efficient power ICs will promote this advancement.

Home Appliance - Room Air Conditioners

Home appliances are also benefiting from power electronics advances. All season room air conditioners, for example, are one of the main products in this area which owes much to this technology. Primary requirements of room air conditioners with heat pumps include energy savings, operation at high capacity from the start of comfort cooling or heating, and quieter operation.

Air conditioners employ three motors including a compressor motor, outdoor fan motor and indoor fan motor. The compressor motor, employing a PWM (pulse width modulation) inverter operative with a variable speed control, contributes to the energy savings and quieter operation. Referring to energy savings, continuous control of the compressor motor by the inverter realizes a 20% cut in overall power consumption as compared with the conventional on-off control system.

Because the compressor's load varies to a great extent according to the revolving position, mechanical vibrations are produced causing noise. To reduce such noise, recently, a new control system is being applied. The new system makes motor torque conform to compressor torque by means of a learning control. This system functions to reduce the range of speed variation of the compressor, hence reducing the mechanical vibrations. Consequently, it realizes a reduction of noise by 5dB as compared with conventional systems.

In the future, the speed control range of the compressor will be expanded in order to improve its capacity. In such a case, the outdoor fan motor should be controlled by means of an inverter to be synchronized with the speed of the compressor operating under variable speed control. The indoor fan motor will have to be capable of continuously adjusting and controlling the amount of air to be supplied for greater user comfort.

Automobiles - Impacts of Power Electronics Technology

The introduction of power electronics technology into the area of automobiles started with the application of power transistors to the maintenance-free contact-less ignition. Since the oil crises in the 1970's, more efforts relating to the application of power electronics have been centered around energy-savings and low exhaust gas emission. As a result, microcomputer control of engines has been introduced. The microcomputer optimizes fuel injection, ignition timing, recirculation of exhaust gas, and so on, through the adequate control of their actuators. Electric vehicles once actively studied as non-polluting vehicles in the 1970's employed chopper controlled DC motors and inverter-controlled AC motors. They have not, however, advanced to a practical stage yet because of their weight and economic disadvantages.

Lately, with demand growing for more luxury, greater driving comfort and safety, there is a marked tendency for power electronics and microcomputers to be introduced into a broader range of uses. For example, an electronically controlled throttle system under development is intended to control engine output precisely by means of air mass flow control. An electronic automatic transmission system is designed to control clutch hydraulic pressures so as to eliminate backlash. An active suspension system controls damping characteristics of shock absorbers according to the road condition.

The IC regulators which have been applied from an early stage to the control of alternator output, will tend to become more multifunctional as they will be required to satisfy the whole automobile power supply. The trend for circuit integration of car electronics including power devices is expected to continue.

The demands for mobile communication and information equipment such as a telephone, TV, facsimile, navigation system, and so on are growing and will continue to do so in the future. For this reason, a number of robust, reliable power ICs and application specific ICs are being developed for use on board.

Power ICs - Their Applications

Lately power ICs have been introduced into a wide range of application areas as shown in Fig. 4, because they are able to satisfy growing demands for compactness, cost reduction, and improved reliability of power control systems.

The introduction of power ICs started with application to audio-visual (AV) instruments in an attempt to miniaturize the sizes of cassette tape recorders, audio amplifiers or television units. Now, they have come to be used in VTRs and OA equipment on a large scale.

They are also finding applications in miniature motors for floppy disk or hard disk drives, and in other driving circuits for printer heads, electroluminescent or plasma display panels, in addition to the car electronics as previously referred to. However, most of these power ICs are of pn-junction isolation types, and cannot be used for high voltage applications.

On the other hand, high voltage power ICs

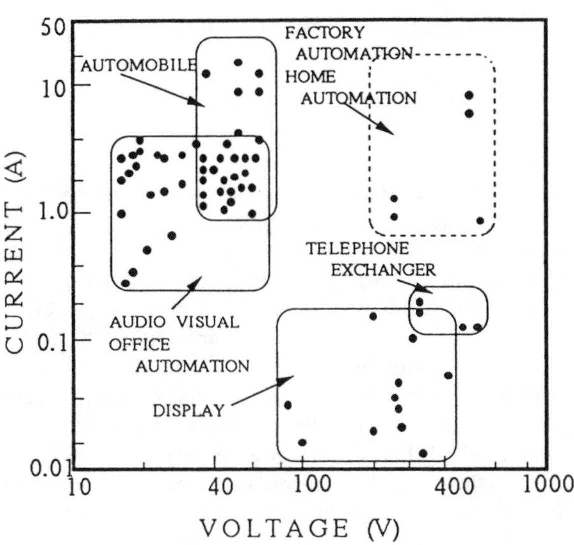

Fig. 4. Application areas of power ICs.

Fig. 5. Micro-photograph of 250-V,1-A three-phase monolithic inverter IC.

adopting the dielectric isolation method were used in the early stage for the subscriber line interface circuit (SLIC) in telephone exchangers. Now a fully solid state circuit has been introduced with improved reliability.

Power ICs were seldom employed for home appliances which would require rather high voltages(100/200V) for operation. Lately, however, the introduction of advanced isolation technology has prompted the development of one-chip inverter ICs to be used for brushless motors of a few tens of watts, which are expected to provide for a broad range of applications. Fig. 5 shows a micro-photograph of a 250-V, 1-A three-phase monolithic inverter IC. IGBTs are employed in the main circuit.

Low voltage ICs are expected to be employed for much broader areas of applications in the future including AV equipment, OA equipment and automobiles. High voltage ICs may have a bigger voltage capacity so as to be able to accept 200V. Power ICs in general are expected to attain much higher intelligence including self-protection, self-diagnosis, programability, communication functions, etc.

Ⅳ. SUMMARY

Diversity of power electronics will continue into new application areas. Power electronics have been accepted as one of the key technologies indispensable to almost any type of advanced systems. Power electronics have played important roles in energy savings in many applications including electric power utilities, transportation, automobiles, home appliances, and manufacturing industries. Thus, they may contribute to mitigation of global warming in the future. Power electronics are also essential to new energy systems, considering inverters operating in power utility lines with fuel cells or solar cells and power supplies for excitation of superconducting coils in nuclear fusion systems.

Power electronics will continue to progress as a vital technology, and provide more comfortable lives for everyone.

Power Electronics in the Minicomputer Industry

WILLIAM W. BURNS, III, MEMBER, IEEE, AND JOHN KOCIECKI, MEMBER, IEEE

Invited Paper

An overview of modern minicomputer power systems is presented. Requirements placed on the power systems by computer loads, power source characteristics, and product market forces are described. A brief review of the genesis of switching power converter technologies in the minicomputer industry is presented. Based on power and packaging considerations, four distinct types of computers are identified: laptop computers, workstations, rack-mount systems, and superminicomputers. The attributes of each of these types of computers, as they relate to power system requirements, are described, and the power system architectures and technologies which meet these requirements are presented. The paper concludes with a discussion of the basic technologies which are currently being explored as the vehicles for meeting new performance goals and product requirements.

INTRODUCTION

Remarkable advances in integrated semiconductor logic circuits and memory devices have helped to reduce the size and cost of modern minicomputers to a point where individuals can afford powerful computers packaged in small desktop enclosures, and large computer users can get the computing power they need at attractive prices and in packages suitable for office environments. In order to function properly, these complex electronic machines require precisely regulated electrical power at specified voltage levels and profiles. However, the sources of electrical power normally available to the machines do not match these requirements. They may be worldwide utility voltages with their attendant variations, battery systems, diesel motor generator sets, or a number of other unconventional sources of power. It is the challenge of the power electronics engineer to develop the electronic interface which matches the numerous variations in the characteristics of the sources of energy to the characteristics of the computer loads.

When computers were first developed and experimental in nature, they were bulky and expensive, and the physical attributes of the power supply were not a concern. However, as progress was made in both computer technology and market development, the size, cost, and performance of a product's power system became more of a factor. Today, the design of a computer's power system can have a significant affect on the market appeal of the product.

Interest in improving the characteristics of computer power systems began in the early 1970s, as minicomputers began to penetrate many new markets. At that time, power system designers began to take advantage of some of the research which had been done for aerospace and military power systems, and high density "switching" power supplies began to replace more conventional "linear" power supplies. As the benefits of these new technologies were recognized, computer companies realized that investments in power system technologies, in addition to semiconductor and memory technologies, were also needed for their success. Today, most large computer companies make substantial investments in power system design groups, and some even support research projects for power electronics development.

The purpose of this paper is to review the current state of technology in modern minicomputer power systems, and to look at what work is planned for future developments in this field. The nature of the problem is explored first, with an examination of the requirements which modern computer systems place on their power systems. Next, the evolution of computer power system architectures and technologies is explored to help put today's technologies into perspective. The bulk of the paper focuses on the challenges and solutions for powering today's complex computer systems, from both the "market pull" and the "technology push" perspectives.

COMPUTER POWER SYSTEM REQUIREMENTS

Load Characteristics

Since the primary function of a computer power system is to match the electrical characteristics of the source to the load, the design of the power system is, of course, influenced by both. Load characteristics of a typical computer system are summarized in Table 1. The power level of each of these loads is dependent on the type of system. Modern

Manuscript received July 24, 1987; revised January 14, 1988.

W. W. Burns, III, is with the Power and Environmental Engineering Department, Data General Corporation, Westboro, MA 01580, USA.

J. Kociecki was with Data General Corporation, Westboro, MA. He is now with A. L. E. Systems, Inc., Ashland, MA 01721, USA.

IEEE Log Number 8820252.

Reprinted from *Proc. IEEE*, vol. 76, no. 4, pp. 311–324, April 1988.

Table 1 Load Characteristics of a Typical Computer System

Computer Subsystem	Type of Assembly	Voltage (Vdc)		Usage	Load Profile
CPU (logic)	printed circuit boards	5.0 −5.2 −2.0	±5% ±5% ±5%	TTL ECL ECL	up to 10% step changes in less than 10 μs
RAM memory	printed circuit boards	5.0 −5.2 −2.0	±5% ±5% ±5%	TTL ECL ECL	up to 50% step changes in less than 1 ms
I/O control	printed circuit boards	5.0 ±12.0	±5% ±10%	TTL analog	up to 10% step changes in less than 10 μs
Mass storage	tape and disk drives	5.0 ±12.0	±5% ±10%	TTL analog, motors	large turn on surge and up to 150% step change in less than 10 ms
Display	CRT monitor	5.0 12.0 HV	±5% ±5%	TTL analog, tube bias and focus	relatively constant
Input	keyboard	5.0	±5%	TTL	relatively constant

minicomputers employ logically dense gate arrays which consume 10–20 W of power each, which can lead to circuit board dissipations of 100–300 W. An example of such a computer circuit board is shown in Fig. 1.

Disk drives often present transient load problems for the power system. Current surges of 150 percent of the steady-state load can be required to bring the storage media up to speed or to quickly position the read/write heads for data transfers. These surge conditions can last many milliseconds, and must be considered in the design of the power supply. If this surge condition is not accommodated, the power supply voltage will sag out of regulation and cause the system to shut down.

Source Characteristics

There is a similar diversity of requirements imposed on the computer power system by the source of power. Table 2 gives a listing of the various power utility voltages which are found around the world. Since most computers are marketed throughout the world, attempts are made to develop universal power systems so that one system can be designed and manufactured rather than developing different products for each country. However, this leads to some signif-

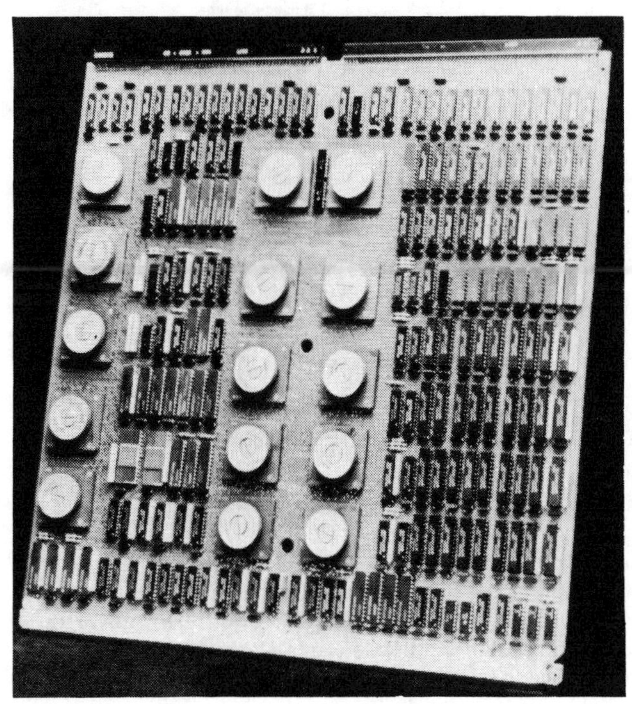

Fig. 1. Computer printed circuit board assembly.

Table 2 Listing of Various Worldwide Power Utility Voltages

Country	Frequency (Hz)	Residential Voltage (*V*)	Commercial Voltage (*V*)
Australia	50	240	240/415 wye
Brazil	60	127/220	220/380 wye, 220 delta
Continental Europe	50	220	220/380 wye
Israel	50	230	230/400 wye
Japan (East)	50	100/200	200 delta
Japan (West)	60	100/200	200 delta
North America	60	120/240	120/208 wye
United Kingdom	50	240	240/415 wye

icant tradeoffs in terms of size, cost, and performance, and cannot be achieved in all cases.

In addition to the variations in voltage and frequency of worldwide power sources, the computer power system must also be able to accommodate power line transients and outages. This topic has received considerable attention over the past two decades [1]–[4], and is the subject of an IEEE Standard [5]. In this standard, two waveforms are proposed as being representative of the disturbances which any line powered equipment, located in typical building environments, should be able to withstand. These waveforms are shown in Fig. 2. Failure to accommodate these

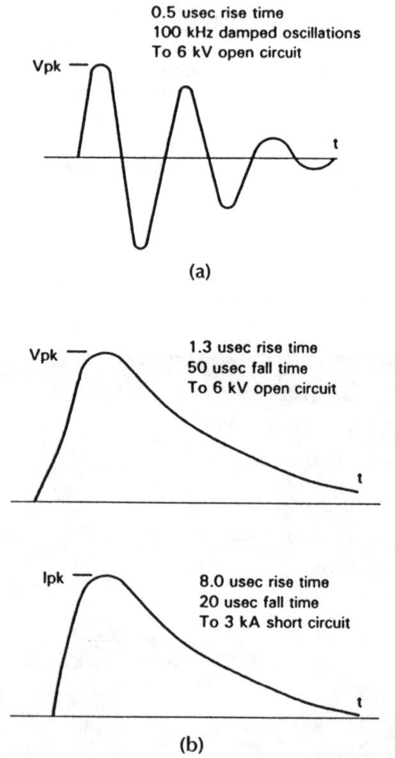

Fig. 2. IEEE 587 line transient test waveforms. (a) Ring wave. (b) Unipolar wave.

conditions in the design of a power system could lead to unreliable operation and customer dissatisfaction.

Also to be considered when designing for power source variations is the power system's response to power outages. The designer must determine if the computer should be partially backed up with batteries to ride through short outages, or if it should be completely backed up with an uninterruptable power system (UPS). These decisions can be made correctly only if the designer has a thorough understanding of the function of the complete computer system and its particular application.

Market Requirements

In addition to designing a power system which accommodates the characteristics of the load and the source, other requirements are imposed on a designer by the market for which the product is developed. These requirements are sometimes driven by customer appeal, such as size and cost of the product, whereas others are a result of government or independent regulatory agency standards. Examples of the latter include design practices which must be followed in order to have the product listed or certified by Underwriters Laboratories (UL), the Canadian Standards Association (CSA), and the equivalent German agency, VDE, as meeting safety requirements, or VDE and the Federal Communications Commission (FCC) for meeting electromagnetic interference (EMI) standards [6]–[10]. In order to meet some of these requirements, new technologies, such as opto-couplers with improved isolation capabilities and new EMI filtering techniques, have been and continue to be developed. Others are being met through a thorough understanding of the standards documents and careful attention to details in a system implementation. When considered as a whole, meeting all of these requirements presents a formidable task to the power system designer, and many design tradeoffs must be made.

Historical Perspective

Whereas the invention of the semiconductor integrated circuit brought sudden and dramatic improvements in the size, cost and performance of computers, it also brought with it more stringent requirements for the computer's power system. More precise regulation of the supply voltages and carefully planned protection features became critical to the operation of these powerful new machines. Early minicomputer power supplies consisted of utility-line-frequency transformers for the high to low voltage transformation, followed by rectifiers and linear dissipative regulators. The low-frequency transformers were sometimes linear and sometimes ferroresonant regulated (also known as constant voltage transformers or CVTs), but always big and heavy. In addition, the inefficiency of the linear regulators required using large heat sinks for cooling, thereby adding even more to the size and weight of the power supply. As long as computers themselves were large and bulky, large power supplies did not present a problem. However, as computing circuitry became smaller through advances in semiconductor processing, bulky and inefficient power supplies became unacceptable.

Fortunately, work sponsored during the 1960s by the U.S. Navy, NASA, and other aerospace organizations led to practical "switching" power supply technologies which enabled dramatic reductions in the size, weight, and efficiency of computer power systems [11]–[13]. Significant work on switching power converter techniques had been done many years earlier [14], [15], but the lack of an efficient high-frequency power switch limited the practical application of these techniques until the power transistor and the silicon controlled rectifier (SCR) became available in the 1950s. These new semiconductor switches enabled the development of multikilohertz switching power converters which used transformers and filter components which were much smaller than their 60-Hz counterparts. Also, it was found that pulsewidth and pulse frequency modulation techniques could be used to control these switching power converters and regulate their outputs, thereby providing a very efficient alternative to series or shunt dissipative regulators. With these developments, the stage was set for advancing the state of the art in commercial power electronics technology.

The history of these early developments in switching

power supply technology is replete with examples of creative engineers developing new circuits to take advantage of evolving components, and component engineers developing new devices to meet evolving application needs. These complementary efforts were key factors in the rapid progress which was made during the 1960s and 1970s. In addition, new analysis and design techniques were developed in the 1970s to help power electronics engineers use these new technologies effectively [16]–[19]. As a result of these advances, switching power supplies began appearing in minicomputer systems in the mid-1970s.

At first, low-voltage dc-to-dc converters, or switching regulators, replaced the linear regulators on the secondary side of the line-frequency transformers. These converters achieved regulation by varying the duty cycle of the power switch rather than by dropping excess voltage across a "variable resistance" transistor as in the case of the linear regulator. This approach improved power system efficiency, but the bulky line-frequency step-down transformers remained. Very soon thereafter high voltage (500–1000 Vceo) power switching transistors became available and enabled the development of high-frequency (20–50-kHz) "direct-off-line" switching power supplies. Off-line switchers, as they have come to be known, rectify the utility line directly, without any step-down transformers, and filter the rectified input with large electrolytic capacitors. This unregulated dc voltage is chopped into a high-frequency square wave so that a much smaller transformer can be used to change the voltage level. The regulation function can be accomplished through controlling the duty cycle of the power switches. Thus, both the large step-down transformers and the inefficient linear regulators are eliminated with this technology. Fig. 3 illustrates the impact of switching converter technology on the size of a typical minicomputer power supply.

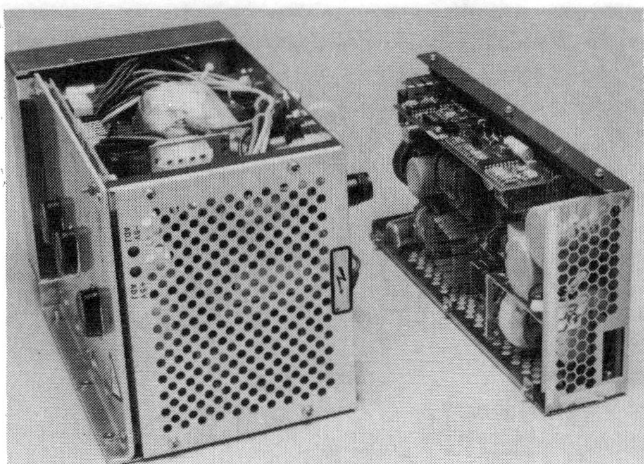

Fig. 3. Comparison of a 150-W multi-output linear power supply (left, circa 1973) and a 150-W multi-output direct-off-line switching power supply (right, circa 1983).

The early years of switching power supply design were fraught with problems. The high-voltage high-frequency power transistors were not yet fully understood, and unexplained failures were common and exasperating. Eventually, new operating characteristics, such as reverse biased second breakdown, were discovered and accommodated [20]–[23], and most of these problems are now just memories. Another common problem was that of electromagnetic interference (EMI). Switching hundreds of volts and tens of amperes in a few microseconds made previously negligible parasitic circuit inductances and capacitances quite significant, and electromagnetic emissions skyrocketed. In fact, many noise-sensitive devices, such as high-density disk drives, were not able to use switching power supplies during these early years. The problem was so severe that new companies were formed to offer services as EMI consultants. Since that time, much progress has been made in understanding and resolving this problem, but controlling EMI is still a major challenge for power system designers.

As power electronics engineers became more comfortable with the technology, and as system designers became more appreciative of the benefits of switching power supplies, more research and development was done on power electronics technology for computer applications. As a result, numerous options became available to the power electronics engineer for reaching design objectives. Many different power circuit "topologies" were proposed and evaluated for use in various minicomputer systems. The most frequently used circuits were the "flyback" for applications requiring less than 150 W, the "forward" converter for applications in the 150–500-W range, and the "half-bridge" for applications requiring more than 500 W [24]. The operation of all of these converters is based on the fundamental principles of "chopping" an unregulated dc voltage into a high-frequency quasi-square wave, changing the voltage level by means of a high-frequency transformer, and rectifying and filtering the transformed square wave to yield the desired dc voltage. Regulation of this voltage against changes in line and load conditions is accomplished through pulse-width modulation (PWM) techniques. Numerous variations of these basic square-wave switching converters have been proposed over the years [25], but the majority of applications in the minicomputer industry have relied on the flyback, forward, and half-bridge converters.

Today, experienced power electronics engineers in the minicomputer industry have a wealth of tools and knowledge at their fingertips. They are in a position to make design tradeoffs at the system level so that they can help to contribute to the overall market appeal of a new product. The power supply is not an add-on box, but rather it is an integral part of the system, and it is designed differently depending on the product and the market for which it is intended. The next section of this paper describes the power system solutions of today, with special emphasis on the technologies which are necessary to enable these solutions and the market requirements which drive the need for them.

Power Systems in Present-Day Minicomputers

For purposes of discussion in this paper, minicomputer systems are grouped into four distinct categories:

1) laptop, or portable systems,
2) personal computers, or workstations,
3) rack-mount systems intended primarily for OEM (original equipment manufacturer) applications,
4) superminicomputers.

Each of these types of systems is designed for a specific market with specific packaging, cost, and functional requirements. The power systems which are designed for each of these products must also accommodate these requirements and incorporate technologies which optimize the products for their intended markets. A brief description of each of these product categories and their incorporated power technologies follows.

Laptop Systems

Truly portable computers have only been available since the mid-1980s. These machines have been made possible through the development of powerful CMOS microprocessors, high-density 3.5-in disk drives, and flat panel display technologies such as liquid crystal displays (LCD) and electroluminescent (EL) displays. In order to be considered portable, these machines must be able to operate on batteries, weigh no more than 10 lb, and fit into a small carrying case. In addition, the unit should consume less than 50 W of power so that internal cooling fans are not required and several hours of battery powered operation can be sustained. Such a portable system is shown in Fig. 4.

Fig. 4. Portable laptop computer.

A block diagram of a power system which accommodates these requirements is shown in Fig. 5. It should be noted that this system can be powered from rechargeable internal batteries or the ac line. In addition, the unit may be plugged directly into the 12-Vdc power system of an automobile.

The ac line is converted to 12 Vdc through a simple single transistor direct off-line switching power supply such as shown in Fig. 6. This is a single output flyback converter switching at 100 kHz, with PWM regulation provided via a commercially available integrated circuit controller. This "ac power pack" is normally packaged in a detachable housing in order to keep the computer as small and light as possible during portable battery operation.

A multi-output dc-to-dc converter, the batteries, and the battery charger are all packaged in the computer housing.

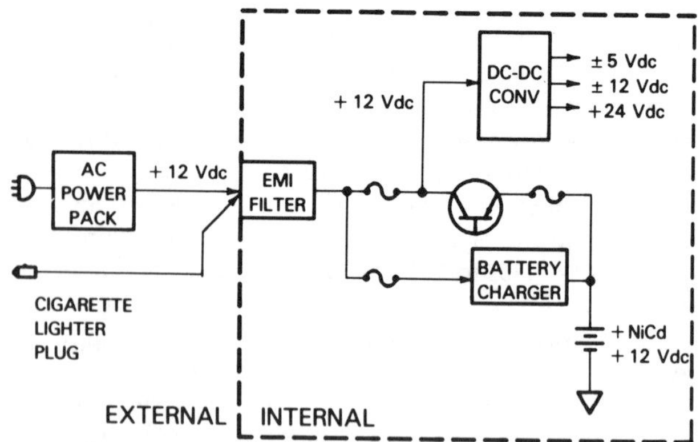

Fig. 5. Laptop computer power system block diagram.

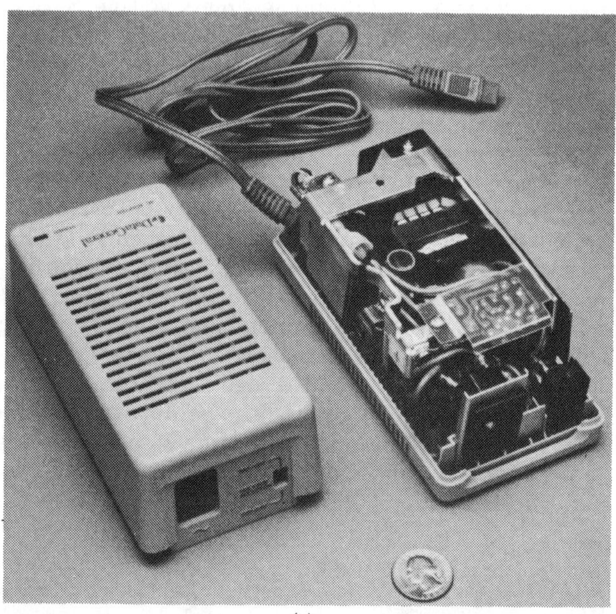

(a)

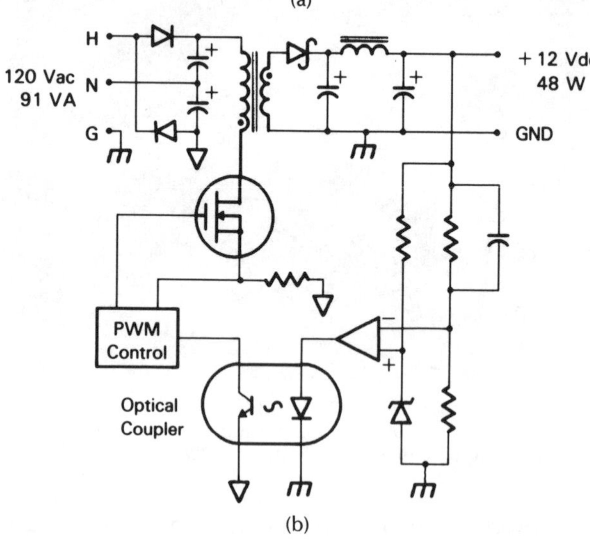

(b)

Fig. 6. (a) Laptop computer ac power pack and (b) schematic diagram.

The dc-to-dc converter converts the 12 Vdc into the regulated voltages needed to power the logic circuits, disk drives, and flat panel display. In order to minimize the size and weight of the dc-to-dc converter, switching frequencies greater than 100 kHz, and surface mount packaging technologies are used. Current, low cost designs for this application achieve a power density of 8 W/in^3, an efficiency of 80 percent and a cost of 50 cents/W. Future work in this area will focus on achieving higher power densities so as to become smaller and lighter, and higher efficiencies to minimize cooling requirements and to increase the time that the system can sustain battery powered operation.

Workstations

As the computer industry entered the 1980s, a new type of machine was introduced which met immediate and surprising success. This type of computer has come to be known by many names, including "personal computer," "small office computer," and "workstation." One common attribute which is found in all of these machines is that they are packaged for the office environment. This means that they must be cooled with "quiet" air movers, they must be able to use conventional power outlets available in the office, and they must be transportable and compatible with office furnishings.

All computer system functions, central processing unit (CPU), disk drives, input/output (I/O) devices, etc., are contained in this single package with a monitor and keyboard attached via cables. The most common approach to powering this type of system is to use multi-output direct-off-line switching power supplies. These multi-output power supplies can range in power from less than 100 W for small personal computers to 750 W for powerful technical workstations with full graphics capabilities. The power supply shown in Fig. 7 is capable of delivering 375 W of power split

Fig. 7. Workstation power supply.

among +5, +12, and −12 Vdc. In order to achieve packaging densities greater than 2 W/in^3, switching frequencies of greater than 100 kHz are employed. In addition, this particular power system was designed to be modular so that the customer can buy an entry level system with one power supply having a 375-W capability and later add a second 375-W module to power additional system components for a total capability of 750 W.

The most significant power system design problem facing this type of product today is encountered in the larger systems. As stated previously, these systems are required to operate in an office environment. Therefore, they must be able to be powered from the commonly available 15-A wall outlets. Underwriters Laboratories requires that the maximum current drawn from this outlet be derated to 80 percent of 15 A, or 12 A, at the nominal line voltage of 120 V. This results in a volt-ampere capability of 1440 VA. Considering the relatively low power factor of capacitive input power supplies (typically 70 percent), and the efficiency of the multi-output power supply (typically 70 percent), a power utilization factor of less than 50 percent results. Therefore, of the 1440 VA available from the 120-V 15-A line, only 720 W of usable power are available to the computer.

In order to increase the amount of power which can be delivered to the system, work has been done to improve power supply efficiencies [26], [27] and to correct power factor. Both passive and active power factor improvement circuits have been discussed in the literature, with performance as high as 90 percent being reported [28]–[30]. Also, some switching power supplies are achieving efficiencies of 80 percent, which in combination with a power factor of 90 percent yields a power utilization factor of 72 percent and thus a power delivery capability of more than 1000 W. These improvements add cost and complexity to the overall system, and must be weighed against the additional performance and functionality which can be delivered by the workstation at the higher power level.

In recent years, personal computers have found wide acceptance in many businesses. As a result, users have become quite dependent on them for many of their job functions, and they cannot afford to lose access to them during power outages. Therefore, it is often necessary to add standby power supplies (SPS) to these machines. The SPS uses batteries as the back-up power source. During normal operation, these batteries are kept fully charged with power from the ac line via an electronic charger. When power line outages are sensed, a dc-to-ac line-frequency sinusoidal inverter is activated and replaces the ac line as the source of power for the computer system. Since all elements of the computer are integrated into one package, the complete system can be backed up simply by connecting the system power cord to the SPS. Capacitive energy storage in the computer holds the system up during the switchover transition from line power to battery power. More conventional uninterruptable power supplies (UPS) can also be used in this application, but they are less efficient because they process power continuously, not just during power outages. Low cost SPS units have been developed for the full range of this type of system, from small personal computers to high performance technical workstations.

Rack-Mount Systems

As the name implies, these systems are designed to mount easily in the cabinet of an "original equipment manufacturer's (OEM)" product such as an automatic test set or a robotic system. The salient characteristics of this type of product, as compared to superminicomputers, are lower cost and minimum features. Functionality is added by the system integrator. To be consistent with these requirements, the power system approach most frequently chosen for this type of product is the multi-output off-line switching power supply.

The power required for this type of system typically ranges from 100 W to 1 kW. It can be powered from a single-phase line for the small systems, or a three-phase line for full systems, including disk drives and other peripherals, which require more than a kilowatt of power in total. These systems usually incorporate higher performance air movers which are not appropriate in office based workstations, and therefore can dissipate more power. A photograph of a typical rack-mount computer chassis with its multi-output off-line switching power supply is shown in Fig. 8. This power supply is a dual forward converter switching at 80 kHz. A schematic diagram of this converter is given in Fig. 9.

Fig. 8. Rack-mount computer chassis with 1-kW power supply.

In addition to providing the fundamental power conversion and regulation requirements for these systems, it is often necessary to provide a battery back-up capability. This is needed when the computer is controlling machinery or other equipment which must remain available to the user during power outages. In order to back-up an off-line switching power supply, a dc-to-dc converter which steps the battery voltage up to the power supply input voltage is required. A block diagram of such a system is shown in Fig. 10. The batteries must be charged while power is available from the line so that they are available to support the system during a power outage. This is a full back-up system in which the entire load continues to receive power. Battery sizing for this application usually achieves 2 min of full power hold-up time which accommodates more than 80 percent of the power outages in the U.S. [2]. Some applications require that only the system memory be powered during a power outage. System memory usually accounts for approximately 5–10 percent of the total system load, so that 10 min of hold-up time can be provided without excessive battery capacity.

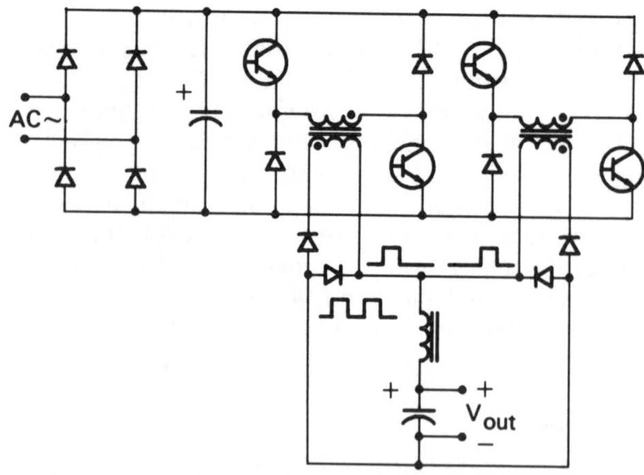

Fig. 9. Dual forward converter used in the rack-mount computer power supply.

Rack-mount computer systems are becoming more powerful while occupying less space. This is due to the many advances being made in semiconductor technology. These trends put similar pressure on the power system designer to reduce the size and cost of the power supply. Therefore, current work in this area includes increasing the switching frequency and conversion efficiency to reduce size, while reducing cost through simpler circuits and component standardization.

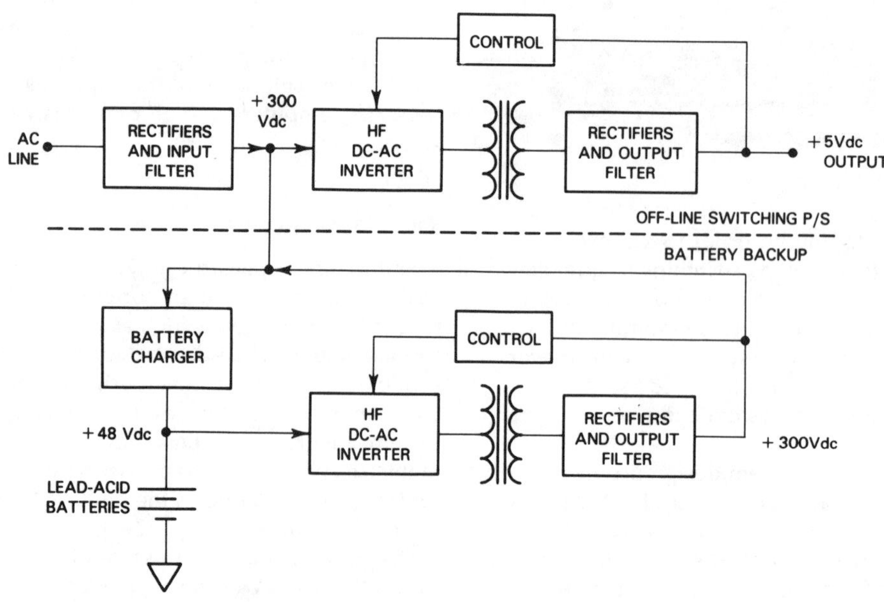

Fig. 10. Voltage step-up, full power battery back-up block diagram.

Superminicomputers

The superminicomputer, first appearing in the late 1970s, is a relative newcomer to the minicomputer industry. Phenomenal advances in semiconductor and electronic storage technologies have enabled the packaging of 12-MIPS (millions of instructions per second) computers in small, single cabinets as shown in Fig. 11. These systems outperform the mainframe computers of the 1970s which cost millions of dollars and required large air-conditioned rooms, with raised floors for cabling and cooling, to house the many cabinets which comprised the system.

Fig. 11. Single cabinet, 12-MIPS superminicomputer.

The power systems for these new superminicomputers have seen similar advances in technology and architectural flexibility [31]. These advances have led to the development of high performance "distributed regulation" power systems. A block diagram of such a distributed power system is shown in Fig. 12. In this approach, the ac line is rectified and converted to an intermediate dc bus voltage, normally in the range of 40–60 Vdc. This dc power bus is distributed to the computer printed circuit board chassis where it supplies power to CPU, memory and I/O cards via board-mounted or adjacent dc-to-dc converters.

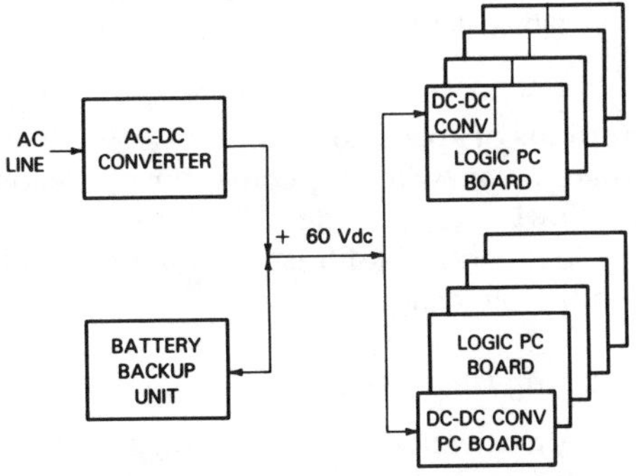

Fig. 12. Distributed power system block diagram.

These distributed converters process tens to hundreds of watts of power as compared to "lumped regulation" power systems in which kilowatts of power are processed in large multi-output converters. Processing power in smaller quantities provides several advantages over the lumped approach. First, higher switching frequencies can be used, thereby reducing the size of the energy storage components in the converters. Secondly, small, modular converters can be developed, using standard components, and assembled via automated manufacturing processes. These "power cells" can be assembled directly on portions of larger system boards as shown in Fig. 13, or they can be prepackaged in encapsulated modules as shown in Fig. 14. The advantage of the assembled-on-board approach is that the cell is cheaper and smaller because of the use of the larger printed circuit board for mounting and interconnecting components. The prepackaged approach, however, yields a versatile, pretested unit which can be placed easily throughout a distributed power system. In both cases, the advantages of the distributed system architecture can be realized.

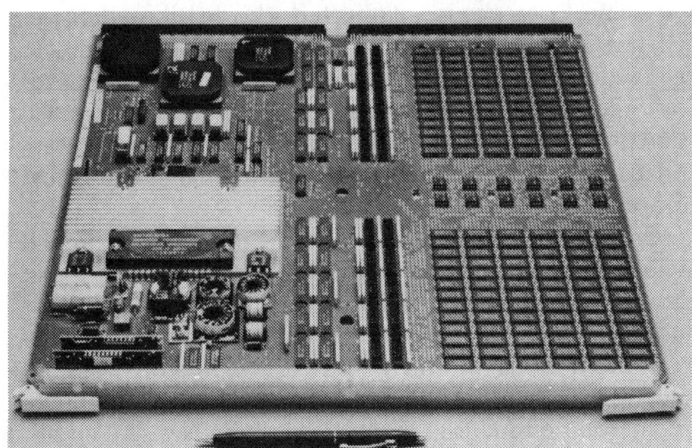

Fig. 13. Distributed regulator assembled on a circuit board.

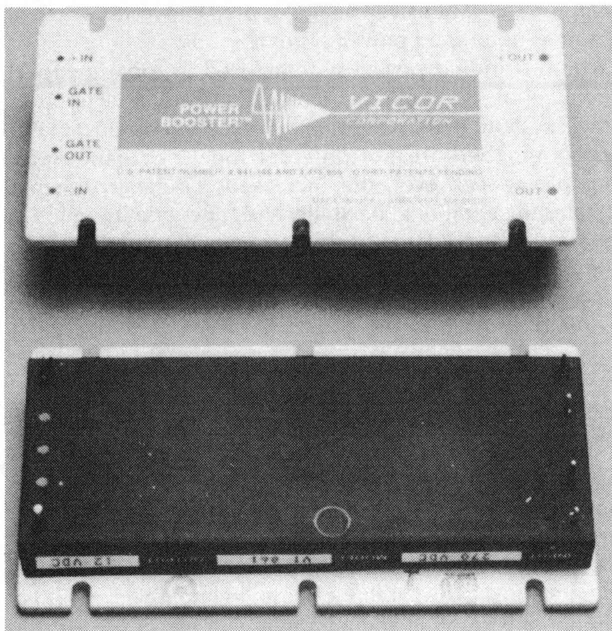

Fig. 14. Encapsulated dc-to-dc converter module suitable for use as a distributed regulator.

The primary motivation for employing a distributed power system is to be able to allocate regulated power to specific loads. In this way, pieces of the system can be independently powered up or powered down, thus enhancing system fault isolation capabilities and enabling subsystem repair without powering down the entire system. Also, this feature has made it easier to develop fault tolerant computers through the allocation of power cells to redundant system failure groups. These "failure groups" are functional blocks of circuitry which are duplicated in the system so that if one set fails the other continues to operate and system performance is not affected. The distributed power cells are incorporated into the failure groups so that a power cell failure will not cause a system failure. Microprocessor controllers are used to orchestrate and monitor the operation of the various pieces of the distributed power system and to report power system status and anomalies to the host computer.

Additional system benefits derived from this approach include simpler power distribution systems and simpler battery back-up systems. The higher voltage distribution bus (40–60 Vdc instead of 5 Vdc) reduces the current flow by an order of magnitude thereby simplifying bus bar construction, system backplane construction, and the mechanism for conducting current onto the system circuit boards. The 40–60 Vdc distribution bus also enables a very simple battery back-up system. Instead of converting the battery voltage to the high voltage dc bus as required with direct off-line switching power supplies, the battery can be switched directly onto the low voltage distribution bus during a power outage. This can be done with a controlled semiconductor switch and relay instead of the far more complex and expensive voltage step-up converter which is required in lumped power systems.

The distributed power systems used in today's superminicomputers are more complex than traditional lumped power systems in that there are more pieces comprising the system and there are more interdependencies of these various pieces. However, this increased complexity is what enables the additional flexibility and functionality which is required in these large computers. In addition, these systems are less expensive than lumped power systems when the added features of battery back-up or fault tolerance are required.

Power System Technologies

The power system solutions described above are the result of two major influences. First, the system requirements; the power system must be designed to meet the performance requirements of the computer and to contribute to the market acceptance of the product. The second major influence is the availability of base technologies; circuits, components, cooling and packaging, for use in the system design. Once the system requirements are understood, the power system designer must draw on the available technologies to implement an optimum and attractive solution. This section presents a brief description of the current state of the art in computer power system technologies, and highlights those technologies which are currently in transition as power electronics researchers and system designers strive to keep pace with the rapidly evolving power requirements of the minicomputer industry.

Forces Driving the Technology

With the rapid advances in computer semiconductor and storage technologies being achieved today, it is not surprising that the major goals in the power systems arena are 1) to reduce the size of the power conversion subsystem, and 2) to reduce its cost. The research activities which are currently addressing the first goal of reducing the size of power converters, together with business issues such as automated manufacturing and component standardization, also contribute to the second goal of reducing cost. Therefore, the following discussion will focus on the miniaturization activities which are currently in progress.

There are three major directions which are currently being explored in the pursuit of higher power conversion densities. These are:

1) higher switching frequencies,
2) higher levels of circuit integration, and
3) improved thermal performance.

The motivation for each of these directions can be surmised from the pie chart shown in Fig. 15. This chart shows the

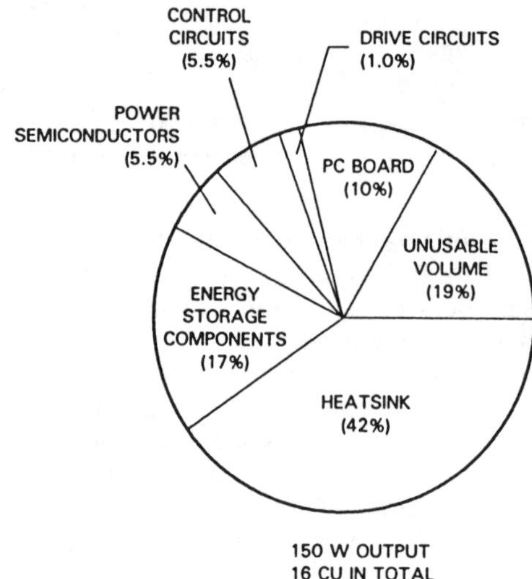

Fig. 15. Relative portions of space consumed in a dc-to-dc converter operating at 400 kHz.

relative portions of space consumed in a 60-Vdc to 5-Vdc, 150-W square-wave switching converter operating at 400 kHz. The following sections describe how the three directions described above address the various categories depicted in the pie chart.

Higher Switching Frequencies

The primary motivation for progressing to higher switching frequencies is to reduce the size of the transformers and the energy storage capacitors and inductors. As shown in Fig. 16, significant reductions in the size of these components are realized when the switching frequency is increased from tens of kilohertz to hundreds of kilohertz. The shift from hundreds of kilohertz to the megahertz range yields less significant size reductions, but other advantages come into play. For example, in the megahertz range, parasitic elements such as leakage inductance in transformers and intrinsic capacitances in power MOSFETs become com-

Fig. 16. Comparison of 150-W power transformers as the switching frequency is increased from 40 kHz (left), to 400 kHz (right).

parable in magnitude to discrete components. If these parasitic elements can be adequately controlled during the manufacturing process, they can be used in the design of a circuit, thereby replacing additional discrete components.

Current research in this area is focused on resonant and quasi-resonant circuits which convert power at frequencies in the 1-20-MHz range [37], [38]. Resonant converters have been used in various power electronics applications for many years [32]–[35], but the quasi-resonant approach is a more recent development and is still very much under investigation [36], [37]. Examples of these types of circuits are shown in Fig. 17, together with some characteristic waveforms. The fundamental difference between resonant circuits and square-wave circuits is the use of resonant *LC* tank circuits to form sinusoidal current and/or voltage waveforms in the resonant converter power semiconductor switches, as compared to the rectangular waveforms found in the square-wave converter switches. This helps to reduce switching losses which tend to increase significantly at high frequencies in square-wave converters.

In order to take advantage of the benefits which can be derived at higher switching frequencies, careful attention must be given to the design of the magnetic components [40]–[43]. New magnetic structures which yield low profile form factors and minimize losses due to skin effect and proximity effect are being developed. Such a transformer is shown in Fig. 18. Also, different capacitor technologies are required at these higher frequencies. Conventional electrolytic capacitors are plagued by high equivalent series resistance (ESR) and inductance (ESL) at high frequencies. Ceramic capacitors, however, retain their capacitive characteristics into the megahertz range [44]. The lower value

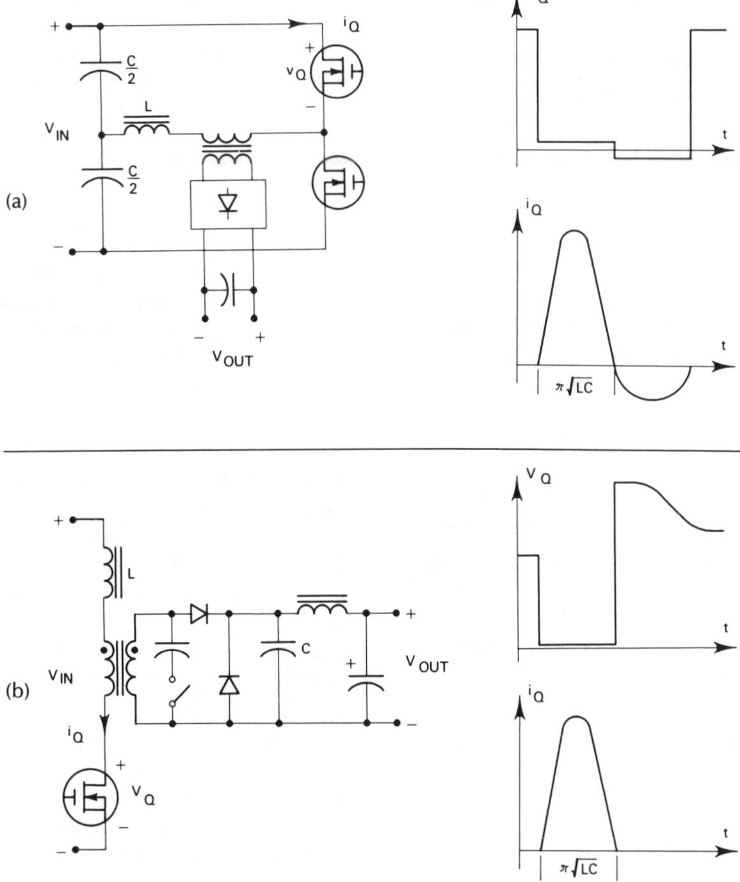

Fig. 17. Schematic diagrams with characteristic voltage and current waveforms for the (a) resonant converter and (b) quasi-resonant converter. (For transformer reset circuit, see [39].)

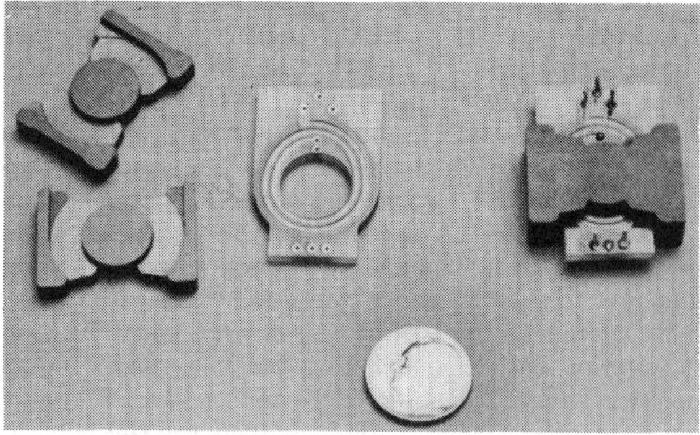

Fig. 18. High-frequency magnetic structure with printed coils and low profile ferrite core.

of capacitance afforded by ceramic capacitors is not a problem because less capacitance is needed at these frequencies.

Higher Levels of Integration

When combined, the sectors of the pie chart of Fig. 15 labeled "power semiconductors," "control circuits," and "drive circuits" account for only 12 percent of the total converter volume. This is a relatively small portion of the total volume because of the application of circuit integration techniques. Prior to the use of circuit integration, these components accounted for 50 percent of converter volume.

The first step in this integration process occurred in the mid-1970s with the introduction of linear integrated circuit implementations of pulse-width modulation (PWM) control algorithms [45], [46]. This technology is now well established, and as new control algorithms are derived, they are routinely implemented through integrated circuit techniques. A second, more recent step, has been the use of hybrid integrated circuits. These hybrid ICs incorporate functional blocks of circuitry in single packages comprising ceramic substrates, thick film conductors and resistors, chip capacitors, and "chip and wire" or SOT/SOIC semiconductor mountings. An example of a hybrid module which incorporates the power semiconductor devices of a dc-to-dc converter is shown in Fig. 19. This module is capable of

Fig. 19. Thick film hybrid IC incorporating power semiconductors.

processing 150 W of power and can dissipate up to 50 W. An example of a signal level hybrid is shown in Fig. 20. This control hybrid incorporates the PWM and protection circuitry which controls the performance of the dc-to-dc converter.

Fig. 20. Thick film hybrid IC incorporating low power control circuitry.

A third level of integration which is still in the early stages of evolution is a process which has come to be known as "smart power." This process combines high voltage and high current power conversion capabilities with the attendant low power control circuitry into a single monolithic silicon integrated circuit [47]. In addition to the significant reduction in size which this IC affords, other advantages include better electrical performance at high frequencies due to the elimination of relatively long circuit board interconnections, and a simpler and less expensive end product because there are fewer parts to procure, test and assemble. There are still some questions today regarding the viability of this approach. These questions have been raised because of the difficulties which have been encountered in integrating different semiconductor technologies into a single silicon chip, and because of the concern that the power dissipated in the high voltage/high current section of the chip will raise the temperature and thus lower the reliability of the lower power control circuitry. However, in spite of these concerns, significant progress is being made in this new technology.

Improving Thermal Performance

The largest piece of the pie chart shown in Fig. 15 is labeled "heat sink." The size of the heat sink required in a given application depends on many factors, including ambient air temperature, velocity or volume of air flow, and the shape and size of the heat sink fins. However, there are two factors in the design of the converter itself which can make a significant difference in the size of the heat sink required. The first is, of course, efficiency. If fewer watts are dissipated there is less heat to be removed from the circuit. The second factor is the thermal impedance between the devices in the converter which dissipate the power and the heat sink for those devices. If this thermal impedance is low, there will be less of a temperature rise between the heat sink and the device being cooled. Therefore the heat sink can be designed to be smaller and run hotter. Both of these factors are being addressed with current research.

A breakdown of where power is lost in a 150-W, 60-Vdc to 5-Vdc, 400-kHz square-wave switching converter is given in Fig. 21. It is clear from this chart that the most significant opportunity for improving converter efficiency is in the output rectifiers. The output rectifiers in low voltage power converters must pass large currents, and they account for approximately 40 percent of the losses in the power conversion process. The most commonly used rectifier in this application today is the Schottky diode. The Schottky diode is now a mature device and is quite reliable. However, ongoing research into new barrier metals and fabrication pro-

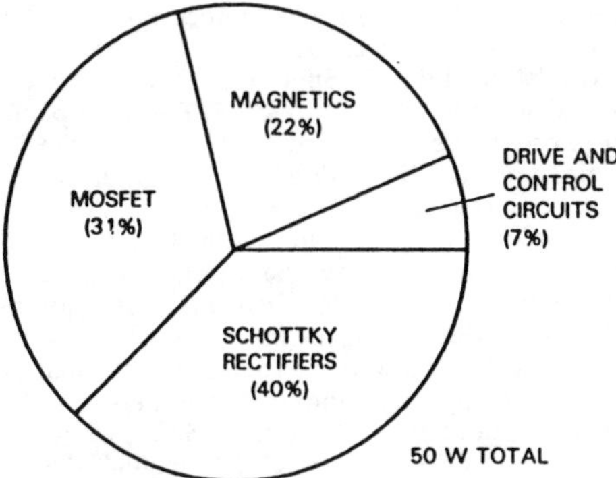

Fig. 21. Relative losses within a 400-kHz dc-to-dc converter.

cesses is promising to yield some improvement in the forward voltage drop in these rectifiers.

A second approach to the problem of improving the efficiency of the output rectifiers has been the development of the "synchronous rectifier" [48]–[50]. The synchronous rectifier is a controllable switch, such as a bipolar or field effect power transistor, which can be turned on and off in synchronization with other switching elements in the converter so as to accomplish the rectification function. The reason for developing this more complex approach is the promise of very low resistances to the flow of current in the forward direction. An example of such a synchronous rectifier, proposed by Archer [50], is given in Fig. 22. Developers of the synchronous rectifier have predicted that they will be able to reduce the losses in output rectifiers by approximately 50 percent. However, it is not clear at this time if such devices will become practical for low cost computer applications.

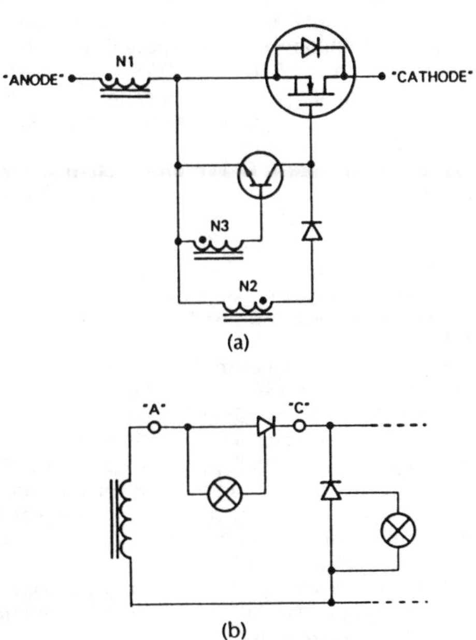

Fig. 22. Synchronous rectifier (a) schematic diagram and (b) proposed schematic symbol [50] in a typical application.

The second most significant opportunity for improving converter efficiency is in the area of the primary power switches. Although not as significant as the losses in the output rectifiers, the losses in the primary power switches can reduce overall converter efficiency by 5–10 percent. The losses in these switches can be split into two components: 1) the switching losses, and 2) the conduction losses. These two components are illustrated in Fig. 23. As switching frequencies increase, switching losses also increase because the fixed amount of power dissipated during each cycle is repeated more frequently. Conduction losses, on the other hand, remain relatively constant, and are a function of the converter load and the voltage drop across the power switch during its conduction interval. The first of these components, switching losses, can be virtually eliminated when using resonant or quasi-resonant converters. As illustrated in Fig. 17, the switch current is at zero during switching transitions. Efforts to reduce the second component, conduction losses, are focused on improving the on-state resistance of power MOSFETs, which are most frequently used as the power switch in high-frequency applications.

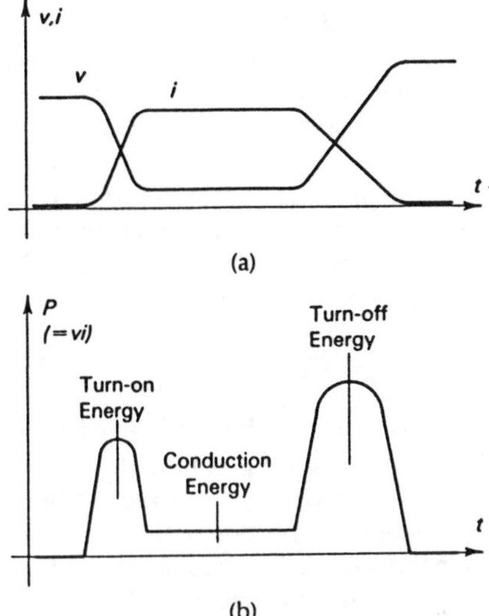

Fig. 23. Power semiconductor switch (a) voltage and current waveforms and (b) dissipated power waveform.

As mentioned previously, a second approach to reducing heat sink size is to reduce the thermal impedance of the interface between the power dissipating semiconductors and the ambient air. With conventional packaging, there can be as many as 5 layers of materials between the semiconductor junction and the heatsink. A typical stackup is shown in Fig. 24. Depending on how well each of these interfaces is designed, the resultant thermal impedance could be as high as several degrees centigrade per watt of dissipation. Thus, 10–20 W of dissipation in a large semiconductor device could lead to a junction temperature of

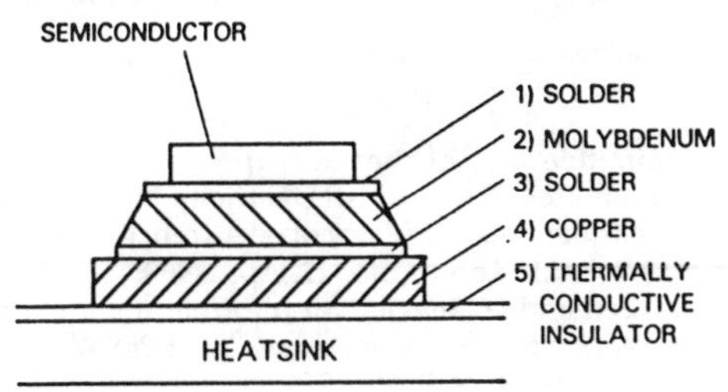

Fig. 24. Layers of material between the power semiconductor and the heat sink.

20–40 degrees above the heat sink temperature. This temperature differential leads to a large heat sink. Keeping the thermal impedance below 1.0°C/W keeps the silicon temperature very close to the heat sink temperature. In order to do this, most of the thermal interfaces shown in Fig. 24 must be eliminated. The best possible solution would be to bond the semiconductor device directly to the heatsink. This would eliminate all thermal interfaces except for the bonding material. However, due to factors such as mismatches between thermal coefficients of expansion of different materials, and voltage isolation requirements, this approach is not practical. Practical implementations are being studied, however, and research into new substrate and bonding materials gives hope that thermal impedances less than 1.0°C/W might be achievable.

Conclusions

As advances continue to be made in computer architectures and semiconductor technologies, the size and cost of the computer power system continues to be a significant, and perhaps increasing, portion of the overall product. Also, as the dimensions of IC features shrink to less than 1 μm, a new lower voltage standard (3.3 Vdc) is being proposed to replace the accepted 5-Vdc standard of today [51]. This will present a significant challenge to power electronics designers as they attempt to meet regulation and efficiency specifications at this lower voltage. These are just two of many reasons why research and development in power electronics technologies for computer applications will continue at a significant level for the foreseeable future.

One of the primary goals of this research will be to develop very small, low cost power conversion modules which can be fully characterized and applied like components. The availability of such modules will provide the flexibility needed to configure new power systems for new products very quickly and with very little additional engineering resources. Other system issues, such as power line interface requirements, energy storage back-up systems, and power system control and diagnostic capabilities will continue to be addressed on a system-by-system basis, so that each product can be tailored for its intended market.

As in other areas of power electronics, computer power system designers have enjoyed a very broad range of challenges in their work. These designers must understand and be able to work with magnetic components, power semiconductor devices, linear and nonlinear control theory, circuit analysis and design techniques, and numerous other electrical engineering disciplines. Power electronics engineers have met the challenges of this multi-disciplinary field and have provided excellent solutions for the minicomputer industry. The challenge continues, and the engineers are better equipped than ever to meet the challenge.

References

[1] Subcommittee M.4 of the measurement and communications committee of the British Electricity Board, "A survey of the amplitudes and frequency of occurrence of surges on MV systems," A.C.E. Report, no. 22, Apr. 1969.

[2] G. W. Allen and D. Segall, "Monitoring of computer installations for power line disturbances," *IEEE PES Winter Meeting Conf.*, Paper no. C74 199-6, 1974.

[3] E. M. Gulachenski and D. P. Symanski, "Distribution circuit power quality considerations for supply to large digital computer loads," *IEEE Trans. Power App. Syst.*, vol. PAS-100, no. 12, pp. 4885–4892, Dec. 1981.

[4] M. Goldstein and P. D. Speranza, "The quality of U.S. commercial ac power," *IEEE Intelec '82 Record*, pp. 28–33, 1982.

[5] Surge protective devices committee of the IEEE Power Engineering Society, "IEEE guide for surge voltages in low-voltage ac power circuits," *IEEE Std* 587-1980.

[6] Bureau Central de la Commission Electrotechnique Internationale, Geneve, Suisse, "Safety of information technology equipment including electrical business equipment," IEC Publication 950, 1st ed., 1986.

[7] Underwriters Laboratories, "Safety of information processing equipment," UL Standard 478, 5th ed. 1978.

[8] Canadian Standards Association, "Safety of data processing equipment," CSA Standard C22.2, no. 154, 1983.

[9] Federal Communications Commission, "Radio frequency interference suppression of radio frequency equipment," FCC rules part 15, subpart J.

[10] VDE Specification 0871/6.78, "Radio frequency interference suppression of radio frequency equipment for industrial, scientific, and medical (ISM) and similar purposes," English translation by EMACO EMC Consultants, San Diego, CA, 1978.

[11] "Voltage regulation and conversion in unconventional electrical generator systems," General Electric Company Report prepared under Bureau of Naval Weapons, Department of the Navy, Contract NOW 62-094-d, Aug. 31, 1963.

[12] B. P. Schweitzer and A. B. Rosenstein, "Free running—switching mode power regulator: Analysis and design," *IEEE Trans. Aerosp. Electron. Syst.*, vol. AES-2, pp. 1171–1180, Oct. 1964.

[13] E. T. Moore and T. G. Wilson, "Basic considerations for dc-dc conversion networks," *IEEE Trans. Magn.*, vol. MAG-2, no. 3, pp. 620–624, Sept. 1966.

[14] F. N. Tompkins, "The parallel type inverter," *AIEE Trans.*, vol. 51, pp. 707–714, Sept. 1932.

[15] B. D. Bedford, "Electric amplifying circuits," U.S. Patent 1 874 159, Aug. 30, 1932.

[16] A. Capel, G. Ferrante, and R. Prajoux, "State variable stability analysis of multi-loop PWM controlled dc/dc regulators in light and heavy mode," *IEEE PESC '75 Record*, pp. 91–103, 1975.

[17] R. D. Middlebrook and S. Cuk, "A general unified approach to modelling switching-converter power stages," *IEEE PESC '76 Record*, pp. 18–34, 1976.

[18] W. W. Burns, III, and T. G. Wilson, "State-plane trajectories used to observe and control the behavior of a voltage step-up dc-dc converter," *IEEE PESC '76 Record*, pp. 212–222, 1976.

[19] J. G. Kassakian, "Simulating power electronic systems—a new approach," *Proc. IEEE*, pp. 1428–1439, Oct. 1979.

[20] P. L. Hower, "Collector charge dynamics and second breakdown energy of power transistors," *IEEE PESC '74*, pp. 149–153, 1974.

[21] P. L. Hower, D. L. Blackburn, F. F. Oettinger, and S. Rubin, "Stable hot spots and second breakdown in power transistors," *IEEE PESC '76*, pp. 234–246, 1976.

[22] B. Bailey, "Safe reverse bias operation—a new approach," *Proceedings of Powercon 3*, pp. C3-1–C3-7, June 1976.

[23] W. R. Skanadore, "Load line shaping considerations for the high speed switching transistor in switching regulators and other highly inductive environments," *Proceedings of Powercon 4*, pp. H4-1–H4-18, May 1977.

[24] L. E. Jansson, "A survey of converter circuits for switched-mode power supplies," Mullard Technical Communications, no. 199, pp. 271–278, July 1973.

[25] R. P. Severns and G. Bloom, *Modern DC-DC Switchmode Power Converter Circuits.* New York, NY: Van Nostrand Reinhold, 1985.

[26] A. Levy, "The use of magnetic amplifier pulse width modulator in high frequency dc-dc converters," *IEEE PESC '76 Record*, pp. 223–232, 1976.

[27] C. E. Mullett and R. A. Mammano, "Using an integrated controller in the design of mag-amp output regulators," Unitrode Corp. application note U-109.

[28] D. Chambers and D. Wang, "Dynamic power factor correction in capacitor input off line converters," *Proceedings of Powercon 6*, pp. B3-1–B3-6, May 1979.

[29] M. J. Kocher and R. L. Steigerwald, "An ac to dc converter with high quality input waveforms," *IEEE PESC '82 Record*, pp. 63–75, 1982.

[30] M. F. Schlecht, "Novel topological alternatives to the design of a harmonic-free, utility/dc interface," *IEEE PESC '83 Record*, pp. 206–216, 1983.
[31] J. Kociecki, U. B. Goerke, and W. W. Burns, III, "A high power-density dc-dc converter board," *IEEE APEC '87 Record*, pp. 169–180, 1987.
[32] N. Mapham, "An SCR inverter with good regulation and sine-wave output," *IEEE Trans. Ind. Gen. Appl.*, vol. IGA-3, pp. 176–187, Mar./Apr. 1967.
[33] F. C. Schwartz, "A method of resonant current pulse modulation for power converters," *IEEE Trans. IECI*, vol. 17, no. 3, pp. 209–221, May 1970.
[34] E. E. Buchanan and E. J. Miller, "A resonant switching power conversion technique," *IEEE PESC '75 Record*, pp. 188–193, 1975.
[35] V. Vorperian and S. Cuk, "A complete dc analysis of the series resonant converter," *IEEE PESC '82 Record*, pp. 85–100, 1982.
[36] P. Vinciarelli, "Forward converter switching at zero current," U.S. Patent 4 415 959, Nov. 15, 1983.
[37] T. Zeng, D. Y. Chen, and F. C. Lee, "Variations of quasi-resonant dc-dc converter topologies," *IEEE PESC '86 Record*, pp. 381–392, 1986.
[38] L. F. Casey and M. F. Schlecht, "A high frequency, low volume, point-of-load power supply for distributed power systems," *IEEE PESC '87 Record*, pp. 439–450, 1987.
[39] P. Vinciarelli, "Optimal resetting of the transformer's core in single ended forward converters," U.S. Patent 4 441 146, Apr. 3, 1984.
[40] A. F. Goldberg, J. G. Kassakian, and M. F. Schlecht, "Issues related to 1–10 MHz transformer design," *IEEE PESC '87 Record*, pp. 379–386, 1987.
[41] J. M. Dishman, F. T. Dickens, and R. Rodriguez, "Optimization of energy storage inductors for high frequency dc-to-dc converters," *Proceedings of Powercon 7*, pp. B1-1–B1-11, Mar. 1980.
[42] P. S. Venkatraman, "Winding eddy current losses in switch mode power transformers due to rectangular wave currents," *Proceedings of Powercon 11*, pp. A1-1–A1-11, Apr. 1984.
[43] A. Dauhajre and R. D. Middlebrook, "Modelling and estimation of leakage phenomena in magnetic circuits," *IEEE PESC '86 Record*, pp. 213–226, 1986.
[44] J. Prymack, "MLC capacitor designs for switch mode power supplies," AVX Corp. technical information paper.
[45] R. A. Mammano, "Simplifying converter design with a new integrated regulating pulse width modulator," *Proceedings of Powercon 3*, pp. E3-1–E3-7, June 1976.
[46] C. J. Aswell, "A new monolithic switching regulator," *Proceedings of Powercon 3*, pp. H3-1–H3-15, June 1976.
[47] C. E. Harm, K. J. Timm, D. Kinzer, and D. Tam, "A universal input, fixed output, solid state, dc-dc converter," *IEEE PESC '87 Record*, pp. 76–85, 1987.
[48] M. W. Smith and K. Owyang, "Improving the efficiency of low output voltage switched-mode converters with synchronous rectification," *Proceedings of Powercon 7*, pp. H4-1–H4-13, Mar. 1980.
[49] R. S. Kagan and M. Chi, "Improving power supply efficiency with MOSFET synchronous rectifiers," *Proceedings of Powercon 9*, pp. D4-1–D4-5, July 1982.
[50] W. R. Archer, "Current-driven synchronous rectifier," TMOS Power FET Design Ideas, Motorola Inc. publ. BR316, pp. 9–20, 1985.
[51] S. Chou and C. Simonsen, "Chip voltage: Why less is better," *IEEE Spectrum*, vol. 24, no. 4, pp. 39–43, Apr. 1987.

Paper 2.5

Technology Trends in Microcomputer Control of Electrical Machines

BIMAL K. BOSE, SENIOR MEMBER, IEEE

Abstract—**Computer automation of factories, homes, and offices is ushering a new era of industrial revolution. Our automated factories, homes, and offices of the future will significantly advance our industrial civilization and profoundly influence the quality of human life on this planet. Microcomputer-based intelligent motion control systems which constitute the workhorses in the automated environment will play a significant role in the forthcoming era.**

Electronic motion control technology has moved a long way since the introduction of power semiconductor devices in the mid-1950's. In course of its dynamic evolution during the last three decades, the area of motion control has grown as diverse interdisciplinary technology. The frontier of this technology has taken a new dimension with the advent of today's powerful microcomputers, VLSI circuits, power integrated circuits, and advanced computer-aided design (CAD) techniques.

The paper gives a comprehensive review of state-of-the-art motion control technology in which the salient technical features of electrical machines, power electronic circuits, microcomputer control, VLSI circuits, machine controls and computer-aided design techniques have been discussed, and wherever possible, appropriate trends of the technology have been indicated.

I. Introduction

MICROCOMPUTER-based intelligent motion control systems are playing a vital role in today's industrial automation. In an automated industrial environment, a hierarchical computer system makes decisions about actions based on a preset strategy, and a motion control system, as a workhorse, translates these decisions into mechanical action.

Today's motion control is an area of technology that embraces many diverse disciplines, such as electrical machines, power semiconductor devices, converter circuits, dedicated hardware signal electronics, control theory, and microcomputers (Fig. 1). More recently, the advent of VLSI/ULSI circuits and sophisticated computer-aided design techniques has added new dimensions to the technology. Each of the component disciplines is undergoing an evolutionary process, and is contributing to the total advancement of motion control technology. The motion control engineer today is indeed facing a challenge to keep abreast with this complex and ever-growing multidisciplinary technology.

Motion control is a new term defined by the present generation of engineers. It is an offspring of electrical machine drives technology, which has grown at a rapid pace over the last two decades. The era of electronic motion control essentially started with the advent of power semiconductor devices in the late 1950's, though hydraulic, pneumatic, and other mechanically driven actuation systems were known for a long time. Gradually, the use of integrated signal electronics simplified the electronic control hardware. The introduction of microcomputers in the early 1970's profoundly influenced motion control systems, not only by simplifying the control hardware, but by adding intelligence as well as diagnostic capability to the system.

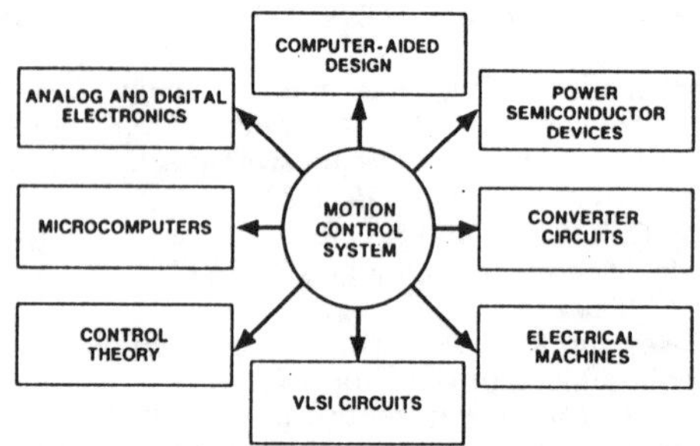

Fig. 1. Motion control system—An interdisciplinary technology.

We have seen an explosive growth in the application of motion control systems during recent years. Mechanical motion control systems found widespread acceptance in industry since the invention of the steam engine started the first industrial revolution in the eighteenth century, when mass industrial manufacturing replaced manual labor. Since then, the evolution of motion control engineering has been influenced by the development of electrical machines, vacuum tube electronics, gas tube electronics, saturable reactor magnetics, solid-state electronics, and control theory. The advent of computer technology and microelectronics during recent years has brought us to the doorstep of a second industrial revolution. Today, a tremendous momentum has developed for computer automation of our factories, homes, and offices. The principal motivation for this automation is improvement of productivity and and quality and minimization of less predictable human elements; and these motives in turn are being inspired by international competition. Computer-aided design (CAD) and computer-aided manufacturing (CAM) are playing increasingly important roles in factory automation. The concept of computer-integrated manufacturing (CIM), in which business decisions are translated to designs, which are then translated to manufacturing through a hierarchy of

Manuscript received September 9, 1986; revised February 18, 1987. This paper was the keynote address in the International Conference on Microcomputer Control of Small Machines (sponsored by IEEE Industrial Electronics Society), University of Padova, Italy, July 14–15, 1986.

The author was with General Electric Company, Corporate Research and Development, Schenectady, NY. He is now with the Department of Electrical Engineering, Ferris Hall, University of Tennessee, Knoxville, TN 37996, and also with Power Electronics Applications Center, 10521 Research Drive, Knoxville, TN 37932.

IEEE Log Number 8716647.

Reprinted from *IEEE Trans. Ind. Electron.*, vol. 35, no. 1, pp. 160–177, February 1988.

computers and motion control systems, will become a reality in the near future.

A motion control system, as mentioned before, is the workhorse through which higher level computer decisions are translated into mechanical actions. Motion control applications in industry include robots, numerically controlled machine tools, general-purpose industrial drives, computer peripherals, and instrument type drives. In the home, applications include home appliance drives for washers, dryers, air-conditioners, blenders, mixers, etc. In a typical computer-controlled manufacturing system on a factory floor, as illustrated in Fig. 2, there are three layers of control. The master control (usually a minicomputer) operates the entire network. It includes parts transportation and material handling on machine tools by robots. The direct numerical control (DNC) unit, usually a second minicomputer, collects programs for the microcomputers which directly control the machine tools. The computerized numerical control units (CNC), in addition, contain diagnostic programs that can detect mechanical and electronic malfunctions in a machine tool and report them to central controllers. The data entry units allow communication between the operator and the DNC computer.

In motion control systems, the application of robots is of significant interest today. The robot essentially symbolizes the challenge of synthesizing all state-of-the-art component technologies shown in Fig. 1. The modern industrial robot was introduced by Japan in 1980, and since then, it has evolved from performing simple tasks, such as handling and transferring, to performing sophisticated work including welding, painting, assembling, inspection, and adjustment. In Japan, the world leader in factory automation, almost two hundred thousand robots are in operation today. This is about 60 percent of all industrial robots in the world. One noticeable trend is the growth of robot use in non-manufacturing fields, for example, nuclear power generation, medical service and welfare, agriculture, construction, transport and warehousing, underwater work, and space exploration. More intelligent robots that will mimic the brain and muscles of human beings will be put to work in the future, for factory, home, or office automation.

The application of motion control has growth at a phenomenal rate in the computer peripheral industry. For example, in the U.S. alone, electronic printers, disk drives and tape drives used 24 million motors in 1983, and this figure is expected to rise to a staggering 80 million by the year 1988. It has been estimated that an average American home uses 50 motors in all the household appliances, and this amounts to a staggering 12.5 billion motors in all U.S. homes. Eventually, all these motors will be controlled by microcomputer. In an automated home of the future, all the motors will have a central home computer-based control through an integrated power-and-signal wiring system. Similar integrated motion control concepts will be applied to automobiles, airplanes, and so on.

This report is intended to review the technology trends of motion control that relate to electrical machines, power semiconductor devices, converter circuits, microcomputers, VLSI circuits, control of machines, and computer-aided control design techniques. Particular emphasis will be paid to

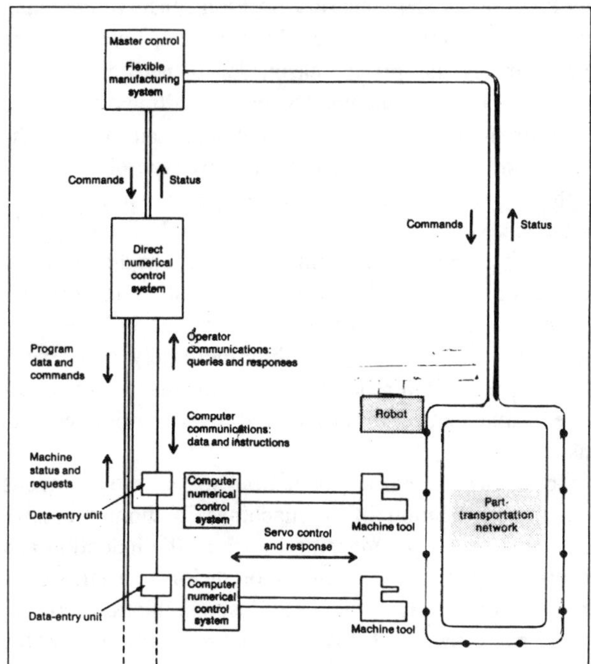

Fig. 2. Computer-controlled manufacturing system, showing interface with motion control systems.

intelligent motion control based on microcomputers. Again, motion control systems that use small machines will be our main theme of discussion. The literature on motion control has grown enormously, and proliferated so diversely that it is impossible to deal with all the aspects of the technology. Therefore, only the salient features will be highlighted.

II. Electrical Machines

An electrical machine is an electromagnetic energy conversion device that translates its input electrical energy into output mechanical motion. Electrical machines have been available for nearly a century,[1] and during this period the world's leading universities, research laboratories, and industries have made extensive studies of them. The evolution of machine technology, unlike that of electronics and computer science, has been long and slow, and we have not seen any dramatic invention in this area for a long time. The first machines were bulky, expensive, and had poor performance. Better understanding of machine principles coupled with evolution of new and improved materials has contributed to the improvement of machine design. The advent of modern digital computers and more recently the theory of finite element design have helped in further design optimization.

In motion control applications, the prime competitive candidates in electrical machines are dc machines, induction machines, synchronous machines (in brushless dc form), step motors, and switched reluctance machines. Recent literature on motion control has extensively discussed the behavior of these machines. To a unified machine analyst, the generic behavior of all the machines is the same. A dc machine is essentially an ac machine internally, where commutators and

[1]This year the Polytechnic di Torino, Italy, is celebrating the hundredth anniversary of induction machines.

brushes function as elements of a position-sensitive mechanical inverter. Here, the orthogonal disposition of field mmf and armature mmf is the prime reason for enhanced speed of response. This type of machine has been traditionally favored in electronic motion control applications, and by far the majority of industrial drives today use this type of machine. Although its control principle and converter equipment are somewhat simple, a dc machine, in general, is bulky and expensive compared to ac machines. In addition, the principal problem of a dc machine is that its commutators and brushes make it less reliable, and unsuitable to operate in a dusty or explosive environment. A dc machine definitely needs periodic maintenance. High reliability and maintenance-free operation are prime considerations in industrial motion control systems.

For these reasons, we are beginning to see a tremendous surge in the application of ac machines in motion control systems. Historically, ac machines, such as the induction and synchronous types, have been favored for constant-speed applications. In the last two decades, ac motion control technology has grown by leaps and bounds. Traditionally, the induction machine, particularly the cage type, has been the workhorse in industry because of its ruggedness, reliability, efficiency, and low cost. Although ac machines are simple, the cost of conversion and control equipment is generally high, which makes the total drive system expensive.The scenario has been changing recently, however, because of the advent of the integrated converter and microcomputer-based controllers. One reason for the control complexity of an ac machine is its complex dynamic behavior, which must be taken into consideration in feedback control systems. An ac machine is basically a nonlinear multivariable system with coupling between direct and quadrature axes, and its dynamic model is usually specified by a state-space equation in a synchronously rotating reference frame.

An induction motor always operates at a lagging power factor because its rotor field excitation has to be supplied from the stator side. In a permanent magnet synchronous machine, however, the field is established by the magnets. The stator will supply reactive current only (leading or lagging), if mismatch between supply voltage and induced voltage demands it. The concept of a brushless or commutatorless dc motor using a synchronous machine was developed by Ohno *et al.* [8]. A dc machine is a synchronous machine internally with magnets on the stator and armature on the rotor (commutators and brushes serve as the rotor position commutated inverter, as mentioned before). The same operation mode is possible if magnetics are transferred to the rotor, and the stator which contains the armature winding is supplied with ac power through an electronic inverter. The inverter commutation or gating signals must now be derived from a rotor position encoder to maintain absolute synchronism between magnet fluxes and stator winding induced fluxes. The reward of eliminating mechanical commutators and brushes is offset to some extent by the penalty of an absolute position encoder in the rotor and an expensive electronic inverter with the complex control. Besides in this new configuration, a dc machine-like transient response may not be straightforward.

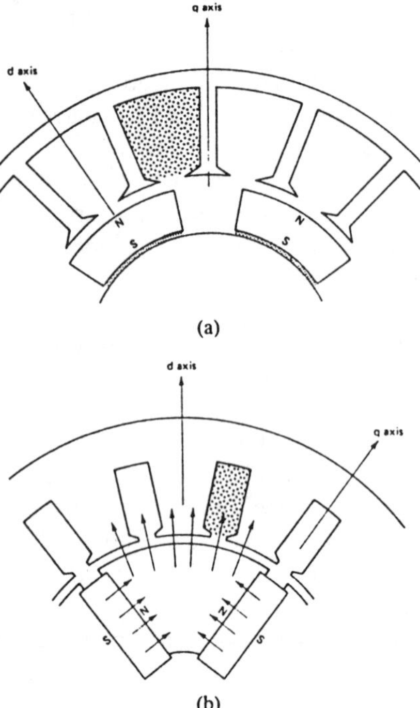

Fig. 3. Profile of permanent magnet machines. (a) Surface magnet machine. (b) Interior magnet machine.

It is important to mention that PM machines have essentially two different configurations. The conventional surface magnet machine (Fig. 3(a)) is essentially nonsalient (it has a large airgap) and is popularly used in a brushless drive. The large airgap again weakens the armature reaction effect, and therefore the operation is essentially restricted to a constant torque region. Recently, synchronously machines have been introduced with interior or buried magnets (Fig. 3(b)), which, because of their narrow airgap, overcome the above drawback of surface magnet machines. A buried magnet machine is essentially a hybrid machine in which torque is contributed by the reluctance component as well as the field component. The evolution of magnet materials is contributing to the size reduction of PM machines. Fig. 4 shows characteristics of several viable magnet materials. Ferrite material, which is low in cost and has excellent demagnetization linearity, is traditionally used in PM machines, but the machine tends to be bulky because of low remanence. Cobalt-samarium has a higher energy product and excellent temperature insensitivity, but its high cost restricts its use for specialized applications. The neodymium-iron-boron magnet, which has been introduced only recently (June 1983), has maximum remanence and coercive force force, and because of its reasonably low cost, shows great promise for future applications. This material, however, has some temperature sensitivity which must be taken into consideration during machine design.

In incremental motion control applications, the most widely used class of machines is step motors. While the machines discussed so far are characterized by continuous motion, step motors are characterized by discrete steps of motion and respond directly to digital command pulses. Step motors have been available for nearly half a century, but much attention has been focused on them recently because of the surge of

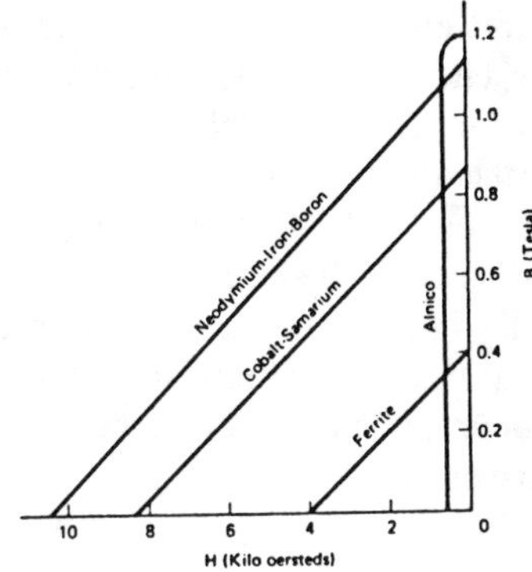

Fig. 4. Permanent magnet characteristics.

applications in the incremental motion control industry. Basically, step motors have characteristics similar to synchronous machines and are constructed in PM hybrid form or variable reluctance form. An example of a variable reluctance step motor with 1.8° step movement is shown in Fig. 5(a). A step movement of the rotor corresponds to the effective angular rotation of stator poles created by the stator winding mmf's. The inherently simple and economical construction of this "brushless" machine coupled with its simple open-loop control makes it extremely popular in the motion control industry. However, a number of performance penalties must be paid for these good features. Besides limited angle resolution, the open-loop synchronous machine-like operation gives load-dependent position accuracy, underdamped step response, high loss, and a tendency to lose synchronism as speed is increased. However, these characteristics are not limitations in application such as printer and disk drives and remote indicators, where these machines are most popularly used. As the market for motion control systems grew, the proponents of step motors came out with sophisticated controls using position encoder signals to solve some of the above problems. With these modifications, however, the appeal of inherent simplicity and economy is lost, and the margin of difference between step motor drive and brushless dc drive is narrowed. In summary, the points in favor of the closed-loop controlled step motor in comparison with the brushless dc motor include the following.

1) Below a few hundred watts of power, a PM step motor is cheaper than a PM synchronous motor, mainly because the former needs only one magnet, whereas the latter needs four (four poles).
2) A large holding torque and a high stiffness near the detent position are inherent in a step motor, whereas in the brushless dc motor the feedback mechanism (which may be sluggish) is responsible for establishing the above parameters.
3) A step motor requires a simple incremental position encoder, whereas a brushless motor needs an absolute position encoder.

The switched reluctance machine (SRM), the principle of which has been known for over a century, has seen a revival of interest in recent years for small-machine drives. Basically, the SRM is a variable-reluctance, continuous-movement machine (Fig. 5(b)), which is structurally identical to the single-stack, reluctance-type step motor. In this machine, continuous movement is regulated by current magnitude control and rotor synchronized commutation of stator phases, where commutation signals are derived from an absolute position encoder. The control is analogous to that of a concentrated winding brushless dc machine, and speed can be smoothly increased beyond the constant torque region. One drawback of this machine is its large pulsating torque, which makes it difficult to apply in position servo drives. Pulsating torque compensation has been proposed through such schemes as pole shaping, current command profiling and adaptive feedback control, and these show good promise.

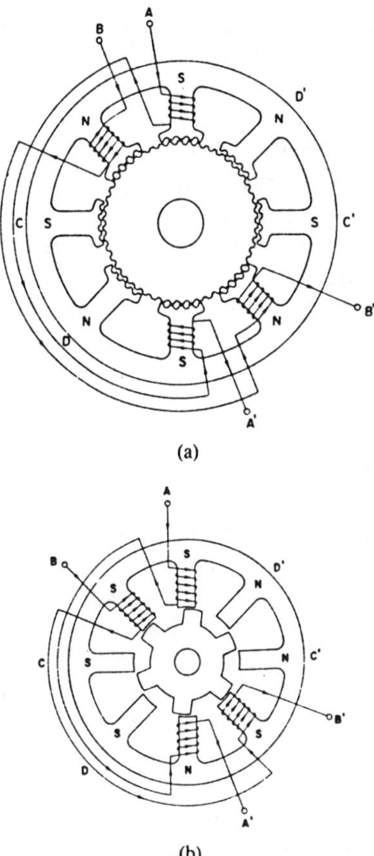

Fig. 5. Profiles of step and switched reluctance machines. (a) Variable reluctance single stack step motor (1.8° step). (b) Switched reluctance machine.

III. Power Converters

An electronic power converter translates the control signal at the input to the power actuation signal for the machine. The modern era of electronic motion control technology came into existence because of the advent of power semiconductor devices. These devices have grown in power rating and performance by an evolutionary process in the last two and a half decades. The improvement of device model, computer-aided simulation and design techniques, and semiconductor processing improvement have contributed to performance enhancement. Silicon is the principal material and will remain so in the foreseeable future. Phase-control thyristors were first introduced in the late 1950s; they found ready acceptance in rectifier controlled dc machine drives and variable-voltage constant-frequency controlled induction machine drives. The devices that are primarily important for small machine control applications are power transistors and power MOSFET's.

Bipolar Darlington transistors have been established as power switching devices for the high end of motion control converters. Second breakdown effects were the prime killers of power transistors for a long time. Today, these phenomena are understood better, and devices and circuits are being designed for better reliability and higher utilization factor.

Power MOSFET devices were introduced in the late 1970's, and these devices have found a tremendous growth of applications in converters up to several hundred watts. This frontier is expanding with the introduction of higher power devices in the market. Unlike the bipolar transistor, the MOSFET is a majority voltage-controlled device. Its second breakdown effect is minimal. One great demerit of the MOSFET is its high conduction drop; this drop increases with higher voltage rating and operating temperature. The on-resistance of the device has been improved over the last several years, but there seems to be a fundamental limit for silicon. While the conduction loss of the MOS device is high, its switching loss is almost negligible. In sinusoidal-output inverter applications, the PWM frequency can be extended to a high value so that conduction loss is offset by an improvement of the machine harmonic loss.

Very recently, we have seen the emergence of several hybrid power semiconductor devices. An example is the insulated-gate transistor (IGT), which is also known as the GEMFET or COMFET. It is essentially a MOSFET-driven bipolar transistor, and, therefore, combines the advantages of both the devices. It has the high input impedance of the MOSFET but the low conduction drop of the bipolar device. The switching speed is slow because the minority carrier storage and the second breakdown effect of the bipolar device are retained. The device has thyristor-like reverse voltage blocking capability. IGT's have been introduced in the 500-V 50-A range, and soon this range will be extended. Another hybrid device worth mentioning is the MOS-controlled thyristor. The device, as the name indicates, is designed in such a way that a MOSFET can control the turn-on and turn-off operations of a thyristor.

The converter in a motion control system is expensive, primarily because of the high cost of discrete power devices. The bulk of device cost is due to packaging complexity. The trend toward integration in low power signal electronics is being applied to power circuits also. Hybrid integration of half-bridge of full-bridge converters with or without control electronics has been available for some time. A more significant change is in monolithic integration of power circuits with embedded signal electronics. Such a circuit not only reduces cost and size, but eliminates EMI and interface problems. Further, integration of power devices and control electronics is so-called "smart" power devices brings in easily the additional functions, such as temperature control and overvoltage and overcurrent protections. This would not be possible with discrete power devices. The principal technical hurdles in this area are isolation between high-voltage devices and low-voltage circuits, and efficient thermal management. The birth of power integrated circuit (PIC) technology has brought us to the doorstep of what we call the "second electronic revolution." The first electronic revolution started with the integration of small signal electronics. Power IC's are already appearing in the low end of motion control applications. Eventually, as the technology advances, these will appear in our home appliances, automobiles, robots, and other factory floor drives. Researchers in this area are optimistic that eventually PIC's will incorporate sensing signal processing, and will directly interface speed and position encoders. Hall sensors, temperature sensors, and so on. If sensing, power control, and signal processing can be combined, a standalone, single-chip system that will interface with a central microcomputer can be constructed, and mounted on the drive machine directly.

Computer-aided power circuit design techniques have evolved over a number of years. Compared to trial-and-error design with the help of a breadboard, computer-based design systems are very convenient for design optimization. Because of its switching elements, a converter is essentially a discrete time system. Therefore, it can be simulated on a digital computer as a time-varying network topology, i.e., in each switching state of a converter, a linear state-space equation can be described and solved by Fortran-like programs. Alternately, the network can be described as a graph by nodes and branches, and programs such as SPICE II (University of California, Berkeley) can be used. CAD techniques for signal electronics (both logic and analog) and control systems have reached a stage of maturity, and therefore the problem of how to integrate various design and simulation tools of an integrated power system remains. Fig. 6 illustrates a CAD of a converter circuit with conversions and links to the various programs [18]. In the beginning, the user defines a circuit schematic from given specifications and requirements by preliminary analysis and design. The P-CAD (Personal CAD Systems Inc.) programs capture the schematic, extract the netlist, and produce the SPICE input file. The SPICE–NIP translator converts the SPICE input file into the NIP (nodal description input program—California Institute of Technology) input file. The function of NIP is to generate (from a nodal description input file) the state-space equations, output equations, and feedback/feedforward equations associated with linear switched networks that a converter goes through in each switching cycle. The SCAP (switching converter analysis program—California Institute of Technology) program generates a state-space-averaged model of the converter that can be used to study steady-state and frequency-response behaviors. SIMNON (nonlinear simulation program—Lund Institute of Technology, Sweden) accepts the state-space equations from NIP through a translator and permits the simulation of time domain behavior SIMNON will be further discussed in Section VI. After optimizing the converter design with several iterations, the program can be integrated with controller simulation and/or used to generate the layout of a power integrated circuit.

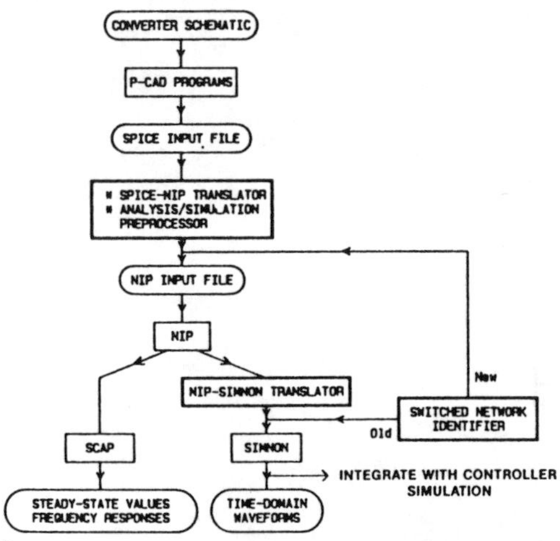

Fig. 6. CAD of a converter from a schematic entry.

IV. Control of Electrical Machines

The advent of gas tubes, such as thyratrons and ignitrons in the 1930's, and then, magnetic amplifier or saturable devices in the 1940's gave birth to the first generation of motion control systems using dc machines. Advancement of feedback control theory in post World War II years intensified evolution of the technology, but modern motion control technology was truly born with the advent of power semiconductor devices. In a feedback control system, the machine as well as the converter are elements in feedback loops, and therefore their dynamic models should be taken into consideration. A dc machine, particularly a small machine with a permanent magnet field, can be modeled as a linear second-order system between applied armature voltage and speed-neglecting armature reaction, saturation, temperature, and brush nonlinearity. However, a converter-machine system with digital control is a discrete time system because of the sampling effect. It is convenient to analyze, simulate, and design such a system on a computer.

Control of a dc machine is considerably simpler than that of an ac machine. A dc machine can be interfaced with utility ac supply through a phase-controlled converter, and the output (speed, position, or torque) can be regulated by controlling the converter firing angle. A universal motor can be controlled by anti-parallel thyristors or triac devices. A high-performance dc servo, in which dc power is obtained from a rectified ac supply or from a battery and then controlled by a pulsewidth modulated chopper, is shown in Fig. 7. The addition of inner current control (which is indirectly torque control) and speed control loops not only expand the system bandwidth but help in limiting the excursion of the state variables.

Control of an ac machine with a feedback loop is considerably more complex, and this complexity increases as higher performances are demanded. The main reason for this complexity is that ac machine dynamics are more complex; they must be represented by nonlinear multivariable state-space equations. For example, an induction motor model can be represented by a sixth-order state-space equation, where voltage and frequency are inputs to the stator and the outputs may be speed, position, torque, flux stator currents, or a

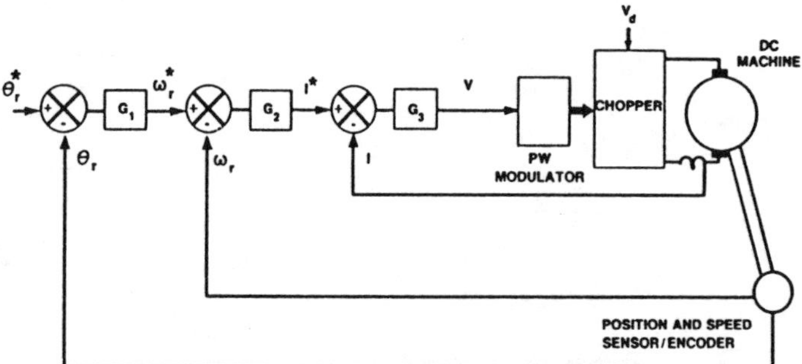

Fig. 7. Control block diagram of a dc machine.

combination of them. The additional reasons for complexity in ac drives are intricate feedback signal processing and the requirement for complex control of the variable-frequency power supply.

Many different control techniques of varying degrees of complexity have appeared in the evolution of ac drives. The acceptance of a particular method depends on the nature of the application. A simple and economical method of control of an induction motor is to vary the stator voltage at utility frequency through a phase-controlled anti-parallel thyristor or a triac converter. Such a scheme, though inefficient, is used in blower and appliance drives. A simple open-loop volts/Hz control method has been popularly used for a long time. It will continue to be used in the future for low-performance, low-power, and cost-effective industrial drives. Feedback flux control, torque control, slip control, angle control, etc., have been used extensively where better performance is demanded. The penalty in such feedback controls is the difficulty of feedback signals synthesis using distorted ac voltage and current waves. Problems arise in such a "scalar" control method, because of the nonlinearity of the machine model and the inherent coupling effect between the direct (d) and quadrature (q) axes. The poles and zeros of machine transfer functions vary at each operating point. The control can be optimized at a certain operating point, but the performance will deteriorate if the operating point shifts. Besides, the coupling effect causes sluggish transient response.

The field oriented or vector control techniques are now being accepted almost universally for control of ac machines. Such control methods were developed in Germany in the early 1970's. Blaschke [21] introduced the direct or feedback method of vector control and Hasse [22] invented the indirect or feedforward method. But the world ignored these techniques because of the complexity of their implementation. With the advent of the microcomputer era, such control complexity is no longer a problem.

The vector or decoupling control considers the generic analogy between ac and dc machines (Fig. 8). The underlying principle of vector control is to eliminate the coupling problem between the d and q axes; then an ac machine will behave like a separately excited dc machine. The fundamentals of vector control implementation with the machine model in a synchronously rotating reference frame are explained in Fig. 9. The phase and coordinate transformations within the machine are cancelled by two stages of inverse transformation in the control so that i_{ds}^* and i_{qs}^* currents correspond to i_{ds} and i_{qs},

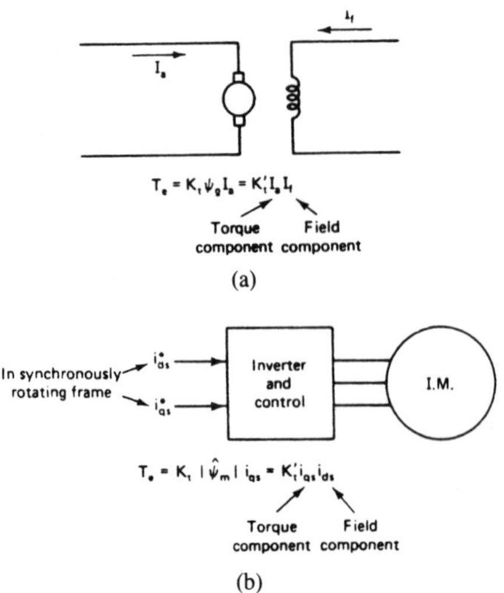

(a)

(b)

Fig. 8. DC machine and induction motor analogy in vector control.

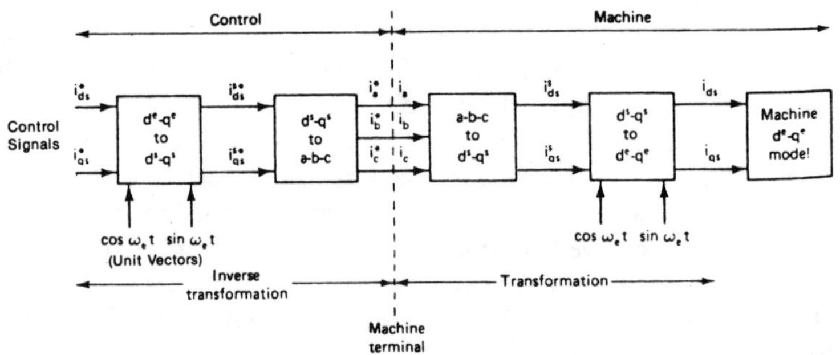

Fig. 9. Vector control implementation technique with d^e–q^e machine model.

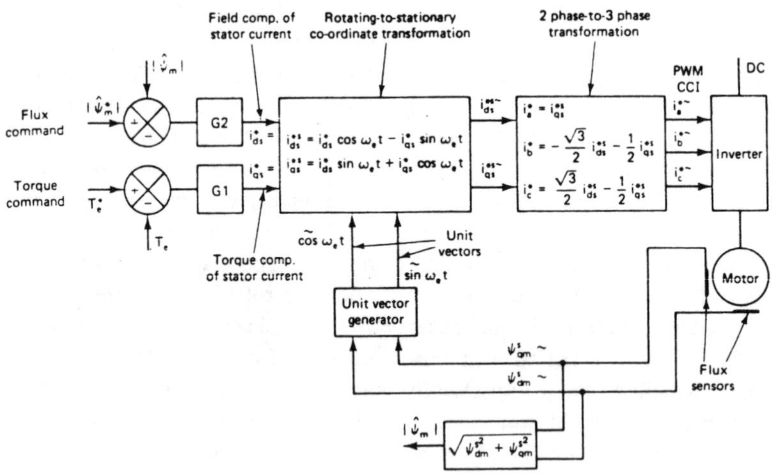

Fig. 10. Direct or feedback method of vector control of induction motor.

respectively. The converter dynamics and sampling delays are omitted for simplicity. The unit vectors cos $\omega_e t$ and sin $\omega_e t$ assume alignment of i_{ds} (field component) with the flux and i_{qs} (torque component) orthogonal to it, in order to have dc machine-like decoupling. The vector control not only gives the advantage of fast transient response, but also eliminates the conventional stability limit of the induction motor. The torque relation becomes linear with i_{qs}, and the drive can be easily designed for four-quadrant operation. Of course, the price to be paid for all the benefits is complex coordinate transformation, phase conversion, and intricate feedback signal processing.

Blaschke's direct method for a PWM voltage-fed inverter with current control is illustrated in Fig. 10. The principal control parameters i_{ds}^* and i_{qs}^*, which are dc quantities, are converted to a stationary reference frame with the help of unit vectors as shown. These are then converted to phase current commands for the inverter. The unit vectors are generated from d and q components of airgap flux with the help of the phase-locked loop so that cos $\omega_e t$ and sin $\omega_e t$ are cophasal to

ψ^s_{dm}, and ψ^s_{qm}, respectively. The flux components can be measured directly by Hall-effect sensors or flux coils, or can be estimated from stator voltage and current signals with the help of a partial observer. Blaschke has shown that rotor fluxes instead of airgap fluxes, as shown in Fig. 10, should be used in order to avoid undesirable stability problems. It is possible to reconstruct rotor fluxes from airgap fluxes with the help of stator currents.

The direct method of vector control as discussed above can operate typically above 10 percent of the base speed, because of the difficulty in accurate flux signal synthesis at low speed. In fact, the flux signal obtained by direct integration of stator voltages can be used only in a higher speed range. The resulting coupling effect, although small at higher speed, may become significant as the speed is reduced. In applications such as servo drives, the drive system must operate at truly zero speed with best possible transient response. The accurate stator drop compensation near zero speed is very difficult. Blaschke derived flux estimation equations which use speed and stator current signals. These equations are valid at any speed (including zero speed), and can be given as follows:

$$\frac{d\psi^s_{qr}}{dt}=\frac{L_m}{T_R}\,i^s_{qs}+\omega_r\psi^s_{dr}-\frac{1}{T_R}\,\psi^s_{qr} \tag{1}$$

$$\frac{d\psi^s_{dr}}{dt}=\frac{L_m}{T_R}\,i^s_{ds}+\omega_r\psi^s_{qr}-\frac{1}{T_R}\,\psi^s_{dr} \tag{2}$$

where $T_R = L_r/R_r$ is the rotor circuit time constant, and all other parameters are in standard symbols. The estimation block diagram for unit vectors and rotor flux from these equations is shown in Fig. 11. Note that the estimation is machine parameter dependent; the rotor resistance variation due to temperature and skin effect, and the inductance variation due to saturation, are all important.

Hasse's method generates unit vectors indirectly from rotor position and feedforward slip signal, the control method otherwise remaining the same as before. Fig. 12 explains the indirect vector control principle with the help of a phasor diagram, and Fig. 13 shows a position servo implementation using this method. In order to satisfy the criteria of decoupling control, the following equations can be established from the rotation frame equivalent circuit [1]:

$$\omega_{sl}=\frac{L_m R_r}{L_r|\hat{\psi}_r|}\,i_{qs} \tag{3}$$

$$\frac{L_r}{R_r}\frac{d\hat{\psi}_r}{dt}+\hat{\psi}_r=L_m i_{ds}. \tag{4}$$

In Fig. 13, the i^*_{ds} signal for the desired rotor flux $\hat{\psi}_r$ is determined from (4). The i^*_{qs} signal, which is proportional to torque, is derived from the speed control loop. The set value of slip ω_{sl} is related to current i_{qs} by (3). The slip angle vectors sin θ_{sl} and cos θ^*_{sl}, which determine the desired electrical axis with respect to rotor mechanical axis, are generated from i^*_{qs} in a feedforward manner. The rotor position vectors are then added with the slip angle vectors to generate the desired unit

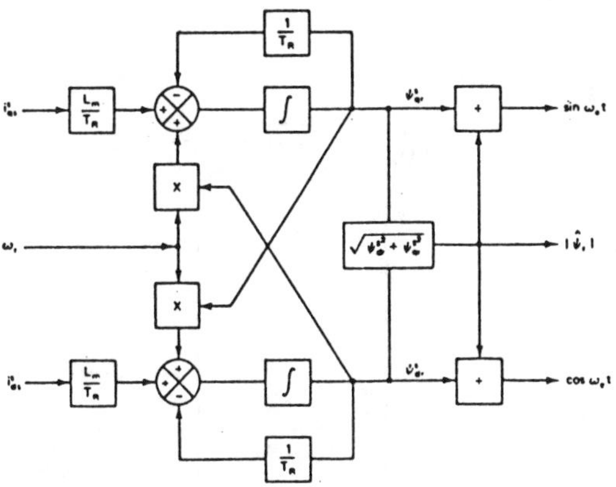

$$\frac{d\psi_{qr}{}^s}{dt} = \frac{L_m}{T_R}\,i_{qs}{}^s + \omega_r\psi_{dr}{}^s - \frac{1}{T_R}\psi_{qr}{}^s$$

$$\frac{d\psi_{dr}{}^s}{dt} = \frac{L_m}{T_R}\,i_{ds}{}^s + \omega_r\,\psi_{qr}{}^s - \frac{1}{T_R}\psi_{dr}{}^s$$

Fig. 11. Unit vectors and rotor flux estimation from speed and stator currents.

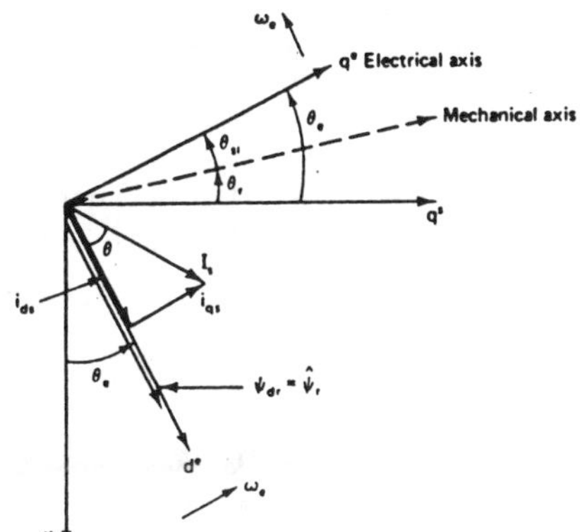

Fig. 12. Phasor diagram for indirect vector control.

vectors for coordinate transformation. Since induction motors can locate the field flux at any position, an absolute shaft position encoder is not needed. In fact, the rotor speed can be added directly with the slip signal, and then unit vectors can be synthesized by a VCO, counter, and SIN/COS waveform generator. Both the indirect method and the direct method are dependent on machine parameters. The dominant parameter to be considered is rotor resistance, which has been estimated on-line by various techniques giving improved performance in decoupling control. Fig. 13 can be modified to incorporate control in the field-weakening region as shown in Fig. 14. Below base speed, the machine operates at constant flux, and, therefore, operation is identical to that in Fig. 13. Above base speed, $|\hat{\psi}_r|$ is weakened to be inversely proportional to speed so that the drive system remains under the vector control mode. Note that here flux is controlled in an open-loop manner by solving (4).

Control of synchronous machine drives is, in many ways, similar to control machine drives. Synchronous machines may have essentially two different modes of operation. One is the open-loop true synchronous machine mode, where a simple volts per hertz method of control locks the machine speed with

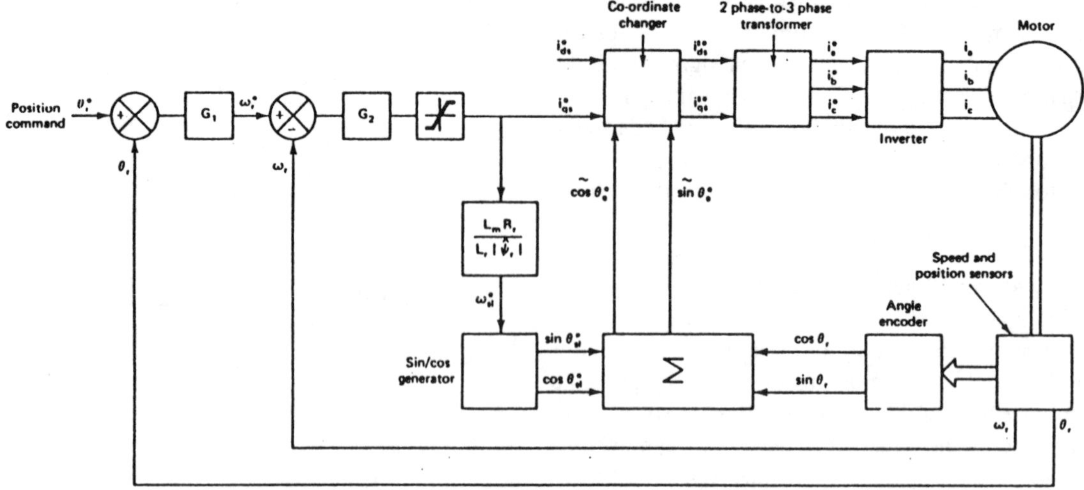

Fig. 13. Induction motor position servo using indirect or feedforward method of vector control.

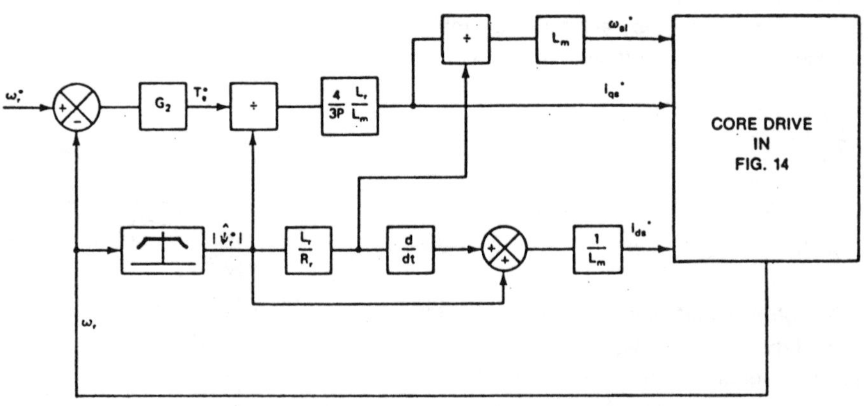

Fig. 14. Indirect vector control principle in field weakening constant power region.

the frequency of an independent oscillator. This method of speed control is popular in multiple reluctance or PM machine drives where close speed tracking is essential in such applications as a fiber-spinning mill. The other is the self-control mode, in which variable-frequency inverter control pulses are derived from an absolute position encoder. A self-controlled machine, as mentioned before, is known as an electronically commutated motor (ECM), brushless dc motor (BLM), or commutatorless brushless motor (CLM).

Fig. 15 shows a control scheme of a brushless dc drive using a trapezoidally wound surface-type PM machine. Since the induced phase voltages of the machine are trapezoidal in shape, it can be shown that a six-step line current wave in phase with the induced voltage wave will maintain constant developed torque. A Hall-effect or optical encoder properly aligned on the shaft with respect to rotor poles generates three-phase, 180° square pulses, which are shaped to six-step waves by a decoder as shown. The speed loop generates the current magnitude command, which is multiplied by the decoder output to generate phase current command waves. The current control loop generates the voltage command, which is pulse-width modulated (PWM) by a fixed frequency triangular carrier wave. The simplicity of the machine, the position sensor, and the control electronics makes this type of brushless

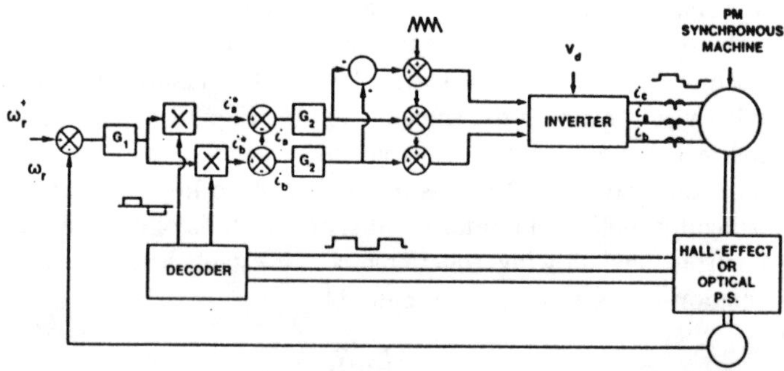

Fig. 15. Control scheme of trapezoidally wound PM (surface) machine in brushless dc motor mode.

drive very popular in industrial motion control systems. However, the drive has a pulsating torque problem because of the mismatch of current switching instants and the machine counter emf wave. Besides, an extra tachometer is needed for a speed control system as shown in the figure.

For a sinusoidally wound PM machine, the inverter can synthesize sine wave line current, and then the pulsating torque problem does not arise. Since in a surface magnet machine the armature reaction effect is very weak, the stator current phasor can be positioned orthogonal to the magnet flux

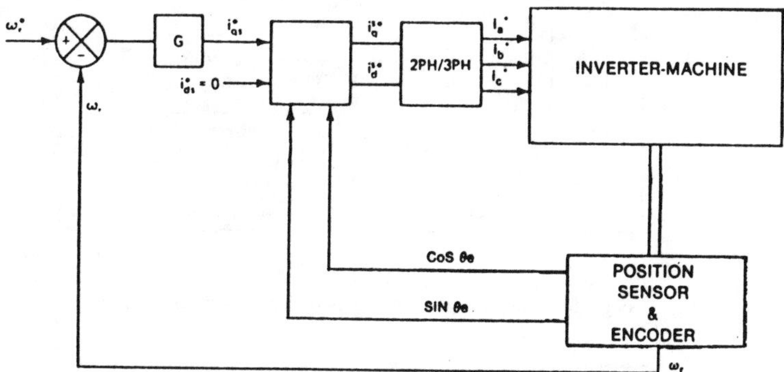

Fig. 16. Vector control scheme of sinusoidal PM (surface) machine in brushless dc motor mode.

(i.e., in phase with counter emf) with the help of an absolute position sensor. Such a decoupling or vector control method, as discussed before, will give true dc machine-like response from a sinusoidal brushless dc motor. Fig. 16 shows a speed control system using such a control scheme. This scheme can be derived from the induction motor vector control method shown in Fig. 13 with the modifications $\omega_{sl} = 0$, $\theta_r = \theta_e$, and $i^*_{ds} = 0$. Since the rotor establishes the airgap flux, the stator need not supply any reactive current. Generally, an expensive position resolver is required in such a control scheme. If a resolver/digital converter is used with an analog resolver, then its outputs can be used not only for vector transformation, (i.e., commutation), but for speed and position control loops as well.

A simple open-loop step motor control scheme (Fig. 17) consists of sequence logic, a power converter and the machine. The sequence logic receives a step input pulse train and direction signal from the host controller, and these are then translated into sequential drive signals to the converter such that the machine stator poles advance by a step in response to a step input pulse. With a step input of constant frequency, the machine runs in the specified direction with the corresponding number of steps per second. In such a "time-dependent commutation" (unlike the position-dependent commutation in a brushless dc machine), the step motor behaves as a synchronous motor, and, therefore, oscillatory response and loss of synchronism are possible, as indicated before. There is also a possibility that the machine may miss step pulses. These disadvantages can be eliminated by a closed-loop control using an incremental position encoder (Fig. 17). Adding the complexity of closed-loop control, step motors have been used for more accurate position control, much higher and smoother speed, and greater versatility in many other aspects. A commonly used closed-loop control, where the phase switching angle is rotor-position-synchronized with advance angle excitation as a function of speed, is shown in Fig. 17. Schemes have been proposed in which rotor position is estimated by observer techniques.

It was indicated before that the switched reluctance machine (SRM) is nothing but a variable reluctance step motor with different controls. An SRM is a continuously controlled machine in which holding torque is established by feedback method. An absolute position encoder is essential for an SRM to provide rotor position synchronized excitation to the stator

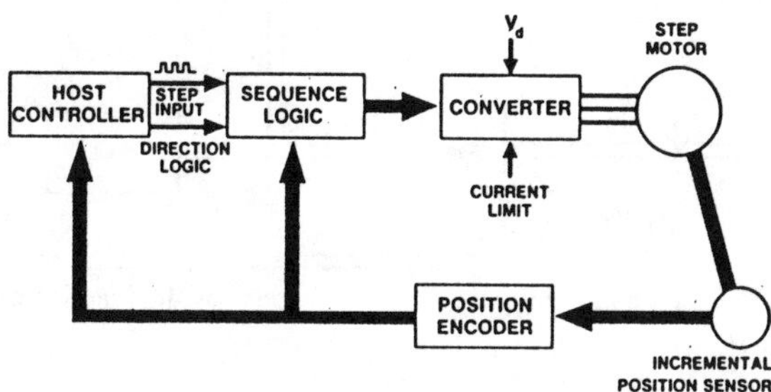

Fig. 17. Step motor control system.

windings. Fig. 18 shows an SRM position servo with an inner speed control loop. An inner high bandwidth torque loop can be provided to compensate pulsating torque at low speed. An absolute position encoder generates commutating signals for converter switches. The machine operates with full performance in all four quadrants. In the forward motoring mode, the stator phases are turned on at an advance angle (θ_0) with respect to positive inductance slope so that full active stator current can be established. The torque is then controlled by chopping the level of current I. Beyond the constant torque region, chopping control is lost, and then turn-off angles can be controlled in the constant power region.

There has been a recent interest in applying modern control theories to motion control systems. The theories have been advanced since the 1960's, but in general, they have not found practical applications. They were initially applied to aerospace systems and general process control applications, but the advent of inexpensive and powerful microcomputers has made it possible to apply them to time-critical motion control systems as well. Although dc drives are receiving most of the attention, ac drives are being considered as well. Applying modern control theory to motion control systems in general is difficult because of large time-critical computation requirements.

Optimal control theory, such as Pontryagin's minimum principle, or the dynamic programming technique, which is based on extensive iterative computation, can be generally applied to a single optimal profile of the drive system. The optimal precomputed profile can be generated, for example, on the basis of minimum time of transit or minimum energy consumption subjected to a number of control constraints. Such optimal control principles are extremely difficult to apply in general motion control systems.

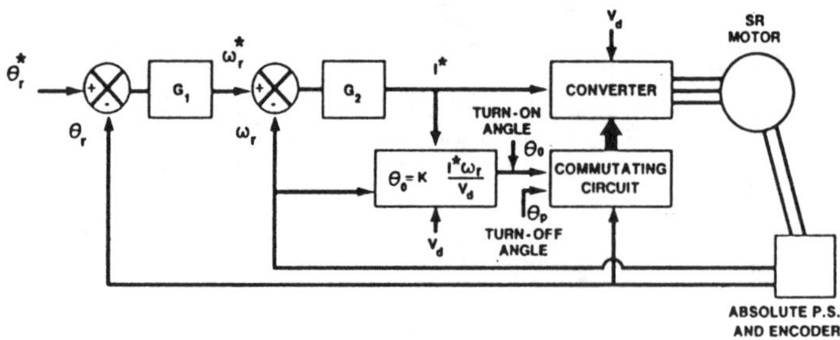

Fig. 18. Position servo using switched reluctance machine.

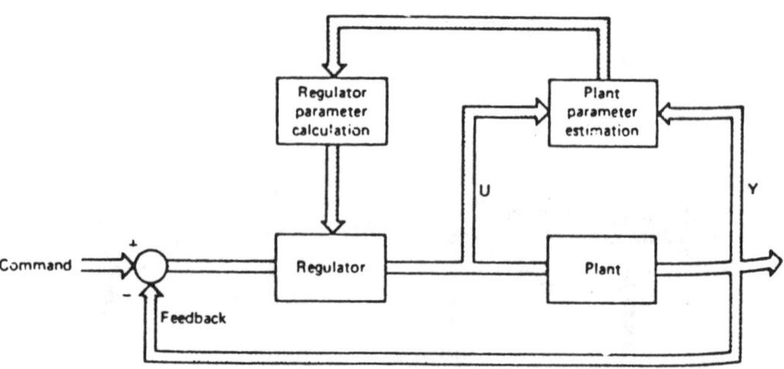

Fig. 19. Self-tuning regulation of drive system based on on-line parameter estimation.

The applications of adaptive control theories, still just beginning, are growing at a rapid pace. They are extremely useful in systems such as robots and machine tool drives, where the system has to be robust, on insensitive to parameter variations. A conventional PI (proportional-integral) or PID (proportional-integral-derivative) controller with fixed parameters cannot generate optimal response in a plant parameter varying system. In self-tuning adaptive control, the controller parameters are tuned to adapt to plant parameter variations. Such a general control scheme is indicated in Fig. 19. The plant parameter estimation algorithm solves the plant model in real-time and updates the plant parameters on the basis of recursive least square identification techniques. A tuning algorithm then adjusts the regulator parameters based on plant parameters. The tuned system may have pole-assignment control, but dead-beat, state-space, or design of time-series control can also be used. The regulator parameters may be updated at a slower rate than the main control loop sampling rate if the plant parameters vary slowly (which may not be necessarily true). For successful operation of the global system, stability is essential.

In a model referencing adaptive control (Fig. 20), the plant response is forced to track the response of a reference model irrespective of plant parameter variation. The reference model with fixed parameters is stored in microcomputer memory, and therefore the response of the plant becomes insensitive to parameter variation. The speed command ω_r^* generated by the position control loop in Fig. 20 is applied in parallel to the reference model and plant controller. The reference model output ω_{rm} is compared with the measured plant speed ω_r, and the resulting error signal e actuates the adaptation algorithm. The feedforward and feedback gains K_f and K_B, respectively, of the plant controller are iterated by the adaptation algorithm so as to dynamically reduce the error e to zero. The plant can track the reference model without saturation, provided the parameters in the reference model are defined on a worst-case basis. Therefore, the desired robustness of the control system is obtained at the sacrifice of optimum response speed. In general, the structure of the reference model and the plant should be the same, and the parameters should be compatible for satisfactory adaptation. The global stability of the system can be analyzed by Popov's hyperstability theorem.

A model referencing adaptive control system with a PI controller that is based on an on-line search strategy is shown in Fig. 21. For example, the plant under consideration may be a vector-controlled induction motor, where rotor resistance variation causes a coupling effect and torque sensitivity with I_{qs}^* changes. The parameters of PI torque controller can be adapted to compensate the plant parameter variation, so that the system tracks the reference model. The controller parameters K_1 and K_2 are varied by trial-and-error so that the error between actual and desired responses remains bounded within a hysteresis band. Again, the reference model is to be determined on the basis of worst-case parameters of the plant so that the torque loop can physically track the reference model.

A sliding-mode or variable-structure control technique has been applied successfully to both dc and ac drive systems. Basically, it is an adaptive model-referencing control (MRAC), but is easier to implement by microcomputer than the conventional MRAC system. The sliding mode control is ideally suitable for position servo, such as robot and machine tool drives, where problems related to mechanical inertia variation and load disturbance effect can be eliminated. The control can be extended to multiple drives where close speed or position tracking is desired. In sliding mode control, the "reference model" or a predefined trajectory in the phase is stored in a microcomputer, and the drive system is forced to follow or "slide" along the trajectory by a switching control algorithm, irrespective of plant parameter variation and load torque disturbance. The microcomputer detects the deviation of the actual trajectory from the reference trajectory and correspondingly changes the switching topology to restore tracking. Fig. 22 shows sliding mode control applied to a vector-controlled induction motor drive system, and Fig. 23 shows the sliding trajectory for both forward and reverse motions in phase plane. The sliding trajectory of the reference contour defines acceleration (δ_1), constant speed (δ_2), and deceleration (δ_3) segments which are beyond the drift band, so that the system always remains controllable. The actual sliding curve that follows the defined trajectory is given by a zigzag line in the direction of the arrow. The phase plane trajectory

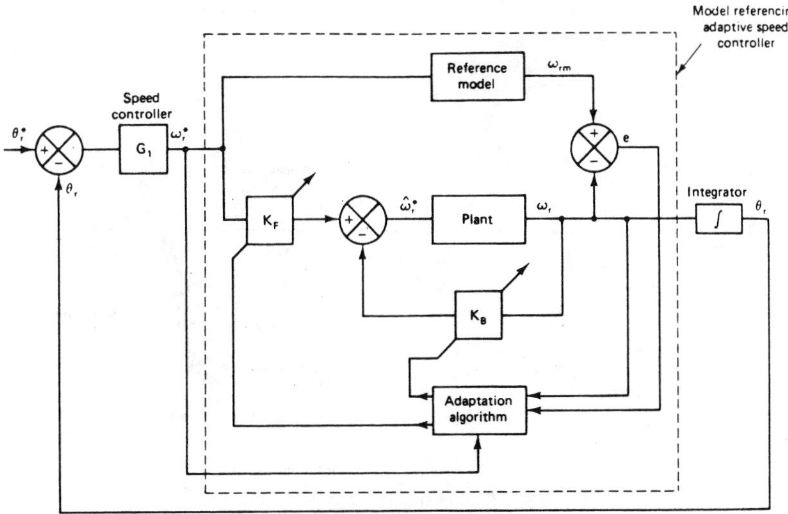

Fig. 20. Model referencing adaptive control (MRAC) system.

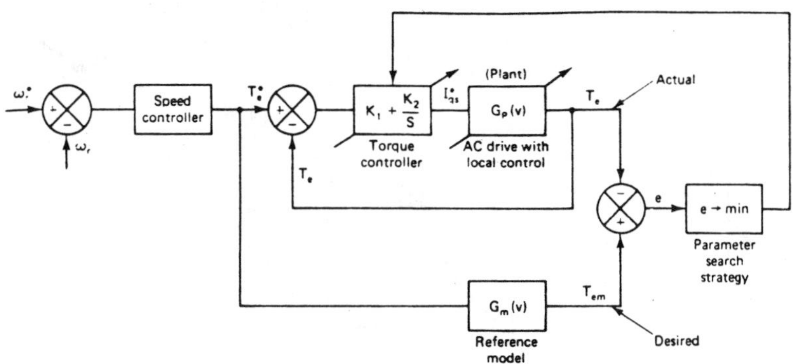

Fig. 21. Self-optimizing controller based on search strategy.

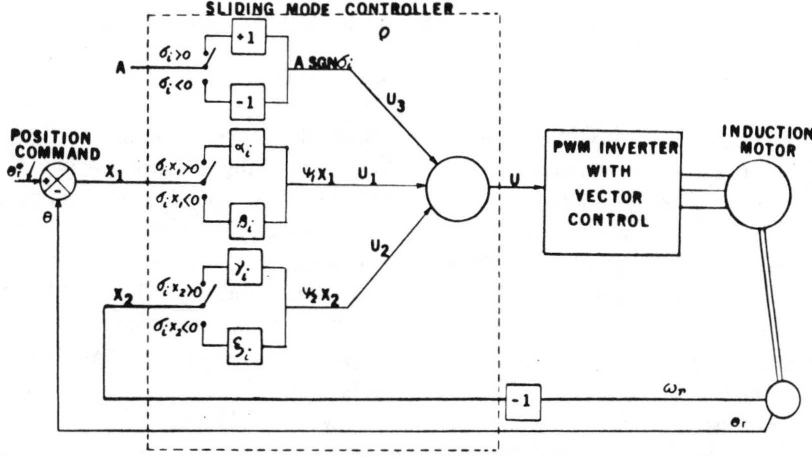

Fig. 22. Sliding mode control of induction motor.

can easily be translated into a corresponding time domain response. In a sliding mode controller, the position loop error (X_1), its derivative (X_2), and a constant A are transmitted through single-pole double-throw (SPDT) switches and the respective gains to constitute the effective control input U. The position of SPDT switches is determined by the operating point with respect to the defined trajectory. The jitter in the response can be regulated by good resolution of signals, small sampling time of computation, and high switching frequency of the inverter.

V. Microcomputer Control

The advent of microcomputers has brought a new dimension in motion control technology. The impact of this evolution is as significant as the advent of power semiconductor devices in the 1950s. It is interesting to see that both ends of the spectrum

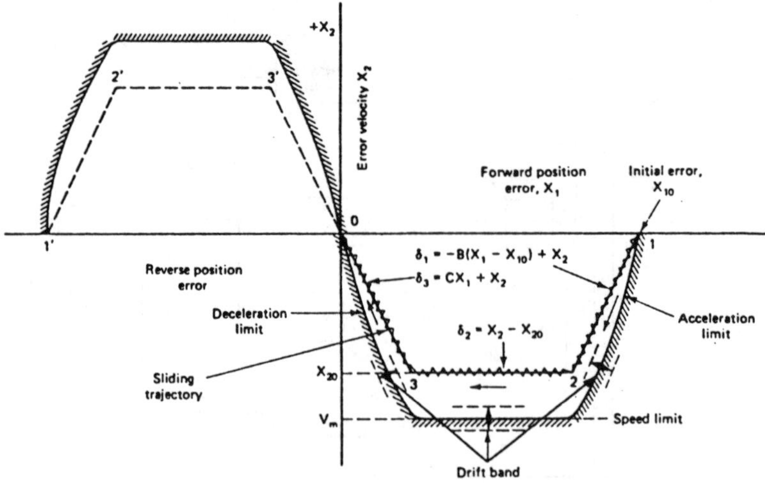

Fig. 23. Sliding trajectory in phase plane.

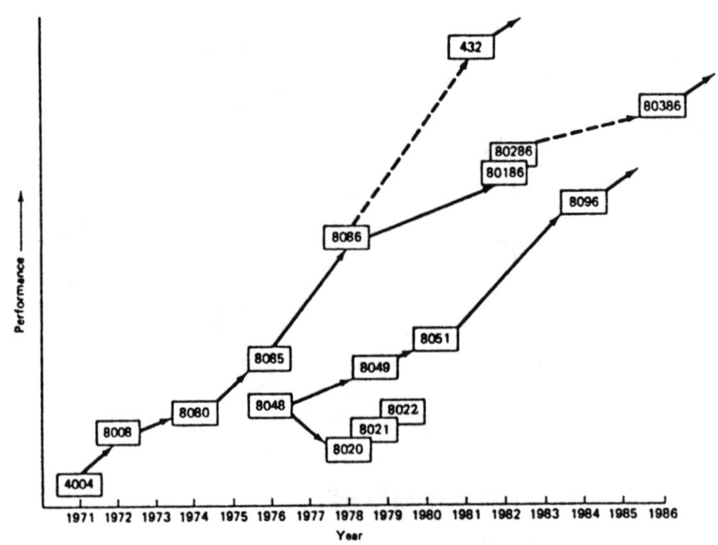

Fig. 24. Intel microprocessor evolution.

are digital: power semiconductors provide the muscle, whereas microcomputers provide the brain. Microcomputers have now found universal acceptance in motion control systems.

The advantages of microcomputers, seem obvious. They provide significant cost reduction in control electronics, improve reliability, and eliminate drift and electromagnetic interference (EMI) problems. They also permit design of universal hardware and flexible software control. Software can be updated or altered as the system performance demands change. "Micro" has the powerful capability of complex computation and decision-making. With the present trend toward computer-automated factories, microcontrol provides a compatible communication link in the computer hierarchy.

Microcontrol has the disadvantage of signal quantization and sampling delay. It is sluggish compared to dedicated hardware. In motion control, micro has time-critical functions which are unheard of in general process control applications. Of course, computation speed can be enhanced by parallel processing, use of more dedicated hardware, and assembly language programs.

Since the introduction of microcomputers in 1971 by Intel Corporation, the technology has gone through an intense evolution in the last two and a half decades. Intel microcomputers have dominated in motion control systems; other key competitors in the market are Motorola, Zilog, Texas Instruments, and National Semiconductor. Fig. 24 shows an overview of Intel microcomputer evolution. Here, the performance can be considered as a weighted average of bit size, components, improvement of hardware and software features, and so on. The 8080 is, in fact, the first generation microcomputer, which was once the industry's most commonly used micro. The evolution indicates two general directions: the multi-chip and single-chip families. Both 8- and 16-bit microcomputers are widely used, but as the price is coming down and system functions are increasing, the 16-bitters are finding more acceptance. A very dominant member of the Intel family is the 16-bit, single-chip 8096 microcontroller, which is designed for real-time control applications. The key features of the 8096 are summarized in Table I; Fig. 25 shows its architecture. It has a built-in A/D converter that can accept unipolar signals and a PWM output that can be used for

TABLE I
KEY FEATURES OF INTEL 8096 MICROCONTROLLER

* 8K-byte on-chip ROM
* 232-byte register space (RAM)
* 10-bit, eight-channel A/D converter
* Five 8-bit I/O ports
* Full-duplex serial port
* High-speed pulse I/O
* Pulse-width-modulated output
* Eight interrupt sources
* Four 16-bit software timers and two 16-bit hardware timers
* Watchdog timer
* Hardware (microcoded) signed and unsigned multiply/divide

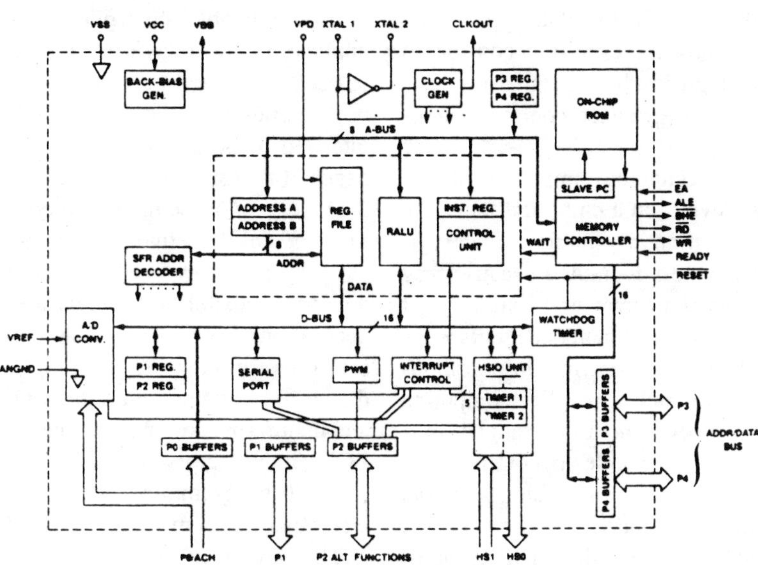

Fig. 25. Architecture of Intel 8096 microcomputer.

D/A conversion. With a 12-MHz clock frequency, the 8096 can do 16-bit addition in 1.0 μs and a 16 $\times$ 16 multiply or 32/16 divide in 6.5 μs. The other interesting features are high-speed trigger inputs (HSI's) and high-speed outputs (HSO's). The HSI's look for transition of input lines and record the times at which external events occur. The HSO's trigger external events at preset times and therefore can be used to generate interrupts at preset times. This microcomputer is expected to find wide applications in motion control.

Digital signal processors are high-speed microcomputers than generally act as peripheral components to a central processor and help in processing I/O signals. A very dominant member in this family is the TMS32010, which was introduced by Texas Instruments several years ago. The key features of this chip are given in Table II. The 16-bit microcomputer has 160 ns instruction cycle time (32010-25), which includes 16 $\times$ 16-bit multiply instruction. More recently, a CMOS version (320C25) has been announced in which the speed has been enhanced to 100 ns. Faster program execution has been possible in the TMS320 family by using what is called modified Harvard architecture, which permits overlap of instruction fetch and execution of consecutive instructions. In addition, the chip uses a dedicated hardware multiplier and barrel shifter. The TMS32020, which represents a considerable enhancement of its predecessor, the TMS32010, contains 544-word on-chip RAM, 128 K-words of ROM, sixteen input and output channels, three external interrupts, and one hardware timer.

TABLE II
KEY FEATURES OF TMS32010 DIGITAL SIGNAL PROCESSOR

* 160-ns instruction cycle
* 144-word on-chip data RAM
* 1.5 K-word on-chip program ROM-TMS320M10
* External memory expansion to a total of 4 K words at full speed
* 16-bit instruction/data word
* 32-bit ALU/accumulator
* 16 $\times$ 16-bit multiply in 160 ns
* 0 to 15-bit barrel shifter
* Eight input and eight output channels
* 16-bit bidirectional data bus with 50 megabits/s transfer rate
* Interrupt with full context save
* Signed two's complement fixed-point arithmetic
* NMOS technology
* Single 5-V supply
* Two versions available
  TMS32010-20—20.5 MHz clock
  TMS32010-25—25.0 MHz clock

We are beginning to see the emerging growth of 32-bit microcomputers in the market. Though National Semiconductor originally introduced 32-bit architecture four years ago, the age of the 32-bit machine truly started with the introduction of Motorola's 68020. At present, the other prominent members of the 32-bit family are Intel's 80386, Zilog's Z8000, AT&T's WE32100, and National's NS32C532. In terms of data processing capability, microcomputers can now successfully complete with mainframes and minicomputers. An interesting architecture of 32-bit machine is RISC (reduced instruction set computer) architecture which, because of its simplicity and single-cycle per-instruction operation, can considerably enhance the capabilities of microcomputers. The Inmos "Transputer" family are the first commercially available RISC machines. An example is the 32-bit T414 (1.5 micron, 200,000 transistors), which runs at 10 MIPS (million instructions/s) with memory transfer rate up to 25 MHz. The 32-bit machines will initially make inroads for data processing applications, but as prices come down, they will be considered for real-time control. Besides high-resolution signal processing, they will be useful in high-performance control systems using modern control theories.

As semiconductor processing technology improves, it will be possible to integrate more devices in a chip, and therefore to achieve more functional integration in a microcomputer. At present, the speed of microcomputers is limited because they operate in an inherently sequential manner. Using VLSI techniques, systems can be built in which many elements work in parallel on the same problem, thus allowing an enormous increase in processing speeds. In such a parallel computing system,[2] a large number of processors are arranged in a rectangular grid, with each processor able to communicate with its nearest neighbors on the grid, and, using a global communication system with any other processor in the machine. The machine operates in a single-instruction, multiple-data mode, which means that all component processors execute the same instruction at the same time. Super microcomputers based on parallel machines will be very expensive initially for real-time control applications.

What role can the microcomputer play in digital motion control systems? Practically all the control functions discussed so far can be implemented by microcomputer. The application areas may include gate-firing control of phase-controlled converters, closed-loop control, nonlinearity compensation, digital filtering, programmable delay, sequencing of control modes, programmable set point commands, system signal monitoring and warning, and data acquisition. Microcomputers have been used for optimal PWM wave generation of an inverter. Powerful micros are permitting vector control and optimal and adaptive control in motion control systems with intricate signal processing. The cost of a drive system can be reduced by using cheap sensors and by reconstructing precise signals with the micro's intelligence. In many cases, sensors can be completely eliminated, or redundant sensor information can be provided by observer computation. System reliability can be enhanced by micro-assisted fault-tolerant control. As the micro's speed and functional integration improve, it will be used in real time or quasi-real time for simulation of motion control systems. Artificial intelligence, another area where the microcomputer will find applications will be discussed later.

[2] The CRAY2, generally acknowledged as the fastest supercomputer currently available, has four processors that execute up to a billion operations per second.

The micro will play an increasingly important role in system tests and diagnostics. The data from a system under test can be captured and processed to determine efficiency, power factor, etc. A personal computer is an important tool in such an application. Automated tests can be performed on a system, and structure and parameters can be identified. System diagnostics can be designed on either an on-line or an off-line basis. On-line diagnostics indicate the healthiness (or sickness) of system operation and give warnings if problems arise. Off-line diagnostics help in troubleshooting a system and minimize plant outage time. Diagnostic programs can be very user-friendly, and can be exercised by unskilled technicians.

Programmable controllers (PC's are finding increasing applications in today's factory floor environments. A PC is basically a general-purpose microcomputer controller that can be programmed for any application. Originally, it was intended to be an electronic replacement of industrial relay panels. Interestingly, the development of this application led to the invention of the microcomputer. From their initial applications in on-off sequencing of motors, solenoids, actuators, etc., PC's have evolved into intelligent workhorses with such advanced capabilities as data acquisition and storage, report generation, execution of complex mathematical algorithms, servo motor control, stepping control, axis control, self-diagnosis, system troubleshooting, and talking to other PC's and mainframe computers. The reasons for the proliferation of PC's on the factory floor are low off-the-shelf hardware cost, ease of programming and reprgramming by an ordinary electrician, system reliability, and ease of maintenance.

The supremacy of the microcomputer has been challenged recently by semi-custom or custom-VLSI circuits. Typically, a chip containing 100,000 or more devices is defined as a VLSI chip. All the peripheral chips of a micro can be integrated into a single chip, or both micro and peripheral chips can have a large single VLSI chip replacement. The advantages of VLSI design are low cost at high volume application, improvement of speed, reliability, and lower power consumption. The semi-custom design in VLSI is shown increasing popularity. The dominant member in this group is the gate array system, which is based on logic system synthesis using identical NAND or NOR gates. The chip may have analog devices to give more functional capability. The design and fabrication of gate array systems are highly computer-aided. Reasonably simple logic functions can be directly translated to gate-array design through what is known as a "silicon compiler." A programmable gate array permits flexible logic system design which can be erased and reprogrammed like an EPROM. In a standard cell VLSI design, individual cell or device parameters may be specified to gain tighter performance control of the circuit. The standard cell approach of semi-custom design normally permits large system design using logic analog, ROM, RAM, and even complete microcomputer function.

VI. Computer-Aided Control System Design

CAD tools are playing an increasingly important role in motion control system design. It is convenient to design and simulate a newly developed control system on a computer before building a breadboard. The traditional paper-and-pencil design of a control system and then trial-and error experiment in the laboratory may be very time-consuming, expensive, and frustrating, especially if the control system is complex and a lot of uncertainty is involved in performance. Both analog and digital computers have been used in the past for system design and simulation. In a hybrid computer, the control system can be appropriately partitioned for analog, logic, and digital simulation. Digital computers have found preference in recent years, and more and more powerful and user-friendly CAD programs are appearing in the market. By way of illustration, two general groups of CAD programs will be briefly reviewed.

The VAX-based federated CAD system [39] essentially consists of several independently developed subsystems tied together (Fig. 26) by a system supervisor and unified data base. The objective is to provide the user with a unified system that spans the entire control design problem: modeling, design, and simulation. In a federated system, the subsystems are loosely coupled, and each subsystem can be used as a standalone program. The additional advantages are that component programs can be added, deleted, or altered without affecting the main system. The first package, called IDPAC, is used for data analysis and identification of linear system. It can manipulate and plot data, and make correlation analysis, special analysis, and model identification. The next package, CLADP, permits frequency domain design methods. These include Bode, Nyquist, and root-locus design. The SSDP is a state-space design package that provides time domain design techniques. The MATLAB, which stands for "matrix laboratory," is used to solve matrix-related problems. The SIMNON is a Fortran-based simulation program for nonlinear dynamic systems. Both continuous and discrete time systems can be simulated on a VAX using SIMNON. The simulation of a discrete time system with prescribed sampling time is of particular importance to a microcomputer-based control system. SIMNON accepts descriptions of a dynamic system in state-space form; i.e., a continuous system is described by differential equations and a discrete time system by difference equations. For simulation, a large system is normally resolved into small interconnected subsystems. A connecting system routine links the subsystems by I/O signals. SIMNON can interface specially formatted FORTRAN to expand its capabilities.

CTRL-C, developed by Systems Control Technology, is an interactive computer language for the analysis and design of multivariable linear control systems and signal processing. Systems may be described in state-space, transfer function, or continuous or discrete-time forms. Transformations between representations are simple and straightforward. A powerful matrix environment provides a workbench for system simulation, signal generation, matrix analysis and graphics. The ACSL is a continuous system simulation language that can be used for simulation of nonlinear dynamic systems, both in continuous and discrete time form. It can be integrated with CTRL-C (Fig. 27) to form a complete CAD design and simulation package. Both the programs are Fortran based, and the completed package is available for VAX and other computers.

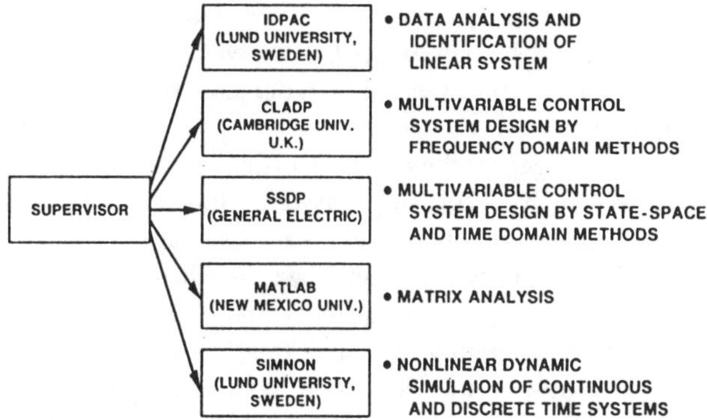

Fig. 26. Federated CAD of control system.

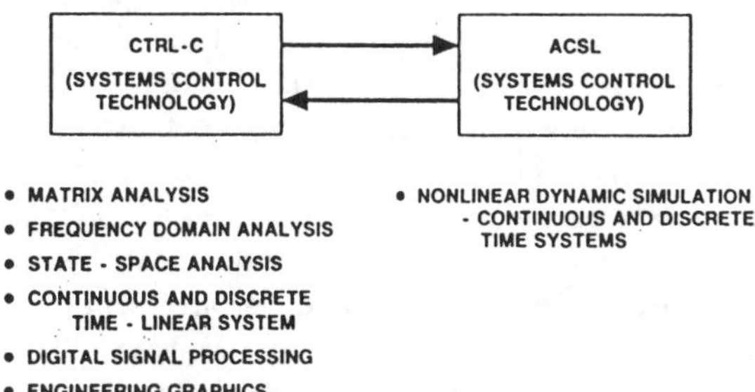

Fig. 27. CTRL-C/ACSL CAD system.

The tools for design of control systems can be divided into two categories: computer-aided control system design (CACSD), which is based on a mathematical model of a system, has been discussed above; the other is hardware/software architecture simulation for microcomputer-based control systems. An example in the latter category is HCSE (Hierarchical Control System Emulation), which was originally developed by Bolt, Beranek and Newmans, Inc. [42] for the National Bureau of Standards to support the development of their Automated Manufacturing Research Facility. The VAX-based HCSE simulation tool set permits emulation of a multiprocessor/multitasking system in the form of finite state machine (FSM) [47]. As mentioned before, only the hardware/software architecture is considered in the emulation without regard to actual implementation in hardware and software. The controller emulation in HCSE can be linked with plant simulation in SIMNON to evaluate design tradeoffs. When performance criteria are established, prototype hardware and software can be designed.

Computer-aided system design tools are in the process evolution and will undergo many changes in the future. The personal computer is expected to play an increasingly important role in this area. As microcomputer speed improves and memory becomes cheaper, more time-critical controls will be implemented in high-level languages. Eventually, the simulation software will be down-loaded directly to prototype microcomputer memory and use as real-time control software.

VII. Artificial Intelligence in Control

A significant advance has been made recently in control and CAD techniques by the introduction of artificial intelligence, or expert systems. Artificial intelligence involves programming a computer so that it can mimic human thinking. An expert system essentially tends to mechanize the expertise of a human being. A human expert has knowledge, an experience base, and the power of reasoning, judgment, and intuition. In a sense, conventional computer programs have some degree of artificial intelligence: they make decisions on questions which have clear-cut "yes" or "no" answers. But human thinking is often qualitative, involving ideas such as "large," "small," or "medium." Fuzzy logic[3] and fuzzy set[4] theories have been developed for computers to quantify and objectively evaluate the subjective ambiguity of human thinking.

There is now a tremendous surge of activity in expert systems applications. These include robotics, industrial process control, computer-aided design and diagnostics, medical diagnosis and prescription, medical knowledge automation, chemical and biological synthesis, mineral and oil exploration, space defence, air-traffic control, VLSI design, speech understanding, and knowledge-based management. An expert system can help in designing control structures and parameters for a desired performance goal. For example, a pole-placement design of a multivariable control system can be obtained automatically if a plant model and the desired set of poles are furnished to the computer. Expert-system-based diagnostics can locate faults in a complex control system with extensive man-machine dialogues. Such troubleshooting methods have already been used for diesel electric locomotives and jet engines. Expert systems are also being used for real-time control applications. In such a system, a controller can tune itself as it monitors the process and learns the dynamics of the operation, much as an experiences human operator would do. An example of such an auto-tuning regulator is the Foxboro Model 760, which can control a system that is not well understood and difficult to model. It is essentially a microcomputer-based PID controller with some 200 production rules. The self-tuning method is a pattern recognition approach that allows the user to specify desired temporal response to disturbances in the controlled parameter or in the controlled set point. The controller than observes the actual shape of these disturbances and adjusts its PID values to restore the desirable response.

A typical architecture of real-time expert control system is shown in Fig. 28. The plant under consideration may be unknown or difficult to model. A set of sensors measures the important variables that characterize the state of the process, and the pattern recognizers extract the features to detect important events. The rule base contains the knowledge of expert operators or designers and of the overall control strategy for all the regimes. The "meta control" can select the control strategy and define the control parameters. The speed of computation, system stability and robustness are serious issues in expert system control, and generally it requires extensive computer simulation study before actual implementation.

[3] Fuzzy logic is a kind of logic using graded or qualified statements rather than ones that are strictly true or false. The results of fuzzy reasoning are not as definite as those derived by strict logic.

[4] Fuzzy sets that do not have a crisply defined membership, but rather allow objects to have grades of membership from 0 to 1.

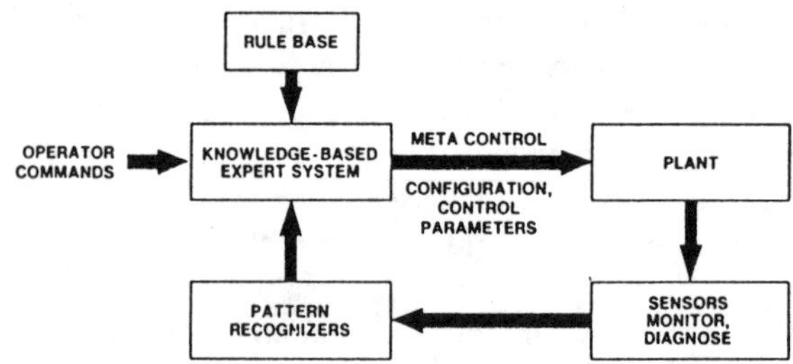

Fig. 28. Architecture of real-time expert control system.

VIII. Conclusion

This report has presented a comprehensive review of technology trends in microcomputer control of electrical machines. Although microcomputer control and computer-aided design techniques are our main themes of discussion, motion control as multidisciplinary technology has been reviewed in the broad perspective of electrical machines, power semiconductor devices, converter technology, microcomputers, and VLSI circuits. The concepts discussed in this report are valid not only for small machines, but for large machines as well.

Before concluding, I think that it is relevant to give some thought to the consequences of the "new" industrial revolution. Will it create more affluence for a privileged segment of society—thus furthering the gap between haves and have nots? Will it create a massive unemployment problem? Will the material prosperity deprive us of peace and tranquility and fill us with hypertension and restlessness, and consequently, aggravate the problems of our society? Will technological accomplishments bring more power rivalry in the world and bring us closer to war, and eventually destroy us with the results of our "accomplishments?" I think that we—the engineers, the creators of this technological society—should involve ourselves in answering these questions and help in shaping the future of our society. We, the human beings of this planet, are collectively responsible for our destiny. If accomplishments in technology have adverse influence on the society, that is not a justification for halting the march of technology.

References

[1] B. K. Bose, *Power Electronics and AC Drives.* Englewood Cliffs, NJ: Prentice-Hall, 1986.

[2] ——, "Motion control technology—Present and future," *IEEE Trans. Ind. Appl.*, vol. IA-21, pp. 1337–1342, Nov./Dec. 1985.

[3] ——, "Adjustable speed AC drives—A technology status review," *Proc. IEEE*, vol. 70, pp. 116–135, Feb. 1982.

[4] F. Fukuchi and H. Awane, "Recent trends and the future of Hitachi robots," *Hitachi Rev.*, vol. 34, pp. 1–3, 1985.

[5] E. J. Lerner, "Computer-aided manufacturing," *IEEE Spectrum*, pp. 34–39, Nov. 1981.

[6] D. Jones, "Trends in factory automation," *Motion*, p. 28, 2nd. quarter, 1985.

[7] S. Saba, "Electronics challenges for innovation in industrial and social systems," in *Int. Power Elec. Conf. Rec.*, Tokyo, Japan, pp. 1–4, 1983.

[8] E. Ohno *et al.*, "The thyristor commutatorless motor," *IEEE Trans. Magn.*, vol. MAG-3, pp. 236–240, Sept. 1967.

[9] T. Kenjo *et al.*, "A closed-loop control of a five-phase hybrid step motor," in *Proc. 13th Ann. Symp. of Inc. Motion Control Conf.*, pp. 167–181, June 1984.

[10] B. C. Kuo, Step Motors and Control Systems, SRL, Champaign, IL, 1979.

[11] L. F. Wade, "Step motors versus dc motors—which one?" in *Motor Con Conf. Rec.*, pp. 345-351, Oct. 1985.
[12] C. Oudet and D. J. Ettelman, "An alternative to choosing between dc and stepper motors," in *Power Conv. Intl.*, pp. 50-58, May 1985.
[13] J. V. Byrne, "High performance variable reluctance drive: A new brushless servo," in *Motor Con Conf. Rec.*, pp. 147-160, Oct. 1985.
[14] A. Cogan and R. A. Blanchard, "Discrete semiconductor switches: still improving," in *Power Conv. and Int. Motion Control*, pp. 15-22, Jan. 1986.
[15] V. A. K. Temple, "MOS controlled thyristors, " in *IEDM Proc.*, pp. 282-285, 1984.
[16] B. J. Baliga *et al.*, "The insulated gate transistor, a new three-terminal MOS-controlled bipolar power device," *IEEE Trans. Electron Devices*, vol. ED-31, pp. 821-828, 1984.
[17] V. Rumennick, "Power devices are in the chips," *IEEE Spectrum*, pp. 42-48, July 1985.
[18] M. H. Kuo and K. D. T. Ngo, "Modeling and simulation of PWM dc-dc converters," in *IEEE Applied Elec.Conf. Rec.*, New Orleans, LA, pp. 184-192, 1986.
[19] R. H. Comstock, "Trends in brushless permanent magnet and induction motor servo drives," *Motion*, pp. 4-12, 2nd. quarter, 1985.
[20] B. K. Bose *et al.*, "Microcomputer control of switched reluctance motor, " in *IEEE/IAS Ann. Meet. Conf. Rec.*, pp. 542-547, 1985.
[21] F. Blaschke, "The principle of field orientation as applied to the new TRANSVECTOR closed loop control system for rotating field machines," *Siemens Rev.*, vol. 34, pp. 217-220, May 1972.
[22] K. Hasse, "Zur dynamik drehzahlgeregelter antriebe mit stromrichtergespeisten asynchronkurzschlublaufermaschinen," Darmstadt Tech. Hoch. diss. 1969.
[23] R. Gabriel *et al.*, "Field oriented control of a standard ac motor using microprocessors," in *IEEE/IAS Ann. Meet. Conf. Rec.*, pp. 910-916, 1979.
[24] A. Brickwedde, "Microprocessor-based adaptive speed and position control of electrical drives," in *IEEE/IAS Annu. Meet. Conf. Rec.*, pp. 411-417, 1984.
[25] U. Itkis, *Control Systems of Variable Structures.* New York: Wiley, 1976.
[26] G.Fromme, "Self-optimizing controller employing microprocessor," in *Proc. Microelect. Power Elec. Electr. Drives*, Darmstadt, pp. 117-125, 1982.
[27] B. K. Bose, "Sliding mode control of induction motor," in *IEEE/IAS Ann. Meet. Conf. Rec.*, pp. 479-486, 1985.
[28] F. Harashima *et al.*, "MOSFET converter-fed position servo system with sliding mode control," in *Power Elec. Spec. Conf. Rec.*, pp. 73-79, June 1983.
[29] Y. D. Landau, *Adaptive Control.* New York: Dekker, 1979.
[30] G. Kaufman *et al.*, "High performance servo drives for machine tool applications using ac motors," in *IEEE/IAS Ann. Meet. Conf. Rec.*, pp. 604-609, Oct. 1982.
[31] W. Schumacher, "Microprocessor controlled ac servo drive," *Proc. Microelec. Power Elec. Electr. Drives*, Darmstadt, pp. 311-320, 1982.
[32] B. K. Bose, Ed., *Adjustable Speed AC Drive Systems.* New York: IEEE Press, 1981.
[33] J. Voelker, "Microprocessors-technology '86," *IEEE Spectrum*, pp. 46-48, Jan. 1986.
[34] "Parallel processors enter the marketplace," *The Institute*, June 1986.
[35] G. Zorpette, "The beauty of 32 bits," *IEEE Spectrum*, pp. 65-71, Sept. 1985.
[36] P. Wallich, "Toward simpler, faster computers," *IEEE Spectrum*, pp. 38-45, Aug. 1985.
[37] R. K. Jurgen, "Industry's workhorse gets smarter," *IEEE Spectrum*, pp. 34-38, Feb. 1982.
[38] D. K.Frederick, "Computer packages for the simulation and design of control systems," Arab School on Science and Tech., 4th Summer Session, Bloudan, Syria, Sept. 1981.
[39] H. A. Spang, "The federated computer-aided control design system," *Proc. IEEE*, vol. 72, pp. 1724-1731, Dec. 1984.
[40] J. N. Little *et al.*, "CTRL-C and matrix environments for the computer-aided design of control system" *Control. Syst. Tech. Manual*, 1983.
[41] Mitchell & Gaunther Assoc., *ACSL Manual*, July 1985.
[42] T. L. Johnson *et al.*, "Hierarchical control system emulation user's manual," Rep. 5096, Bolt, Beraneck and Newman, Inc., Cambridge, MA, Aug. 1982.
[43] R. G. Phillips and H. S. Sutherland, "Performance evaluation of alternate robot controller architectures using a finite state machine emulator," in *IEEE Int. Conf. on Robotics and Automation, St. Louis, MO, Mar. 1985.*
[44] G. Kaplan, *Technology 1986-Industrial Electronics*, pp. 62-64, Jan. 1986.
[45] W. B. Gevanter, "Expert systems: limited but powerful," *IEEE Spectrum*, pp. 39-45, Aug. 1983.
[46] L. A. Zadeh, "Making computers think like people," *IEEE Spectrum*, pp. 26-32, Aug. 1984.
[47] H. A. Sutherland *et al.*, "A state language for the sequencing in a hybrid vehicle," *IEEE Trans. Ind. Electron.*, vol. IE-30, pp. 318-322, Nov. 1983.
[48] T. R. England, "Neodymium Iron Boron; key to future servo motor performance," in *Motor Con. Proc.*, pp. 223-233, 1985.
[49] B. K. Bose, Ed., *Microcomputer Control of Power Electronics and Drives.* New York: IEEE Press, 1987.

Selected Bibliography

[1] T. A. Lipo, "Recent progress in the development of solid state ac motor drives," *IEEE Trans. Power Electron.*, vol. 3, pp. 105-117, Apr. 1988.

[2] K. Shenai, R. S. Scott, and B. J. Baliga, "Optimum semiconductors for high-power electronics," *IEEE Trans. Electron Devices*, vol. 36, pp. 1811-1823, Sept. 1989.

[3] W. McMurray, "Survey of controlled electronic power converters," *First IFAC Symp. Contr. Power Electron. Elec. Drives*, pp. 39-62, 1974.

[4] E. Ohno, "The semiconductor evolution in Japan—A four decade long maturity thriving to an indespensible social standing," *Int. Power Electron. Conf. Rec.*, Tokyo, pp. 1-10, 1990.

[5] B. K. Bose, "Adjustable speed ac drives—A technology status review," *Proc. IEEE*, vol. 70, pp. 116-135, Feb. 1982.

[6] B. K. Bose, "Recent advances in power electronics," *Proc. IECON'90*, pp. 829-838, 1990.

[7] P. C. Sen, "Electric motor drives and control—Past, present and future," *IEEE Trans. Ind. Electron.*, vol. 37, pp. 562-575, Dec. 1990.

[8] N. Mohan, "Power electronic circuits: An overview," *Proc. IECON'88*, pp. 522-527, 1988.

[9] V. Rajagopalan, "Computer-aided analysis of power electronic systems," *Proc. IECON'88*, pp. 528-533, 1988.

[10] W. Leonhard, "Adjustable speed ac drives," *Proc. IEEE*, vol. 76, pp. 455-471, April 1988.

[11] R. D. Middlebrook, "Power electronics: An emerging discipline," *IEEE Int. Symp. Circuits Systs.*, vol. 1, pp. 225-229, April 1981.

[12] B. K. Bose, "Motion control technology—Present and future," *IEEE Trans. Ind. Applicat.*, vol. IA-21, pp. 1337-1342, Nov./Dec. 1985.

[13] K. Heumann, "Power electronics—State of the art," *Int. Power Electron. Conf. Rec.*, Tokyo, pp. 11-20, 1990.

[14] R. G. Hoft, "Power electronics: Historical review, present status and future prospect," *Int. Power Electron. Conf. Rec.*, Tokyo, 1983.

[15] V. R. Stefanović and S. P. Peterlongo, "Current developments in ac drives," *Int. Power Electron. Conf. Rec.*, Tokyo, pp. 382-390, 1983.

[16] E. L. Owen, M. M. Morack, C. C. Herskind, and A. S. Grimes, "AC adjustable speed drives with electronic power converters—The early days," *IEEE/IAS Ann. Meet. Conf. Rec.*, pp. 854-861, 1982.

[17] V. Rajagopalan, "Computer aided analysis of power electronic systems," *Proc. IECON'89*, pp. 528-533, 1989.

Part 3
Power Semiconductor Devices and Power Integrated Circuits

Paper 3.1

The Evolution of Power Device Technology

MICHAEL S. ADLER, SENIOR MEMBER, IEEE, KING W. OWYANG, MEMBER, IEEE, B. JAYANT BALIGA, FELLOW, IEEE, AND RICHARD A. KOKOSA, SENIOR MEMBER, IEEE

Abstract—Power semiconductor devices and their associated technology have come a long way from their beginnings with the invention of the bipolar transistor in the late 1940's. Presently, the spectrum of what are referred to as "power devices" span a very wide range of devices and technology from the massive 4 in, 3000-A thyristor to the high-voltage integrated circuit and the power MOSFET, a device of VLSI complexity containing up to 150 000 separate transistors.

In this paper, the past, present, and future of power devices will be reviewed. The first section will be a historical perspective indicating the key events and developments of the past that brought the power devices of today to their present state. The second section of the paper will review the technology and characteristics of bipolar power devices with separate subsections on thyristors, the gate turn-off thyristor (GTO), and the bipolar transistor. Within the thyristor subsection there will be discussions of the phase control thyristor, the inverter thyristor, the asymmetric thyristor (ASCR) the reverse conducting thyristor (RCT), the gate-assisted turn-off thyristor (GATT), and finally the light-triggered thyristor (LTT).

The third section of the paper is devoted to the new field of integrated power devices and will review the evolution to the present power MOS devices including the power MOSFET, the insulated gate transistor (IGT), and the high voltage IC (HVIC).

The last section of the paper reviews the future of power devices with projections as to future ratings of power devices for both the traditional bipolar devices, such as the thyristor, GTO, and bipolar transistor, as well as the integrated devices such as the MOSFET and the IGT. In case of the former, in particular the thyristor, the maximum device ratings will be tied to the availability of large area float zone material, currently difficult to obtain in the high resistivities needed for power devices. In the case of integrated devices, the maximum ratings will be limited by the maximum die area for which acceptable device yields can be obtained. This is identical to the situation for conventional IC's since much of the unit processing is the same.

I. Historical Perspective and Introduction

Process Technology

TODAY it is difficult to imagine a world of power conversion and control without silicon power devices. Forty years ago, the introduction of selenium rectifiers was heralded as a major advance over the thyratrons, ignitrons, and even copper-oxide devices of that time. However, the selenium era proved to be short-lived. In the late 1940's a number of important successive developments initiated the dawn of today's semiconductor era. Although point contact diodes were in use in the 1940s, most important was the discovery of the point contact transistor in 1947 [1], [2] and the invention of the junction transistor in 1949 [3] at Bell Labs. Supported by countless process innovations, device concepts, and developments in physical understanding, the junction transistor formed the foundation for today's integrated circuits and power electronics businesses.

Manuscript received July 1, 1984; revised July 15, 1984.

The authors are with General Electric Company, Corporate Research and Development Center, Schenectady, NY 12301.

In 1952, Hall [4] demonstrated the first significant power devices based upon semiconductor technology. The devices were fabricated using germanium mesa alloy junctions and resulted in a rectifier with impressive electrical characteristics for that time, i.e., a continuous forward current capability of 35 A and a reverse blocking voltage of 200 V. Hall also used the recently developed theories of carrier recombination, generation [5], [6], and current flow [7] to successfully model the electrical characteristics of power rectifiers and transistors.

In the mid 1950's power device characteristics capitalized on the development of single-crystal silicon technology. The larger band gap of silicon rectifiers resulted in higher reverse voltage capability and higher operating temperatures. By the late 1950's, 500-V rectifiers were available in alloy junctions. The introduction of diffused junctions combined with mesa technology in the late 1950's proved to be the step necessary to realize reverse blocking capability of several kilovolts in later years. By the mid 1960's, theoretical avalanche breakdown voltages of up to 9000 V [8] had been achieved by optimized contouring of mesa junctions [9]. Increased current handling capability became a possibility by optimizing device packaging for minimum thermal and mechanical stress on the chip. Today, 77-mm diam silicon rectifiers are available with continuous current ratings of 5000 A and reverse voltages of 3000 V.

To put this development in perspective, while the first commercially available silicon transistors were announced by TI in 1954 [10], it was almost a decade later that their practical application to high-power conversion and control began. Emitter current crowding [11], reliability, and materials processing challenges precluded economic justification. The introduction of the planar process by Fairchild [12] plus the application of photolithography techniques to wafer processing resulted in the birth of the power transistor business in the 1960's. A decade of effort in the industry related to second breakdown [13], power/speed performance and unique processes such as epitaxy deposition [14] paid off. By the late 1970's 200-A 500-V bipolar Darlington transistors with a gain of 50 were available together with 100-V 10-A transistors which could operate at frequencies up to 1 MHz. Since then, however, the application of MOS technology to power transistors has been a major focus of the industry due to the promise of high-speed and high-input impedance in many low-voltage applications.

Reprinted from *IEEE Trans. Electron Devices*, vol. ED-31, no. 11, pp. 1570–1591, November 1984.

Device Technologies

Beyond the important developments in material and process technology described above, there have been many significant device developments. One of the first of these was the publication of the P-N-P-N transistor switch concept in 1956 by Moll *et al.* [15]. Although probably envisioned to be used for Bell's signal applications, engineers at General Electric quickly recognized its significance to power conversion and control and within nine months announced the first commercial silicon controlled rectifier in 1957. This three-terminal power switch was fabricated using a 5-mm square alloy-diffused mesa silicon chip and had a continuous current rating of 25 A and a blocking voltage capability of 300 V. The shorted emitter concept [16] plus the planar process resulted in planar diffused SCR's in 1962. These processes resulted in high-voltage blocking capability at junction temperatures of 125°C and made practical power control and conversion possible.

Since the early 1960's, thyristor producers have capitalized upon the process innovations of the signal industry while introducing new devices or structural improvements to existing devices. In 1961 a gate turnoff thyristor (GTO) was disclosed [17] which combined the switching properties of a transistor with the low conduction losses of an SCR. In 1964 a bidirectional ac switch (TRIAC) was introduced by General Electric [18] principally for 60-cycle consumer lighting and motor speed control. In 1965, light-triggered thyristors were developed [19] which later found significant application in optoelectronic couplers. In the late 1960's a number of advances were made in the design of thyristor cathode gate structures. Incorporation of interdigitated gates made possible high-power 20-kHz inverters. Similarly, the inclusion of pilot gating techniques [20] decreased the gating requirements as well as improved high-frequency and pulse-duty operation. The reverse conducting thyristor (RCT) and asymetrical SCR were developed in 1970 [21] to provide higher speed capability in those inverter applications where reverse blocking voltage was not required. In the mid 1970's, thyristor designers were intrigued with electric field (or voltage) controlled thyristors [22] which held promise for higher speed performance. The later, however, never came to fruition and the application of MOS concepts has proven to offer similar benefits, but with greater ease of manufacture.

The most recent trend in power devices has been to utilize VLSI technology to create a whole new generation of integrated power devices. This started with the power MOS transistor in the late 1970's [23] and has evolved toward totally new devices such as the MOS-gated thyristor [24], [25] and, most recently, the insulated gate transistor (IGT) [26] also known as the COMFET [27]. This latter device combines the best features of the MOSFET and the bipolar transistor in a device that conducts more current in a unit area than either. In addition to the new discrete devices, monolithic high-voltage integrated circuits (HVIC) that combine power and signal circuitry on a chip have come on the scene. These devices are a dramatic extension of the trend towards mixed technologies in the IC industry and for the first time allow the cost efficiencies of integrated circuitry to be applied in the power area. The initial application areas have been in telecommunications [28], power supplies [29], high-voltage displays [30], and most recently power circuits [31], [32]. However, this is just the beginning and these new devices and HVIC's represent a genuine revolution in the power electronics area. The net result could well be a vast extension of electronics into many new application areas in the home and industry that have been precluded because of the limited capabilities and high cost of power electronics.

Foreword

In this paper, the current status of power device technology will be reviewed in several sections. The first and largest section of the paper will be in the traditional area of high-power devices and will include reviews of thyristors, gate turn-off thyristors (GTO), and bipolar transistors. The second section will deal with the new field of integrated power electronic devices. This will include a review of the evolution of power MOS technology together with a presentation of the characteristics of some of the recent new power devices such as the IGT. Also included in this section will be a review of the important area of HVIC's. The final section of the paper will be projections of device ratings for thyristors, GTO's and bipolar transistors, IGT's, and MOSFET's over the next 10 years. This will include both ratings of terminal currents and voltages as well as a comparison of these devices for power switching applications that will aid the power circuit designer in selecting the optimum device. The comparison will be based on switching efficiency and will be done as a function of frequency in 5 distinct voltage ratings.

II. Bipolar Power Devices

Thyristors

Ever since its introduction, circuit design engineers have been subjecting the thyristor to increasing levels of operating stress and demanding that these devices perform satisfactorily there. The different stress demands that the thyristor must be able to meet are:

1) Higher blocking voltages
2) More current carrying capability
3) Higher di/dt's
4) Higher dv/dt's
5) Shorter turn-off times
6) Lower gate drive
7) Higher operating frequencies.

There are many different thyristors available today which can meet one or more of these requirements but, as always, an improvement in one characteristic is usually only gained at the expense of another. As a result, different thyristors have been optimized for different applications. Today's thyristors can be classified into six general types, namely:

a) Phase Control Thyristor
b) Inverter Thyristor
c) Asymmetrical Thyristor
d) Reverse Conducting Thyristor (RCT)
e) Gate-Assisted Turn-Off Thyristor
f) Light-Triggered Thyristor.

The voltage and current capabilities of various thyristor types are summarized in Fig. 1. The salient design features, structures, and applications of these different SCRs are discussed in the following subsections:

a) *Phase control thyristors:* "Phase Control" or "Converter" thyristors generally operate at line frequency. They are turned off by natural commutation and do not have special fast-switching characteristics. Current ratings of phase-control thyristors cover the range from a few amperes to about 3000 A, and the voltage ratings from 50 to around 4000 V.

For a 77-mm diam phase-control thyristor, conduction voltages vary from 1.5 for 600 V rated devices, to 2.3 for 3000 V rated devices, and to 2.6 for 4000 V rated devices. For a given size device with a given voltage design, the widths of the bases and the junction profiles are fixed by punchthrough and current-gain considerations. Because of this, the forward drop becomes mainly dependent upon the diffusion length L (or lifetime, τ) in the wide n-base region and the ohmic contact losses at the end regions of the device and careful consideration of the diffusion profiles and diffusion technique must be taken to insure low forward drop.

Other key considerations of present day phase control thyristors are enhancement of the dynamic dv/dt capability and improvement of the gate sensitivity. In case of the former, the rate of rise of the voltage reapplied at the end of the turn-off interval (dv/dt effect) in conjunction with the device capacitance produces a displacement current which can turn on the device if sufficiently large. The use of emitter shorting structures which provide a shunting path for the displacement current has greatly improved dynamic dv/dt capabilities with typical dv/dt ratings of greater than 100 V/μs routinely achieved. The high-temperature performance has been improved significantly by emitter shorting, since the shorts will also bypass thermally generated currents around the emitter.

In order to simplify the gate-drive requirement and increase sensitivity, the use of amplifying gate, which was originally developed for fast switching "inverter" thyristors, is widely adopted in phase control SCR. As a result, gate drive can usually be limited to 1 to 2 A for a 50-mm device.

b) *Inverter thyristors:* The most common feature of an inverter thyristor which distinguishes it from a standard phase control type is that it has fast turnoff time, generally in the range of 5 to 50 μs, depending upon voltage rating. Maximum average current ratings of 1500 and 1200 A have been achieved with 1200 and 2500 V rated inverter thyristors, respectively.

Inverter thyristors are generally used in circuits that operate from dc supplies, where current in the thyristor is turned off either through the use of auxiliary commutating circuitry, by circuit resonance, or by "load" commutation. Whatever the circuit turn-off mechanism, fast turn-off is important because it minimizes sizes and weight of commutating and/or reactive circuit components.

For inverter/thyristors, the turn-off time is dependent upon the stored charge at the time of current reversal, the amount of charge removed during the recovery phase, the rate or recombination during the recombination phase, and the amount of charge injected during reapplication of the forward voltage.

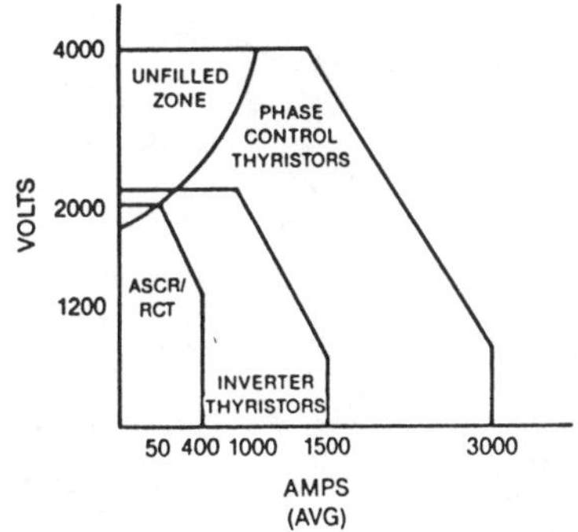

Fig. 1. Summary of present day thyristor rating capabilities.

The general practice for achieving short turn-off times reduction is to "kill" the lifetime by introducing recombination centers in the device structure using gold or platinum doping and electron irradiation. However, one of the problems in doing this is the adverse effect it has on the forward conduction drop [33], the turn-on time, and the plasma spreading properties of the device [34]. As a result, a trade-off has to be made in selecting the appropriate lifetime. Incorporating cathode shorting will aid in this trade-off by reducing the initial stored charge and the amount of charge injected during the reapplication of the forward voltage. While it will not speed up the recovery and the recombination process, the advantage of emitter shorting over lifetime reduction is that it has a much less adverse effect on forward drop.

In addition to fast turn off, fast turn-on time and di/dt capability are usually important for inverter thyristors. Achieving this requires proper design of the gate structure with the objective being to design the device so that no part of the cathode has a potential greater than that of the gate electrode. This mandates the use of a gate electrode with a large perimeter ensuring that the adjacent cathode area is as large as possible. A number of interdigitated designs have been developed to achieve this goal. Perhaps the most effective design in achieving good utilization of the device area is a structure in which both the gate and the cathode have an involute pattern [35]. Fig. 2 presents the geometric aspects of one arm (gate or cathode) of such a structure. Typically, a center gate is used to maintain maximum symmetry. The use of involute gate structures has resulted in an improvement in the di/dt capability of inverter thyristors by a factor of as much as 25. Modern devices of this type can be designed to have di/dt ratings in excess of 100 A/μs. Involute gate structures are widely used in inverter thyristors with 40-mm diam and below. Other distributed gate structures, such as the "snow flakes" pattern, are being used for inverter thyristors with larger diameter.

c) *Asymmetrical thyristors (ASCR):* One of the main salient characteristics of asymmetrical thyristors (ASCR) is that they do not block significant reverse voltage. They are typically designed to have a reverse blocking capability in the range of 400 to 2000 V. The ASCR finds applications in many voltage-fed inverter circuits that require antiparallel feedback rectifiers that keep the reverse voltage to less than 20 V.

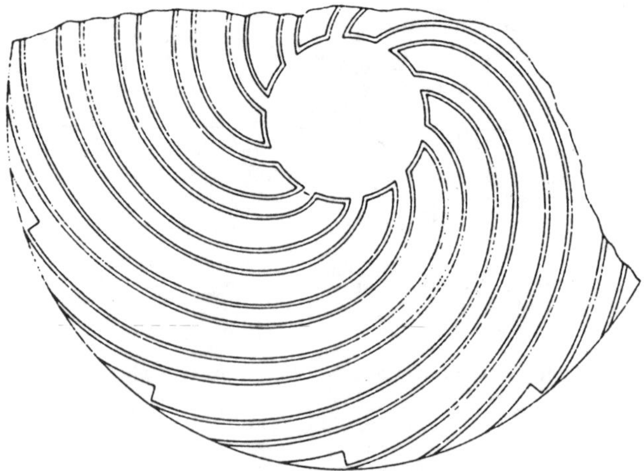

Fig. 2. The involute gate structure used in inverter thyristors.

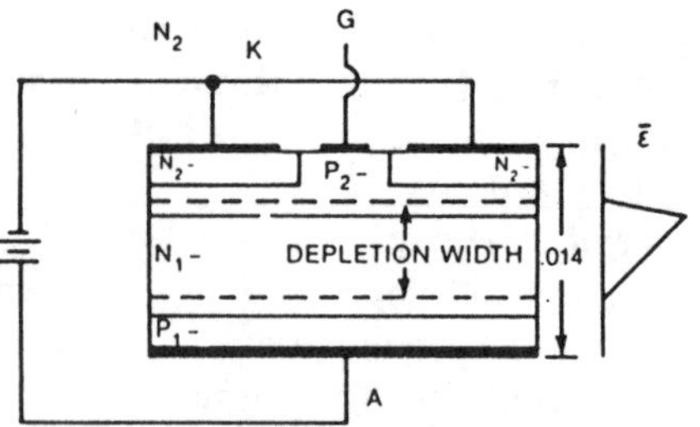

Cross-Sectional View of Conventional Center Gate SCR and Electric Field During Off-State.

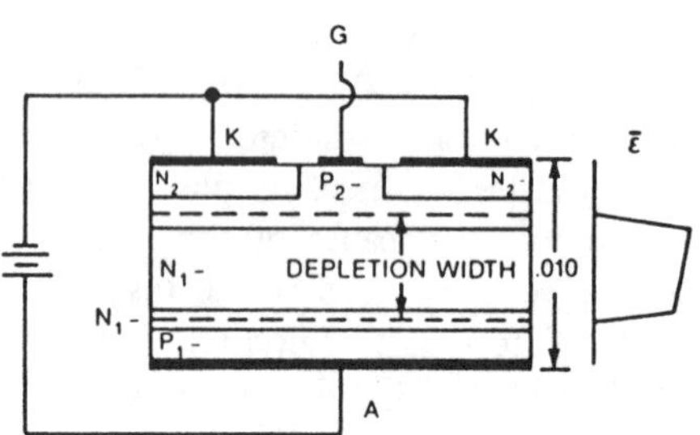

Asymmetric SCR Cross-Sectional View.

Fig. 3. Symmetrical and asymmetrical thyristor structures.

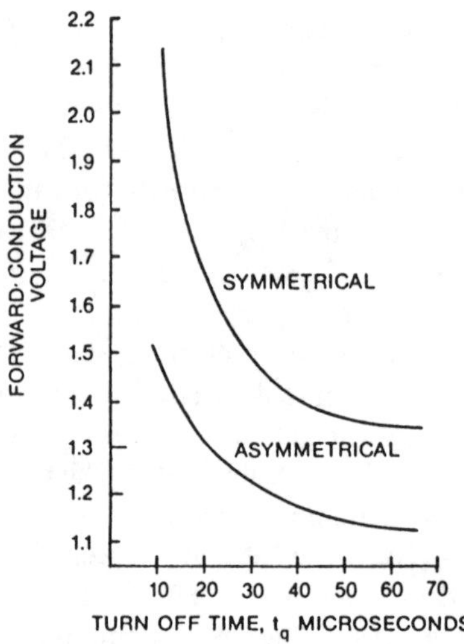

Fig. 4. Typical forward conduction voltage versus turn-off time, t_q for 1200 V rated symmetrical and asymmetrical thyristors.

The fact that ASCR needs only to block voltage in the forward direction provides an extra degree of freedom in optimizing turn-off time, turn-on time, and forward voltage drop. Fig. 3 compares the basic structure of an ASCR with that of a conventional thyristor. The main difference is the insertion of a N buffer layer between the N base and the P^+ anode. The buffer N-layer serves as a "field stopper" and allows the N base region to be reduced to half the width of a conventional thyristor. Because the forward voltage across the thyristor depends on $(d^2/D\tau)$ where d is the N base width, D is the diffusion coefficient and τ is the minority-carrier lifetime, halving d allows the lifetime to be reduced by 4 times, while maintaining the same forward drop. This translates to 50 percent or more improvement in turn-off time as shown in Fig. 4, which compares the typical forward voltage drop versus turn-off time τ_q for a 1200-V symmetrical and asymmetrical thyristor. The thinner N base width also improves the di/dt capability during turn-on because the spreading velocity is inversely proportional to the N base width. As a result, the ASCR can be made to have faster turn-on without compromising significantly the di/dt capability and turn-off time.

The spectrum of voltages and current ratings presently covered by ASCR's is shown in Fig. 1. The ASCR market is still in its infancy stage, but is gathering momentum. As the market develops, other ASCR types will certainly appear and extend the present rating boundaries.

d) *Reverse conducting thyristor (RCT):* The reverse conducting thyristor (RCT) represents the monolithic integration of an asymmetrical thyristor with an antiparallel rectifier. Beyond obvious advantages of the parts count reduction, the RCT eliminates the inductively induced voltage within the thyristor-diode loop (virtually unavoidable to some extent with separate discrete components) and essentially limits the reverse voltage seen by the thyristor to only the conduction voltage of the diode.

Features such as the asymmetrical structure, lifetime control, high-density cathode shorts, and amplifying gates that are used in ASCR can be effectively implemented in RCT. However, the monolithic incorporation of the antiparallel diode presents a special problem. A cross section of the RCT is shown in Fig. 5. When the voltage across the device is reversed, the monolithic anitparallel diode ($p_2{}^{n-n+}$) becomes forward biased, thereby flooding the n-base region with minority carriers. The device will fail to achieve forward blocking unless a long interval of time is provided during which no anode-to-cathode voltage is present. To meet a high commutating dv/dt requirement, the monolithic diode is integrated into the structure at a distance from the main thyristor (a few diffusion lengths) causing it to divert the flow of injected carriers during the supply reversal phase. To further provide isolation, a groove is etched in the p_2 region. These methods have proved to be largely effective and are able to provide a dynamic dv/dt larger than 1000 V/μs [36].

The spectrum of voltage and current ratings of the RCT is

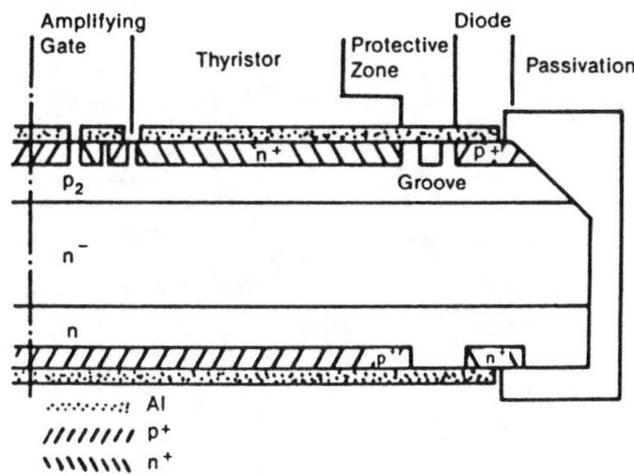

Fig. 5. Cross section of the RCT.

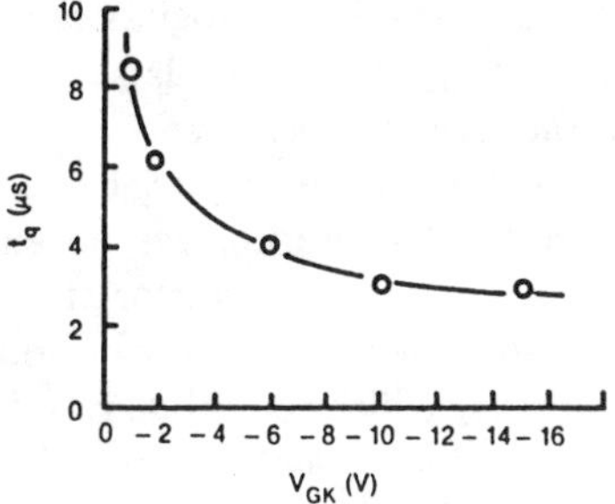

Fig. 6. Turn-off time versus reverse gate bias for GATT ($TJ = 125^\circ$C).

similar to ASCR and is shown in Fig. 1. The one drawback of the RCT is that the ratio between the thyristor and diode current carrying capabilities is fixed for a given design. The RCT is, therefore, likely to serve specific "dedicated" applications, while the ASCR should find more general industry-wide usage.

e) *Gate-assisted turn-off thyristor (GATT):* Gate-assisted turn-off is the name given to the method for turning off a thyristor with the usual commutation of the anode current, but with the addition of a negative pulse applied to the gate during the time when forward anode voltage is being reapplied. Fig. 6 gives typical data that show how the turn-off time is decreased by the negative gate drive. By using gate assisted turn-off, the normal trade-off between turn-off loss and conduction loss can be relaxed. Typically, a 50-percent reduction in turn-off time can be achieved for the same on-state voltage. It was generally believed [37] that the effect of the gate-assist pulse was to sweep out excess carriers. Works by Schlegel [38] prove that this is not the case. In actuality, the gate assist reverse bias works to reduce the injection efficiency of the cathode junction to assist in breaking the regenerative thyristor action during turn-off.

GATT's are designed with interdigitated cathodes in order to achieve both fast, low-loss turn-on and effective gate-assisted turn-off. Cathode shorts were not generally used in GATT design because it was thought that their inclusion would only add parasitic gate current. It is found that [38], [39] cathode shorts not only improve dv/dt capability as in standard thyristor design, but actually direct the current paths in such a manner that the effect of the gate-assist bias becomes more reliable and requires lower drive voltage.

Overall, the GATT has extended the operating frequency of the thyristor into the 20-kHz range. Turn-off time of less than 4 μs has been reported for a 1200-V 400-A GATT [40].

f) *Light-triggered thyristors:* Most recent developments in thyristors have been in the area of light-triggered thyristors. Direct irradiation of silicon with light creates electron–hole pairs which, under the influence of an electric field, produce a current that triggers the thyristors.

The turn-on of a thyristor by optical means is an especially attractive approach for devices that are to be used in extremely high-voltage circuits. A typical application area is in switches for dc transmission lines operating in the hundreds of kilovolts range, which use series connections of many devices, each of which must be triggered on command. Optical firing in this application is ideal for providing the electrical isolation between trigger circuits and the thyristor which floats at a potential as high as hundreds of kilovolts above ground.

The main requirement for an optically-triggered thyristor is high sensitivity while maintaining high dv/dt and di/dt capabilities. Because of the small and limited quantity of photo energy available for triggering the thyristor from practical light sources, very high gate sensitivity of the order of 100 times that of the electrically triggered device is needed. However, high gate sensitivity always leads to higher sensitivity to noise or low dv/dt capability. This design problem has reportedly been solved [41], [42], [43] by going to small light active regions and physically small initial turn-on regions. Typical gate regions have areas about 10 to 100 times smaller than the gate or pilot thyristor of the corresponding electrically fired device. The main problem dealing with the dv/dt sensitivity trade-off in this manner is the reduction of the di/dt capability of the thyristor. The general approach to this has been to use multiamplifying gates [44], [45], each providing increased current to gate the following stage. Computer models [44] have been developed to assist in the design of amplifying stage devices, which otherwise become difficult as the number of stages increases.

Prototype light-triggered thyristors rated 4 kV and 1500 A, requiring light-triggering power as low as a few tens of milliwatts and having dv/dt ratings of 1500 to 2000 V/μs, and di/dt ratings of 250 A/μs have been developed. Significant progress has been made not only in higher device ratings, but also in new device features [46], [47] such as "controlled turn-on" which protect thyristors from destructive di/dt failure during turn-on and "voltage breakover" (VBO) protection, which prevents destructive failure due to triggering by avalanche current.

Gate Turn-off Thyristors

The gate turn-off thyristor (GTO) is a thyristor-like latching device that can be turned off by application of a negative pulse of current to its gate. This gate turn-off capability is advantageous because it provides increased flexibility in circuit application, where it now becomes possible to control power in dc circuits without the use of elaborate commutation circuitry.

a) *Performance considerations:* Prime design objectives for GTO devices are to achieve fast turn-off time and high current turn-off capability and to enhance the safe operating area during turn-off. Significant progress has been made in both areas during the last few years, largely due to a better understanding of the turn-off mechanisms.

The GTO's turn-off occurs by removal of excess holes in the cathode-base region by reversing the current through the gate terminal. Similar to the transistor, the electron-hole plasma is squeezed toward the center [48] during the turn-off process, thereby creating a high current density filament which not only slows down the turn-off process, but can lead to device failures [48]-[51].

An expression for the controllable current I_{ATO} which can be turned off and which takes into account the two-dimensional nature of the problem can be written

$$I_{ATO} = \frac{4G\,V_{GK}}{R_B}$$

where V_{GK} is the breakdown voltage of the cathode gate junction, and R_B the lateral resistance of the p-base layer below the cathode, and G is the turn-off gain of the device. In order to obtain high I_{ATO}, R_B is required as low as possible and therefore, it is necessary that the p-base impurity concentration in GTO's be higher than that in conventional thyristors. However, the high p-base impurity concentration results in lowering the breakdown voltage for the emitter junction and increases the on-state voltage and gate trigger current (I_{GT}). As a result, a balance must be made in choosing the optimum p-base doping profile. It is reported [52] that the p-base impurity concentration at the cathode junction should be kept in the 0.5×10^{18} to 1.5×10^{18} cm^{-3} range to provide a satisfactory compromise for the different conflicting requirements.

b) *Cathode structures and designs:* New cathode-gate structures and advanced cathode designs are being investigated to further improve turn-off performance of GTO's. For high current GTO, a mesa structure as shown in Fig. 7 is used at the cathode junction for the purpose of obtaining higher breakdown voltage and also to facilitate contact of the cathode region in a conventional press pak package. A modified planar structure [52] as shown in Fig. 7 has been proposed to alleviate problems such as a complicated passivation process and variation in etching depth encountered in the standard mesa structure. Improvements in I_{GT} and I_{ATO} have been demonstrated with the modified planar gate structure which is being used by many commercial GTO devices.

In order to further increase the gate-cathode reverse breakdown voltage, a buried-gate structure [53] has been proposed and developed. It has been demonstrated that with this structure the reverse breakdown voltage of gate-cathode junction can be extended to 60 and to 100 V. This improvement, in turn, translates to higher controllable current that can be turned off.

Cathode patterns used in GTO's are highly interdigitated as compared to conventional thyristors. In order to reduce the lateral resistance of the p-base layer. Experimentally it has been demonstrated [54] that the maximum gate turn-off current I_{ATO} increases with decreasing cathode finger width. However, because of the variations in the etching process to form the cathode junction, a larger finger width has to be

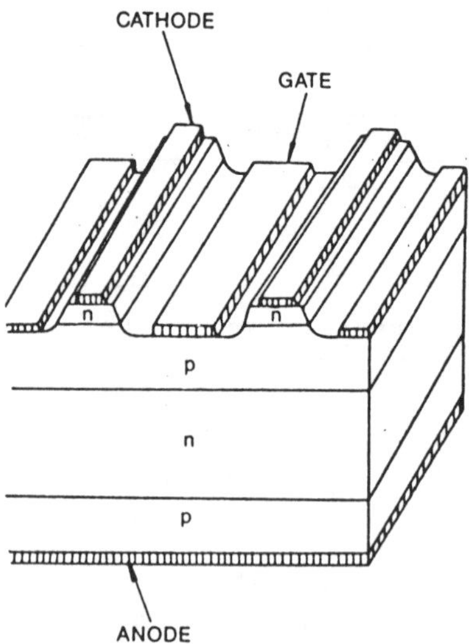

Fig. 7. MESA emitter structure for GTO's.

maintained than is ideal. Typical finger widths used in today's GTO designs range from 10 to 12 mils. Some advanced cathode pattern designs have been reported and demonstrated to make significant improvements in the device. One of these [55] uses a two interdigitating level (TIL) pattern which is formed of alternating shallow and deep diffused n± cathode layers. The purpose is to minimize current crowding at the center of the cathode finger during turnoff. This is similar to two-step emitter designs for bipolar transistors [56] which is described below. A 20-percent improvement in I_{ATO} and a turn-off gain G of greater than 10 are reported with the TIL cathode pattern. In addition, a very high dynamic dv/dt capability is found (> 1 kV/μs) and, unlike the cathode shorts in conventional thyristors, the TIL design does not degrade the turn-on sensitivity.

Another cathode design that is aimed at minimizing current pinching at the center of the cathode finger during turn-off has been proposed by Becke [57]. In this approach, the standard high concentration phosphorous cathode is replaced with a resistive ion-implemented layer. In addition, the center of the cathode is insulated so that only the edge is contacted with the metal electrode. This is shown in Fig. 9. The resistively ballasted cathodes are reported to widen the operational range and improve safe turn-off for GTO's by counteracting the formation of high-current density filaments.

c) *Lifetime control and anode design:* In addition to the cathode design, the turn-off time of GTO's also depends on the anode design and lifetime control in the wide n-base region. To achieve a better trade-off between turn-on and turn-off characteristics, work [57] has been performed to vary lifetimes vertically across the n-base region. A nonsymmetric gold distribution profile which is high in the vicinity of the p-base, n-base junction and low in the vicinity of the anode junction is used to improve the trade-offs.

In many applications, reverse blocking capability is not needed since the GTO is normally provided with an antiparallel diode for inverter operation. In such cases anode shorting can be used to improve the switching characteristics. With the use of anode shorting, the carrier lifetime in the n-base

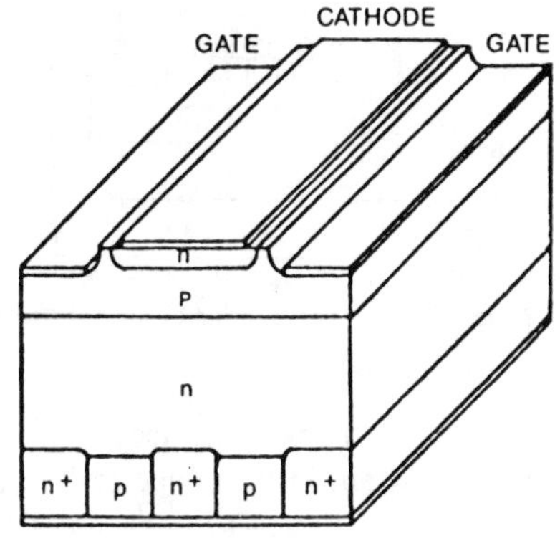

Fig. 8. Modified planar structure for GTO's.

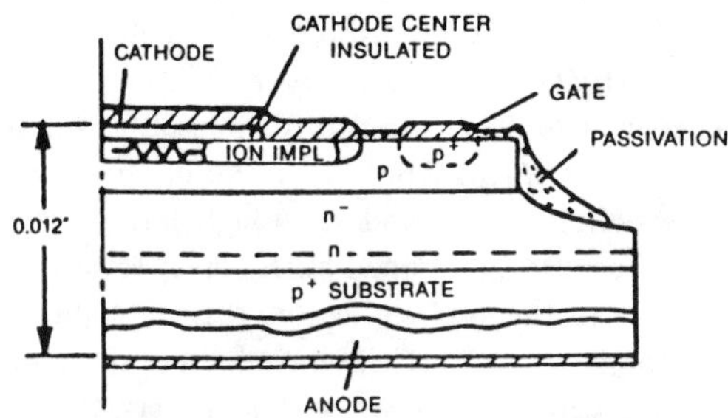

Fig. 9. Schematic of epi-GTO featuring a resistive cathode with isolated center to achieve dynamic ballasting (defocusing).

need not be reduced as much to achieve a given switching time since many carriers in the wide base can be swept out and need not be recombined. GTO's without reverse blocking capability can also be made with an additional n^+ layer in the n-base adjacent to the anode emitter junction, which is similar to the asymmetric thyristor (ASCR). This provides favorable trade-offs between on-state voltage and turn-off performance and is generally preferred for high-voltage (>2000 V) applications. Overall, the anode shorted and asymmetric GTO offer the best tradeoff between forward drop and switching time. However, the gold diffused device is technically simpler to fabricate and is currently more widely available in high-power versions. The asymmetric GTO probably represents the optimum design approach, but is also technically more difficult and, therefore, more costly to produce.

d) *Device characteristics:* It is apparent from the above discussions that GTO device technology represents a marriage between that of transistor and thyristor. The design and structure of the cathode-emitter are similar to those of transistors, but the vertical structures resemble those of thyristors. It is instructive to compare some of the salient features and operating characteristics with that of the other members of the thyristor family. This is shown in Table I.

With improved cathode emitter geometries and better optimized vertical structures, today's GTO's have made significant progress in turn-off performance—the prime weakness of earlier day GTO's. Fig. 10 shows the available GTO ratings and, as can be seen, they cover quite a wide spectrum. However, the main applications lie in the higher voltage end (>1200 V) where bipolar transistors and power MOSFET's are unable to compete effectively. The GTO with the highest

TABLE I

Phase SCR	Inverter SCR	ASCR/RCT	Assisted Turn-off SCR (GATT)	GTO
Rev. Blocking	Rev. Blocking	Nonreverse	Rev. Blocking	Rev. Blocking*
Amplifying Gate	Amplifying Gate	Amplifying Gate	Amp. Gate with By-pass Diode	No Amp. Gate
Noninterdigated	Interdigitated and Noninterdigitated	Interdigitated and Noninterdigitated	Medium Interdigitated	Fine Interdigitated
$50 < \tau_q < 300$ μs	$15 < \tau_q < 75$ μs	$5 < \tau_q < 75$ μs	$4 < \tau_q < 30$ μs	$2 < \tau_{fall} < 15$ μs $5 < \tau_{storage} < 30$ μs

*In practice, most devices are made without reverse blocking capability to optimize for speed.

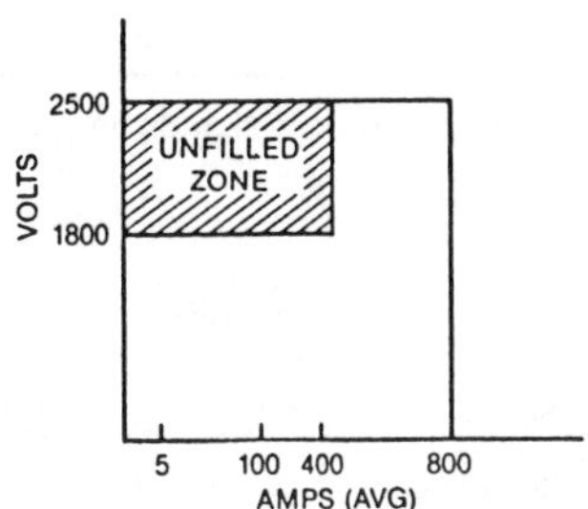

Fig. 10. Ratings covered by available GTO's.

voltage-current ratings reported to date is a 2500 V rated device with a 1000-A turn-off capability [58]. The *di/dt* and *dv/dt* ratings are reported to be 2500 A/μs and 200 V/μs, respectively.

Power Transistors

During the last few years, attention has been focused on high power transistors as switching devices in the use of high-speed inverter applications. New devices with faster switching speeds and lower switching losses are being developed that offer performance beyond that of thyristors. With their faster speed, they can be used in an inverter circuit operating at frequencies over 100 kHz. In addition, these devices can be readily turned off with a low-cost reverse base drive without the costly commutation circuits required by thyristors. Most of these improvements have resulted from significant progress made in the last few years in understanding the switching dynamics of high-voltage transistors [59], [60] and implementing improvements based on this understanding.

The prime design objectives for high-voltage power transistors designed for power switching applications are similar to those mentioned for GTO's. These are to achieve high switching efficiency in a high-voltage transistor structure and to achieve a large reverse bias safe operating area (RBSOA) without sacrificing forward drop current gain. In this subsection, the key design and performance considerations will be reviewed.

a) *Emitter structure:* The emitter design has a great impact on the turn-off performance of power transistors. An innovative "two step" emitter structure, as shown in Fig. 11, has been developed [56] and used in many high-performance power transistors commercially available today. In this emitter structure, the center portions of the emitter fingers consist of shallow diffused n^+ regions with doping concentrations just slightly higher than that of the base region. As a result, the injection efficiency at the centers of the emitter fingers is negligible compared to that near the edges. This structure reduces

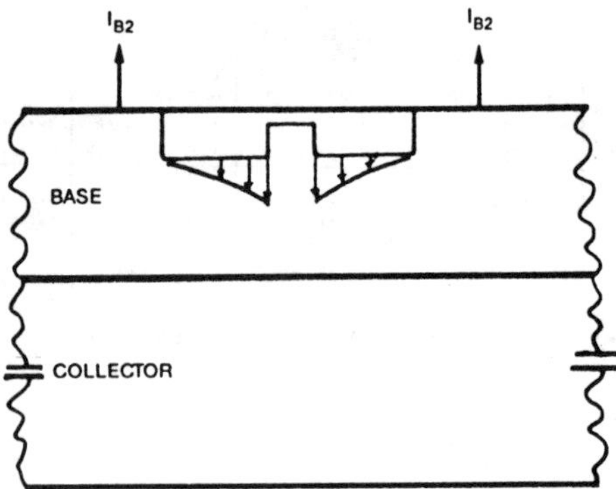

Fig. 11. New transistor design during turn-off.

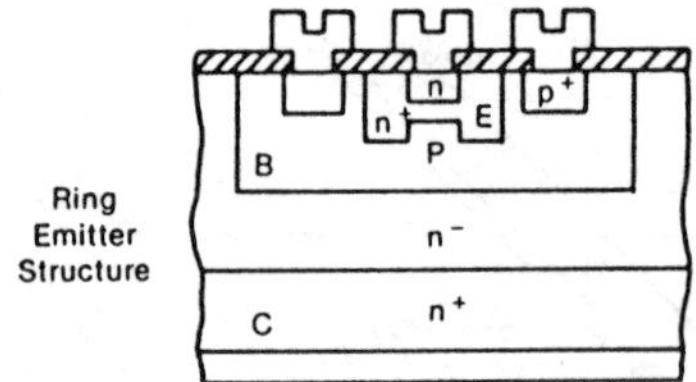

Fig. 12. Ring emitter structure for bipolar transistors.

conduction at the center of the fingers during the turnoff and confines conduction to the deeper emitter region where stored charge is more easily removed. This feature minimizes voltage "tailing" and results in reduced turnoff times. In addition, because of the more uniform current density across the emitter fingers, the device will be more rugged in reverse second breakdown. It also should be noted that little performance is sacrificied in the on-state due to this emitter design because conduction occurs mostly near the emitter periphery.

The "two step" emitter has been shown [56] to reduce switching loss by 3 times, fall time by 4 times and improve RBSOA performance by 15 percent. It can be implemented with very little change in the standard transistor processing and can be used in conjunction with any of the existing transistor emitter patterns such as the "comb-" or "spine-like" emitter geometry.

A natural evolution of the "two step" emitter concept is the dot emitters approach where many small individual emitter islands are connected in parallel. When emitter islands are so connected, it is necessary to provide a means of distributing the current uniformly between the emitter islands in order to operate at a safe current density. A practical implementation of the dot emitters approach has been achieved by the Ring Emitter Transistor (RET) [61]. The RET typically consists of several hundred small, ring-shaped emitters connected by a common emitter electrode through diffused resistors. These resistors act to ballast the current and insure uniform distribution of current, thus preventing thermal runaway. A cross section is shown in Fig. 12. Each ring emitter island is basically a "two step" emitter structure, but with an addition of a diffused ballast resistor at the center. It has been demonstrated that the RET transistor is far superior compared to conventional power transistors for applications where high RBSOA and fast switching speed are required. In high switching regulators, a 400-V 15-A RET transistor [61] is reported to achieve 80 percent efficiency at a switching frequency of 0.5 MHz.

b) *Collector structure:* The collector structure plays an important role in determining switching loss and RBSOA performance. Switching loss is found to increase with collector thickness. This is to be expected since transistors with larger collector thickness will have a larger quasi-saturation region, which results in more voltage tailing during turn-off. On the other hand, RBSOA performance improves with increasing collector thickness due to lower induced field caused by the space charge limited current in the collector [59], [60].

The trade-off between switching loss and RBSOA performance can be greatly relaxed if a multiple epitaxial collector structure [56] is used. It consists of a n-epitaxial layer collector first grown on the n^+ substrate which is slowly graded to a high resistivity n- epitaxial layer. With a properly graded epitaxial layer structure in a 400-V transistor, a dramatic 60-percent improvement in RBSOA can be obtained while maintaining low switching loss and good high current gain hold up. This occurs because the graded buffer layer lowers the current induced field at the n-n^+ collector, substrate junction when the transistor is turning off in an inductive switching circuit. Similar results can be achieved with single crystal silicon using a carefully-controlled triple-diffusion process. However, this process cannot be extended to 5-in silicon due to the increased wafer thickness and thus the epitaxial process will be more cost effective in the long term.

c) *Darlington design:* For a given collector current and current gain requirement, the current density (J_E) of a transistor declines rapidly as the sustaining voltage [V_{CEO} (SUS)] increases. This is due to the current-induced base widening effect [62]. For a Darlington where a monolithic driver transistor is driving the base of the main transistor, the current density is much improved as compared to that of the transistor. This is shown in Figs. 13 and 14. In Fig. 13, the current density of the transistor is calculated as a function of V_{CEO} (SUS) for a current gain H_{FE} of 14. From Fig. 14 it can be see that the current density is significantly higher than that of a transistor, even though the current gain for the Darlington is 50. In applications requiring higher V_{CEO} (SUS) voltage, the use of a power Darlington will result in a smaller, less expensive device for a given collector current and current gain. Another view on this is that for a given chip size and current level, the power Darlington is much higher in current gain and, thereby, minimizes base-drive requirements and system costs.

In Darlington design, the area ratio between the driver-stage and output-stage can be varied to obtain the smallest total chip area for a given collector current and gain requirement. For example, for a 400-V Darlington, the optimum design occurs when the output stage area is approximately twice that of the driver [63]. This is arrived at based strictly on static parameter considerations. If switching speed is taken into account, the area of output stage is usually 3 to 4 times that of the driver transistor. The reason is that during turn off of a Darlington, switching loss to first order is determined by the output stage and a lower current density in the output transistor will give lower turn-off loss.

d) *Device characteristics and ratings:* The spectrum of

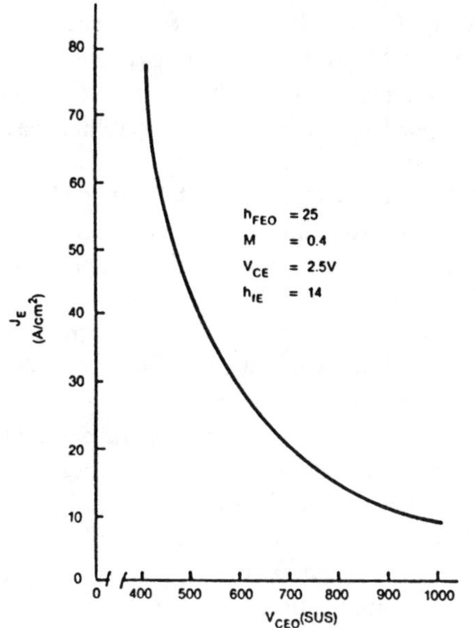

Fig. 13. Current density as a function of V_{CEO}(SUS).

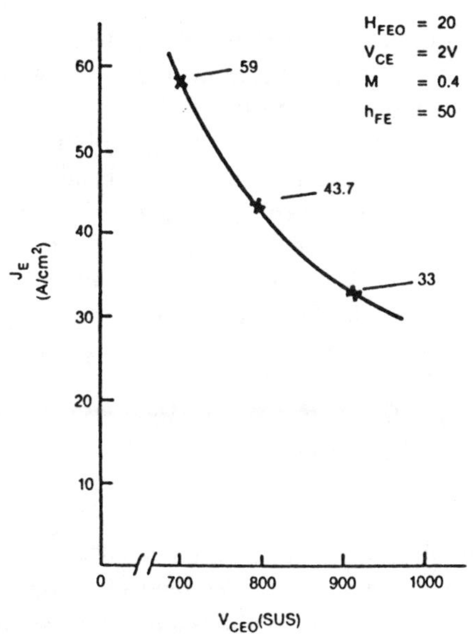

Fig. 14. Current density as a function of V_{CEO}(SUS) for a power Darlington transistor.

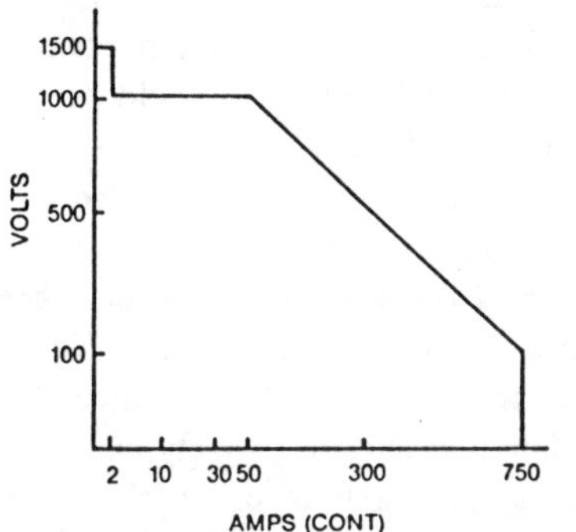

Fig. 15. Summary of present-day power transistor rating capabilities.

voltage and current ratings presently covered by power transistors/Darlingtons is shown in Fig. 15. The majority of the devices fall into three voltage ranges: V_{CEO}(SUS) $\leqslant$ 120 V, V_{CEO} (SUS) $\leqslant$ 450-500 V, and V_{CEO}(SUS) $\leqslant$ 1200 V. For the 120-V type, peak currents are being offered up to 1200 A. Most of the high current products are fabricated with a simple single-diffusion process and may be offered with multiple chips in one package. Switching peformances are characterized by very slow speed, but very rugged performance. These are used in battery-operated inverter/chopper circuits that switch at 500 Hz or below.

In the 450- to 500-V range, devices are fabricated with the triple diffusion process or with the epitaxial collector approach. Devices above 50 A are usually monolithic Darlington rather than discrete transistors. These devices are mainly targeted for 230-V line applications either in motor control or in switching power supplies.

In the 1000- to 1200-V range, devices are predominantly fabricated with a single-crystal substrate using a triple diffusion process. The epitaxial approach is not widely used because of higher defect density associated with the thicker epitaxial layer required by the 1000 to 1200 V. In addition, good lifetime is required with the thicker collector in order to maintain good current gain holdup and the epitaxial collector usually has lower lifetime than single crystal. Except at the very low current range ($\leqslant$ 5 A), practically all devices in this voltage range are Darlingtons or triple Darlingtons with many of these multiple chips either in parallel or in a multiple stage Darlington configuration. These devices are mainly used for 480-V line applications.

III. Integrated Power Electronic Devices

Evolution of Power MOS Technology

The power MOS Field-Effect Transistor (MOSFET) is a device that evolved from MOS integrated circuit technology. The motivation for the development of these devices arose from the large base drive current required by power bipolar transistors and their limited switching speed capability. The first attempts to develop high-voltage MOSFET's were performed by redesigning lateral MOSFET's to increase their voltage blocking capability [64]. This work was motivated by the interest in developing high-speed switches for driving piezoelectric devices in medical electronics. The technology developed for these devices was lateral, double-diffused MOS (DMOS), as illustrated in Fig. 16. Parallel with this effort, several groups were working on the development of vertical power MOSFET's. This effort was motivated by the improved breakdown voltages and higher current ratings that could be obtained by moving the drain from the top to the bottom of the wafer, as shown in Fig. 17(a) and (b). Although the vertical DMOS structure has been adapted by virtually all manufacturers of power MOSFET's today, the initial work in the early 1970's began with the use of the V-groove process. One of the first high-voltage (600 V) V-MOS power FET's was developed at the General Electric Research Laboratory in 1978 [65] with lower voltage devices (200 V) having been developed and marketed by Siliconix. The initial focus on the VMOS process was based upon the belief that the JFET pinchoff action caused by current flowing between the p-base regions of adjacent cells in region A (see Fig. 17(a)) would result in a significantly higher resistance for the DMOS devices

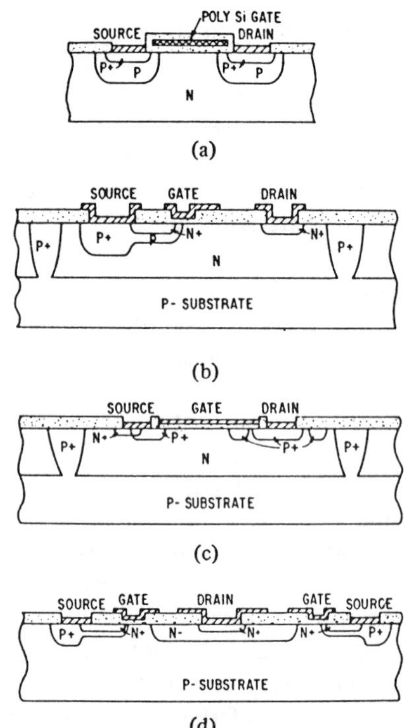

Fig. 16. Lateral DMOS structure for high-voltage drivers in integrated circuits.

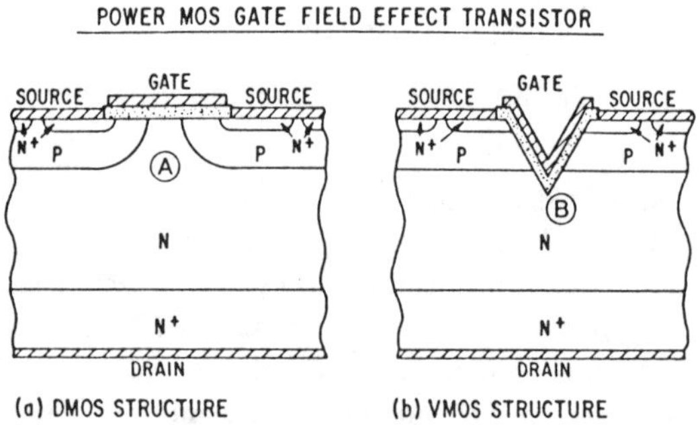

Fig. 17. Vertical power MOSFET structures for power switching output devices.

compared with the VMOS devices. However, detailed modeling studies of breakdown voltage of these devices pointed out the existence of very high electric fields at the bottom *B* of the V-grooves (see Fig. 17(b)). This high field resulted in a significant reduction in the breakdown voltage compared to the DMOS geometry for the same drift layer doping and thickness. Since the on-resistance of the power MOSFET increased as the 2.5 power of the breakdown voltage rating, the VMOS structure was found to have a higher on-resistance than the DMOS structure for the same breakdown voltage [65], [66]. Further, the V-groove process exposed the gate oxide to ionic contamination resulting in unstable device threshold voltages which compromised production yield and device reliability.

The introduction of DMOS power FET's was originally regarded as a major threat to the power bipolar transistor. Initial claims of infinite current gain for the power MOSFET's were diluted by the need to design the gate drive circuit to account for the pulse currents required to charge and discharge the high input capacitance of these devices. This was especially true in high-frequency applications where the power MOSFET was particularly valuable due to its inherently high switching speed. The high-speed capability was the result of current transport occurring solely via majority carriers. This eliminated the large storage and fall times observed in bipolar transistors due to minority-carrier transport. The power MOSFET's were also found to exhibit superior safe-operating-area and output characteristics for paralleling when compared with the bipolar transistor. However, these merits of the power MOSFET were offset by a higher on-resistance per unit area and a much larger processing cost when compared to the bipolar transistor. In order to derive good characteristics, high-resolution lithography with good registration between masking levels was crucial to power MOSFET fabrication, and the yield was much lower than for bipolar transistors of the same size. Consequently, the high cost of power MOSFET's restricted their application to high-frequency circuits (such as those used in switch-mode power supplies) and to low-voltage (<100 V) circuits where their on-resistance reached acceptable values.

With improvements made in process technology to obtain better yields and performance, the ratings of power MOSFET's continued to grow over the last 10 years. At present, devices are available with breakdown voltages of up to 1000 V at current levels of about 1 A and current handling capability of over 20 A at breakdown voltages below 100 V. The maximum pellet size that is in production today is about 250 mils × 250 mils in size although larger devices (300 mils × 300 mils) have been reported in the literature [67]. These large area, low-voltage devices are being developed for use as synchronous rectifiers which are very low forward drop diodes that are aimed at replacing the Schottky output rectifiers in low voltage (<5 V) switching power supplies.

MOS-Bipolar Hybrid Devices

With the discovery that power MOSFET's are not in a strong position to displace the power bipolar transistor, many researchers began to look at the possibility of combining these technologies to achieve a hybrid device which has a high input impedance and a low on-resistance. The most obvious step in this direction was to simply drive the bipolar transistors with a power MOSFET in the Darlington configuration shown in Fig. 18(a). This circuit element could now be gated on like a power MOSFET and yet have a lower on-resistance because most of the output current was handled by the bipolar transistor. One application for this configuration was the development of motor drives and processes to integrate these devices together on a monolithic chip [68]. The drawback to this approach was again the poor performance of the power bipolar transistor. The low current gain (typically 10) of high-voltage bipolar transistors made it essential to use a high-voltage MOSFET of equal size as a driver. In addition, the usual reverse base drive current applied to the bipolar transistor during turn-off could not be used without the addition of another expensive power MOSFET as illustrated in Fig. 18(b). It is also worth pointing out that this hybrid approach could only result in an average current density which was in between

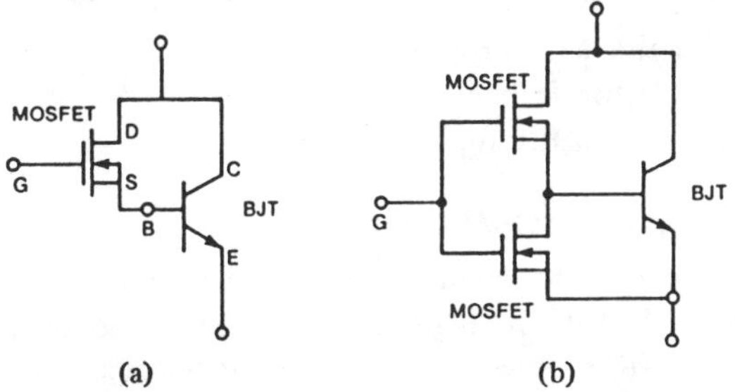

Fig. 18. Hybrid MOSFET bipolar transistor configurations for achieving a high input impedance and low on-resistance.

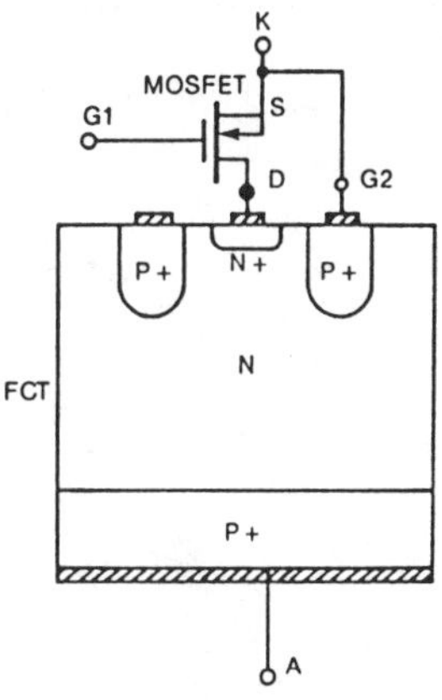

Fig. 19. Hybrid MOS/bipolar configuration for achieving high input impedance and high forward conduction current density by using a power MOSFET and field-controlled thyristor.

that obtainable for the power MOSFET and bipolar transistors, while requiring process technology that must optimize the performance of both devices simultaneously.

An interesting alternative hybrid approach to obtaining an MOS high-input impedance device configuration with a high forward conduction current density was also developed in the late 1970's. In this approach, the power field controlled thyristor was used as the main current carrying high-voltage device as illustrated in Fig. 19 and a power MOSFET was used to control the output current [69]. The field controlled thyristor (FTC) is a device which operates like a p-i-n diode in its forward conduction mode. This results in very high current densities in this device compared with the bipolar transistor even at high breakdown voltages. Before the development of this gating scheme shown in Fig. 19, it had been necessary to apply a negative voltage to the gate of the FCT to hold it in the offstate and to provide large gate current pulses to achieve high-speed turn-off [70]. These problems were eliminated by the circuit shown in Fig. 19 with the use of a low-voltage power MOSFET connected in series with the FCT. These MOSFET's were considerably smaller than those required for the Darlington configuration in Fig. 17(b). Yet it was highly desirable to integrate the MOSFET with the FCT to obtain a single monolithic device.

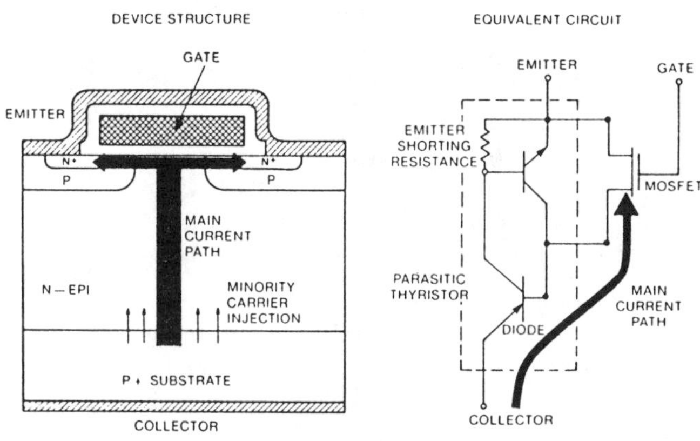

Fig. 20. The insulated gate transistor structure and its equivalent circuit.

MOS-Bipolar Functional Integration

The process of integration of the series MOSFET with the field-controlled thyristor led to the invention of the insulated gate transistor (IGT) shown in Fig. 20 [26]. This device structure is deceptively similar to that of the DMOSFET shown in Fig. 17. At first glance, it appears like the DMOSFET with its N+ substrate (drain region) was replaced with a P+ substrate (collector region). However, this simple substitution creates a four-layer (p^+-n-p-n^+) thyristor structure as illustrated in the equivalent circuit for the IGT in Fig. 20. This MOS gated thyristor structure had been conceptualized in the early 1970's and experimentally demonstrated for the first time in 1978 [71]. These devices had also been built in the triac form [72], [24] and later introduced by Motorola as a commercial product [25]. Their application was limited by the loss of gate control after turn-on which made them unacceptable as replacements for bipolar transistors.

It took a conceptual breakthrough in the early 1980's to realize that the parasitic thyristor inherent in the IGT could be defeated by adequate emitter shorting as illustrated in Fig. 20. This was achieved at the General Electric Research Laboratory by a combination of strengths in two-dimensional device modeling capability [73] and extensive experience with process development for DMOSFET's and other novel device structures. (The device was also disclosed independently by the RCA Research Laboratory [27].) The modeling indicated that it was necessary to include a highly doped P^+ region in the center of each DMOS cell to reduce the lateral resistance in the p-base in order to suppress latchup of the parasitic thyristor. The ability to incorporate this P^+ region into a power MOSFET production process with a minimum of process modification allowed device development and transition into production to occur within 6 months. The very first devices [IGT (A) in Fig. 21] exhibited excellent characteristics with forward conduction current densities 20 times higher than for MOSFET's and 5 times greater than for a bipolar transistor operating at a current gain of 10. These results demonstrated the value of functionally integrating the physics of an MOS structure for controlling current and bipolar physics for conducting the current. However, the introduction of minority car-

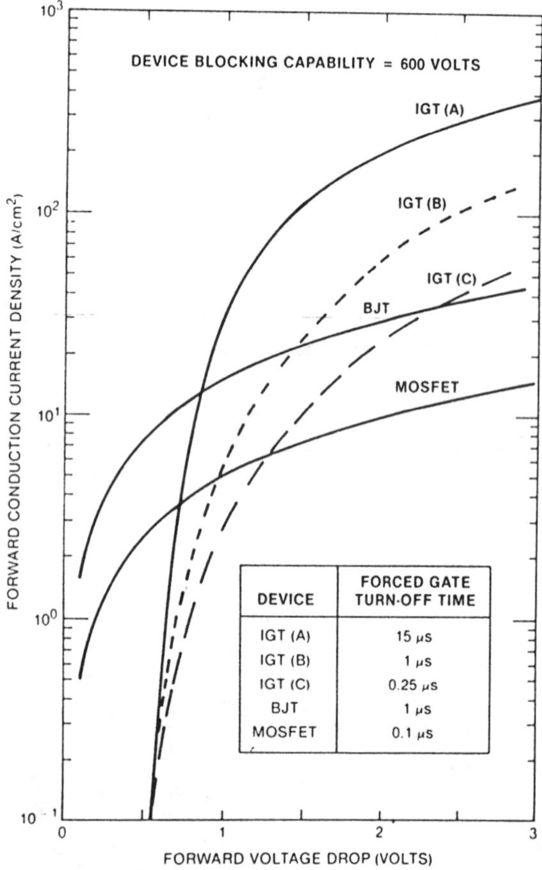

Fig. 21. Comparison of IGT with power MOSFET and bipolar transistor.

riers for current transport resulted in a slower switching speed. The first IGT's had forced gate turn-off times of 10 to 20 μs. This relatively slow switching speed would have restricted the application of these devices to circuits operating at low frequencies such as directly off the ac power line. In order to use the device for a wider range of applications, including motor drives, it became necessary to develop a lifetime control process by which the turn-off speed could be controlled without degrading the MOS gate structure. This was achieved by using an electron irradiation process [74] originally developed for controlling the speed of p-i-n rectifiers [75]. This process created the ability to control the switching speed of the IGT in the range of turn-off times from 0.2 to 20 μs. This made the IGT a unique and versatile device which could be optimized to achieve the lowest combination of conduction and switching power losses for each application depending upon the operating frequency [76].

With the advent of these devices, the bipolar transistor is seriously threatened with replacement. The high operating current density of the IGT more than offsets the higher cost of MOS fabrication. Its advantages of a much lower gate-drive power which can be derived from low cost, integrated electronics, its unique reverse blocking capability, superior safe-operating area, and high temperature performance make it an ideal choice for high-voltage ($>$100 V), lower-frequency ($<$50 kHz) applications. Since the power MOSFET offers significantly superior performance compared to the bipolar transistor at breakdown voltages of less than 100 V and at frequencies above 50 kHz, it can be predicted that the power bipolar transistor is likely to be replaced with power MOS devices in the near future.

High-Voltage Integrated Circuits

One of the more exciting trends in power electronics has been the advent of the high-voltage integrated circuit (HVIC). The first HVIC's were primarily used for telecommunications [28] and display applications [30] with the former being built in dielectrically isolated material and the latter using junction isolation. There is also another class of devices that do not combine multiple high-voltage devices on a chip but rather have a single vertical power device together with on-chip logic devices. Power supply applications dominate the applications for these devices [29]. Figs. 22, 23, and 24 show examples of cross sections for these three types of HVIC's, with the first two having multiple 400-V devices and the latter having a single 80-V device.

These early HVIC's all were somewhat limited in their capabilities to handle a wide variety of applications because they either lacked the necessary voltage rating for the high-voltage devices or the flexibility to handle the many different device types and circuits often found in power circuits. Recently, several new HVIC processes have been disclosed which offer both extended device voltage ratings and capabilities [31], [32]. Figs. 25 and 26 show a new junction isolated HVIC and process which has over a 500-V rating for the high-voltage devices together with flexibility to have both 20-V complementary MOS and bipolar devices. In addition, the process makes it possible to make resistors and capacitors giving it a full range of digital and analog current capabilities. This flexibility has largely been possible because of the use of a thin epitaxial layer and the lateral charge control technique [77], [78] for making lateral high-voltage devices. By doing this instead of using the thick epitaxial layers needed to make vertically oriented high-voltage devices, it is possible to make high quality 20-V bipolar transistors using buried layers.

One of the key early questions about this procedure was the issue of the yield of the high-voltage elements, particularly in view of the need to control the doping thickness product of an epitaxial layer. The problem was solved by use of a charge control implant by which 90 percent of the charge is put in using the precise control inherent in ion implantation. This made control of the epitaxial charge less critical [78]. This can be seen on Fig. 27 which shows the voltage variation across a 3-in wafer as a function of the drift layer length for HVIC's made with both ion implanted charge control and charge control done using only control of the epitaxial process.

Another of the unique features of the above HVIC process has been achieving 500-V devices that are largely free of unwanted parasitics while using low-cost junction isolation technology. One example of how this is done is shown in the bottom device cross section in Fig. 25. This device is a 500-V bipolar transistor which does not inject charge into the substrate when saturated. This happens because the emitter and base regions are surrounded by a heavily doped N^+ region which breaks the gain of the parasitic substrate p-n-p. This

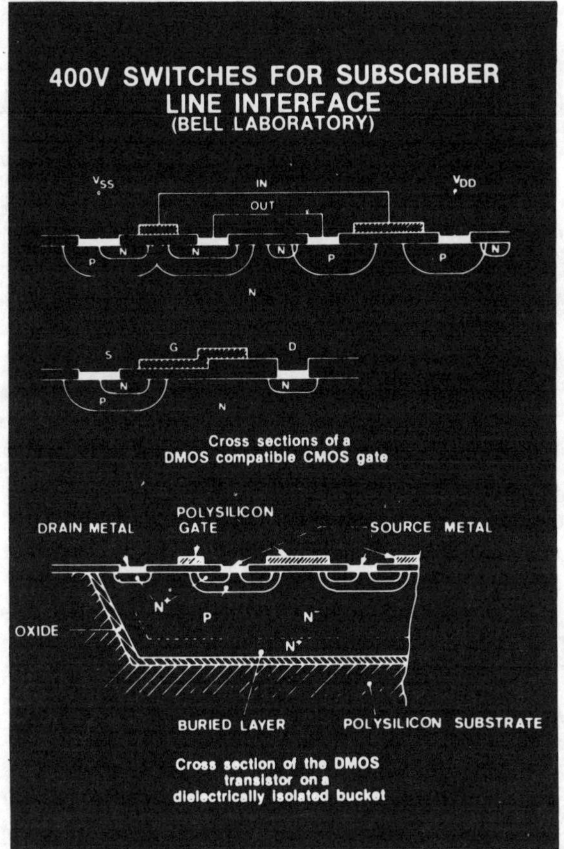

Fig. 22. Cross section of 400-V devices used in dielectrically isolated IC used for telecommunications (after Mattheus).

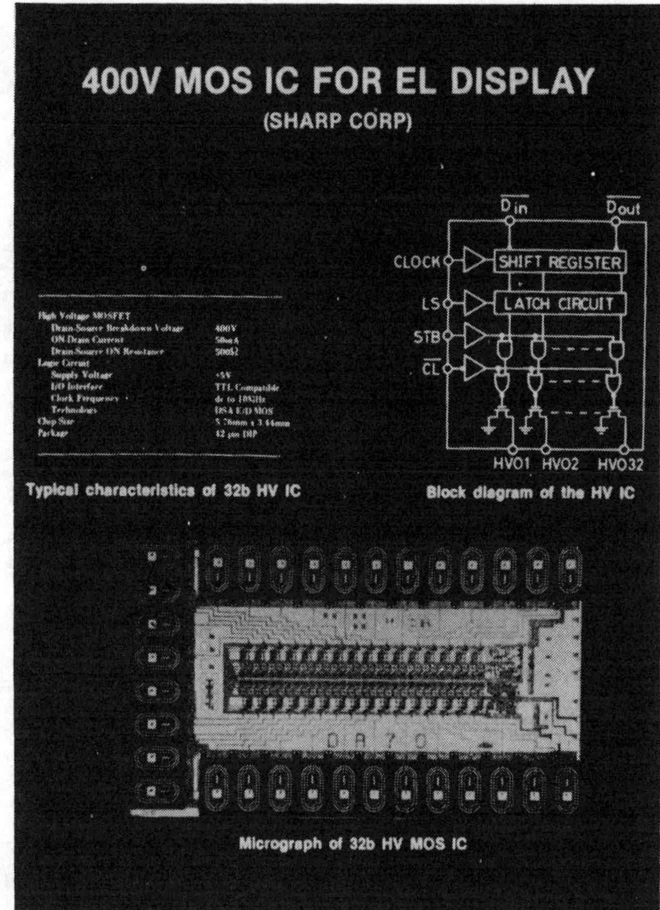

Fig. 23. Description of micrograph of power supply chip (after Ruggles).

same N^+ region would otherwise preclude high-voltage operation, but this problem is solved because the N^+ region forms the source of a self-biasing lateral JFET as shown. When the device is in a blocking state, the N^+ region floats up in potential until the channel under the junction gate (which is tied to the substrate) is pinched off. When the device is turned-on, electric charge injected from the emitter reduces the potential of the N^+ region allowing current to flow through the lateral JFET.

The commonly accepted practice for achieving parasitic free 500-V devices required the use of the much more expensive dielectric isolation (DI) technology. In the long run, however, DI will be required to achieve even higher levels of parasitic free operation, circuit flexibility, and performance. This is particularly true at high temperature and in circuits requiring high-voltage complementary devices or devices that must be referenced in both polarities relative to the substrate. Achieving these goals in a cost-effective DI technology will require a significant breakthrough in the present cumbersome method to make DI and/or progress in the silicon on insulator (SOI) technologies. Examples of promising SOI approaches include recrystalization of polysilicon or massive implantation of oxygen (nitrogen) to form a buried insulating layer [79]. In both cases it will be necessary to have advances both in the material and production equipment technologies.

An additional key issue is that of high-voltage interconnection. An effective means for doing this must be solved since without it a true HVIC is not possible. Presently most HVIC's sidestep the issue by bonding directly out from the high-voltage devices. Methods such as the use of field shields or thick insulators must be devised to make high-voltage interconnects a reality. Fig. 28 shows several approaches to this problem.

IV. Projections of Device Ratings

As one charts the future of power semiconductor devices, there are several facets involved. The first is the evolution of existing devices such as the thyristor, the bipolar transistor, and the power MOS transistor. The second is the emergence of new devices such as the insulated gate transistor (IGT) and the high voltage integrated circuit (HVIC). In this section both of these subjects will be reviewed starting first with a projection on ratings for existing devices.

Thyristors and Rectifiers

The history and evolution of thyristors and rectifiers has been closely associated with the availability of ever increasing sizes of silicon wafers. Fig. 29 shows the availability of float zone wafers and the time lag between their introduction and thyristors using that size of silicon. Some of the questions confronting the high power semiconductor industry is whether ever increasing sizes of float zone material will continue to become available or whether the industry will have to adapt

Fig. 24. Description and micrograph of 400-V electroluminescent driver chip (after Fujii).

to the Czochralski grown material being grown in larger wafer sizes as directed by the IC industry. The major issue here is the high oxygen content of the Czochralski material and the resultant low carrier lifetime. This problem is magnified because the thyristors most likely to use larger diameter wafers are those at the highest voltage, since the larger wafer is used to offset the increased forward drop for these devices. These high-voltage devices are, in turn, the ones requiring the highest lifetime because of the increased width of the N-base. As a result, it is the projection here that thyristors larger than 100 mm will not be available unless larger, high resistivity float zone material becomes available. Since the IC industry is driving the materials developments, this is not likely.

Figs. 30 and 31 give a projection of the maximum thyristor average current rating and peak reverse voltage rating, respectively, with the year of the projection shown as a parameter. In Fig. 30, it can be seen that the projections for average current have historically been low due to increases in the available sizes of wafers. However, a change in this pattern has now occurred in the last 5 years because silicon larger than 100 mm has not occurred as explained above. As a result, the peak current ratings can be expected to saturate at 3000 A unless larger silicon becomes available. It can also be expected that even if this occurs, there may be little increase because the larger silicon will most likely be used for higher voltage devices and most of the benefit in the increased area will be lost due to the resultant lower current densities.

The curves in Figs. 29–31 are updates of curves previously done [80]. The biggest change from the previous set of projections made in 1975 is the likelihood of 10 000-V thyristors emerging in the next several years. These devices are being developed for HVDC applications where, because of

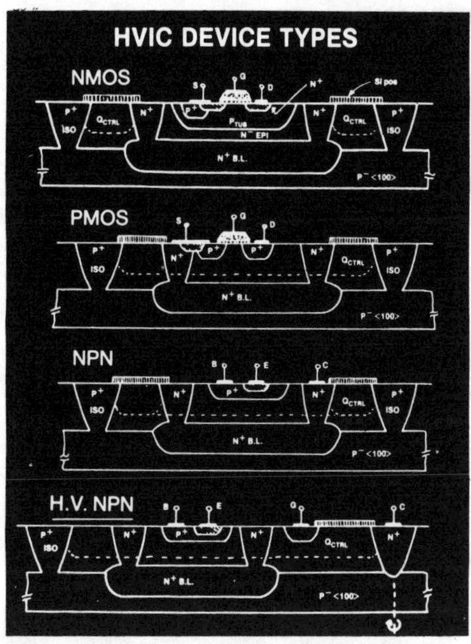

Fig. 25. Cross section of devices implemented in 500-V junction isolated HVIC.

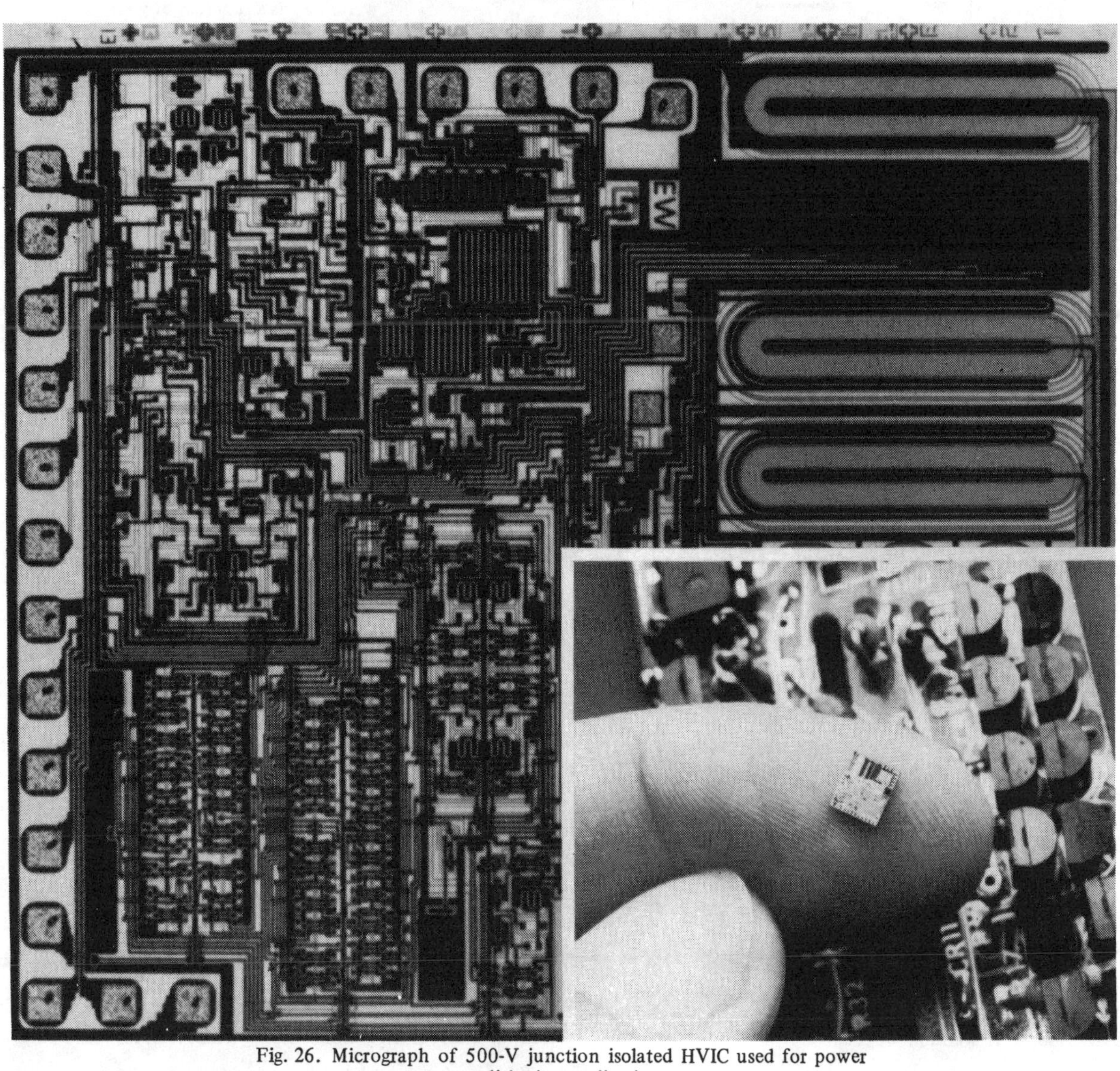

Fig. 26. Micrograph of 500-V junction isolated HVIC used for power conditioning applications.

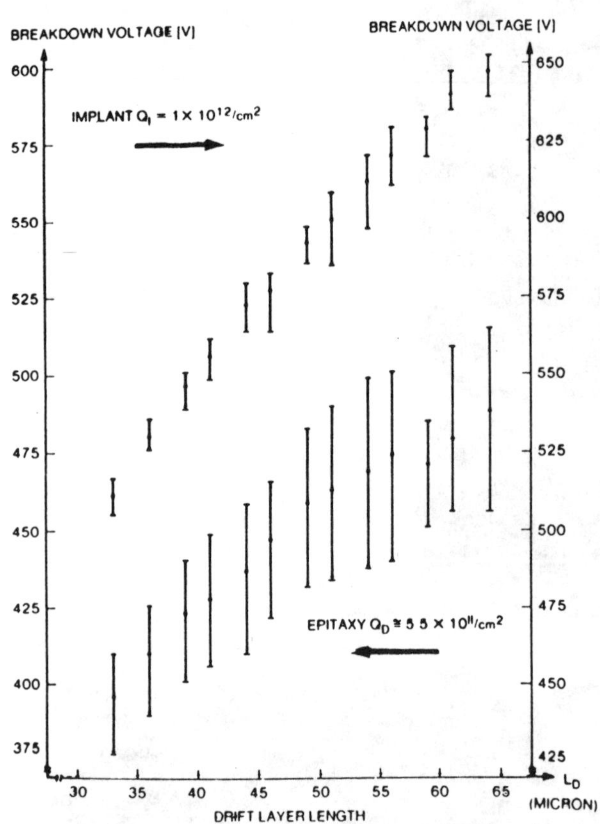

Fig. 27. Breakdown voltage for HVIC's as a function of drift region length for implanted drift region and drift region implemented using epitaxial layer.

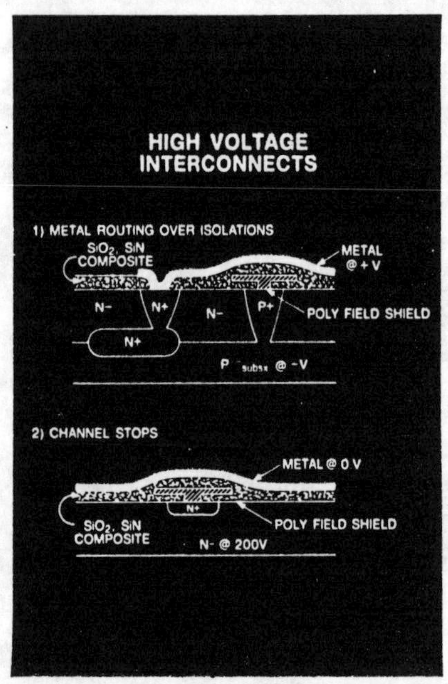

Fig. 28. Cross section of high-voltage interconnection approaches using field shields to present premature breakdown when metal runs cross heavily doped regions in HVIC's.

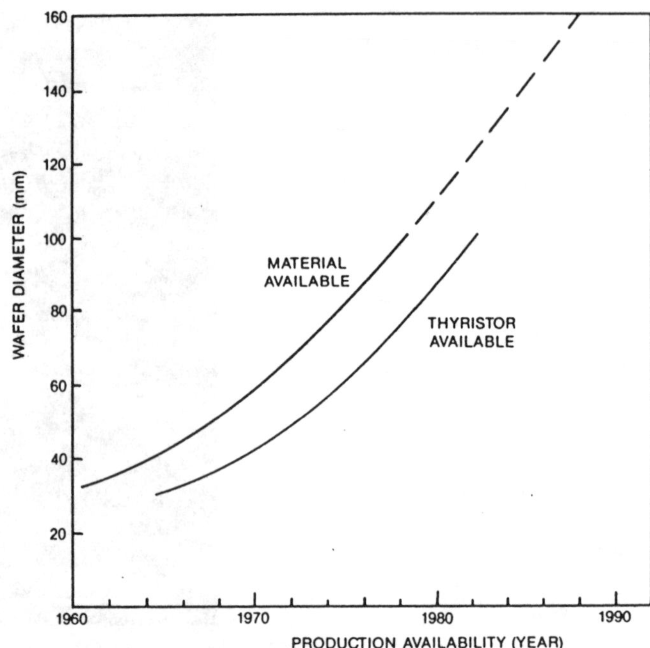

Fig. 29. Prediction of wafer size and availability of thyristor using wafer size as a function of year.

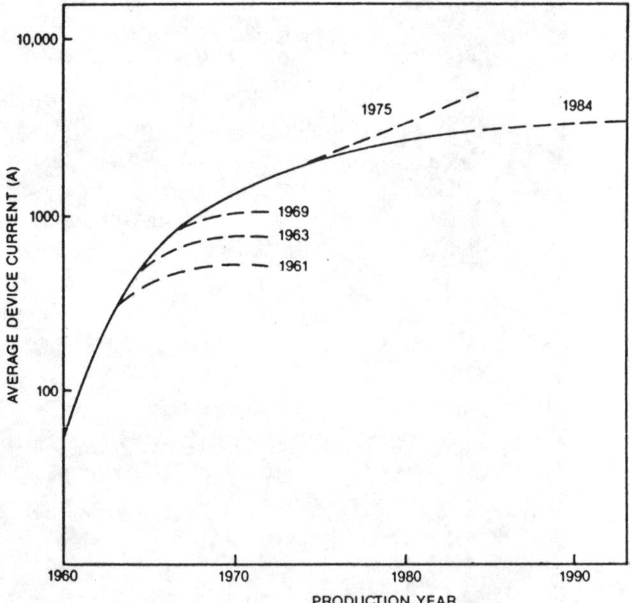

Fig. 30. Maximum average current rating for thyristor as a function of year with year of production as a parameter.

the extremely high voltages being switched (>100 kV), economies can be realized by going from 5000 to 10 000 V due to the halfing the number of devices. However, due to the fact that at rated temperatures (125°C) the background doping of the substrate is approaching the intrinsic carrier concentrations, these devices are likely to be asymmetrical, having only forward blocking capability. While higher blocking voltages

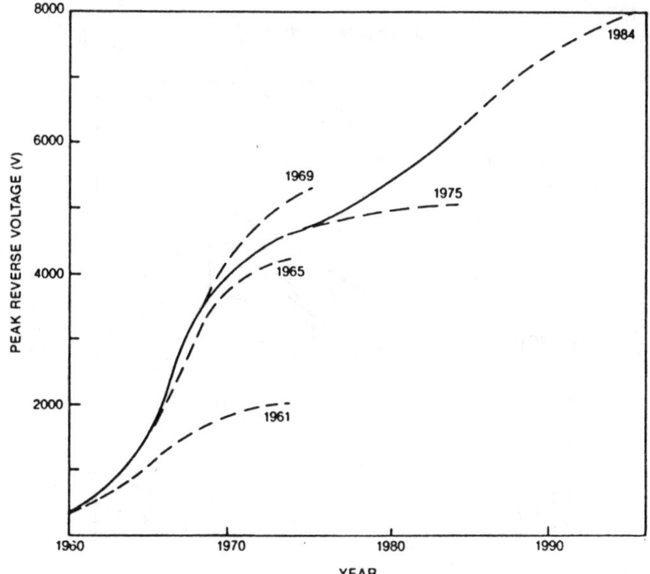

Fig. 31. Maximum voltage rating of thyristors with year of prediction as a parameter.

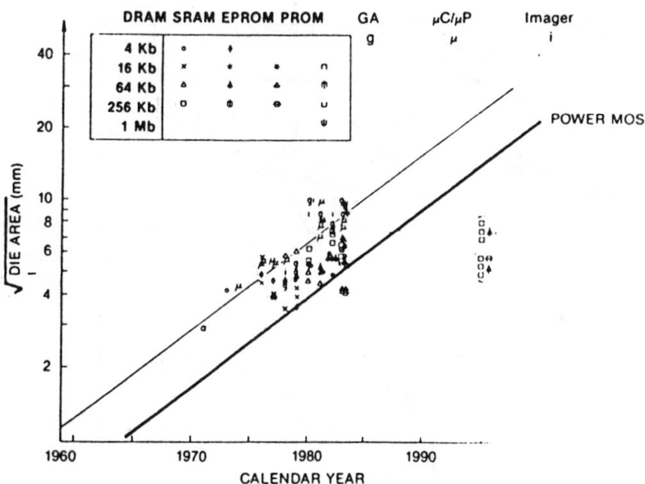

Fig. 32. Die size as a function of year for integrated circuits with curve shown for integrated power MOS devices (after Meindl).

110 VAC (≥ 250 VDC)

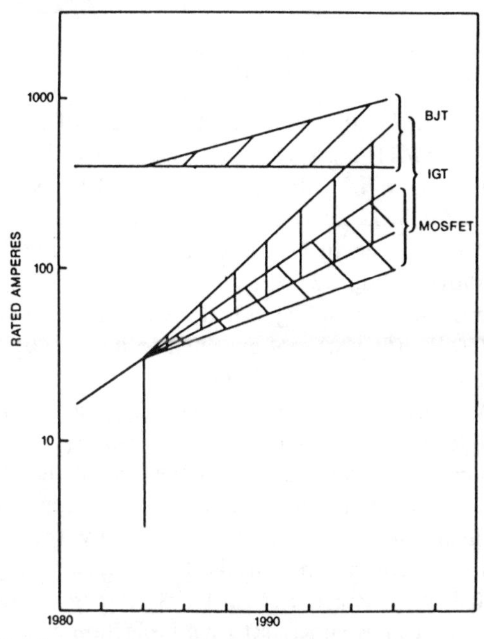

Fig. 33. Maximum current ratings for devices rated at 250 V over the next ten years.

are possible for asymmetrical devices, this is not considered likely because of the poor tradeoff against forward conduction [8]. The problem is that carrier lifetimes greater than several hundred microseconds are difficult to achieve and it makes better economic sense to partition the device voltage ratings at a voltage where the base width is no larger than several diffusion lengths.

Transistors, GTO's, IGT's, and MOSFET's

The maximum ratings for the class of devices that can be turned off, unlike thyristors, is not set by the size of silicon wafers that are available. These ratings are set by a combination of factors ranging from cost performance competition among devices and demand based on what applications are being served, to technological issues such as the rapid yield fall off for MOS-gated devices for chips larger than 6 mm on a side.

Dealing with this latter issue first, the maximum die size will track the rapid progress in device fabrication skills and in new processing equipment much as is the case for IC's. A projection as to the latter can be seen in Fig. 32 where die size is projected up until the year 2000. Similar behavior can be expected for integrated MOS-gated devices, such as the MOSFET and the IGT, since these devices have similar unit process steps as are found in IC's and progress in IC fabrication will rapidly be translated into progress for power MOS devices. Taking the 6-mm die size as a starting point, Fig. 32 shows a projection of die size for power MOS devices. On this basis, the die size can be expected to triple over the next ten years from 6 to 18 mm.

Turning now to the actual device ratings, this is most conveniently done separately for three distinct device voltage ratings corresponding to power switching applications from the 110-V ac, 220-V ac, and 440-V ac lines. These in turn correspond to dc device blocking voltage ratings of 250, 450, and 1000 V, respectively. Taking the 250-V rating first, Fig. 33 shows the projection for device current ratings from the present up through 1994. Only the bipolar transistor (BJT), the insulated-gate transistor (IGT), and MOSFET are considered, since at this low voltage the GTO is not available. The ratings shown for each device span a range starting at the maximum rating for devices available today. The upper projection is the maximum technological rating (MTR) set by issues such as maximum die size. The lower rating is the maximum likely rating (MLR) set by applications demand and

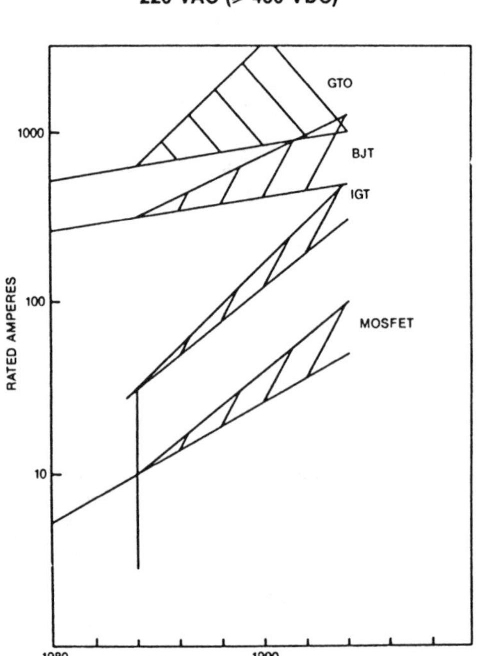

Fig. 34. Maximum current ratings for devices rated at 450 V over the next ten years.

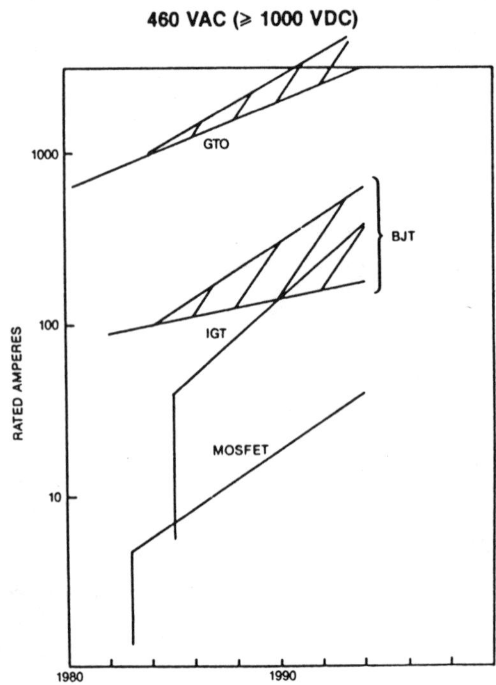

Fig. 35. Maximum current ratings for devices rated at 1200 V over the next 10 years.

competition with other devices. In the case of the BJT and the GTO, the MTR is set by an expectation that the maximum device die area will be under 75 mm for the next 10 years. The MTR for MOS-gated devices is set by the maximum die size that is believed to be consistent with acceptable device yield as shown in Fig. 32.

As can be seen from Fig. 33, the current rating for BJT's at the 250-V rating are not expected to increase beyond the 400-A rating of today because of a lack of probable demand for such a high current device serving applications requiring 250-V blocking. This particular device corresponds to a 35-mm Toshiba Grant Transistor. In the case of the MOSFET, the MLR is set by a belief that most of the applications requiring high currents will best be served by the IGT since these applications are not likely to need switching speeds above 50 kHz (where the MOSFET is the best choice). The MLR for the IGT is largely set by a projection of where most of the volume of applications for this voltage rating will occur.

Fig. 34 shows the projections for devices rated at 450 V and it can be seen that there is less spread between the MLR and the MTR since applications for devices at this voltage demand higher currents. For example, at the 110-V ac line, motor drives above 1 to 2 hp (requiring devices with rating 20 to 40 A at 250 V ac) are uncommon while, at a 220-V ac line, motor drives up to 10 hp are found (requiring devices with 100-A 450-V ratings). This trend continues, of course, with motor drives above 10 hp usually being built for the 460-V ac line. This is the main reason why the MLR for IGT's is only 300 A in 1994. The story for GTO's at this voltage rating is quite different. This is the lowest voltage rating at which GTO's are used and there is a large difference between the MTR and the ratings that are required by applications at this voltage.

The last of this set of figures is shown in Fig. 35 for the devices rated at 1000 V. Except for the BJT, most of the devices' ratings are set close to their MTR's since applications at this high voltage require high currents and most of the limiting issues are technological. In the case of the BJT, however, the MLR is set by a belief that most of the applications requiring devices above 100 A will be best served by the GTO in the near term and possibly by the IGT in the years after 1990 (up to 400 A). The problem for the BJT at this voltage is that the device areas required for current gains greater than 10 make the device economically noncompetitive with the GTO (or the IGT when available).

Devices Above 2000 V and Under 100 V

The regime or power switching devices at the extremes of voltage, either high or very low, is somewhat specialized since the choice narrows to only one device in each case. Above 2000 V the GTO is the only turn-off device that is or will be available. Presently GTO devices of 3000 V and 1000 A are being reported [58] based on 40-mm wafer sizes. By going to 75-mm wafers, it can be expected that the ratings will increase to over 3000 A. It should also be noted that at these and higher voltages, competition between the GTO and the SCR is intense with the cost of gate drives and snubbers being traded off against forced commutation circuits, respectively. The actual choice in a given application will depend on the specific details.

In the case of devices rated under 100 V, the MOSFET is the device of choice because of a combination of the ease of the MOS-gating relative to the BJT and the low forward drop of MOSFET's at this voltage relative to the IGT. In the case of the latter, the penalty of the built-in series diode drop proves to be too significant at these low voltages and the MOSFET is the device of choice. The only exception to this would be applications where the built-in parasitic

Fig. 36. Large area power MOSFET chip containing 150 000 separate cells in a 330 mil × 330 mil die.

diode in the MOSFET is a problem and it becomes necessary to put a diode in series to prevent current flow from source to drain when the drain voltage goes negative. In this case, the IGT would be perferable since this blocking diode is inherent in the device and thus one gets the diode plus the overall benefits of a much lower forward drop than the MOSFET/series diode combination. Presently MOSFET devices with on-resistance values as low as 12 mΩ have been reported [67] in a 300 mil × 300 mil chip. This gives a specific on-resistance of 7×10^{-3} Ω · cm^2. Over the next 10 years this specific on-resistance will drop to under 2×10^{-3} Ω · cm^2 because of improvements in design and processing. When combined with larger die areas of over 3 cm^2, this will produce devices of 6×10^{-4} Ω resistance. For applications such as a synchronous rectifier, in switching power supplies, this could be used as a 300-A rectifier with a 0.2-V drop. Such devices would also be very attractive in other applications, such as in automotive electronics, for switching virtually all the loads in an automobile. A micrograph of a device which represents the first step in this direction can be seen on Fig. 36, which shows a developmental 330 mil × 330 mil chip that is expected to have less than 0.003-Ω resistance and contains over 150 000 cells. This chip was fabricated at the GE Research and Development Center as a MOSFET synchronous rectifier under contract to the Naval Research Laboratory.

Comparison Between Devices

The previous sections discussed the probable evolution of device ratings over the next 10 years. In this section the question of how to select the optimum device type for a given application will be discussed. Of course, the issue is only a relevant one where multiple devices of a particular current and voltage rating are available. Consequently, much of the following analysis will be largely academic for applications requiring devices of very high currents where only GTO's or SCR's are available.

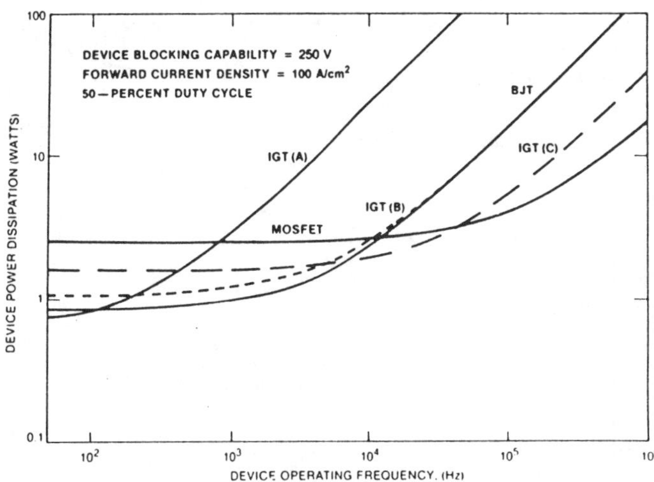

Fig. 37. Comparison of power dissipation of power switches rated at 250 V as a function of switching frequency.

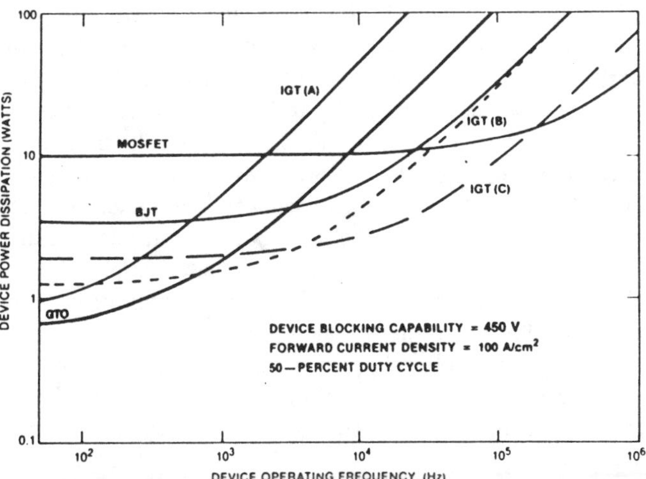

Fig. 38. Comparison of power dissipation of power switches rated at 450 V as a function of switching frequency.

Figs. 37, 38, and 39 show comparisons based on power dissipation for devices rated at 250, 450, and 1000 V, respectively. This discussion will purposely leave out any comparison with SCR's since in applications that do not require a turn-off type device, the SCR is the logical choice and in most applications requiring turn off, the SCR is largely precluded. The discussion here will largely be centered on the issue of power dissipation since for most power switching applications the device size is largely determined by a requirement that the chip temperature is kept under a maximum junction temperature such as 150°C. As such, the relative chip areas for two devices (and to first order, cost), are approximately related to the square root of the ratio of power dissipation levels (the square root relation is exact for resistive devices). Additional issues, such as savings due to loss of gate drive and to different fabrication costs for devices of different technologies, can then be factored in to the degree required. In each of the figures, the power dissipation is plotted as a function of switching frequency for inductive switching with a duty cycle of 50 percent. All of the devices have equal chip areas of 0.01 A/cm^2 and carry 1 A or current (translating to a current density of 100 A/cm^2). At low frequency, the power loss is dominated by conduction loss and at high frequency by switching loss,

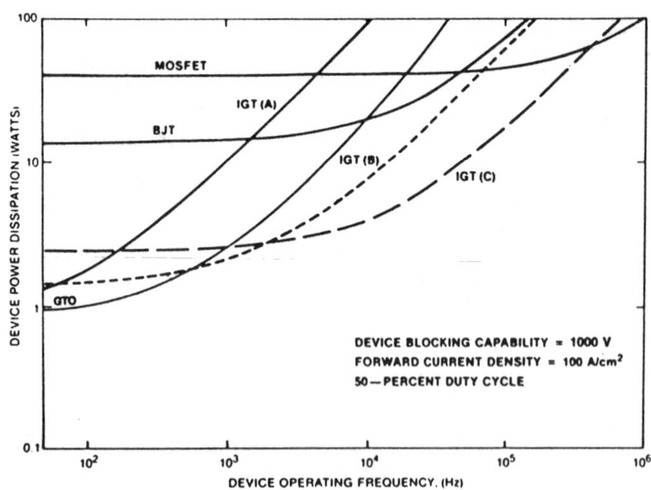

Fig. 39. Comparison of power dissipation of power switches rated at 1000 V as a function of switching frequency.

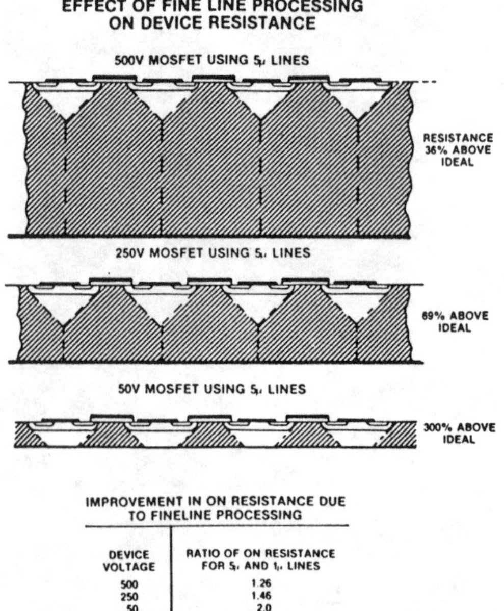

IMPROVEMENT IN ON RESISTANCE DUE TO FINELINE PROCESSING

DEVICE VOLTAGE	RATIO OF ON RESISTANCE FOR 5μ AND 1μ LINES
500	1.26
250	1.46
50	2.0

Fig. 40. Effect of design rule on the specific on-resistance of power MOSFET's.

which is proportional to frequency and becomes the dominant factor. Additional discussion on this means of making device comparisons can be found elsewhere [83]. It should also be noted that for each figure 3 IGT curves are presented. These correspond to the three different IGT's discussed in the context of Fig. 21, where increased switching speed has been traded off against increased conduction losses. This can easily be done by electron irradiating the devices after the fabrication sequence has been otherwise completed. This ability to customize the IGT for a given application is one of the significant advantages that the IGT possesses.

Looking first to low-frequency performance, it can be seen that the MOSFET has the highest power dissipation of all of the devices for all three voltages for frequencies below 10 kHz. At the lowest frequencies (<100 Hz), the GTO has the lowest loss with the IGT being a close second. At this same low-frequency regime, the losses for the BJT lie above that for the IGT but below that of the MOSFET. This pattern of relative performance is most pronounced for the 1000-V comparisons and the smallest for the 250-V devices. As noted earlier, below 100-V the MOSFET becomes the device of choice, and in the context of the present discussion this occurs because the MOSFET is the lowest loss device at this voltage.

The situation in the medium frequency regime (500 Hz $< f <$ 10 kHz) is much more complicated. However, the IGT is a good choice at these frequencies because device B (see Figs. 37–39) is close to being the lowest loss device in all cases and, when this is combined with the circuit savings inherent with MOS gate drives, the IGT is a very attractive device (assuming it is available in the required ratings).

At frequencies above 100 kHz the MOSFET is the obvious choice for all these voltages, but IGT device C makes a good choice for applications with frequencies under 50 kHz. Additional factors alluded to earlier, such as the desirability or lack of having the parasitic diode inherent in the MOSFET, will also contribute to the decision as to optimum device type.

Future Directions in Power Devices

When viewed together, it is clear that for the last several years a revolution has been occurring in power electronics with the introduction of the class of integrated power devices such as the MOSFET, the IGT, and the HVIC. These new devices have been made possible by the increasing sophistication of integrated circuit processing technology, since much of the technology inherent in these devices is borrowed from advances in IC fabrication. The MOSFET described earlier in Fig. 36, which contains 150 000 cells, is the best example to date of VLSI technology implemented in power electronics. This trend will continue as IC technology advances further with increasing levels of integration being applied to both increase the size and improve the performance of MOS power devices.

There is an example of the latter in Fig. 40 that illustrates the effect that finer line width has on the specific on-resistance of low-voltage MOSFET's. As can be seen, a reduction of a factor of three is possible by reducing the minimum feature size from the present 5-μ design rule to a 1-μ design rule. This occurs due to the fact that the resistance from current spreading from the top surface of the device into the bulk is the dominant component of resistance in low-voltage MOSFET's. This effect is magnified in low-voltage MOSFET's where the vertical epitaxial thickness is small compared to the pitch of the unit cell. This makes most of the area of the device inactive in conducting current (cross-batched area in Fig. 40). Thus as one can see, dramatic improvements in the low-voltage MOSFET can be expected over the next 10 years as power device manufacturers continue to take advantage of improvements coming from IC technology.

The trend to combining MOS and bipolar in monolithic structures, begun with the IGT, will also continue. In particular, the IGT which combines the best features of MOSFET's and bipolar devices in a totally new device that is distinct from the simple constituent devices can be referred to as an example of vertical integration. This is distinct from horizontal integration found in IC's which combine multiple devices as a single chip. The IGT is an early example of devices and other devices with mixed technologies can be expected. As a general comment, the trend to mix technologies with logic and driver devices added to discrete power devices will continue.

HVIC's can also be expected to increase in capability and complexity. This will include the integration of higher gate count logic and analog circuitry together with smart sensors and high-voltage devices with higher levels of output power capabilities. One should expect that, as the chip areas increase as shown in Fig. 32, single-chip power circuits with over a 10-A capability at the 110-V ac line will emerge.

Second Electronic Revolution

The effect of the recent revolution in integrated power electronics with the introduction of both new discrete devices, such as the IGT and power MOSFET, and the HVIC, has been to achieve up to a factor of twenty cost reduction in power electronics in the low to medium power area. These cost reductions rival the effect that the IC has had on signal level electronics over the past 10 years. This in turn is opening up new applications for electronics, in general, where the major impediment in many cases had become the cost of power electronics after the signal IC had reduced the cost of the control function. Examples of this are the many consumer products such as appliances, air conditioners, and lighting which is all electrical but has been devoid of electronics due to the high cost. Examples in the industrial area include programmable controls, machine tool controls, and robotics. This new generation of integrated power electronic devices will open up a second electronic revolution that could surpass the size and scope of the IC-based revolution in its impact on the entire scope of consumer and industrial electronics.

REFERENCES

[1] J. Bardeen and W. H. Brattain, "The transistor, a semiconductor triode," *Phys. Rev.*, vol. 74, pp. 230–231, 1948.

[2] —, "Physical principles involved in transistor action," *Phys. Rev.*, vol. 75, pp. 1208–1225, 1949.

[3] W. Shockley, "The theory of p-n junctions in semiconductors and p-n junction transistors," *Bell Syst. Tech. J.*, vol. 28, pp. 435–489, 1949.

[4] R. N. Hall, "Power Rectifiers and transistors," *Proc. IRE*, vol. 40, no. 11, pp. 1512–1518, 1952.

[5] R. H. Hall, "Electron-hole recombination in germanium," *Phys. Rev.*, vol. 87, pp. 387–392, 1952.

[6] W. Shockley and W. T. Read, Jr., "Statistics of recombination of holes and electrons," *Phys. Rev.*, vol. 87, pp. 835–842, 1952.

[7] —, *Electronic and Holes in Semiconductors.* Princeton, NJ: Van Nostrand, 1950.

[8] R. A. Kokosa and R. L. Davies, "Avalanche breakdown of diffused silicon p-n junctions," *IEEE Trans. Electron Devices*, vol. ED-13, pp. 874–881, 1966.

[9] R. L. Davies and F. E. Gentry, "Control of electric fields at the surface of p-n junctions," *IEEE Trans. Electron Devices*, vol. ED-11, pp. 313–323, 1964.

[10] G. K. Teal, "Some recent developments in silicon and germanium materials and devices," presented at National IRE Conf., (Dayton, OH), 1954.

[11] N. H. Fletcher, "Some aspects of the design of power transistors," *Proc. IRE*, vol. 43, no. 5, pp. 551–559, 1955.

[12] J. A. Hoerni, "Planar silicon transistors and diodes," presented at IRE Electron Devices Meet., (Washington, DC), 1969.

[13] H. A. Schafft, "Second breakdown–A comprehensive review," *Proc. IEEE*, vol. 55, no. 8, pp. 1272–1287, 1967.

[14] E. S. Wajda, B. W. Keppenhan, and W. H. White, "Expitaxial growth of silicon," *IBM J. Res. Develop.*, vol. 4, pp. 288–296, 1960.

[15] J. L. Moll, M. Tanenbaum, J. M. Goldey, and N. Holonyak, Jr., "p-n-p-n transistor switches," *Proc. IRE*, vol. 44, p. 1174, 1956.

[16] R. W. Aldrich and N. Holonyak, Jr., "Multi-terminal p-n-p-n switches," *Proc. IRE*, vol. 46, pp. 1236–1239, 1958.

[17] J. M. Goldey, I. M. Makintosh, and I. M. Ross, "Turn-off gain in p-n-p-n triodes," *Solid-State Electron.*, vol. 3, p. 119, 1961.

[18] F. E. Gentry, R. T. Scace, and J. K. Flowers, "Bidirectional triode p-n-p-n switches," *Proc.* IEEE, vol. 53, pp. 355–369, 19.

[19] E. K. Howell, "The light actuated SCR," Appl. Note 200.34, General Electric Co., Schenectady, NY, 1965.

[20] F. E. Gentry and J. Moyson, "The amplifying gate thyristor," presented at IEEE Int. Electroc Device Meet., Washington, DC, 1968.

[21] R. A. Kokosa and B. R. Tuft, "A high-voltage, high temperature reverse conducting thyristor," *IEEE Trans. Electron Devices*, vol. ED-17, no. 9, pp. 667–672, 1970.

[22] D. E. Houston, S. Krishna, D. Piccone, R. J. Finke, and Y. S. Sun, "Field-controlled thyristor (FCT)–A new electronic component," presented at IEEE Int. Electron Device Meet., Washington, DC, 1975.

[23] V.A.K. Temple and R. P. Love, "A 600 V MOSFET with near ideal on-resistance," in *IEDM Tech. Dig.*, pp. 664–666, 1978.

[24] J. D. Plummer and B. W. Scharf, "Insulated gate planar thyristors," *IEEE Trans. Electron Devices*, vol. ED-27, pp. 380–394, 1980.

[25] A. Pshaenich, "The MOS-SCR, A new thyristor technology," Motorola Engineering Bull. ED-103, 1982.

[26] B. J. Baliga, M. S. Adler, P. V. Gray, R. P. Love, and N. Zommer, "The insulated gate rectifier (IGR): A new power switching device," in *IEDM Tech. Dig.*, pp. 264–267, 1982.

[27] J. P. Russell, A. M. Goodman, L. A. Goodman, and J. M. Neilson, "The COMFET–A new high conductance MOS-gates device," *IEEE Electron Device Lett.*, vol. EDL-4, pp. 63–65, 1983.

[28] P. W. Shackle, A. R. Hartmen, T. J. Riley, J. C. North, and J. E. Berthold, "A 500 V monolithic bidirectional 2 × 2 crosspoint array," *ISSCC Dig. Tech. Papers*, pp. 170–171, 1980.

[29] T. E. Ruggles and G. V. Fay, "Mixed process puts high power under fine control," *Electron. Design*, pp. 69–73, 1982.

[30] K. Fujii, Y. Torimaru, K. Nakagawa, T. Fujimoto, and Y. Aoko, "400 MOS-IC for EL display," in *ISSCC Dig. Tech. Papers*, pp. 46–47, 1981.

[31] P. W. Shackle and R. S. Pospisil, "Using the HV-100 induction motor energy saver," Harris Semiconductor Application Note no. 542, Jan. 1983.

[32] E. J. Wildi and T. P. Chow, "A 500 V junction isolated BIMOS high voltage IC," in *Proc. Electro 1984*, Session 25, paper no. 4, 1984.

[33] M. Otsuka, "The forward characteristics of thyristors," *Proc. IEEE*, vol. 55, no. 8, Aug. 1967.

[34] T. Matsuzawa, "Spreading velocity of the on-state in high speed thyristors," *Trans. IEEE* Japan, 1973.

[35] H. F. Storm and J. G. St. Clair, "An involute gate-emitter configuration for thyristors," *IEEE Trans. Electron Devices*, vol. ED-21, no. 8, pp. 520–522, 1974.

[36] A. A. Jaecklin, "Structure of an efficient high power reverse conducting thyristor," presented at IEEE Power Division Colloquium, London, England, Dec. 1, 1978.

[37] P. S. Raderecht, "The development of a gate-assisted turn-off thyristor for use in high frequency applications," *Int. J. Electron.*, vol. 36, pp. 399–416, 1974.

[38] E. S. Schlegel, "Gate-assisted turn-off thyristor," *IEEE Trans. Electron Devices*, vol. ED-23, pp. 888–892, 1976.

[39] J. Shimiza *et al.* "High-voltage high-power gate-assisted turn-off thyristor for high-frequency use," *IEEE Trans. Electron Devices*, vol. ED-23, no. 8, pp. 883–887, 1976.

[40] A. Tada, T. Nakagawa, H. Iwamoto, and K. Ueda, "1200 V, 400 Amperes, 4 μs gate-assisted turn-off thyristor for high frequency inverter use," in *Proc. Industry Application Society IEEE IAS Ann.* Meet., pp. 731–734, 1981.

[41] V.A.K. Temple and A. P. Ferro, "High power dual gate light-triggered thyristors," *IEEE Trans. Electron Devices*, vol. ED-23, p. 893, 1976.

[42] P. DeBruyne and R. Sittig, "Light sensitive structure for high voltage thyristors," in *Tech. Dig. IEEE Power Electronics Specialists Conf.*, p. 262, 1976.

[43] E. Schlegal and D. Page, "A high power light activated thyristor," in *IEDM Tech. Dig.*, p. 483, 1976.

[57] H. W. Becke and R. P. Misra, "Investigation of gate turn-off structures," in *IEDM Tech. Dig.* pp. 649-653, 1980.

[58] T. Nagano, T. Yatsuo, and M. Okamura, "Characteristics of a 3000 V, 1000 A gate turn-off thyristor," in *Proc. IEEE Industry Application Society Conf.*, pp. 750-753, 1981.

[59] P. L. Hower and V. G. Reddi, "Avalanche injection and second breakdown in transistors," *IEEE Trans. Electron Devices*, vol. ED-17, pp. 320-335, April 1970.

[60] S. Krishna and P. L. Hower, "Second breakdown of transistors during inductive turn-off," *Proc. IEEE*, vol. 61, no. 3, pp. 393-395, Mar. 1973.

[61] Y. Nakatani, H. Nakazawa, Y. Nawata, K. Ono, M. Kobayashi, and M. Kohno, "A new ultra-high speed high voltage switching transistor," in *Proc. Power Conf.* 7, 1980.

[62] L. E. Clark, "High current density beta diminution," *IEEE Trans. Electron Devices*, vol. ED-17, pp. 661-666, Sept. 1970.

[63] P. L. Hower, "Optimum design of power transistor switches," *IEEE Trans. Electron Devices*, vol. ED-20, pp. 426-435, Apr. 1973.

[64] M. J. Declereq and J. D. Plummer, "Avalanche breakdown in high voltage D-MOS devices," *IEEE Trans. Electron Devices*, vol. ED-23, pp. 1-6, 1976.

[65] V.A.K. Temple and P. V. Gray, "Theoretical comparison of DMOS and VMOS structures for voltage and on-resistance," in *IEDM Tech. Dig.*, pp. 88-93, 1979.

[66] S. C. Sun and J. D. Plummer, "Modeling of the on-resistance of LDMOS, VDMOS, and VMOS power transistors," *IEEE Trans. Electron Devices*, vol. ED-27, pp. 356-367, 1980.

[67] R. P. Love, P. V. Gray, and M. S. Adler, "A large area power MOSFET designed for low conduction losses," *IEEE Trans. Electron Devices*, vol. ED-31, pp. 817-820, 1984.

[68] N. Zommer, "The monolithic HV BIPMOS," in *IEDM Tech. Dig.*, pp. 263-266, 1981.

[69] B. J. Baliga, "High gain power switching using field controlled thyristors," *Solid-State Electron.*, vol. 25, pp. 345-353, 1982.

[70] —, "The asymmetrical field-controlled thyristor," *IEEE Trans. Electron Devices*, vol. ED-27, pp. 1262-1268, 1980.

[71] —, "Enhancement and depletion mode vertical channel MOS gated thyristors," *Electron. Lett.*, vol. 15, pp. 645-647, 1979.

[72] L. Leipold, W. Baumgartner, W. Ladenhauf, and J. P. Stengl, "A FET-controlled thyristor in SIPMOS Technology," in *IEDM Tech. Dig.*, pp. 79-82, 1980.

[73] M. S. Adler and V.A.K. Temple, "The dynamics of the thyristor turn-on process," *IEEE Trans. Electron Devices*, vol. ED-27, pp. 483-494, 1980.

[74] B. J. Baliga, "Fast switching insulated gate transistors," *IEEE Electron Device Lett.*, vol. EDL-4, pp. 42-454, 1983.

[75] B. J. Baliga and E. Sun, "Comparison of gold, platinum, and electron irradiation for controlling lifetime in power rectifiers," *IEEE Trans. Electron Devices*, vol. ED-24, pp. 685-688, 1977.

[76] B. J. Baliga, "The new generation of MOS power devices," in *Proc. Drive/Motors/ Controls Conf.*, pp. 139-141, 1983.

[77] J. A. Appels and H.M.J. Vaes, "High voltage thin layer devices (resurf devices)," in *IEDM Tech. Dig.*, pp. 238-241, 1979.

[78] E. J. Wildi, P. V. Gray, T. P. Chow, and H. R. Chang, "Modeling and process implementation of implanted resurf devices," in *IEDM Tech. Dig.*, pp. 268-271, 1982.

[79] H. W. Lam, "Silicon on insulating substrates–Recent advances," in *IEDM Tech. Dig.*, pp. 348-351, 1983.

[80] J. D. Harnden, "1977 solid-state power technology," General Electric TIS Rep. no. 77CRD114.

[81] V.A.K. Temple, "Development of a 10 kV light triggered thyristor with built-in self-protection," General Electric Technical Proposal Prepared for Electric Power Research Institute, Nov. 1982, no. CRD5110.001E.

[82] J. D. Meindl, "Theoretical, practical, and analogical limits in ULSI," in *IEDM Tech. Dig.*, pp. 8-13, 1983.

[83] M. S. Adler and S. R. Westbrook, "Power semiconductor switching devices–A comparison based on inductive switching," *IEEE Trans. Electron Devices*, vol. ED-29, pp. 947-952, 1982.

Paper 3.2

POWER MOSFETS - A STATUS REVIEW

Brian R. Pelly
International Rectifier
El Segundo, California

Abstract

This paper gives an overview of the present technical status of power MOSFETs and discusses the features of these devices that are luring more and more designers to use them. A summary of available MOSFET ratings and packages is presented, and information is given on the exacting quality and reliability levels that are now being achieved.

INTRODUCTION

Power MOSFETs were introduced to the marketplace about five years ago, and have now gained a strong foothold in a multitude of applications, at power levels from a few watts to a few kilowatts -- in a few cases, to several hundreds of kilowatts. Typical uses include switching and linear power supplies, speed control of dc and ac motors, stepper motor controllers, relays, lighting controls, solenoid drivers, medical equipment, robotics, appliance controls, induction heating, and instrumentation.

Useage is expected to increase significantly over the next few years, as engineers become more aware of the electrical performance characteristics, quality, and reliability of power MOSFETs. Stimulating the trend will be continuing reductions in prices.

This paper presents a brief technical overview of the present status of the power MOSFET market, and shows -- by reference to key technical comparisons with conventional bipolar transistors -- why power MOSFETs will continue to gain a greater share of the marketplace.

POWER MOSFET TECHNOLOGY

Power MOSFETs differ fundamentally from signal-level field Effect Transistors, in that the current flow is vertical rather than lateral through the silicon. Vertical current flow is vital in a power device in order to utilize the silicon effectively.

The first power MOSFETs to be introduced employed a surface groove technique -- called V-groove, or VMOS. This structure is generally no longer favored, as it is limited in voltage capability, and most manufacturers now use a planar DMOS (double diffused MOS) construction. A DMOS power MOSFET is exemplified by the HEXFET structure shown in Figure 1.

The basic principle of operation of a MOSFET is that application of a potential to a control (gate) electrode alters the conductivity of an adjacent "channel" region, thus allowing the flow of current through the main terminals of the device to be controlled. Because the gate is isolated, the power gain is extremely high; and because the MOSFET is a majority carrier device, switching speeds are very fast, thermal stability is assured, and second breakdown -- a common problem in bipolar transistors -- is absent.

The manufacturing technology needed to achieve the fine geometrical structure of a power MOSFET is borrowed largely from that previously reserved

Reprinted with permission from *Int. Power Electron. Conf. (IPEC) Rec.*, vol. 1, pp. 19–32, March 1983. © 1983 IEE of Japan.

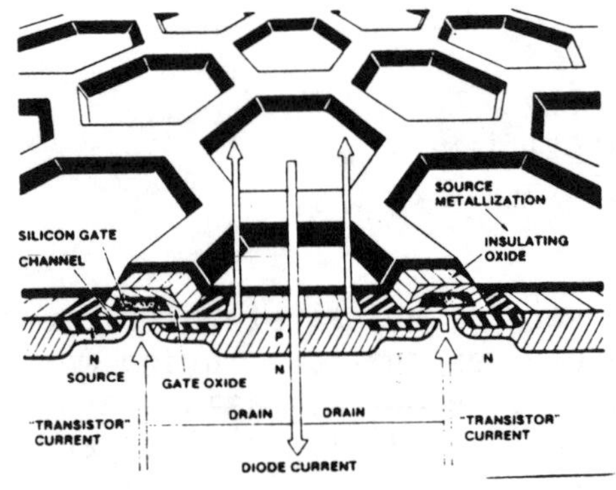

Fig. 1. Basic structure of a HEXFET Power MOSFET

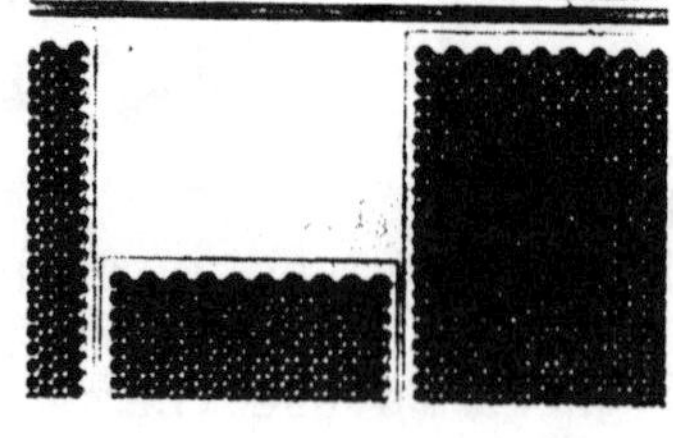

Fig. 2. HEXFET geometry

for Large Scale Integrated circuits. Ion implantation, which allows very precise controlled formation of shallow layers, and very fine-line photolithographic techniques are commonplace in the production of power MOSFETs. The HEXFET structure shown in Figure 1, for example, contains about 1000 hexagonal source cells per square millimeter of silicon. This is the same order of cellular density that is used in today's intricate integrated circuits. Figure 2 shows a magnified view of the HEXFET's surface geometry.

A common (but incorrect) argument when comparing fundamental costs of bipolars and MOSFETs is that since the MOSFET inherently requires greater manufacturing precision and more manufacturing steps, it will inherently be more expensive. This point of view ignores the fact that the manufacture of all MOSFETs, whether high voltage, low voltage, small-chip or large-chip, follows largely the same standard processing steps. Substantially the only variable is the starting silicon material. Real practical economies of scale will therefore be possible as MOSFET manufacturing volumes grow, because of the uniformity with which MOSFETs can be manufactured. By comparison, literally hundreds of different manufacturing processes exist for bipolar transistors, each optimized for the specific mix of parameters needed for the particular application. Bipolar transistor manufacturers are always fine-tuning their processes to optimize the trade-offs between gain, Safe Operating Area, switching speed, and voltage, which inevitably increases manufacturing costs, and narrows any real cost differences with MOSFETs.

ELECTRICAL CHARACTERISTICS -- COMPARISONS WITH BIPOLARS

Power MOSFETs have a number of major performance advantages over bipolar transistors. These are discussed in the following sections.

MOSFETs are voltage controlled

To switch a MOSFET ON, it is necessary simply to apply a voltage -- typically 10 volts for "full enhancement" -- between gate and source. The gate is isolated by silicon oxide from the body of the device, and the dc gain is virtually infinite. Drive power is negligible, and drive circuitry is generally considerably simpler than for a bipolar transistor. A typical comparison between the base drive current of a bipolar transistor and the gate current of a MOSFET in a switching application is illustrated in Figure 3. Note the change of scales between the bipolar and MOSFET oscillograms. Whereas drive current for the bipolar must be supplied continuously during the whole conduction period, gate current for the MOSFET flows only for the short periods needed to charge and discharge the self-capacitance, during the turn-on and turn-off transitions.

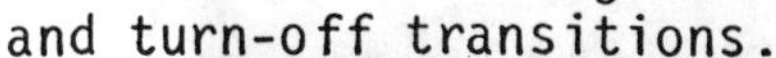

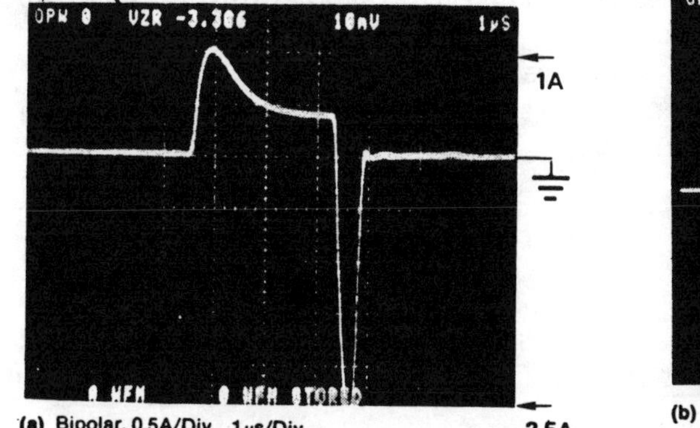

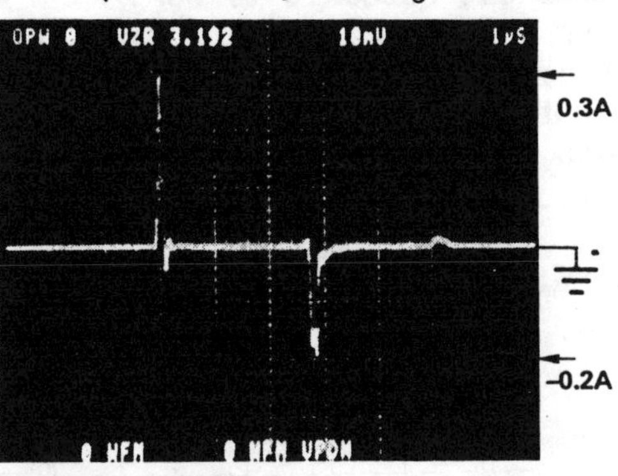

Fig. 3. Drive current waveforms for (a) bipolar transistor and (b) HEXFET
Collector (drain) current = 2.5A
Collector (drain) voltage = 270V
Frequency = 100kHz

A comparison of typical drive circuitry for a bipolar and a power MOSFET is shown in Figure 4. In this example the bipolar uses a "proportional" drive circuit, base current being taken from the collector via a current transformer. A second winding on the current transformer provides electrical isolation to the primary drive circuit. The bipolar's drive transformer is relatively large, because it must handle the relatively large base current, throughout the duration of the collector conduction period. The drive transformer for the HEXFET, by comparison, can be an order of magnitude or more smaller, since it carries current only for the short charging period of the gate-source capacitance (considerably less than a microsecond). Also, in this particular circuit, the size of the drive transformer is <u>independent</u> of the conduction time -- because the MOSFET "holds" its own gate drive voltage, by virtue of its own gate-source self-capacitance (discharge being blocked by the small auxiliary MOSFET drivers).

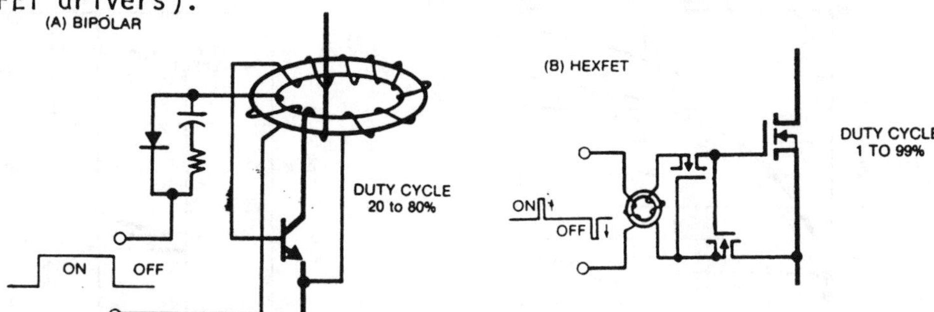

Fig. 4. Typical isolated drive circuits for (a) bipolar and (b) MOSFET

<u>Absense of storage time</u>

The MOSFET has no inherent delay and storage times, though it does, as mentioned above, have self-capacitance, which must be charged and discharged when switching. The time constant formed by the self-capacitance in conjunction with gate circuit and drain and source circuit impedances determines the switching times. Practical switching times range from less than 10 nanoseconds for small MOSFETs rated 1 ampere or less, to 50-100 nanoseconds for the largest ones, rated 10 to 30A.

The absence of storage time increases circuit utilization factors by reducing or eliminating "dead times" that must be built into circuits that use bipolar transistors. It also permits much faster response when reacting to overload and fault conditions, allowing fault current to be arrested much more effectively -- as illustrated in Figure 5.

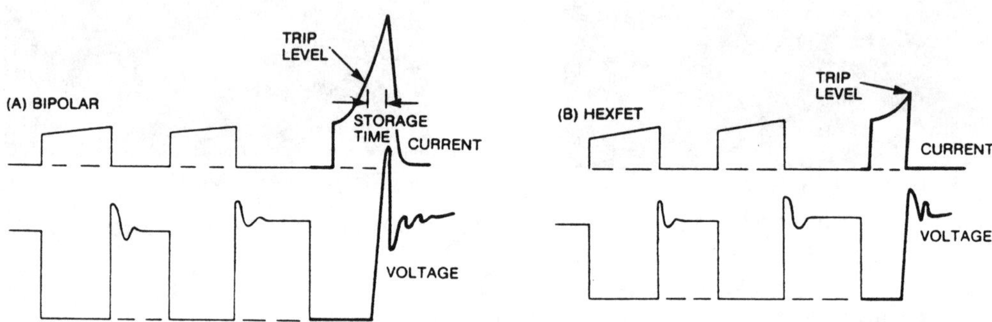

Fig. 5. Response to overload in switching power supply (a) bipolar transistor (b) HEXFET

High peak current capability

The gain of a bipolar transistor decreases with increasing current, but the transconductance of a MOSFET increases with increasing current, as illustrated in Figure 6. High peak current in a bipolar transistor tends to "pull it out of saturation" and destroy it through overheating. The on-resistance of a MOSFET does increase with increasing current -- as shown in Figure 7 -- but the effect is much more benign than with a bipolar, and the MOSFET has a much higher peak current carrying capability. For example a 400V HEXFET with a continuous drain current rating of 5.5A has a useable peak current of 20A. A comparable bipolar transistor would have a useable peak current of perhaps 7.5A.

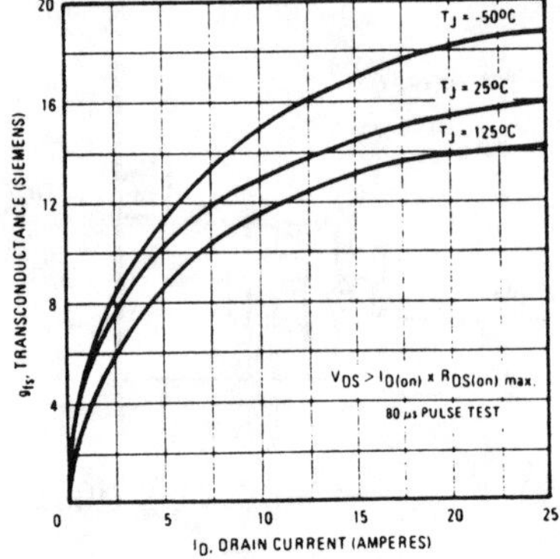

Fig. 6. Typical transconductance vs. drain current IRF450 HEXFET

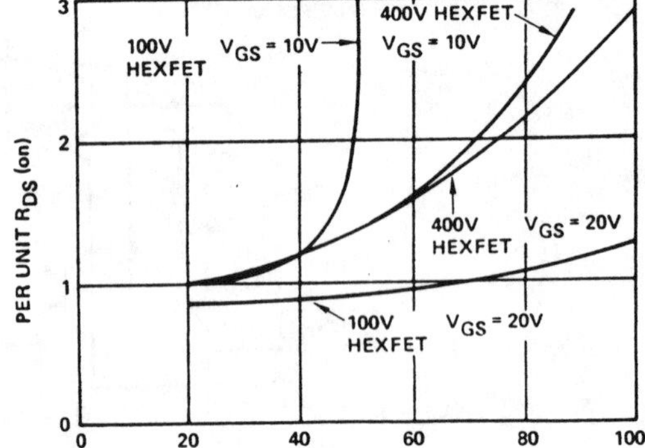

Fig. 7. Typical variation of on-resistance with drain current. 100% $I_{DM} \doteq 4 \times I_D$ @ $T_C = 25^oC$.

A practical example of the use of the HEXFET's peak current carrying capability is illustrated in Figure 8. In this example, the IRF150 HEXFET, rated 40A continuous, carries a peak capacitive load charging current of 150A, with a time constant of about 10msec.

The underlying limitation on current handling capability of a HEXFET is junction heating. It is able to handle peak current well in excess of its continuous current rating, just so long as the rated maximum junction temperature is not exceeded. This is true both for non-repetitive and repetitive operation.

A comparison of typical die sizes and current ratings of 400V rated bipolar and HEXFET devices is shown in Figure 9.

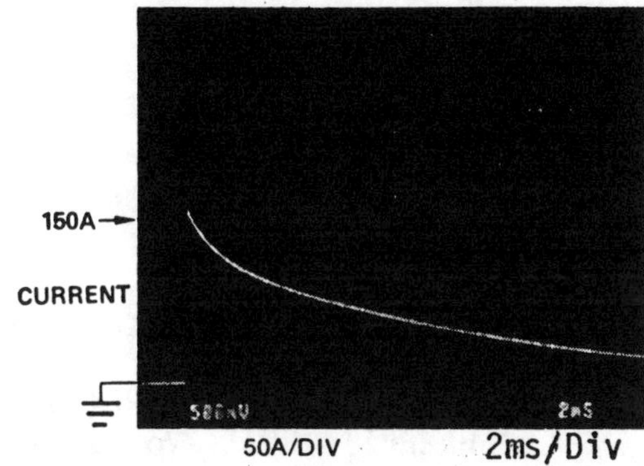

Fig. 8. Single shot 150A peak exponentially decaying pulse applied to the IRF150. Time constant ≑ 8msec.

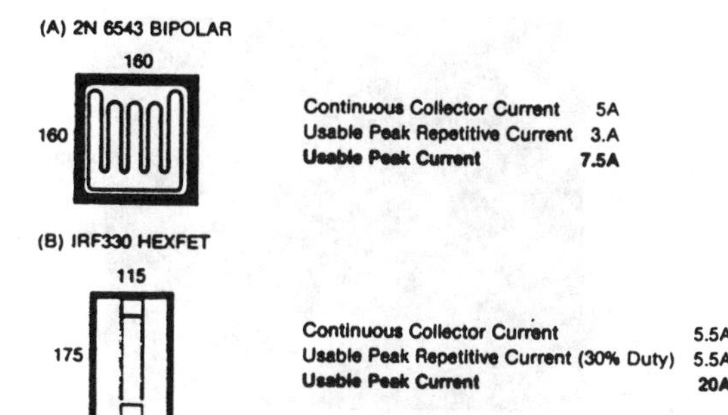

Fig. 9. Comparison of typical bipolar and MOSFET chips

Wide Safe Operating Area

The Safe Operating Area of a power MOSFET is much better than that of a bipolar. The MOSFET, being a majority carrier device, has a positive temperature coefficient of resistance, and is immune from the hotspot formation and second-breakdown phenomena that plague the bipolar transistor. MOSFETs are therefore generally much more rugged than bipolars, and snubber/clamp circuitry can be smaller and less dissipative, as illustrated in Figure 10.

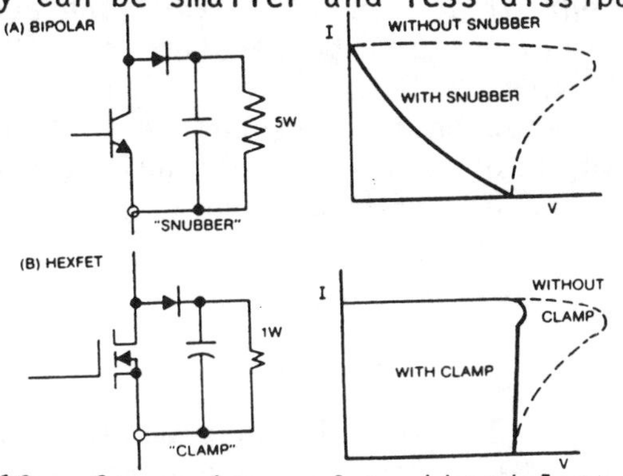

Fig. 10. Comparison of snubber/clamp circuitry for (a) bipolar and (b) MOSFET

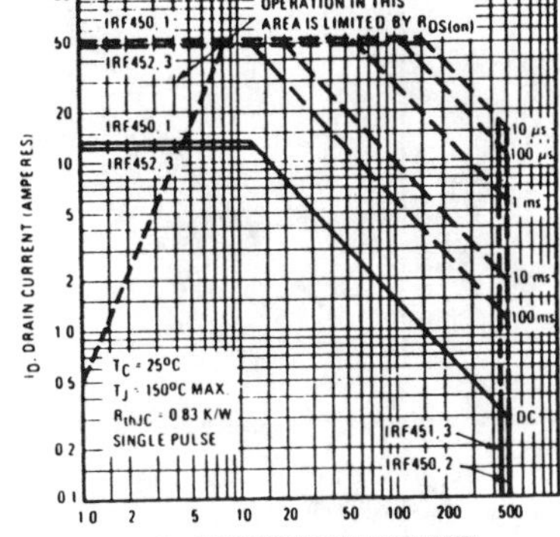

Fig. 11. Maximum Safe Operating Area IRF450 HEXFET

MOSFET data sheets usually show Safe Operating Area curves that cover current and voltage values up the rated I_{DM} and V_{DS} values respectively. Typical SOA data for a HEXFET is shown in Figure 11. This data is based simply on junction temperature rise, and is for a case temperature of 25°C, and an internal dissipation that raises the junction to the rated maximum value of 150°C. SOA curves for each pulse duration follow a line of constant power, and are actually nothing more than a graphical statement of the absence of second breakdown.

A verification of this particular SOA data is shown by the oscillograms in Figure 12. In this example, a 10μs, 50A pulse current is applied to the IRF450, at an applied drain-to-source voltage of 400V. Reference to Figure 11 shows that this point lies beyond the published SOA.

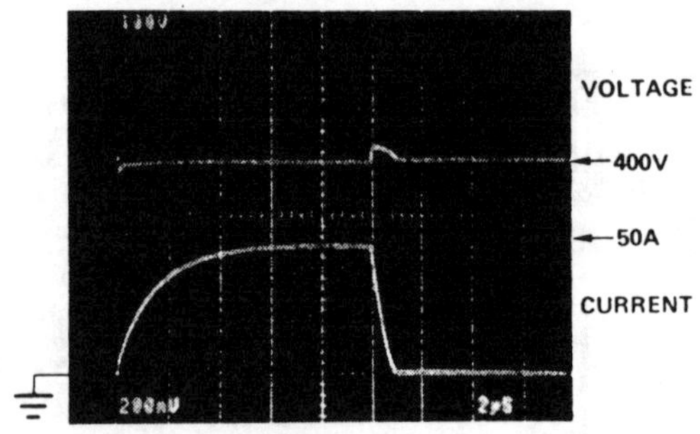

Fig. 12. Verification of IRF450 HEXFET's SOA. Voltage=400V. Peak current=50A

MOSFETs are more efficient at high frequency

The on-resistance of a MOSFET is one of its key characteristics, because it determines the device's conduction losses in switching applications. Today's largest 100V MOSFETs have on-resistance in the order of 30-50mOhms at 25°C. The corresponding conduction voltage drop at 30A at 25°C is 1 to 1.5V, and at rated maximum junction temperature of 150°C, it is 2 to 3V. For a given chip size, on-resistance increases with voltage rating. The largest 500V rated power MOSFETs have on-resistance in the order of 0.4 ohms at 25°C. The corresponding conduction voltage drop at rated useable continuous current of 10A is 4V at 25°C and about 8V at a junction temperature of 150°C. Figure 13 shows a typical relationship between on-resistance and voltage rating, for a HEXFET chip having dimensions of 6.5mm X 6.5mm.

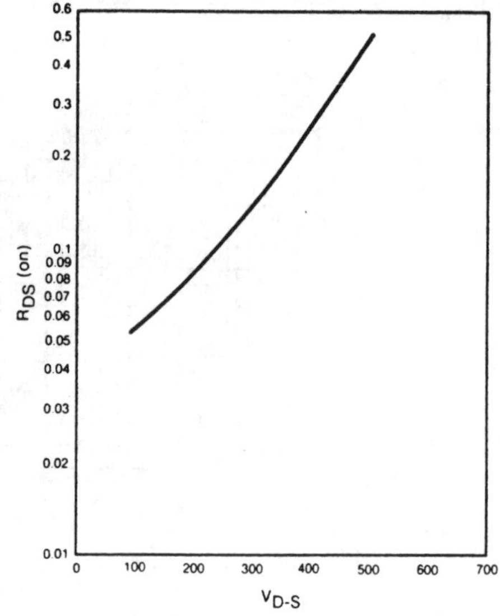

Fig. 13. Relationship between on-resistance and voltage rating. 6.53 X 6.53mm HEXFET

Comparisons between power MOSFETs and bipolars often center around the fact that the conduction voltage of a MOSFET is higher than for a bipolar, and becomes progressively more so as voltage rating increases. Conduction losses of a MOSFET when operating near rated current are therefore generally greater than for a bipolar. Switching losses of a MOSFET, on the other hand, are almost negligible -- while the switching losses of a bipolar are often greater than its conduction losses, particularly at high frequency. The bipolar is therefore usually more energy-efficient at low frequency, while the MOSFET is more energy-efficienct at high frequency. The frequency cross-over point depends upon specific circumstances, but is generally somewhere between 10 and 40kHz.

A comparison between the switching waveforms for a bipolar and a HEXFET is shown in Figure 14; note the sharper waveforms for the HEXFET. Figure 15 shows a comparison between power dissipation for the IRF330 HEXFET, the industry standard 2N6542/3 bipolar, and a recently introduced fast switching bipolar transistor. Power losses were gauged by measuring the case temperature of the device on a calibrated heatsink. The "full" curves represent only the device dissipation. Additional power is dissipated in the external base drive circuit of the bipolar, and the dashed curve includes 1.3W of external base drive power for the fast switching bipolar.

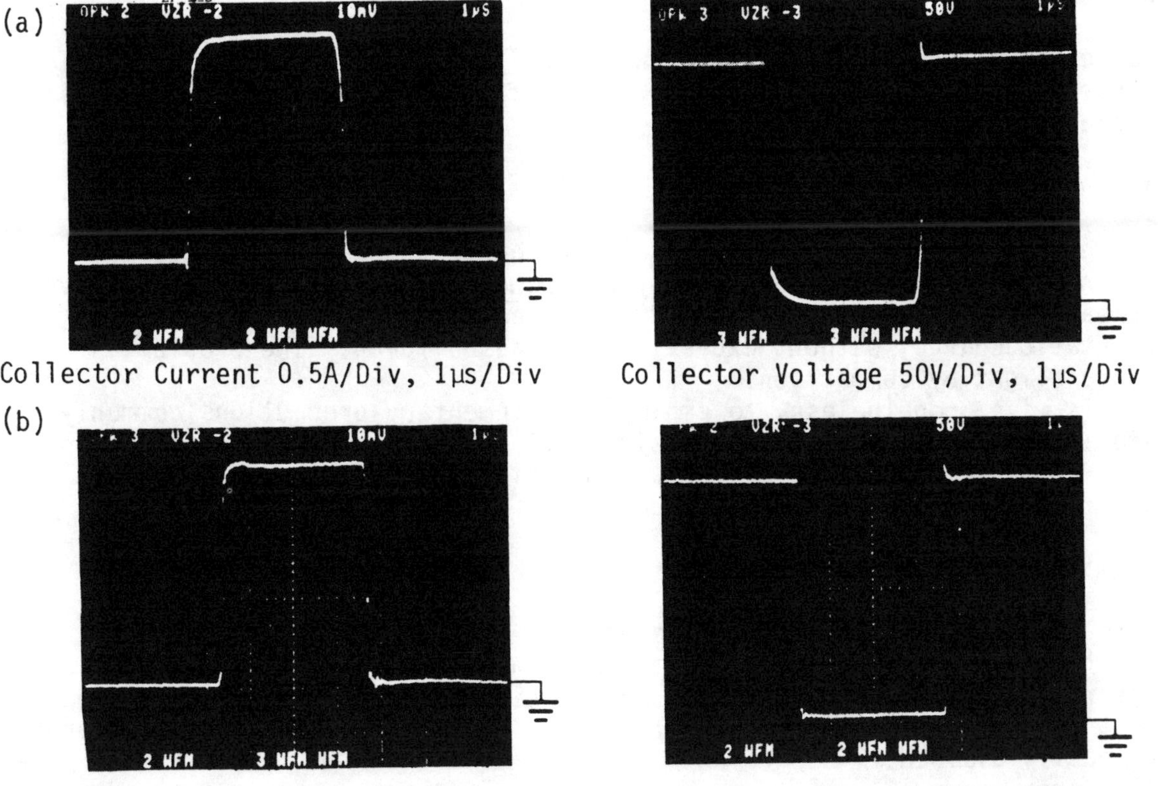

(a) Collector Current 0.5A/Div, 1µs/Div — Collector Voltage 50V/Div, 1µs/Div

(b) Drain Current 0.5A/Div, 1µs/Div — Collector Voltage 50V/Div, 1µs/Div

Fig. 14. Switching waveforms for (a) bipolar transistor and (b) MOSFET operating at 100kHz

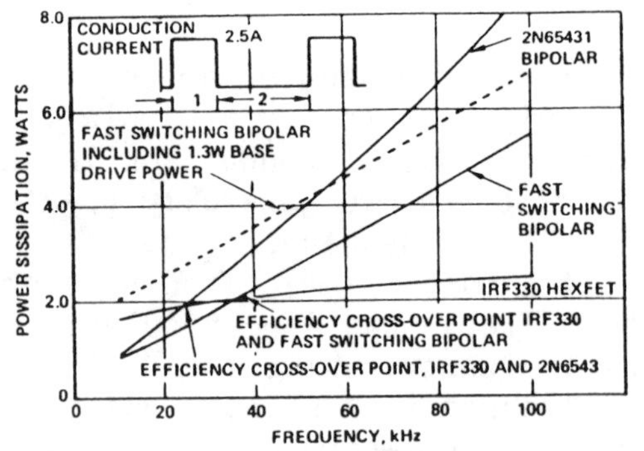

Fig. 15. Power dissipation versus frequency for 2N6542/3, a fast switching bipolar and IRF330 HEXFET. Supply voltage=270V. Conduction duty cycle=0.33 current amplitude =2.5A

It would not be correct to conclude from this discussion that power MOSFETs will find use only in higher frequency applications, and will not also be the preferred choice at lower frequency. Although MOSFETs certainly "shine" at high frequency, their higher conduction losses actually are often inconsequential, when viewed from the standpoint of the overall system design. Considerations such as circuit simplification, ruggedness, cost effectiveness and reliability of the overall system will frequently favor the MOSFET, even in low frequency applications.

Precautions

Like any other semiconductor, power MOSFETs do have their own subtleties, and these must be recognized and understood if these devices are to be applied successfully.

Static Charge

Power MOSFETs can be damaged by static charge when handling, testing, or installing into a circuit. Since they are <u>power</u> devices, however, they have much greater self-capacitance than CMOS devices, and are much more able to absorb static charge, without excessive voltage build-up. The problem is therefore slight by comparison.

It is wise, nonetheless, to employ the elementary precautions commonly used for other types of static-sensitive devices, such as the use of grounded wrist-straps, electrically grounded work stations, and grounded soldering irons.

Gate Voltage Transients

Excessive voltage applied to the gate of a power MOSFET will punch through the gate oxide and cause permanent damage. A typical gate-source voltage rating is $\pm$20V. Gate-source overvoltage failures have probably been the most common application problem to date -- but fortunately these failures can be easily avoided.

The problem usually stems from the fact that designers do not immediately recognize that voltage transients in the drain circuit can be coupled to the gate via the drain-gate self-capacitance. The amplitude of the voltage transient induced at the gate may or may not be dangerous (often it isn't), and it depends upon the impedance of the drive circuit. The simplest solution where gate voltage transients are suspected is to connect a clamping zener diode between the gate and source, physically as close as possible to the terminals.

A more subtle circuit mechanism for producing overvoltage at the gate has been observed. This is due to induced voltage in common source inductance when commutating "freewheeling" current from the internal body-drain diode. If this is a problem (in nearly all applications it isn't), it can be overcome by minimizing common source inductance -- and by keeping this inductance as symmetrical as possible for each MOSFET in the circuit.

Drain Voltage Transients

The extremely fast switching speed of the MOSFET is obviously conducive to self-inflicted overvoltage transients when switching off, due to stray drain circuit inductance -- even though the drain supply voltage may be well within the drain-source voltage rating.

The solution is to minimize stray circuit inductance, and if necessary (usually it is) to use a voltage clamp. Figure 10(b) shows an example.

High Let-Through Fault Current

Because power MOSFETs are not gain-limited to nearly the same degree as bipolar transistors, let-through fault currents can be much higher before self-limiting occurs. If left to flow unabated, or if allowed to reach the very high self-limiting level of the MOSFET, this fault current can be destructive to the MOSFET, as well as to other components in the circuit.

In applications where high let-through currents can occur, the first "line of defense" is to reduce the amplitude of the MOSFET's gate drive voltage, so that the peak let-through current is limited to a more moderate value. A more positive approach, however, is to use current sensing circuitry that turns OFF the MOSFET at a present level of current (as illustrated for example by the waveforms in Figure 5), thereby avoiding operation in a high-dissipation mode for more than a short transient interval.

Body Drain Diode

All power MOSFETs have an integral body-drain diode built into their structure (see Figure 1). In many applications this diode is inactive, and its presence can be ignored. In other circuits the body-drain diode does conduct, and actually performs a necessary circuit function "free of charge", obviating the need for a separate "freewheeling" or "clamping" rectifier.

In other cases, however, the reverse recovery time of the internal diode can be a problem, because this is relatively long by comparison with the switching speed of the MOSFET, and switching losses can become excessive. More subtly, the dv/dt capability of the body diode during its recovery period is limited, and in circuits that apply dv/dt during this period MOSFET failures can occur, if the dv/dt is excessive.

Fortunately, there are relatively simple circuit solutions to these problems when they arise (and in the majority of applications, they don't).

POWER MOSFET RATINGS AND PACKAGES

Power MOSFET ratings and packages cover the spectrum shown in Figure 16.

A typical family of N-Channel MOSFET die, with their associated voltage and current ratings, is illustrated in Figure 17.

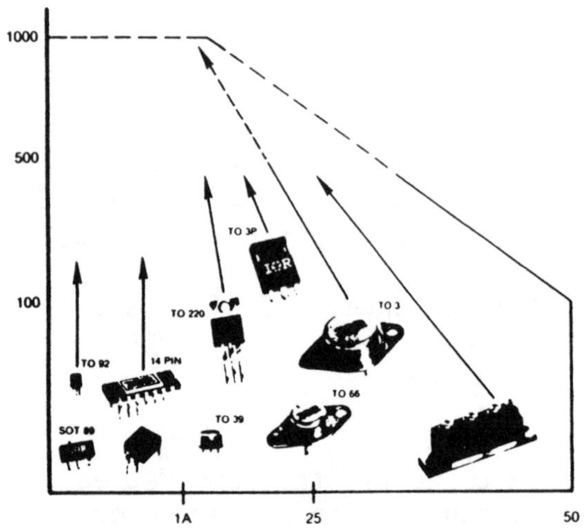

Fig. 16. Summary of power MOSFET ratings and packages

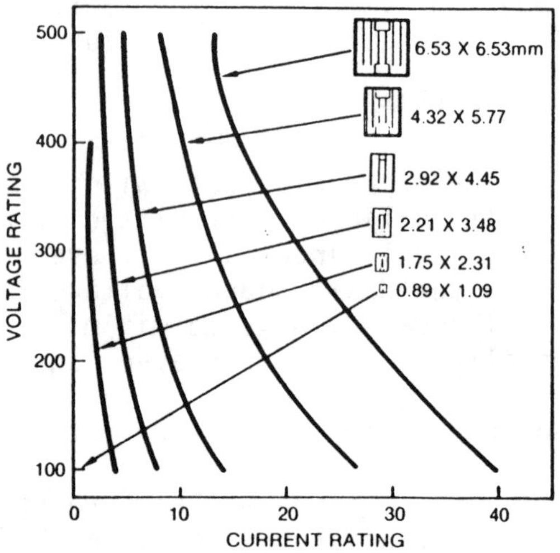

Fig. 17. Voltage versus current ratings. HEXFET family of power MOSFETs

As voltage capability increases above 500V, the power MOSFET requires an increasingly larger silicon die area than a bipolar transistor. Manufacture of MOSFETs above this voltage rating also becomes more difficult, reducing manufacturing yields and further contributing to costs. These are reasons why most of the power MOSFET market is presently at 500V and below.

Two or three years ago, the main packages offered were the industry-standard TO-3, TO-220AB, and TO-92 types. Today's spectrum of packages is broadening considerably, to cover both higher and lower power applications.

Noteable among the packages in Figure 16 are the "HEXPAK", and the 4-pin and 14-pin dual in-lines. The former package style has been popular for several years for SCRs and rectifiers; it is a natural development to put parallel chip HEXFETs in this package, for high power applications such as motor drives and uninterruptible power supplies.

The DIP package -- popular for line drivers, stepper motor controllers, automatic test equipment, instrumentation, and the like -- are automatically insertable, and are ideal where space is at a premium.

Power MOSFETs are being increasingly used in high reliability, space and military applications. Several special packages are now being offered to meet these special needs. Some of these packages are shown in Figure 18.

Hybrids -- containing additional circuitry peripheral to the MOSFET itself -- are also a natural development, and are beginning to appear for special applications. An example is shown in Figure 19.

Fig. 18. Typical packages for high reliability/military applications

Fig. 19. Typical HEXFET hybrid package

QUALITY AND RELIABILITY

The sophisticated processes and modern facilities necessary to the production of power MOSFETs create a manufacturing environment that is ideally conducive to high standards of quality and reliability. As of January, 1983, HEXFETs, for example, are being delivered to an AQL of 0.04% (i.e. a statistical maximum of 400 defective parts per million). Bipolar transistors and related bipolar power semiconductors, by comparison, typically achieve AQL levels that are twenty-five to fifty times inferior -- in the range of 10,000 to 20,000 defective parts per million.

The stringent AQL levels being obtained with power HEXFETs are achieved through rigid in-process controls -- which include numerous computerized monitoring checks during wafer fabrications, inspection of die mount-down, wire bonding, ultrasonic cleaning, and cap welding, pre-cap visual, and 100% computerized testing to electrical specifications.

HEXFETs also undergo an additional 100% batch Reliability Certification Program, that includes accelerated gate stress and high temperature reverse bias, along with tests to destruction, such as Safe Operating Area, gate dielectric breakdown, and avalanche energy failure. These tests determine the ultimate limits of performance, and verify that safety margins lie well beyond published data sheet specifications.

Reliability

Separate from -- but obviously related to -- the very tight quality levels now being achieved are equally impressive reliability specifications. Extensive long term reliability testing of TO-3 and TO-220AB package power HEXFETs, for example, for a total of 680,000 device hours, has demonstrated a relationship between Random Failure Rate and junction operating temperature shown in Figure 20.

This graph gives 23 failures in 10^9 device operating hours at a continuous junction operating temperature of 90°C. This level of reliability matches or exceeds that of the most advanced LSI memories.

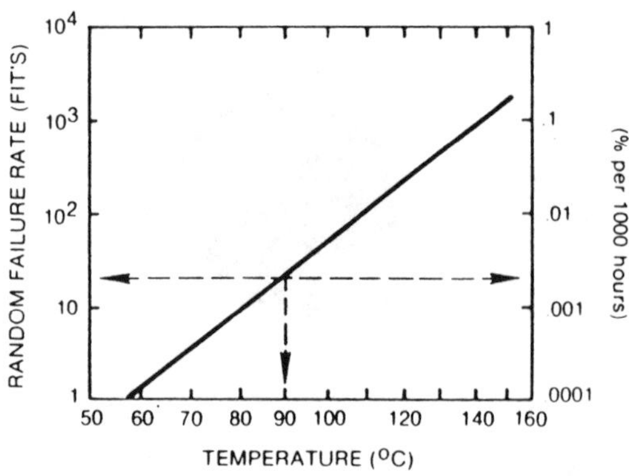

Fig. 20. Random failure rates versus junction operating temperature of HEXFETs

Reliability testing such as this is expected to lead many users to reduce or eliminate their own burn-in test programs, thus accelerating the user trend to power MOSFETs.

Military Approvals

Several power MOSFET types are now qualified to JAN, JANTX, JANTV, and CECC specifications, and many more are in the process of qualification.

Such approvals, for example, have been conferred on all TO-3 package HEX-3 and HEX-5 types (Figure 19).

Radiation Resistance

The effects of radiation are critically important in military and space applications. Testing by various agencies has now demonstrated the suitability of power MOSFETs for use in these environments, provided that the appropriate circuit design features are observed.

The primary effect of ionizing radiation is to cause a decrease in gate threshold voltage of N-Channel types, and an increase for P-Channel types. Typical test results are shown in Figure 21. The change of threshold voltage depends on the gate biasing conditions, particularly at radiation doses that are sufficient to change the polarity of the threshold voltage (N-Channel HEXFETs). A negative bias voltage applied to the gate during the OFF period -- typically -10V -- allows reliable switching operation at doses up to 1 megarad (Si) -- a greater dose than would actually be accumulated in most space applications.

The primary effect of neutron radiation is to cause an increase in on-resistance. This depends on the resistivity of the silicon -- and hence on the voltage rating of the device. The effect is not too pronounced for a 100V rated HEXFET, but can be appreciable for a 400V rated device, as illustrated in Figure 22.

The increase of on-resistance due to neutron radiation produces increased conduction losses in switching applications, but will have little effect in linear applications. It can be allowed for at the design stage, by appropriate choice of MOSFET and heatsink.

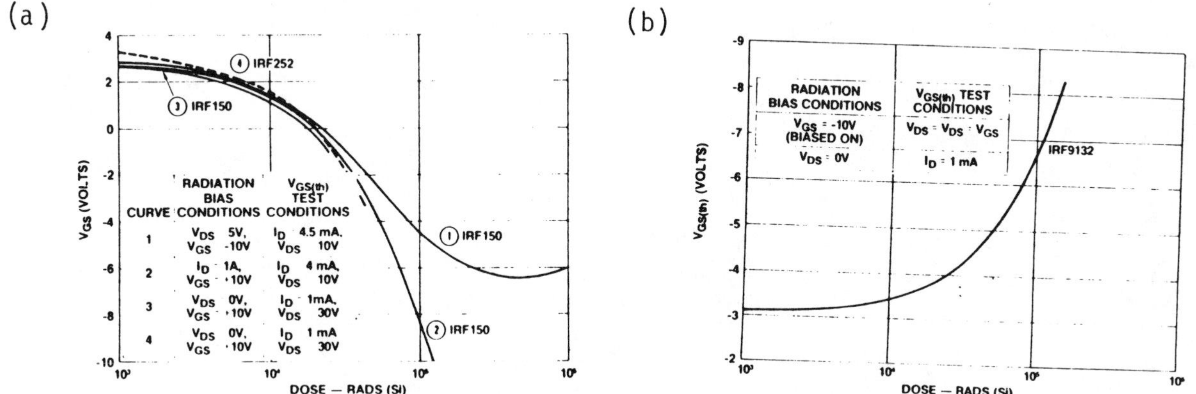

Fig. 21. Typical effects of ionizing radiation on (a) N-Channel and (b) P-Channel HEXFETs

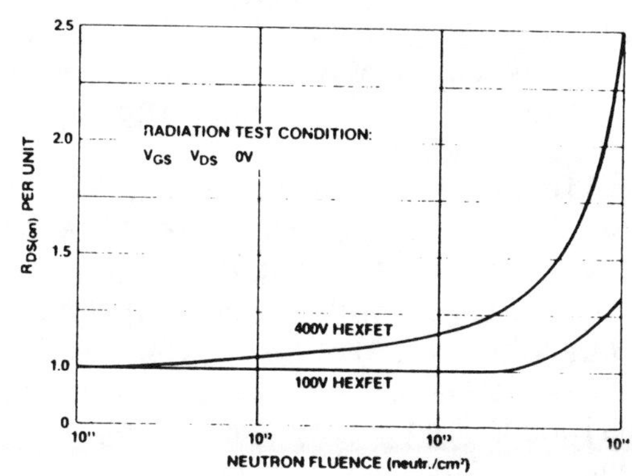

Fig. 22. Typical relationship between on-resistance and neutron fluence level

CONCLUSIONS

MOSFETs are now firmly established, and useage is continuing to increase rapidly. From a fairly modest range of product offerings two or three years ago, users now have at their disposal a variety of different types, in a variety of different packages.

Today MOSFET prices are often quite close to those of bipolars, and overall system costs are frequently lower using MOSFETs, because of the circuit simplifications that result from their use. Price is much less a consideration than it used to be -- and will become even less so in the future. Designers, no longer shackled by overriding cost considerations, are turning in droves to MOSFETs for the technical advantages that they offer. These advantages are summarized as follows:

(a) Quality and reliability of MOSFETs are an order of magnitude better than for bipolar transistors, providing much better system reliability.

(b) Drive circuitry is simpler and cheaper, and often can be standardized for a whole range of products.

(c) MOSFET's fast switching speeds permit much higher switching frequencies (well above 1MHz), much better efficiency at high frequency, and often much smaller overall circuit size and weight.

(d) Overload and peak current handling capability are high. MOSFETs are generally much more rugged and "forgiving" than bipolars.

(e) Absence of second breakdown reduces snubber circuitry in switching applications, and gives more power handling capability in linear applications.

(f) MOSFETs have more linear characteristics and have better temperature stability -- giving better performance in linear applications, and reducing complexity of feedback circuitry.

(g) MOSFETs are easy to parallel for higher current.

(h) MOSFET's leakage current is relatively low -- typically in the order of nanoamperes. This is important in critical applications such as Automatic Test Equipment and relay switching.

(i) Drain-source conduction threshold voltage is absent, eliminating electrical noise in sensitive A-C switching applications.

(j) MOSFETs are able to operate in hazardous radiation environments, and are suitable for space and military use. A number of different types have now received JAN, JANTX, JANTXV and CECC approval, and many more will follow.

(k) MOSFETs are easy to design with. Their operation is "clean" and predictable, and is easily analyzed.

Paper 3.3

ULTRA HIGH VOLTAGE, HIGH CURRENT GATE TURN-OFF THYRISTORS

Tsutomu YATSUO, Takahiro NAGANO, Hiroshi FUKUI, Masahiro OKAMURA
Hitachi Research Laboratory, Hitachi, Ltd.
AND Shuroku SAKURADA
Hitachi Works, Hitachi, Ltd.
Hitachi, Ibaraki, Japan

Abstract

A high power GTOs with ratings of 2,500 V · 2,000 A has been developed, and 4,500 V · 2,000 A GTO trial fabricated and performance tested, for use in traction motor control equipment. Their low on-state voltage was attained by applying a unique anode emitter shorting structure which does not require doping of a lifetime killer such as gold to obtain suitable GTO characteristics. Their high interrupt current was obtained by introducing a ring shaped gate structure which has uniform operation between many segments in the devices during turn-off process.

1. INTRODUCTION

Gate turn-off thyristors (GTOs) have been applied to high power inverters and choppers for traction motor drive.[1),2),3)] For these applications, 1,200 to 2,500 V, 600 to 1,000 A GTOs were developed.[4),5),6)] However, higher current, higher voltage GTOs are needed in order to realize substantial reductions in equipment size and weight.

There are two major factors to be resolved in designing high power GTOs. One is to reduce the on-state voltage, which increases remarkably when producing a high blocking voltage due to the inherently thick n-base layer, and due to the short carrier lifetime required in conventional GTOs. The second factor is to increase the maximum gate turn-off current without causing device failure.

To resolve these two points, the basic structure consisting of an anode emitter shorting was introduced and its structural parameters were optimized by experimental fabrications and characterizations of small size test samples. As a result, a high voltage, high current GTO with the rating of 2,500 V · 2,000 A was developed, and a 4,500 V · 2,000 A GTO trial fabricated and performance tested.

In this paper, various design considerations, device structures and electrical characteristics of the newly developed high power GTOs are described.

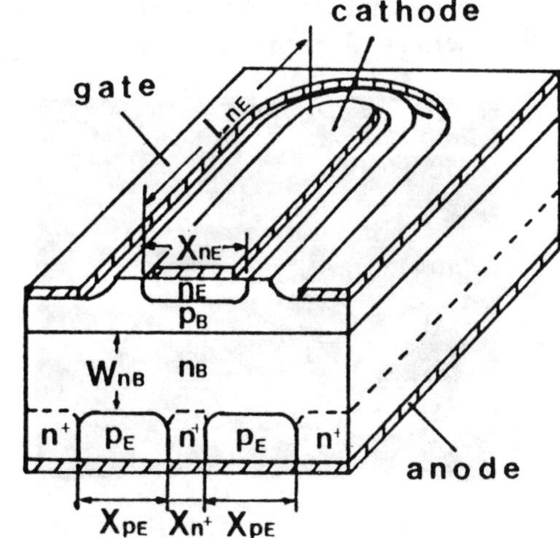

Fig. 1. Schematic structure of the unit-GTO with anode emitter shorting.

Reprinted with permission from *Int. Power Electron. Conf. (IPEC) Rec.*, vol. 1, pp. 65–74, March 1983.

2. DESIGN CONSIDERATIONS

2.1 Typical GTO Characteristics and the Shorted Emitter Structure

In general, GTO has a multi-emitter structure consisting of a plurality of narrow emitter strip surrounded by the gate electrode, which is called a unit-GTO. It is easy for the gate current to drive out electrons and holes from the current conducting area during the turn-off process.

Figure 1 shows a schematic structure of the unit-GTO with anode emitter shorting.[7] This structure dose not require a particular reduction in carrier lifetime to obtain good turn-off performance, because p-emitter shorting could reduce the carrier concentration in the base layer at the current conducting state, and have an effect of sweeping out carriers during the turn-off phase, similar to a reduction of carrier lifetime by doping with lifetime killer such as gold.[8] Thus it is easier here to decrease the on-state voltage than in a conventional GTO structure.

From a design viewpoint, it was important to estimate the electrical characteristics of the unit-GTO. The relations between turn-off characteristics, as well as on-state voltage and the structural parameters of the unit-GTO were investigated by using a group of small-size test samples.

Figure 2 shows examples of turn-off waveforms for the unit-GTO with different p-emitter shorting structures. The samples consisted of a single n-emitter strip with constant width and length of 0.3 and 5.8mm, respectively, and with various p-emitter shorting factors Xn^+/Xp_E. It can be seen that turn-off time t_{GQ} and the tailing part of the anode current are strongly related to the shorting factor Xn^+/Xp_E.

Figure 3 shows the effect of p-emitter shorting structure on turn-off time t_{GQ} and a turn-off gate charge Q_{GQ}, where Q_{GQ} was defined as the gate current integral during the turn-off time. The sample having $Xn^+/Xp_E = 0$ was a conventional structure without p-emitter shorting. As is evident from Fig. 3, both t_{GQ} and Q_{GQ} decrease with an increase in the value of Xn^+/Xp_E, and a saturating tendency can be seen at higher values of Xn^+/Xp_E.

Figure 4 shows anode currents as a function of time in a late stage of the gate turn-off period for the various unit-GTOs. In the tailing part of the anode current, I_A decays linerly the semi-logarithm plots, so I_A can be expressed as the following relation, $I_A \propto e^{-Rt}$, where R represents a shorting resistance which decreases with an increase in

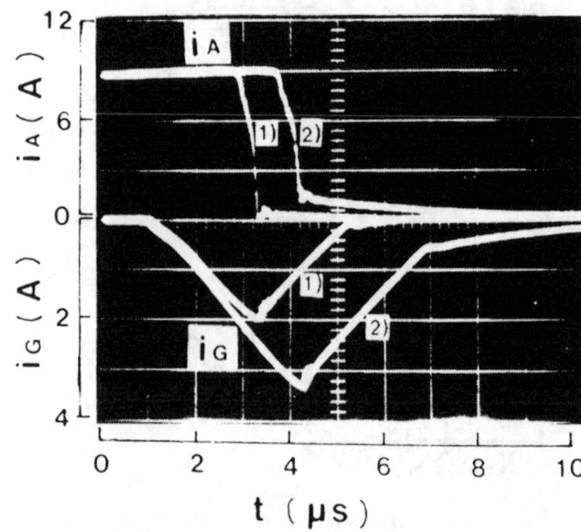

Fig. 2. Turn-off waveforms for the unit-GTOs with different p-emitter shorting structures.

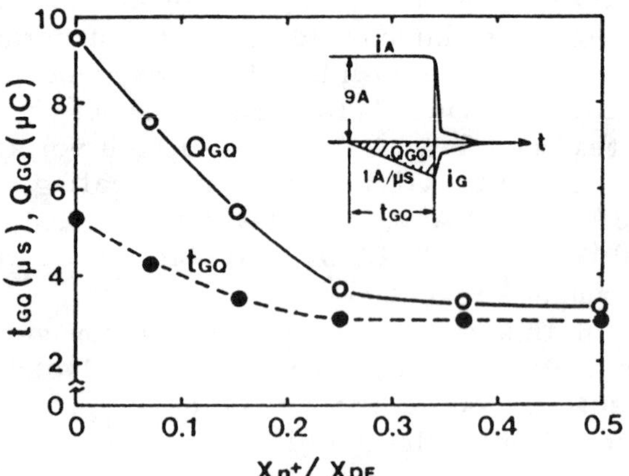

Fig. 3. Effect of shorting factor Xn^+/Xp_E on the turn-off time t_{GQ} and turn-off gate charge Q_{GQ} of the unit-GTOs.

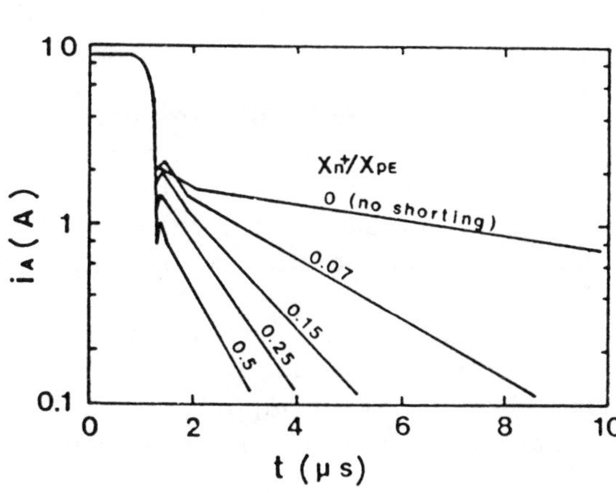

Fig. 4. Anode currents as a function of time in a late stage of the gate turn-off process.

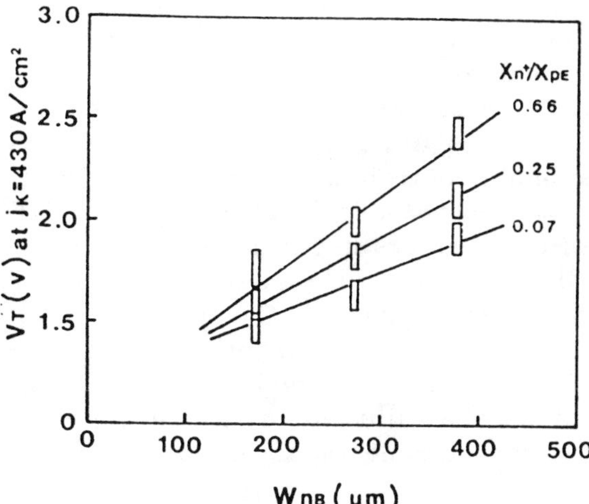

Fig. 5. On-state voltage vs. n-base width W_{nB} for various shorting factors.

X_{n^+}/X_{pE}. From the results, it is seen that power dissipation in the turn off process can be reduced by an increase in the p-emitter shorting of an actual GTO device.

Figure 5 plots the on-state voltage V_T versus n-base width W_{nB} for various shorting factors. The V_T increases with an increase in W_{nB} and with the shorting factor X_{n^+}/X_{pE}. A lowering of V_T below 2.5 volts can be obtained by optimizing the p-emitter shorting structure, even for such thick n-base widths as 0.4 - 0.5 mm or more.

Summarizing the above investigation, it was found that unit-GTO characteristics, such as on-state voltage, turn-off speed and gain, and turn-off power dissipation, depend primarily on the p-emitter shorting structure, and the degree of the shorting can be controlled by the p-emitter width X_{pE} and the n^+-shorting width X_{n^+}.

2.2 Maximum Gate Turn-Off Currents and GTO Structure

2.2.1 Safe operating area of unit-GTOs

In designing high current GTOs, it is important to increase the maximum gate turn off current I_{TCM} , witch is restricted by possible device failure due to current crowding in the respective unit-GTOs during the gate turn-off process.

Therefore, in order to increase I_{TCM} , it is first necessary to increase the maximum controllable current of the unit-GTO.

Several authors have mentioned the importance of a low p-base sheet resistiveity, narrow width of n-emitter strips, and high reverse breakdown voltage of the n-emitter junction in obtaining high I_{TCM}.[9),10)] Recent studies on turn-off failure have shown that the I_{TCM} is related to spike voltage during the fall period,[10)] and that failure happens at a critical value of the voltage, which increases in W_{nB}. According to these results, the concept of a safe operating area (SOA) for GTOs, which is similar to the reverse safe operating area for transistor has been introduced.[11)]

Figure 6 shows SOAs for unit-GTOs with various n-base widths W_{nB}. The SOAs extend towards the higher voltage region as W_{nB} increases. It is expected that a high I_{TCM} can be obtained for a higher voltage GTO with an inherently thick n-base layer, and that the p-emitter shorting structure is superior in terms of increasing I_{TCM} , because of the lower on-state voltage.

Figure 7 shows the effect of the number of unit-GTOs N_{nE}, in parallel operation, on SOA. The SOAs extend towards the higher current region as N_{nE} increases, however, a saturating tendency is seen and the voltage limit does not increase in the lower current region. Therefore, only an increase in the number of unit-GTOs can not lead to hgiher I_{TCM} values.

2.2.2 Arrangement of the unit-GTOs

In designing a large area GTO device, it is important not only to increase the maximum controllable current of the unit-GTOs, but also to provide operation which is as uniform as possible in all of the unit-GTOs during the turn-off process. Uniformity of turn-off currents in the device are strongly affected by unbalance in lateral conductance of the gate electrode on the p-base layer, between the contact of the external gate lead and the respective unit-GTOs.

Figure 8 shows experimental results for arrangement effects on I_{TCM} in the unit-GTOs. All of the sample GTOs had the same diameter of 40 mm, but different gate structures as illustrated in the figure. The ring shaped gate sample shows a higher interrupt current than that of the center gate sample, which is probably caused by

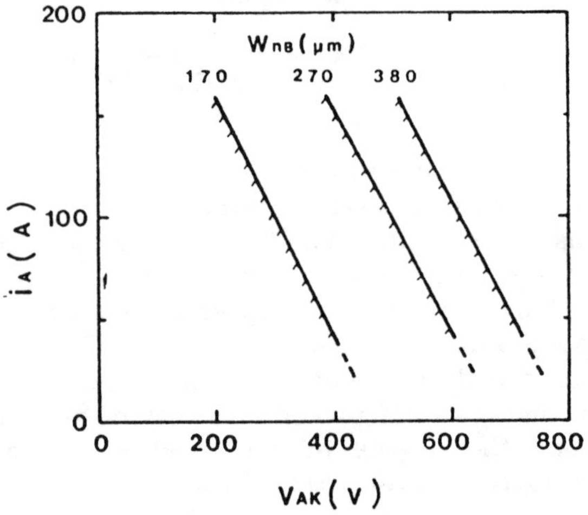

Fig. 6. SOAs for unit-GTOs with various n-base widths.

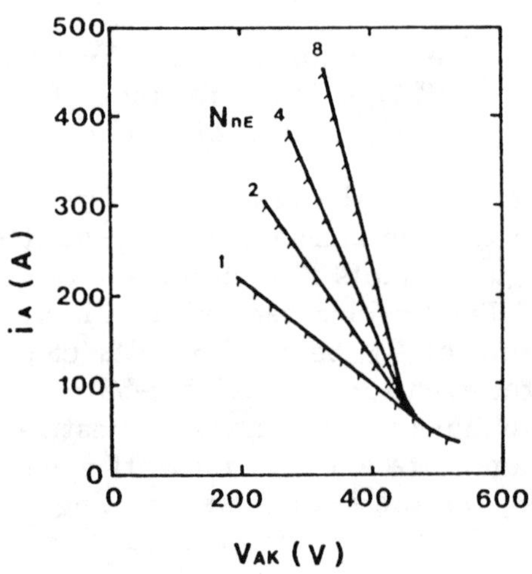

Fig. 7. Effects on SOA by the number N_{nE} of unit-GTOs in parallel operation.

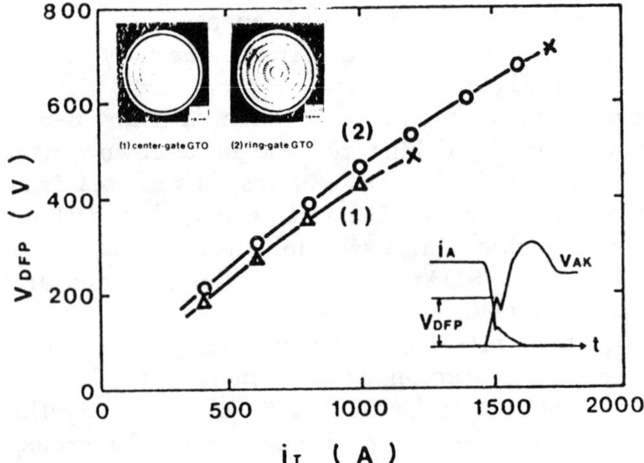

Fig. 8. Comparision of the maximum interrupt current I_{TCM} and of spike voltage V_{DFP} for the different gate structures.

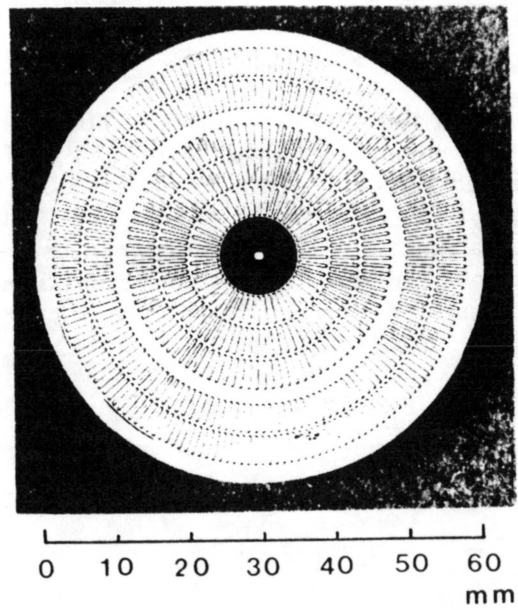

Fig. 9. A top view of the GTO pellet.

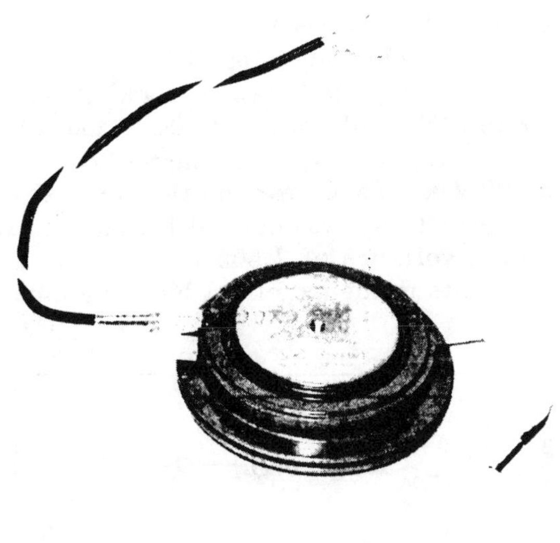

Fig. 10. An exterior view of the packaged device.

sufficiently uniform operation between many unit-GTOs which are arranged on both sides of the ring shaped gate electrode. Based on the result, a ring shaped gate structure was introduced in the newly developed high power GTOs.

3. DEVICE STRUCTURE AND FABRICATION PROCESS

3.1 Device Structure

Design of the 2,000 A GTO structure was done taking into account the above mentioned considerations. Figure 9 shows a top view of the GTO pellet which has a 60 mm diameter. Many unit-GTOs are arranged in five concentric circles on the pellet, and the external gate electrode, which has a ring shape makes contact on the internal circuler area. Eath of the unit-GTO is composed of the n-emitter strip of 0.26 mm in width and 4 mm in length, provided with the p-emitter shorting structure as descirbed in Fig. 1.

3.2 Fabrication Process

The devices are fabricated by using a gallium and selective phosphorus diffusion, and conventional photo masking technologies. First, phosphours is diffused selectively into the anode side of the wafer in the 200 to 250 Ω·cm resistiveity range, to form the anode emitter shorting n^+ region. Then, gallium is diffused into both sides of the wafer, to form the p-emitter and the p-base layer. Next, phosphorus is diffused again into the cathode side of the wafer to form the n-emitter junctions. Chemical etching is applied to etch down the part of the p-base surface surrounding the n-emitter strips to form the gate contacts. After the resulting wafer is alloyed with a tungsten plate using aluminum, the cathode and gate contact are plated, and the wafer is contoured and covered by silicone rubber for the main junction protection.

Figure 10 shows an external view of the packaged device.

4. ELECTRICAL CHARACTERISTICS

4.1 Static Characteristics

4.1.1 Voltage blocking capability

Figure 11 plots forward blocking voltage V_{DRM} as a function of junction temperature T_J for the trial fabricated 2,500 V and 4,500 V GTO devices. The V_{DRM} is defined as the applied voltage at a leakage current of 20 mA. The peak blocking voltage is about 3,000 V and 5,200 V at 125°C, for the two devices respectively.

Figure 12 shows forward leakage current I_R as a function of T_J. The I_R is measured at applied voltages of 2,500 V and 4,500 V respectively. A very low I_R can be obtained, which results in the excellent blocking characteristics stated above.

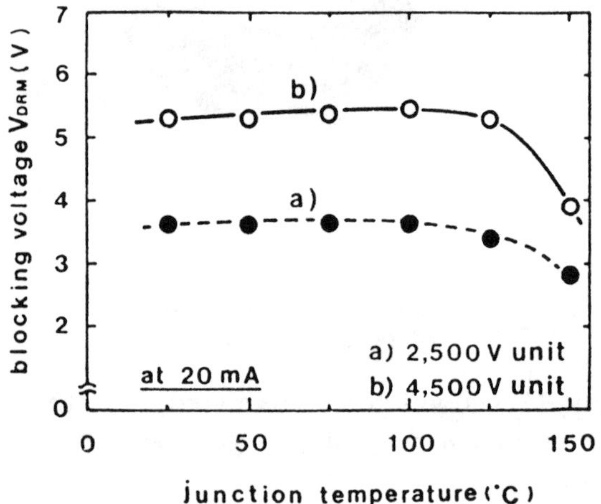

Fig. 11. Forward blocking voltage V_{DRM} vs. junction temperature.

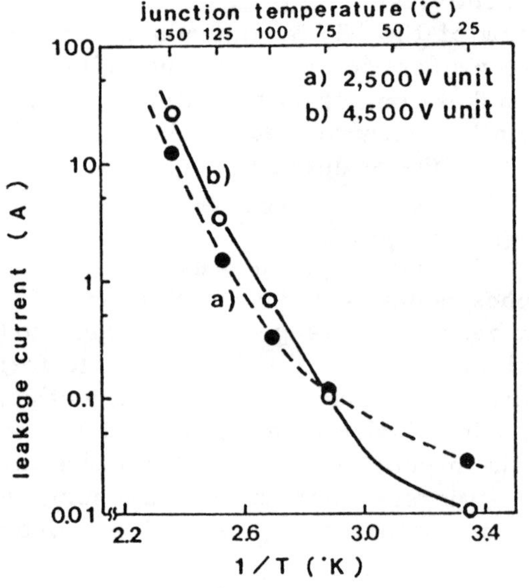

Fig. 12. Leakage current at forward blocking state.

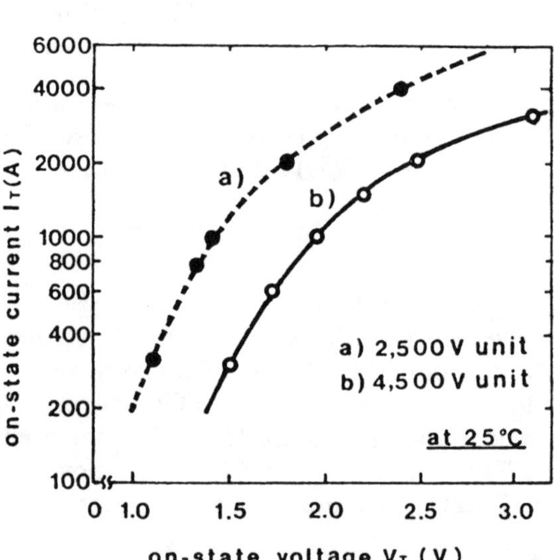

Fig. 13. Forward currnt conducting characteristics.

4.1.2 On-state voltage

Figure 13 shows the forward conducting characteristics, V_T vs. I_T, at the junction temperature of 25°C. At a current of 2,000 A, V_T is less than 1.8 V and 2.5 V, for the devices respectively. These values are lower compared with those of gold doped type GTOs.

From above results, advantages of the p-emitter shorted GTO, such as low on-state voltage and high blocking voltage at high temperature are comfirmed.

4.2 Dynamic Characteristics

4.2.1 Turn-on responce

Figure 14 shows typical turn-on waveforms of the 2,500 V · 2,000 A GTO. In this case, it took a relatively long time, about 6 μs, to turn-on. Measured turn-on time t_{GT} is plotted as a function of triggering gate current in Fig. 15.

The t_{GT} decreases to 4 μs at the maximum gate current of 30 A. The minimum triggering gate current of the GTO is about 0.8 A. Therefore, it is necessary to have a large gate current as much as 40 times the minimum triggering gate current, to trigger the GTO in a sufficiently short time.

4.2.2 Turn-off characteristics

Figure 16 shows turn-off waveforms during the gate turn-off period. In the test circuit, the load is inductive, and a snubber circuit composed of a diode, a resistance of 10Ω and a capacitance of 6 μF is used. In this case, anode current of 2,000 A is interrupted by a peak turn-off gate current of 400 A.

The anode current begins to fall rapidly 23 μs after the gate puls is applied, then decreases slowly for about 15 μs. The tailing current consists of a displacement current due to the rapid rise of the anode voltage and a base current due to stored carrier in the base layer.

In this figure, there is a relatively large tailing current, but it can be reduced by changing the p-emitter shorting structure, as previously described. During the current fall period, a peak value in the anode voltage can be seen. This is the spike voltage, which is induced in the snubber circuit due to a voltage drop in the diode and capacitance, and due to stray inductance in their wiring. The spike voltage is an important value related to the maximum interrupt current of the device, as described later.

Figure 17 shows turn-off time t_{GQ} and turn-off gate charge Q_{GQ} as a function of turn-off current I_T. It is known that t_{GQ} and Q_{GQ} depend on the gate drive condition, especially the rate of current rise dig/dt. In this test, a gate pulse of dig/dt of 15A/μs is used. When the anode current of 2,000 A is interrupted at 125°C, the turn-off time is about 29 μs, and gate charge is 6000 μC.

Figure 18 shows a typical example of the spike voltage V_{DFP} as a function of turn-off current I_T, and the breakpoint for 2,500 and 4,500 V devices. As is evident from the figure, V_{DFP} increases with increasing I_T, and has the maximum value of 610 and 640 V obtained at the breakpoint, respectively. The maximum interrupt current is 2,400 and 2,600 A. This result agrees well with the results of SOA (Fig. 6), because the 4,500 V device has a thicker n-base width than that of the 2,500 V device.

4.2.3 Ratings and typical characteristics

Ratings and typical characteristics of the newly developed 2,500 V · 2,000 A GTO are described in Table 1.

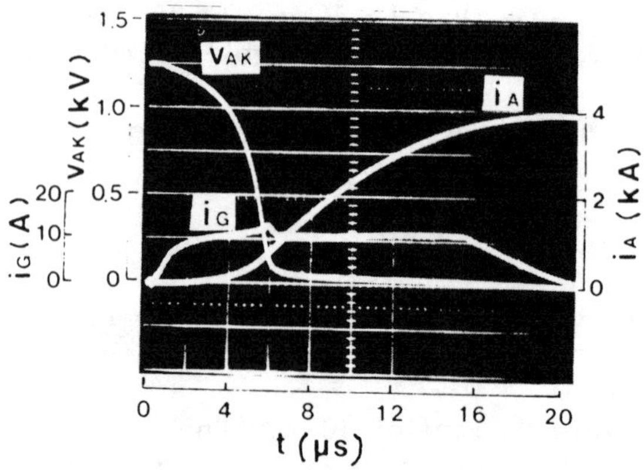

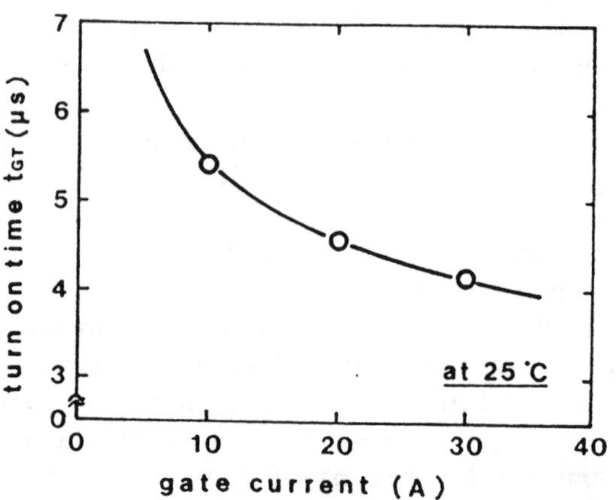

Fig. 14. Typical turn-on responses (T_j = 25°C).

Fig. 15. Turn-on time t_{GT} vs. gate current I_G.

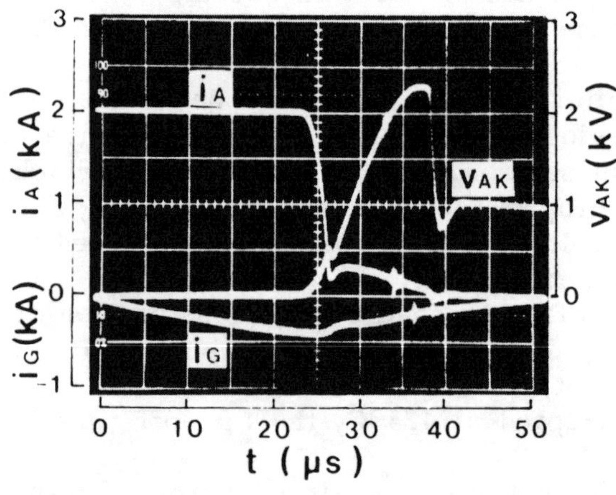

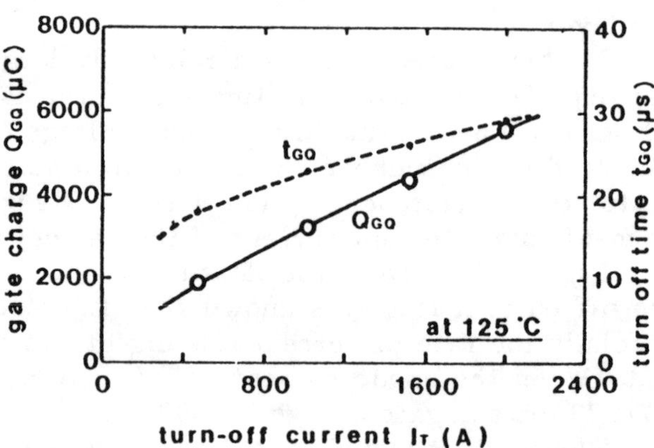

Fig. 16. Waveforms at 2,000 A turn-off (T_j = 125°C).

Fig. 17. Turn-off time t_{GQ}, turn-off gate charge Q_{GQ} vs. turn-off current.

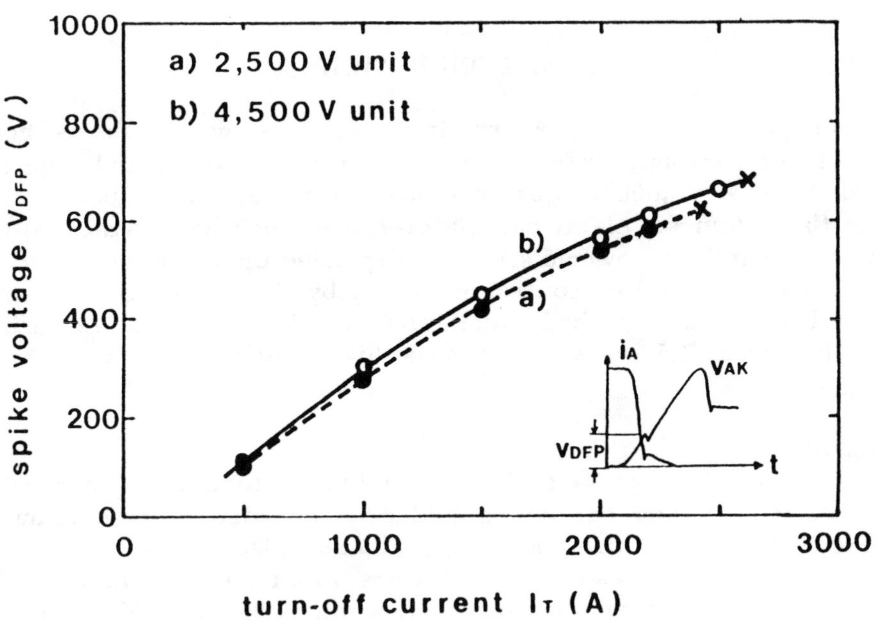

Fig. 18. Spike voltage V_{DFP} as a function of turn-off current.

Table 1. Ratings and electrical characteristics

Ratings/Characteristics	Symbol	Units	GFP2000B25
Ratings			
off-state voltage	V_{DRM}	V	2,500
maximum controllable current	I_{TCM}	A	2,000
RMS on-state current	$I_{T(RMS)}$	A	800
surge on-state current	I_{TSM}	A	14,000
gate reverse voltage	V_{GRM}	V	16
junction temperature	T_J	°C	-40 to 125
Characteristics (typical value)			
on-state voltage	V_{TM}	V	1.8
gate trigger current	I_{GT}	A	0.8
turn-on time	t_{GT}	μs	6
turn-off time	t_{GQ}	μs	30
turn-off gate charge	Q_{GQ}	μC	6,000
thermal impedance	Rth (j-f)	°C/W	0.02

5. CONCLUSION

Using a unique anode emitter shorting structure, which shows good switching performance without particular lifetime control, a high voltage and high current GTOs with ratings of 2,500 V · 2,000 A was developed, and 4,500 V · 2,000 A GTO was trial fabricated. In these devices, electrical charcteristics such as on-state voltage, turn-off time and gain, and switching power dissipation depended upon the degree of the p-emiter shorting structure which could be controlled mainly by the width of the p-emitter and n^+-shorting layer. The new devices had excellent forward blocking characteristics, low on-state voltage, less than 2.5 volts and a peak higher allowable gate turn-off current, 2,400A.

Acknowledgements

The authors wish to express their sincere thanks to Dr. T. Takasuna, Messrs. T. Tsuboi, H. Kawakami for their continuing guidance and encouragement, and Messrs. H. Amano, Y. Ikeda and A. Ueda for many valuable discussions. They also wish to acknowledge the significant roles played by Messrs. S. Oikawa, I. Sampei and S. Okano in the fabrication of the device, and by Messrs. S. Kimura, M. Sato, Y. Sato and K. Koga in the electrical measurments.

References

1) A.Ueda et al. "GTO Inverter for AC Traction Drives" IEEE - IAS '82 Annual meeting Rec. p.645 (1982-10)
2) M.Ohta et al. "Gata Turn-off Thyristor Application Technology for Rolling Stock" IEEE - IAS '82 Annual Meeting Rec. p.239 (1982-10)
3) T.Kanzaki et al. "Inverter Control system for Driving Induction Motors in Papid Transit cars Using High Power Gate Turn-Off Thyristors" IEEE - ISPCC '82 Meeting Rec. p.145 (1982)
4) T.Nagano, T.Yatsuo and M.Okamura "Characteristics of a 3000 V, 1000 A Gate Turn-off Thyristor" IEEE - IAS '81 Annual Meeting Rec. p.750 (1981)
5) M.Azuma, M.Kurata, and K.Takigami "2500-V 600-A Gate Turn-Off Thyristor (GTO)" IEEE Trans. Electron Devices, ED-29, p.270 (1981)
6) A.Tada and H.Hagion "A High-Voltage, High-Power, Fast-Switching Gate Turn-Off Thyristor" IEEE - ISPCC '82 Meeting Rec. p.66 (1982)
7) T.Nagano, M.Okamura, and T.Ogawa "A High-Power, Low-Forward-Drop Gate Turn-Off Thyrsitor" IEEE - IAS '78 Annual Meeting Rec., p.1,003 (1978)
8) Y.Shimizu et al. "Numerical Analysis of Turn-Off Characteristics for a Gate Turn-Off Thyristor with a Shorted Anode Emitter" IEEE Trans. Electron Devices, ED-28, p.1,043 (1981)
9) E.D. Wolley "Gate Turn-Off in p-n-p-n Devices" IEEE Trans. Electron Devices ED-13, p.590 (1966)
10) H.Ohashi and A.Nakagawa "A Study on GTO Turn-Off Failure Mechanism" IEEE-IEDM Conf. Rec. p.414 (1981)
11) T.Nagano et al. "A Snubber-Less GTO" IEEE - PESC '82 Rec. p.383 (1982)

Paper 3.4

THE INSULATED GATE TRANSISTOR (IGT) - A NEW POWER SWITCHING DEVICE

By

B. Jayant Baliga
General Electric Company
Corporate Research and Development
Schenectady, New York

Mike Chang, Peter Shafer, and Marvin W. Smith
General Electric Company
Semiconductor Products Department
Auburn, New York

The Insulated Gate Transistor (IGT) is described in this paper. It is a new power switching device that combines Power MOSFET and bipolar technology to provide the circuit designer with a device that has Power MOSFET input characteristics and bipolar output characteristics. Device ratings, characteristics and applications are discussed. Practical operating frequencies, voltage, and current limits, as well as interface requirements with other devices are defined.

Introduction

The ideal semiconductor device for power switching applications should exhibit a low forward voltage drop in order to keep the forward conduction losses small and a high turn-on/turn-off speed in order to keep the switching losses small. In addition, the device should operate at a high-current density in order to minimize the size of the chip (and, hence, the cost required) for any desired current handling capability. The gate drive power requirements for the ideal device should also be low. For applications that do not require gate turn-off capability, the thyristor has been the best choice because of its high forward conduction current density, even when designed for handling high operating voltages. However, many thyristors require reversal in the anode potential to achieve turn-off. Consequently, for applications where the load current is controlled by the input signal, the power bipolar transistor has been extensively used. Bipolar transistors are capable of turn-off speeds of less than 1 microsecond, but have the disadvantage of requiring high base drive current both during the on-state and during turn-off. Other competitive devices that have been developed for gate turn-off applications are the gate turn-off thyristor (GTO) and the Power MOSFET. The GTO has the advantage of operating at higher current densities than the bipolar transistor but cannot operate at high switching speeds and requires very high gate turn-off currents. In contrast, the Power MOSFET is capable of very high switching speeds and requires low gate drive currents. However, these devices operate at much lower current densities than the bipolar transistor and have more costly and complex processing requirements. Thus, these power devices do not meet the requirements of an ideal switch. The Insulated Gate Transistor (IGT) is a new three-terminal gate turn-off power semiconductor device whose electrical characteristics approach those of an ideal switch. This paper discusses the IGT structure, its operation, and presents the characteristics of typical devices.

IGT Structure

One form of IGT structure is shown in cross-section in Figure 1. In this structure, current flow is prevented when negative biases are applied to the collector with respect to the emitter because the lower (collector)

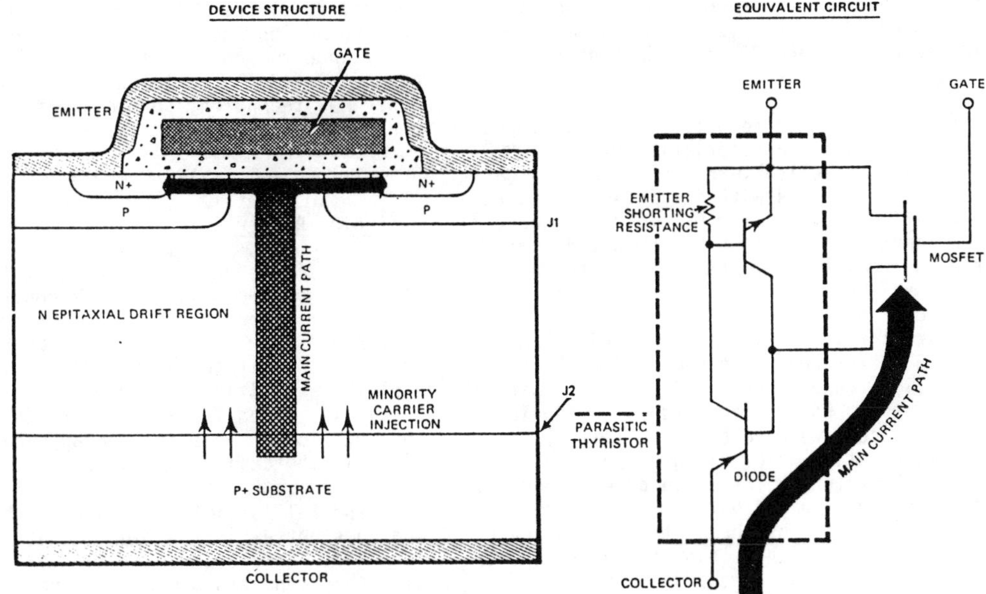

FIG. 1 Insulated Gate Transistor (Power MOS IGT)

Reprinted from *IEEE/IAS Ann. Meet. Conf. Rec.*, pp. 794-803, 1983.

junction, (J2), becomes reverse biased. This provides the device with its reverse blocking capability (see Figure 2). When positive voltages are applied to the collector with the gate biased at the emitter potential, the upper junction, (J1), becomes reverse biased and the device operates in its forward blocking mode. However, if a positive gate-to-emitter voltage is applied

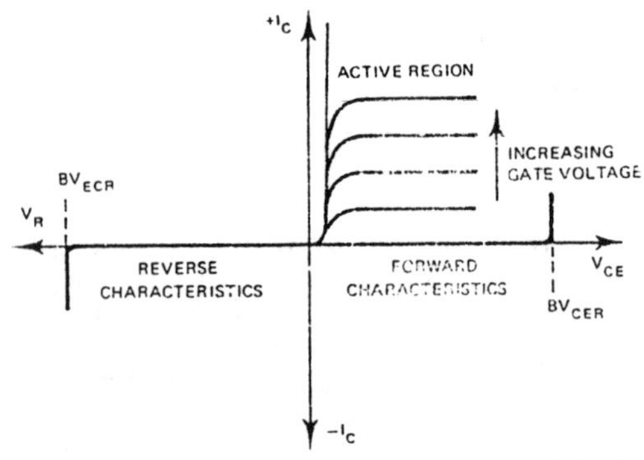

FIG. 2 Blocking Characteristics.

of sufficient magnitude to invert the surface of the p-base region under the gate, the device switches to its forward conducting state because current can now flow from the emitter N+ region into the n-base region via the inversion layer. In this forward conducting state, the junction J2 becomes forward biased and the collector P+ region injects holes into the n-base region. In this regime of operation, the device operates at high current densities like a forward biased p-i-n diode.

The significantly improved current conduction of the IGT is illustrated in Figure 3 where its forward conduction current density is compared to that of the bipolar transistor and Power MOSFET. Due to its rectifier-like forward conduction characteristics, the current density of the IGT exceeds that of the bipolar transistor and Power MOSFET for forward voltage drops above 1 Volt. At a forward voltage drop of 2 Volts, the IGT current density is observed to be 5 times that of the bipolar transistor and 20 times that of the Power MOSFET.

The IGT is also designed to obtain the high input impedance gate controlled characteristics of Power MOSFET's. This allows controlled turn-on, as well as gate controlled turn-off. Devices with intrinsic gate turn-off time capabilities ranging from 0.2 to 20 microseconds have been constructed. It should be noted that decreasing the turn-off time of the IGT results in a sacrifice in forward current capability per unit area of silicon (current density). This is indicated in Figure 3 where curves for IGT's with gate turn-off times of 15, 1 and 0.25 microseconds are compared to that of the bipolar transistor and Power MOSFET. These characteristics point out two notable advantages of the IGT. First, in these devices, we have a unique ability to tailor its characteristics which allows trading-off conduction losses with switching losses in power circuits. Second, even after reducing the gate turn-off time of the IGT devices to 0.25 microseconds, the current density is still substantially higher than that of the Power MOSFET. As an example, at a current density of 100 Amps/cm^2, IGT (C) exhibits a forward drop of 5 Volts compared to 35 Volts for the equivalent (same die size and blocking voltage) MOSFET.

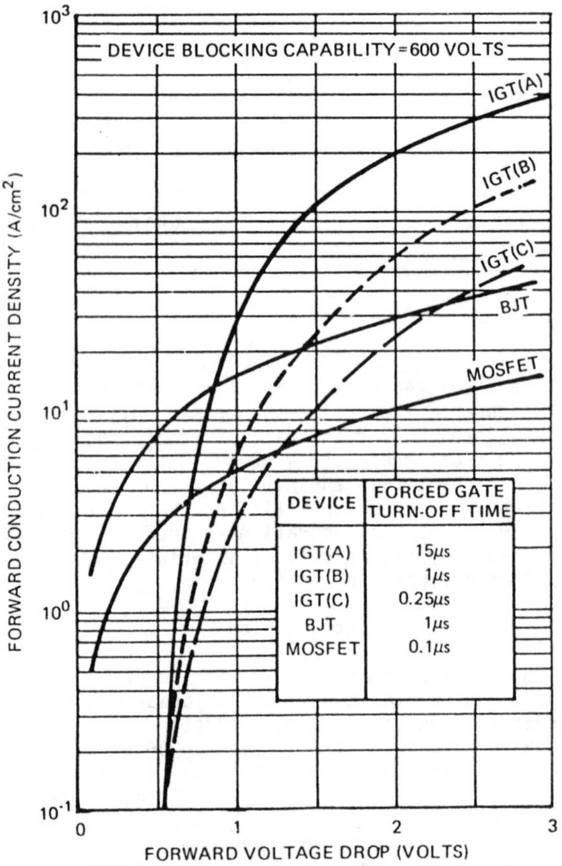

FIG. 3 Forward Voltage Drop vs. Current Density.

It is worth pointing out that the IGT structure shown in Figure 1 contains a parasitic p-n-p-n thyristor structure between the collector and the emitter terminals as illustrated in the equivalent circuit. If this thyristor latches on, the current can no longer be controlled by the MOS gate. Consequently, it is important to design the device with a low emitter shorting resistance to suppress this thyristor action. This has been achieved in the IGT devices using high resolution Power MOS technology to provide margin over the gate controlled current density.

IGT Operation

Switching Properties

The IGT is designed such that the turn-on and turn-off times of the device can be controlled by the gate-to-emitter source impedance. Its equivalent input capacitance is lower than a Power MOSFET with a comparable current and voltage rating. The device is turned on by applying a positive voltage between the gate and emitter terminals. When V_{GE} is greater than $V_{GE(th)}$, collector current flows. In switching applications where $V_{GE} \gg V_{GE(th)}$, the device saturates.

The IGT is similar to a Power MOSFET during turn-on and does not exhibit a significant storage time during turn-off. However, during turn-off, it exhibits a fall time that consists of two distinct time intervals - designated hereafter as t_{f1} and t_{f2}. Typical switching waveforms for a resistive load are shown in Figure 4 using two types of IGT's. The two time intervals are

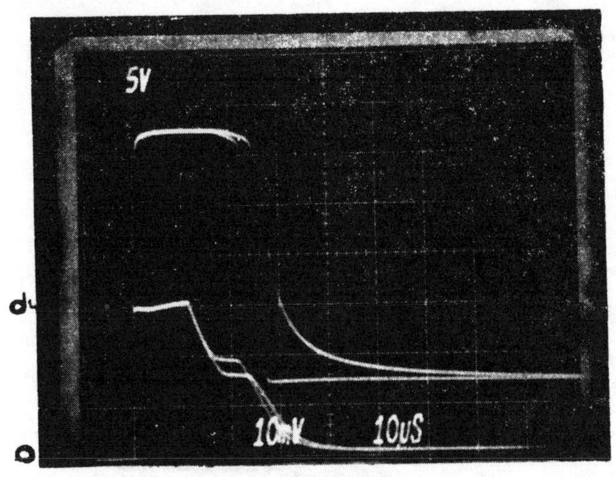

TOP (I_C)

VERT = 2A/cm

BOTTOM (V_{GE})

VERT = 5V/cm

FIG. 4 Resistive Load Switching.

very distinct for the slow device and hardly noticeable for a fast device. The turn-off delay is caused by the discharge time constant of the effective gate-to-emitter capacitance and R_{GE}.

Controlling Current Fall Time

The current fall time of the IGT can be controlled by use of external circuitry. t_{f1} is directly controlled by the value of R_{GE} (Figure 5). This dependence is shown in Figure 6. t_{f2} is not controllable and is an inherent characteristic of the type of IGT that is selected (that is, - slow, medium or fast switching types).

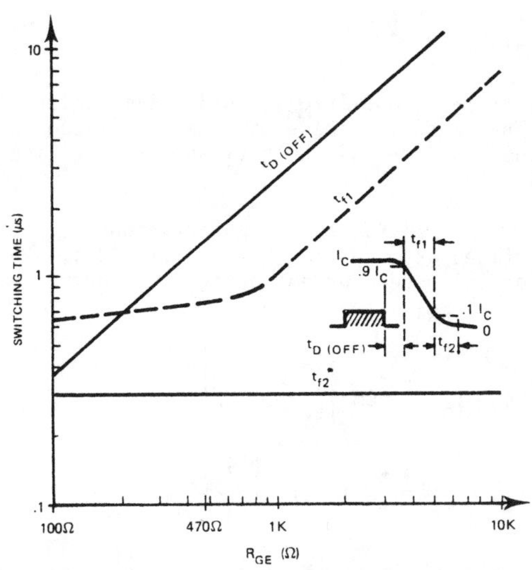

FIG. 5 Typical Turn-off Time vs. R_{GE}.

Since t_{f1} and t_{f2} contribute significantly to switching losses, the control feature of t_{f1} by a resistor (R_{GE}) is a definite advantage. For example, in the case of an inductive load, the fall time can be controlled to the extent that snubberless operation is possible, since E_L = -L dI/dt. Figures 6 and 7 are idealized representations of the two phases of the device turn-off. That is, a slow device can be used for d.c. and low fre-

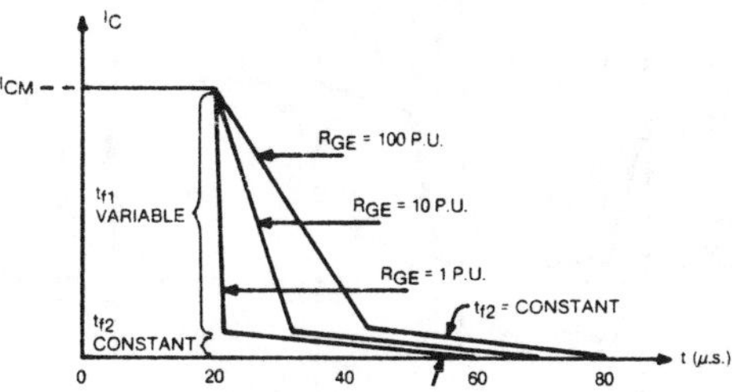

FIG. 6 Fall Time Control for a Slow Device.

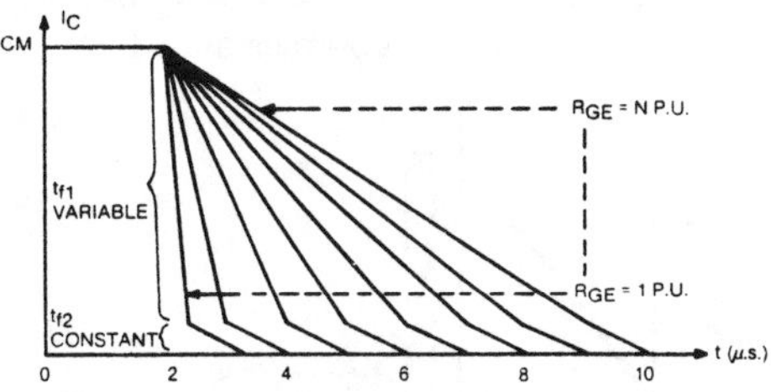

FIG. 7 Fall Time Control for a Fast Device.

quency applications with minimal gate turn-off current or a fast device can be used with a linear turn-off characteristic [R_{GE} = N per unit (p.u.), and N > 1 Figure 7]. For higher frequency operation, a fast device with R_{GE} = 1 p.u. will minimize switching losses due to t_{f1} and t_{f2}.

Conduction and Switching Losses

In switching applications, power losses in the IGT will consist of: (1) drive losses, (2) conduction losses, (3) off-state losses, and (4) switching losses. In dc or low frequency applications, where the total switching times are much less than the period, switching losses are generally negligible. Also, if the ambient temperature extremes are limited, the off-state losses are generally insignificant.

Using the waveforms in Figure 8 as a reference, switching losses can be determined as a function of time, current, and voltage. Note that this is a general procedure and that individual applications may differ. However, the procedure for calculating losses would be similar for any given set of waveforms. Figure 8(a) and (b) show typical resistive and clamped inductive load switching waveforms. For purely inductive loads, turn-n losses are very small because the transistor turns on at essentially zero current each cycle. Therefore, for a purely inductive load, switching losses will be determined by the turn-off losses.

Note the deviation from normal rise and fall time definitions (i.e., instead of 10% to 90% and 90% to 10%, 0 to 100%, and 100% to 0 is used to determine power dissipation).

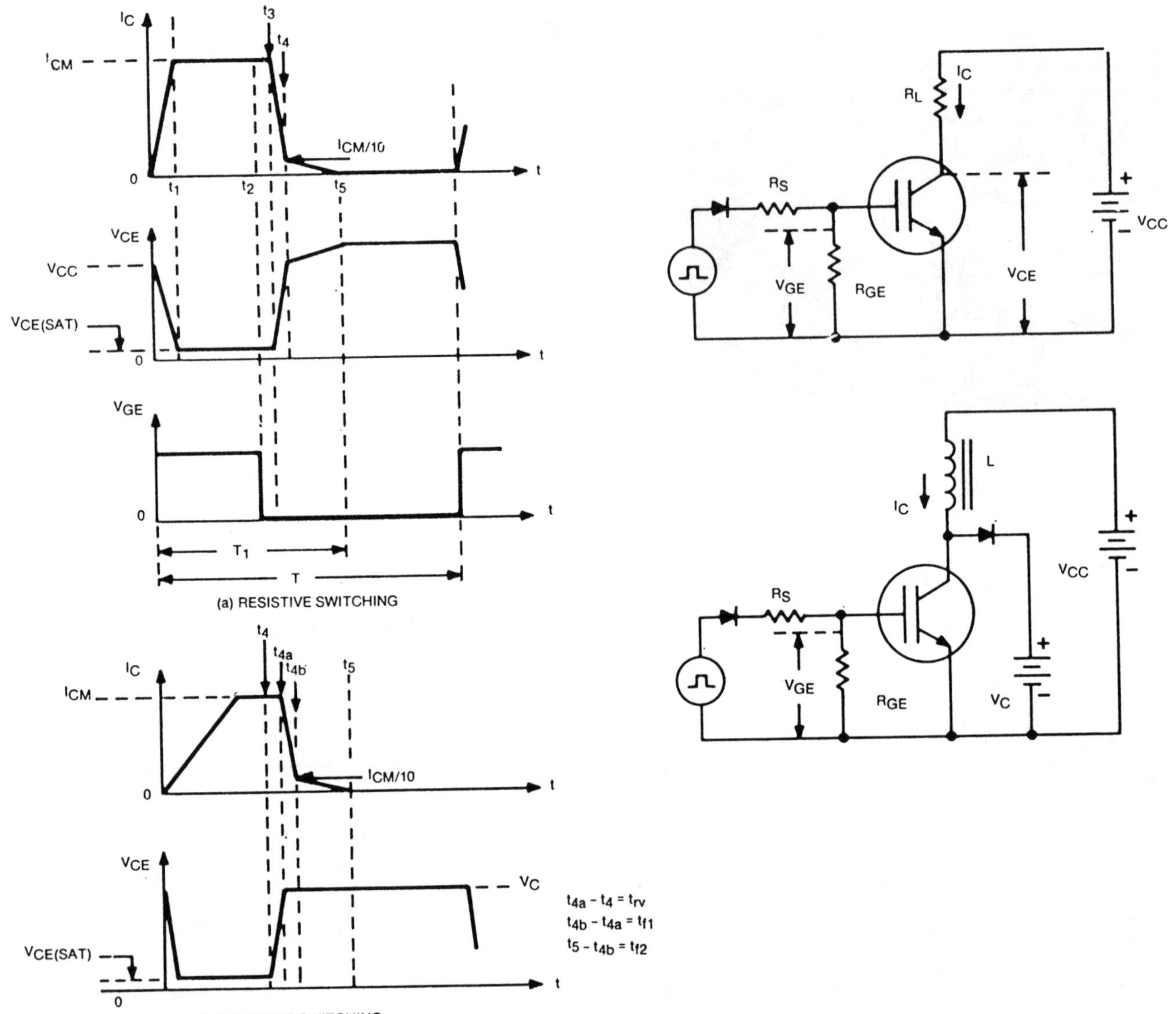

(a) RESISTIVE SWITCHING

(b) INDUCTIVE SWITCHING

FIG. 8 Idealized Switching Waveforms.

$0 - t_1 = t_r$ = rise time, $t_2 - t_1 = t_c$ = conduction time;

$t_3 - t_2 = t_d$ = turn-off delay,

$t_4 - t_3 = t_{f1}$ = fall time one;

$t_5 - t_4 = t_{f2}$ = fall time two;

$T = 1/f$ = period, I_{CM} = maximum collector current;

$V_{CE(SAT)}$ = collector-to-emitter saturation volts;

V_{GE} = gate-to-emitter volts, V_{CC} = collector-to-emitter power supply voltage.

Switching Mode Application. When gate voltage is applied to an IGT operating in a saturated switching mode, the collector-to-emitter voltage decreases and goes into hard saturation if sufficient gate voltage is available. The sequence of events for a resistive load is shown in Figure 8(a). Notice the conduction region defined by $V_{CE(SAT)}$ and $I_{C(MAX)}$ during time interval $t_3 - t_1$. The switching losses can be summarized and are contained in intervals 0 to t_1 and $t_3 - t_5$ [see Figure 8(a)].

Total Power Dissipation. Instantaneous collector power is defined as: $P_p = [V_{CE}(t)]\,[I_{CE}(t)]$. The equation for collector current during the period T [assume $I_C \gg I_{CER}$] is:

$$i_C(t) = \frac{I_{CM}t}{t_r}\Big|_0^{t_1} + I_{CM}\Big|_{t_1}^{t_2} + I_{CM}\Big|_{t_2}^{t_3} + \ldots$$

$$I_{CM}\left(\frac{-.9\,t}{t_4 - t_3} + 1\right)\Big|_{t_3}^{t_4} + \ldots$$

$$\frac{I_{CM}}{10}\left(\frac{-t}{t_5 - t_4} + 1\right)\Big|_{t_4}^{t_5} + I_{CER}\Big|_{t_5}^{T}$$

While the corresponding $V_{CE}(t)$ is (assume $V_{CE(SAT)} \ll V_{CC}$):

$$V_{CE(t)} \cong V_{CC}\left(1 - \frac{t}{t_r}\right)\Big|_{o}^{t_1} + V_{CE(SAT)}\Big|_{t_1}^{t_2} + \ldots$$

$$V_{CE(SAT)}\Big|_{t_2}^{t_3} + \left(\frac{.9\ V_{CC}}{t_4 - t_3}\ t\right)\Big|_{t_3}^{t_4} + \ldots$$

$$V_{CC}\left(\frac{.1\ t}{t_5 - t_4} + .9\right)\Big|_{t_4}^{t_5} + V_{CC}\Big|_{t_5}^{T}$$

Note that the average power is given as:

$$P_{AV} = \frac{1}{T}\int_o^T V_{CE}(t)\ i_C(t)\ dt = \frac{1}{T}\sum_o^T V_{CE}(t)\ i_C(t)\ \Delta t$$

$$= \frac{1}{T}\sum_o^T P\ \Delta t$$

After substitution and integration,

$$P_{AV} = \frac{1}{T}\left[\frac{V_{CC}\ I_{CM}\ t_r}{6} + V_{CE(SAT)}\ I_{CM}\ (t_c + t_d) + \ldots \frac{I_{CM}\ V_{CC}\ t_{f1}}{5.55} + \frac{V_{CC}\ I_{CM}\ t_{f2}}{21.5} + V_{CC}\ I_{CER}\ (T - T_1)\right]$$

$$P_{AV} = \underbrace{V_{CC}\ I_{CM}\ f\left[\frac{t_r}{6} + \frac{t_{f1}}{5.55} + \frac{t_{f2}}{21.5}\right]}_{\text{Switching Loss}} + \ldots$$

$$\underbrace{\frac{V_{CE(SAT)}\ I_{CM}\ (t_c + t_d)}{T}}_{\text{Conduction Loss}} + \underbrace{V_{CC}\ I_{CER}\ \frac{T-T_1}{T}}_{\text{Off-State}} \quad \text{(Eqn. 1)}$$

Therefore, the switching power losses are directly proportional to frequency and are independent of duty cycle or pulse width. Conduction losses are proportional to duty cycle ($D = T_1/T$), while off-state losses are proportional to 1 - duty cycle.

In order to assess the significance of Equation 1, idealized switching losses for a resistive load are given in Equation 2.

$$P_{AV} = V_{CC}\ I_{CM}\ f\left(\frac{t_r + t_f}{6}\right) \quad \text{(Eqn. 2)}$$

Where t_r, t_f = current rise and fall times from 0 to 100% and 100% to zero, respectively.

By inspection of Equation 1, it is observed that t_{f2} adds another component to the switching losses and will be a limiting parameter for high speed switching applications. For example, if the switching frequency is 10 kHz, $t_r = t_{f1} = .5(10^{-6})$, $t_{f2} = 2(10^{-6})$, I_C = 10 Amps, and V_{CC} = 400 Volts. Switching losses would be (per Equation 1):

$$P_{AV(SW)} = 400 \times 10 \times 10^4 \times 10^{-6}\left[\frac{.5}{6} + \frac{.5}{5.55} + \frac{2}{21.5}\right]$$

$$= 10.72\ \text{W}$$

Now, per equation 2 (let t_f = .555 μs to account for 100% fall time):

$$P_{AV(SW)} = 400 \times 10 \times 10^4 \times 10^{-6}\ [(.5 + .555)/6]$$

$$\cong 7\ \text{Watts}$$

That is, a 53% increase in switching losses due to t_{f2}.

It is instructive to consider the case of an inductive load [Figure 8(b)]. It will be assumed that turn-on losses are negligible, since the IGT turns on into zero collector current. Therefore, only the turn-off interval t_3 to t_5 will be considered. The collector current is given as:

$$i_C(t) = I_{CM}\Big|_{t_4}^{t_{4a}} + \left(-\frac{.9\ I_{CM}}{t_{4b} - t_{4a}}\ t + I_{CM}\right)\Big|_{t_{4a}}^{t_{4b}} + \ldots$$

$$\left(-\frac{.1\ I_{CM}t}{t_5 - t_{4b}} + .1\ I_{CM}\right)\Big|_{t_{4b}}^{t_5}$$

Assume $V_{CE(SAT)} >> V_{CC}$, then $V_{CE(t)}$ is:

$$V_{CE(t)} = \frac{V_{CC}}{t_{4a} - t_4}\ t\ \Big|_{t_4}^{t_{4a}} + V_{CC}\Big|_{t_{4a}}^{t_{4b}} + V_{CC}\Big|_{t_{4b}}^{t_5}$$

After substitution and integration:

$$P_{AV(SW)} = V_{CC}\ I_{CM}\ f\left(\frac{t_{rv} + 1.1\ t_{f1} + .1\ t_{f2}}{2}\right) \text{(Eqn. 3)}$$

That is, collector-to-emitter voltage rise time and current fall times $t_{f1} + t_{f2}$ contribute to switching losses. The idealized switching losses for an inductive load (t_{f2} = 0 and t_{f1} goes from 100% to 0%) are given as:

$$P_{AV(SW)} = V_{CC}\ I_{CM}\ f\left(\frac{t_{rv} + t_f}{2}\right) \quad \text{(Eqn. 4)}$$

When Equation 4 is compared to Equation 3, it is observed that t_{f2} contributes to increased power losses. For example, using f = 10 kHz, $t_{f1} = .5(10^{-6})$, $t_{f2} = 2(10^{-6})$, $t_{rv} = .5\ (10^{-6})$, I_C = 10 Amps, and V_{CC} = 400 Volts, switching losses would be (per Equation 3):

$$P_{AV(SW)} = 20\ (.5 + .55 + .2) = 25\ \text{Watts}$$

per Equation 4,

$$P_{AV(SW)} = 20\ (.5 + .55) = 21\ \text{Watts}$$

That is, the contribution of power loss due to t_{f2} is not as much as one would intuitively believe at first glance - a 19% increase when compared to devices with a linear current fall time from 100% to zero.

Gate Drive

The input characteristics of the IGT are similar to a Power MOSFET. That is, it has a gate-to-emitter threshold voltage and a capacitive input impedance. In order to turn the device "on", the input capacitance must be charged up to a value greater than $V_{GE(th)}$ before collector current can begin to flow. The collector-to-emitter saturation voltage decreases with an increase in magnitude of V_{GE}. That is, for lowest values of "on" state voltage, V_{GE} should be much greater than $V_{GE(th)}$. Typical output characteristics are shown in Figure 9.

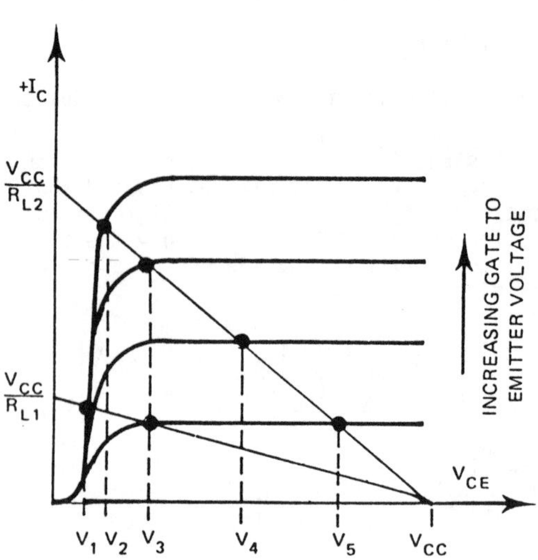

FIG. 9 Output Characteristics.

In order to turn the IGT off, a resistor between gate and emitter is all that is required. This resistor provides a path for the gate-to-emitter input capacitance to discharge. It must be emphasized that R_{GE} has a lower limit that cannot be exceeded. The IGT has a maximum controllable collector current that is dependent on the gate-to-emitter dV/dt. That is, the higher the gate-to-emitter turn-off dV/dt, the lower the controllable collector current. A typical device will have a minimum value of R_{GE}, which will vary from slow device types to fast device types.

The controllable current will also be dependent on the nature of the load. That is, the controllable current will be specified with an inductive and a resistive load at V_{CE} maximum.

Some typical drive circuits are shown in Figures 10(a) thru 10(d). There can be many variations in the drive circuit. It is safe to conclude that most circuits common to Power MOSFETs can be used to drive the IGT with minor modifications. In most cases, a negative turn-off voltage is not required between gate and emitter.

In Figure 10(a), a symmetrical drive is utilized to drive a lamp load. R_{GE} would be quite large and would minimize drive current. Required turn-on and turn-off times would be slow, tens of microseconds.

In Figure 10(b), a high speed asymmetrical drive is utilized. Isolation between primary and secondary is realized by the transformer T1. A diode is used in conjunction with R_{S1} to provide fast turn-on time without effecting turn-off time. Therefore, R_{S1} and R_{GE} would determine turn-on and turn-off times, respectively.

In Figure 10(c), an asymmetrical drive is utilized for a relay or solenoid driver. R_S determines turn "on" time, while R_{GE} determines turn-off time. CR1 is normally required for this type of application in order to prevent excessive collector-to-emitter voltage due to effects of L dI/dt during turn-off of Q_1. Since t_{fl} can be controlled, it is possible to eliminate CR1 in some applications or, in many cases, the need for critical layouts is minimized when CR1 must be used.

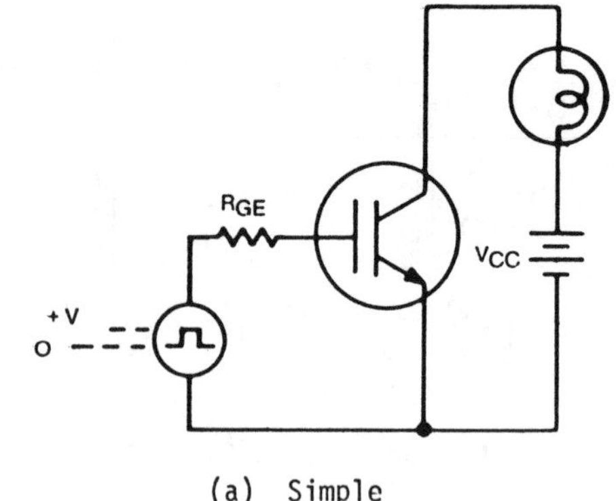

(a) Simple

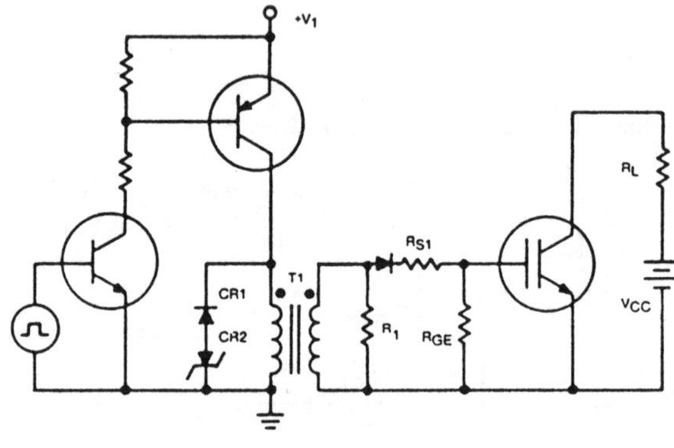

(b) Isolation

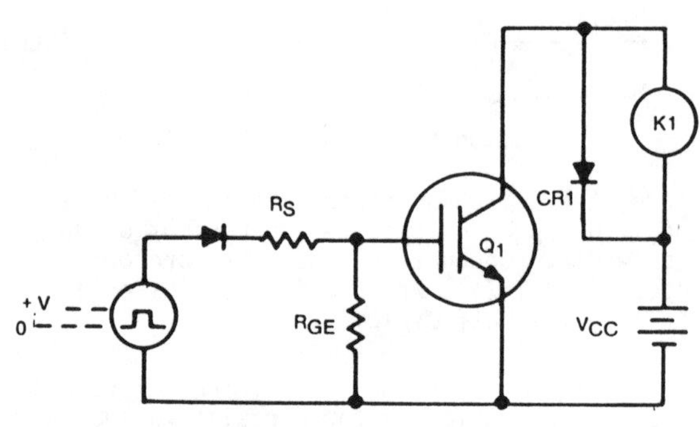

(c) Asymmetrical

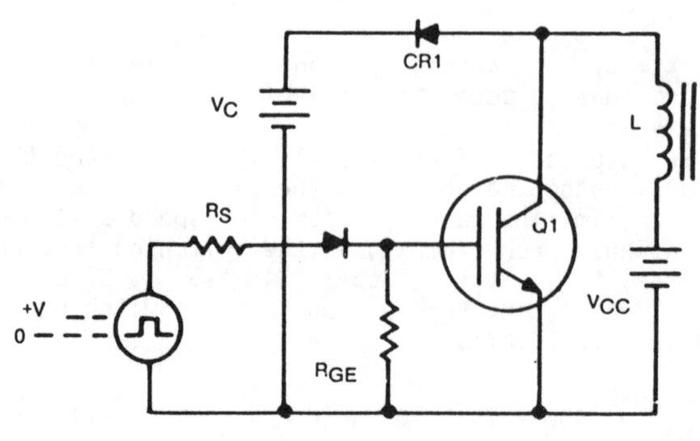

(d) Clamped Inductive

FIG. 10 IGT Drive Circuits.

In Figure 10(d), a high speed device would be used. The drive is asymmetrical, since R_S determines turn "on" time and R_{GE} determines turn "off" time. The collector-to-emitter voltage is clamped by CR1 and V_C. Depending on the value of L, I_C and t_{f1}, the need for the clamp can be determined. In this type of application, the IGT is subjected to the same stress [V_{CE} and I_C simultaneously during turn-off [Figure 8(b)] as any other power switching device. A snubber may be required to increase controllable collector current or to decrease power dissipation within the IGT by load line shaping.

Snubbers

The use of snubbers for load line shaping is well-known.[1] In the case of the IGT, the need for snubbers must be determined for the particular application. Figure 11 is an illustration of IGT turn-off characteristics with and without a polarized snubber. The snubber is used for load line shaping and functions to reduce switching losses within the IGT. The snubber also reduces turn-off dV/dt of the collector-to-emitter voltage. The controllable collector current capability is also increased since it varies proportional to V_{CE}. That is, at low values of collector-to-emitter voltage ($V_{CE} << V_{CER}$), controllable collector current is much greater than the specified maximum value.

It has been shown earlier that switching losses in the IGT increase significantly due to the presence of t_{f2}. By use of a snubber, device heating is minimized. In Figure 11, operation at point A with no snubber, t_{rv1}, t_{f1} and t_{f2}, the IGT has switching losses equal to:

$$P_{AV(SW)} = V_{CC}\, I_{CM}\, f\, \frac{t_{rv1} + 1.1\, t_{f1} + .1\, t_{f2}}{2}$$

When the polarized snubber is used (cases B and C with t_{rv2} and t_{rv3}, respectively), these losses are reduced. One can write equations for each case to get an exact expression or use graphical analysis. Since equations were used earlier, a graphical solution will be employed to determine peak power dissipation for each case. It is readily observed that snubbering definitely reduces the peak power and average power that the IGT must dissipate.

Parallel Operation

Parallel operation of the IGT presents two problems --static and dynamic. In the static case, the magnitude of the individual collector currents must be balanced. In the dynamic case, the turn-on time, turn-off time, and magnitude of collector current must be balanced. In order to assess the performance of the IGT, the "on" state voltage as a function of current, turn-on time, and turn-off times must be evaluated over the operating temperature range of the device. Figure 13 shows typical "on" state voltage as a function of current and temperature with constant V_{GE}. It is of interest to note that a typical IGT rated at 10 Amps has a negative temperature coefficient at collector currents less than 7 Amps. ΔV_{CE} varies from -.5 mV/°C at I_C = .5 Amps to a zero temperature coefficient at approximately 7 Amps.

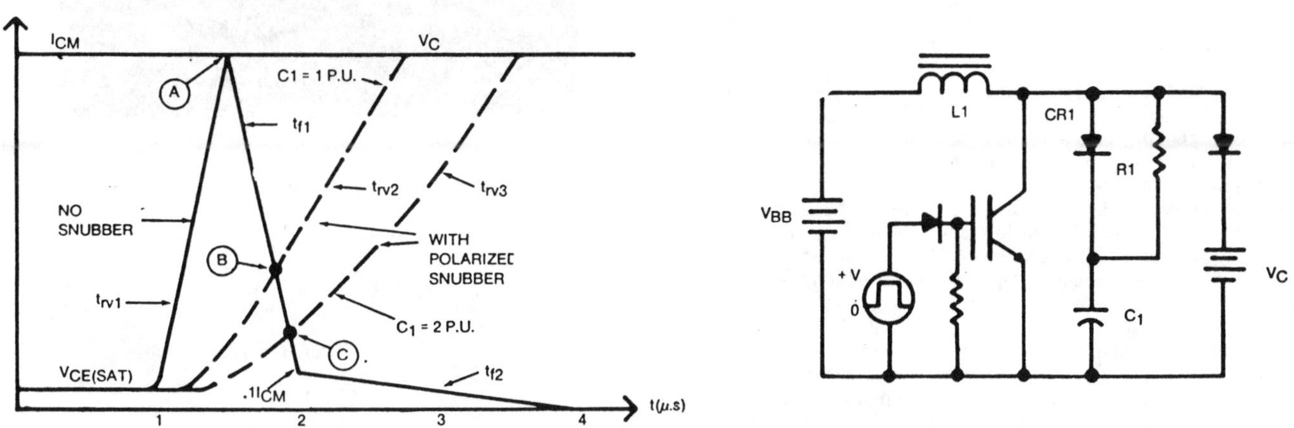

FIG. 11 IGT Turn-off with/without Polarized Snubber.

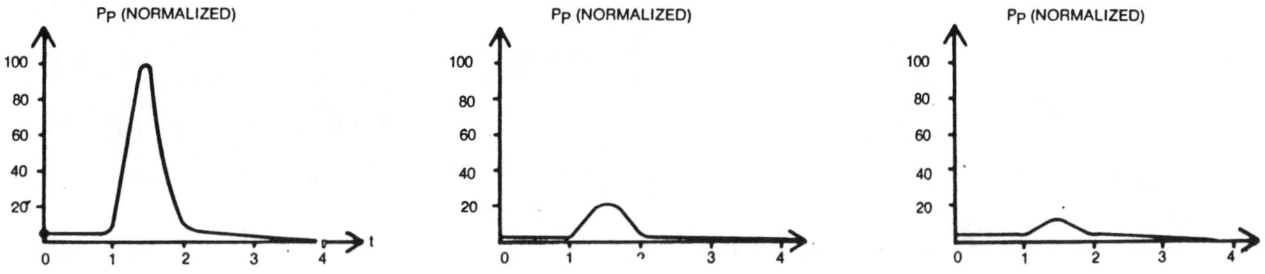

FIG. 12 IGT Peak Power with and without Snubbers.

[1] GE Transistor-Diode Manual, 1st Edition, M. Smith, editor, 1982, Chapter 8.

For currents greater than 7 Amps, the temperature coefficient is positive. At an I_C of 9 Amps, the temperature coefficient is approximately +.75 mV/°C. Therefore, the IGT behaves similar to a Power MOSFET and a bipolar. If the IGT is compared to a Power MOSFET with equivalent current and voltage ratings, it is clearly superior at elevated junction temperatures - since the on-state voltage of the Power MOSFET increases as much as 2.5 times from T_J = 25°C to T_J = 150°C.

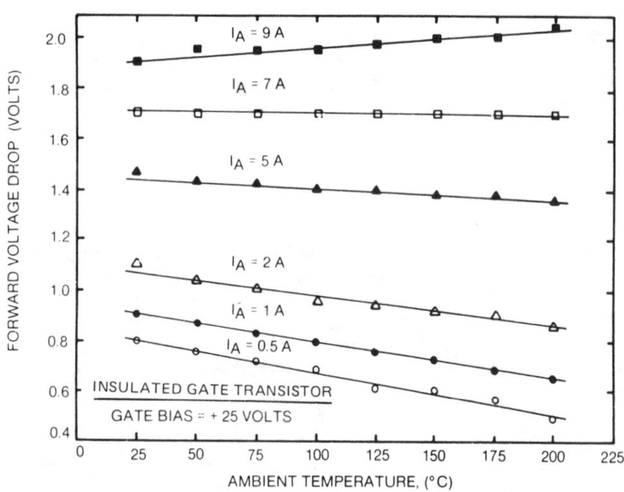

FIG. 13 V_{CE} vs. I_C and T_J for a 10 Amp Device.

Two IGT's can be connected in parallel. In order to achieve the best current sharing, the devices should be matched for gate-to-emitter threshold voltage $[V_{GE(th)}]$ and transconductance $\left(g_{fs} = \frac{I_C}{V_{GE}} \right)$. In addition, the physical layout must be such that there is geometric balance in the gate-to-emitter and collector-to-emitter areas. This is illustrated in Figure 14. In low frequency applications, the dynamic unbalance due to differential turn-on and turn-off times is insignificant and only the degree of static current unbalance between Q_1 and Q_2 is of concern. However, as the operating frequency increases, package inductance and series resistance [R and L in Figure 14(b)] in each lead of the device can cause dynamic unbalance. R_{S1}, R_{S2}, R_{GE1} and R_{GE2} are recommended to prevent oscillation and to tailor turn-on and turn-off times of each device. All connecting leads to the devices must be as short and symmetrical as possible.

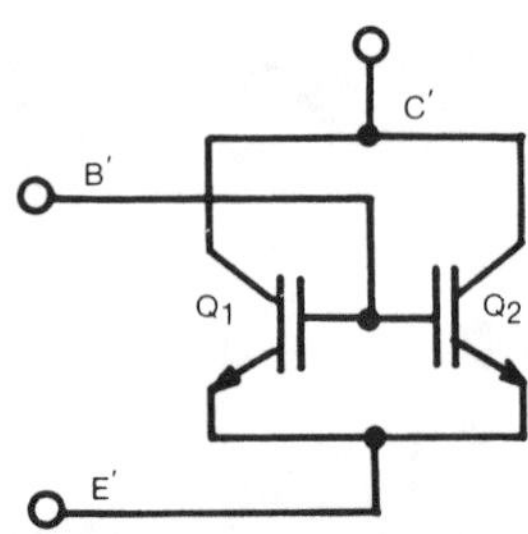

14(a) Low Frequency Equivalent Circuit.

For high frequency switching, the magnitude of the collector current is not a problem. However, differential switching times could cause a problem. The problem is illustrated in Figure 15.

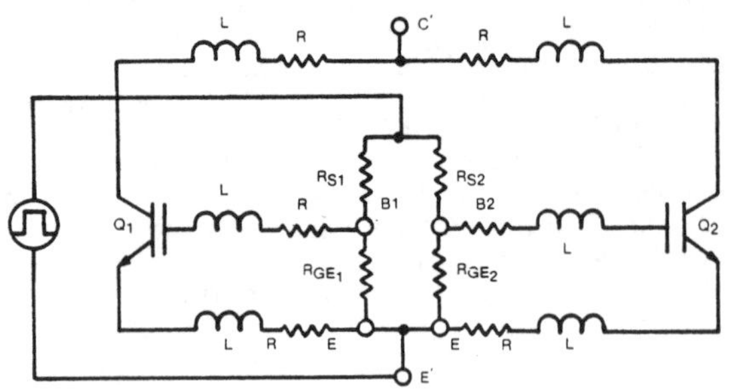

14(b) High Frequency Equivalent Circuit.

FIG. 14 Parallel Connection.

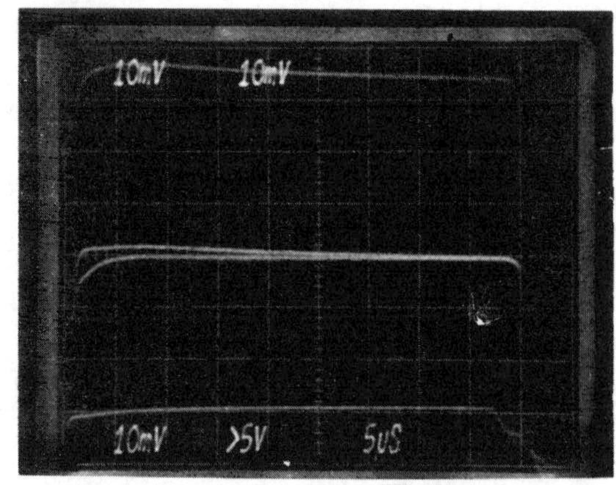

TOP (I_T)

VERT = 2A/cm

MIDDLE ($I_1 + I_2$)

VERT = 2A/cm

BOTTOM

V_{GE} = 20V/cm

15(a) Switching Times Equal.

In Figure 16(b), an extreme unbalance exists ($R_{S1} \neq R_{S2}$ and $R_{GE1} \neq R_{GE2}$) due to Q_1 turning on before Q_1 and Q_1 turning off before Q_2. This problem can be minimized by matching transconductance and tailoring the drive circuitry to provide equal turn-on and turn-off times. That is, adjust R_{S1} and/or R_{S2} [Figure 14(b)] for equal turn-on time and R_{GE1} and/or R_{GE2} for turn-off time. The results of balancing switching times by use of gate resistors using two units selected at random are shown in Figure 16(b).

TOP (I_C)

VERT = 2A/cm

BOTTOM (V_{GE})

VERT = 5V/cm

15(b) Unequal Switching Times.

FIG. 15 Parallel Operation in the Switching Mode.

If a further degree of balance is required other than drive compensation, bucking inductors may be employed in addition to matching transconductance.

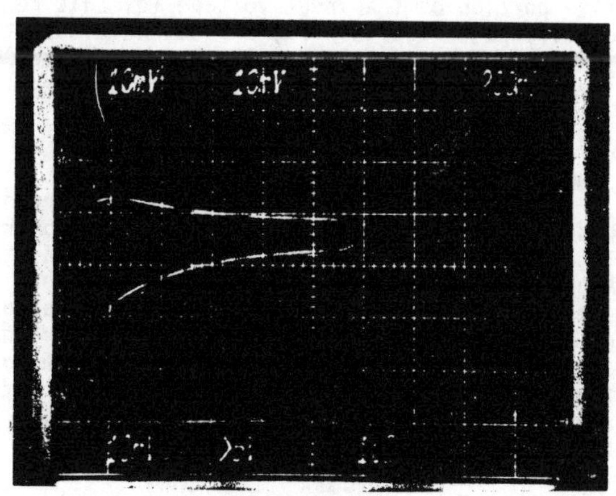

TOP (I_{TOTAL})

VERT = 2A/cm

BOTTOM ($I_{C1} + I_{C2}$)

VERT = 2A/cm

16(a) Switching Time Unbalance.

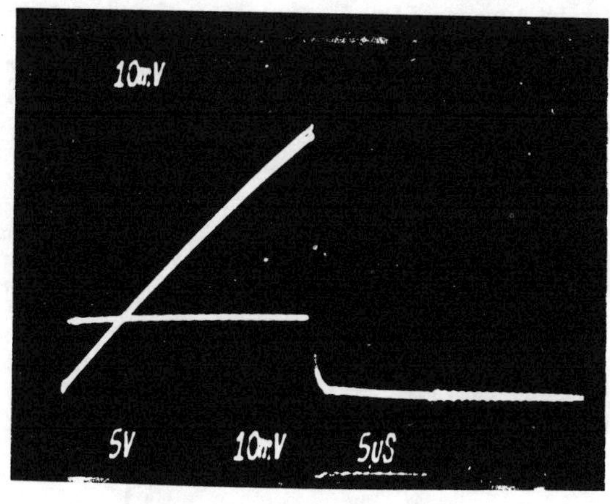

TOP (I_C)

VERT = 2A/cm

BOTTOM (V_{GE})

VERT = 10V/cm

16(b) Balanced Switching Time Using R_{GE} and R_{S1}.

FIG. 16 Parallel Operation.

Switching Times as a Function of Temperature

The IGT has a positive temperature coefficient associated with its fall time. It is approximately .27%/°C. In critical applications where increased fall time will result in excessive power dissipation, the device turn-off time can be controlled by choosing the temperature coefficient of R_{GE} to compensate for device characteristics. If R_{GE} is a thermistor, it should be sized to minimize the effects of self-heating due to the application of constant power. If the thermistor is properly chosen, minimal change in the fall time will result - a definite advantage. The rise time of the IGT is relatively constant over temperature and is similar to a Power MOSFET. Therefore, no temperature compensation is required for turn-on time.

Protection

The IGT can latch "on" if the maximum controllable collector current is exceeded for a specified minimum value of R_{GE}. The value of R_{GE} is specified as a minimum value to guarantee that the device cannot latch for any rated combination of use conditions which include a resistive or inductive load, with and without snubbers and permissible maximum operating junction temperatures.

The latching mode of operation should be generally avoided, since loss of gate control results. If the device latches, it can be turned off if the collector current falls below the holding current for the device, or if the devices are force commutated similar to an SCR. The device can be easily controlled to prevent latching. Since the magnitude of collector current is controlled by V_{GE}, a limit on $V_{GE(max)}$ will not allow excessive collector current to flow. However, current source operation results if the load is shorted, thereby forcing the device to dissipate excessive power until it can be turned off. This is entirely possible in inverter circuits. The FBSOA characteristics are such that the device can survive full voltage and current for 5 µs. During the maximum intrapulse period, the device can be safely turned off to insure device

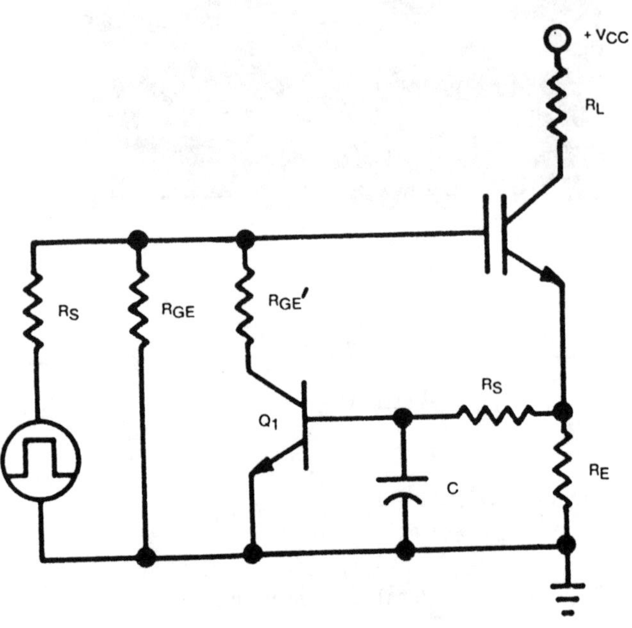

17(a) Current Viewing (Low Frequency)

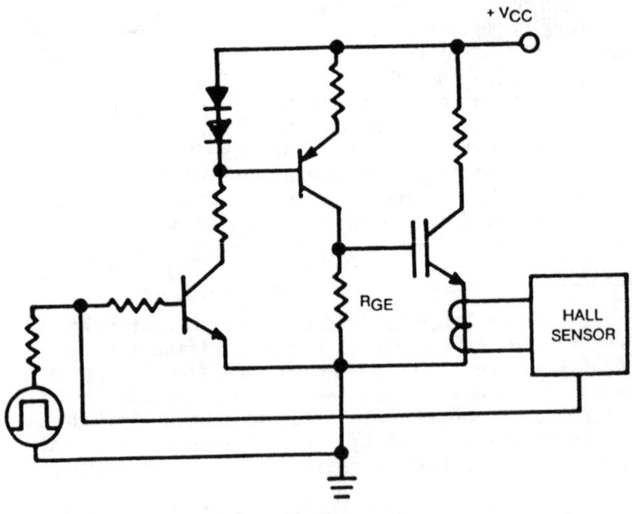

17(b) Hall Effect

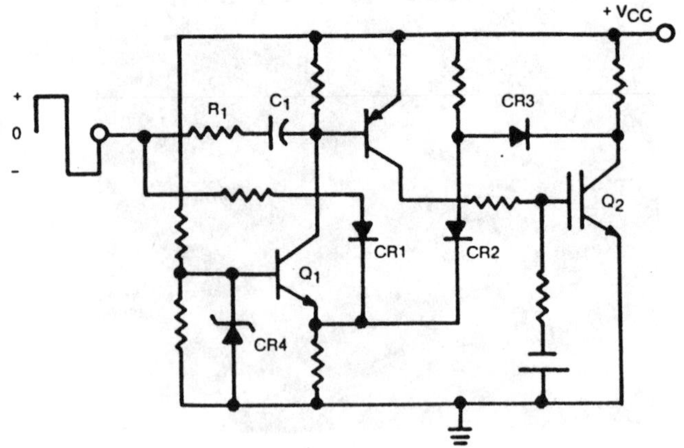

17(c) Intrapulse Sensing

FIG. 17 Typical Current Limiting Circuits.

survival. Current sensing can be implemented by use of a current viewing resistor in the emitter circuit. Hall Effect devices may also be used to eliminate excessive power dissipation in the resistor. Some typical current limiting circuits are shown in Figure 17. All circuits turn off the IGT when excess collector current exists. The circuit of Figure 17(a) functions to remove drive from the IGT when I_C R_E is greater than V_{BE} of Q_1. The disadvantage of this scheme is power dissipation in R_E. The Hall sensor in Figure 17(b) is free of excess power dissipation but is costly. The circuit of Figure 17(c) senses excessive current by turning off Q_1 if $V_{CE(SAT)}$ of Q_2 rises due to excessive current or collector-to-emitter voltage during the intrapulse period. If during the negative portion of the input voltage (circuit requires negative pulse for turn-on) a fault develops, the V_{CE} of Q_2 rises. This increase in V_{CE} reverse biases Q_1 and provides instantaneous shutdown of Q_2.

Conclusion

The Insulated Gate Transistor (IGT) is a new power switching device that features simple control circuitry, low on-state losses, fast (or slow) switching speeds and has FBSOA and RBSOA characteristics similar to a Power MOSFET. Devices have been constructed which are rated at 25 Amps and 600 Volts. Typical applications for the device would include relay drivers, motor speed control, switching power supplies, lamp drivers and fluorescent lighting. Samples of the device are available now.

MOS-Controlled Thyristors—A New Class of Power Devices

VICTOR A. K. TEMPLE, MEMBER, IEEE

Abstract—A new class of power devices is described that is based on an optimal combination of MOS and thyristor elements. Devices of this class function in the ON-state and OFF-state in a manner indistinguishable from a thyristor yet can switch from on-to-off or off-to-on by applying a voltage to its MOS gate. Thus, the devices exhibit extremely low forward drop, high surge current capability, and enjoy negative thermal feedback. To turn off the device, one activates the gate so that FET's are turned on to effectively short one of the emitting junctions of the thyristor. These FET's need only block a maximum of about 1 V when off and carry a sizable current for about 1 μs when on. To turn on the device, any of the normal methods may be employed. However, it is most convenient to use the same MOS gate electrode (and polysilicon layer) and a voltage of the opposite polarity to turn on the thyristor with another FET—just as if it were a normal MOS gated thyristor. The current density that can be turned off depends on the density and effective resistance of the turn-off FET's while turn-on speed and *di/dt* rating depend on the initial turn-on area, which in turn depends on the density of the ON-FET's. If the OFF-gate voltage is maintained during the desired OFF-state period, the device has, effectively, an infinite *dv/dt* capability. Switching speed is most similar to, but somewhat faster than, that of gate turn-off thyristors (GTO's) and, as in other bipolar devices, depends chiefly on carrier recombination time, device thickness, and turn-off *di/dt*.

I. Introduction

There have been a number of investigations of various MOS bipolar device alternatives [1], [2] described in the literature that benefit from either high FET input impedance as in the Darlington configuration of Fig. 1(a), for example, or from high FET switching speed as in the parallel MOS bipolar transistor (MOS-BT) configuration of Fig. 1(b). There are advocates, as well, for the series low-voltage MOS high-voltage BT configuration of Fig. 1(c) to improve turn-off performance of the BT without the normal second breakdown phenomena. In all of these devices shown schematically in Fig. 1 there are performance drawbacks. In the Darlington, forward drop is increased. In the parallel combination, we still have to drive the bipolar device (in concert now with the FET) to achieve faster less lossy turn-off with the BT, however, still limiting the useful cut-off frequency. In the series combination, forward drop is increased, and two gates must be driven.

In the MOS thyristor (MOS-T) combination [3], [4], there are two devices of note as shown in Fig. 2. One is the MOS-gated thyristor of Fig. 2(a) where one has a MOS element connected between the anode and gate with an ability to turn on a large portion of the device simultaneously without having to supply the large (though short) gate current pulse that must be supplied to a typical inverter thyristor. In the recently described [5], [6] "insulated gate transistor" (IGT), illustrated schematically in Fig. 2(b), it is not clear that the device should be classified as a thyristor, since in the ON-state the devices effectively resembles a series-diode low, voltage MOSFET. In the ON-state, the thyristor is parasitic and, if it latches, will prohibit gate control. In the OFF-state and in device construction, the device is a thyristor and therefore blocks voltage in both directions. If the device is compared at the 600-V level to a transistor (at a forced gain of 3), it can carry about three times the current density at a 2-V forward drop. Compared to a 600-V MOSFET, it has about a 20 times higher current density at 2 V. This is significant because the single control electrode is the MOS gate. However, the series FET, the electron spreading resistance, the low level of modulation, and the nonuniform flow of current lead to a quite different story when its forward drop is compared to that of a thyristor. Now the IGT has a 10 times smaller current density at 1 V and a 50

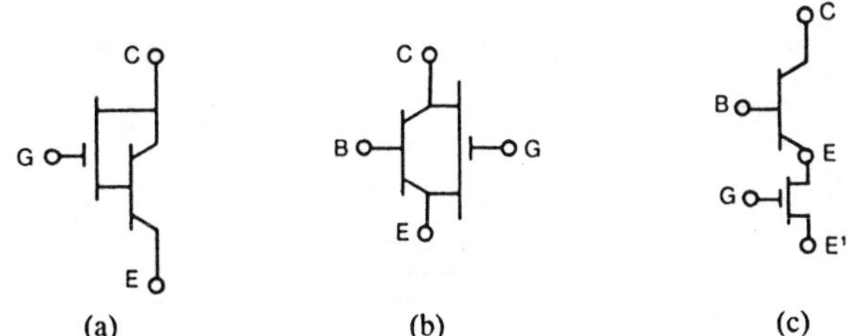

Fig. 1. Schematic diagrams of some MOS/bipolar transistor device combinations. (a) Darlington. (b) Parallel. (c) Series.

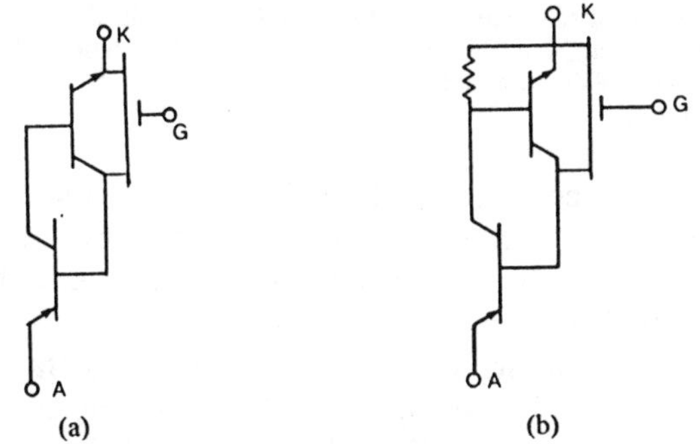

Fig. 2. Schematic diagrams of two MOS/thyristor device combinations. (a) MOS gated SCR. (b) Insulated gate transistor.

Manuscript received October 21, 1985; revised April 16, 1986.
The author is with Corporate Research and Development, General Electric Co., Schenectady, NY 12301.
IEEE Log Number 8609830.

Reprinted from *IEEE Trans. Electron Devices*, vol. ED-33, no. 10, pp. 1609–1618, October 1986.

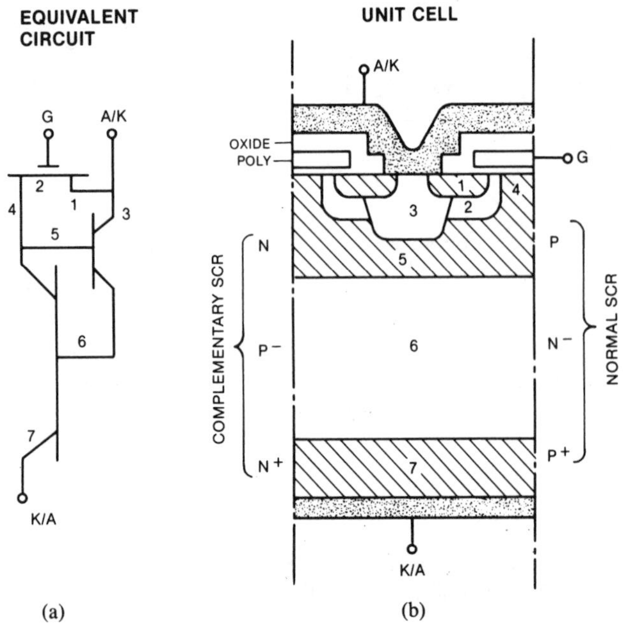

Fig. 3. (a) Circuit schematic of the typical MCT unit cell. (b) Cross section of a typical MCT unit cell. 1) FET source. 2) Channel. 3) SCR emitter. 4) FET drain. 5) and 6) SCR upper/lower base, respectively. 7) SCR emitter.

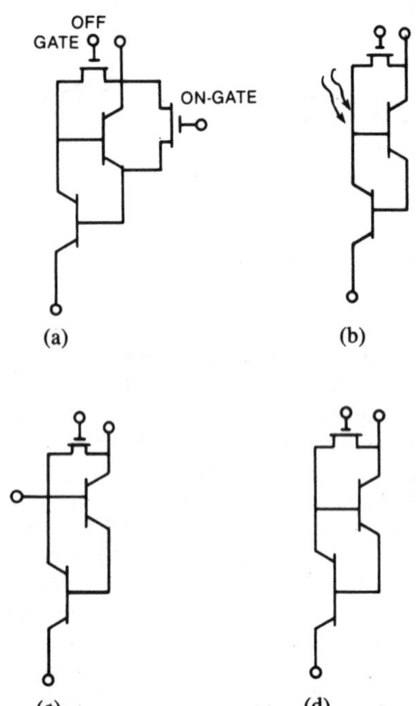

Fig. 4. Schematic diagrams of various possible MCT turn-on alternatives. (a) MOS on-gate. (b) Light triggered. (c) Normal gate. (d) Noise gate.

times smaller current density at 2 V than a comparable 600-V thyristor with the same doping and carrier lifetime profiles. Obviously what is needed is a thyristor that can be MOS controlled in turn-off as well as turn-on.

Scharf and Plummer [7] describe several lateral low-current devices that combined MOS, transistor, and thyristor structures, some of which included MOScontrolled turn-off. Later, Remmerie and Bossche [8] combined several lateral devices using the Plummer approach. However, for real power (devices of [7] and [8] were 4 and 10 Ω, respectively) and for power electrode simplicity, nothing beats a vertical power device as we described in an earlier paper [9].

The key to accomplishing this turn-off function, as first described in [7], is to realize that thyristors have a holding current capability that is normally dictated by p-base resistivity and emitter short density with low short density giving the lowest forward drop and holding current. What our FET's must do is to control the short density, making it very high when we want to turn off and very low (even zero) when we want to be on. Fig. 3 indicates how this can be most easily accomplished. On the left, the FET element is seen to short the upper transistor emitter junction while on the right we see a unit cell cross section of a practical device. Table I can be consulted for a complete list of symbols used in the following discussion.

TABLE I
LIST OF VARIABLES

Variable	Definition
α_L , α_U	lower and upper transistor current gains
$\alpha_{T,U}$	upper transistor base transport factor
β	transistor gain
ρ, ρ_{ef}	unmodulated and modulated resistivity in ohm-cm of the upper base layer
$\rho_{\square}$	sheet resistance of the upper base layer
$\rho_{\square DR}$	FET channel and drain overlap region sheet resistance
I, I_T	device current
I_R	current in the off-FET path
J	current density
J_{OFF}	current density prior to turn-off
J_{E1} , J_{H1}	electron and hole current densities at the upper emitter base junction
J_R	current density flowing through the off-FET
L_1	Half width of a 1cm long cell
L	channel length
R, R_{ef}	FET path resistance
$R_{lateral}$	lateral component of off-FET current path resistance
R_{SPR}, $R_{spreading}$	off-FET spreading resistance
R_{CH}, $R_{channel}$	off-FET channel resistance
$V_J, V_J(x,J)$	upper emitter base junction voltage
$V_{T,ON}$	threshold voltage for latch-up with the off-FET not conducting
$V_{T,OFF}$	upper emitter base voltage at the highest current density that can be turned off.

II. Device Turn-On

The unit cell of Fig. 3 has been shown without any turn-on capability, partly because the ON-state can rapidly spread to this cell from a remote part of the device through a plasma spread that, due to the lack of emitter shorts, is even more rapid than normal, and partly because there are so many ON-gate alternatives as illustrated in Fig. 4. In Fig. 4(a), one or more cells include what will be termed an ON-FET that, when turned on, initiates thyristor action. Those cells latch on, and plasma spreads from those cells to the remaining device area. Fig. 5 shows an example of a cell that would accomplish the purpose. If this

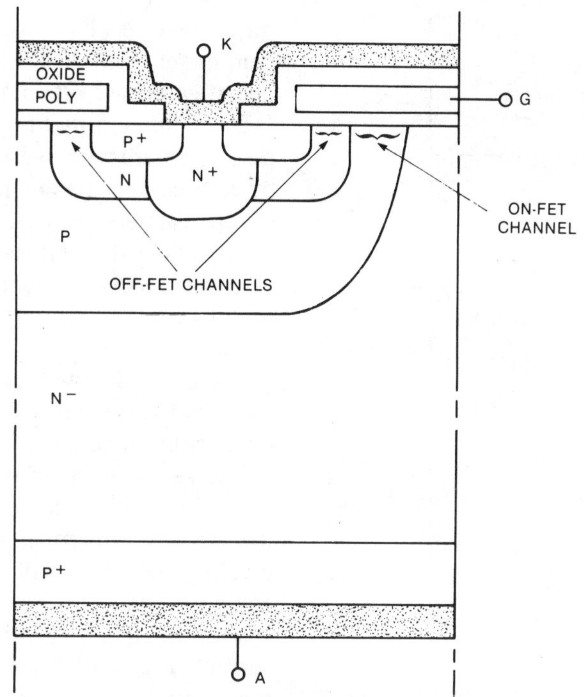

Fig. 5. Cross section of an MCT unit cell with both turn-on and turn-off FET's.

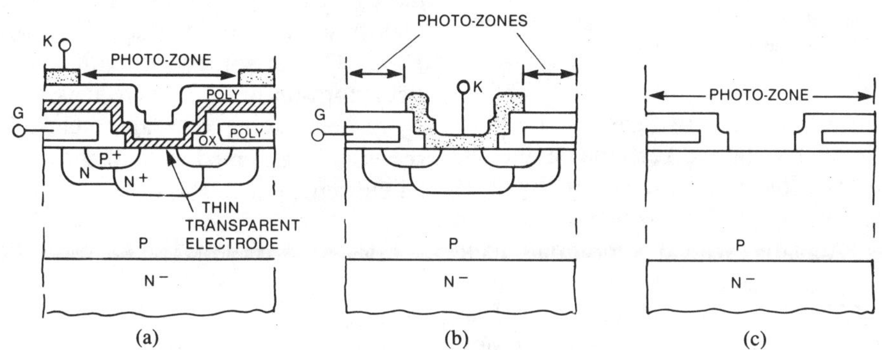

Fig. 6. Some possible unit cell cross sections for photo turn-on. (a) Transparent electrode. (b) Patterned cathode. (c) Photo-p-n-p cell.

cell and that of Fig. 3 are compared, it can be seen that by including an ON-gate on one side of the cell, the cell size has been increased in that direction. This will later be seen to lower the current density that can be turned off in that cell.

In Fig. 4(b), the device is turned on by light that infers either a transparent electrode, a portion of the device with the metal emitter electrode removed in selected areas, or cells with the emitter electrode removed entirely. All three alternatives are illustrated in Fig. 6. In Fig. 6(a), the thin transparent electrode is connected to the major emitter electrode by a polysilicon layer. In Fig. 6(b) openings are made in the emitter electrode carefully aligned such as to miss the source–emitter contact areas. Finally, in Fig. 6(c), a structure is shown in which some cells are sacrificed, having no emitter or source contacts. Fig. 6(c) is also shown as having no channel, source, or emitter diffusion but could, without affecting turn-on to any large extent, have any or all of these regions.

In Fig. 4(c), turn-on is accomplished with a normal ON-gate while Fig. 7 shows a possible ON-gate unit cell. Here gate metal directly contacts the upper base layer with the source included to make good contact. Note that a device turned on in this fashion must have another contact to the OFF-MOSFET's. Perhaps the most important role of cells such as that of Fig. 7 is their use, not as a normal ON-gate, but as a permanent (normal) emitter short. This would occur if the cell metal shown here were continued to become part of the emitter contact metalization.

One of the most interesting turn-on methods is noise or leakage current turn-on that can occur where all unit cells look like that of Fig. 3. In other words, with the OFF-FET's off there are no emitter shorts so that leakage current or dv/dt current can turn on the device if it exceeds a critical amount. This amount is roughly being given by the 1-V leakage current of the OFF-FET.

In these devices, in contrast to devices with one or more permanent shorts where the OFF-gate FET's need be on

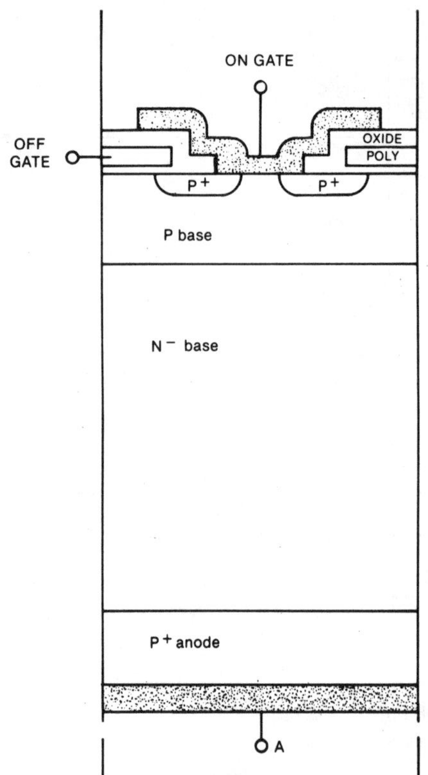

Fig. 7. Cross section of a unit cell with both a normal on-gate and a FET off-gate.

for only a few microseconds, the OFF-gate FET's now must be maintained in the ON-state to keep the device off. However, unlike the MOS ON-gate structure of Fig. 4(a) and (c), only a single polarity gate signal is required with respect to the emitter. Actually, with an appropriate fixed interface and oxide charge, it is theoretically possible to control both the ON-FET and OFF-FET of Fig. 4 with three voltage levels of a single polarity. The same result, namely sufficiently different threshold voltages of the same polarity, could be achieved if one FET were made a depletion FET while the other were made an enhancement FET. Because, in a more complex process, both ON- and OFF-FET's can be chosen to be enhancement or depletion and because, to some degree, we can control fixed surface and oxide charge, it is possible to gate the device with a single polarity, either positive or negative, or with both polarities. In the following sections, however, all FET's are assumed to be the inversion channel variety, needing one polarity to turn on and the other to turn off.

III. Turn-Off Design

In this section the device is assumed to be a normal, rather than a complementary, thyristor with blocking capability in both directions. A device is composed of as many cells as required to meet average current rating, surge current rating or forward drop, whichever is most restrictive. As in the GTO, it is clearly maximum turn-off current that normally limits the device performance unless a complex control allows ride-through during surges without attempting to turn off. In the GTO, this means a turn-off current density of several hundred amperes per square centimeter, which is about twice the maximum current densities turned off in a bipolar transistor. And, like the GTO, a turn-off that turns off most but not all of the cells may be destructive. Also, like the GTO, turn-off proceeds by 1) breaking the latched condition, and 2) recombining excess carriers in the two base layers of the device. In both devices the first stage must be rapid since it is in that period that current from areas that have unlatched will be moving as a plasma, at velocities approaching the turn-on spreading velocity, to areas that are still latched on. This will lead to an OFF-FET gate voltage rise time requirement that is the dual of the GTO turn-off gate current rise time requirement.

The key to turn-off is to break the latched condition in multiple parallel cells such as that of Fig. 3. For simplicity, the minimum design requirement's estimate for breaking latching will now assume this to be an MCT composed of 1-cm-long rectangular cells with dimensions and parameters as given in Fig. 8. To break the latching current, it is simply assumed that holes from the p-anode must prefer the FET path (solid arrows) to the thyristor-emitter junction path (the dashed arrows). In a worst case calculation, it is assumed necessary to divert nearly all of the current to the FET while holding the maximum emitter-base junction voltage (V_J) below some threshold $V_{T,\mathrm{ON}}$. This is somewhat similar to $V_{T,\mathrm{ON}}$ in normal thyristor turn-on design where it is assumed to be on if the V_J exceeds some critical voltage. $V_{T,\mathrm{OFF}}$ was first conservatively assumed to be 0.5 E_G or ~0.5 V. $V_J(X)$ can be written, in general, as

$$V_J(x, J) \approx V_{\mathrm{Lateral}} + V_{\mathrm{Spreading}} + V_{\mathrm{Channel}} \tag{1a}$$

or

$$V_J(x, J) = J|R_{\mathrm{Lateral}} + R_{\mathrm{Spreading}} + R_{\mathrm{Channel}}| = JR \tag{1b}$$

where R values are in ohms times square centimeters. The maximum value of V_J occurs at $X = 0$. Thus $V_{J,\max}$ becomes for a given current density

$$V_J(0, J) = JL_1^2\, \rho_\square/2 + J\, R_{\mathrm{Spreading}} + JL_1 L\rho_{\square CH}. \tag{2}$$

At 100 A/cm² for the dimensions of Fig. 8 ($L_1 \approx 10\ \mu$) this would give

$$V_J(0, 100) = 0.25 + 100R_{\mathrm{Spreading}} + 0.10\ \mathrm{V}, \tag{3}$$

for $\rho_\square = 500$ and $\rho_{\square CH} = 10\,000$.

If the spreading component is assumed to be of the same order as the channel contribution, the $V_J(0) = 0.5$ V would occur at about $J = 220$ A/cm²—about one-sixth the surge capability of a 600-V thyristor and somewhat less than the rated maximum turn-off current capability for a 600-V transistor of GTO. Naturally, (2) is an approximation that does not consider such things as the modulation level that lowers $\rho_\square$, nor does it attempt to calculate $R_{\mathrm{Spreading}}$.

However, (2) shows clearly that the most important design consideration is cell size L_1 followed by FET channel

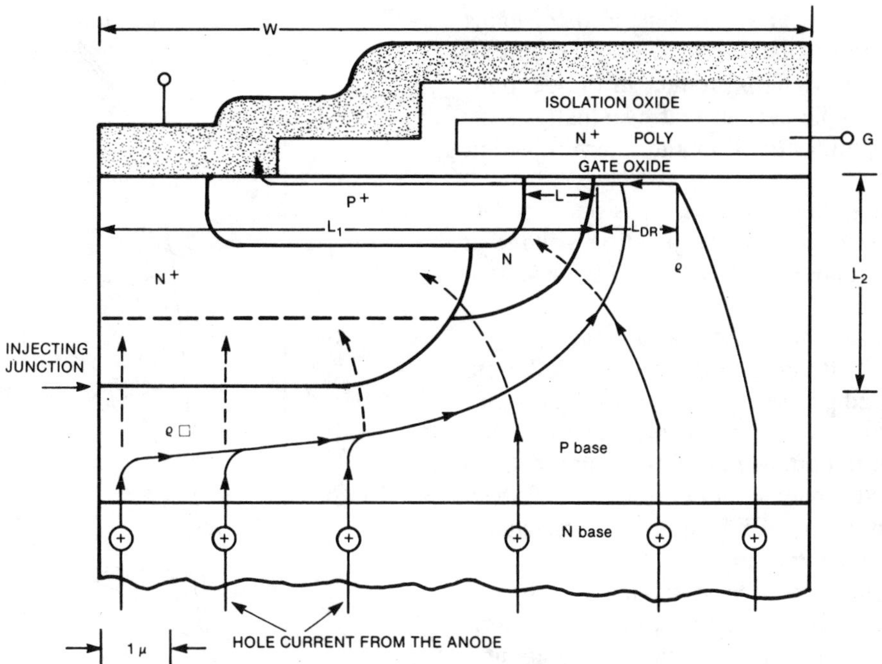

Fig. 8. Enlarged half-unit cell cross section of an MCT showing hole-current path when on (dashed curve) and during turn-off (solid curve).

and spreading resistance, though not necessarily in that order.

There are, however, at least three reasons why the 220-A/cm^2 estimate is on the low side. Most obvious is the fact that only holes flow in the FET path and that these comprise somewhat less than 50 percent of the device current in the p-base layer in the ON-state. This will be born out by a computer modeled example in a later section of this paper.

The second important correction is in the resistivities—in $\rho_\square$, in ρ, and at very high current densities, even in $\rho_{\square DR}$ and $\rho_{\square CH}$—due to modulation effects. For example, at 100 A/cm^2, $\rho_\square$ is closer to 50 Ω/□ than 500.

The third correction factor lies in our low estimate of the critical emitter–base junction voltage to cause turn-off. Rather than being ~0.5 V as one would find $V_{T,\,\mathrm{ON}}$ (the junction voltage at approximately the latching current density of a thyristor), $V_{T,\,\mathrm{OFF}}$ is, instead, the junction voltage at the maximum rated turn-off current that is more like 0.85 V at room temperature.

To see why this should be so, one needs to follow a turn-off in some detail. For simplicity it is assumed that the OFF-FET becomes fully on instantly. At this point some of the hole current is diverted to the FET. For the device to remain on, this must be a stable operating point with the loss of gain of the upper transistor made up for by an increase in the lower transistor current gain. Thus there will be a range of stable operating points until we call for a lower transistor gain to be larger than its maximum value—a range from a β of perhaps about 2 to about 10. More explicitly, in the p-base, the junction current

$$J_{H1} + J_{E1} = K_1 \ln K_2 V_J \tag{3}$$

and

$$RJ_R = V_J \tag{4}$$

with J_{H1} being the injected hole current into the emitter and J_R being the diverted portion. But $J_{H1} + J_R$ is about 40 percent of the total current in our modeling results (to be described later), which means that, at least in this case

$$J_{H1} + J_R \approx 0.66\, J_{E1}. \tag{5}$$

Selecting $J_{H1} = J_{E1}/\beta_{\max}$ gives for the turn-off condition

$$J_{E1} + J_{E1}/\beta_{\max} \approx K_1 \ln K_2 V_{J,\,\mathrm{Threshold}}. \tag{6}$$

In other words, with the device conducting its maximum turn-off current, up to $(\beta - 1)/\beta\, J_H$ hole current must be diverted through the FET while the emitter junction voltage is reduced an amount approximately given by ΔV_J.

$$\Delta V_J \approx \frac{kT}{q} \ln \left| J_E(1 + 0.66)/J_E \left| 1 + \frac{1}{\beta} \right| \right|$$

or

$$\Delta V_J \approx \frac{kT}{q} \ln 1.66 \tag{7}$$

if $1/\beta$ is neglected. In other words, very little reduction in injecting junction voltage need occur to cause the MCT to turn off.

Before using our computer modeling capability to calculate turn-off, it is first useful to examine the predicted current that can be turned off when the three correction factors are taken into account. Equation (2) becomes

$$J_{\mathrm{OFF}} = \frac{V_{T,\,\mathrm{OFF}}}{\alpha_{T,\,U}\alpha_L R_{ef}} \tag{8}$$

where α_U and α_L are the upper and lower transistor gains and R_{ef} the effective impedance of the OFF-FET current path. The reason for the $\alpha_L \alpha_{T,U}$ product in the denominator is that this is the hole current that eventually is injected into the upper emitter to allow the return injection of electrons.

In our computer modeling case, which is discussed in the next section, it is found that the junction voltage at 440 A/cm^2 was more than 0.8 V and, at 1000 A/cm^2 it was about 0.85 V.

Setting $V_{T,\mathrm{OFF}}$, therefore, to be 0.85 V, and taking $\alpha_L = 0.4$, $\alpha_{T,U} = 0.9$, $L_1 = 10$ μm, and R_{ef} to be 1.33 Ω · cm (R_{ef} assumes modulated p-base resistances.) J_{OFF} becomes 1733 A/cm^2 rather than the uncorrected value of 267 A/cm^2. However, the importance of having small cell repeat distance L_1, short channel length L, low channel sheet resistance $\rho_{\square CH}$, and a low FET spreading resistance through a low R_{ef} remains the same.

Although these factors are process related and the example structure given may already be difficult to fabricate, there is one thing that can be done to give about a twofold improvement and also increase process yield. That change is to convert the device cell of Fig. 8 from a normal to a complementary thyristor so that the FET current is electron instead of hole current. All unmodulated resistance values are close to 3 times lower while modulated resistance regions are only slightly more conductive. The only negative aspect is the fact that α_L will be larger, closer to 0.6 rather than 0.4, giving a net increase in J_{OFF} from 1773 A/cm^2 to about 3546 A/cm^2.

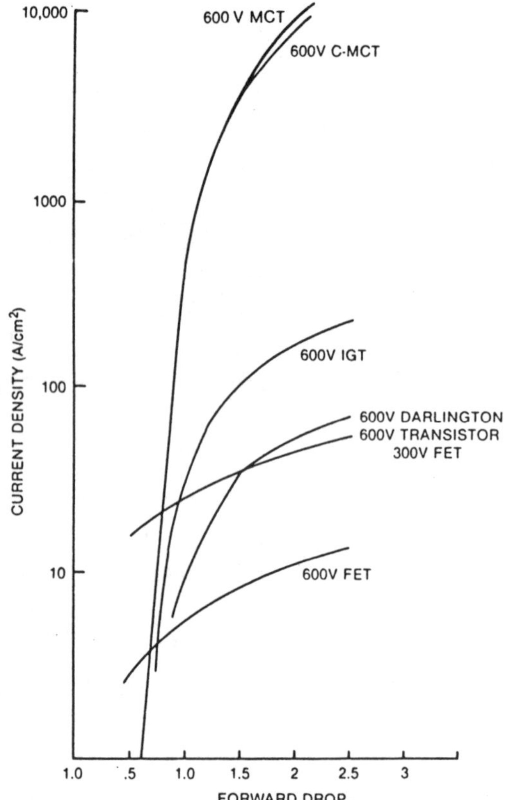

Fig. 9. Comparison of high gain turn-off device forward drop. The IGT and MCT are calculated based on the same identical doping and lifetime profiles.

IV. Computer Calculations

In this section the forward drop and turn-off of an MCT unit cell was considered. For both of these the calculations were one-dimensional. In the case of forward drop, this can be easily understood because the only place that current is somewhat constricted is in the upper emitter region that, however, is so highly doped that little increase in emitter drop is possible. Nor is there any sizeable reduction in upper transistor gain through the somewhat reduced emitter efficiency largely because, in a thyristor, upper transistor gain at high current is of the order of 0.6. Thus, a drop in emitter efficiency from 0.99 to 0.97 for example, is of little consequence. In addition, cell size is a small fraction of total thyristor base thickness so that even in the base regions the current flow is quasi-one-dimensional.

A. Forward Drop

Fig. 9 shows a comparison of 600-V turn-off devices with the FET, bipolar transistor, and IGT data taken from the comparison curves of [5] and the MCT and C-MCT (complementary MCT) taken from this work. The IGT curve is a calculated curve fitting the actual IGT device very closely. For the most accurate comparison between MCT and IGT in calculating the MCT curve in Fig. 9 the entire doping and carrier lifetime profiles of the parasitic thyristor inherent in the IGT were modeled as an MCT in the ON-state. This profile is shown schematically in Fig. 10. For the complementary MCT or C-MCT of Fig. 9, the profiles were again those of Fig. 10 but with the n- and p-labels reversed. Because of the fact that transistors block voltage in one direction only. The IGT (and MCT) devices were chosen to be asymmetric.

B. Turn-Off

The ON-state calculations were relatively simple. However, turn-off calculations were more complex. What was done was to add resistors (admittances) between the upper base nodes and upper emitter contact in the one-dimensional version of the program that would only allow upper base majority-carrier current flow—in this case, holes. The admittance values were given a Gaussian distribution with an abrupt cutoff at the n$^+$ emitter and n-base boundaries and a net resistances R that was then varied as a function of time. Since the program assumes 1 cm^2 of area, R is then in ohms times square centimeters.

Fig. 11 shows the result with various quantities of interest plotted as a function of R from its initial value of ∞ to a final value of about 10 mΩ · cm^2 at which time the program would no longer converge even with a very, very small reduction in R. This point was taken as the point at which latching was broken. It was also inferred, from our convergence problem, that the transition from latched thyristor to unlatched open-base transistor would be very fast, of the order of several base transit times.

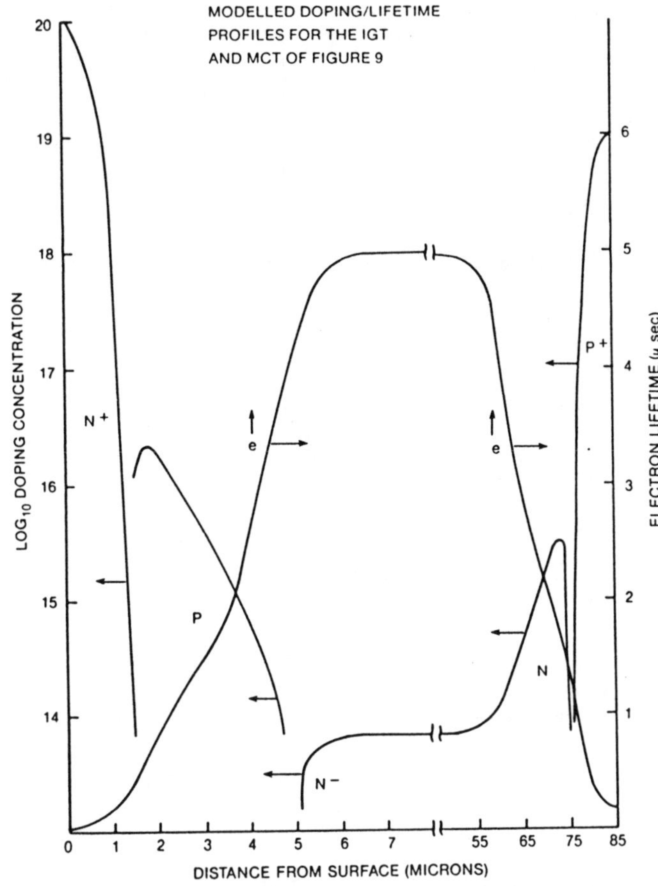

Fig. 10. Doping and lifetime profiles used in the computer model in generating the MCT and IGT I-V curves. The C-MCT was calculated by changing the sign of the doping.

An R of 60 mΩ is seen to have little or no effect with I_{HB} (the hole current entering the p-base from the n-base), I_{HE} (the hole current reaching the emitter), I_R, I_T, and V_J (plotted as V_{BE}) asymptotically approaching their fully unshorted values. At this point, for example, $I_{HB} = 0.38$ I_T and $I_{HE} = 0.30$ I_T while $V_J = 0.838$ V. At the final stable operating point in Fig. 11, $I_{HB} = 0.41$ I_T while I_{HE} has dropped to 0.16 I_T—i.e., the upper transistor emitter efficiency has increased to help keep the device on with the shorting resistor in place. This partially offsets the resistor so that a smaller increase in the lower transistor gain is sufficient to keep the device on. The resistor (FET) current is interesting, having increased from 13 A at $R = 60$ mΩ to 81 A at the turn-off point where it comprises only 24 percent of the net device current. Further, from considering V_J, it has only been necessary to reduce the upper emitter junction voltage to 0.814 V to turn off the device at its 338-A final operating point, a change of only 24 mV, a change in keeping with the analysis leading to (7). Careful examination of the currents at this point reveals that the total current of 338 A at the last stable operating point is composed of 54 A of hole current and 213 A of return electron current into the emitter and 81 A of hole current in the resistor (FET) path whereas at $R = 60$ mΩ · cm², one has a 413-A total current composed of 131 A of hole current into the emitter, 269 A of return electron current, and a resistor current of 13 A. These give injection ratios r_E of 3.94 and 2.05, respectively, leading to injection efficiencies of 0.80 and 0.67. From taking the ratio of I_{EB}/I_{EE} where I_{EB} is the electron current reaching the n-base-p-base junction, one gets the effective upper transistor base transport factors α_T, and multiplying by the injection efficiency, the transistor current gain. These are tabulated at R-values from 60 to 10 mΩ · cm² in Table II.

From examining this table, one can see that the upper transistor's effective α value ($\alpha_{U,ef} = \alpha_U - I_R/I_T$) is decreasing, as it should, as R is reduced. However the reduction is slowed considerably by a partly compensating increase in the injection ratio of the upper emitter as measured by I_{EE}/I_{HE}. Further, that the thyristor remained latched to the $R = 10$ mΩ level means that the reduction in the effective α_U is being met with an increase in α_L such that

$$\frac{\Delta\alpha_{U,ef}}{\Delta R} = \frac{-\Delta\alpha_L}{\Delta R} \tag{9}$$

where ΔR is the change in resistor value. Turn-off occurs where increases in α_U and α_L no longer match increases in I_R/I_T. Thus, as seen in the computer example in Fig. 11, one need not divert all hole current from the upper emitter, since at turn-off, 53 A/cm² of hole current was still injected into the upper emitter while 81 A/cm² was diverted. In fact, the R at which turn-off occurs can be found from rewriting [9] as the condition for breaking, latching, as

$$\frac{d}{dR}\left|\alpha_1 + \alpha_2 - \frac{I_R}{I_T}\right| = 0 \tag{10}$$

which unfortunately is not generally soluble to any degree of accuracy.

Although (10) may not be soluble (except perhaps for $d/dR\, I_R$), it provides an alternative view to (8) by allowing α values to be dynamic functions.

Following (10) to it logical conclusion, we find that diverting

$$I_R = |\Delta\alpha_L + \Delta\alpha_U|\, I_T \tag{11}$$

is, by definition, sufficient to break the latching if $\Delta\alpha_L$ and $\Delta\alpha_U$ are defined as α differences from before and after latch. Our modeling experience has shown that α_L is slowly varying compared to α_U from a dynamic standpoint and that

$$J_{\mathrm{OFF,MIN}} \approx \frac{V_{T,\mathrm{OFF}}}{L_1\, R_{ef}}\frac{1}{\Delta\alpha_U}. \tag{12}$$

Since α_U is mostly controlled by injection efficiency for the high currents we are interested in, we find that $\Delta\alpha_U$ can be replaced by a log function of current density as in (13a) or by a log function in R^{-1} since J_{OFF} is proportional to R^{-1}. Note that since $\Delta\alpha_L$ is nonzero, (12) will tend to overestimate turn-off capability.

Thus, we tested the following approximations against

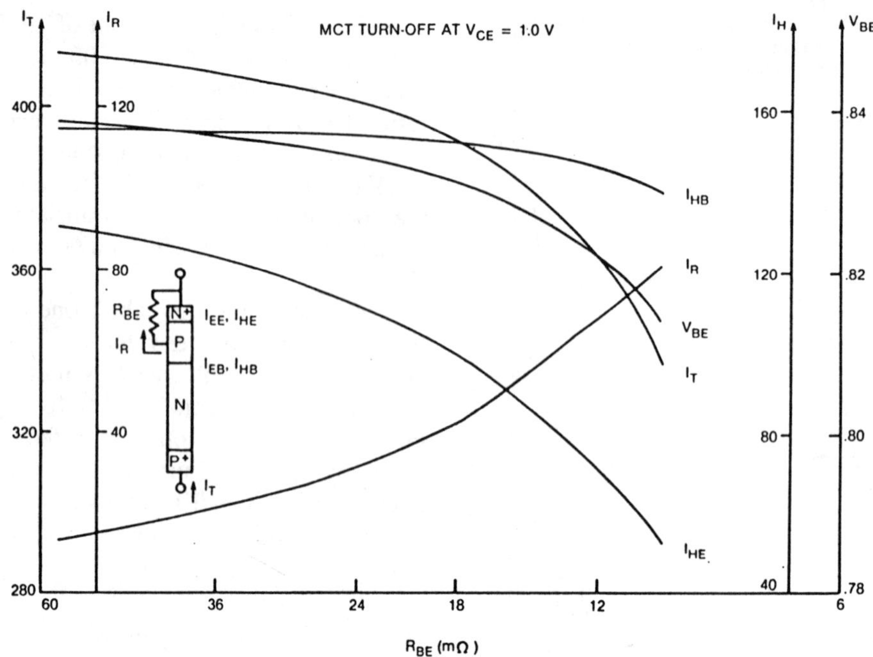

Fig. 11. Base–emitter voltage and various device currents (see inset diagram) during turnoff as a function of R_{BE}. Note that R_{BE} only carried hole current for MCT devices and only electron current for C-MCT devices. At $R = \infty$, I_T was 440 A/cm².

TABLE II
MCT TURN-OFF AT 1 V
(See Fig. 11.)

R (mΩcm²)	V_J	I_T	I_{EB}	I_{HB}	I_R	I_{EE}	I_{HE}	$\gamma_{UE} = \frac{I_{EE}}{I_{EE}+I_{HE}}$	$\alpha_{UT} = \frac{I_{EB}}{I_{EE}}$	$\alpha_U = \gamma_E \alpha_{UT}$	$\alpha_{U,ef} = \frac{I_{EB}}{I_T}$	$\alpha'_{UT} = \frac{I_{HE}}{I_{HB}}$
60	.838	414	259	155	13	269	131	.673	.963	.648	.626	.845
36	.836	408	254	154	21	264	123	.682	.962	.656	.623	.799
24	.834	401	248	153	31	258	112	.697	.961	.670	.618	.732
18	.831	393	241	152	42	251	100	.715	.960	.687	.613	.658
12	.822	364	218	146	68	225	71	.760	.969	.736	.599	.486
10	.814	338	199	139	81	203	54	.790	.980	.774	.589	.388

our computer-modeled one-dimensional device

$$J_{\mathrm{OFF}} \approx \frac{V_{T,\mathrm{OFF}}}{L_1 R_{ef} \alpha_L} \log \frac{J_{\mathrm{OFF}}}{J_D} \tag{13a}$$

$$J_{\mathrm{OFF}} \approx \frac{V_{T,\mathrm{OFF}}}{L_1 R_{ef} \alpha_L} \log R_o/R_{ef}. \tag{13b}$$

The α_L values in the denominator, since they have been assumed constant through the breaking of the latched state, do not effect the shape of (13). The justification for including them was that when included in (13), we could fit both MCT and C-MCT data, such as those in Fig. 11 and Table II by a single R_0 or J_0 value. Best fit, for example, to computer data was with $R_0 = 65\ \Omega$.

V. Device Feasibility

A series of small approximately 1100-V (ideal breakdown voltage) C-MCT devices were fabricated with the geometry of Fig. 8 but with square cells having $\rho_\square$ measured at 500 Ω/□ and ρ at 1.5 Ω · cm. The devices had no ON-gates but were turned on, in the absence of emitter shorts, by leakage current. They were principally intended to see if a latched thyristor could be turned off. Some of the results on the one-, four- and sixteen-cell devices will be described briefly with a more complete description of the device processing and larger device results on the wafer to be given in a later paper.

Fig. 12 shows a photograph of some of the test devices with a blow up of the 16-cell device just after the contact

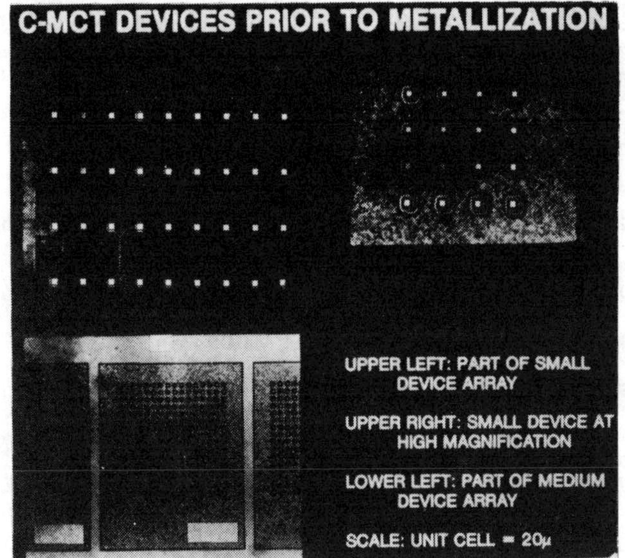

Fig. 12. Photographs of some of the devices processed with mask set MCT-1.

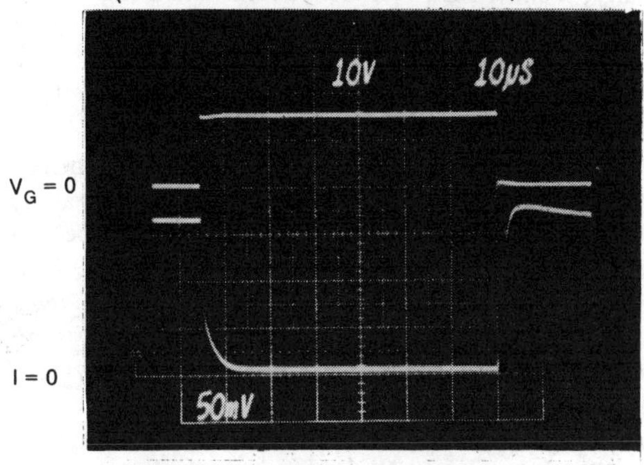

Fig. 14. Measured turn-off in a 50-V resistive circuit with a 16-cell device using a 15-V gate. The turn-off limit for size device at $V_G = 15$ ranged from 1000 to 2000 A/cm^2 at room temperature for this test circuit.

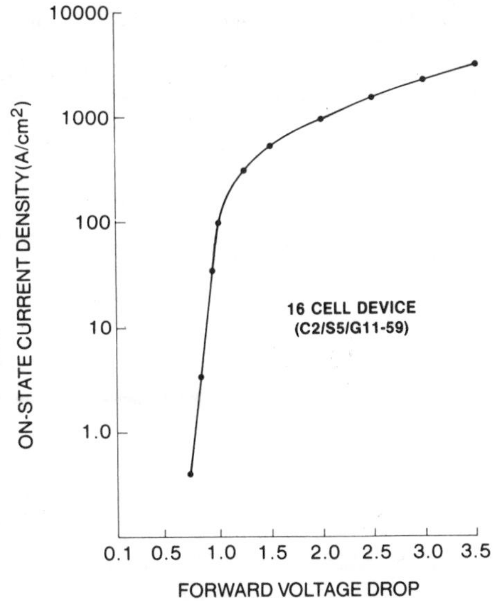

Fig. 13. Forward drop of a 16-cell device with $V_{GATE} = 15$ V. This device was made with twice the lower base thickness of the device of Fig. 10 so that it could block voltage in both polarities.

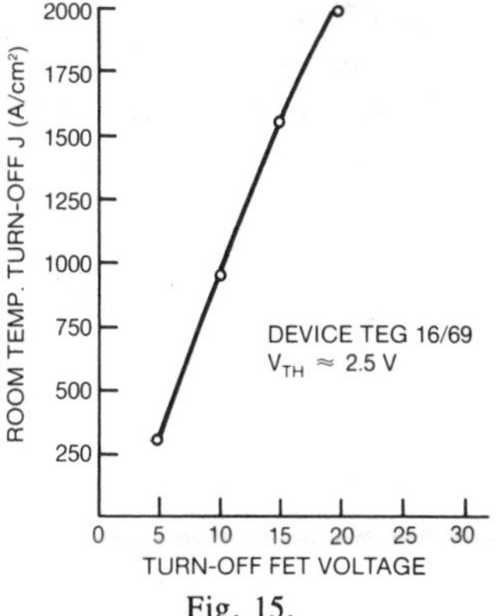

Fig. 15.

window step while Fig. 13 shows the typical forward drop normalized to the active area of the device. The device, unlike the modeled example, had a 100-μm lower base that, with proper termination, would have blocked voltage in both polarities. A spreading resistance profile is given in Fig. 14. Ideal breakdown voltage should be about 1100 V in the n-base–p-base junction and 80 V in the n$^+$ emitter–p-base junction. As it was, devices were tested on a probe station, unpassivated, and in wafer form where they blocked 400 V in the n-base–p-base junction and at least 50 V in the n$^+$ emitter–p-base junction.

Fig. 14 shows a turn-off of 1000 A/cm^2 using a 15-V gate signal with a resistive load and a 50-V anode-cathode potential. Turn-off is similar to the GTO or IGT, having an initial rapid fall as the latched condition is broken, and then a recombination tail.

Turn-off densities in the one-cell device, which, therefore, does not have uneven turn-off problems, were typically 6000 A/cm^2 at $V_G = 60$ and 2000 A/cm^2 at $V_G = 15$. The $V_G = 15$ value of about 2000 A/cm^2 is about twice the typical thyristor surge current rating and about 5 to 10 times the current density that can be turned off in a GTO.

To attempt to resolve the relative importance of the FET and base region resistance contribution an experiment was performed where turn-off current density of the 16-cell device was correlated with applied FET gate voltage. The result, shown in Fig. 15, showed that the turn-off current was nearly proportional to $V_G - V_{GT}$ as indicated by the dashed curve. This would argue that the lateral and spreading resistance were secondary in nature, which is an argument in favor of the use of the modulated base resistances in turn-off calculations.

VI. Summary

A new power device concept has been presented that combines thyristor power handling capability with MOS turn-on and turn-off control. Turn-off is accomplished by a MOS-gated emitter "short" in every cell of the device.

To reduce the resistance of this short requires a high short density, a short FET channel length, and a high FET g_m.

The analysis presented along with computer model turn-off indicates that under resistive load conditions, or conditions under that the device voltage is relatively constant, the current density that can be turned off is of the order of several thousand amperes/per square centimeter.

No temperature-dependent or load-dependent analyses were given although several predictions can be made. First, V_{OFF} will fall as $1/T$ where T is in degree Kelvin. Second, R will increase as T increases through reduced carrier mobility. In going from 25 to 125 K, this might amount to a twofold derating factor. Third, if device voltage increases substantially with little reduction in current, some reduction in J_{OFF} should result. Work on this aspect of MCT behavior will be presented later.

Device results at 25°C and turning off a resistive load at 50 V showed that turn-off current density in the better devices ranged from 2000 A/cm^2 with a 15-V gate to 6000 A/cm^2 with a 60-V gate. Note that this indicates that the prime contributions to R are in channel and spreading resistance, both of which are reduced with gate bias.

Elevated temperature and circuit-dependent modeling as well as further device results will be presented in a later paper.

Parallel work on the same device concept has been reported recently by Stoisiek and Strack [10] at Siemens who have called the device an MOS-GTO, a term that will be shown in a later paper to be too restrictive.

References

[1] G. R. David, J. C. Vallee, and J. Lebailly, "A new VMOS/bipolar Darlington transistor for power applications," in *IEDM Tech. Dig.*, p. 83, 1980.

[2] J. Tihanyi, "Functional integration of power MOS and bipolar devices," in *IEDM Tech. Dig.*, p. 75, 1980.

[3] B. W. Scharf and J. D. Plummer, "A MOS-controlled triac device," in *Int. Solid-State Circuit Conf. Dig.*, p. 222, 1978.

[4] B. J. Baliga, "Enhancement and depletion mode vertical channel MOS gated thyristors," *Electron. Lett.*, vol. 15, p. 645, 1979.

[5] B. J. Baliga, M. S. Adler, P. P. Gray, R. P. Love, and N. Zommer, "The insulated gate rectifier," in *IEDM Tech. Dig.*, p. 264, 1982.

[6] J. P. Russel, A. M. Goodman, L. A. Goodman, and J. M. Neilson, "The Comfet, a new high conductance MOS-Gater device," *IEEE Electron Device Lett.*, vol. EL-14, p. 63, 1983.

[7] J. D. Plummer and B. W. Scharf, "Insulated gate planer thyristors," *IEEE Trans. Electron Devices*, vol. ED-27, p. 380, 1980.

[8] G. Remmerie and L. Van Den Bossche, "High voltage switches for line circuit applications," *IEEE J. Solid-State Circuits*, vol. SC-19, p. 406, 1984.

[9] V. Temple, "Mos controlled thyristors (MCT's)," in *IEDM Tech. Dig.*, p. 282, 1984.

[10] M. Stoisiek and H. Strack, "MOS-GTO—A turn-off thyristor with MOS-controlled emitter shorts," in *IEDM Tech. Dig.*, p. 158, 1985.

Paper 3.6

Discrete Semiconductor Switches: Still Improving

by
Dr. Adrian Cogan,
Siliconix Inc.
Dr. Richard A. Blanchard,
Siliconix Inc.

Traditional semiconductor power switches continue to show improvement. In addition, new technologies offer higher speed and higher power switching.

The rapid evolution presently occurring in power-switching device technology presents many challenges to the circuit or systems designer. The goal of a designer — to obtain the most satisfactory solution for the least total investment — is greatly complicated by the continual changes. Not only is the performance of familiar devices such as bipolar and power MOS transistors improving, but new classes of devices such as MOS-gated four-layer devices and structures that combine power MOS and bipolar transistors are being touted as the "ultimate switch."

One basis for comparing power-switching devices is shown in *Figure 1*, which compares devices as a function of power-handling capability and operating frequency.[1] *Figure 2* provides additional information, showing the current and voltage handling capability of these devices.[2]

Bipolar Transistors

The bipolar transistor remains the switching device workhorse because of its performance per dollar. Its drawbacks include secondary breakdown, high base drive requirements, and a 20 to

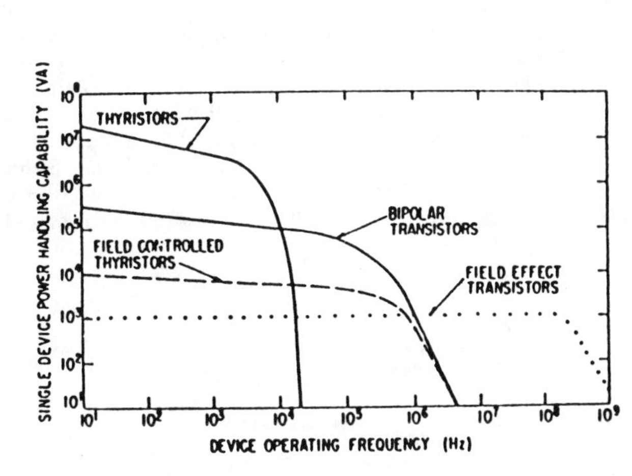

Figure 1. Power-handling capability vs. operating frequency of power-switching devices.

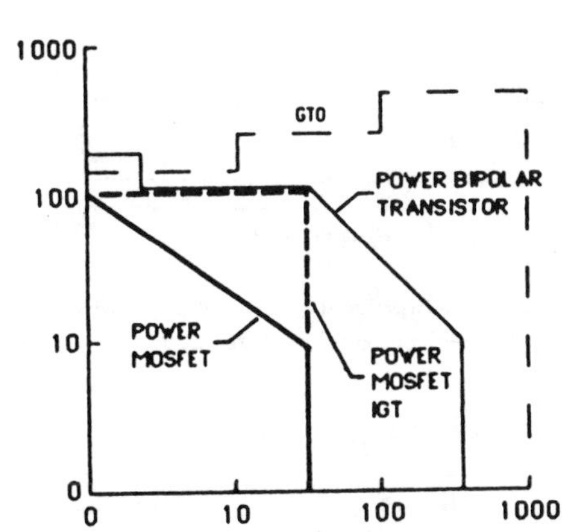

Figure 2. The current and voltage handling capabilities of commercially available power-switching devices.

Reprinted with permission from *Powerconversion & Intelligent Motion (PCIM)*, pp. 15–22, January 1986.

40 kHz switching speed. However, its low cost per ampere and the body of knowledge regarding its use represent advantages that are difficult to overcome.

New bipolar transistors increase the cost-performance advantage. Bipolar transistor technology advanced slowly during the 1970s due, in part, to the lack of competition from other devices. This state was altered by the introduction of power MOS devices in the late 1970s. In response, the use of finer line widths and more complex process sequences proved that enhanced bipolar transistor performance was attainable when process improvements were made.

The primary focus for these process improvements was transistor ruggedness. The positive feedback mechanism leading to device failure was addressed in a variety of ways. *Figure 3a* shows a cross section of an epitaxial base transistor whose emitter injects carriers only at the edges.[3] The shallower region in the center of the emitter remains inactive due to the lateral transverse voltage drop when the perimeter of the device is active. When the transistor switches, the absence of carrier injection in the center of the transistor avoids current crowding, increasing both switching speed and ruggedness.

The "ring emitter" structure of *Figure 3b* deals with current crowding by adding a series "debiasing" or "ballast" resistor at every emitter site.[3] This series resistor prevents rrent crowding by "debiasing" any emitter site that begins to dra excessive current.

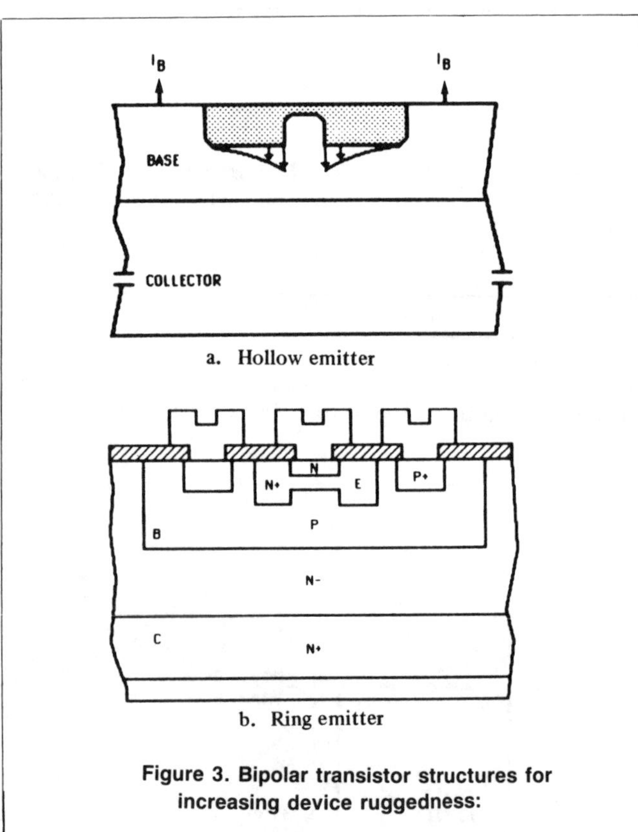

a. Hollow emitter

b. Ring emitter

Figure 3. Bipolar transistor structures for increasing device ruggedness:

Figure 4 documents the gains made using the hollow emitter and the ring emitter structures by showing the current and voltage capabilities of commercially available power bipolar transistors.[3]

A recent innovation in power bipolar technology is the introduction of a device with a large emitter-to-base breakdown voltage. This voltage rating allows the transistor to be used as a synchronous rectifier by reversing its normal bias during operation. This device makes synchronous rectification more viable for certain applications, as shown in *Figure 5*. The efficiencies of its primary competitors — Schottky diodes, and power MOS transistors — are also shown in this figure.[4]

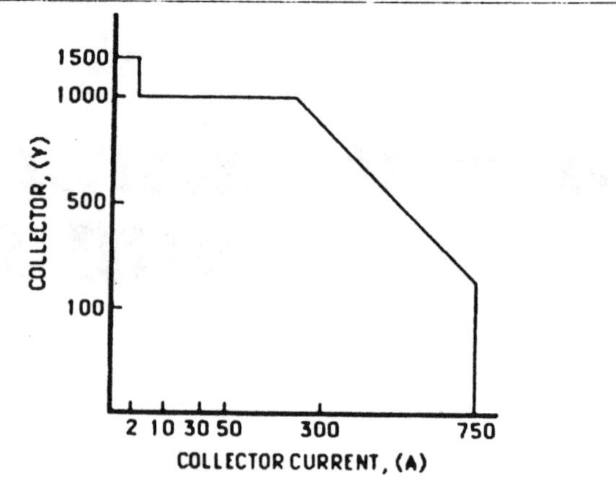

Figure 4. Rating capabilities for state-of-the-art bipolar transistors.

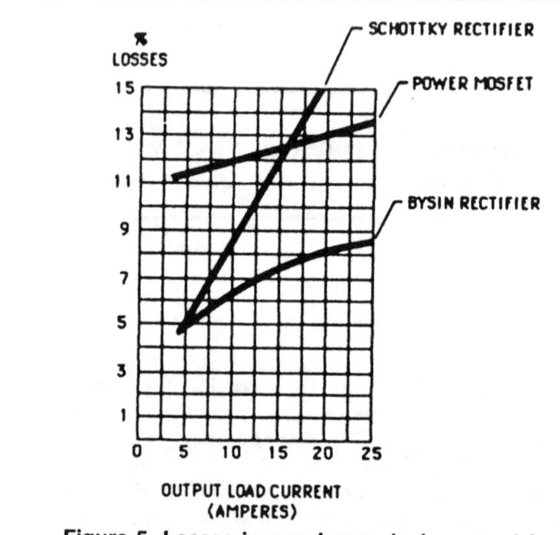

Figure 5. Losses in equal area devices used for low-voltage power rectification.

Thyristors and GTOs

Thyristors or silicon controller rectifiers (SCRs) exhibit bistable characteristics and can be switched between a high-impedance off-state and a low-impedanace, high-current on-state. Thyristors are available for voltages up to 4000V and currents to 3000A *Figure 6*.[3] The basic thyristor structure latches in the on-state and cannot be turned off by merely modifying the gate potential. As large minority currents flow through the device while in the on-state, device turn-off is slow, thus limiting the maximum frequency of operation which is typically below 1 kHz. A representative device cross section and its equivalent circuit are shown in *Figure 7a* and *7b*, respectively.[5]

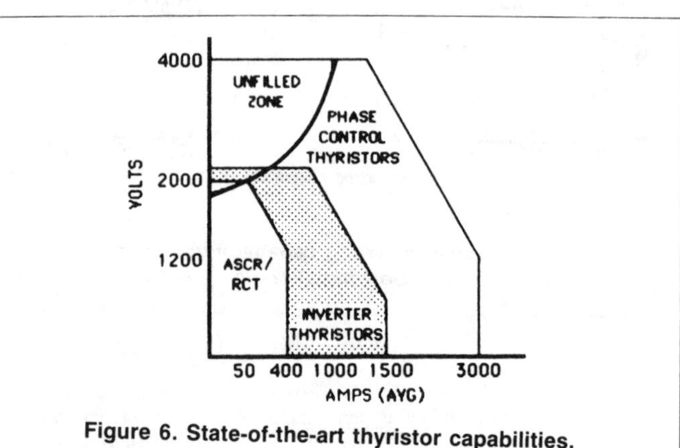

Figure 6. State-of-the-art thyristor capabilities.

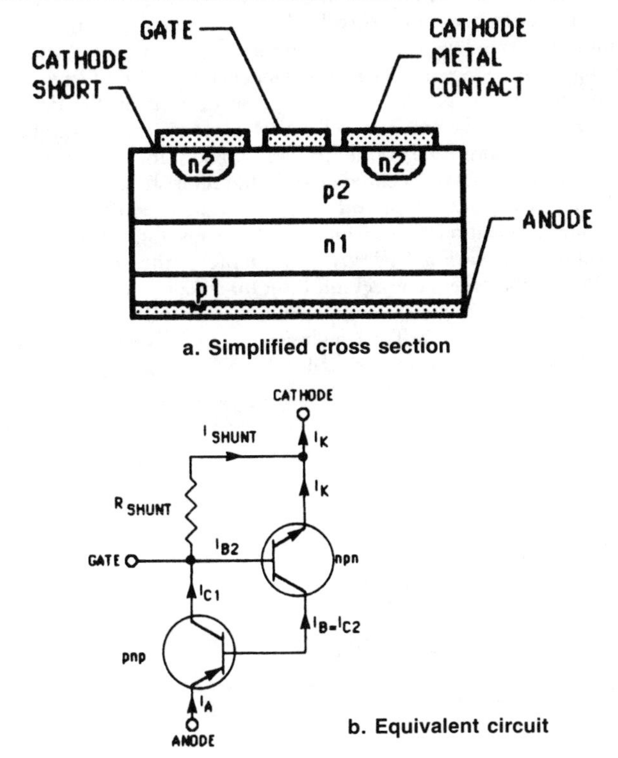

a. Simplified cross section

b. Equivalent circuit

Figure 7. Shortened cathode thyristor:

A "basic" thyristor can block current flow in both directions when in the off-state. Deviations from this are the asymmetrical thyristor (ASCR) and the reverse-conducting thyristor (RCT) which do not block current in the reverse direction. These devices were developed for their fast turn-off characteristics.

The gate turn-off thyristor (GTO) is a device which can be turned off by a negative gate current. A simplified device cross section is shown in *Figure 8*.[6] High-power SCRs and GTOs are typically used at low frequencies, while controlling hundreds or thousands of amperes.

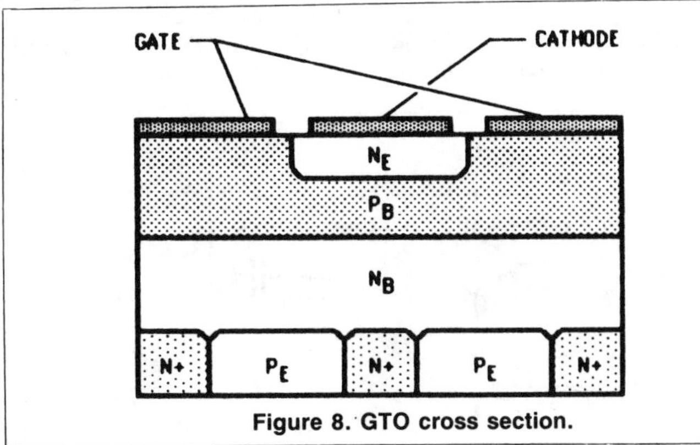

Figure 8. GTO cross section.

Power MOSFETs

Over the last eight years, power MOS transistors have changed from a laboratory curiosity to a strong competitor in the power semiconductor market. By 1990, it is expected that the power MOSFET market will reach $1 billion.

The MOSFET is a voltage-driven device in which a gate, isolated by silicon dioxide from the conductive channel, controls the flow of the drain-to-source current *Figure 9*. Two successively diffused junctions define the channel length — hence, the double-diffused MOS (DMOS) name. To achieve high-channel packing density, the drain is placed on the opposite side of the source and gate. Highly conductive polysilicon layers, isolated to silicon dioxide, are used for the gate electrode, thus allowing for the source metal to continuously cover the whole device.

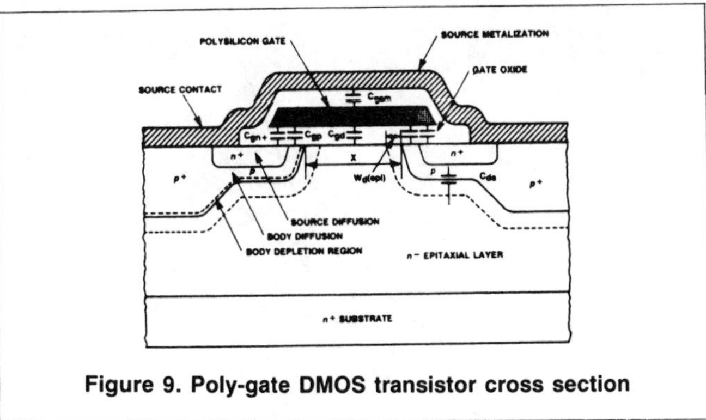

Figure 9. Poly-gate DMOS transistor cross section

Two factors influence optimal MOSFET design: device cell layout and the operating voltage. As devices are designed for minimum on-resistance per area, junction impurity profiles and drain resistivity must be properly selected. *Figure 10a* shows the resistive components of the device on-resistance which must be minimized. Current density is increased by combining a large number of elementary cells into a large power device *Figure 10b*.[7] Sixty thousand cells are combined into a high-power DMOS FET recently fabricated by Siliconix, giving a total source perimeter of 360 cm in a 200 by 200 mil chip.

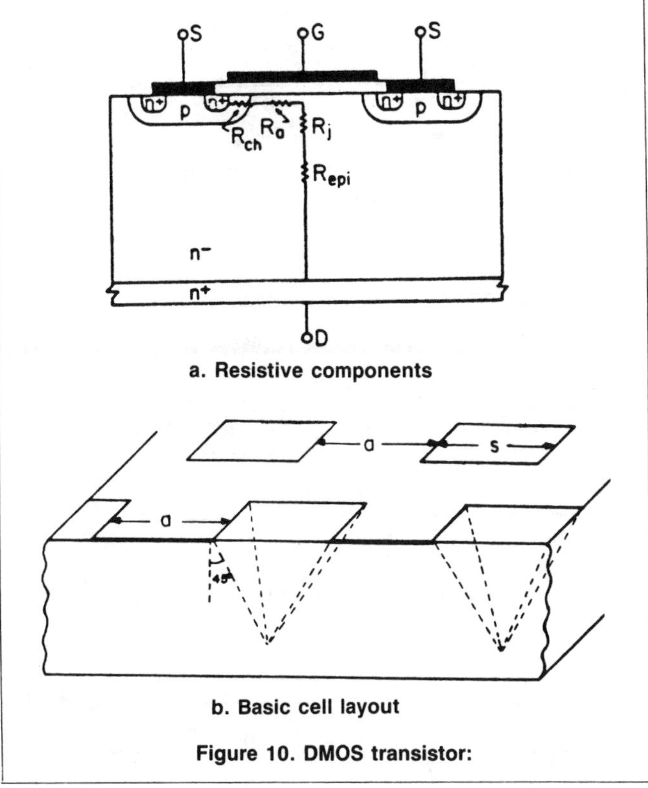

a. Resistive components

b. Basic cell layout

Figure 10. DMOS transistor:

Presently, the DMOS FET has become more cost effective than the bipolar transistor in applications requiring device breakdown below 100V. As new DMOS FETs become available, this crossover limit moves to higher voltages. One of the key parameters in this race is the specific on-resistance. *Figure 11* shows the evolution of this parameter, including predictions, for Siliconix power DMOS FETs. The solid line represents the silicon theoretical limit.

Static Induction Transistors

Static induction transistors (SITs) are short-channel junction FETs in which the current, flowing vertically between the source and drain, is controlled by the height of an electrostatically-induced potential barrier under the source *Figure 12*. Because the channel current is due to majority carriers (electrons),

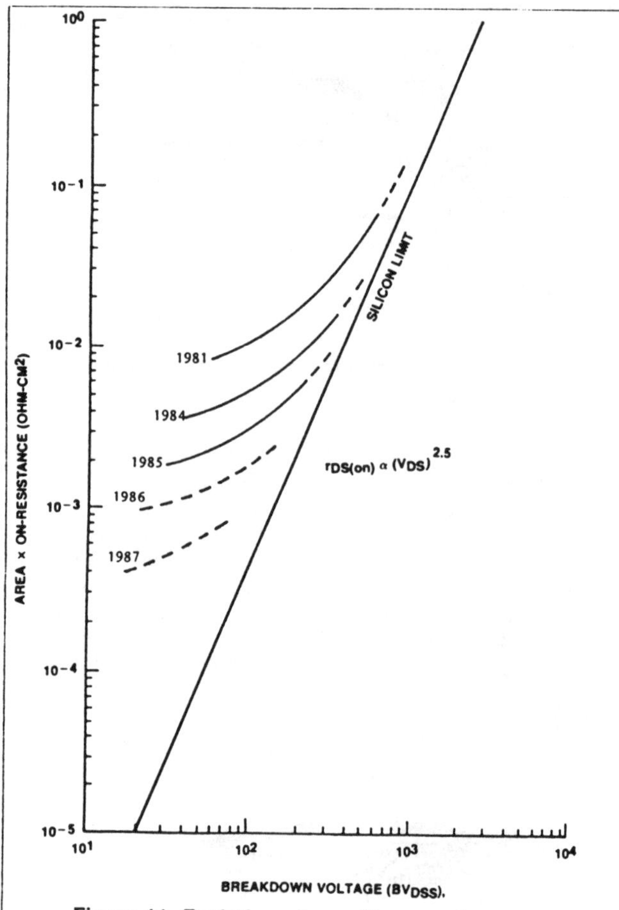

Figure 11. Evolution of specific on-resistance for power DMOS transistors.

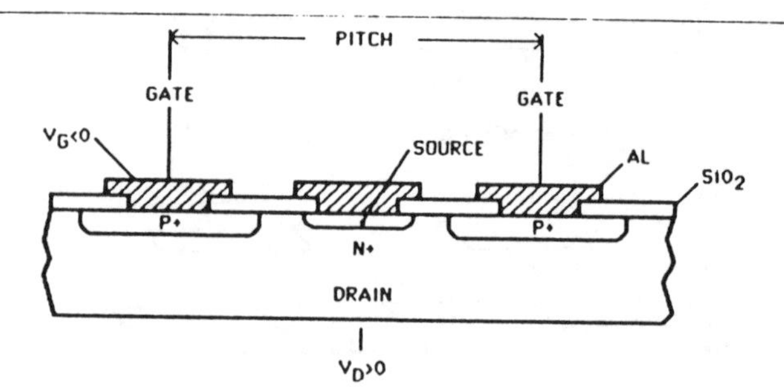

Figure 12. Surface-gate SIT cross section. [8]

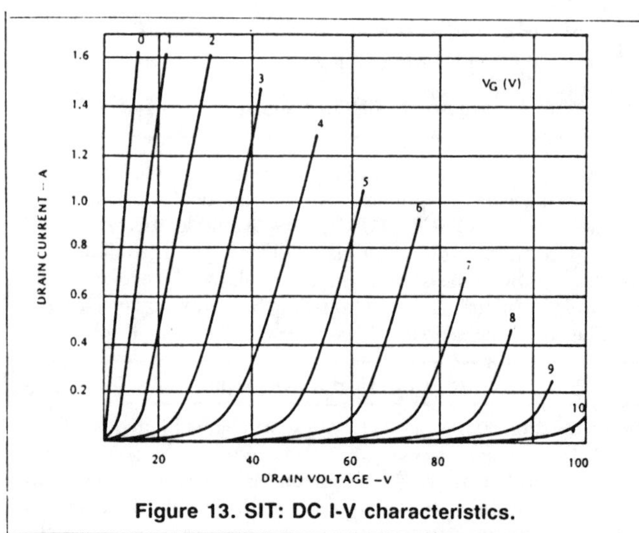

Figure 13. SIT: DC I-V characteristics.

minority-carrier-stored-charge (hole) effects are eliminated. Moreover, as the electrons travel between drain and source at maximum saturated velocity, SITs can operate at high speed while under high bias voltage.[8] The short-channel effect in the SIT results in an exponential dependence of the drain current on the drain voltage *Figure 13*. Hence, the SIT I-V characteristics are similar to that of a vacuum tube triode. By comparison, the bipolar and DMOS transistors have "pentode-like" characteristics.

SITs perform better than other conventional semiconductor devices in applications requiring simultaneous high-speed and high-voltage operation. *Figure 14* depicts the theoretical breakdown-voltage frequency-cutoff limit for silicon semiconductor devices. The figure includes a comparison of state-of-the-art bipolar, MOS transistors, and SITs. The conclusion — the SIT operates closer to the silicon theoretical materials limit.

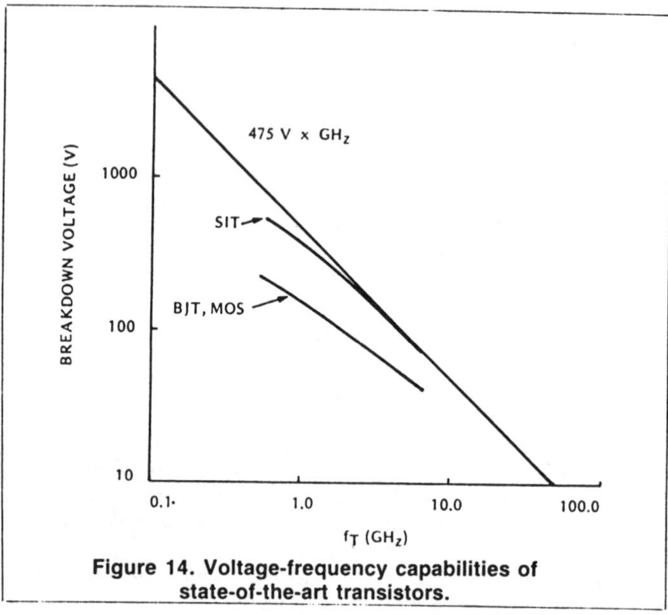

Figure 14. Voltage-frequency capabilities of state-of-the-art transistors.

Merged MOS-grated Devices

By combining bipolar and MOS transistors into single "merged" devices, improved terminal characteristics may be achieved.[9,10] *Figure 15* shows some of the possible bipolar-MOS combinations, which produce devices with the high input impedance of MOS

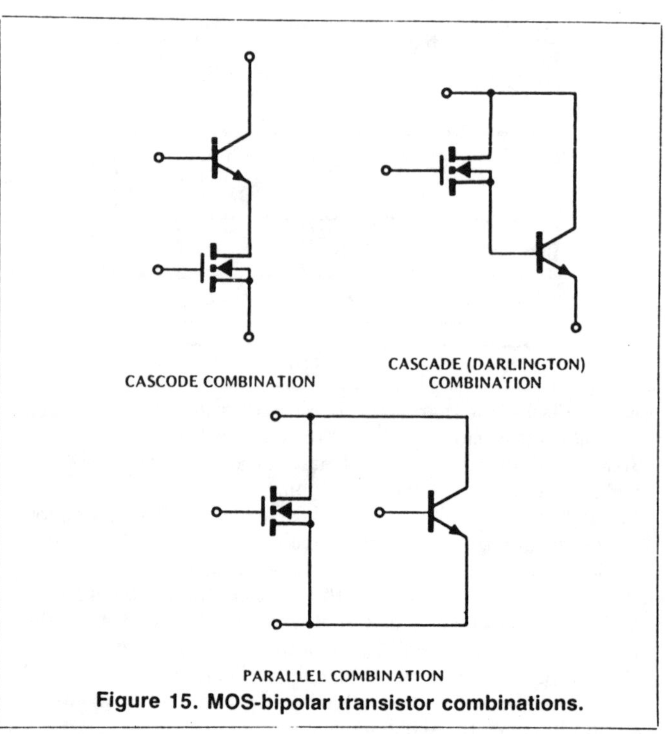

Figure 15. MOS-bipolar transistor combinations.

transistors and the low saturation voltage and high current-carrying capability of high-voltage bipolar transistors. In *Figure 16*, a performance comparison is made between high-voltage bipolar, MOS, and bipolar-MOS transistor combinations during inductive switching.[10]

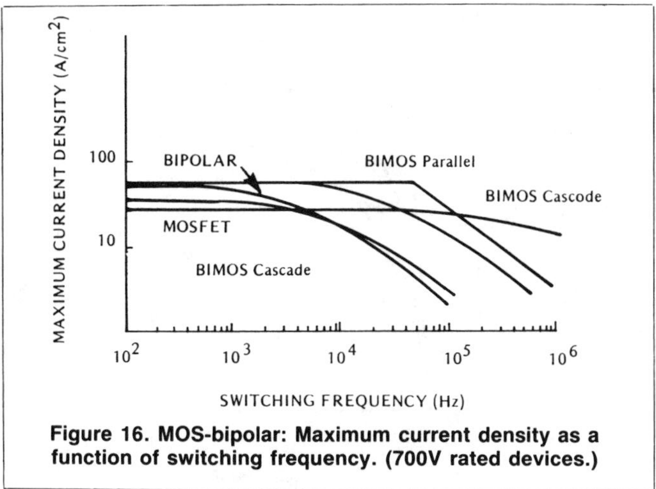

Figure 16. MOS-bipolar: Maximum current density as a function of switching frequency. (700V rated devices.)

By merging two lateral DMOS transistors in a back-to-back configuration, a novel switching device with triac-like characteristics[11] (called "TRIMOS") is obtained. A TRIMOS cross section and equivalent circuit are shown in *Figure 17*.

Overvoltage, overcurrent, and temperature-sensing functions may be easily integrated on a DMOS FET chip, thus creating a "smart" power device *Figure 18*. For DMOS FETs which are as large as 250 by 250 mils, these "sense" functions add to the device capabilities without a significant increase in area and, hence, cost. Several companies are now developing such "SMART" transistors.

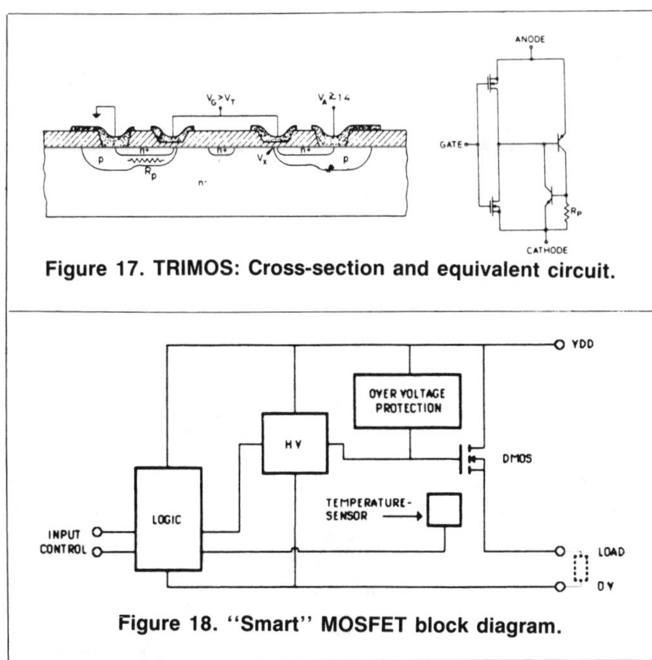

Figure 17. TRIMOS: Cross-section and equivalent circuit.

Figure 18. "Smart" MOSFET block diagram.

MOS-grated Conductivity Modulated Devices

MOS-grated conductivity modulated devices (CMD) represent a new class of power devices which combine bipolar and MOS capabilitis. One of the best known MOS-CMDs is the insulated gate transistor (IGT), also referred to as GEMFET or COMFET.

A typical IGT cross section and its equivalent circuit are shown in *Figure 19*. This figure shows that an IGT is similar to a vertical power DMOS transistor, with the exception of the p/n junction which represents the device anode.[12] The device is controlled by applying the proper polarity voltage to the gate.

IGT operation relies on the minority carrier injection by the backside p/n junction. As shown in *Figure 19b*, the IGT is equivalent to a four-layer, SCR-like device in parallel with a DMOS transistor. The IGT is designed to prevent the parasitic SCR from latching. This behavior is accomplished by shorting the npn section of the SCR. The anode p/n junction produces an offset voltage when the IGT is on. A typical intermediate-voltage characteristic is shown in *Figure 20*. The similarity with DMOS I-V characteristics is obvious. As minority carriers are injected by the anode junction, they will lower ("modulate") the conductivity of the high resistivity "n" region. Hence, the IGT has a lower dynamic on-resistance than a DMOS transistor fabricated on the same die area and epitaxial

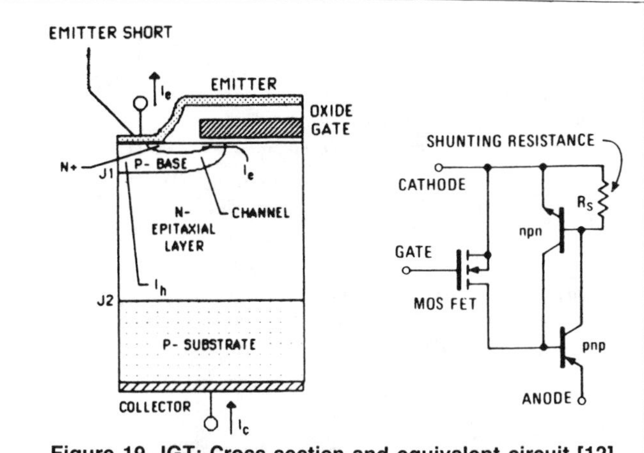

Figure 19. IGT: Cross section and equivalent circuit.[12]

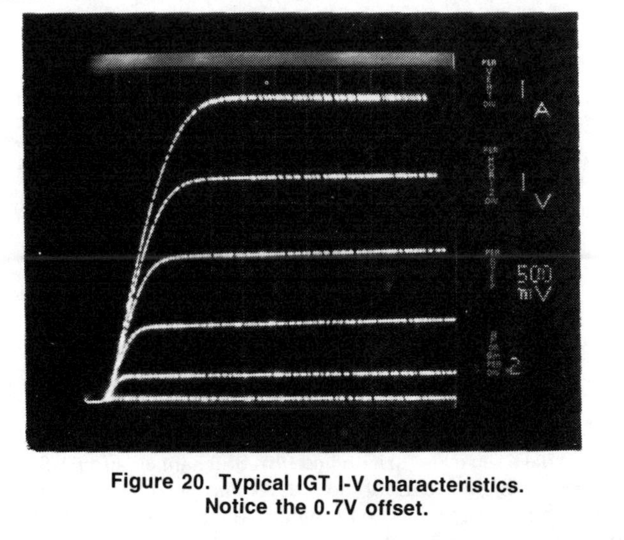

Figure 20. Typical IGT I-V characteristics. Notice the 0.7V offset.

layer resistivity. *Figure 21* shows a comparison between equivalent DMOS transistors and IGTs.[13] This shows that the IGT has a definite on-resistance advantage over the DMOS transistor for breakdown voltages above 300V.

Another IGT advantage is that complementary devices have the same die size. This fact results from the "symmetry" of the conductivity modulation effects for high resistivity n- and p-type material. By comparison, p-channel DMOS transistors require about two times the area of their n-channel counterparts *Figure 22*.[14]

One IGT disadvantage is its relatively long turn-off time, which is due to the presence of the minority carrier charge in the base of the large pnp parasitic bipolar. Switching times are in the tens of microseconds range and depend upon the gate drive circuit.

The latching current of an IGT may be modified by adjusting the value of the base shorting resistor of the npn parasitic transistor. As the latching current is lowered to the mA range, the device becomes a MOS-gated SCR. This device cannot be turned off by the gate.

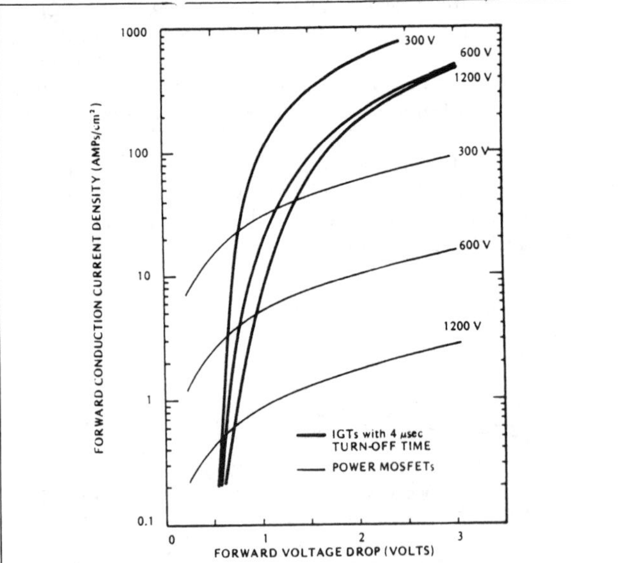

Figure 21. Forward conduction current density vs forward voltage drop for high-voltage IGTs and DMOS FETs.[13]

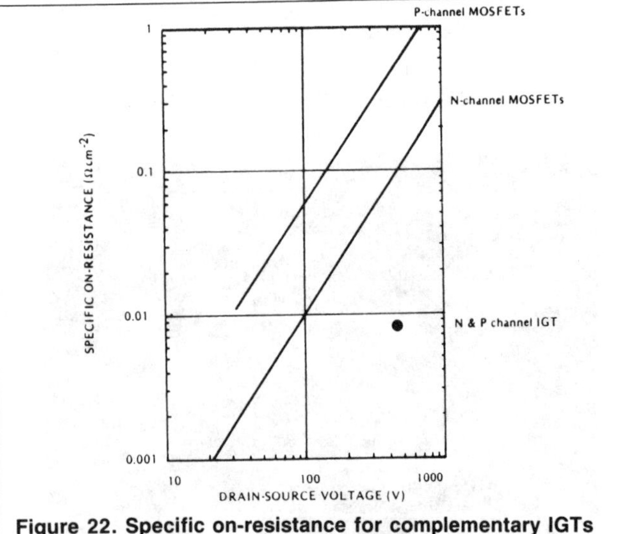

Figure 22. Specific on-resistance for complementary IGTs

Recently, new MOS-gated CMDs were reported by GE.[15] These devices have separate turn-on and turn-off channels *Figure 23* and operate at higher current densities than the IGTs *Figure 24*. Although the switching speed is similar to that of IGTs, much better dV/dt rates are achieved.

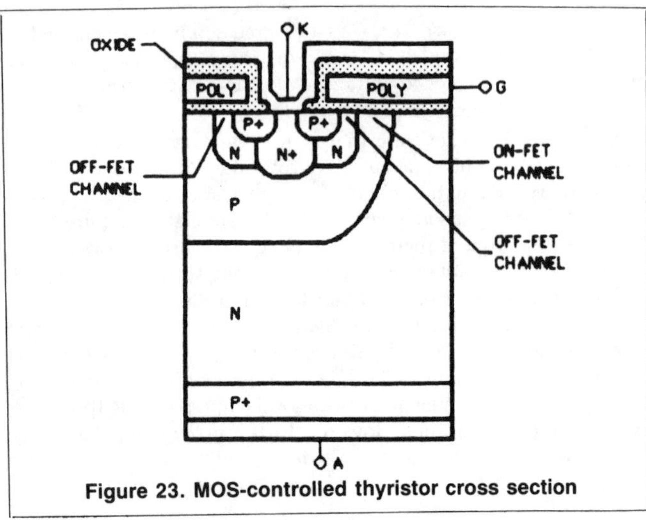

Figure 23. MOS-controlled thyristor cross section

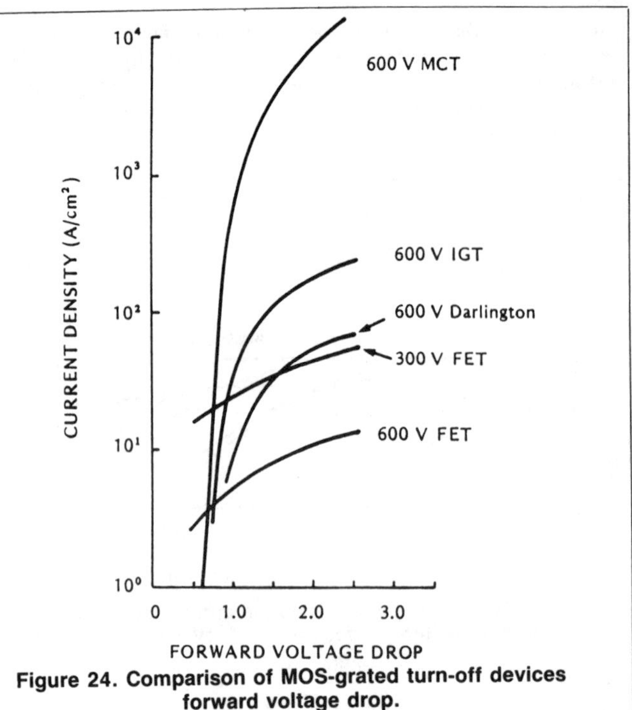

Figure 24. Comparison of MOS-grated turn-off devices forward voltage drop.

Packaging

Rapid advances in power-control devices and circuits face a fundamental limit — dissipation of the power that is the ***natural*** by-product. This limit is further aggrevated by the growth of the average die size. The forecast increase in discrete devices is shown in *Figure 25* [3].

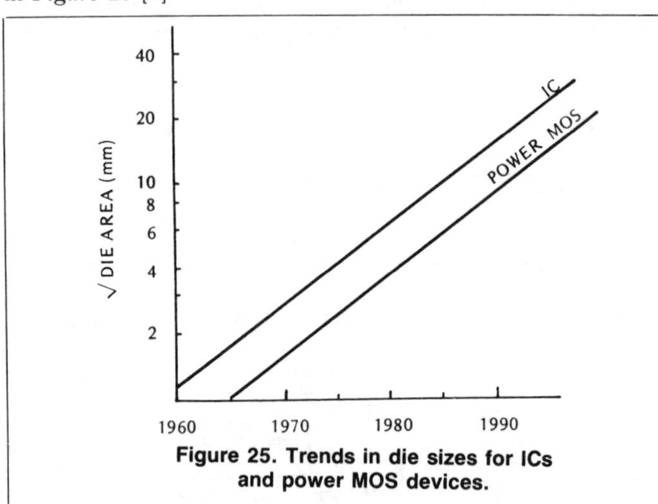

Figure 25. Trends in die sizes for ICs and power MOS devices.

Innovations in power dissipation are essential if future developments are to continue at the same pace as in the last few years. The fundamentals of power handling have not changed, but several improvements promise to significantly enhance thermal performance. One example is seen in *Figure 26*, which shows the

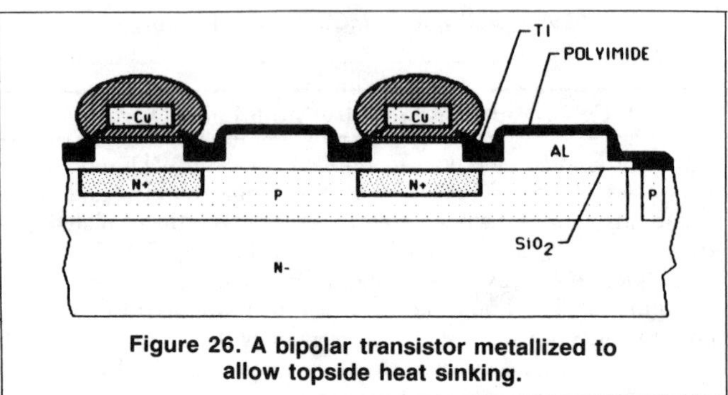

Figure 26. A bipolar transistor metallized to allow topside heat sinking.

use of built-up metal on the emitters to provide both electrical and thermal contact. The use of topside thermal heat sinking significantly increases power dissipation if the package is designed to use it to full advantage.[16]

Advances in power packaging depend on improvements in both materials and assembly techniques. One recently developed hermetic module, shown in *Figure 27*, provides both high-current, high-voltage capability and high power dissipation. This module may be configured to handle a variety of configurations and is capable of dissipating 350W.

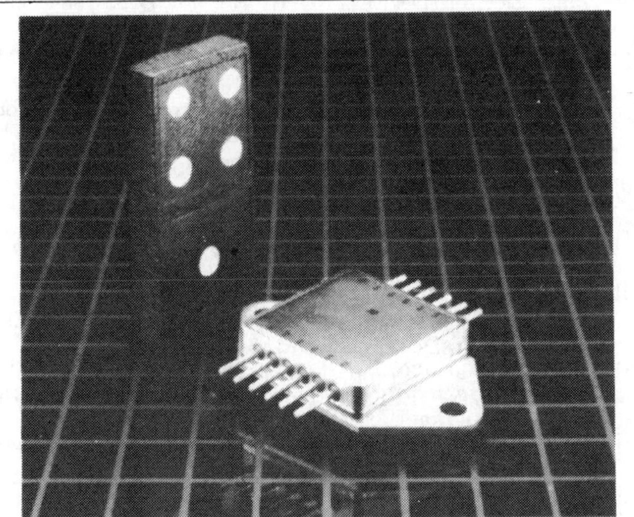

Figure 27. A recently developed hermetic module that has high-current, high voltage, and power dissipation capabilities. (Siliconix)

The large number of discrete power-switching devices indicates both the breadth and the rate of change in power electronics. A decrease in the rate of change is not foreseen before the end of the 80s due to the nature of the new power devices being developed. The combination of majority and minority carries devices promises to provide devices with a continous spectrum of current, voltage, and switching characteristics. However, it is useful to provide a basis for comparison such as that contained in *Table 1.* This table compares the electrical parameters of a variety of power-switching devices.[2] An additional comparison is provided in *Figure 28*, where the normalized transconductance of bipolar transistors, power MOS transistors, insulated-gate transistors, and SCRs is compared.

The increase in device performance anticipated by the end of the decade is best shown by updating two figures used in the introduction. *Figure 29* shows the improvements in power-handling capability that can be expected over the next five years.[2] This graph indicates that the most significant gain will occur in the most recently introduced devices. The power ratings and application ranges of power transistors is shown in *Figure 30*[1], and the projected use of power-switching devices through the year 2000 is shown in *Figure 31*.[17]

Table 1. A comparison of the characteristics of power-switching devices.

DEVICE CHARACTERISTIC	POWER BIPOLAR TRANSISTOR	GATE TURN-OFF THYRISTOR	POWER MOSFET	POWER JFET/SIT	POWER MOS-IGT
NORMALLY ON/OFF	OFF	OFF	OFF	ON	OFF
REVERSE BLOCKING CAPABILITY (VOLTS)	<50 V	500-2500 V	0 V	0 V	200-2500 V
BLOCKING VOLTAGE RANGE (VOLTS)	50-500 V	500-2500 V	50-500 V	50-500 V	200-2500 V
FORWARD CONDUCTION CURRENT DENSITY (A/cm^2)	40	200	10	4	200
SURGE CURRENT HANDING CAPABILITY	3x	10x	5x	5x	5x
MAXIMUM SWITCHING SPEED	50 kHz	10 kHz	20 MHz	200 MHz	50 kHz
GATE DRIVE POWER	High	Medium	Low	Low	Very-Low
dV/dt CAPABILITY	Medium	Low	High	High	High
dI/dt CAPABILITY	Medium	Low	High	High	High
RADIATION TOLERANCE	Poor	Very Poor	Moderate	Good	Moderate

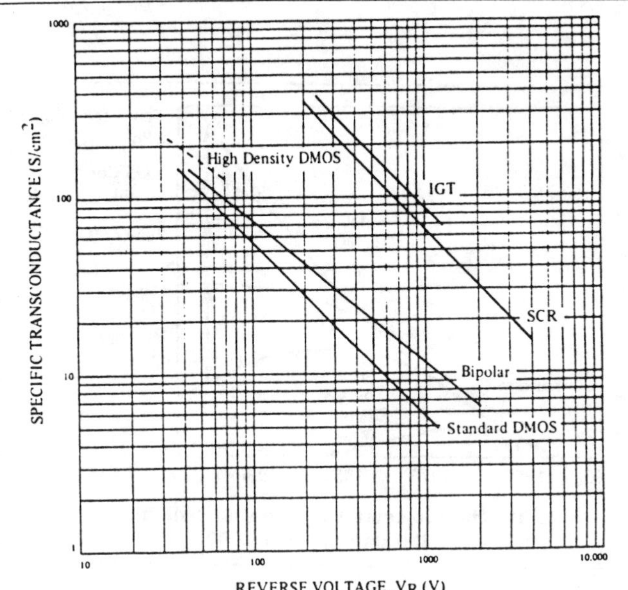

Figure 28. A comparison of the normalized specific transconductance of power-switching devices.

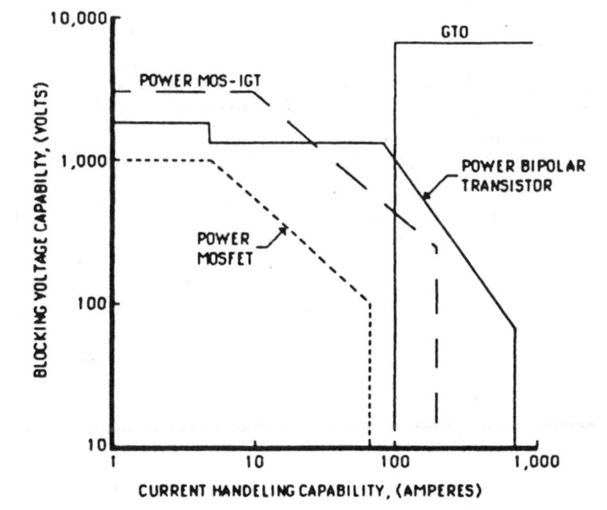

Figure 29. Projected 1990 power rating of power-switching transistors.

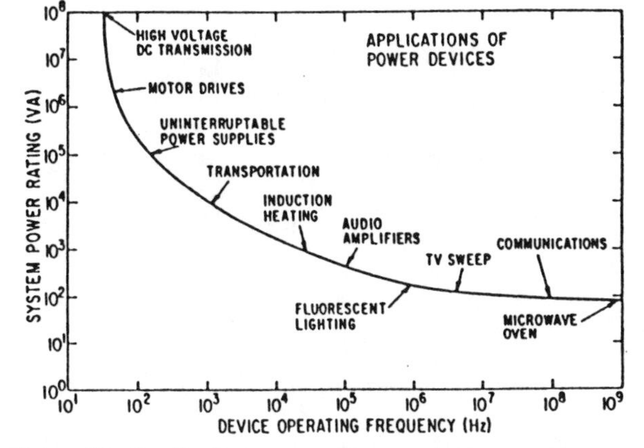

Figure 30. Application ranges of power-switching devices.

In summary, power-switching device technology will continue to evolve as the electrical and thermal limits of materials are better understood. This evolution will provide designers with the opportunity to continually improve system performance.

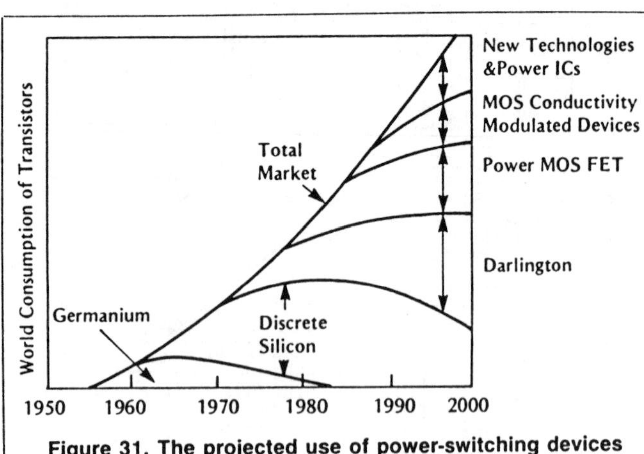

Figure 31. The projected use of power-switching devices through the year 2000.

References

[1] Baliga, B.J., "Silicon Power Field Controlled Devices and Integrated Circuits in 'Silicon Integrated Circuits' " Part B, Academic Press, 1981.

[2] Baliga, B.J., et al., "Power Transistors: Device Design and Applications," IEEE Press, 1984, pp. 1-17.

[3] Adler, M., et al., "The Evolution of Power Device Technology," IEEE Trans. Electron Devices, ED-31, No. 11, Nov. 1984, pp. 1570-1591.

[4] Unitrode, "Symmetrical-Breakdown Bipolar Transistor," EDN, Nov. 15, 1984, p. 150.

[5] Sze, S.M., "Physics of Semiconductor Devices," Chapter 4, Wiley & Sons, 1982.

[6] Nagano, T., et a., "A Snubber-less GTO," PCI-Motorcon, 1982 Proceedings, p. 383-387.

[7] Hu, C., et al., "Optimum Design of Power MOSFETS," IEEE Trans, Electron Devices, ED-31, No. 12, Dec. 1984, pp. 1693-1700.

[8] Cogan, A., et al., "High Performance Microwave SIT," IEDM - 1983 Proc, pp. 221-224.

[9] Blanchard, R., et al., "A New High-Power Transistor for High-Current High-Voltage Switching Applications," Proceedings Powercon-8, 1981, Paper N1-1.

[10] Adler, M., "A Comparison Between Device Types," PCI Meeting, 1982 Proceedings, pp. 371-374.

[11] Plummer, J.D., "Insulated Gate Planar Thyristors," IEEE Trans. Electron Devices, ED-27, Feb. 1980, pp. 380-394.

[12] Baliga, B.J., et al., "The Insulated Gate Transistor, A New Three-Terminal MOS-Controlled Bipolar Power Device," IEEE Trans. Electron Devices, Vol. ED-31, 1984, pp. 821-828.

[13] Cohn, T., et al., "Comparison of 300-, 600-, and 1200-V N-Channel IGTs," IEEE Electron Devices Letters, EDL-6, April 1985, pp. 161-163.

[14] Russel, T.P., "High-Power COMFET with a p-Type Channel," IEEE Electron Devices Letters, EDL-5, Nov. 1984, pp. 437-439.

[15] Temple, V.A.K., "MOS Controlled Thyristors," IEDM 1984 Proceedings, pp. 282-285.

[16] Driscoll, T., "Design Application and Characterization of New Power Semiconductor Devices for PWM Drives," PCI Proceedings, April 1983, pp. 26-36.

[17] Ruggles, T.E., "Power Transistors," EE Times, March 15, 1982, p. 102-104.

Paper 3.7

Designing Intelligent Muscle into Industrial Motion Control

THOMAS M. JAHNS, MEMBER, IEEE

Abstract—**Power electronics integration provides a key approach to reducing the cost and increasing the reliability of future motion control systems. Power integrated circuit (PIC) technology has developed rapidly during recent years, making it possible to combine substantial power handling and sophisticated control functions on the same silicon chip. Sensor integration techniques are further extending the capabilities of new PIC designs. Following a brief discussion of the underlying PIC semiconductor technology, this tutorial paper reviews reported PIC applications in a broad spectrum of stepper, dc, brushless dc, and ac motor drive configurations. PIC designs used in motor drives covering a range of power ratings from < 100 W to > 10 kW are surveyed. Strengths and limitations of present PIC technology are discussed, revealing likely directions for future PIC developments and their potential impact on tomorrow's motion control systems.**

I. Introduction

MOTION CONTROL is an extremely pervasive need throughout industry for accomplishing everything from controlling a pump's speed to accurately positioning a robot's arm. Despite the wide range of specific applications, the generalized motor drive configuration shown in Fig. 1 applies to a wide range of industrial motion controllers. Electrical power applied to the motor flows through the power converter, where it is regulated under authority of the controller, using feedback information from the available sensors. Interface amplifiers or level shifters are typically required to handle the large voltage differences separating the controller and the power semiconductors imbedded in the power converter.

Although motion controllers find wide use throughout industry, there are vast numbers of electric motors that are still directly connected to utility power for constant speed operation, in spite of the potential advantages of adjustable-speed operation. The observation that more than half of all electric power in the United States is consumed by electric motors [1] gives some perspective on the huge scope of opportunities for motion/speed control in commercial, residential, and industrial applications.

Despite widespread opportunities for significant energy savings and productivity improvement from the introduction of adjustable-speed control, many of these remain unrealized. Long-standing concerns about the cost and reliability of the power electronics continue to retard new motion control applications in industry and other market sectors. Payback

Manuscript received January 8, 1989.

The author is with Corporate Research and Development, General Electric Corporation, Schenectady, NY 12301.

IEEE Log Number 9038041.

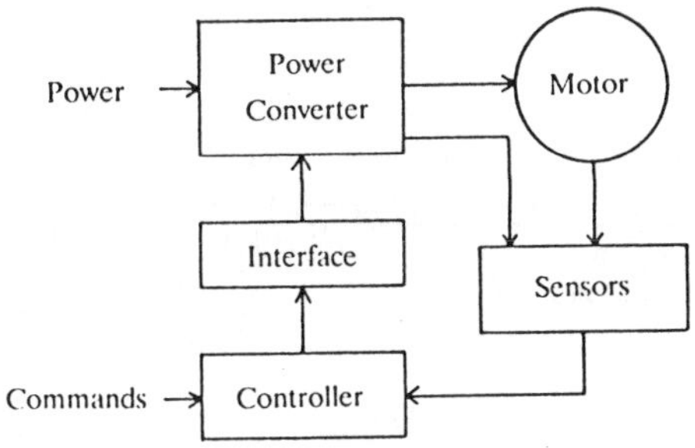

Fig. 1. Generalized motor drive block diagram.

periods must be shortened and maintenance/downtime costs shrunk to almost nothing if adjustable-speed drives are to achieve significant increases in their industrial market penetration.

One of the key strategies being sought to meet the dual challenges of cost and reliability in industrial power electronics is component integration. The rapid development of power integrated circuit (PIC) technology during the 1980's has been responsible for major progress towards the desired objective of power electronics integration [2], [3]. The impact of these PIC's has been greatly amplified by the simultaneous development of important new classes of MOS-gated power semiconductors with high-impedance input gates that are highly compatible with PIC output drive capabilities [4].

Motion control has been one of most important application areas for new PIC's, reflecting the significant implementation advantages they offer. Returning to Fig. 1, this new technology has made it possible to combine control, interface, and power-handling functions on a single piece of silicon, achieving a powerful integration of intelligence and muscle in new motion control systems. Recent PIC technology developments bring sensors onboard the silicon as well.

The purpose of this tutorial paper is to review state-of-the-art PIC technology as it applies to motion control systems. Capabilities and limitations of the present generation of motion control PIC's will be discussed, with a clear focus on PIC functionality rather than on the underlying semiconductor physics. Although specific PIC's are used occasionally for purposes of illustration, this paper should not be misinterpreted as a survey of commercial PIC product offerings. Rather, this paper will attempt to acquaint readers more generally with the opportunities for modern PIC's in new motion control systems. Likely directions for future power electronics integration efforts and the expected impact of these ongoing developments will be addressed in the concluding section of the paper.

Reprinted from *IEEE Trans. Ind. Electron.*, vol. 37, no. 5, pp. 329–341, October 1990.

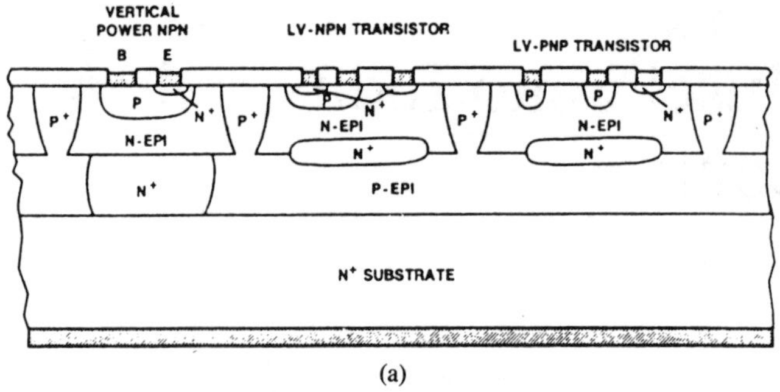

(a)

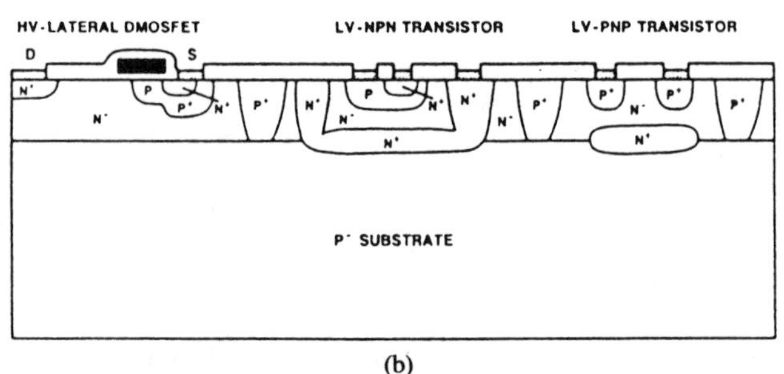

(b)

Fig. 2. Examples of two families of PIC structures [7]: (a) Smart discrete PIC incorporating high-voltage vertical devices; (b) high-voltage integrated circuit (HVIC) including high-voltage lateral devices.

II. Power Integrated Circuits

A. Definition and Underlying Technology

A PIC is defined for purposes of this paper as an integrated circuit combining both logic-level control and/or protection features with the power handling capability of supplying at least 1 A (total) to the load or withstanding at least 100 V. Although far from ironclad, this PIC definition sets some useful limits on the present discussion. The popular term "smart power" will not be used as a general synonym for PIC's in order to avoid the interesting but diversionary debate about what constitutes "smarts."

Only a brief introduction to PIC technology is presented here; interested readers are referred elsewhere for more detailed reviews [5], [6]. The many different PIC processes and architectures that have been developed around the world can generally be separated into two major broad categories [7]: 1) Smart discrete PIC's, combining vertical power device structures with driver and protection circuits on the same silicon chip and 2) high-voltage integrated circuits (HVIC's), consisting of low-voltage analog and digital logic circuitry in combination with high-voltage lateral power devices. Sample architectures for these two types of PIC's are provided in Fig. 2 to illustrate distinguishing features.

Both bipolar and MOSFET power transistors have been successfully implemented as the vertical power device in smart discrete PIC configurations, such as the one shown in Fig. 2(a) [8]. A variety of low-voltage NMOS, CMOS, and bipolar devices can be added to the process to provide logic and analog signal conditioning functions [9]. More than one vertical power device can be implemented on the same chip, but the basic smart discrete PIC architecture is limited to bussed terminal (e.g., common collector/drain) configurations since the back of the chip is shared as a power terminal by all of the vertical devices. Automotive applications have spurred significant amounts of development work on smart discrete PIC's for multiplexed power switching [10], leading to processes yielding high-quality vertical power devices combined with sophisticated low-voltage logic circuitry.

HVIC's incorporate lateral high-voltage device in place of the vertical structures so that the back side of the IC is no longer used as an active electrical terminal for the PIC. Three basic isolation techniques [7]—self-, junction-, and dielectric isolation—are widely used to permit HVIC subcircuits to operate at widely separated voltage potentials. Fig. 2(b) illustrates a junction-isolated structure, which uses reverse-biased p-n junctions to form "islands" in the thin n-epitaxial layer for the isolated HVIC subcircuits, with the p-substrate held at the most negative potential in the circuit [11].

Charge control techniques have been developed for distributing the electric field in the HVIC epitaxial layer so that lateral power transistors can be flexibly designed with breakdown voltages of 500 V or more set by the device physical dimensions [12]. A wide variety of bipolar, CMOS, and I^2L devices can be accommodated in the same HVIC process to form analog and digital logic subcircuits operating at different potentials but communicating via high-voltage level-shifting lateral devices.

Although voltage and current ratings of PIC's are continually expanding, Fig. 3 provides a glimpse of the present voltage-current limits of existing PIC processes. The vertical power device incorporated in the smart discrete PIC tends to yield the highest volt-amp product in the Fig. 3 spectrum (in the vicinity of 3 kVA), but the circuit flexibility tends to be limited by the shared substrate terminal constraint described above. In comparison, the lateral power devices provided by the HVIC process are generally limited to lower currents (in the vicinity of 100 mA for 500 V devices), but the HVIC circuit flexibility is distinctly higher. It should come as little surprise that PIC manufacturers are developing new merged processes to combine the best features of the smart discrete and HVIC architectures [13].

B. PIC Configurations and Packaging

Power IC's are used in a variety of physical configurations, often in conjunction with discrete power semiconductors. Fig. 4 illustrates three of the most common configurations. The monolithic PIC assembly (Fig. 4(a)) combines all of the required power handling, logic, and interface functions on a single piece of silicon, which represents the highest level of assembly integration. Achieving this high integration level typically extracts penalties in the form of extra silicon processing costs due to additional masking steps or performance limitations in the logic or power handling sections. For example, silicon area utilization for a power device included in a smart discrete PIC may be poorer than for the same power device designed as a separate chip.

In light of these tradeoffs, hybrid PIC assemblies (Fig. 4(b)) are sometimes adopted so that the logic and high-voltage interface sections can be optimized on a separate HVIC chip that is independent of the power device [14]. This

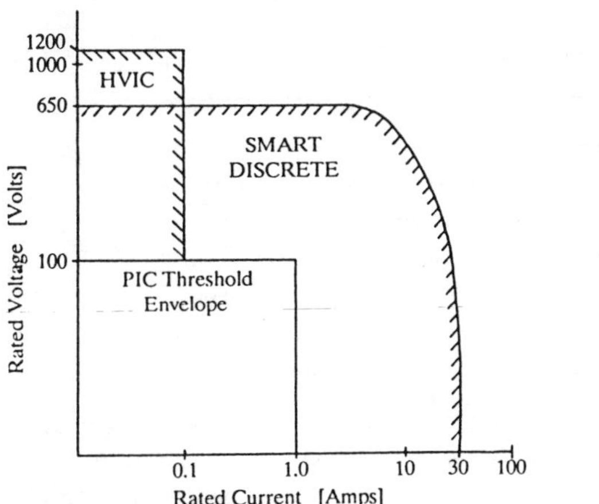

Fig. 3. Approximate voltage-current ratings envelope of present-day PIC's.

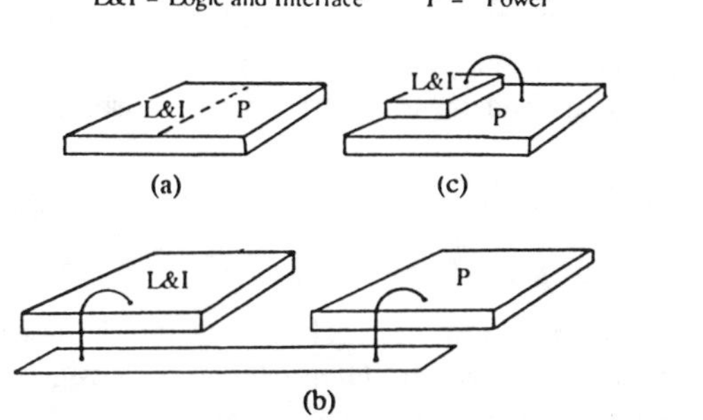

Fig. 4. Alternative PIC assembly configurations: (a) Monolithic; (b) hybrid; (c) chip-on-chip.

approach becomes increasingly attractive as the ratings of the power section (current and voltage) are raised, increasing the difficulty of achieving a practical monolithic PIC solution. Unfortunately, additional packaging costs are entailed with the hybrid configuration in order to mount and interconnect two (or more) chips on a common substrate. Taking this approach a step further, the HVIC and power device can be individually packaged for interconnection in the macrocircuit. However, the growing physical separation of the logic and power functions may add undesirable signal delays and complicate protection, diluting the desired integration advantages.

As a significant variation of the hybrid approach, chip-on-chip PIC configurations (Fig. 4(c)) provide an additional degree of freedom to utilize the vertical dimension by stacking the logic/interface PIC on top of the power device [15]. Electrical isolation and thermal management of the upper chip requires careful attention, but the limited surface area within standard device packages can be used very effectively with this approach. Furthermore, the PIC is well positioned to minimize interconnection (e.g., wire bond) lengths and to sense the power device temperature more directly for fast thermal protection.

Package choice is critical in determining the power handling capabilities of any PIC since the package limits the chip's maximum safe power dissipation. A variety of standard and custom packages have been developed for PIC's ranging from commercial plastic single- and dual-inline packages to military-grade hermetic packages [16]. Power dissipation capabilities for these packages range from 2 to 50 W for a 75°C PIC case temperature. PIC's have been designed to deliver 2 kVA or more to motor loads within these power dissipation constraints [17].

C. PIC Use Evaluation Factors

The decision to use a PIC in a specific application must be based on a thorough engineering evaluation weighing PIC advantages and disadvantages on a case-by-case basis. Key evaluation factors are summarized in Table I.

PIC technology improvements are gradually eroding some of the disadvantages listed in Table I by lowering PIC processing costs and reducing the associated performance compromises. In addition, PIC chip development costs are being reduced by new CAD design tools [18] and the increasing availability of PIC semi-custom [19] and standard cell [20] processes. New opportunities for PIC's in industrial motion control applications are being opened as a result of these advances, as described in Sections IV and V.

III. Sensor Integration Technology

Sensors play critical roles in motion control systems for purposes of feedback control and protection. Nevertheless, the cost, weight, and volume associated with the sensors and their signal conditioning tend to be underestimated when undertaking a motor drive design. Efforts are under way at many locations to reduce these penalties by integrating the sensors into the power devices and PIC's, as described below.

A. Integrated Current Sensors

Current sensors have special significance in motion control systems since the torque in virtually any type of electric motor is directly related (often linearly) to the motor winding current. Furthermore, fast current sensors are crucial to protecting the power switches from dangerous overload and fault conditions. Conventional current sensors suffer from disadvantages that include the power dissipation in shunt resistors and the significant weight/volume of current transformers.

The development of a variety of new MOS-gated power devices (power MOSFET's, IGBT's, etc.) has opened important opportunities for integrating the current sensor directly into the power device. By taking advantage of the cellular nature of these devices, device designers can segregate a few of the identical device cells to divert a small but fixed fraction of the main device current to a separate sensing terminal. This small current signal can then be conveniently amplified and conditioned to provide a valuable device current feedback signal. A sketch of this integrated current configuration based on classic current mirror techniques is sketched in Fig. 5 for a power MOSFET [21].

Both power MOSFET's and IGBT's with integrated current sensors are now available from device manufacturers with ratings up to several hundreds of volts and several tens of amps. These integrated sensors can be manufactured with very good linearity and wide bandwidth, making them useful

TABLE I
PIC APPLICATION DECISION FACTORS

Advantages	Disadvantages
• **Lower assembly and inventory costs** from parts count reduction.	• **PIC chip cost may be higher** than sum of replaced components.
• **Improved reliability** by eliminating package interconnections.	• **Lack of long reliability track record** for new PIC technology.
• **Major volume and weight reductions** via circuit integration.	• **Limited PIC power handling capability** in existing packages.
• **Faster dynamic/protection response times** from on-chip logic.	• **Performance compromises** due to integrated power/logic process.
• **Improved features/protection** possible using integrated sensors.	• **High engineering cost** of developing a full-custom PIC design.

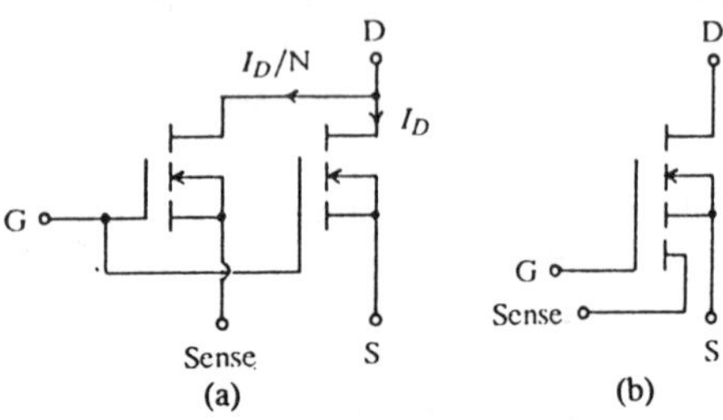

Fig. 5. Equivalent circuit and symbol for power MOSFET with integrated current sensor: (a) Schematic; (b) symbol.

for both feedback control and protection circuits. Advantages of these sensors include their negligible size and the modest incremental cost associated with the higher power device pin count. However, system designers must recognize that the integrated current sensor is not galvanically isolated from the power circuit (unlike a current transformer or Hall-effect sensor), and the sensor is designed to measure current only when the power switch is "on." As a result, special control techniques are required to properly apply these integrated current sensors in new motor drive systems [22].

B. Temperature Sensors

The power handling capability of any power device is ultimately limited by the maximum tolerable junction temperature, which is typically limited to 150°C in silicon power devices. Although solid-state temperature sensors are far from new, the ability to combine these sensors and their conditioning circuitry on the same chip as the power device being monitored opens major new opportunities for fast thermal protection. Sophisticated thermal protection schemes can be designed into the PIC logic to provide coordinated warning and shutdown protection features using integrated temperature sensors with multiple detection thresholds.

C. Integrated Hall-Effect Sensors

Hall-effect sensors are small semiconductor sheet transducers that are sensitive to magnetic field lines impinging on the sensor [23]. These sensitive magnetic sensors can be configured as either linear or digital transducers. For example, Hall-effect sensors are commonly used as discrete sensors in brushless permanent-magnet motors to detect rotor position, delivering digitized level outputs in the presence of the spinning rotor magnets. As linear sensors, the Hall-effect transducers are used to measure the magnetic field encircling an adjacent current conductor, providing a galvanically isolated measurement of the instantaneous current.

Recent developments have succeeded in integrating Hall-effect sensors directly into PIC processes, providing a family of versatile sensors that complement the power devices and logic [24]. Although the full range of opportunities opened by the availability of integrated PIC Hall elements has not yet been explored, some interesting applications have already been announced, and these will be briefly discussed in Section V.

IV. INTEGRATED POWER CONVERTER APPLICATIONS

A. Smart Switch Building Block

The most basic building block of any motor drive power inverter is a single switch. Given the pervasiveness of this switch element, one can conceive of a powerful generic "smart switch" block incorporating not only the fast-switching power semiconductor device but also many of its key auxiliary functions as sketched in Fig. 6. One of the most basic functions associated with each power device is the amplifying driver interfacing the external on–off command signal to the control (gate or base) terminal of the power device. Level shifting means is envisioned, which permits the common terminal (source or emitter) of the power switch to float freely above the controller ground.

In addition, the smart switch block in Fig. 6 includes circuitry that protects the power device from dangerous electrical conditions including overcurrent, overtemperature, and overvoltage protection. This protection should be fast enough to safely turn off the device even for sudden short-circuit faults, making the switch block as indestructible (bulletproof) as possible. Diagnostic status information is delivered back to the controller by means of a level-shifted interface. Given the importance of instantaneous current information, the generic smart switch block also includes a current sensor that provides a wide-bandwidth current feedback signal (level shifted or, preferably, galavanically isolated) back to the controller.

Despite its conceptual appeal, the smart switch in Fig. 6 is too ambitious to be realizable as shown using today's PIC technology. Nevertheless, impressive progress is being made in several locations towards achieving integrated power switches that incorporate key subsets of the features included in Fig. 6. Automotive "high-side" switches developed using smart discrete PIC technology have demonstrated that driver, protection (including short circuit), and status-reporting features can be incorporated onto the same chip with the main

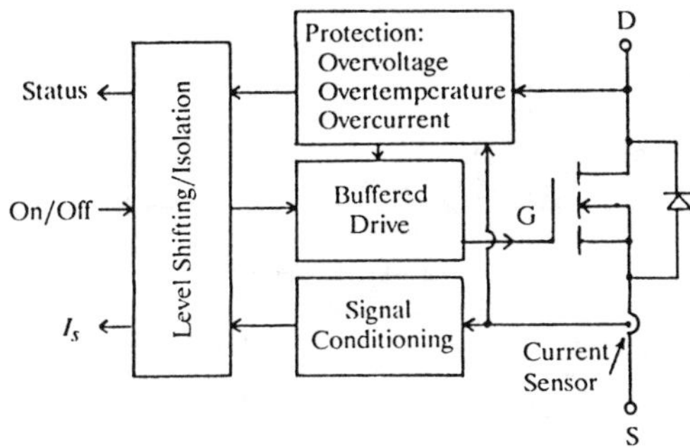

Fig. 6. Conceptual block diagram of generic smart switch module using power MOSFET.

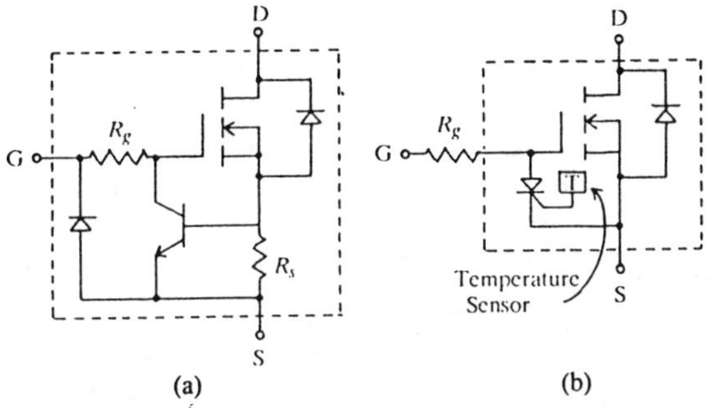

Fig. 7. Two schemes for providing power MOSFET short-circuit protection: (a) Using sensing resistor in source lead; (b) using chip-mounted temperature sensor.

power MOSFET switch [8], [25]. Consistent with automotive requirements, these high-side switches are typically rated at 50 to 100 V, delivering currents of 10 to 20 A. Higher current versions rated at 50 to 100 A have recently been reported using a chip-on-chip configuration [15]. However, these automotive PIC's are principally intended as buffered switches for energizing lamps and solenoids in multiplexed power bus systems rather than as high-frequency modulated switches for use in motor drives.

Given the importance of overcurrent protection, some smart discrete PIC's are commercially available, and these provide this single feature as an inexpensive addition to the basic power MOSFET switch. For example, the Motorola scheme shown in Fig. 7(a) uses a resistor in series with the source to develop a voltage drop that turns on an integrated n-p-n transistor, shunting the gate capacitance and turning off the 80-V power MOSFET when the source current gets too high (> 1.1 A) [26]. Alternatively, a Siemens chip-on-chip approach illustrated in Fig. 7(b) uses a small temperature-sensitive latching thyristor across the gate-source terminals to turn off the power MOSFET (rated at 50 V, 27 A) whenever the junction temperature exceeds 155°C [27]. Although simple and cost-effective, both of these approaches suffer from a need to incorporate minimum values of gate resistance R_g, which slow down the MOSFET switching times to 2 to 4 μs, limiting their usefulness in high-performance motion control applications.

Monolithic smart switch configurations more closely approaching the capabilities of the Fig. 6 conceptual scheme are presently under development at various locations. One of the more ambitious of these smart discrete PIC configurations, reported recently by SGS-Thomson incorporates a 200-V,

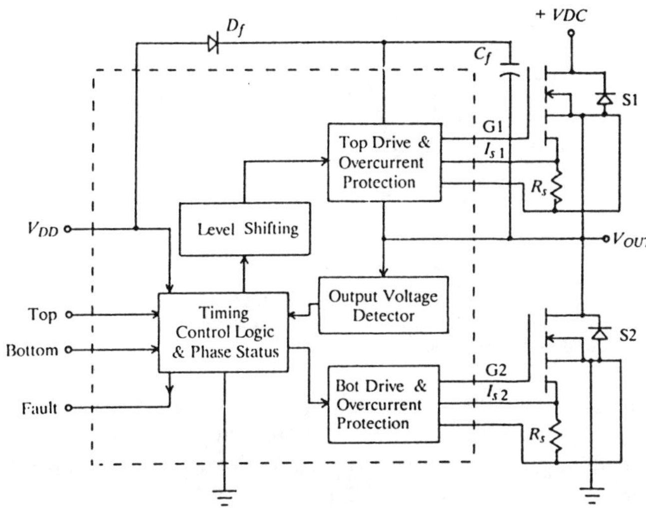

Fig. 8. Block diagram of HVIC driving two power MOSFET's with integrated current sensors in half-bridge configuration (based on Harris GS600/1).

18-A power MOSFET with protection features and a high-speed driver for sub-microsecond switching [28]. An integrated current sensor is included to provide overcurrent protection and linear current feedback using an on-chip operational amplifier. Other protection features include overtemperature and undervoltage when the supply voltage drops too low. Although level-shifting and full-status reporting capabilities are not included, this configuration illustrates the significant progress being made towards realizing sophisticated smart power switches for integral-horsepower motor drives.

B. High-Voltage Half-Bridge Drivers

Although the single power switch represents the most basic building block of any power inverter, the half-bridge consisting of two power switches connected as a series totem pole spanning the dc power bus appears as a recurring unit in many motor drive converter configurations. Output power to the motor winding is extracted from the half-bridge center point, and level shifting is typically required to refer one or both of the switch drivers to the controller ground. The controller logic must ensure that both switches are never turned on at the same time, which would short the low-impedance power bus.

Monolithic PIC's are available, which incorporate the two half-bridge switches plus the necessary level shifting at ratings up to at least 50 V and 8 A. These low-voltage half-bridge PIC's (< 100 V) are typically designed with bipolar transistors (2 n-p-n's or an n-p-n, p-n-p pair). Multiple-chip PIC configurations are generally adopted at higher voltages (> 100 V) and higher output power (> 1 hp) using an HVIC driver chip combined with two discrete MOS-gated power switches, as is sketched in Fig. 8 [29]. Two n-channel power MOSFET's (or IGBT's) are preferred for such applications due to the superior performance characteristics of n-channel devices.

If the ground of the HVIC driver chip is referenced to the negative power bus terminal, as is indicated in Fig. 8, the gate drive command for the upper switch $S1$ must be level shifted in order to accommodate the $S1$'s floating source

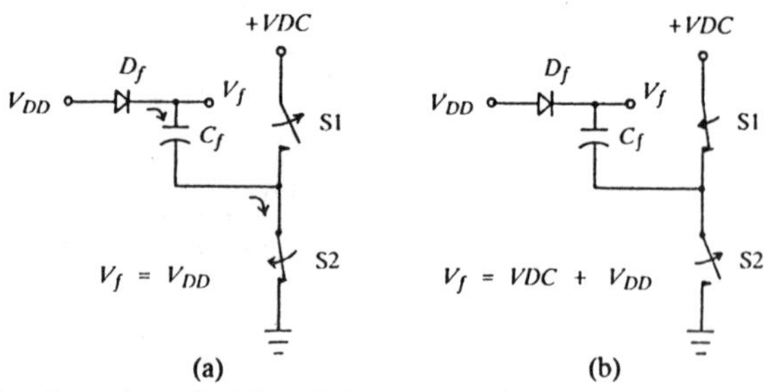

Fig. 9. Operating principles of charge pump for upper-switch gate drive supply: (a) Capacitor charges when $S2$ is closed; (b) capacitor supplies charge to $S1$ gate when $S2$ is open.

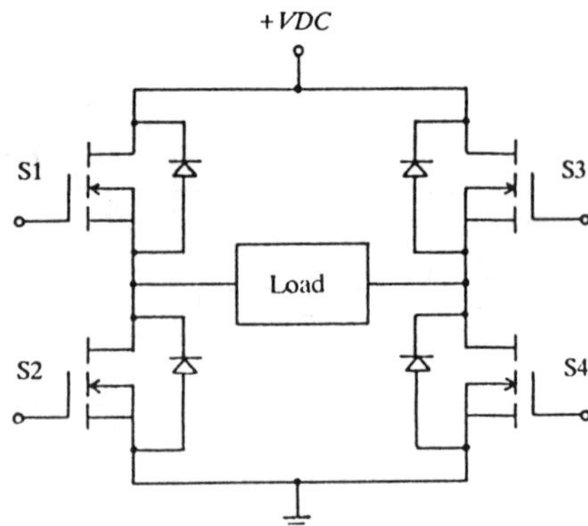

Fig. 10. Basic *H*-bridge inverter topology using four power MOSFET switches.

terminal reference potential. Supplying gate charge to the upper $S1$ switch is further complicated by the fact that the on-state gate voltage for $S1$ must be higher than the positive power bus potential +VDC by 10 to 15 V.

The most common technique for supplying the modest gate charge requirements of $S1$ is by means of a simple diode-capacitor charge pump. As illustrated in Fig. 9, capacitor C_f is charged by the low-voltage supply V_{DD} when $S2$ is on and then delivers the charge to the $S1$ gate at a voltage above VDC when $S1$ is on. Switch $S2$ must be turned on often enough to refresh the charge extracted from C_f, placing an upper limit on the duty cycle of the upper switch. Alternatively, more complicated charge pump configurations using independent free-running oscillators can be adopted to circumvent these duty cycle limitations.

HVIC half-bridge drivers using 500-V junction isolation PIC technology are commercially available with various combinations of features [30], [31]. The block diagram in Fig. 8 illustrates key features of a Harris chip [32], which is representative of the most sophisticated of the available HVIC half-bridge driver offerings. In addition to the level-shifting functions, the HVIC logic includes half-bridge lockout protection to ensure that $S1$ and $S2$ are never gated on at the same time. Other protection features include overcurrent for both $S1$ and $S2$ (using integrated current sensors, if desired), logic supply V_{DD} undervoltage detection, and an output state monitor to detect when V_{out} is not following the input logic command. Detected faults are reported by the HVIC to a central controller. Packaged with the power devices in hybrid assemblies [33] or separately in dual-inline (DIP) packages, HVIC half-bridge drivers are available with sufficiently high voltage and current drive capabilities to be used in integral-horsepower motor drives rated at 10 hp or higher.

C. H-*Bridge Power Stage Integration*

The next higher level of the power circuit hierarchy reviewed here is the *H*-bridge topology consisting of two totem-pole half bridges with a load connected between the two output terminals (see Fig. 10). This versatile circuit is capable of applying voltages of both polarities across the load by controlling the gating sequences of the four switches. Both dc motors and bipolar stepper motors are conveniently controlled using the *H*-bridge power circuit (see Section V), and the six-switch inverter that is commonly used in ac and brushless dc motor drives is closely related [34].

As a result of the *H* bridge's broad usefulness, a variety of integrated implementations are commercially available with a wide spectrum of features and current/voltage ratings. Since the *H* bridge consists of two half bridges, requirements for gate drive level shifting and half-bridge lockout protection described above for the single half bridge apply equally to the full *H* bridge. In addition, pulse width modulation (PWM) controllers can be added to control the switching instants of the four power devices in order to adjust both the polarity and the effective voltage amplitude applied to the load at any time instant.

The lowest level of integration provides an unadorned *H* bridge consisting of four discrete power transistors packaged together in a single compact module without any level shifting or protection features. All ''smarts'' are sacrificed in order to provide the *H*-bridge ''muscle'' in a compact package, typified by the 100-V, 8-A power MOSFET *H*-bridge module produced by Motorola [35]. Controller PIC's that can directly drive this type of *H*-bridge switch module are available.

At the next step up the integration ladder are monolithic PIC implementations of the buffered *H*-bridge power stage, which provide low-voltage logic-level inputs to directly control the switch states. This type of configuration includes the necessary level shifting to gate the upper half-bridge switches ($S1$ and $S3$ in Fig. 10) as well as various protection features, but it stops short of providing on-chip PWM control circuitry. Early generations of these *H*-bridge PIC's used all-bipolar technology yielding typical output ratings of 50 V and 2 A. Newer versions based on merged bipolar-MOS PIC technology are expanding the voltage-current envelope, with a recently announced SGS-Thomson unit rated at 250 V and 1.5 A [36]. Most of the newer buffered *H*-bridge offerings include the four reverse diodes in Fig. 10 as part of the PIC.

Despite the variety of input signal formats with various names used to designate the *H*-bridge switching states, it is important to recognize that there are only four valid states for current conduction, as is shown in Fig. 11. Neglecting semiconductor voltage drops for the moment, one of these states applies +VDC across the load (Fig. 11(a)), another applies −VDC (Fig. 11(b)), and two states apply 0 V (Figs. 11(c) and (d)), effectively short circuiting the load.

H-bridge control is simplified if only the +VDC and −VDC states (Figs. 11(a) and (b)) are used, ignoring the zero states, since a single input logic level is then sufficient to

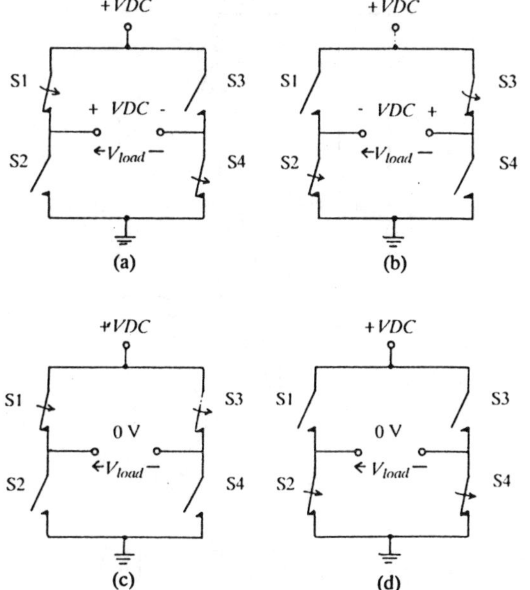

Fig. 11. Diagram of four valid H-bridge switching states (excluding open-circuit load state): (a) Supplies +VDC to load; (b) supplies −VDC; (c), (d) both supply zero voltage (short-circuited load).

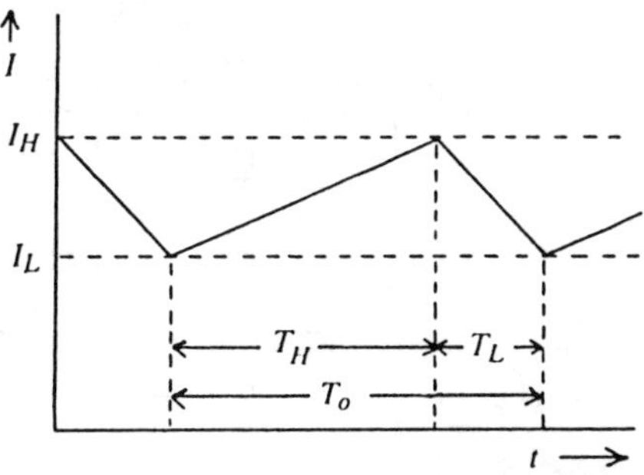

Fig. 12. Typical steady-state load current waveform during current-regulated PWM operation with purely inductive load.

control the *H*-bridge switching state. This type of control is referred to as "locked antiphase" since the adjacent switches in the two half bridges making up the *H* bridge are always in opposite states. Although locked antiphase control increases simplicity, it does not take full advantage of the *H* bridge's capabilities since the two zero voltage states can be very useful in reducing the di/dt current rise and fall rates in inductive motor loads. Lowered di/dt levels can be used to reduce either the current ripple amplitude or the switching frequency during PWM operation.

A good example of the buffered *H*-bridge PIC in its mature form is a 55-V, 3-A monolithic PIC, which was developed jointly by National Semiconductor and International Rectifier [37]. Provisions are made for controlling the *H* bridge in either the simple two-state locked antiphase mode or an alternate four-state "sign-magnitude" mode, which makes use of the zero voltage states. In addition to the level-shifting charge pumps, the unit includes a rather complete set of protection features as well as a current sensing output. Instantaneous current information is derived from integrated current sensors imbedded in the two upper half-bridge switches (*S*1 and *S*3 in Fig. 10) so that current feedback is available at an output pin as long as either *S*1 or *S*3 are conducting forward current to the load.

D. H *Bridge Controls Integration*

At the highest level of integration are monolithic PIC's, which bring PWM voltage or current control logic on board the chip to drive the buffered *H* bridge. Current-regulated PWM control generally provides the basis for higher performance motor control than voltage regulation since torque is directly related to the motor winding current amplitude.

Basic PWM voltage regulation is accomplished by means of high-frequency duty cycle control. One straightforward PWM implementation compares the desired voltage level to a fixed-frequency ramp signal, switching the *H*-bridge output state when the ramp exceeds the command level. Using the *H*-bridge locked antiphase control mode described above, the ramp comparison PWM strategy varies the average *H*-bridge output voltage over the full range from −VDC to +VDC by adjusting the relative widths of the −VDC and +VDC output pulses.

Several different algorithms are available for implementing current-regulated PWM control using current feedback information from the load. The simple current waveform for an inductive load shown in Fig. 12 will be used to briefly describe three of the alternative current PWM algorithms:

1) *Fixed frequency*. The PWM frequency is fixed so that T_o is constant; +VDC is applied until the load current reaches the upper I_H threshold; −VDC is applied during the remaining T_L interval until +VDC is applied again at the end of each T_o period.
2) *Fixed off-time*. Similar to *Fixed frequency* except that the T_L interval for applying −VDC is fixed in duration so that the PWM period T_o varies as the load and command change.
3) *Hysteresis control*. The switching points are determined when the load current reaches the upper I_H and lower I_L thresholds set by the current command; intervals T_H, T_L, and period T_o are all variable.

Each of these algorithms has its own advantages and disadvantages, and there are other alternatives as well [38]. One important difference worth noting is that the first two algorithms above only require current feedback information during the T_H interval when +VDC is being applied, whereas hysteresis control requires current feedback during the full T_o period. Since integrated current sensors in the power devices only provide current information when the switches are on, the selection of a current-regulated PWM algorithm is sensitive to the type and placement of the current sensors in the *H* bridge.

Fig. 13 sketches a monolithic *H*-bridge PIC based on a Unitrode device (40 V, 1 A), which includes provisions for current regulation using the fixed off-time algorithm described above [39]. The basic simplicity of the PWM implementation using a comparator and monostable generator is apparent in this figure. A small resistor in series with the negative power bus provides the current feedback information, and the monostable sets the fixed off-time interval,

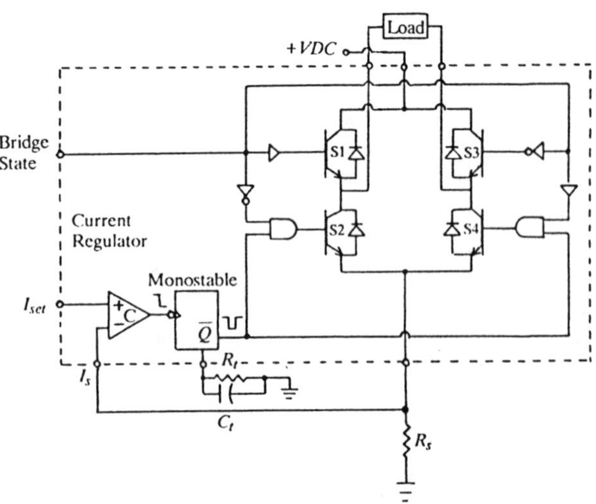

Fig. 13. . Monolithic H-bridge PIC including buffered drivers for the four switches and fixed off-time PWM current regulator (based on Unitrode UC3717).

which is user selected by means of external R-C components.

V. Motion Control PIC Applications

A. Stepper Motor Drive Integration

Stepper motors are widely used in motion control systems to provide open-loop shaft position control in fixed discrete increments without the need for closed-loop servo control [40]. Stepper motors are conveniently compatible with digital control systems since each input pulse can be decoded to deliver a single rotational step, which typically corresponds to 3.6 mechanical degrees (100 steps per revolution) or less. Fractional horsepower ratings are typical, although integral horsepower stepper motors are made for special applications [41].

Stepper motors are typically designed with windings oriented along two electromagnetically orthogonal axes, making it possible to step the motor shaft in either direction by controlling the timed sequence of the excitation delivered to the two stator windings. There are two major alternatives for conventional stepper winding configurations, and the choice between them has a significant impact on system performance capabilities and power converter configuration [42].

The unipolar stepper motor drive configuration shown in Fig. 14(a) uses a center-tapped winding along each axis with the supply voltage +VDC connected to both taps. Current flows in only one direction through each half winding during stepping operation (hence, unipolar), and the two halves making up each phase winding are never both excited at the same time. This winding configuration yields an appealingly simple power converter consisting of only four switches and four diodes, with all four transistor emitters (sources for MOSFET's) sharing the same reference point. No level shifting is necessary to drive the base terminals of the four switches, and there is only one power semiconductor voltage drop in each winding current path.

However, the simplicity of the unipolar configuration extracts some penalties. The fact that only half of each phase

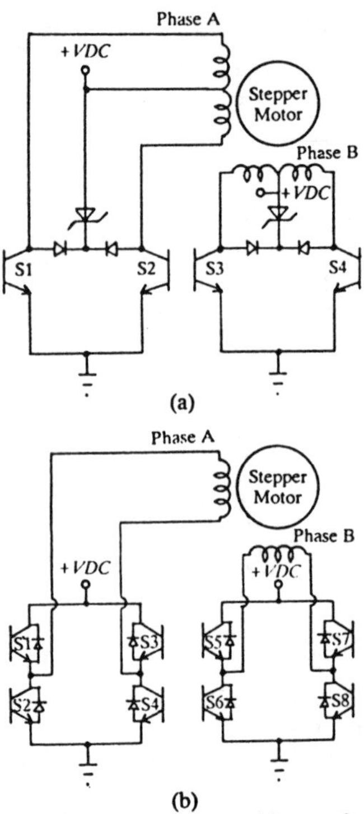

Fig. 14. Standard two-phase stepper motor drive configurations: (a) Unipolar drive with zener diodes for winding energy dissipation; (b) bipolar drive using two H bridges.

winding can be excited at any time penalizes copper utilization, increasing the motor size. Circuit means must be provided (e.g., zener diodes or resistors) to dissipate inductive energy stored in the windings when they are deenergized at the end of each step, adding losses to the power converter.

These disadvantages are avoided by eliminating the center taps and exciting each of the full phase windings in both polarities (bipolar) using H bridges, as is shown in Fig. 14(b). Winding utilization improves considerably, giving the bipolar-wound stepper motor a torque advantage of approximately 40% over a unipolar-wound machine in the same frame. Stored inductive energy can be conveniently returned to the source by the H-bridge diodes at the end of each step. However, there are now twice as many switches and diodes in the power converter combined with the complications of level-shifted switch gating. The relative advantages of each approach must be weighted in each application.

Beyond the choice of winding configuration, there are also alternative excitation control modes that must be considered. The simplest means of controlling winding currents, particularly for a small stepper, is to apply the full source voltage +VDC across each winding and use the winding resistance (plus additional series resistance if necessary) to directly limit the current amplitude. Although some PIC's use this basic voltage stepping control, higher efficiency and faster step response are achieved by using current-regulated PWM techniques (discussed in Section IV) to actively control the current amplitudes.

A variety of discrete stepping modes yielding rotational steps of varying lengths at differing torque levels are available (wave-front, full-step, half-step, and microstep), which are determined by the exact sequence in which the stepper

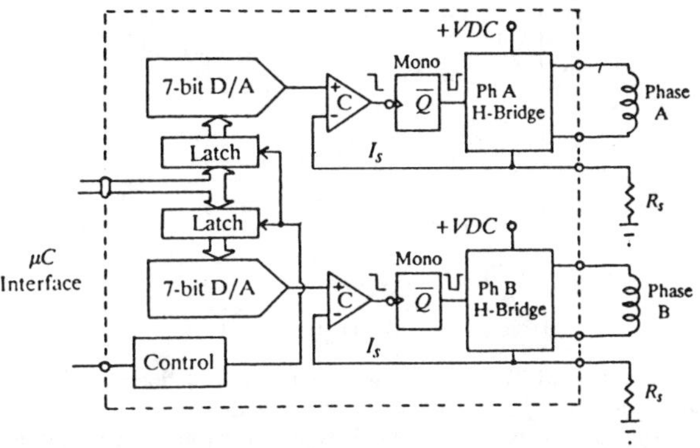

Fig. 15. Monolithic bipolar stepper motor drive PIC including two H bridges plus microcomputer interface for current-regulated microstepping control of both phase currents (based on SGS-Thomson L6217A).

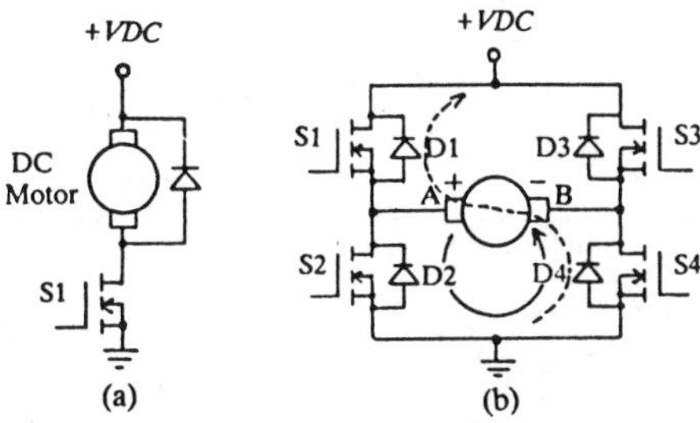

Fig. 16. Two basic dc motor drive configurations: (a) Simple unidirectional drive without braking capability; (b) four-quadrant H-bridge drive for bidirectional motoring and braking. Solid line = dissipative braking; broken line = regenerative braking.

motor windings are excited. Microstepping can yield extremely small incremental step sizes at the price of control complexity, requiring that the two phase winding currents be precisely controlled in amplitude according to a quadrature sinusoidal relationship.

Stepper motor control PIC's have been developed in a variety of configurations at varying levels of integration that parallel H-bridge choices described in the preceding section. Buffered stepper motor power stages are available in both unipolar and bipolar drive configurations with all of the power switches and diodes included in a monolithic PIC (typical ratings are 50 V, 1 A per phase) [43]. These buffered power stages offer minimal control functions and are typically intended for use in multiple-chip stepper drive designs. A separate low-voltage controller chip can then be used to implement the winding current PWM regulation and stepping sequence (translation) control.

Newer stepper motor PIC's move up the integration ladder to include both the power stage and translation control logic on a single chip. One interesting example of this approach is an SGS-Thomson PIC, which is designed for microstepping control of a bipolar stepper motor with two H-bridge power stages located on-chip [44]. Although not packing as much muscle as some of the more basic stepper PIC's (each bridge can deliver 500 mA at 18 V), the controller features are more extensive. As sketched in simplified form in Fig. 15, the PIC includes two current-regulated H-bridge blocks, each of which has a configuration very similar to that of Fig. 13. In addition, two 7-b D/A converters are included in the PIC design to generate analog current references for the two H bridges, making it possible to subdivide each discrete step into 128 microsteps. The digital PIC inputs are designed to conveniently interface to a microcontroller, which issues the appropriate commands for achieving either full-step, half-step, or microstep sequencing.

B. DC Motor Drive Integration

DC motors find wide usage in industrial and commercial applications for both speed and position control systems. Servo control of dc motors is simplified by the fact that the torque is directly proportional to the input armature current, and the motor back-EMF varies linearly with the speed [45]. Although integral-horsepower dc machines often contain stator field windings that can be separately excited, fixed permanent-magnet fields are typical in fractional horsepower sizes.

Two basic power converter drive configurations for dc motors shown in Fig. 16 are widely used, with the choice depending on the desired performance capabilities and cost constraints [46]. The unidirectional dc motor controller in Fig. 16(a) uses a single power switch and circulating diode to regulate either the average voltage applied to the motor (speed control) or the delivered armature current (torque control). The price for this simplicity is rotation in only one direction with no braking capability.

The versatile H bridge reappears in Fig. 16(b) to serve as the power converter for a "four-quadrant" dc motor drive. The term "four-quadrant" indicates that both the motor speed and torque are bidirectional, which permits the machine to operate in all four quadrants of the two-dimensional torque-speed plane. The availability of four switches makes it possible to apply average voltages in both polarities across the dc motor terminals ("on" switches $S1$ and $S4$ apply one polarity, and the $S2$–$S3$ pair applies the other), as is required for bidirectional rotation. The motor is in a braking (generating) mode when the torque and speed are of opposite polarities.

DC motor braking is achieved with the Fig. 16(b) H bridge using one of two modes. Assume first that the motor is rotating so that the motor internally generates back-EMF biasing terminal A positive with respect to B in Fig. 16(b). If only switch $S2$ is closed, braking current flows out of the motor terminal A (positive) through $S2$ and diode $D4$ and back to motor terminal B (negative). Under these conditions, energy extracted from the motor/load rotating inertia is dissipated entirely in the internal dc motor resistance (lossless switches and diodes assumed).

Although internally-dissipated braking is adequate for small dc motors (< 300 W), braking energy in larger motors must be returned to the source to avoid overcurrents and motor overheating. More specifically, if all H-bridge switches are gated "off," stored inductive energy in the motor can be "regenerated" back to the power source by means of current flowing out of motor terminal A through diode $D1$ to the supply and then back to terminal B via $D4$. The choice of braking modes depends entirely on the details of the PWM switching sequences applied to the four switches.

Integrated dc motor drives have been developed using PIC technology implemented in single- and multiple-chip config-

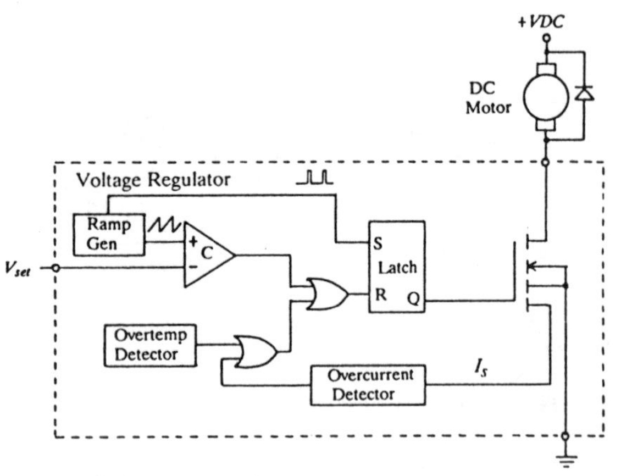

Fig. 17. Monolithic unidirectional dc motor drive PIC with simple PWM voltage-regulated speed control and integrated overcurrent/overtemperature protection features (based on Motorola MPC1700).

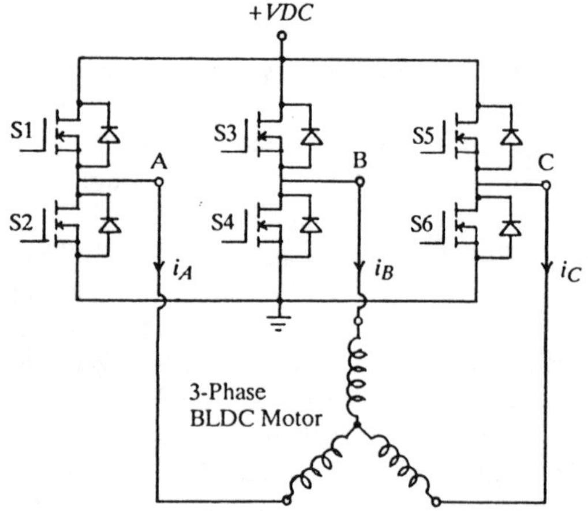

Fig. 18. Basic six-switch full-bridge inverter configuration with power MOSFET switches for driving BLDC motor and other types of ac motors.

urations. Fig. 17 illustrates the basic elements of a Motorola PIC providing a unidirectional dc motor drive on a single chip [47]. Key features include voltage-regulated PWM control logic for speed control, overtemperature protection, and an integrated current sensor to provide overcurrent protection for the 100-V, 20-A output power MOSFET.

As many as four independent *H* bridges, including two small dc motor controllers, have been designed into a monolithic PIC that was developed for a specific consumer product application [48]. Multiple-chip dc motor drive configurations are also available using a current-regulated *H*-bridge PIC for the four-quadrant output power "muscle"; separate low-voltage control chips provide the outer position and velocity control loops including optical encoder feedback processing and a digital input interface [49].

C. Brushless dc Motor Drive Integration

Brushless dc (BLDC) motors have been the subject of increasing attention during recent years for a variety of industrial and commercial applications. The absence of commutator brushes accounts for much of this appeal, using rotor-mounted permanent magnets to provide the necessary "field" excitation [50]. The commutation function is per-

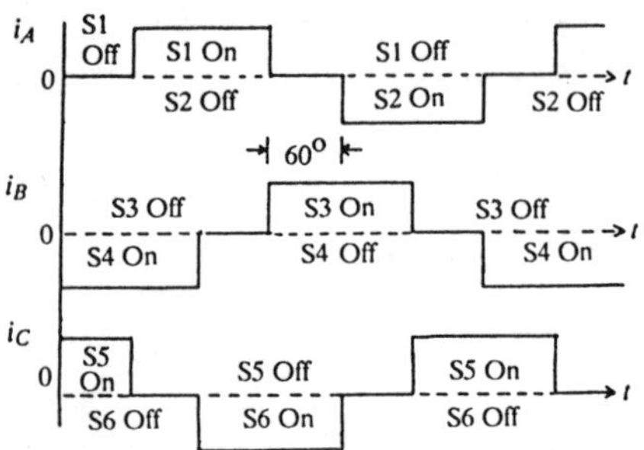

Fig. 19. Standard BLDC motor phase current excitation waveforms during fixed-speed steady-state operation with inverter switch states marked on waveform segments (excluding effects of high-frequency PWM switching).

formed electronically in the BLDC motor drive, with excitation supplied sequentially to the stator windings (typically three phase) in synchronism with the rotor position. The relative simplicity of the controls for a BLDC motor has contributed to making it an attractive alternative to other types of brushless ac motors (e.g., induction motors) requiring sinusoidal excitation for comparable performance.

Fig. 18 shows the basic six-switch full-bridge inverter used to excite three-phase BLDC motors. Unipolar BLDC motor drives analogous to the unipolar stepper motor configuration in Fig. 14(a) are sometimes used with small BLDC motors but will not be discussed here. Each of the three motor phases in Fig. 18 is excited by a half bridge of the type described previously in Section IV. Only one of the three upper switches (*S*1, *S*3, or *S*5) and one of the three lower switches (*S*2, *S*4, or *S*6) are "on" at any time instant so that one of the three motor phases is disconnected from the power supply (i.e., open circuited) at all times.

The standard current excitation waveforms for all three BLDC motor phases are sketched in Fig. 19, indicating that the selection of active switch pairs changes only six times per electrical cycle (60° intervals). The BLDC motor is specifically designed with trapezoidal back-EMF waveforms so that the square-top phase current waveforms in Fig. 19 produce minimum torque ripple. Three Hall-effect sensors mounted in proximity to the rotor magnets are typically used to provide sufficient rotor position feedback information to control the commutation process. Simple gated logic is adequate to decode the sensor signals into the desired switch gating sequence for motoring and braking torque production.

Although simple voltage control is adequate in some applications, means for achieving phase current regulation are typically provided in BLDC motor drives to improve the output torque control. Understanding the basis for current regulation is simplified by noting that one of the three motor phases and its associated inverter phase leg are inactive during each commutation interval. By mentally stripping away the unexcited phase, one finds that the Fig. 18 BLDC drive configuration reduces to a familiar *H* bridge (Fig. 10) with the two excited phase windings connected in series between the bridge output terminals.

All of the techniques described previously for regulating *H*-bridge load current extend in a quite natural way to the BLDC motor drive for both motoring and braking operation. A single resistor in series with one of the inverter power

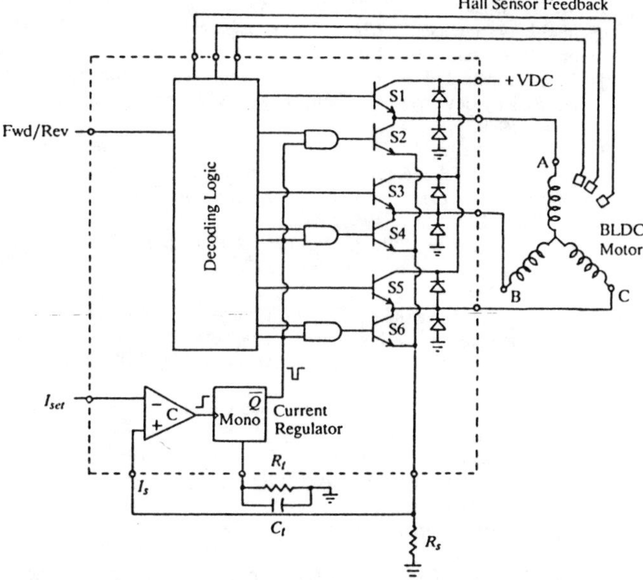

Fig. 20. Monolithic BLDC motor drive PIC including six-switch inverter, current regulation of motor phase currents, and Hall-effect position sensor decoding for electronic commutation (based on Unitrode UC3620).

buses is often used as the current sensor, although integrated current sensors in the inverter switches are also appealing sensor candidates because they avoid the resistor's power dissipation. Although small BLDC motors used in computer disk drives often control the inverter switches to linearly regulate the winding current amplitudes (non-saturating switch operation) for minimum electrical noise [51], PWM control is highly preferable in larger BLDC drives to reduce inverter losses. Appropriate PWM control of the switches makes it possible to brake the BLDC motor using either internal motor dissipation or regeneration back to the supply based on the same principles as for the dc motor described above.

Integrated BLDC motor drives can be assembled for a wide range of output power ratings using a variety of available combinations of specialized PIC's and controller chips. Single-chip PIC drives are available for small BLDC motors that are rated in the vicinity of 100 W. Fig. 20 provides a simplified block diagram for a 40-V, 2-A Unitrode BLDC drive PIC, which includes a six-switch power stage (Fig. 18), Hall sensor decoding logic, current-regulated PWM control of the lower switches, and thermal/undervoltage protection features [52]. Higher power levels are typically achieved by separating the controller and power stage onto separate chips. Versatile controller chips are available with a variety of features and drive capabilities [53], [54], which can be used to control buffered six-switch inverter PIC's or multiple half-bridge PIC's. HVIC phase-leg driver chips (see Section IV-B) simplify the controller-power stage interface in larger integral-horsepower BLDC drives [22].

A more aggressive approach to BLDC motor drive integration implemented by Sprague [24] combines the Hall-effect position sensors directly into the power stage PIC, including the sensor decoding and switch control logic. The integrated drive electronics is then mounted inside the motor housing in proximity to the rotor magnets to couple the rotor magnetic fields to the PIC sensors. Although only used presently for small specialty BLDC motors, this combined motor/electronics packaging approach indicates the high level of integration that can be achieved using modern PIC technology.

D. AC Motor Drive Integration

Reported applications of PIC's for the integration of other types of ac motor drives, such as the versatile induction motor drive, are relatively rare. Single-chip PIC drive implementations including both the power stage and controls are presently unavailable for ac motors due to a combination of technical and market-related issues. However, the power stage configurations used for single- and multiphase ac motors are identical to the *H*-bridge and six-switch inverter topologies introduced previously for stepper, dc, and BLDC motor controllers. As a result, PIC power stage components such as the HVIC half-bridge driver discussed in Section IV-B can be effectively applied in sinusoidal ac motor drives as well [55]. Special ac motor drive logic controller chips or chip sets are occasionally reported in the literature [56], and other custom-design IC controller implementations have been developed at various locations for proprietary use in ac-drive product lines [57].

A limited number of special-purpose ac motor control PIC's have been introduced to serve particular market segments. One interesting example is a Harris PIC that is designed to improve the average efficiency of a single-phase induction motor by adjusting the motor voltage amplitude [58]. Dielectric isolation (500-V rating) is used so that the PIC can be connected directly across the 240-VAC power line, controlling trigger pulses to a phase-controlled triac in series with the motor.

Another ac motor control PIC application, which has been investigated at GE, is a solid-state replacement for the mechanical centrifugal start switch used in many small induction motors (capacitor start) to remove excitation from an auxiliary winding at the end of startup. A Hall-effect sensor integrated into the PIC provides a shaft speed signal used to control the triggering of a discrete triac in series with the auxiliary winding. Like the Harris chip described above, this start-switch PIC is designed to be housed inside the induction motor end bell for minimum overall size and cost.

VI. Concluding Remarks

This paper has attempted to provide a broad tutorial review of the growing impact of power integrated circuit (PIC) technology on motion control systems. Virtually all types of motor drives commonly used in industry including stepper, dc, brushless dc, and ac motor drives are being positively influenced by the new PIC developments. The common theme linking all of these motion control applications is the universal desire to integrate the power electronics "muscle" with the control logic "smarts" in order to eliminate parts and improve system reliability. A continually expanding variety of PIC motor drive applications is being pursued, extending from the basic smart switch building block to single-chip PIC servo drives.

Where is PIC technology likely to go from here, and what will be its eventual impact on motor drive product markets?

New PIC developments are expected to continue to expand the voltage-current application envelope (Fig. 3) in both dimensions. Maximum power handling capabilities of smart discrete PIC's are likely to increase from approximately 2 to 3 kVA presently to 5 kVA and beyond during the 1990's. This progress will be achieved by developing higher performance PIC power devices (which will reduce losses) and improved PIC packaging techniques (which will dissipate internal losses more effectively). More cost-effective dielectric isolation processes will expand PIC functional capabilities, opening new avenues that will increase logic sophistication and incorporate appealing MOS-bipolar power devices such as the IGBT and MCT [59]. Sensor integration techniques are also likely to see expanding use in new PIC designs in order to bring additional control and protection functions onboard the chip.

Market impact of PIC technology is more difficult to predict with certainty due to the complex combination of factors influencing its acceptance [60]. Penetration of PIC's into the vast automotive electronics market during the 1990's will exert a dominant influence on PIC availability and cost effectiveness in more specialized smaller-volume industrial markets. In particular, progress towards increasing PIC chip processing yields and reducing production costs will play a major role in determining market growth opportunities for PIC-based motor drives. Improved CAD design techniques for new PIC's and availability of semi-custom PIC processes will also be very important for reducing initial engineering costs, making PIC's more attractive in new drive designs.

Despite the difficulties in predicting technical advances and market growth rates, the benefits of increased motor drive integration made possible by PIC technology are indisputable. Relentless competitive pressures to cut motor drive costs and improve product reliability ensure that the 1990's will bring increased market pressures to design smarter and more powerful intelligent muscle into new industrial motion control systems.

References

[1] A. D. Little, Inc., "Energy efficiency and electric motors," Final Rep. prepared for U.S. Fed. Energy Admin., Contract No. C0-04-50217-00, May 1976.

[2] B. J. Baliga (Ed.), *High Voltage Integrated Circuits.* New York: IEEE Press, 1988.

[3] M. W. Smith (Ed.), *Smart Power Economics, Technology, and Applications.* Ventura: CA, Intertec Communications, 1988.

[4] M. S. Adler, K. W. Owyang, B. J. Baliga, and R. A. Kokosa, "The evolution of power device technology," *IEEE Trans. Electron Devices*, vol. ED-31, pp. 1570-1591, Nov. 1984.

[5] V. Rumennik, "Power devices are in the chips," *IEEE Spectrum*, pp. 42-48, July 1985.

[6] P. Antognetti (Ed.), *Power Integrated Circuits.* New York: McGraw-Hill, 1986.

[7] B. J. Baliga, "Power integrated circuits—A brief overview," *IEEE Trans. Electron Devices*, vol. ED-33, no. 12, pp. 1936-1939, Dec. 1986.

[8] R. S. Wrathall, "The design of a high power solid state automotive switch in CMOS-VDMOS technology," in *Rec. 1985 IEEE Power Electron. Spec. Conf.*, June 1985, pp. 229-233.

[9] S. P. Robb, J. L. Sutor, and L. E. Terry, "Smart discretes, A new trend in power MOSFET industry," in *Proc. Electrochemical Soc. Spring Mtg.* (Los Angeles), May 1989, pp. 413-414, vol. 89-1.

[10] M. J. Hillyer, "Using motors in automotive multiplex systems," *Preprint-SAE Int'l Cong. Expo.* (Detroit), Feb. 1986, Paper 860394.

[11] M. F. Chang *et al.*, "Lateral HVIC with 1200-V bipolar and field-effect devices," *IEEE Trans. Electron Devices*, vol. ED-33, pp. 1992-2001, Dec. 1986.

[12] J. A. Appels and H. M. J. Vaes, "High-voltage thin-layer devices (RESURF) devices," in *Tech. Dig. IEEE Int'l Electron Devices Mtg.*, 1979, pp. 238-241.

[13] A. A. Andreini, C. Contiero, and P. Galbiati, "A new integrated silicon gate technology combining bipolar linear, CMOS logic, and DMOS power parts," *IEEE Trans. Electron Devices*, vol. ED-33, pp. 2025-2030, Dec. 1986.

[14] J. F. Dickson and W. A. Peterson, "High performance, hermetic power hybrid circuits," in *Proc. PCI Conf.* (Chicago), Oct. 1985, pp. 216-234.

[15] L. Leipold, R. Sander, and J. Tihanyi, "Chip-on-chip high-side switch technology for high current smart devices," in *Proc. Electrochemical Soc. Spring Mtg.* (Los Angeles), May 1989, pp. 469, vol. 89-1.

[16] P. R. Emerald, "Power IC's for motor control: The challenges and the concerns of military versions, applications, and specifications," in *Proc. Motor-Con. Conf.* (Dearborn, MI), Oct. 1988, pp. 127-135.

[17] S. Raciti and M. Paparo, "A 2.0 KVA fully integrated PWM motor controller opens the way to a new perspective on motor ICs design," *Power Conv. Intell. Motion*, June 1987, pp. 42-46.

[18] N. J. Elias and J. L. Woo, "A CAD system for ASPIC (applications specific power IC), in *Proc. Electrochemical Soc. Spring Mtg.* (Los Angeles), May 1989, pp. 445-457, vol. 89-1.

[19] N. Friedman, "Semi-custom, smart power IC family operates at 20, 40, 80 V," *Power Conv. Incremental Motion*, pp. 15-20, March 1989.

[20] S. L. Wong, M. J. Kim, and S. Mukherjee, "A 60 V, compact flexible-cell library for high current PIC applications," in *Proc. Electrochemical Soc. Spring Mtg.* (Los Angeles), May 1989, pp. 458-459, vol. 89-1.

[21] W. Schultz, "Lossless current sensing with SenseFETs enhances motor drive design," *Power Conv. Intell. Motion*, Apr. 1986, pp. 30-34.

[22] T. M. Jahns, R. C. Becerra, and M. Ehsani, "Integrated current regulation for brushless ECM drive," in *Proc. IEEE Appl. Power Electron. Conf.* (Baltimore), Mar. 1988, pp. 81-90.

[23] T. Wood, "The Hall-effect sensor," in *Hall-Effect and Optoelectronic Sensors.* Concord, NH: Sprague Databook SN-500, 1987, pp. 7:38-41.

[24] P. R. Emerald, "Bipolar IC merges Hall effect, control logic, and power outputs," in *Proc. IEEE Industry Appl. Soc. An. Mtg.* (Atlanta), Oct. 1987, pp. 515-520.

[25] W. Dunn and R. Frank, "Smart power automotive issues," in *Smart Power Electronics, Technology, and Applications.* Ventura, CA: Intertec Communications, 1988, pp. 503-533.

[26] F. Goodenough, "Inhibit short circuit current with power MOSFET IC," *Electronic Design*, Jan. 26, 1989, pp. 148-149.

[27] M. Glogolja, "Built-in protection makes TEMPFET resistant to catastrophic failures," *Power Conv. Intell. Motion*, pp. 19-23, Mar. 1989.

[28] B. Nadd, "500 V/8A MOSFET integrating protections and gate drive simplifies the design of power circuits," in *Proc. Electrochemical Soc. Spring Mtg.* (Los Angeles), May 1989, pp. 405-406, vol. 89-1.

[29] D. Henderson *et al.* "HVIC half bridge driver—Applications and reliability," in *Smart Power Economics, Technology and Applications.* Ventura, CA: Intertec Communications, 1988, pp. 385-395.

[30] S. Young, "High-speed, high-voltage IC driver for HEXFET or IGBT bridge circuits," Int. Rectifier Application Note AN-978, 1988.

[31] A. Wegener and M. Amato, "A high voltage interface IC for half-bridge circuits," in *Proc. Electrochemical Soc. Spring Mtg.* (Los Angeles), May 1989, pp. 476-477, vol. 89-1.

[32] J. Mansmann *et al.*, "ASIC-Like HVIC for interfacing to half-bridge based power circuits," in *Rec. IEEE Power Electron. Spec. Conf.* (Tokyo), Apr. 1988, pp. 1319-1324.

[33] D. MacIntyre, "Power hybrid hoists logic to motor drive levels," *Electron. Products*, pp. 57-60, Nov. 3, 1986.

[34] M. H. Rashid, *Power Electronics—Circuits, Devices, and Applications.* Englewood Cliffs, NJ: Prentice-Hall, 1988, pp. 230-233.

[35] D. Artusi and R. Frank, "Power multiples for motion control systems," *Power Conv. Intel. Motion*, Feb. 1988, pp. 33-35.

[36] C. Cini and C. Diazzi, "250 V integrated full bridge with driving stages with logic inputs, in multipower BCD technology," in *Proc. Electrochemical Soc. Spring Mtg.* (Los Angeles), May 1989, pp. 474-475, vol. 89-1.

[37] M. Izadinia *et al.*, "A next generation high performance CMOS/bipolar/DMOS H-bridge," in *Proc. Motor-Con Conf.* (Long Beach, CA), Oct. 1987, pp. 117-124.

[38] D. M. Brod and D. W. Novotny, "Current control of VSI-PWM inverters," *IEEE Trans. Industry Appl.*, vol. IA-21, pp. 562-570, May/June 1985.

[39] R. Neidorff, "Smartpower ICs employ bilevel current control to improve step motor performance," *Power Conv. Intell. Motion*, pp. 74-80, Aug. 1988.

[40] T. Kenjo, *Stepping Motors and Their Microprocessor Controls*. Oxford, England: Clarendon, 1985.

[41] R. Welburn, "Ultra-high torque motor system for direct drive robotics," in *Proc. Motor-Con Conf.* (Atlantic City), Apr. 1984, pp. 17-24.

[42] A. C. Leenhouts, *The Art and Practice of Step Motor Control*. Ventura, CA: Intertec Communications, 1987.

[43] "High-power, dual-bridge IC's ease stepper motor drive design," *Motion Contr. Application Manual*, SGS, pp. 61-67, 1987.

[44] T. L. Hopkins, "Microstepping controller IC supports proportional current control," *Power Conv. Intell. Motion*, pp. 57-60, Mar. 1989.

[45] *DC Motors, Speed Controls, Servo Systems*, Electro-Craft Handbook, Hopkins, MN, 1980, 5th ed.

[46] M. H. Rashid, *Power Electronics-Circuits, Devices, and Applications*. Englewood Cliffs, NJ: Prentice-Hall, 1988, pp. 313-321.

[47] D. Artusi and R. Frank, "Power MOS IC technology perspective," in *Smart Power Economics, Technology, and Applications*. Ventura, CA: Intertec Communications, 1988.

[48] R. Janikowski, "Portable CD player uses smart power IC to control four motors," *Power Conv. Intell. Motion*, Mar. 1989, pp. 45-48.

[49] "A designer's guide to the L290/L291/L292 dc motor speed/position control system," *Motion Contr. Application Manual*, SGS, pp. 107-125, 1987.

[50] T. J. E. Miller, *Brushless Permanent-Magnet and Reluctance Motor Drives*. Oxford, England: Oxford Univ. Press, 1989.

[51] R. A. Mammano and J. J. Galvin, "Linear, three-phase BDC driver IC cuts losses and EMI," *Power Conv. Intell. Motion*, pp. 20-26, June 1989.

[52] C. de Sa e Silva, "Brushless dc motors, drivers, and speed controllers," *Power Conf. Intell. Motion*, pp. 46-50, Sept. 1987.

[53] J. H. Alberkrack, "Brushless motor controller implements three-or four-phase system," *Power Conv. Intell. Motion*, pp. 80-90, May 1987.

[54] R. Neidorff, "New integrated circuit produces robust, noise immune system for brushless dc motors," in *Proc. Motor-Con Conf.* (Dearborn, MI), Oct. 1988, pp. 65-74.

[55] T. M. Jahns, "Electric controls for a high-performance EHA using an interior permanent magnet motor drive," in *Proc. IEEE Nat. Aerospace Electron. Conf.* (Dayton), May 1989, pp. 346-354.

[56] E. S. Tez, "Custom chipset controls variable-speed ac drives," *Power Conv. Intell. Motion*, pp. 82-85, May 1989.

[57] S. J. Bailey, "New ac drives emphasize motor-drive power matching," *Contr. Eng.*, pp. 101-104, Feb. 1989.

[58] R. S. Pospisil, P. W. Shackle, and J. D. Beasom, "A line powered induction motor energy saver," in *Proc. IEEE Custom Integrated Circuit Conf.*, May 1983, pp. 412-416.

[59] B. J. Baliga, "Integrable high voltage devices for power integrated circuits," in *Proc. Electrochemical Soc. Spring Mtg.* (Los Angeles), May 1989, p. 398, vol. 89-1.

[60] M. W. Smith, "Economics of smart power," in *Smart Power Economics, Technology, and Applications*, Ventura, CA: Intertec Communications, 1988.

Selected Bibliography

[1] P. L. Hower, "Power semiconductor devices: An overview," *Proc. IEEE*, vol. 76, pp. 335–342, April 1988.

[2] J. L. Hudgins, W. W. Glen, S. Menhart, and W. M. Portnoy, "Comparison of MOS devices for high frequency inverters," *IEEE/IAS Ann. Meet. Conf. Rec.*, vol. 2, pp. 1594–1596, 1990.

[3] B. J. Baliga, M. S. Adler, R. P. Love, P. V. Gray, and N. D. Zommer, "The insulated gate transistor: A new three-terminal MOS-controlled bipolar power device," *IEEE Trans. Electron Devices*, vol. ED-31, pp. 821–828, June 1984.

[4] T. Tanaka, Y. Yasuda, and M. Ohayashi, "A new MOS-gate bipolar transistor for power switches," *IEEE Trans. Electron Devices*, vol. ED-33, pp. 2041–2045, Dec. 1986.

[5] Y. Nakatani, H. Hakazawa, and Nawata, "A new ultra high speed high voltage switching transistor," *Proc. Powercon*, pp. j3–j3-8, 1980.

[6] B. J. Baliga, "Evolution of MOS-bipolar power semiconductor technology," *Proc. IEEE*, vol. 76, pp. 409–418, April 1988.

[7] D. Y. Chen, "Power semiconductors: Fast, tough, and compact," *IEEE Spectrum*, vol. 24, pp. 30–35, Sept. 1987.

[8] B. J. Baliga, "High gain power switching using field controlled thyristors," *Solid State Electron.*, vol. 25, pp. 345–353, 1982.

[9] B. J. Baliga, "The new generation of MOS power devices," *Drives/Motors/ Controls Conf. Proc.*, pp. 139–141, 1983.

[10] B. J. Baliga, "Revolutionary inventions in power discrete devices," *IEEE Int. Electron Devices Meet. Tech. Dig.*, Abstract 5.1, pp. 102–105, 1986.

[11] M. Azuma and M. Kurata, "GTO thyristors," *Proc. IEEE*, vol. 76, pp. 419–427, Apr. 1988.

[12] E. D. Wolley, "Gate turn-off in p-n-p-n devices," *IEEE Trans. Electron Devices*, vol. ED-13, pp. 590–597, July 1966.

[13] T. C. New, W. D. Frobenius, T. J. Desmond, and D. R. Hamilton, "High power gate-controlled switch," *IEEE Trans. Electron Devices*, vol. ED-17, pp. 706–710, Sept. 1970.

[14] H. R. Chang and A. V. Radun, "Performance of 500V, 450A parallel MOS-controlled thyristors (MCTs) in a resonant dc-link circuit," *IEEE/IAS Ann. Meet. Conf. Rec.*, vol. 2, pp. 1613–1617, 1990.

[15] T. Suzuki, T. Ugazin, M. Kekura, T. Watanabe, and T. Sueoka, "Switching characteristics of high power buried gate turn-off thyristor," *IEEE Int. Electron Devices Meet. Tech. Dig.*, pp. 492–495, 1982.

[16] M. Azuma, M. Kurata, and K. Takagami, "2500-V 600-A gate turn-off thyristor (GTO)," *IEEE Trans. Electron Devices*, vol. ED-28, pp. 270–274, Mar. 1981.

[17] 0. Hashimoto, H. Kirihata, M. Watanabe, and A. Nishiura, "Turn-on and turn-off characteristics of a 4.5 kV 3000 A gate turn-off thyristor," *IEEE/IAS Ann. Meet. Conf. Rec.*, pp. 876–881, 1985.

[18] R. L. Steigerwald, M. H. Kuo, G. S. Claydon, and K. C. Routh, "A high-voltage integrated circuit for power supply applications," *IEEE Appl. Power Electron. Conf. Rec.*, pp. 221–229, 1987.

[19] E. J. Wildi, T. P. Chow, M. S. Adler, M. E. Cornell, and G. C. Pifer, "New high voltage IC technology," *IEEE Int. Electron Devices Meet. Tech. Dig.*, Paper #10.2, pp. 262–265, 1984.

[20] V. Rumennik, "Power devices are in the chips," *IEEE Spectrum*, vol. 22, pp. 42–48, July 1985.

[21] P. Antognetti (Ed.), *Power Integrated Circuits.* New York: McGraw-Hill, 1986.

[22] B. J. Baliga, "Power integrated circuits—A brief overview," *IEEE Trans. Electron Devices*, vol. ED-33, pp. 1936–1939, Dec. 1986.

[23] S. P. Robb, J. L. Sutor, and L. E. Terry, "Smart discretes, a new trend in power MOSFET industry," *Proc. Electrochemical Soc. Spring Meeting*, Los Angeles, vol. 89-1, pp. 413–414, 1989.

[24] Y. Tokiwa, F. Ichikawa, S. Miyazaki, K. Itoh, T. Takahashi, and T. Horiuchi, "Development of static induction thyristor applications for high-voltage converter," *Power Conv. & Intelligent Motion Proc.*, pp. 357–365, 1988.

[25] K. Muraoka, Y. Kawamura, Y. Ohtsubo, S. Sugawara, T. Tamamushi, and J. Nishizawa, "Characteristics of the high speed SI thyristor and its application as the 60kHz, l00kW and the efficiency of more than 90% inverter," *IEEE PESC Rec.*, pp. 94–103, 1986.

[26] T. Yatsuo, T. Nagano, H. Fukui, M Okamura, and S. Sakurada, "Ultrahigh-voltage high-current gate turn-off thyristors," *IEEE Trans. Electron Devices*, vol. ED-31, pp. 1681–1686, Dec. 1984.

[27] Y. Nakamura, H. Tadano, M. Takigawa, I. Igarashi, and J. I. Nishizawa, "Very high speed static induction thyristor," *IEEE Trans. Ind. Applicat.*, vol. IA-22, pp. 1000–1006, Nov./Dec. 1986.

[28] K. Shenai, "Technology trends in high frequency power semiconductor discrete devices and integrated circuits," *Fourth Int. High Freq. Power Conv. Rec.*, pp. 1–23, 1989.

[29] B. J. Baliga, "Switching lots of watts at high speed," *IEEE Spectrum*, vol. 18, pp. 42–48, Dec. 1981.

[30] M. S. Adler and S. R. Westbrook, "Power semiconductor switching devices—A comparison based on inductive switching," *IEEE Trans. Electron Devices*, vol. ED-29, pp. 947–952, June 1982.

[31] V. A. K. Temple, "MOS controlled thyristors," *IEEE Int. Electron Devices Meet. Tech. Dig.*, pp. 282–285, 1984.

[32] B. Murari, "Power integrated circuits: Problems, tradeoffs, and solutions," *IEEE J. Solid-State Circuits*, vol. SC-13, pp. 307–319, June 1978.

[33] T. Driscoll, "Design application and characterization of new power semiconductor devices for PWM drives," *Power Conv. & Intelligent Motion Proc.*, pp. 26–36, April 1983.

[34] T. M. Jahns, R. W. De Doncker, J. W. A. Wilson, V. A. K. Temple, and D. L. Watrous, "Circuit utilization of MOS controlled thyristors," *IEEE/IAS Ann. Meet. Conf. Rec.*, vol. 2, pp. 1248–1254, 1989.

[35] H. Berg, B. Thomas, and H. Schlangenotto, "GTO thyristor with improved switching behaviour," *IEEE/IAS Ann. Meet. Conf. Rec.*, pp. 700–705, 1984.

[36] H. Matsuda, M. Takeuchi, Y. Tsunoda, K. Mase, Y. Hashiya, and K. Murakami, "2.5kV-800A monolithic reverse conducting gate turn-off thyristor," *IEEE/IAS Ann. Meet. Conf. Rec.*, pp. 871–875, 1985.

[37] O. Hashimoto, H. Kirihata, M. Watanabe, K. Endo, T. Mizuno, and A. Nishiura, "Reverse blocking 4.5 kV, 3000 A gate turn-off thyristor," *IEEE/IAS Ann. Meet. Conf. Rec.*, pp. 384–387, 1986.

[38] E. Ho and P. C. Sen, "Effect of gate drive circuits on GTO thyristor," *IEEE/IAS Ann. Meet. Conf. Rec.*, pp. 706–714, 1984.

[39] A. P. Connolly, J. Baab, and M. Hauswirth, "Application of GTO thyristor modules," *IEEE/IAS Ann. Meet. Conf. Rec.*, pp. 955–959, 1985.

[40] G. L. Skibinski and D. M. Divan, "Characteristics of GTO's for soft switching applications," *IEEE/IAS Ann. Meet. Conf. Rec.*, pp. 638–649, 1988.

[41] R. W. De Doncker, T. M. Jahns, A. V. Radun, D. L. Watrous, and V. A. Temple, "Characteristics of MOS-controlled thyristors under zero voltage soft-switching conditions," *IEEE/IAS Ann. Meet. Conf. Rec.*, vol. 2, pp. 1597–1603, 1990.

Part 4
AC-to-DC and AC-to-AC Converters

Paper 4.1

NEW SINGLE-PHASE UNITY POWER FACTOR PWM CONVERTER-INVERTER SYSTEM

Masayuki Morimoto, Katsumi Oshitani, Kiyotaka Sumito,
Shinji Sato, Muneaki Ishida* and Shigeru Okuma**

Mitsubishi Heavy Industries,Ltd.
*Mie University
**Nagoya University

Abstract

A new single-phase, unity power factor converter-inverter is presented. The converter circuit which delivers sinusoidal input current regulates dc voltage. The inverter which is with the magnetic flux control PWM method generates variable voltage, variable frequency PWM waveform in order to minimize the output voltage distortion factor. The experimental result shows that the motor efficiency is as high as that of the sinusoidal output voltage. As a result, the system efficiency and the power factor are improved.

1 Introduction

Variable Voltage, Variable Frequency (VVVF) drive of an induction motor is widely used both in industrial and household applications. Especially in household, single-phase-input and three-phase-output inverters for motor drive become popular. A voltage source PWM inverter is a key device for such VVVF drives of small induction motors.

For the converter circuit of the PWM inverter, a capacitor-input-type rectifier converter has been used. However, it causes the harmonic distortion of the ac current and the low power factor operation.

Recently, a unity power factor converter circuit for ac to dc voltage regulator has been reported [1][2]. This PWM converter is one of the solutions for the problems of the converter circuit.

The converter-inverter systems for motor drive have been reported. Hombu *et al* [3] reported mainly on the control scheme of the converter circuit of the converter-inverter system. Nonaka *et al* [4] reported the control method of inverter circuit based on dc link voltage. B.T. Ooi *et al* [5] reported the design method of the converter-inverter system based on the loss of controllability and the output harmonic distortion. However, in designing high efficiency VVVF drive system for practical application, it is the motor efficiency that should be taken into consideration.

In this paper, new control strategy of the converter-inverter system for motor drives is studied. For the new system, the single phase, unity power factor ac to dc voltage converter is used. The magnetic flux control PWM method is used as the PWM strategy of the inverter. The modulation factor of the inverter which uses controllable dc voltage is studied in order to make motor efficiency high. It is shown that over-modulation resulting from low dc link voltage is a key design factor.

2 Control strategy of the converter

Fig. 1 shows the circuit configuration of the new converter-inverter system. The single phase converter is connected to the three phase inverter circuit through dc link. The converter is a so called "Buck-Boost" converter with a single power switch. The inverter circuit is a conventional bridge circuit which has six power switches. The control strategy of the converter is described hereafter.

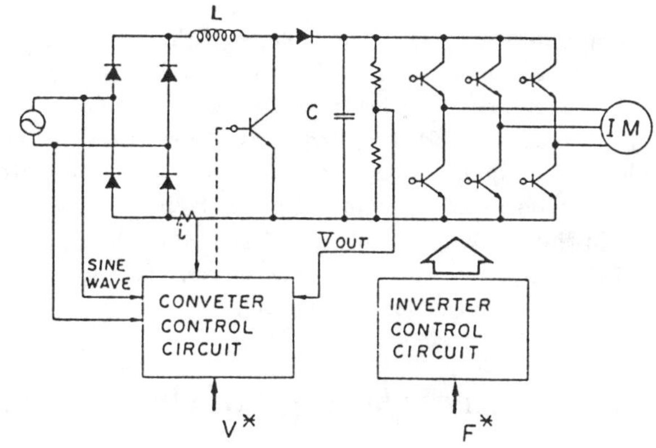

Fig.1. Circuit configuration.

Reprinted from *IEEE Power Electron. Specialists Conf. (PESC) Rec.*, pp. 585–589, 1989.

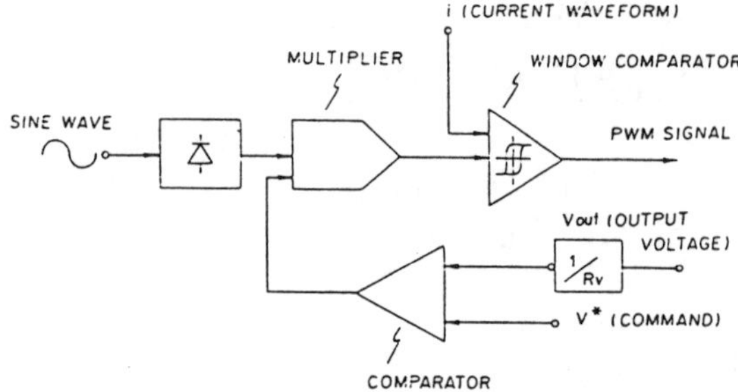

Fig.2. Control diagram of converter.

Fig. 2 shows the control diagram of the converter circuit. The PWM control of the converter has a double control loop. The input current waveform is controlled with the window comparator so that it follows phase and shape of the source voltage. The rectified source voltage is used as the sinusoidal reference waveform. The output dc voltage of the converter is controlled by the outer control loop so that the dc voltage of the inverter circuit may change. The feedback dc voltage and the command voltage are compared. The error is multiplied in order to make instantaneous reference waveform. In the inner current control loop, the feedback current waveform and the reference waveform are hysterisis-controlled with the window comparator. The output signal of the window

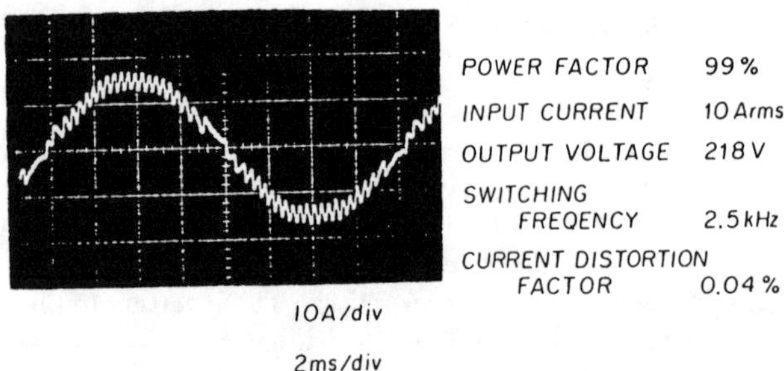

Fig.3. Ac line current waveform.

comparator is the PWM waveform of the converter.

Fig. 3 shows the typical ac line current waveform of the converter. The input power factor is nearly unity, although, the switching frequency is below several kilohertz. A bipolar transistor is used as the power switch, and it contributes to improve power factor.

In this system, the voltage V^* is used as the command of the converter control because the converter operates as the voltage source for the inverter.

3 Control strategy of the inverter

The control strategy of the inverter is the magnetic flux control PWM method[6], which is based on eight kinds of voltage vectors made of a inverter bridge, shown in Fig. 4. In the figure, on state of the upper inverter bridge denotes "1", and off state, "0".

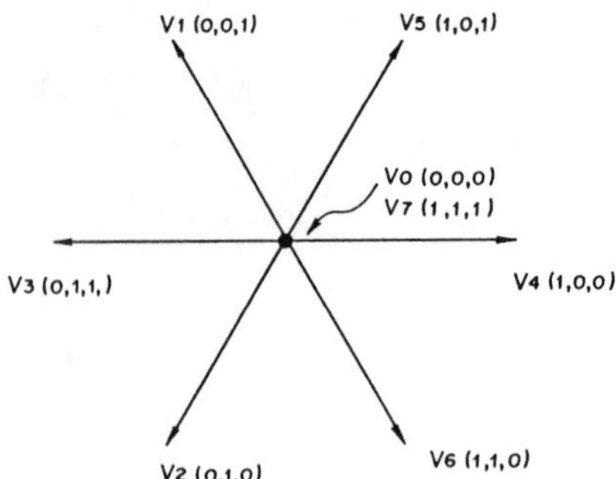

Fig.4. Voltage vectors made by inverter.

The flux locus produced from the inverter output voltage is divided into equal blocks. Each block corresponds to the digital control interval of the PWM pattern. The voltage vectors are selected every time interval so that the flux vectors produced from inverter output line to line voltage may move along the ideal circle.

In the converter-inverter system, dc link voltage can be controlled by the PWM control of the converter. In order to make motor efficiency high, the modulation scheme of the magnetic flux control method with controllable dc input voltage is discussed hereafter.

3.1 The fundamental component of the PWM waveform

In the high efficiency VVVF drives of induction motors, the design of the fundamental component of the motor terminal voltage is the major design factor, because it affects motor characteristics such as torque, efficiency, etc.

The principle of the conventional triangular-sinewave PWM method is shown in Fig.5. The output PWM pulses are generated by comparing the sinewave and the triangular wave. Ideally, the amplitude of the sinewave corresponds to that of the output fundamental voltage. The rms value of output fundamental line to line voltage of the conventional PWM pulses is expressed as follows:

$$V_f = \frac{\sqrt{3}}{\sqrt{2}} A_f \frac{E_{DC}}{2} \qquad (1)$$

where

V_f : fundamental component of the line to line voltage (rms value)
A_f : modulation factor ($0 < A_f < 1$)
E_{DC}: dc link voltage.

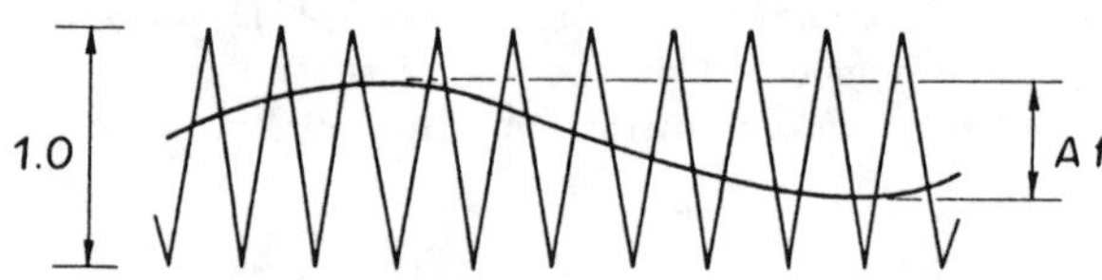

Fig.5. The principle of triangular-sinewave PWM

The voltage utilization factor is defined by the amplitude of the fundamental component when $A_f = 1.0$. That is:

$$\frac{\sqrt{3}}{2} = 0.866$$

On the other hand, in the magnetic flux control PWM method, the output fundamental voltage is proportional to the radius of the flux locus, and is expressed as:

$$V_f = \frac{\sqrt{3}}{\sqrt{2}} A_f^* \frac{E_{DC}}{2} \quad (2)$$

$$A_f^* = \frac{4}{\pi}(1-\gamma) \quad (3)$$

where

A_f^* : modulation factor of the flux control PWM method

γ : ratio of the zero vectors in the PWM pattern.

The radius of the flux locus is determined by the ratio of zero vectors in the PWM pattern. The circle of the flux locus is made from six voltage vectors (V1 $\sim$ V6), although, the PWM pattern consists of eight vectors including zero vectors(V0, V7) which indicate zero output voltage. Accordingly, $(1-\gamma)$ is proportional to the modulation factor. The maximum value of A_f^* is

$$\frac{4}{\pi} = 1.27$$

when the flux locus is a hexagon. The modulation factor can be varied from 0 to 1.27 in the magnetic flux control PWM method.

In the conventional inverter, as shown in equation (1), output voltage is controlled by changing the modulation factor A_f, because the dc link voltage E_{DC} is constant. On the other hand, in the new system, both dc link voltage E_{DC} and the modulation factor A_f^* , in equation (2), can be controlled. In the next subsection, the procedure of determing A_f^* when E_{DC} is controllable is discussed.

3.2 The effect of A_f^*

The inverter PWM pattern design by the magnetic flux control method with controllable dc voltage is studied experimentally. The motor used is a two pole, 800W three phase induction motor.

Fig. 6 shows the effect of the modulation factor A_f^* on motor efficiency. The fundamental component of the motor terminal voltage is kept at 120V. The experimental result shows that the motor efficiency is high when A_f^* is large, as the voltage distortion factor is small.

Fig. 7 shows the motor efficiency η_M when the distortion factor is varied by changing the number of blocks k so that the fundamental component of the motor terminal voltage will be kept constant. Fig. 8 shows the motor

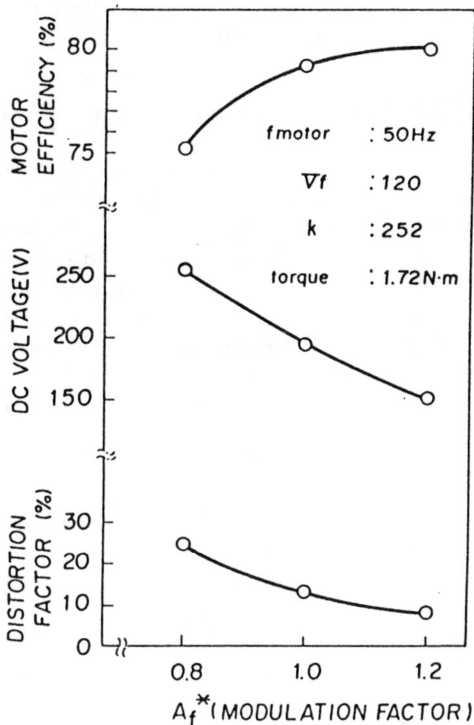

Fig.6. The effect of the modulation factor A_f^*.

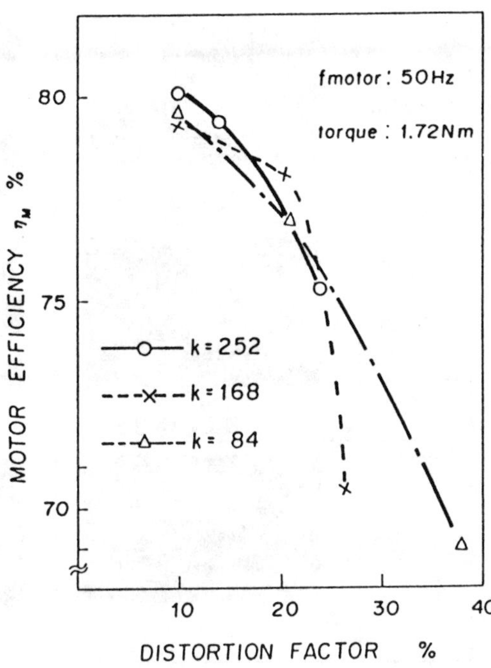

Fig.7. The effect of distortion factor on motor efficiency.

line current waveforms of various distortion factors. Over-modulation($A_f^* > 1.0$) with low dc link voltage is a key design factor of the new system.

4 VVVF drive of the new system

A new VVVF drive system is realized by using controllable dc voltage of the converter and the magnetic flux control PWM method of the inverter. In Fig. 9, the voltage distortion factor of the new system and that of the conventional inverter with an uncontrolled rectifier circuit are shown. The distortion factor of the conventional system is high especially at low motor frequency, while that of the new system is low for all motor frequencies. The over-modulation can reduce the distortion factor.

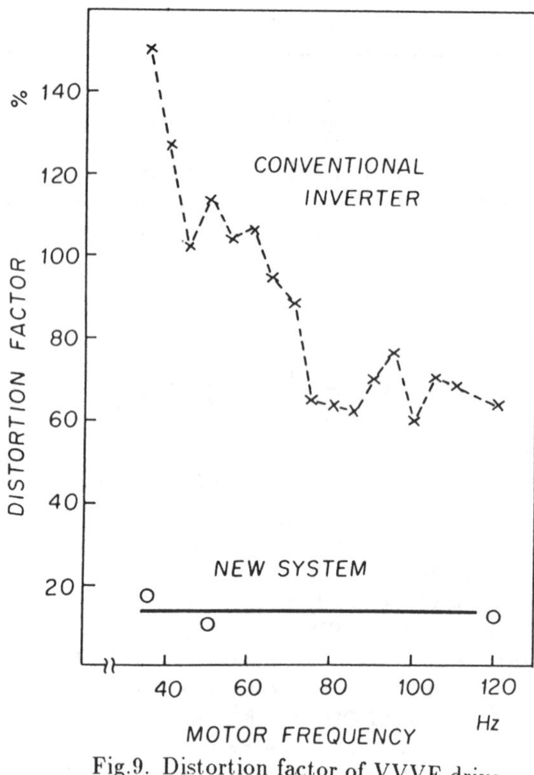

Fig.9. Distortion factor of VVVF drive.

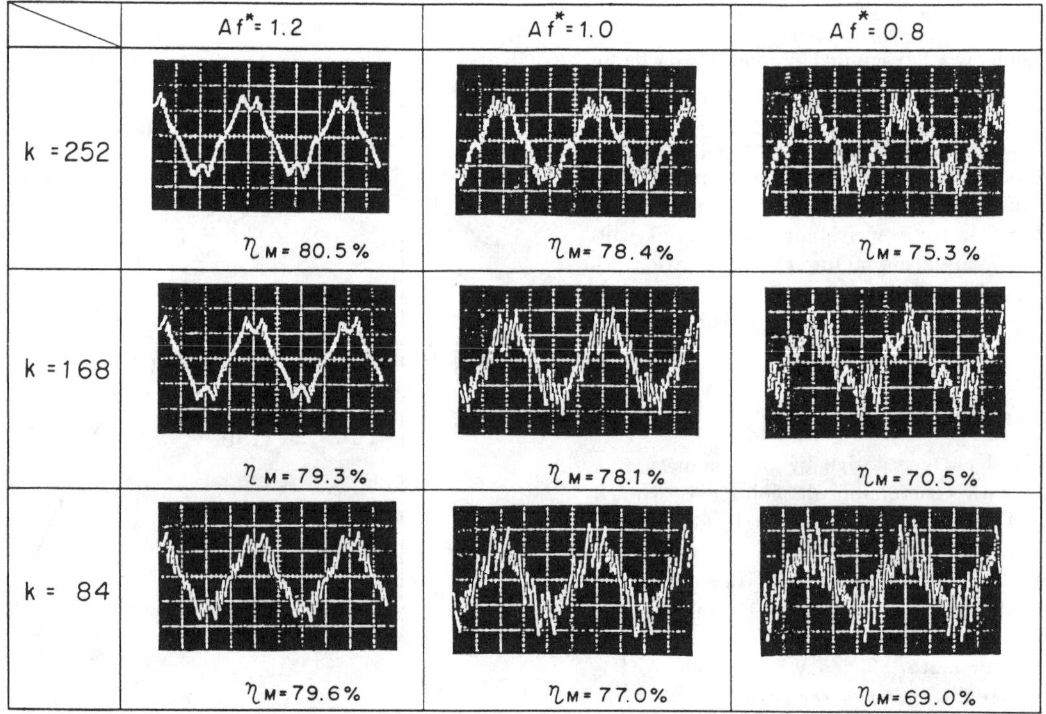

MOTOR FREQUENCY : 50Hz 5A/div, 2ms/div

Fig.8. Motor line current waveforms.

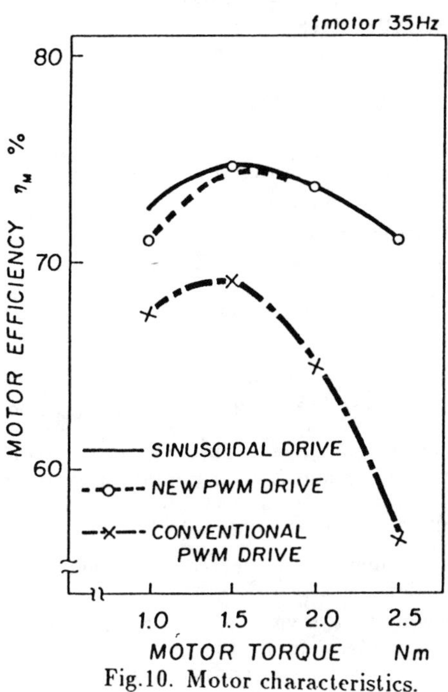

Fig.10. Motor characteristics.

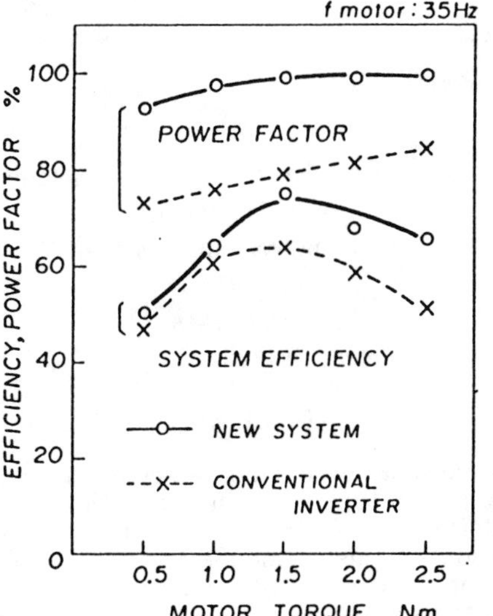

Fig.11. System efficiency and power factor.

Fig.10 shows the motor characteristics at 35 Hz. The motor efficiency of the new system is as high as that of the sinusoidal drive. On the other hand, the motor efficiency driven with the conventional inverter is low.

Fig.11 shows the system efficiency and the power factor. The system efficiency is defined by (motor shaft output power) /(system input power) . The power factor is calculated by the system input rms value. High efficiency and high power factor VVVF drive system has been achieved.

5 Conclusion

A control strategy of a new VVVF drive system is presented. The new system which delivers sinusoidal current, supplies PWM waveforms by the magnetic flux control method. The modulation factor of the magnetic flux control method with controllable dc link voltage is studied. As a result, the distortion factor is reduced by the overmodulation with low dc link voltage. The experimental result shows that the motor efficiency is as high as that of sinusoidal output voltage. High efficiency, high power factor VVVF drive system has been achieved.

References

[1] C. P. Henze and N. Mohan, "A DIGITALLY CONTROLLED AC TO DC POWER CONDITIONER THAT DRAWS SINUSOIDAL INPUT CURRENT", *IEEE-PESC Conference Record*, p531-540(1986).

[2] K.K. Sen and A.E. Emanuel, "UNITY POWER FACTOR SINGLE PHASE POWER CONDITIONING", *IEEE-PESC Conference Record*, p516-524(1987).

[3] M. Hombu, S. Ueda and A. Ueda, "A CURRENT SOURCE GTO INVERTER WITH SINUSOIDAL INPUTS AND OUTPUTS", *20th IEEE-IAS Annual Meeting Conference Record*, p1033-1039(1985).

[4] S. Nonaka and Y. Neba, "A PWM GTO CURRENT SOURCE CONVERTER-INVERTER SYSTEM WITH SINUSOIDAL INPUTS AND OUTPUTS", *22th IEEE-IAS Annual Meeting Conference Record*, p247-252(1987).

[5] B.T. Ooi, J.W. Dixon A.B. Kulkarni and N. Nishimoto, "AN INTEGRATED AC DRIVE SYSTEM USING A CONTROLLED-CURRENT PWM RECTIFIER/INVERTER LINK", *IEEE-PESC Conference Record*, p494-501(1986).

[6] M. Morimoto, S. Sato, K. Sumito and K. Oshitani, "Single-Chip Microcomputer control of the Inverter by the Magnetic Flux Control PWM Method", *IEEE Trans. Ind. Electron.*, vol.IE-36, No.1, p42-47(1989).

Paper 4.2

AN ACTIVE POWER FACTOR CORRECTION TECHNIQUE FOR THREE-PHASE DIODE RECTIFIERS

A.R. PRASAD * P.D. ZIOGAS * S. MANIAS **

* Department of Electrical Engineering
Concordia University
1455 De Maisonneuve Blvd W.
Montreal, Quebec
Canada, H3G 1M8
Tel.:514-848-3091

** Department of Electrical Engineering
Faculty of Technology
Demokritus University of Thrace
Xanthi, 67100
Greece

ABSTRACT

In this paper a novel active power factor correction method for power supplies with three-phase front-end diode rectifiers (Fig. 1) is proposed and analyzed. The implementation of this method requires the use of an additional single switch boost chopper. The combined front-end converter draws sinusoidal ac currents from the ac source with nearly unity input power factor while operating at a fixed switching frequency. Moreover this paper shows that when the active input power factor correction stage is also used to regulate the converter dc bus voltage, the converter performance can improve substantially in comparison with the conventional three-phase ac to dc converters. These improvements include component count reduction, simplified input synchronization logic requirements, and smaller reactive components. Finally selected theoretical results are verified experimentally.

1. INTRODUCTION

Traditionally, conversion of ac line voltages from utilities has been dominated by phase controlled or diode rectifiers. The non-ideal character of the input current drawn by these rectifiers creates a number of problems for the power distribution network and for other electrical systems in the vicinity of the rectifier including:

(i) phase displacement of the current and voltage fundamentals requires that the source and distribution equipment handle reactive power increasing their volt-ampere ratings;

(ii) high input current harmonics and low input power factor;

(iii) lower rectifier efficiency because of the large rms values of the input current;

(iv) input ac mains voltage distortion because of the associated higher peak currents;

(v) high reactive components size.

To combat these disadvantages system designers are increasingly incorporating active input power factor correction methods [2-4]. For medium to high power applications the input rectifier is fed from a three-phase ac source. Application of the bang-bang hysteresis control method to improve the input power factor of a three-phase ac to dc converter has been discussed by several authors [2-4]. In these references the three-phase ac to dc converter has been realized using three single-phase ac to dc converters (Fig. 2) using suitable input and output connections. This topology yields unity input power factor and is clearly much superior than the original phase controlled ac to dc topologies. However it also exhibits some disadvantages including;

(i) it requires complicated input synchronization logic;

(ii) owing to the variations in power circuit control parameters among the three individual converters, a complete triplen harmonic elimination from the input line current (I_{ia}) can not be achieved;

(iii) the switching frequency is load dependent;

(iv) the number of components required for three-phase ac to dc converter is three times the single-phase ac to dc converter;

(v) the advantages of using a three-phase inverter and transformer (better transformer core and copper utilization etc.) can not be achieved.

This paper addresses the analysis and design of a three-phase ac to dc converter which draws high quality input current waveforms from the ac source and exhibits none of the above mentioned disadvantages. However it has the disadvantages of substantially increasing the current stresses of the switching devices and the high frequency ripple content of the pre-filtered ac input currents. The principles of operation of the proposed converter are discussed in the next section.

2. PRINCIPLES OF OPERATION

The proposed three-phase ac to dc converter (Fig. 1) consists of two main power conversion stages. The first stage is a three-phase ac to dc rectifier consisting of an input filter, a boost inductor, a three-phase diode rectifier, an active power factor correction stage, and a dc link filter capacitor. The second stage can be modeled as any type of load requiring a regulated or unregulated dc bus such as general purpose single-phase or three-phase inverters or dc-dc converters with high frequency isolation. The active waveshaping of the input current waveform is obtained through the use of the three boost chopper components L_b, Q_b, and D_b, as shown in Fig. 1. The boost switch, Q_b, is turned on at constant frequency. The duty cycle of Q_b, is varied for load variation only and it is such that the input current is always discontinuous. During the 'on' period of the

Reprinted from *IEEE Power Electron. Specialists Conf. (PESC) Rec.*, pp. 58–66, 1989.

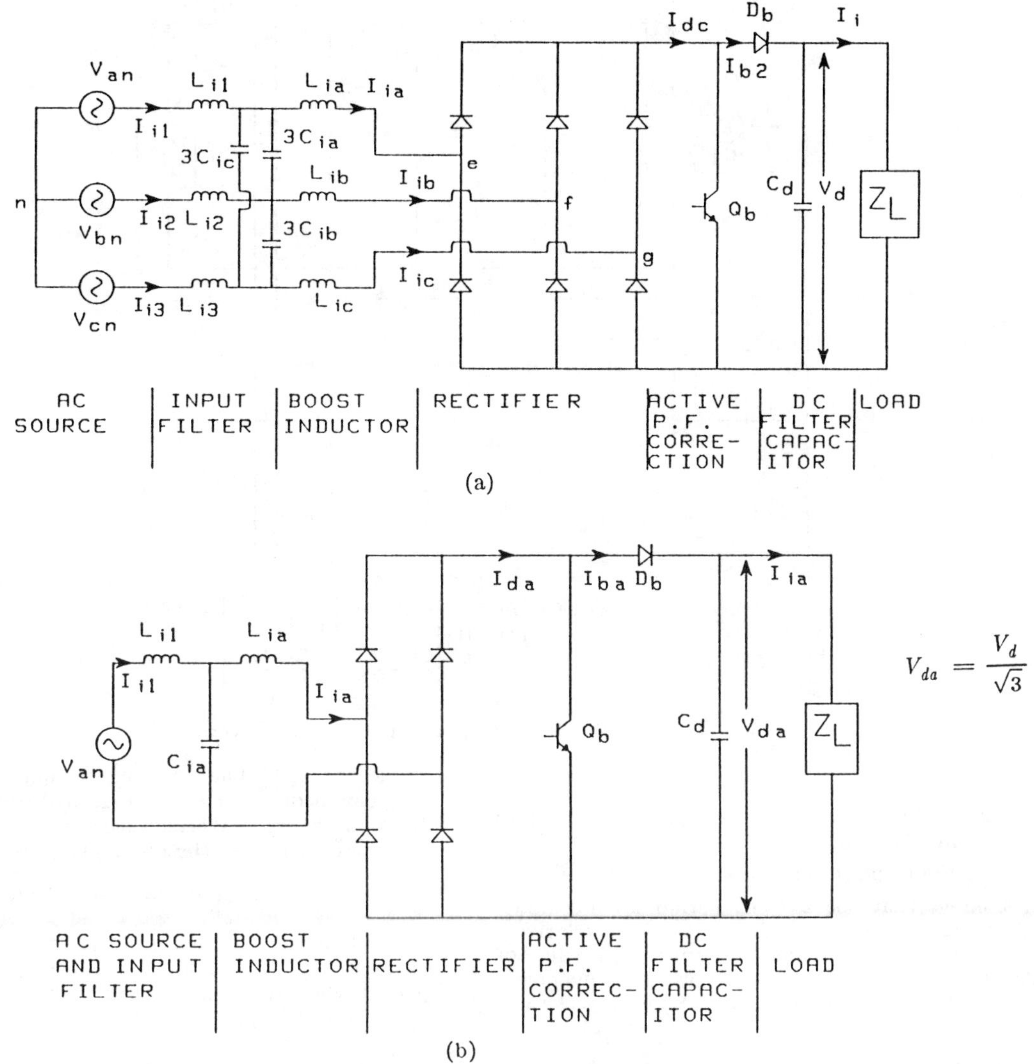

Fig. 1 (a) Proposed three-phase ac to dc converter.
(b) Single-phase equivalent circuit of (a).

boost switch all three input ac phases become shorted through inductors L_{ia}, L_{ib} L_{ic}, the six rectifier diodes and the boost switch. Consequently the three input currents I_{ia}, I_{ib}, and I_{ic} begin simultaneously to increase at a rate proportional to the instantaneous values of their respective phase voltages. Moreover the specific peak current values during each 'on' interval (Fig. 3(c)) are proportional to the average values of their input phase voltages during the same 'on' interval. Since each of these voltage average values varies sinusoidally the input current peaks also vary sinusoidally (Fig. 3(c)). Moreover since the current pulses always begin at zero, it means that their average values also vary sinusoidally. Consequently all three input ac currents consist of the fundamental (60 Hz) component and a band of high frequency unwanted components centered around the switching frequency (f_b) of the boost switch. Since this frequency (f_b) can be in the order of several tens of kHz, filtering out of the unwanted input current harmonics becomes a relatively easy task. From Fig. 3 it is also seen that input power control (or output voltage regulation) can be achieved through pulse width modulation of the boost switch 'on' interval at constant frequency (f_b). Incidently f_b can be easily locked to the mains 60 Hz frequency to avoid 'beat frequency' effects in the input currents.

Finally, under the operating conditions described here the 'displacement input power factor' ($\cos(\phi_1)$) before filtering is unity. Consequently, the overall input power factor (before filtering) becomes equal to the 'harmonic input power factor' and it is given by

$$Power\ Factor = \left[\frac{\frac{I_{ia,1}}{\sqrt{2}}}{\sqrt{\sum_{n=1}^{\infty} \left(\frac{I_{ia,n}}{\sqrt{2}}\right)^2}} \right] \quad (1)$$

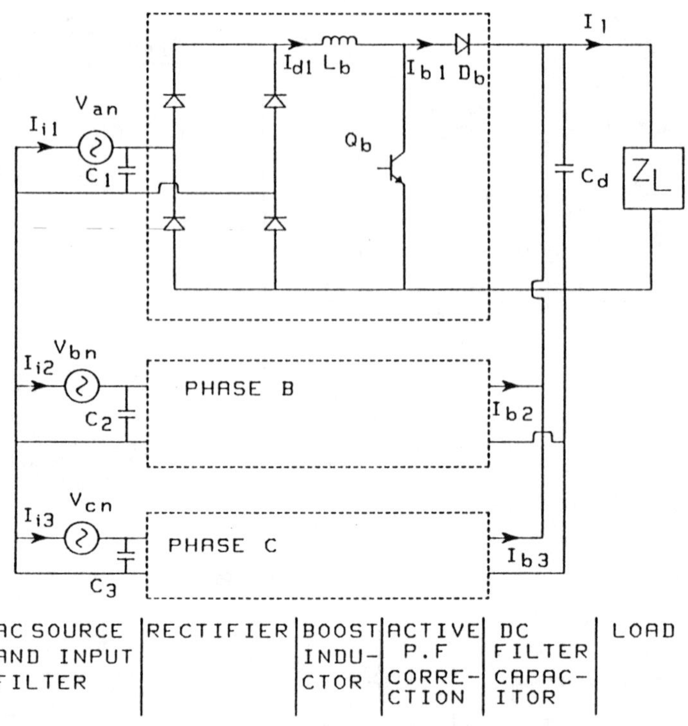

Fig. 2 Conventional three-phase ac to dc converter.

Where

$I_{ia,n}$ is the Fourier component of the nth harmonic component of current I_{ia}.

$\cos \phi_1$ is the displacement factor.

It is noted that the current harmonics associated with this power factor can be suppressed by a relatively small input capacitor (C_{ia}) and inductor (L_{i1}) because of their high frequencies. Therefore the overall input power factor after filtering (i.e. at the ac source) is very close to unity.

3. INPUT CURRENT ANALYSIS

Regarding Fig. 1 during the period when the boost switch (Q_b) is turned on, the equivalent single-phase circuit becomes as shown in Fig. 4(a). The input current (I_{ia}) rises at a rate determined by the input source voltage (V_{an}) and the inductor (L_{ia}). The current (I_{ia}) through the inductor during this period ($\beta \leq t \leq t_1$) is given by

$$E = V_{an} \sin(\omega t) = L_{ia} \frac{dI_{ia}}{dt}$$

Solving the above Eqn. for I_{ia} and substituting the initial conditions, $I_{ia}(\omega t) = 0$, when $t=\beta$ yields

$$I_{ia}(\omega t) = \frac{V_{an(peak)}}{\omega L_{ia}} \left[\cos(\omega\beta) - \cos(\omega t)\right] \quad (2)$$

Where β is the angle at which the boost switch (Q_b) is turned on, with reference to the input voltage V_{an} and t_1 is the boost switch (Q_b) 'on' period. During the period when the boost switch (Q_b) is off the current through the inductor decreases at a rate determined by the input voltage (V_{an}), output dc voltage (V_d), and the inductor (L_{ia}). The single phase equivalent circuit under this condition is shown in Fig. 4(b). Regarding Fig. 4(b) from the boost converter theory the rectifier input phase voltage (V_{en}) when the boost switch is off is given by

$$V_{en}(\omega t) = \frac{1}{1-D} V_{an}(\omega t) \quad (3)$$

where D is the duty cycle of the boost switch (Q_b). The current (I_{ia}) through the inductor (L_{ia}) during the period when the boost switch is off, $t_1 \leq t \leq t_2$, is given by

$$V_{an} \sin(\omega t) = L_{ia} \frac{dI_{ia}}{dt} + V_{en} \quad (4)$$

Solving Eqn. (4) for I_{ia} and substituting the initial condition $I_{ia}(\omega t) = I_{ia}(\omega t_1)$ when $t = t_1$ yields

$$I_{ia}(\omega t) = \frac{V_{an(peak)}}{\omega L_{ia}} \left[\cos(\omega\beta) - \cos(\omega t)\right] - \frac{V_{en}}{L_{ia}}(t - t_1) \quad (5)$$

For the designer the worst operating point is switching on the boost switch (Q_b) at the peak input voltage ($V_{an(peak)}$). Under this condition the current through the inductor (L_{ia}) increases at its maximum rate and reaches its maximum value at the end of t_1. Also under this condition, the time required for the current (I_{ia}) to fall to zero is maximum. Therefore, the frequency of the boost switch (Q_b) is a function of ac input voltage (V_{an}) and output dc voltage(V_d). Substituting $\beta = 90^o$ and t = (90° + t) in Eqn. (2) yields

$$I_{ia}(\omega t) = \frac{V_{an(peak)}}{\omega L_{ia}} \sin(\omega t) \quad (6)$$

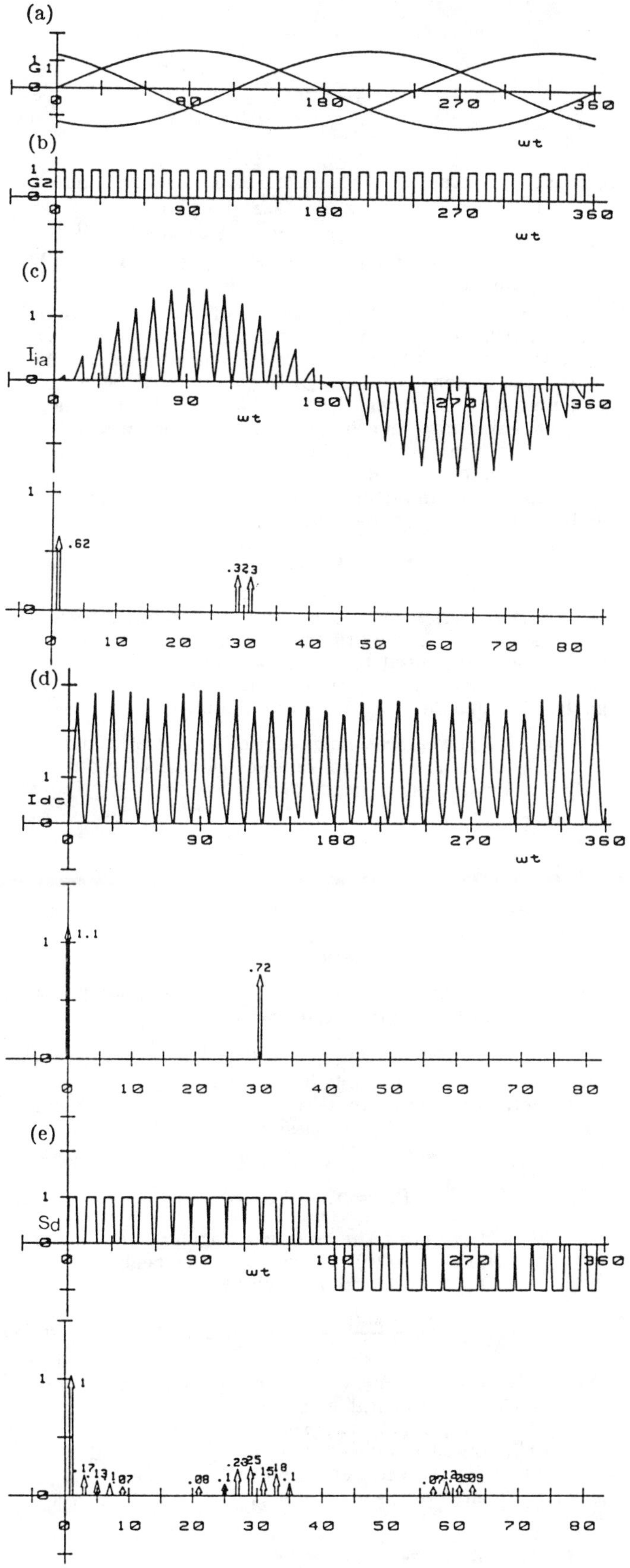

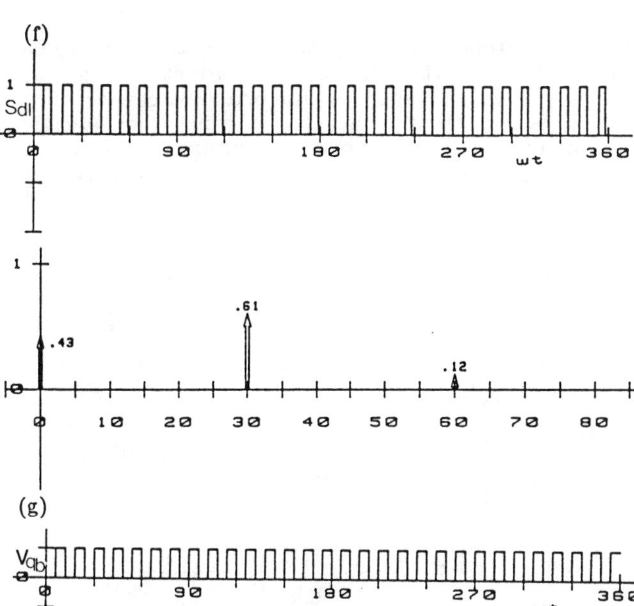

Fig. 3 Simulated waveforms

(a) Three-phase ac source phase voltages.

(b) Boost switch (Q_b) gating signals.

(c) Rectifier input current (I_{ia}) and its spectrum.

(d) Rectifier output current (I_{dc}) and its spectrum.

(e) Three-phase diode rectifier switching function and its spectrum.

(f) Boost diode (D_b) switching function and its spectrum.

(g) Voltage across the boost switch (Q_b).

In practice the boost switch switching frequency, f_b, is on the order of 20-40 kHz and the boost switch 'on' period (t_1) is small in comparison to the input source voltage (V_{an}) time period. For small values of ωt, $\sin\omega t$ is approximately equal to ωt. Consequently Eqn. (6) becomes

$$I_{ia}(\omega t) = \frac{V_{an(peak)}}{L_{ia}} t \qquad 0 \leq t \leq t_1 \tag{7}$$

At time t_1 the inductor current (I_{ia}) reaches its maximum value and the boost switch (Q_b) is turned off by its appropriate control signal. Substituting $\beta = 90^o$ and $t = (90^o + t)$ in Eqn. (5) yields

$$I_{ia}(\omega t) = \frac{V_{an(peak)}}{\omega L_{ia}} \sin(\omega t) - \frac{V_{en}}{L_{ia}}(t - t_1) \tag{8}$$

and substituting ωt for $\sin(\omega t)$, the above equation becomes

$$I_{ia}(\omega t) = \frac{V_{an(peak)}}{L_{ia}} t - \frac{V_{en}}{L_{ia}}(t - t_1) \qquad t_1 \leq t \leq t_2 \tag{9}$$

The current $I_{ia}(\omega t) = 0$ at time $t = t_2$. Substituting this condition in the above equation yields

$$\frac{t_2}{t_1} = \frac{V_{en}}{V_{en} - V_{an(peak)}} \tag{10}$$

Therefore, the minimum output dc voltage, $V_d = V_{en}^{*}\sqrt{3}$

(11)

If the dc output voltage(V_d) is less than the above value then the rate at which the inductor current (I_{ia}) falls to zero decreases. Consequently, the boost switch frequency has to be decreased to a value at which the inductor current (I_{ia}) becomes zero before turning on the boost switch (Q_b) again. In other words the the duty cycle of the boost switch must be decreased for a given boost switch switching frequency (f_b). Therefore the

(a)

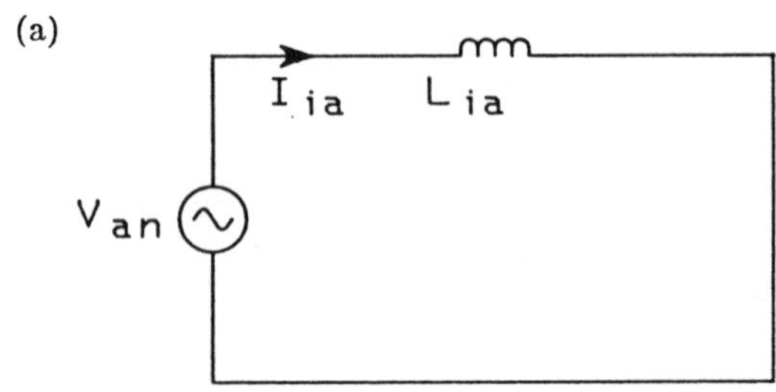

(b)

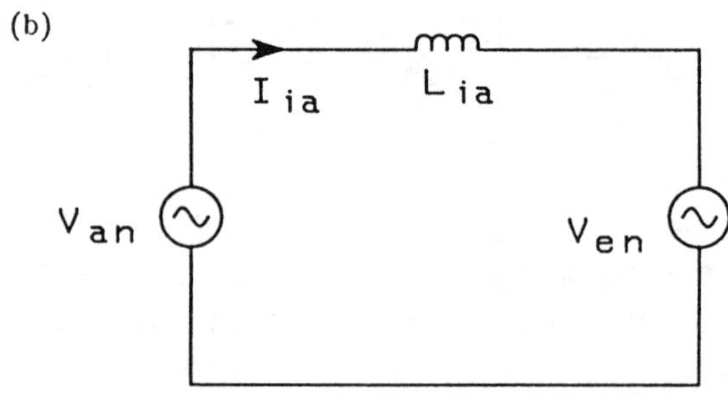

Fig. 4 (a) Equivalent single-phase circuit when the boost switch is on.

(b) Equivalent single-phase circuit when the boost switch is off.

switching frequency of the boost switch (Q_b) is a function of the dc output voltage (V_d). The variation of the minimum dc bus voltage (V_d) with duty cycle of the boost switch is shown in Fig. 5.

From the description presented above, the simulated inductor current (I_{ia}) and its spectrum, the diode rectifier switching function ($Sd(\omega t)$) and its spectrum, and the diode (D_b) switching function ($Sd\,1(\omega t)$) and its spectrum, are derived and shown in Fig. 3. Evaluation of Fig. 3 clearly shows the elimination of the low frequency components from the rectifier input and output currents (I_{ia}, I_{dc}).

The input current (I_{ia}) can be expressed in terms of the Fourier series as

$$I_{ia}(\omega t) = \sum_{n=1,3}^{\infty} \left[A_n \cos(n\omega t) + B_n \sin(n\omega t) \right]$$

Where A_n and B_n are the Fourier coefficients of the current I_{ia}. The above expression can be further simplified to

$$I_{ia}(\omega t) = \sum_{n=1,3}^{\infty} C_n \sin(n\omega t + \theta_n) \qquad (12)$$

Where

$$C_n = \sqrt{A_n^2 + B_n^2} \quad and \quad \theta_n = \tan^{-1}\frac{A_n}{B_n}$$

The values of C_n and θ_n depend upon the value of the operating frequency of the boost switch for a given

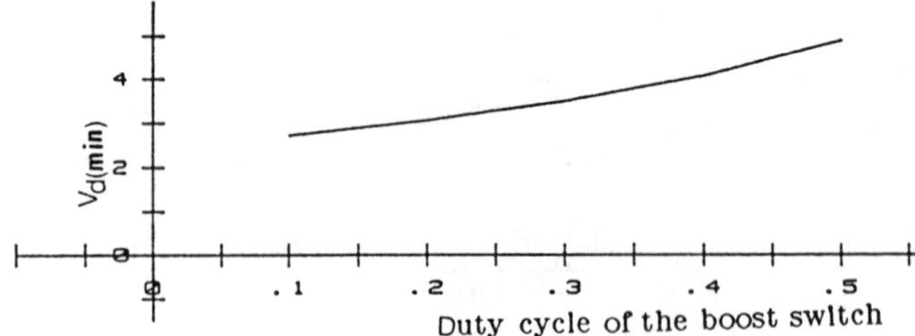

Fig. 5 Variation of minimum dc output voltage (V_d) with the boost switch duty cycle.

inductor value (L_{ia}). The variation of the input power factor (without input filter) with a boost switch duty cycle is shown in Fig. 6. The low input power factor is due to the presence of the high frequency harmonic components in the current (i_{ia}). These high frequency current harmonics can be filtered easily with a small input filter thus providing a nearly unity input power factor. The peak inductor current (I_{ia}) depends upon the value of the inductor (L_{ia}), the operating frequency, and the duty cycle of the boost switch.

4. SYSTEM ANALYSIS

In this section the proposed converter is analyzed under steady-state conditions. The expressions derived are subsequently used to obtain the information necessary for proper converter design. The converter is analyzed under the following assumptions:

(i) all power switching devices are ideal and the forward drop and reverse leakage currents of the diodes are negligible;

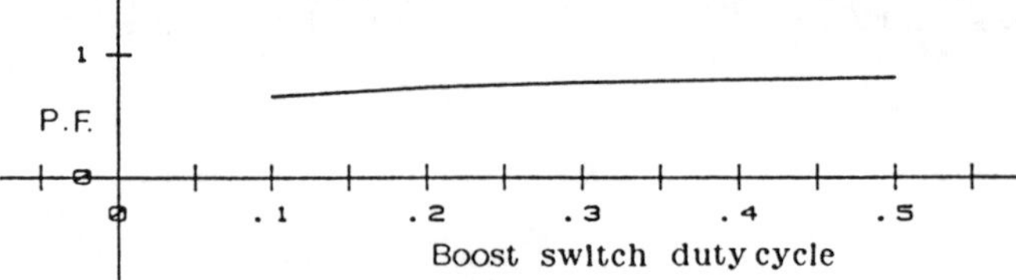

Fig. 6 Variation of power factor (without input filter) with boost switch duty cycle.

(ii) filter components are ideal;

(iii) the load voltage is ripple free.

Moreover, the rated input rms voltage, $V_{an(rms)}$, and rated output power, P_d, are assumed to be

$$V_{an(rms)} = 1.0 \ P.U. \ V$$

$$P_d = 1.0 \ P.U. \ W$$

Further assuming the ac source angular frequency is 1.0 P.U., from Fig. 3(c) the value of the peak current $I_{ia(peak)}$ for $L_{ia} = 0.1$ P.U. is given by

$$I_{ia(peak)} = \frac{V_{an(peak)}}{L_{ia}} * \frac{T_b}{2} = 1.48 P.U. \qquad (13)$$

Where T_b is the boost switch time period. The amplitude of the fundamental component of current $I_{ia,1}$ is 0.62. From Eqn. (13) the peak value of current I_{ia} depends upon the values of L_{ia}, $V_{an(peak)}$, and T_b. From Fig. 3(c) the ratio of current $I_{ia,1(peak)}$ to $I_{ia(peak)}$ is 0.418. Therefore the general expression for the current $I_{ia,1(peak)}$ is given by

$$I_{ia,1(peak)} = I_{ia(peak)} * 0.418$$

$$= \frac{V_{an(peak)}}{L_{ia}} * \frac{T_b}{2} * 0.418 \qquad (14)$$

From Eqn. (14) the maximum value of the inductor L_{ia} for any boost switch switching frequency can be calculated.

4.1 Derivation of rectifier output current and output filter design

Regarding Fig. 3(e) the rectifier output current, I_{dc}, is given by

$$I_{dc}(\omega t) = \left[\sum_{k=0}^{2} I_{ia}(\omega t - \frac{2k\pi}{3}) * S_d(\omega t - \frac{2k\pi}{3}) \right] \qquad (15)$$

Where

$S_d(\omega t)$ is the diode rectifier switching function shown in Fig. 3(e) and it can be expressed in Fourier series as

$$S_d(\omega t) = \sum_{n=1,3}^{\infty} \left[D_n \cos(n\omega t) + E_n \sin(n\omega t) \right]$$

$$S_d(\omega t) = \sum_{n=1,3}^{\infty} F_n \sin(n\omega t + \phi_n) \qquad (16)$$

Where

$$F_n = \sqrt{D_n^2 + E_n^2} \quad and \quad \phi_n = \tan^{-1}\frac{D_n}{E_n}$$

Substituting Eqns. (12) and (16) into Eqn. (15) the diode rectifier output current is given by

$$I_{dc}(\omega t) = \sum_{k=0}^{2} \left[\sum_{n=1,3}^{\infty} C_n \sin(n(\omega t - \frac{2k\pi}{3}) + \theta_n) * \sum_{m=1,3}^{\infty} F_m \sin(m(\omega t - \frac{2k\pi}{3}) + \phi_m) \right]$$

$$= \sum_{k=0}^{2} \left[\left(C_1 \sin(\omega t - \frac{2k\pi}{3} + \theta_1) + C_3 \sin(3\omega t - 2k\pi + \theta_3) + \ldots\ldots \right) * \left(F_1 \sin(\omega t - \frac{2k\pi}{3} + \phi_1) + F_3 \sin(3\omega t - 2k\pi + \phi_3) + \ldots\ldots \right) \right] \qquad (17)$$

Since the harmonic components of $I_{dc}(\omega t)$ are all multiples of six (i.e. 6,12,18...) Eqn. (17) becomes (assuming the boost switch switching frequency, f_b, is also a multiple of six)

$$I_{dc}(\omega t) = 3 \left[\frac{C_1 F_1}{2} \cos(\theta_1 - \phi_1) + \ldots + \frac{C_{f_b-1} F_{f_b-1}}{2} \cos(\theta_{f_b-1} - \phi_{f_b-1}) + \ldots\ldots \right]$$
$$- \ldots\ldots - \left(\frac{3C_1 F_{f_b-1}}{2} \cos(f_b \omega t + \theta_1 - \phi_{f_b-1}) - \frac{3C_1 F_{f_b+1}}{2} \cos(f_b \omega t + \theta_1 - \phi_{f_b+1}) \right)$$
$$- \left(\frac{3F_1 C_{f_b-1}}{2} \cos(f_b \omega t - \phi_1 + \theta_{f_b-1}) - \frac{3F_1 C_{f_b+1}}{2} \cos(f_b \omega t - \phi_1 + \theta_{f_b+1}) + \ldots\ldots \right) \qquad (18)$$

A close examination of Eqn. (18) reveals that the dominant harmonic component of the rectifier output current (I_{dc}) is at f_b. If the boost switch switching frequency is not a multiple of six then the dominant frequency of the rectifier output current (I_{dc}) is a multiple of six around f_b since the harmonics of frequency f_b cancel on the dc side. Evaluation of Fig. 3(c) shows that the dominant harmonic component of the current I_{ia} is at f_b -1, where f_b is the boost switch switching frequency. Furthermore, the switching function (Sd1) of the diode, D_b, shown in Fig. 3(f) can be expressed by the Fourier series

$$S_{d1}(\omega t) = G_0 + \sum_{n=1}^{\infty} \left[H_n \cos(n\omega t) + K_n \sin(n\omega t) \right]$$

$$= G_0 + \sum_{n=1}^{\infty} L_n \sin(n\omega t + \eta_n) \qquad (19)$$

where

$$L_n = \sqrt{H_n^2 + K_n^2} \quad and \quad \eta_n = \tan^{-1}\frac{H_n}{K_n}$$

The dominant harmonic component of the diode (D_b) switching function (sd1) is f_b. Therefore the dominant harmonic component of the output current (I_{b2}) before output filter capacitor is given by

$$I_{b2,f_b(peak)} = L_{f_b} * I_{dc}(0) + G_o(0) * F_{f_b} \qquad (20)$$

The converter output current ($I_{b2}(\omega t)$) consists of a modulated train of pulses and consequently some form of filtering is necessary to separate the dc component from the undesired harmonic components. Furthermore, the amplitude of the f_bth-order voltage harmonic component across the output filter capacitor (C_d) is given by

$$V_{d,f_b} = \frac{I_{b2,f_b(peak)}}{f_b \omega C_d} \qquad (21)$$

where

$I_{b2,f_b(peak)}$ is the amplitude of the f_b^{th} harmonic component of current I_{b2}.

Moreover by assuming that the ripple voltage across the filter capacitor, C_d, is less than 0.01% (i.e. less than 30mV at the load terminals at V_d = 300V) the output voltage (V_d) ripple can be defined by

$$Ripple\ \% = \frac{100 V_{d,f_b(rms)}}{V_{d,o}} \qquad (22)$$

Substituting Eqn. (22) into Eqn. (21) the value of the output filter capacitor (C_d) is given by

$$C_d = \frac{I_{b2,f_b(peak)} * 100}{\sqrt{2} * V_{d,o} * (Ripple\ \%) * f_b * \omega} \qquad (23)$$

Substituting Eqns. (3) and (11) into Eqn. (23) yields

$$C_d = \frac{I_{b2,f_b(peak)} * 100 * (1-D)}{\sqrt{2} * (Ripple\ \%) * f_b * \omega * V_{an(peak)} * \sqrt{3}} \qquad (24)$$

4.2 Input Filter Design

In most specifications for power supplies the total harmonic distortion (THD) content of the input line current (I_{i1}) is $\leq 5\%$. Also it can be shown that if the amplitude of the dominant harmonic component of I_{i1} is reduced to 3% of the amplitude of the respective fundamental then THD $\leq 5\%$ can be ensured. Therefore for the PWM method shown in Fig. 3 the order of the dominant harmonic component of the inductor current (I_{ia}) is f_b - 1. The harmonic equivalent circuit per phase for the input filter is shown in Fig. 7. Reg. Fig. 7 the filter inductor current harmonic components, $I_{i1,n}$, is given by

$$I_{i1,n} = \frac{X_{C_{ia,1}} I_{ia,n}}{n^2 X_{L_{i1,1}} - X_{C_{ia,1}}} \tag{25}$$

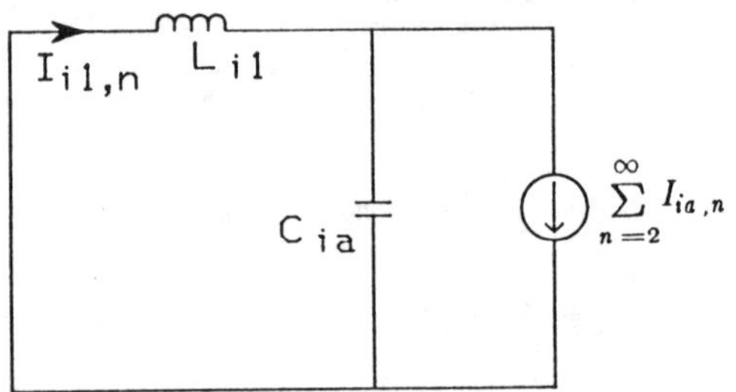

Fig. 7 Single-phase equivalent circuit for input filter design.

where

n is the order of the harmonic;

$X_{C_{ia,1}}$ is the filter capacitor (C_{ia}) reactance at fundamental frequency;

$X_{L_{i1,1}}$ is the filter inductor (L_{i1}) reactance at fundamental frequency.

Equation (25) can be further simplified as

$$\frac{X_{L_{i1,1}}}{X_{C_{ia,1}}} = \frac{1}{n^2}\left[\frac{I_{ia,n}}{I_{i1,n}} + 1\right] \tag{26}$$

The dominant harmonic component of the current I_{ia} is at f_b - 1 therefore Eqn. (24) reduces to

$$\frac{X_{L_{i1,1}}}{X_{C_{ia,1}}} = \frac{1}{(f_b - 1)^2}\left[\frac{I_{ia,f_b-1}}{I_{i1,f_b-1}} + 1\right] \tag{27}$$

Evaluation of Eqn. (25) reveals that size of the filter components is a function of the boost switch switching frequency (f_b). The size of the filter components becomes smaller and smaller for higher switching frequency (f_b). Consequently all the harmonics of the input current (I_{i1}) becomes smaller and smaller and the input power factor is nearly unity.

4.3 Component Ratings

From the aforementioned assumptions and derived analytical expressions the voltage and current ratings of the various system components are as follows.

4.3.1 Inductor L_{ia}

Value of L_{ia} : 0.1

Rms current : 0.54 P.U.

Peak current : 1.48 P.U.

4.3.2 Rectifier Diode

Average current : 0.38 P.U.

Rms current : 0.382 P.U.

Peak current : 1.48 P.U.

4.3.3 Boost switch Q_b

Peak forward voltage : 4.898 P.U.

Peak current : 2.86 P.U.

Rms current : 0.713 P.U.

4.3.4 Boost Diode D_b

Peak reverse blocking voltage : 4.898 P.U.

Rms current : 0.98 P.U.

Average current : 0.69 P.U.

Peak current : 2.86 P.U.

4.3.5 DC filter capacitor C_d

Value : Eqn. (24)

Rms ripple current : 0.98 P.U.

Peak voltage : 4.898 P.U.

5. DESIGN EXAMPLE

To illustrate the significance and facilitate the understanding of theoretical results obtained in preceding sections the following design example is given.

AC source rms voltage ($V_{an(rms)}$) = 50V = 1.0 P.U.

Supply frequency = 60Hz.

Rated output power = 1.0 kW. = 1.0 P.U.

Input ac source angular frequency = 377 rad./sec.

Boost switch switching frequency (f_b) = 24 kHz.

From these values:

$$1 \text{ P.U. current} = \frac{1000}{3*50} = 6.66 \text{ A}$$

$$1 \text{ P.U. impedance} = \frac{50}{6.66} = 7.50\Omega$$

$$1 \text{ P.U. angular frequency} = 2\pi f = 377 \text{ rad/sec.}$$

$$1 \text{ P.U. inductance} = \frac{7.50}{377} = 0.023\text{H}$$

$$1 \text{ P.U. capacitance} = \frac{1}{377*7.5} = 353.66\ \mu\text{F}.$$

Using Eqn. (14) the maximum value of the inductor L_{ia} required at 24 kHz to deliver 1.0 P.U. (rms) current (I_{ia}) is given by

$$L_{ia} = \frac{\sqrt{2}*50}{\sqrt{2}*6.66} * \frac{1}{24000} * \frac{0.418}{2}$$

$$= 65.37\mu H$$

Using Eqns. (3) and (11) the following values are computed:

Duty cycle of the boost switch = 0.5

Rectifier input phase voltage $V_{en} = \frac{50*\sqrt{2}}{1-.5} = 141.4$ Volts.

Minimum output voltage $V_d = \sqrt{3}*V_{en} = 141.4*\sqrt{3}$ = 244.91 V.

Choosing an input filter capacitor (C_{ia}) value of 0.1 P.U. and using the Eqn. (27) the value of the input filter inductor (L_{i1}) value is obtained.

The dominant ripple frequency = 24000 - 1 = 23.99 KHz = 399.98 P.U.

$$L_{i1,1} = \frac{1}{0.1 * (399.98)^2} \left[\frac{0.7}{0.03} + 1 \right] = 0.00152 \ P.U.$$

$$= 34.96 \mu H$$

Using Eqn. (24) the value of the filter capacitor is obtained.

$$C_d = \frac{0.7 * 100 * 0.5}{\sqrt{2} * 0.01 * 400 * 1 * \sqrt{2} * \sqrt{3}}$$

$$= 2.53 \ P.U. \ = 893.63 \mu F$$

6. EXPERIMENTAL RESULTS

To verify the selected predicted results a 1.0 kva experimental converter has been implemented using power MOSFET switch with the following circuit parameters:

Operating frequency of the boost switch $f_b = 25.64$ kHz.

Input ac source rms phase voltage (V_{an}) = 50V

Rectifier input ac rms current $I_{ia} = 11.4$ Amps.

Duty cycle of the boost switch $Q_b = 0.5$

Inductor (L_{ia}) = 45 μH

DC bus voltage (V_d) = 300 V

Rectifier output dc average current $I_{dc} = 4.0$ Amps.

Experimental waveforms obtained with this prototype are shown in Fig. 8. In particular, evaluation of the input current (I_{i1}) shown in Fig. 8(a) is in phase with the ac voltage as predicted. Furthermore the inductor current (I_{ia}), rectifier output current (I_{dc}), and the voltage across the switch are in close agreement with the simulated results shown in Figs. 3(c), 3(d) and 3(g) respectively. However with the conventional method (Fig. 2) the rectifier input rms current to deliver 1200 watts is 8.0 Amps. ($\frac{1200}{3 * 50}$). Moreover with the proposed method the rectifier rms input current drawn from ac the source (11.4 Amps.) is higher in comparison with the conventional three-phase ac to dc converter shown in Fig. 2.

7. CONCLUSIONS

In this paper a novel active power factor correction method for three-phase diode rectifiers is proposed and analyzed. With the proposed method the rectifier draws sinusoidal ac current from the source with unity power factor. Moreover, the proposed method eliminates the complicated synchronization logic requirement, reduces the number of components, and reduces the filter reactive components size. Finally, theoretical results are verified experimentally. However the proposed method has the disadvantage of increasing the switching stresses of the switching devices in comparison with the conventional three-phase ac to dc converter shown in Fig. 2.

REFERENCES

[1] S. Manias, A.R. Prasad, and P.D. Ziogas, "Three-phase inductor fed SMR converter with high frequency isolation high power density and improved power factor," IEE proceedings, Vol. 134, pt. B, No. 4, July 1987, pp. 183-191.

[2] M.J. Kocher and R.L. Steigerwald, "An AC to DC converter with high quality input waveforms," IEEE Trans. Ind. Appl., Vol. IA-19, No. 4, July/Aug. 1983, pp. 586-599.

[3] W.P. Marple, "Low distortion three-phase power regulator," IBM technical disclosure bulletin," Vol. 22, No. 3, Aug. 1979, pp. 970-971.

[4] Dan Gauger et al, "A three-phase off line switching power supply with unity power factor and low TIF," in Conf. Rec. 1986 IEEE INTELEC, pp. 115-121.

(a)

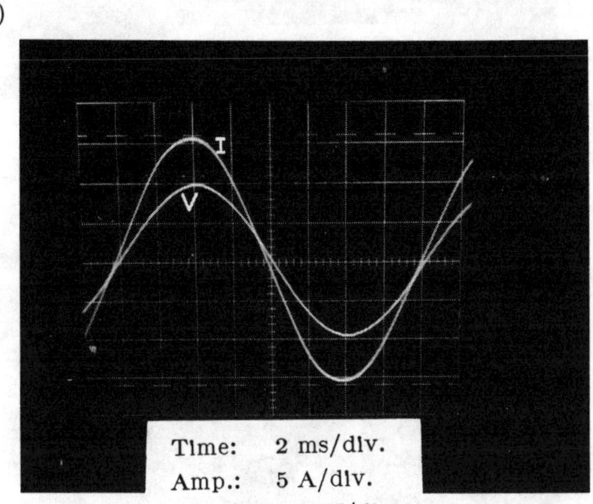

(b)

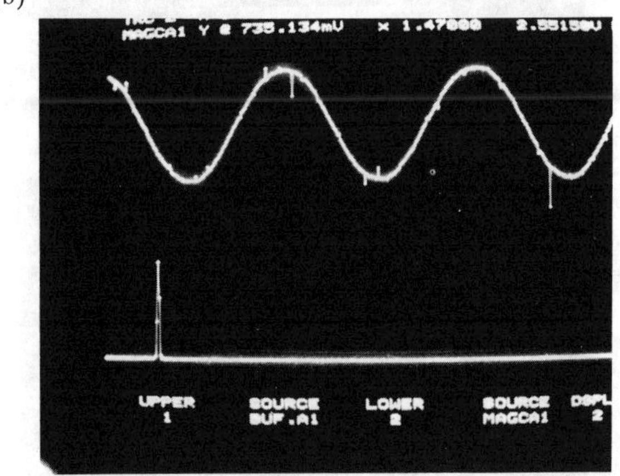

(c)

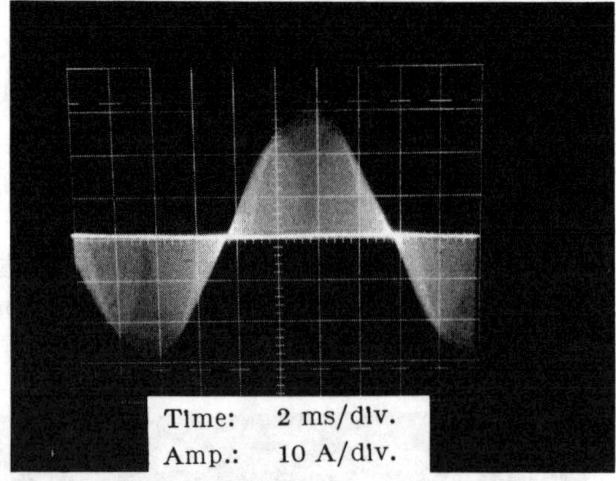

(d)

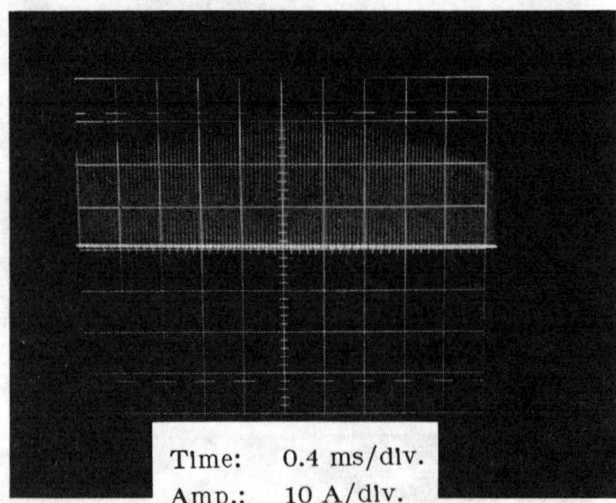

(e)

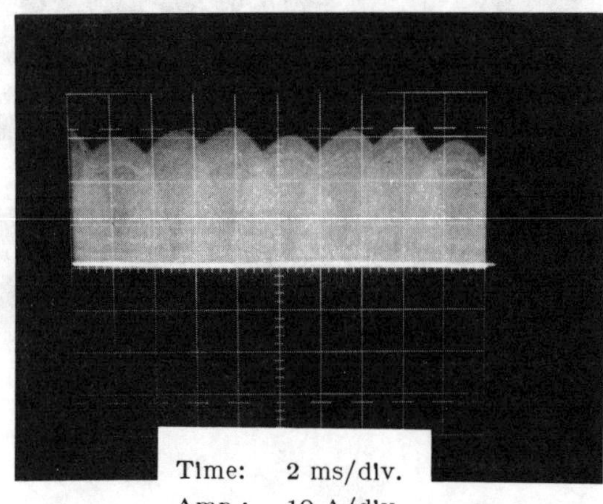

(f)

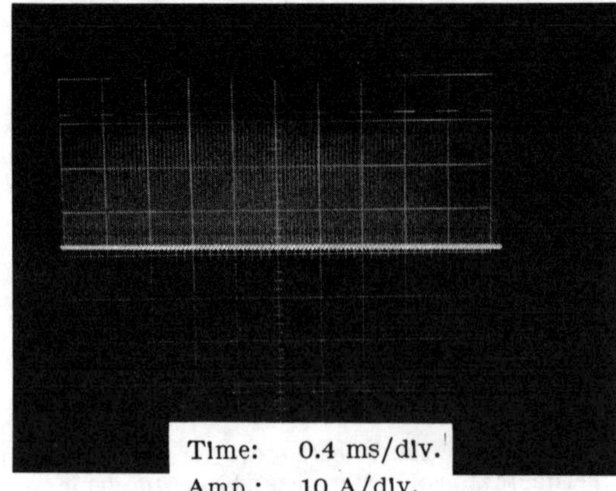

(g)

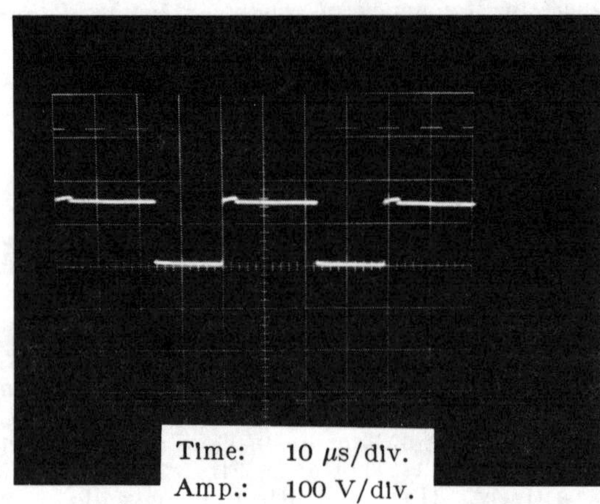

Fig. 8 Experimental waveforms.

(a) Input current (I_{i1}) and ac source phase voltage

(b) Input current (I_{i1}) spectrum.

(c) Rectifier input current (I_{ia}).

(d) Expanded version of (c).

(e) Rectifier output current (I_{dc}).

(f) Expanded version of (e).

(g) Voltage across the boost switch at reduced input voltage.

Paper 4.3

A New Speed Control System for DC Motors Using GTO Converter and its Application to Elevators

HIROMI INABA, SEIYA SHIMA, MEMBER, IEEE, AKITERU UEDA, MEMBER, IEEE, TAKEKI ANDO, TOSHIAKI KUROSAWA, AND YOSHIO SAKAI

Abstract—**A dc motor control system using a new GTO converter, is developed for an intermediate-speed elevator (2.5-m/s rated speed and 1000-kg load). Its features include 1) a main circuit control system composed of pulsewidth and phase controls, 2) a circuit to suppress the overvoltage which occurs when the GTO is turned off, 3) direct digital control which is composed of an acceleration control to compensate for lag time in the field current response and a self-correcting function to compensate for landing error. Application of the control system provided a higher power factor and smaller power consumption than a conventional control system.**

INTRODUCTION

THE THYRISTOR Leonard system and field control method [2] have been used to control the speed of dc motors in elevators. While these offer improved energy consumption and control performance, a number of problems remain.

a) The power factor in a conventional system is rather small at low output voltage. As an elevator usually runs at lower speeds, this disadvantage becomes more serious.

b) Some additional equipment, such as a power transformer for voltage matching and a dc reactor for smoothing the current waveform, are needed.

A method has been proposed to improve the power factor by using an ac–dc converter which is composed of three [3] or six [4] GTO's with pulsewidth control. In the six-GTO converter, GTO's turn on and off several times in a half-cycle of source voltage and the pulsewidth is modulated so as to decrease the third and fifth higher harmonics. So in this six-GTO converter system, the power factor is improved sufficiently and the waveform of the ac line input current becomes similar to a sine wave. However, the problem still remains that for this system the dc output voltage does not reach zero, which hinders its application to elevator speed control.

We have developed a new speed control method for dc motors which is suitable for elevators. This method combines two different current control modes in the GTO converter; pulsewidth control at higher output voltages and phase control with a minimum pulsewidth at lower values. Thus both power factor improvement and good dc output voltage control are realized over the entire voltage range down to nearly zero. Although the three-GTO converter system is used in this paper, the six-GTO converter system can also be used. This three-GTO converter system is used in place of conventional thyristors on the positive polarity side of the three-phase full-wave bridge circuit.

In comparing the three-GTO converter system with the six-GTO converter system, the cost performance of the former system is better than the latter system, but its compensation for higher harmonics is not. However, as compensation of the former system is better than that of the conventional thyristor Leonard system, as described later, the three-GTO converter was used on the basis of its cost performance.

In addition, we adopted a control system in which the armature current is unidirectional, while the field current is bidirectional. This system reduces the cost and power consumption of the converter in comparison with conventional bidirectional armature current control.

DEVELOPMENT OF A GTO CONVERTER WITH A HIGH POWER FACTOR

A. Construction

A block diagram of this system is shown in Fig. 1. The converter which controls the armature current of the dc motor uses three GTO's arranged on the positive polarity side of the six arms. The control circuit is composed of two function generators, a pulsewidth control circuit and a phase control circuit. The function generators produce a pulsewidth control signal and a phase control signal. The pulsewidth control circuit and the phase control circuit which determines the firing angle of the converter are operated by output signals of the function generators. The control signal is produced in response to deviations between a current command and the actual current value. As the power factor is improved by the GTO converter, a transformer to match the power source voltage with the load voltage is unnecessary, and as the waveform of the armature current is smoothed by high-frequency chopping of the GTO converter, a dc reactor is also unnecessary.

B. Operational Principle

Fig. 2 graphically illustrates relationships between the phase angle and pulsewidth to the control signal. In the figure, the control signal is divided into two ranges, the pulsewidth control range and the phase control range.

1) Pulsewidth Control Range: The mode is generated when the absolute value of the control signal is large. The

Paper IPCSD 84-26, approved by the Industrial Drives Committee of the IEEE Industry Applications Society for presentation at the 1983 Industry Applications Society Annual Meeting, Mexico City, Mexico, October 3–7, 1983. Manuscript released for publication July 5, 1984.

H. Inaba, S. Shima, T. Ando, and T. Kurosawa are with the Tenth Department, Hitachi Research Laboratories, Hitachi Ltd., 1070 Ichige, Katsuta City, Ibaraki 312, Japan.

A. Ueda is with the First Department, Hitachi Research Laboratories, Hitachi Ltd., 1070 Ichige, Katsuta City, Ibaraki 312, Japan.

Y. Sakai is with Mito Works, Hitachi Ltd., Ibaraki, Japan.

Reprinted from *IEEE Trans. Ind. Applicat.*, vol. IA-21, no. 2, pp. 391–397, March/April 1985.

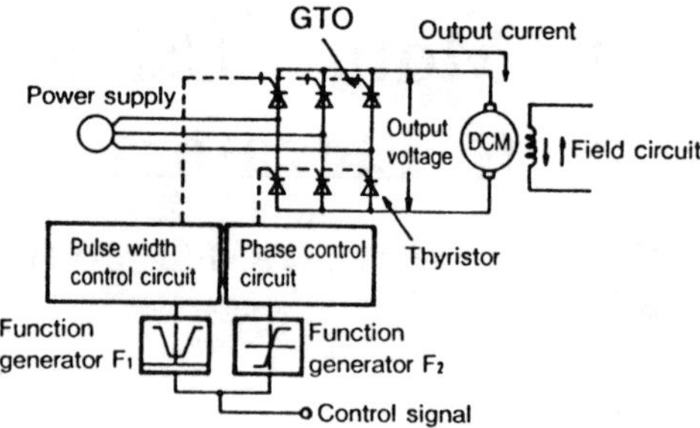

Fig. 1. Block diagram of GTO converter with high power factor.

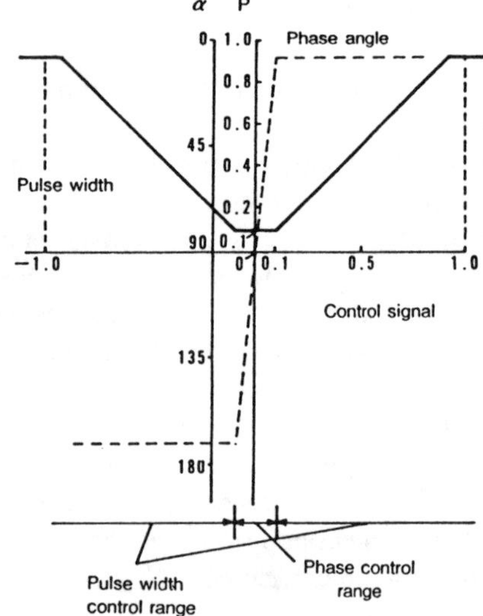

Fig. 2. Phase angle and pulsewidth characteristics.

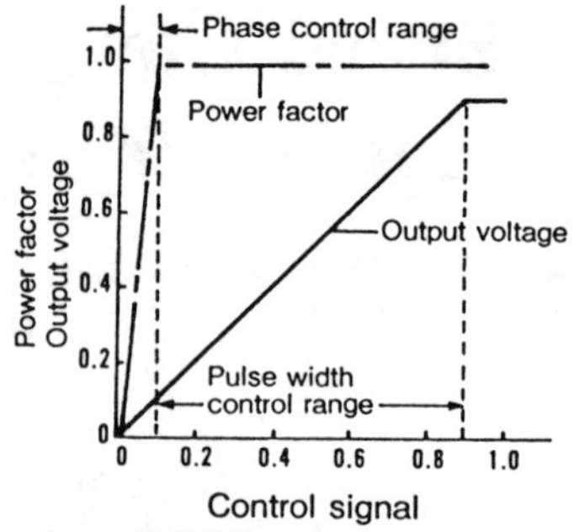

Fig. 3. Output voltage and power factor characteristic.

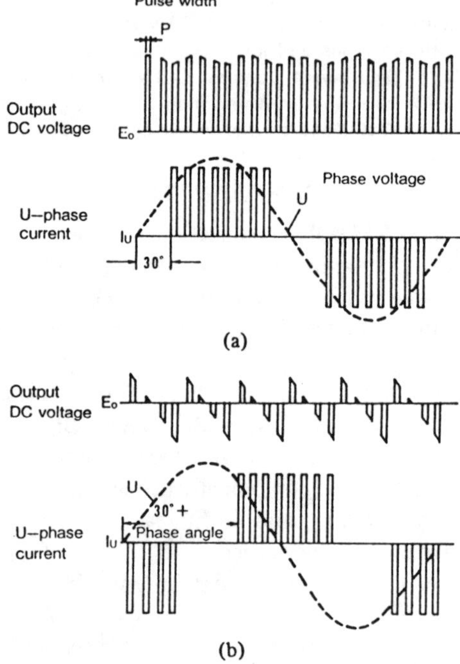

Fig. 4. Waveforms of output dc voltage and current. (a) Under pulsewidth control. (b) Under phase control.

phase angle is constant-controlled near the maximum or minimum value. Pulsewidth increases in proportion to the absolute value of the control signal. As the variable range of the pulsewidth is dependent on GTO turn-on and turn-off times, in this system the range is set from 83.3 to 750 μs for a chopping frequency of 1.2 kHz. In this range the line current is in phase with the line voltage, so the fundamental harmonic power factor is maintained at its maximum value. The output voltage and power factor characteristic versus the control signal are shown in Fig. 3.

2) Phase Control Range: This mode is generated when the absolute value of the control signal is small. As the minimum value of pulsewidth cannot decrease to nearly zero due to restrictions from the GTO turn-on and turn-off times, phase control is introduced to lower the output voltage to zero. Pulsewidth is constant-controlled to the minimum value, and phase angle is controlled bidirectionally to be proportional to the control signal. In this range, as the phase is controlled, the power factor is not a maximum value (Fig. 3). However, as this represents only a small part of the entire range, the fact that the power factor cannot be improved to the maximum value in the phase control range is not critical.

If the minimum turn-off time of the GTO can be improved, the phase control range will be shortened. Waveforms for the phase voltage U, output dc voltage E_0, and U phase current IU are shown in Fig. 4. In these plots, the U phase is representative of the V and W phase as well. As the GTO's chop the ac line voltage with a high frequency, the phase current flows and stops in accordance with the chopping frequency.

This illustration shows the case for a resistor load in which the U phase current flows intermittently. When the output dc voltage is high, power is provided from the source to the load (powering mode). At this time, the U phase GTO and V or W phase thyristor are conducting. When the output dc voltage is zero, the energy which has been stored in the reactance of the load circulates (circulating mode). At this time, the GTO and thyristor of the same phase are conducting.

C. Overvoltage at GTO Turn-Off and Its Suppression Method

We investigated the generation mechanism of overvoltage at GTO turn-off and its suppression method, prior to implementing practical applications. In this circuit method, there are two cases for generation timing of overvoltage: at the end of the circulating mode and at the end of the powering mode. The following analysis on overvoltage is conducted for a positive output voltage.

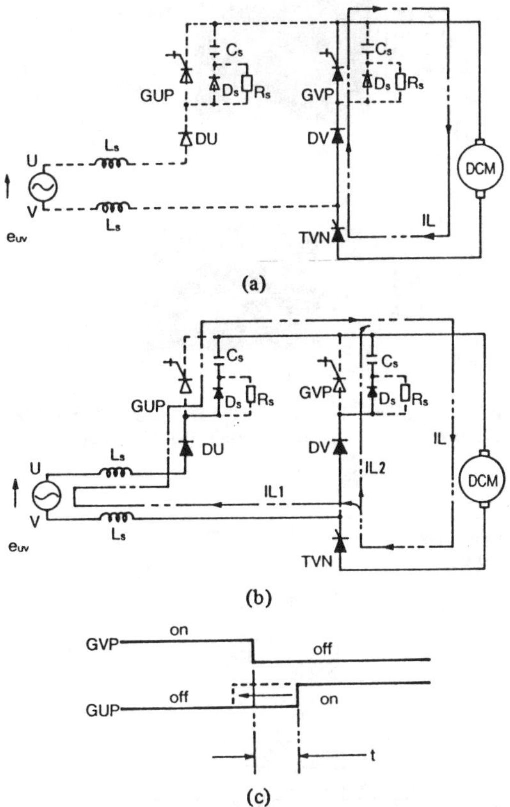

Fig. 5. Generation mechanism of overvoltage (I). (a) Current state (circulating mode). (b) Current state (from circulating mode to powering mode). (c) Relation between two gate-on pulses.

1) At the End of the Circulating Mode: Fig. 5 explains the generation mechanism for an overvoltage at the end of the circulating mode. Fig. 5(a) shows the current state in the circulating mode. The V phase GTO (GVP) and V phase thyristor (TVN) are conducting, and a circulating current flows like I_L. Under this condition, an overvoltage is not generated.

When the control mode changes from the circulating mode to the powering mode, an overvoltage is generated. Fig. 5(b) shows the current state in a transient condition. When GVP turns off, the circulating current I_L separates into I_{L1} and I_{L2}. As each current flows into the snubber capacitors C_s, overvoltage is generated between the anode and cathode of the GUP and GVP.

So as not to make a gap in on-gate pulses between the GVP and GUP (Fig. 5(c)), two on-gate pulses are overlapped with each other. Consequently, as the GVP is turned off by a reverse voltage from the GUP (e_{uv}) after the latter is turned on, the dc output current is not cut off, and overvoltage does not occur.

2) At the End of the Powering Mode: Fig. 6 explains the generation mechanism of overvoltage at the end of the powering mode. Fig. 6(a) shows the current state in the powering mode. GUP and TVN are turned on and the powering current flows like IL. Under this condition, an overvoltage is not generated.

When the control mode changes from the powering mode to the circulating mode, an overvoltage is generated. Fig. 6(b) shows the current state in a transient condition. When the GUP

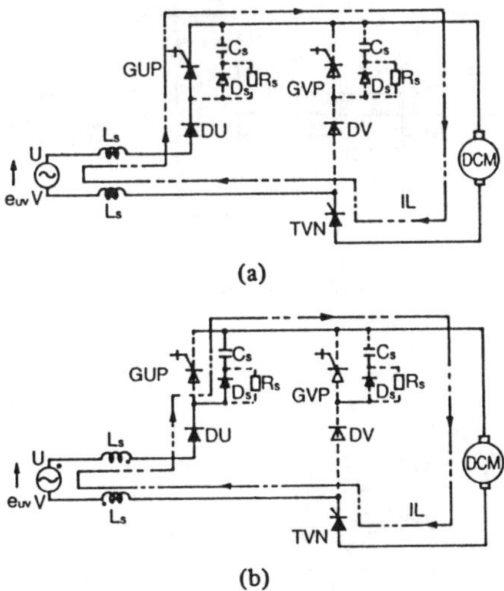

Fig. 6. Generation mechanism of overvoltage (II). (a) Current state (powering mode). (b) Current state (from powering mode to circulating mode).

turns off, powering current I_L which formerly flowed through GUP flows into the snubber capacitor C_s. At this time as a series resonance circuit which is composed of two L_s, LL, and C_s is formed, the overvoltage V_{a-k} is generated and its value is obtained from

$$V_{a-k} \fallingdotseq I_L \cdot \sqrt{\frac{2 \cdot L_s + LL}{C_s}} + e_{uv} \tag{1}$$

where

I_L load current,
L_s reactance of power source line,
LL reactance of load,
C_s capacitance of snubber capacitor,
e_{uv} line voltage.

As we estimated that the overvoltage would be more than 1600 V for an armature current of 300 A, use of a filter circuit was investigated as a suppression method. Initially, the RC filter was examined. When its power loss was shown to be large, other filters were then examined.

Fig. 7 shows a GTO converter circuit with an LC filter used to suppress overvoltage. In the figure, the reactor L_f is inserted to suppress the critical rate of rise of the on-state current (di/dt) to the GTO's. In this filtering system, at the transitional mode, a series resonance circuit composed of two L_s, L_f, LL, and C_f and a series resonance circuit composed of L_f and C_s must be considered. The latter circuit should be considered as a cause of overvoltage V_{a-k}, which is given by

$$V_{a-k} \fallingdotseq I_L \cdot \sqrt{\frac{2/3\ L_f}{C_s}} + e_{uv}. \tag{2}$$

In this converter system, the resonance frequency of the LC filter, chopping frequency of GTO converter, and higher harmonics of power source are limited by the following:

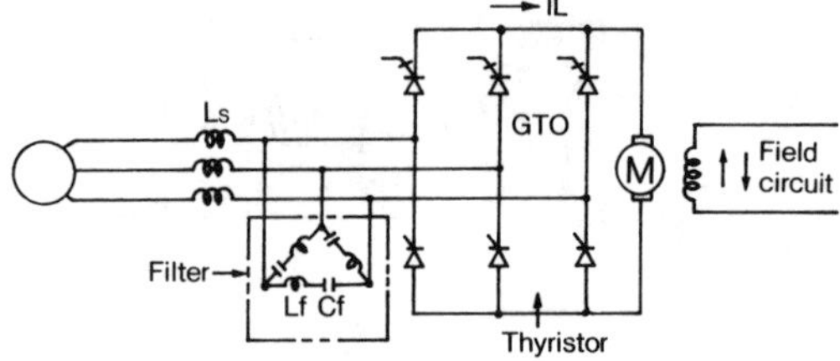

Fig. 7. GTO converter circuit with additional LC filter.

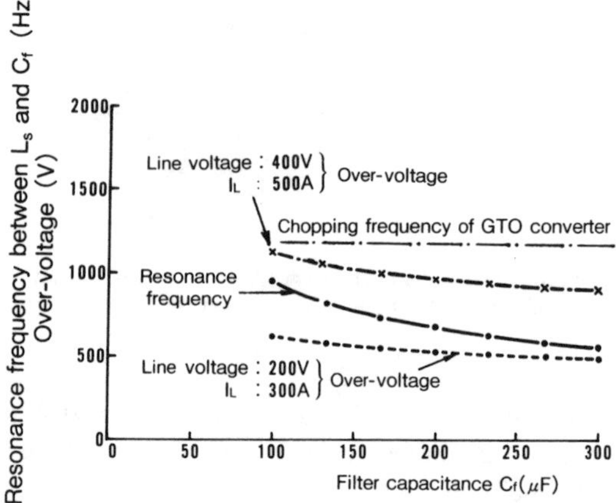

Fig. 8. Characteristics of overvoltage in relation to filter capacitance.

a) the resonance frequency of the LC filter should not coincide with the higher harmonics of the power source, and
b) the resonance frequency should not be close to the chopping frequency of the GTO converter.

The calculation results for overvoltage in relation to filter capacitance are shown in Fig. 8. In the following experiments, 200-μF filter capacitors were used. The filter reactance L_f must be selected after due consideration of both overvoltage V_{a-k} and critical rate of rise of on-state current di/dt.

If the output voltage is negative (polarity of e_{uv} in Figs. 5 and 6 is reverse), overvoltage at the end of the circulating mode resembles that at the end of the powering mode for a positive output voltage.

Fig. 9 shows the voltage waveforms between the anode and cathode of the GTO. Fig. 9(a) shows the waveform of V_{a-k} without a filter circuit and having overlapping of gate pulses. Even if the load current is very small in comparison with its rated value, the overvoltage shows an increase of 100 V above the line voltage. In this experiment, as the line voltage is set at a value below the rated one so as not to damage the GTO's, total overvoltage is not very large. However, if the load current is increased to the rated value (500 A) and the line voltage is set to the rated value (400 V), the overvoltage easily exceeds the maximum allowable rating of the GTO. Fig. 9(b) shows the waveform of V_{a-k} with a filter circuit and overlapping of gate pulses. Overvoltage is sufficiently suppressed.

EXPERIMENTAL RESULTS

Fig. 10 compares the thyristor and GTO converters with respect to apparent power under a static condition. This

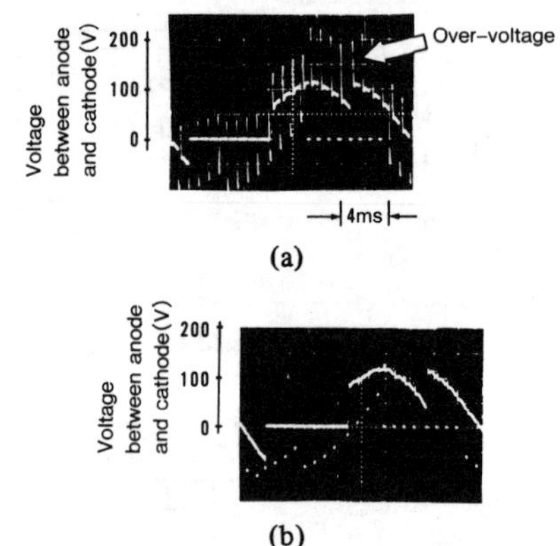

Fig. 9. Voltage waveforms between anode and cathode of GTO (load current I_L:10 A). (a) Without filter circuit. (b) With filter circuit.

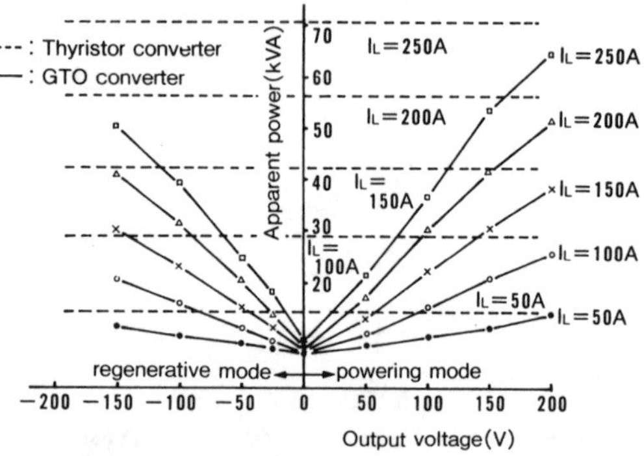

Fig. 10. Comparison of conventional thyristor converter with GTO converter in regard to apparent power.

apparent power means the product between the effective values of primary ac current and voltage. Apparent power is measured as a function of the output voltage with the load current as a parameter. The results may be summarized as follows.

a) The apparent power of the GTO converter method is smaller than that of the thyristor converter method in all regions.
b) The improvement is bigger in the small output voltage region.

For control in the small output voltage region, as for example elevator systems, improvement in the fundamental wave power factor means a reduction in the power source capacity.

Fig. 11 shows the armature current waveforms at a load current of 100 A. A dc reactor (6 mH) is installed in the conventional thyristor converter, and the ripple is 4.7 percent. In the GTO converter, even if there is no dc reactor, the ripple is lowered to 1.7 percent. The high-frequency chopping control of the GTO improves the armature current waveform, thus deletion of the dc reactor still ensures smoothing of the armature current.

Fig. 12 compares the thyristor and GTO converters with respect to higher harmonic current in the ac power line. The current in the GTO converter varies under the influence of pulsewidth control, but the level of the higher harmonic current is smaller than that of the conventional thyristor converter.

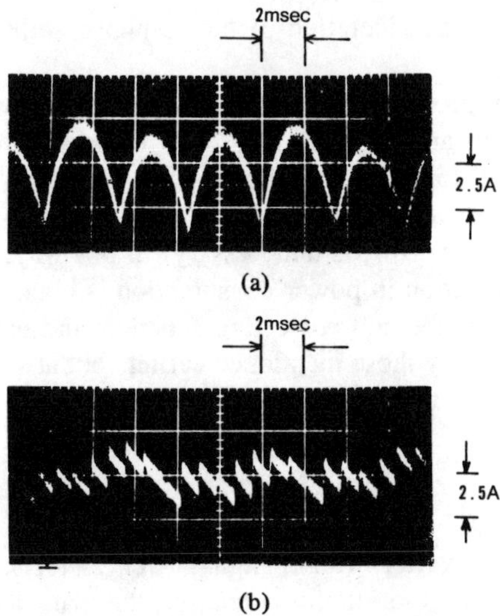

Fig. 11. Current waveforms (at I_L = 100 A). (a) Thyristor converter (dc reactor = 6 mH, ripple = 4.7 percent). (b) GTO converter (dc reactor = 0, ripple = 1.7 percent).

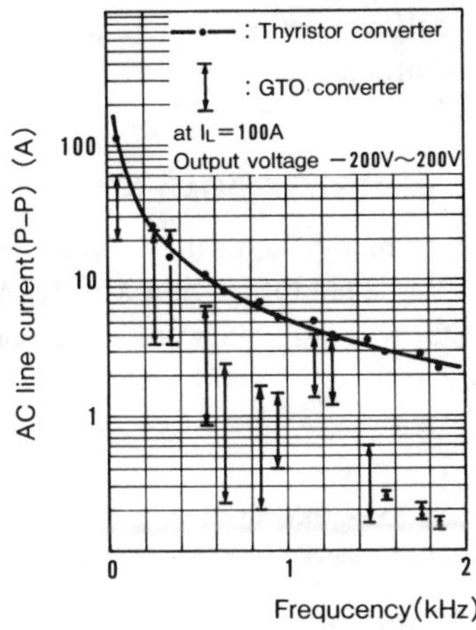

Fig. 12. Higher harmonic current in ac line.

The oscillogram in Fig. 13 compares the apparent power measurements when the conventional and the GTO converter were used in an elevator. The elevator is operated in an upward three-floor run at a speed of 2.5 m/s and 1000-kg load. Apparent power is decreased from that of the conventional system. Under these operating conditions, there are many points where the control mode (pulsewidth control mode and phase control mode) changes during operation, but the waveform of armature current is smoothly controlled.

We also compared the two converter systems with regard to apparent power under other control conditions (load condition, speed, etc.) and saw that the apparent power of the new system is 50 percent that of the conventional one.

Fig. 14 show the energy consumption on repeated up–down movements. The GTO converter was used in an intermediate-speed elevator (8 m/s, 1600 kg). As the main transformer and dc reactor were eliminated, reduction of power consumption is about 20 percent.

Table I shows the maximum allowable ratings of the GTO which is used for the 8-m/s class elevator. Table II compares control methods. Elevator operation using the GTO converter

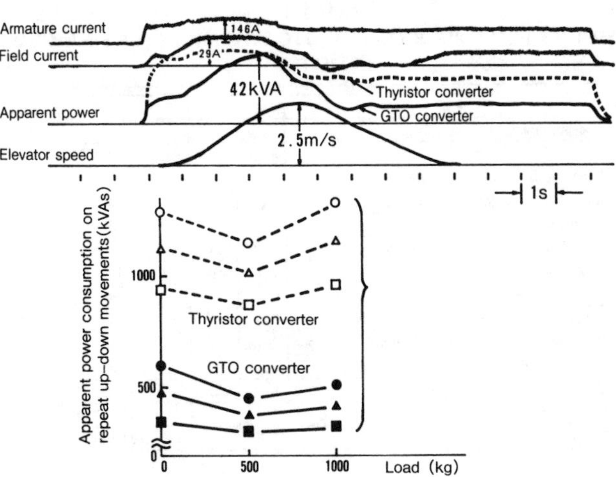

Fig. 13. Oscillogram and comparison of apparent power consumption.

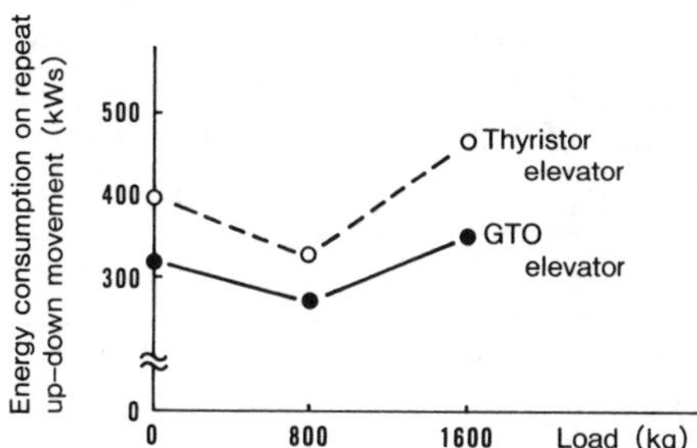

Fig. 14. Energy consumption (8-m/s 1600-kg class elevator).

is superior to that of conventional thyristor converter and recent GTO inverter. However, as this GTO converter is a new device, the present cost is a little higher. Mass production in the near future can be expected to lower this. The mentioned numbers are normalized to the conventional thyristor converter.

DIGITAL SPEED CONTROL SYSTEM

As mentioned previously for the new GTO converter system, the armature current was unidirectional, while the field current was bidirectional, to reduce the cost of the main circuit. However, as the field current should be controlled bidirectionally, the response time of the field current sometimes has a bad effect on the speed control response. A digital speed control system using a microprocessor is effective in compensating for nonlinear factors due to field current control.

Fig. 15 shows flow charts for three characteristic subroutines, as follows.

1) To achieve a smooth elevator start, the traction motor generatores a compensation torque which cancels the unbalance torque between the cage and counter weight. In order to compensate for drift in the compensation value in regard to the start shock, the microprocessor detects this shock and tries to make the most suitable compensation value.

2) To overcome some problems in regard to riding characteristics which depend on nonlinearity of the motor field, the microprocessor generates some suitable speed

TABLE I
MAXIMUM ALLOWABLE RATING OF GTO THYRISTORS FOR 8-m/s CLASS ELEVATOR

Item	Symbol	Units	
Repetitive Peak Off-State Voltage	V_{DRxM}	V	1,600
RMS On-State Current	$I_{T(RMS)}$	A	270(T_c=80°C)
Repetitive Controllable On-State Current	I_{TCM}	A	600
Surge(Non-Repetitive) On-State Current	I_{TSM}	A	6,000
I^2t Limit Value	I^2t	A^2sec.	180,000
Critical Rate of Rise of On-State Current	di/dt	A/μsec.	200
Repetitive Peak Reverse Gate Voltage	V_{GRM}	V	16
Repetitive Average Forward Gate Power Dissipation	$P_{GF(AV)}$	W	30
Repetitive Peak Forward Gate Power Dissipation	P_{GFM}	W	100
Repetitive Average Reverse Gate Power Dissipation	$P_{GR(AV)}$	W	30
Repetitive Peak Reverse Gate Power Dissipation	P_{GRM}	W	2,000
Operating Junction Temperature	T_j	°C	−40to+125
Storage Temperature	T_{stg}	°C	−40to+125
Mounting Force		kg	700±50

TABLE II
COMPARISON OF CONTROL METHODS

Item \ Method	Thyristor elevator	GTO inverter elevator	GTO converter elevator
Control method	Variable voltage + DC gearless motor	Variable voltage and frequency + AC geared motor	Variable voltage + DC gearless motor
Power capacity	1.0	0.8	0.7
Power consumption	1.0	1.0	0.8
Present cost	1.0	1.2	1.2
Noise level	○	△	○

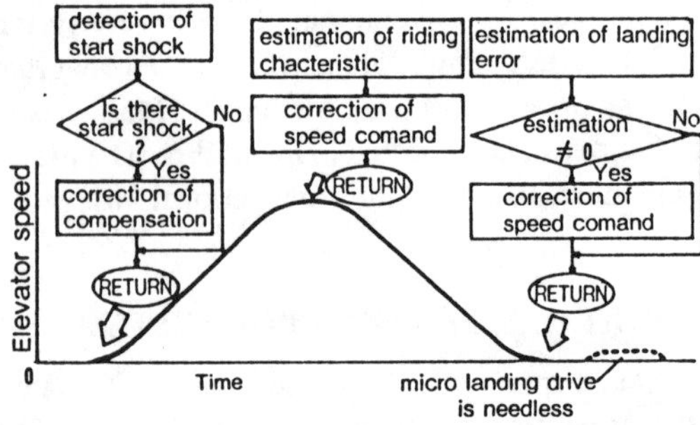

Fig. 15. Characteristic subroutines under digital control.

commands after consideration of the response ability of the motor field.

3) The microprocessor estimates the landing error when the cage is running and corrects the speed command from the standard value to minimize the landing error. With this control, a micro landing run, which is customarily done to cancel the landing error, is unnecessary. In this way, about a ten percent reduction in power consumption is obtained.

The effects of the self-correcting function and estimation control are not only those mentioned earlier, but also serve to minimize traction motor size.

CONCLUSION

The GTO converter with a high power factor has been developed for elevators. In this converter, the firing angle and pulsewidth were controlled at high frequency using GTO's. The application of this converter to dc elevators enabled a reduction in the required capacity of the power supply and power consumption. Riding and landing characteristics were improved by the self-correcting function and estimation control using a microprocessor.

ACKNOWLEDGMENT

The authors wish to recognize to the support and assistance of Mr. T. Hara, of the Head Office and Mr. H. Miyao, Mito Works of Hitachi Ltd. without which this work could not have been accomplished.

REFERENCES

[1] S. Shima *et al.*, "Power converter apparatus," U.S. Patent 4 361 866, Nov. 1982.

[2] H. Inaba *et al.*, "A new speed control system for DC motors and its application to elevator," *IEEE Trans. Ind. Appl.*, vol. IA-16, no. 2, 1979.

[3] T. Kataoka *et al.*, "A pulse width controlled ac to dc converter to improve power factor and wave of ac line current," *IEEE Trans. Ind. Appl.*, vol. IA-15, no. 6, 1979.

[4] D. Alexa and V. Prisacaru, "Selbstgefuhrte Stromrichter für Umkehrantriebe, die keine Blindleistung des Speisenetzes benötigen," *Elektrotech. Z. Ausg. A*, Bd. 94, H. 3, 1973.

Paper 4.4

THE GENERALISED TRANSFORMER: A NEW BIDIRECTIONAL SINUSOIDAL WAVEFORM FREQUENCY CONVERTER WITH CONTINUOUSLY ADJUSTABLE INPUT POWER FACTOR

MARCO VENTURINI

TEXAS INSTRUMENTS LIMITED
BEDFORD

ALBERTO ALESINA

INSTITUTO MATEMATICO
"F.ENRIQUES" UNIVERSITA' DEGLI STUDI DI
MILANO

ABSTRACT

A new frequency converter design is proposed.

The new converter is capable of sinusoidal waveforms at both input and output ports, bi-directionality, continuously controllable input power factor and reactive power generation. The converter operation does not require any reactive element.

INTRODUCTION

Over the last few years, the application of solid state power converters has been continuously and rapidly increasing. Thyristor AC-DC converters, DC-DC choppers, switching power supplies are, with the wide diffusion, but a few examples of the increasing popularity of power electronics.

Despite the variety of the existing designs, however, and the fact that virtually all of the electric energy generated and used in the world is three-phase AC, the "basic" problem of AC power amplitude frequency and power factor control is still unsolved.

The potential impact of versatile and economic frequency conversion on the whole electric power world is enormous. To begin with, the most immediate applications are based on the increased controllability of standard AC machines yielded by such a device. Speed and field control of induction motors, based on load requirements, would result in improved energy efficiency. DC motor replacement in variable speed applications and fast servos would determine a significant upgrading of equipment reliability and performance. Further in time, electronic AC power control can be used to generate controllable amounts of reactive power, for optimal power factor management. Local, intrinsically variable speed energy sources, such as windmills or small IC engines can be synchronised with the line frequency and thus utilised.

The most radical change, however, must be expected from the total redesign, or "rethinking" of all electric machines, due to the release of the traditional, heavily pervasive "either DC or fixed frequency" design constrain. For example, variable frequency induction motors can run at speeds in excess of 200,000 rpm; permanent magnet "brushless" AC machines run with efficiency well over 98%, and power densities as high as 5kw/kg.

The future diffusion of "generalised" AC transformers, or frequency converters, will certainly depend on performance and cost. In particular, if a consistent share of the total AC energy is expected to be utilised through frequency converters in the highly energy conscious future world, two features are essential:

- sinusoidal input current, with controllable input power factor.

- bidirectionality.

Furthermore, as power device technology improves, the cost and size of any power converter tends to be dominated by the reactive elements. Therefore, an "ideal" frequency converter design should not intrinsically need any large reactive elements.

Broadly, the existing frequency converter designs can be grouped into two families : direct and indirect converters. Frequency conversion is performed directly, when a properly operated set of switches connects directly the input lines with the output lines. It is performed indirectly, when the input energy is first transferred into an intermediate storage link (DC or HF) and from the intermediate link to the output.

In general, indirect converters have an intrinsic need for an intermediate storage. Therefore, they are bound to use large reactive elements. Furthermore, the intermediate storage destroys all information about input voltage waveform and phasing, so that bidirectionality is difficult to achieve, and the input current waveform is generally very poor. On the other hand, the intermediate storage decouples the input port from the output port, thus preventing the arising of output subharmonics. Output subharmonics, in turn, tend to affect direct converters. Since their output waveform synthesis is usually not very accurate, some of the input line undulation is present in the converter output. The "beating" between input and output frequency is the most common source of

Reprinted from *IEEE Power Electron. Specialists Conf. (PESC) Rec.*, pp. 242–252, 1980.

output subharmonics, highly undesirable on inductive loads. For this reason, the most used frequency converters are indirect, with a DC link. In addition, AC-DC and DC-AC converter technology is relatively well-established, so that a converter of this type usually consists of well known circuit blocks.

Another basic distinction between converter designs lies in the type of waveform synthesis they perform. In general, only two types of waveform synthesis are possible without large reactive elements :

- step synthesis, where the waveform is improved by an increase in the number of switches.

- high frequency synthesis, where the waveform is improved by increasing the switching frequency.

This paper deals with the properties and limits of high frequency synthesis converters in general. Although DC-AC choppers and PWM inverters are well known members of this family, the extension of high frequency synthesis to any number of input and output phases is possible, and is the basis of the new converter design.

After a brief review of the mathematical tools used in this paper, the basic structure of this family of converters is outlined, and the role played by the switches is discussed. A general condition is then found, which allows the designer to decide whether this type of converter is directly applicable in any given practical case. If the condition is met, a method is proposed which allows a straightforward design of the devised machine. A general low frequency model is also introduced, where all converters in this family are shown to be modelled as two-part, multipole, time-varying linear circuit elements, consisting of a matrix of linear modulators.

Finally, the general design rule is applied to the AC-AC conversion problem: a new AC-AC converter capable of sinusoidal waveforms, frequency, amplitude, phase and power factor changing is designed. Due to its transformer-like characteristics, the new converter can be considered as a "generalised transformer."

MATHEMATICAL PREMISES

BASIC ASSUMPTIONS

Throughout the paper we assume that all the functions we deal with are defined on the non-negative real line, (possibly zero valued on the negative axis), bounded, piece-wise continuous and periodic, their periods having a finite common multiple, unless the contrary is explicitly stated. When dealing with a collection of such functions we assume that a common period τ exists

DEFINITION.

For this kind of function the following definition of Fourier spectrum is applied :

$$\hat{f}(\omega) = \lim_{T\to\infty} \frac{1}{T}\int_0^T f(t).e^{-\iota\omega t}\, dt, \quad \omega \in R.$$

Due to the above assumptions this limit exists for every ω, and it is different from zero only for a countable number of ω's.

NOTATIONS

If Δ is an interval of real line, its length will be denoted by $|\Delta|$. The convolution between two functions f and g will be denoted by $f*g$.

For Fourier transform properties, reference is made to {3,4}

HIGH FREQUENCY SYNTHESIS CONVERTER STRUCTURE

In all power converter designs, efficiency demands that controllable devices, which are intrinsically resistive, are operated as switches. Therefore, within a sufficient approximation, all power converters can be considered as consisting of reactive elements and switches only. For this reason, any analysis of power converters must start from a suitable model of the electronic switch.

SWITCHING MATRIX MODEL

The simplest way to model the electronic switch is to introduce the concept of "ideal" switch. An ideal switch is characterised by a non continuous function M(t) whose value is one when the switch is closed, and zero when it is open. No transition times are considered in this elementary model.
Let $f_I(t)$ be the switch input, then:

$$f_O(t) = M(t)\cdot f_I(t) \qquad (1)$$

is the switch output
The function $M(\cdot)$ has been most referred to as the "existence function" {2,5,12} of the switch; in this context, the perhaps more appropriate denomination of "modulation function" is proposed.

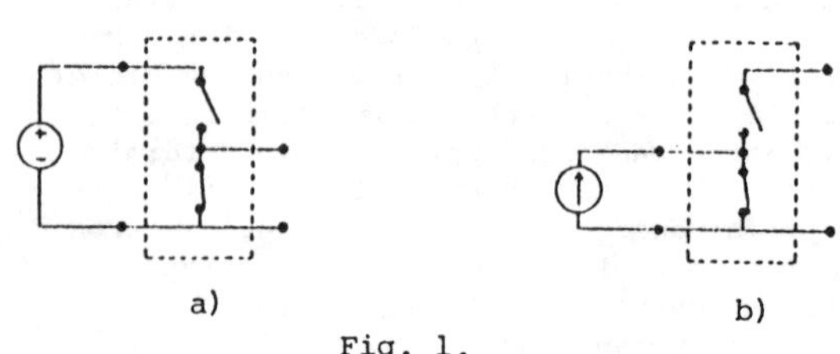

Fig. 1.

In practice the "ideal" switches are realised with electronic switches whose connection topology depends on the nature of the input and output variables. Because of the converter reactive elements, to be discussed later, two types of switches are especially important: the voltage switch (fig. 1a), which is fed from a low impedance supply, and the current switch (fig. 1b), which is fed from a high impedance supply. Notice that the same switch is both a current and a voltage switch depending on the input port considered. Therefore, the elementary switch is modeled by the hybrid relations:

$$V_O(t) = M(t)\cdot V_I(t)$$
$$I_I(t) = M(t)\cdot I_O(t)$$

or

$$I_O(t) = M(t)\cdot I_I(t)$$
$$V_I(t) = M(t)\cdot V_O(t)$$

depending on which port is taken as an input

Consider now the generation of poliphase input, poliphase output switch structures from the connection of several elementary switches. Series connection of voltage fed switches (fig. 2a) and parallel connection of current fed switches (fig.2b) are both possible. Furthermore if n switches are operated so that:

$$\sum_{j=1}^{n} M_j(t) = n - 1$$

or

$$\sum_{j=1}^{n} M_j(t) = 1 \qquad (2)$$

for current and voltage fed switches respectively, the connections can be simplified omitting half of the switches (dotted in fig. 2a', b'). The simplified connection of voltage fed switches is especially important, because several poliphase input, single phase output converters of this type can be parallel connected, thus generating a poliphase voltage fed input, poliphase current fed output switching matrix with minimum component count. For the (either simplified or not) series connection of voltage fed switches:

$$V_O(t) = \sum_j M_j(t).V_{IJ}(t); \qquad (1')$$

i.e. the switches allow a summation of the inputs, besides the basic modulation.

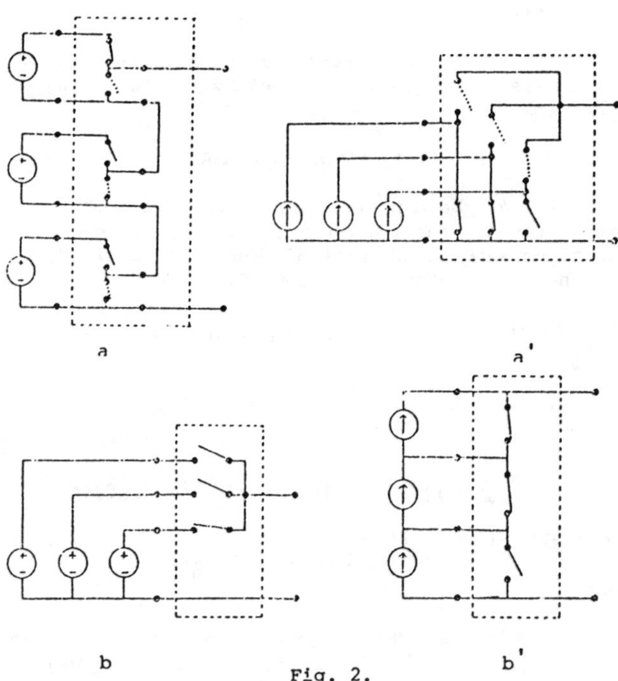

Fig. 2.

In the most general case, a n-input, p-output switching matrix is characterised by a p×n modulation matrix

$$\underline{M}(t) = \{M_{ij}(t)\};\ i=1,..,p\ j=1,..,n$$

where $M_{ij}(t)$ is the modulation function of the switch connecting the j-th input with the i-th output.

REMARK 1. Equation (2) means that none of the input lines is ever shorted and that the output line is never left unconnected. This condition must now be extended to switching matrix operation.

Let $\underline{1}$ be the n (or p; no confusion is possible) dimensional vector whose entries are all equal to 1; for the most general n-input, p-output case equation (2) becomes

$$\underline{M}(t)\cdot\underline{1} = \underline{1}. \qquad (2')$$

Let now

$$\underline{V}_I(t) = \{V_{Ij}(t)\}_{j=1}^{n} \quad \underline{I}_O(t) = \{I_{Oi}(t)\}_{i=1}^{p}$$

$$\underline{V}_O(t) = \{V_{Oi}(t)\}_{i=1}^{p} \quad \underline{I}_I(t) = \{I_{Ij}(t)\}_{j=1}^{n}$$

be the input voltage and output current vectors (impressed), and the output voltage and input current vectors respectively. If condition (2') holds, a general n-input, p-output switching matrix is characterised by the equations :

$$\underline{V}_O(t) = \underline{M}(t)\cdot\underline{V}_I(t)$$
$$\underline{I}_I(t) = \underline{M}(t)^T\cdot\underline{I}_O(t),$$

where the matrix $\underline{M}^T$ is the transpose of $\underline{M}$.

SWITCHING MATRIX OPERATION: WAVEFORM CONTROL.

Consider now an hypothetical converter consisting of switches only. Assume that the converter is fed from any set of sources $\underline{f}_I(t)$ where the $f_{Ij}(t)$'s are continuous functions of t. The converter output is represented by:

$$\underline{f}_O(t) = \underline{M}(t)\cdot\underline{f}_I(t). \qquad (1'')$$

Due to the switches $\underline{f}_O(t)$ is, in general, a non-continuous function with infinite bandwidth. For this reason, most converters generate a quasi square wave or a staircase like output waveform. Unfortunately, converters should generate smooth waveforms, such as DC or sinusoidal waveforms, for best performance. Therefore a converter cannot consist of switches only. Reactive elements are needed to smooth the waveforms generated by the switches.

In general, however, reactive elements have a number of disadvantages, and, in modern circuit design, it is desired to reduce their use to a minimum. For this reason, a general waveform synthesis technique is now described, which allows very little use of reactive elements.

Consider a single-output converter, which is required to generate the waveform $f_d(t)$ whose Fourier components $\hat{f}_d(\omega)$ are such that:

$$\hat{f}_d(\omega) = 0 \quad \text{for } \omega > \omega_{bw};$$

(i.e. f_d has a limited bandwidth).

If the switches can be operated in such a way that:

$$|\hat{f}_O(\omega) - \hat{f}_d(\omega)| < \bar{\varepsilon} \quad \text{for } \omega \leq \bar{\omega},$$

where $\bar{\omega} >> \omega_{bw}$ and $\bar{\varepsilon}$ is arbitrarily small, i.e. the low frequency sides of the actual and desired waveform spectra are similar, then the converter output can be filtered by a low pass filter F with bandwidth ω_F such that :

$$\omega_{bw} << \omega_F << \bar{\omega},$$

thus yielding an output waveform, whose spectrum differs from the desired waveform spectrum by at most $\bar{\varepsilon}$.

Notice that the filter size, and therefore the size of the converter reactive elements, depends on $\bar{\omega}$. Therefore, if an appropriate switching law can be found for any value of $\bar{\omega}$, then the size of the reactive elements needed in the converter can be reduced at will.

DEFINITION 1. An assigned function $f_d(t)$ can be synthesized via high frequency synthesis from an assigned set of input functions

$$\underline{f}_I(t) = \{f_{Ij}(t)\}_{j=1}^{n}$$

if, for each arbitrary pair $(\bar{\varepsilon},\bar{\omega})$, a switching law (i.e. a modulation function $\underline{M}(t)$) can be determined such that:

$$|\hat{f}_O(\omega) - \hat{f}_d(\omega)| < \bar{\varepsilon} \quad \text{for } \omega \leq \bar{\omega},$$

where:

$$f_O(t) = \underline{M}(t)\cdot\underline{f}_I(t).$$

The structure of a general high frequency synthesis converter, complete with its reactive elements, is shown in fig. 5.

SWITCHING MATRIX CONTROL

Consider again a n-input lines, p-output lines switching matrix. Assume that a set of n voltages $\underline{V}_I(t)$ is fed on the input lines, and a set of p desired output waveforms $\underline{V}_d(t)$ is assigned. Two problems are to be solved at this stage:

1) determine which conditions over $\underline{V}_I(t)$ and $\underline{V}_d(t)$ must be satisfied, in order high frequency synthesis to be applicable.

2) If the above conditions are met, determine at least one modulation matrix $\underline{M}(t)$ to synthesize $\underline{V}_d(t)$, when the synthesis parameters $\bar{\varepsilon},\bar{\omega}$ are assigned.

The second problem is discussed first.

INTUITIVE APPROACH

Without loss of generality, consider a single output phase converter (fig. 1a'). Let the converter switches $S_1,\ldots,S_n$ be closed in sequence, so that $\Delta_k^1,\ldots,\Delta_k^n$ are the time disjoint intervals in which the switches $S_1,\ldots,S_n$ are closed during the k-th cycle, with

$$\sum_{j=1}^{n} \Delta_k^j = \Delta_k \qquad |\Delta_k| = \delta \quad k=1,2,\ldots$$

$$\Delta_k \cap \Delta_h = \emptyset \ \text{ if } \ h \neq k \qquad \sum_{k=1}^{\infty} \Delta_k = [0,+\infty)$$

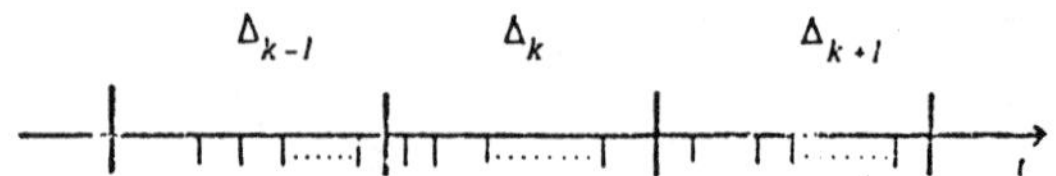

Fig. 3.

The unfiltered converter output consists of "chops" of the input functions $V_{Ij}(t)$ packed together. The output Fourier spectrum, therefore, depends on the input functions as well as on the intervals Δ_k^j. However, the low frequency components

$$\hat{f}_O(\omega) \quad : \quad \omega << \frac{1}{2\pi\delta}$$

of the output Fourier spectrum do not depend greatly on the actual variations of the output inside each sequence, but mainly on the average output value in each sequence. Therefore, if the time intervals $\Delta_k^1,\ldots\Delta_k^n$ are adjusted so that, inside each sequence, the output average varies accordingly to a desired function $f_d(t)$ to be synthesized, the filtered converter output approximates the desired output.

A more rigorous basis for the high frequency synthesis technique is provided by the following theorems.

HIGH FREQUENCY SYNTHESES LEMMA

Let δ,η be a positive, non-negative number respectively, and f,g two real valued, piece-wise continuous, bounded, periodic functions defined on the non-negative real line $[0,+\infty)$ such that:

$$\left|\int_{\Delta_k} f(t)\,dt - \int_{\Delta_k} g(t)\,dt\right| \leq \eta \qquad k=1,2,\ldots$$

Δ_k being the interval $(K-1)\delta\ ,k\delta)$; then:

$$|\hat{f}(\omega) - \hat{g}(\omega)| \leq \sqrt{2}(1 - \cos\tfrac{\omega\delta}{2})^{\frac{1}{2}}\cdot(N(f) + N(g)) + \frac{\eta}{\delta} \qquad \text{for } |\omega| \leq \frac{2\pi}{\delta}, \tag{3}$$

where:

$$N(f) = \{\sup \frac{1}{T}\int_0^T |f(t)|\,dt \ : \ T \in [0,+\infty)\}.$$

The proof of the Lemma, not reported here, can be found in (14).

As a consequence of the High Frequency Synthesis Lemma, a general condition can be derived for the applicability of high frequency syntheses.

EXISTENCE THEOREM.

Consider a set of input functions $f_I(t) = \{f_{Ij}(t)\}_{j=1}^{n}$, and a function $f_d(t)$, all satisfying the initial general assumptions. Then $f_{d(t)}$ can be synthetized via high frequency synthesis if and only if :

$$\inf_{j=1,..,n} f_{Ij}(t) \leq f_d(t) \leq \sup_{j=1,..,n} f_{Ij}(t) \qquad t \in [0,+\infty)$$

The intuitive notion that a converter with arbitrarily small reactive elements cannot synthetize any waveform outside the input range is thus confirmed. A rigorous proof of the existence theorem can be found in (14)

HIGH FREQUENCY SYNTHESIS CONVERTER CHARACTERISATION AND MODELING.

In the previous sections switching matrix performance and control have been discussed. In this section the converter is completed with its filters, and the relationships between switching matrix control and overall circuit performance are analysed.

INTUITIVE APPROACH

Without loss of generality, consider a single output, single output converter first (fig. 4a). Let the filters be perfect, their notch frequency being ω_F. Let the switch be operated at constant high frequency and slowly variable pulse width. Let the pulse width $|\Delta_k'|$ vary according to the law: $|\Delta k'| = m(t_k)|\Delta_k|$ for some $t_k \in \Delta_k$ and some continuous function $m(t)$, such that

$$0 < m(t) < 1,$$

where both m(t) and the converter input do not vary appreciably during each switching cycle. In these conditions, the average value of the output in each cycle, and therefore the converter filtered output, can be approximated by :

$$f_A(t) = m(t)\cdot f_I(t).$$

This intuitive result is confirmed by the following theorem.

MODELING THEOREM.

Let m be a Lipschitz, periodic function

$$m: [0,+\infty) \longrightarrow [0,1]$$

with Lipschitz constant L_m, i.e:

$$0 \leq m(t) \leq 1 \quad |m(t_1)-m(t_2)| \leq L_m|t_1-t_2| \quad t,t_1,t_2 \in R^+.$$

Let f_I be a bounded, periodic, Lipschitz function with Lipschitz constant L_f. Let

$$\{\Delta_k'\}_{k=1}^{\infty},\ \{x_k\}_{k=1}^{\infty}$$

be sequences, of intervals and points respectively, such that:

$$x_k \in \Delta_k; \quad \Delta_k' \subset \Delta_k; \quad |\Delta_k'| = m(x_k)|\Delta_k|$$

for every K.

If $f_O(t)$ and $f_A(t)$ are defined as:

$$f_O(t) = M(t)f_I(t) \text{ and } f_A(t) = m(t)f_I(t)$$

where:

$$M(t) = \sum_{k=1}^{\infty} X\Delta_k',$$

then for every pair $(\bar{\varepsilon},\bar{\omega})$, δ can be chosen such that $|\hat{f}_O(\omega) - \hat{f}_A(\omega)| < \bar{\varepsilon} \quad \omega < \bar{\omega}$.

For a rigorous proof, reference is made to (14)

As a consequence of the above theorem, in high frequency synthesis converters, the switches, completed with their filters, can be modeled as linear modulators (fig. 4b).

The function m(t), analogous to the switch modulation function M(t), is here referred to as the low frequency modulation function of the switch. Practically a low frequency modulation function is a continuous finite bandwidth function of time, whose values are non-negative and not greater than one

If the more general n-input, p-output converter is considered, its operation can be modeled by a pxn low frequdncy modulation matrix $\underline{m}(t)$ (fig. 5), whose entries are the low frequency modulation functions of the switches.

Condition (2') becomes now:

$$\underline{m}(t).\underline{1} = \underline{1} \qquad (2')$$

Practically a low frequency modulation matrix $\underline{m}(t)$ is then a matrix of continuous, finite bandwidth functions of time, such that (2") holds and:

$$0 \leq m_{ij}(t) \leq 1 \quad i=1,..,p \quad j=1,..,n.$$

REMARK 2. So far, only voltage fed input, current fed output switching matrices have been considered. This operating condition is seldom found in practice. However, proper converter operation require that :

$$\frac{1}{\delta} \gg \bar{\omega} \gg \omega_F.$$

Consequently, the converter filters allow very little variation of the input voltage and output current inside each switching sequence. In other words, the filters behave as low and high impedance input and output sources respectively. Therefore, the converter, when completed with its filters, is not restricted to operate from any specific set of sources.

REMARK 3. According to (3), $\bar{\omega}$, and consequently ω_F, can be increased by reducing δ, i.e. increasing the switching frequency. The size of the reactive elements in the filters depends on ω_F. Therefore, due to the high switching frequency which can be achieved with present device technology, the reactive elements needed in this type of converters are small, and their size tends to shrink with solid state device technology improvements.

"GENERALISED TRANSFORMER" SYNTHESIS

As a consequence of the concepts introduced in the previous sections, a general method for high frequency synthesis converter design can now be outlined. As an application of this method, the general and challenging problem of frequency, amplitude, phase and power factor transformation between three phase systems will be considered.

CONVERTER DESIGN

The converter design procedure can be divided in two steps. First, the appropriate low frequency modulation matrix is determined from the desired converter characteristics. The elements of the matrix represent the duty cycles of the corresponding switches in the converter.

Secondly, depending on the switching losses of the actual devices, the required waveform accuracy and the desired total efficiency, the switching carrier frequency and filter notch frequency are chosen, and the actual switch modulation matrix is determined.

In this paper this second phase of the design is not emphasized. For the three phase to three phase converter, a wider discussion on the actual switching frequency and filter sizing can be found in [12].

LOW FREQUENCY MODULATION MATRIX DETERMINATION

In general, the low frequency modulation matrix must satisfy the following system of 2p+n linear equation in nxp variables :

$$\underline{V}_O(t) = \underline{m}(t)\cdot\underline{V}_I(t) \qquad (7)$$

to supply the desired output voltage ;

$$\underline{I}_I(t) = \underline{m}(t)^T\cdot\underline{I}_O(t) \qquad (8)$$

to supply the desired input current;

$$\underline{m}(t)\cdot\underline{1} = \underline{1} \qquad (9)$$

which is condition (2")

SYSTEM DISCUSSION

If the vector $\underline{V}_I(t)$ is not proportional to the vector $\underline{1}$, equations (7) and (9) provide two independent conditions on every line of the matrix $\underline{m}(t)$, while equation (8) provides one condition on every column of $\underline{m}(t)$. Notice that the entries of $\underline{m}(t)$ are the variables of the linear system (7), (8), (9). Therefore, the rank of the matrix of the coefficients of this system is :

$$R = np-(n-2)(p-1) = n+2p-2. \qquad (10)$$

Henceforth, to solve the system (7), (8), (9)

$$2p+n-R = 2 \qquad (11)$$

conditions over the input and output voltages and currents must be satified. These solvability conditions are :

$$\underline{I}_O(t)^T\cdot\underline{V}_O(t) = \underline{I}_I(t)^T\cdot\underline{V}_I(t) \qquad 10)$$

$$\underline{I}_O(t)^T\cdot\underline{1} = \underline{I}_I(t)^T\cdot\underline{1} \qquad 11)$$

i.e., at any time t, the input power must equal the output power, and the sum of the input currents must equal the sum of the output currents (Kirchoff current law).
These conditions can be directly derived from equations (7), (8), and (9) as follows

$$\underline{I}_I^T\cdot\underline{V}_I = \underline{I}_O^T\cdot\underline{m}\cdot\underline{V}_I = \underline{I}_O^T\cdot\underline{V}_O \qquad 8)\ 7)$$

$$\underline{I}_O^T\cdot\underline{1} = \underline{I}_O^T\cdot\underline{m}\cdot\underline{1} = (\underline{m}^T\cdot\underline{I}_O)^T\cdot\underline{1} = \underline{I}_I^T\cdot\underline{1} \qquad 9)\ 8)$$

THREE PHASE TO THREE PHASE CONVERTER

The three phase input, three phase output converter design is now discussed. A limited version of this converter has already been described in [12] from a circuit oriented point of view.

The generalised converter design problem can be stated as follows: Given a set of sinusoidal voltages at input frequency:

$$\begin{cases} V_{I1} = v_I\cos(\omega_I t) \\ V_{I2} = v_I\cos(\omega_I t+ \frac{2}{3}\pi) \\ V_{I3} = v_I\cos(\omega_I t+ \frac{4}{3}\pi), \end{cases}$$

and a set of output sinusoidal currents at output frequency :

$$\begin{cases} I_{O1} = c_O\cos(\omega_O t+ \phi_O) \\ I_{O2} = c_O\cos(\omega_O t+ \frac{2}{3}\pi+ \phi_O) \\ I_{O3} = c_O\cos(\omega_O t+ \frac{4}{3}\pi+ \phi_O), \end{cases}$$

determine a control law for the switches S_{11}, $S_{12},\ldots,S_{33}$ so that the low frequency parts of the synthetized output voltages V_{O1}, V_{O2}, V_{O3}, and input currents I_{I1}, I_{I2}, I_{I3} are sinusoidal with the prescribed output frequency, input frequency, phase and amplitude respectively.

Let now the desired input currents and output voltages be:

$$\begin{cases} I_{I1} = c_I\cos(\omega_I t+\phi_I) \\ I_{I2} = c_I\cos(\omega_I t+ \frac{2}{3}\pi+ \phi_I) \\ I_{I3} = c_I\cos(\omega_I t+ \frac{4}{3}\pi+ \phi_I) \end{cases}$$

$$\begin{cases} V_{O1} = v_O\cos(\omega_O t) \\ V_{O2} = v_O\cos(\omega_O t+ \frac{2}{3}\pi) \\ V_{O3} = v_O\cos(\omega_O t+ \frac{4}{3}\pi). \end{cases}$$

According to the existence theorem, the output voltage and input current high frequency synthesis are possible, in this case, only if

$$v_O \leq \frac{v_I}{2} \quad \text{and} \quad c_I \leq \frac{c_O}{2}.$$

Furthermore, condition (10) requires that:

$$\frac{v_O}{v_I} = \frac{c_I}{c_O} \cdot \frac{\cos \phi_I}{\cos \phi_O},$$

while condition (11) is trivially verified for any balanced poli-phase system. Within these limitations, a solution of the system of equations (7), (8) (9) is the following generalised transformer low frequency modulation matrix $\underline{m}(t)$

$$\frac{1}{3}\alpha_1 \begin{Bmatrix} 1+2q\,CS(0) & 1+2q\,CS(-\frac{2}{3}\pi) & 1+2q\,CS(-\frac{4}{3}\pi) \\ 1+2q\,CS(-\frac{4}{3}\pi) & 1+2q\,CS(0) & 1+2q\,CS(-\frac{2}{3}\pi) \\ 1+2q\,CS(-\frac{2}{3}\pi) & 1+2q\,CS(-\frac{4}{3}\pi) & 1+2q\,CS(0) \end{Bmatrix} +$$

$$+\frac{1}{3}\alpha_2 \begin{Bmatrix} 1+2q\,CA(0) & 1+2q\,CA(-\frac{2}{3}\pi) & 1+2q\,CA(-\frac{4}{3}\pi) \\ 1+2q\,CA(-\frac{2}{3}\pi) & 1+2q\,CA(-\frac{4}{3}\pi) & 1+2q\,CA(0) \\ 1+2q\,CA(-\frac{4}{3}\pi) & 1+2q\,CA(0) & 1+2q\,CA(-\frac{2}{3}\pi) \end{Bmatrix}$$

where:

$$CS(x) = \cos[\omega_M t + x]$$
$$CA(x) = \cos[-(\omega_M + 2\omega_I)t + x]$$
$$\omega_M = \omega_O - \omega_I$$
$$\alpha_1 = \frac{1}{2}[1 + tg(\phi_I)\cdot ctg(\phi_O)]$$
$$\alpha_2 = 1 - \alpha_1 = \frac{1}{2}[1 - tg(\phi_I)\cdot ctg(\phi_O)]$$
$$q = \frac{v_O}{v_I}$$

with:

$$\alpha_1 \geq 0$$
$$\alpha_2 \geq 0$$
$$0 \leq q \leq \frac{1}{2}.$$

CONVERTER REALISATION

From the low frequency modulation matrix (12) a practical three phase to three phase converter can be realised. Let the switches connected to each output phase be closed in sequence with carrier frequency:

$$F_\delta = \frac{1}{\delta} \gg \frac{\omega_I}{2\pi}, \frac{\omega_O}{2\pi}.$$

If, inside each cycle, the closure time of the switches are assembled sequentially, and the switches are operated such that, for example,

$$|\Delta_k^{ij}| = m_{ij}(k\delta)\cdot\delta \qquad \delta = |\Delta_k^i| \;\forall\; i,k \qquad \Delta_k^i = \sum_{j=1}^n \Delta_k^{ij};$$

then, according to the modeling theorem, the converter can be made to synthetize the desired waveform with arbitrary accuracy, just varying the carrier frequency F_δ.

CONVERTER MODEL

When completed with its filters, the converter can be modelled as a two-port, six-pole, time varying linear circuit element, characterised by the hybrid relations:

$$\underline{V}_O(t) = \underline{m}(t)\cdot\underline{V}_I(t)$$
$$\underline{I}_I(t) = \underline{m}(t)^T\cdot\underline{V}_O(t).$$

However, for sinusoidal waveforms, and balanced three phase systems, these relations can be greatly simplified :

$$v_O = q\cdot v_I$$
$$c_I = c_O\cdot q\cdot(\alpha_1^2 + \alpha_2^2 + 2\alpha_1\cdot\alpha_2\cdot\cos(2\phi_O))^{\frac{1}{2}}$$
$$\omega_O = \omega_I + \omega_M$$
$$\phi_I = artg[(\alpha_1 - \alpha_2)\cdot tg(\phi_O)].$$

The type of converter described so far is characterised by sinusoidal waveforms, bidirectionality, independent control over frequency, amplitude and phase transformation. In particular, input and output power factors are separately controllable, up to a complete inversion of the phase displacement between input and output. The converter is thus capable of reactive power generation.

For these reasons the denomination of "generalised transformer" is proposed.

Notice that, if the input frequency is set to zero, the converter degenerates into a Shönung and Stammler inverter [7] . If both input and output frequencies are set to zero, the converter degenerates into a chopper.

Notice also that the converter can either reduce of increase the output voltage. If input and output ports are reversed, the converter becomes a "generalised boost converter", capable of stepping up the input voltage, either for a DC or AC input.

The converter operation has been thoroughly simulated on a digital computer, as well as experimentally tested. Some digital computer simulations of frequency conversion on a reactive load, with different α_1, α_2, and therefore different input phase displacements, are shown in figs. 6,7, 8, 9. A typical converter output voltage spectrum (unfiltered) is shown in fig. 10.

Some of the most interesting applications of the new converter may be :

1) AC variable speed induction motor drive, with regenerative braking capability, and unity or capacitive input power factor.

2) Line synchronisation of variable shaft speed induction generators, for small power

generation plants, with controllable reactive currents.

3). Uninterruptable Power Supplies, where the converter acts as a battery charger and as an inverter, without discontinuity in the operation, and without any transformer.

4) Static reactive power generation, without the use of large reactive elements.

REMARK 4. For motoring and generating applications, the output filters can be usually omitted, due to the inductive nature of the load.

CONCLUSION

In this paper, a wide family of solid state power converters has been considered. These converters can synthetize an assigned, slow varying waveform by means of high frequency switching, with little use of reactive elements.

A condition for the applicability of this method to a general case has been introduced. When this condition is met, a method is proposed which allows straightforward converter design from the desired specifications.

In the second part of this paper, switching matrix control and converter behaviour have been related introducing the concept of low frequency modulation matrix. The low frequency modulation matrix $\underline{m}(t)$, whose entries are the duty cycles of the switches, has been shown to characterize the converter electric behaviour via the hybrid relations.

$$\underline{V}_O(t) = \underline{m}(t)\cdot\underline{V}_I(t)$$

$$\underline{I}_I(t) = \underline{m}(t)^T\cdot I_O(t).$$

Finally, the general converter theory is applied to design a new AC-AC converter. The new converter can be considered a generalized "buck" or "boost" converter: it can reduce or increase the voltage, vary frequency, amplitude, phase and power factor from input to output. The converter is characterized by sinusoidal waveforms, and it is capable of reactive power generation. For these reasons the denomination of "generalized transformer" has been proposed.

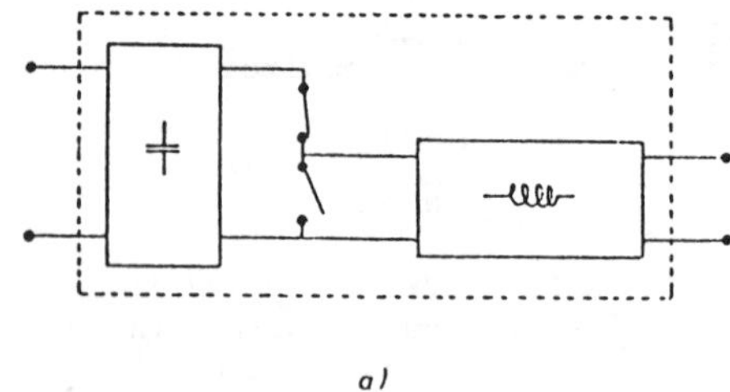

a)

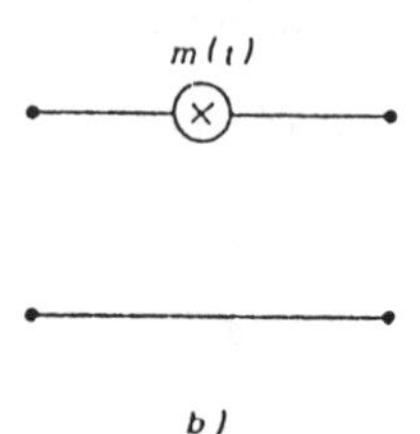

b)

Fig. 4.

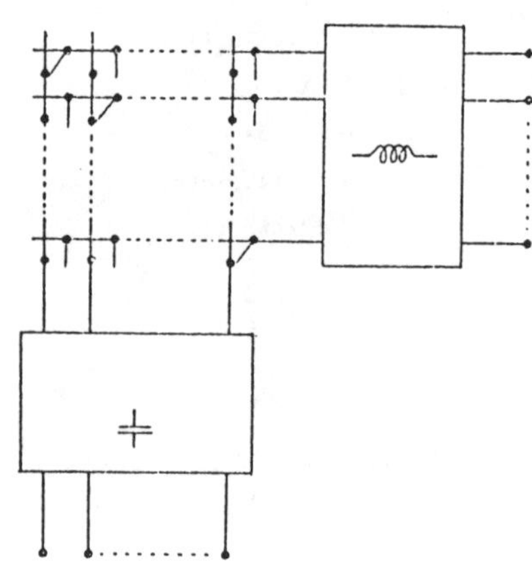

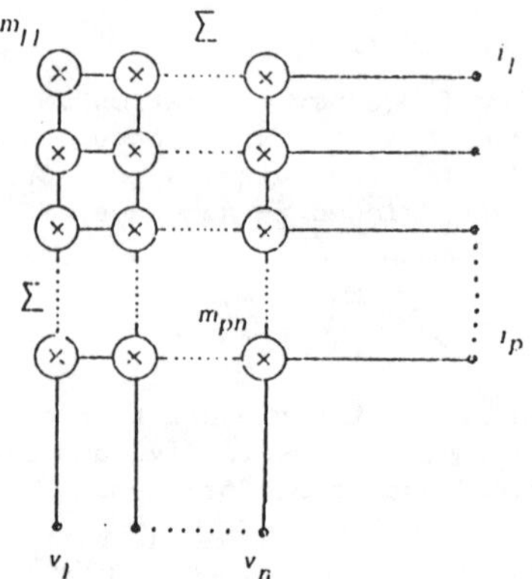

Fig. 5.

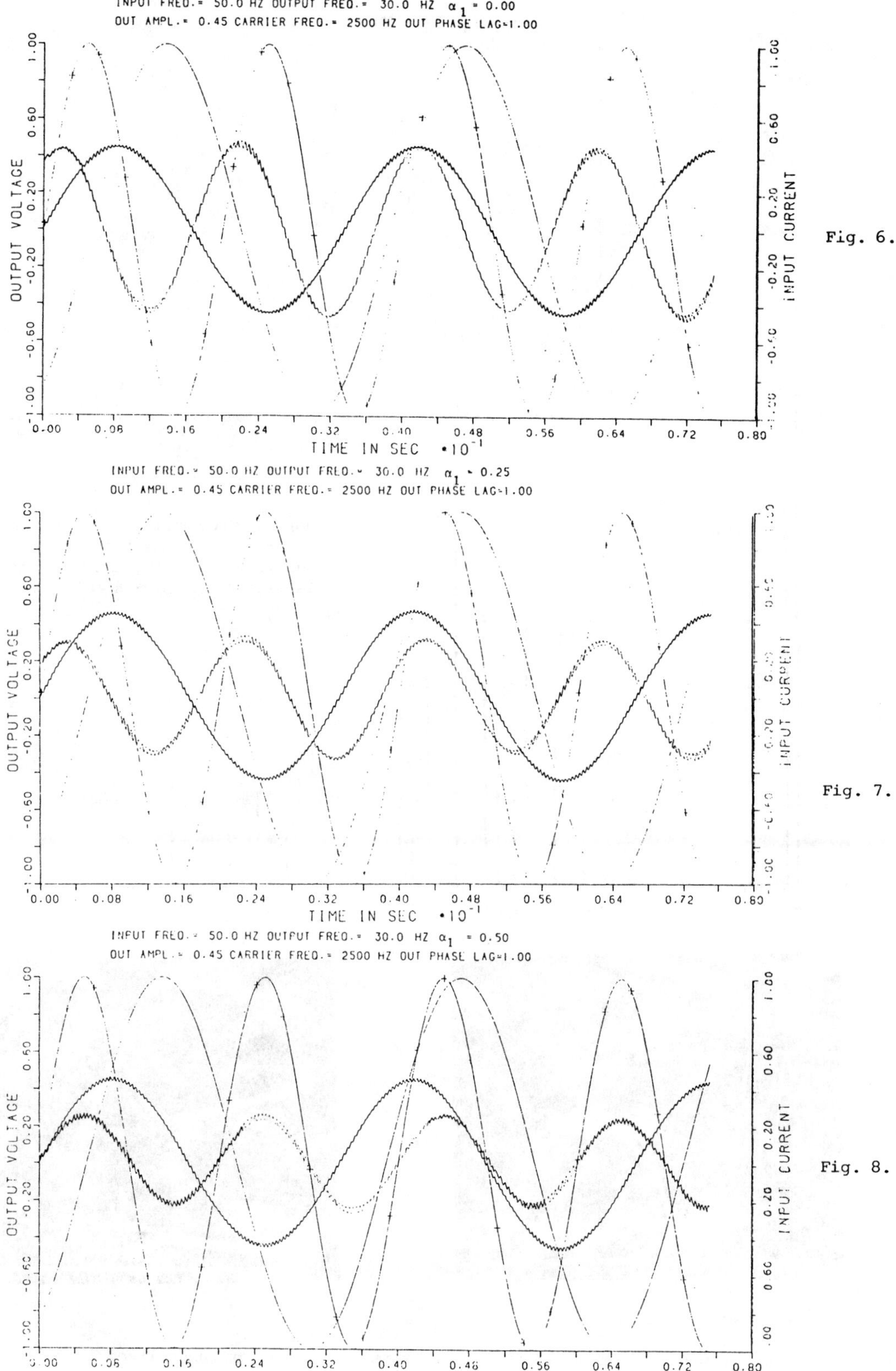

Fig. 6.

Fig. 7.

Fig. 8.

Fig. 9.

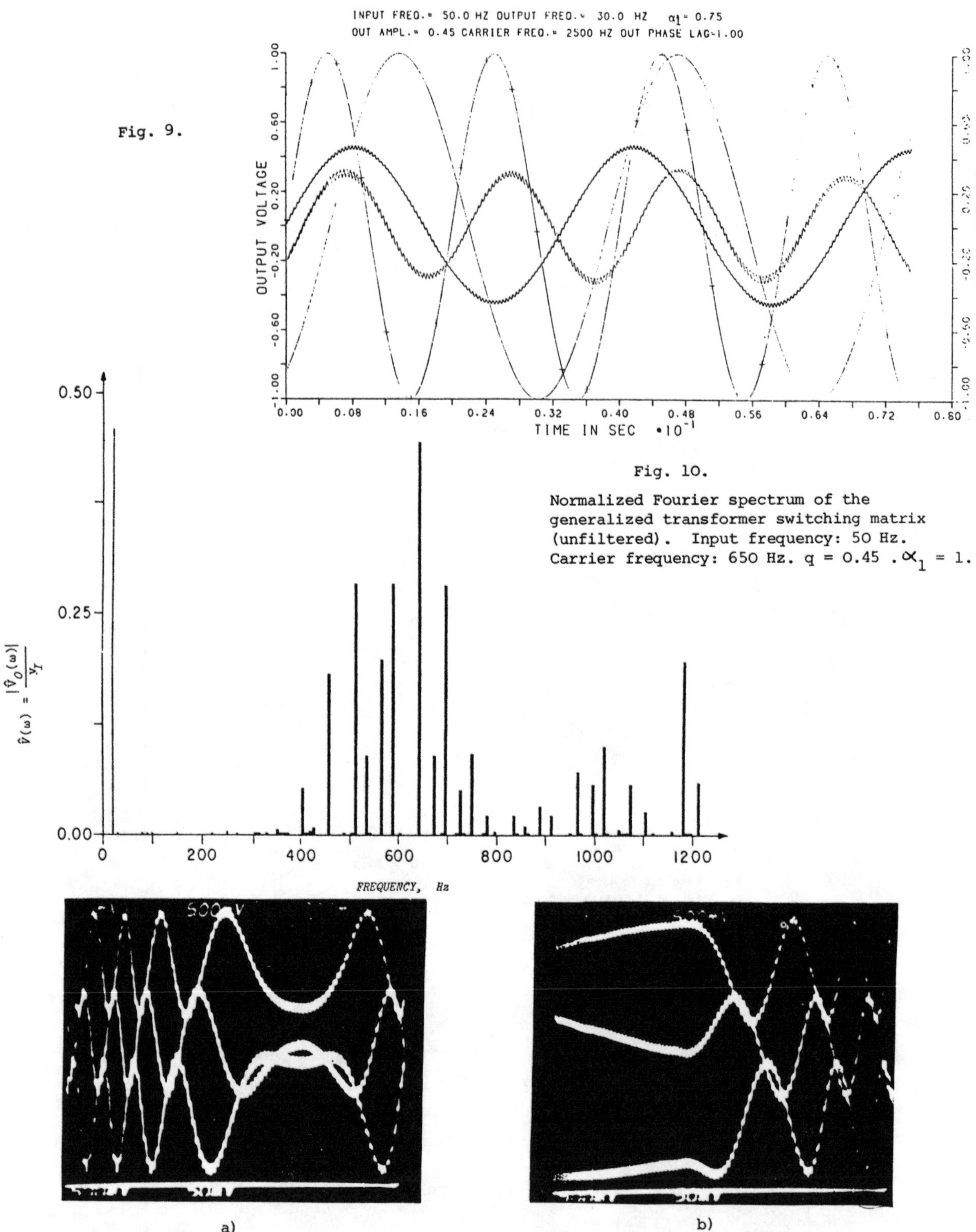

Fig. 10.

Normalized Fourier spectrum of the generalized transformer switching matrix (unfiltered). Input frequency: 50 Hz. Carrier frequency: 650 Hz. q = 0.45 . $\alpha_1 = 1$.

a)

b)

Fig. 11.

Output voltage waveforms of the first prototype of generalized transformer (filtered).

a) Frequency Sweep from 5 Hz, through DC, to 5 Hz with phase sequence inversion.

b) Step change in output frequency with phase sequence inversion.

References

1. B.D. Bedford, R.G. Hoft, "Principles of Inverter Circuits". Wiley, New York, 1964.

2. L. Gjugyi, B. Pelly, "Static Power Frequency Changers". Wiley, New York, 1976.

3. Y. Katznelson, "An Introduction to Harmonic Analysis". Wiley, New York, 1968.

4. A. Papoulis, "The Fourier Integral and its Applications". McGraw-Hill, 1962.

5. P. Wood, "General Theory of Switching Power Supplies". Proceedings of E.S.C., San Diego, 1979.

6. B.R. Pelly, "Thyristor Phase-Controlled Converters and Cycloinverters". Wiley, New York, 1971.

7. A. Shönung, H. Stammler, "Static Frequency Changers with Subharmonic Control in Conjunction with Reversible Variable Speed AC Drives". Brown Boveri Review, Vol. 51, No. 8-9, pp. 555-557, Aug.-Sept. 1964.

8. J. Zubek, A. Abbondanti, C.J. Norby, "Pulsewidth Modulated Inverter Motor Drives with Improved Modulation". IEEE Trans on Ind. Appl., Vol 1A-11, No.6, pp. 695-703, Nov-Dec. 1975.

9. H.S. Patel, R.G. Hoft, "Generalized Techniques of Harmonic Elimination and Voltage Control in Thyristors Inverters: Part I - Harmonic Elimination". IEEE Trans on Ind. Appl., Vol. 1A-10, pp. 666-673, Sept.-Oct. 1974.

10. H. Nayak, R.G. Hoft, "Optimizing the PWM Waveform of a Thyristor Inverter". IEEE Trans. on Ind. Appl., Vol. 1A-11, U.S., pp.526-530, Sept.-Oct. 1975.

11. G.W. Wester, R.D. Middlebrook, "Low Frequency Characterization of Switching DC-DC Converters". IEEE Trans. on Aerospace and Electronic Systems, Vol. AES-9, No. 3, May 1973, pp. 376-385.

12. M. Venturini, "A New High Switching Rate Direct Frequency Converter". Submitted for Publication.

13. M. Venturini, "Convertitore Diretto AC-AC di Elevata Potenza". Italian Patent 20777a-79 March 6, 1979.

14. A. Alesina, M. Venturini, "Solid State Power Conversion: A Fourier Analysis Approach to Generalised Transformer Synthesis". To be published on IEEE Trans. on Circuits and Systems.

Paper 4.5

Theory and Design of a 30-Hp Matrix Converter

Charles L. Neft and Colin D. Schauder
Westinghouse Electric Corporation
Research and Development Center
Pittsburgh, PA 15235 U.S.A

Abstract

The paper describes the control strategy and hardware design for a 30-hp matrix converter (9-switch Forced-Commutation Cycloconverter) which was developed for high-bandwidth four-quadrant motor drive applications. The new switching technique ensures very low distortion of the input currents with unity fundamental displacement factor. Experimental results are presented.

Introduction

Cycloconverters are well established as a means of direct ac-to-ac power conversion. Naturally commutated cycloconverters (NCC) have serious limitations with regard to output frequency range, input power factor, and distortion of the input and output waveforms. Many of these limitations can be overcome with forced-commutation cycloconverters (FCC) comprising bilateral static power switches. Elegant switching control techniques[1] allow FCC structures to be used as unrestricted frequency changers (UFC) which provide regeneration with a moderate switching frequency. The waveform quality achievable with UFC control improves with increasing converter pulse-number, which unfortunately also requires the use of more power switches. Cost considerations, however, make it important to minimize the number of switches, and this has caused the three-pulse FCC, shown in Figure 1, to receive considerable attention. This circuit uses only nine switches and is also known as the matrix converter because it provides exactly one switch for each of the possible connections between input and output lines.

When operated with UFC control, the matrix converter has output voltage limitations and serious waveform distortion, and alternative control techniques have been developed to overcome these problems. In general these methods use high frequency switching and aim to achieve large separation between the fundamental and the distortion components in the input and output waveforms for easy filtering. Venturini[2] has described a high frequency switching strategy which is very effective, but has an output voltage limitation equal to half the input voltage. Another approach[3] controls the switching according to a rectifier-inverter concept which emulates the action of a dc-link inverter and provides maximum theoretical output voltage capability. Ziogas[4] and others have analyzed these methods and suggested variations. This work has yielded improved waveforms but has not fully utilized the potential of the matrix converter to provide sinewave-in/sinewave-out performance over the full output voltage range.

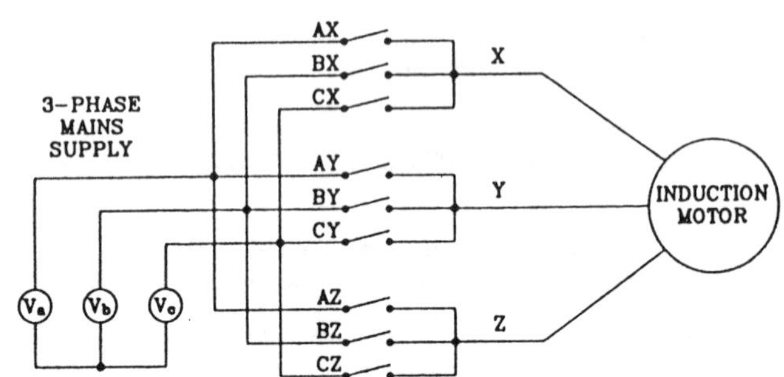

Figure 1: Matrix Converter

A new switching strategy for the matrix converter has been derived based on simplistic considerations of input and output power. Waveform analysis confirms that this method eliminates low order harmonics from the input current spectrum. The technique has further been applied to a 30-hp vector-controlled induction motor drive. Measurements made on this system confirm the analysis.

Switching Control Strategy

The new control technique is a variation of the methods which emulate the action of a dc-link voltage source inverter by considering each of the three-switch groups (see Figure 1) as a hypothetical inverter pole. Using this approach, the switching strategy comprises "rectifier" action, concerned with obtaining either a positive or a negative group output voltage, and "inverter" action, concerned with alternating the group polarities in such a way as to control the output voltage and current.

In the present case, it is anticipated that the inverter action will be dictated by a high-bandwidth closed-loop current control system. Such current control systems are commonly applied to PWM inverters for ac servo drives. It is reasonable to assume that the current controller, responding to current demands from the vector-control system, will ensure that the steady state load power spectrum contains only a dc-level plus high frequency components. The switching control scheme is derived under this assumption.

The rectifier action defines two possible sets of switch control functions for the switches in each group. The "positive" set would generate a predominantly positive group output voltage relative to mains neutral. The "negative" set would generate negative voltage. The difference between the

Reprinted from *IEEE/IAS Ann. Meet. Conf. Rec.*, pp. 934–939, 1988.

positive and negative group output voltages constitutes a hypothetical dc-link voltage. The inverter action ensures that this is the only voltage applied to the motor load at any time. Furthermore, because only one switch in a group can be on at any time, it follows that the dc-link voltage at any time is simply one of the six available mains line-to-line voltages. If we neglect losses in the switching matrix, the current that is reflected through the two active mains lines at each instant is determined by the instantaneous output power and the line-to-line voltage.

Assume that the output power has a dc-level of P watts and consider the interval in Figure 2 between $-\pi/6<\omega t<\pi/6$. During this period either V_{ab} or V_{ac} would be possible choices for the dc-link voltage, but in either case the current will flow through the A-phase input line which will act as the positive rail of the dc-link. The objective, unity power factor, source current during this interval is:

$$i_a(t)=\frac{2P}{3V}\cos\omega t$$

where V is the peak line to neutral voltage. Subject to the constant power and sinusoidal supply voltage constraints, such a current flowing in the A-phase would be sufficient to ensure that the corresponding B- and C-phase currents are balanced sinewaves of the same magnitude and frequency.

Depending on the choice of V_{ab} or V_{ac} there are two possible values of the A-phase current during the interval:

$$i_a(t)=\frac{P'}{\sqrt{3}\,V\cos(\omega t+\pi/6)}\ ,\ \text{if } V_{ab} \text{ is chosen}$$

or

$$i_a(t)=\frac{P'}{\sqrt{3}\,V\cos(\omega t-\pi/6)}\ ,\ \text{if } V_{ac} \text{ is chosen}$$

where $P' = P +$ *high frequency components.*

By rapidly alternating the choice of source voltage with a defined duty cycle the moving average value of A-phase current can be made equal to the desired sinewave. To accomplish this, the fraction of total time to be spent on V_{ac} can be computed as

$$\tau=\frac{\cos(\omega t-\pi/3)}{\cos(\omega t)}$$

Notice that this fraction is independent of power and voltage amplitude and depends only on the mains phase angle.

Similar reasoning can be applied for each succeeding $\pi/3$ interval of the mains cycle, giving the following general expression for the fraction of total time to be spent on the more lagging of the two alternative source voltages in order to ensure that the mains currents are sinusoidal.

$$\tau=\frac{\cos(\phi-\pi/3)}{\cos(\phi)} \quad \text{where } \phi=(\omega t+\frac{\pi}{6})_{mod\,\pi/3}-\frac{\pi}{6}$$

Using PWM approximation of τ, the associated rectifier control functions for positive and negative group output voltages can be determined. These are plotted in Figure 2 for 2880 Hz modulation frequency. These rectifier control functions are what is required to reflect a constant power

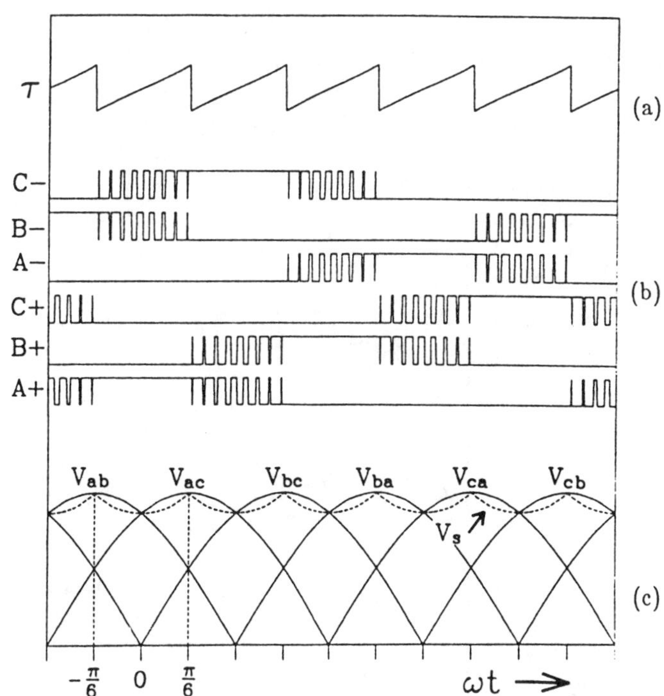

Figure 2: Derivation of Rectifier Control Functions (a) Modulating Function, τ. (b) Rectifier Control Functions. (c) Source Voltage Derivation.

output (plus high frequency components) to the mains as a sinusoidal current set (plus high frequency components). It is of interest to note that these control functions can also be obtained by a process of phase-modulating the natural rectifier control functions. Closed-loop control of input waveform by phase-modulation is therefore also possible.[5]

The rectifier control functions which have been described lead to a dc-link voltage which contains low order harmonics of the mains frequency. The moving average of this voltage is

$$V_s=\frac{3V}{2\cos\phi}$$

V_s is plotted in Figure 2 (c). The varying value of V_s has the effect of introducing low frequency gain variations into the inverter current control loops. A correcting gain factor is therefore generated as a function of mains phase angle. The correction is conveniently applied by amplitude modulating the triangle wave used for voltage control in the forward path of the current loops.

Figure 3 shows a block diagram of the overall control scheme. Notice that both the rectifier control functions and the modulated triangle wave for use in the inverter control are constant functions of the mains phase angle and are generated from lookup tables. The logic which combines the rectifier and inverter action is also fixed and takes the form of a look-up table. Using this approach, all of the switch control timing is derived from the mains phase angle. Carrier frequency for both the rectifier and inverter control is set at the 48th harmonic of the fundamental, 2880 Hz.

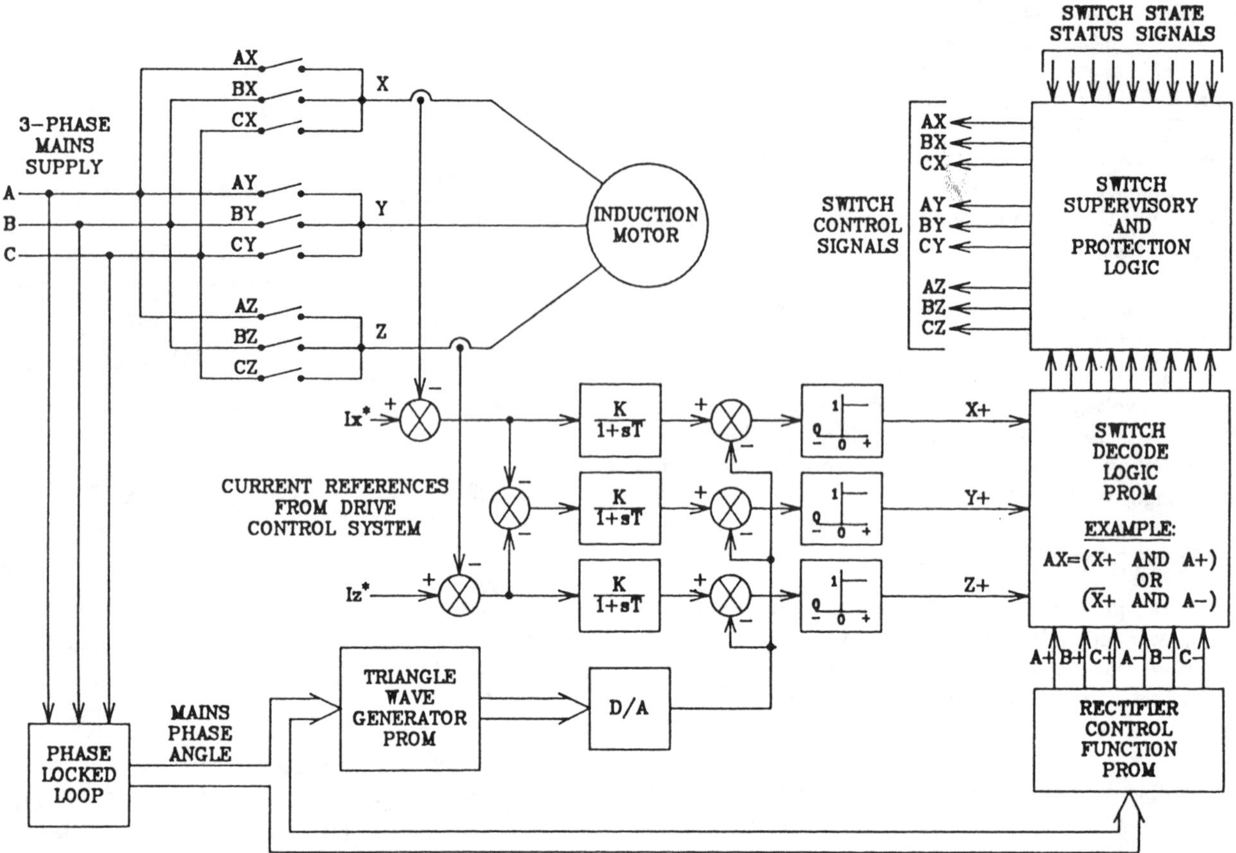

Figure 3: Control Circuit Block Diagram

Figure 4 presents the results of computer simulation of the control strategy. The figure shows the actual hypothetical dc-link voltage, that is the effective dc voltage the inverter control sees. Also shown is the desired ideal dc-link current. This is the current that, in the absence of high frequency power components, will reflect sine wave currents in the mains. The line current, both unfiltered and filtered versions, that results from the dc-link current is shown along with the unfiltered spectrum. The switching frequency used to derive the waveforms shown in this figure is 2880 Hz, the same value used in the drive. Similarly, the filter characteristics used to derive the filtered current are the same as in the drive.

Hardware Description

Bilateral Switch

The matrix converter requires the use of a fully bilateral switch. Since, at the time the program was begun, there were no suitable single packages available, the switch was constructed from discrete components. The switch arrangement shown in Figure 5, consisting of a controllable device, in this case a transistor, embedded in a bridge rectifier, is one of several variations possible. This arrangement was chosen to simplify the snubbing and base drive requirement.

Although in principle, the controllable switch could have been a GTO or MOSFET, a bipolar transistor was chosen as being most appropriate for this particular application. The device had nominal ratings of 300 A, 1000 V, although subsequent analysis showed that a 200-A, 600-V device would have been suitable. The bridge rectifiers were chosen for their soft reverse recovery characteristic, and nominally rated for 70 A, 1000 V. A small local snubber, as shown in Figure 5, provides for some waveshaping of the turn-off pulse. The snubber discharge time constant is coordinated with the minimum allowable switch conduction interval (10 μs) to ensure that the capacitor will fully discharge each interval.

Clamp Circuit

A single voltage clamp circuit is operative for all nine bilateral switches to prevent damaging overvoltages. At switch turn-off, the steering rectifiers, shown in Figure 5, direct current into the clamp capacitors. The strategic use of a voltage clamp permits the use of transistors with a lower voltage rating. Reduction of the magnitude of the local snubber capacitor associated with each individual transistor is also possible, with an effective clamp. Note the clamp is also effective in managing transients due to rectifier recovery.

Two types of capacitors are used for energy storage in the clamp. An electrolytic capacitor for bulk storage is paralleled with a high quality polypropylene capacitor for transient response. As the capacitor voltage will increase with each switching operation, some means is required for removing energy. One method is to switch a resistor across

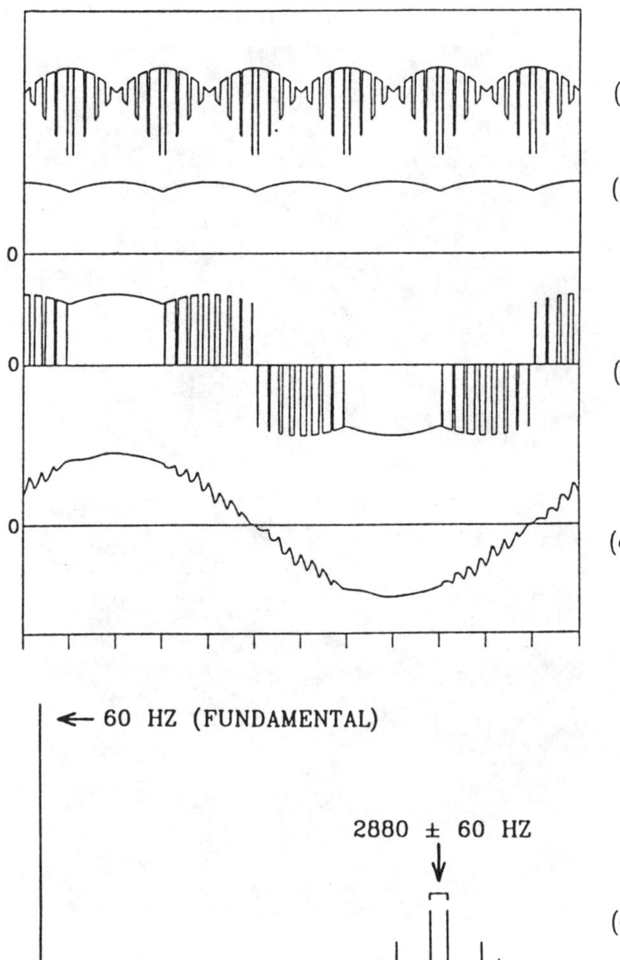

Figure 4: Simulation Results (a) Dc-Link Voltage (b) Dc-Link Current. (c) Unfiltered Line Current. (d) Filtered Line Current. (e) Unfiltered Current Spectrum.

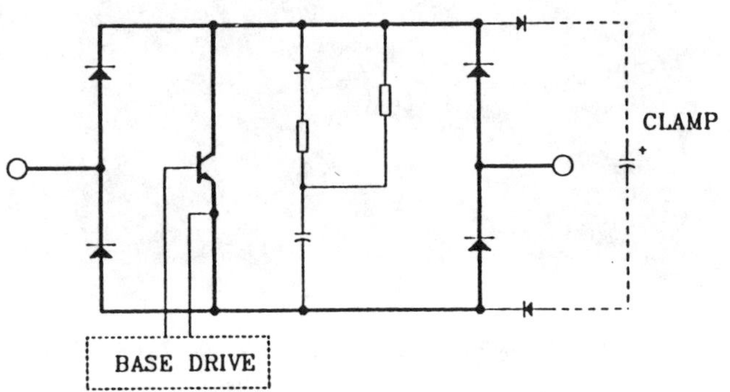

Figure 5: Bilateral Switch

he capacitor when the clamp voltage gets beyond a reselected level. This maintains the clamp voltage, and the ransistor collector-emitter voltage as well, at a safe level, ypically just above the peak line-to-line voltage.

An alternate method of energy removal is to use the lamp energy to power system auxiliaries, for example the ransistor base drives. As each base drive requires an isolated ower supply, the clamp circuit provides a convenient source or that power. Referring to Figure 6, the clamp capacitor serves as an input to a half-bridge inverter power supply operated at 20 kHz. The output drives ten isolated channels, each channel providing power to a transistor's base drive circuit (the tenth channel is for the relatively small transistor still required to dissipate excess clamp energy). This technique improves drive efficiency by 1%. In principle, the clamp energy can be directed into other areas, if appropriate.

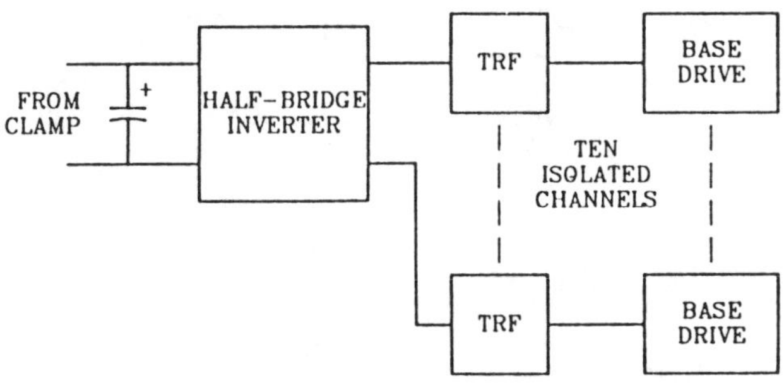

Figure 6: Clamp Energy Recovery

Base Drive

In order to minimize power lost as a result of transistor switching, and to provide optimum converter performance, the base drives in the matrix converter must be fast responding. To effectively isolate the drives from the control circuit, duplex fiber-optic coupling is used. One link provides the on-off signal to the drives. A power amplifier converts this signal to either a turn-on or turn-off drive as appropriate, both current-regulated.

The second link provides status to the control circuit on the transistor's condition. When the base-emitter junction of the transistor has reverse voltage across it, a signal is sent to the control, by this link. Consider a situation where a switch, for example AX in Figure 3, has just received a turn-off signal. Before another switch in the same three-pulse group, BX or CX, can be turned-on, the storage time on AX must elapse. This instant is determined by the base-emitter junction monitor, and the control circuit informed. Thus, the time lag between one device's recovery and the onset of base current to the next, is kept small, about one microsecond.

Several protective features are included on the base drive module. The power supply rails are monitored and shutdown occurs when an out-of-tolerance condition occurs. The transistor's collector emitter voltage is monitored during conduction. If the transistor should come out of saturation, it is immediately turned off. This protects against both erratic base drive problems, and also provides some short circuit protection. The control circuit monitors transistor status by the recovery detector signals. If the transistor status is not normal, the drive is shut down.

Line Filter

In order to provide an appropriate voltage source at the input terminals, as required by the theory, and to bypass the high frequency components in the input current as well, an input line filter is required. A tuned L-C filter was chosen with a damping resistor in parallel across the inductor, as shown in Figure 7. The resistor location provided minimal dissipation in the filter. The resonant frequency of 750 Hz and the damping factor of 0.2 were chosen to provide adequate attenuation of the ripple frequencies, around 2880 Hz, without being significant at the typical rectifier harmonic frequencies, which are likely to be found in practice. The line filter had virtually no effect on the fundamental displacement factor; the final value was above 0.99 at full load.

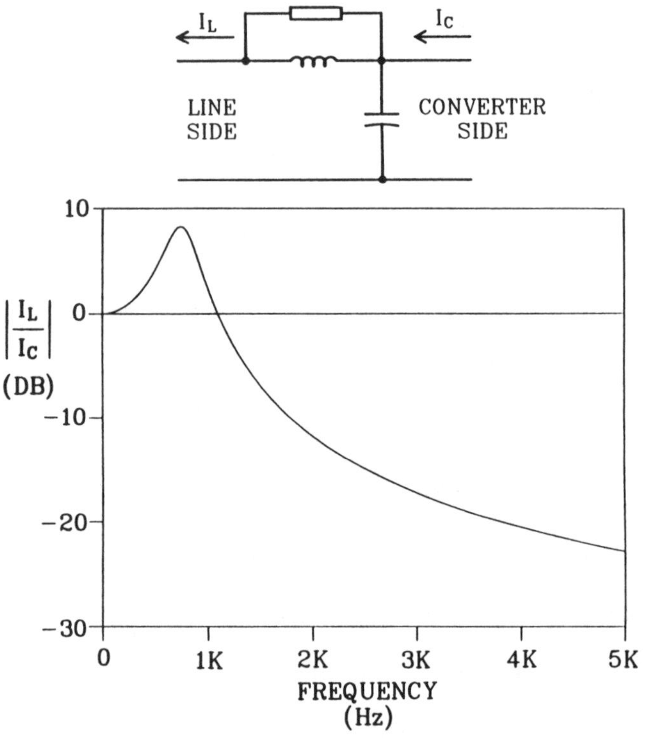

Figure 7: Line Filter Transfer Function

Experimental Results

Input Current Waveform

Figure 8 shows the line and motor current at various speeds, motoring, about 30 and 15 hp, and regenerating, about 10 hp. The motor current is mostly sinusoidal as required by the theory. The input current, also mostly sinusoidal, shows that the filter has removed most of the higher frequency components from the waveform.

The spectrum of the input current is shown, both filtered and unfiltered, in Figure 9. The picture was taken at approximately 50-Hz output, with a fundamental component of 55 *Arms*. The unfiltered spectrum clearly shows the clusters of unwanted components around 2.88 kHz, 5.76 kHz, and 8.64 kHz, as would be expected from the control strategy. The filtered spectrum shows the effect in removing the PWM residue from the waveform. The amplitude of the largest unwanted component has been reduced by a factor of 10. Figure 10 shows the total harmonic distortion (THD) for the line current waveform, plotted versus power, for constant torque loading. At the higher power outputs the waveform distortion is less than an ideal twelve-pulse rectifier waveform.

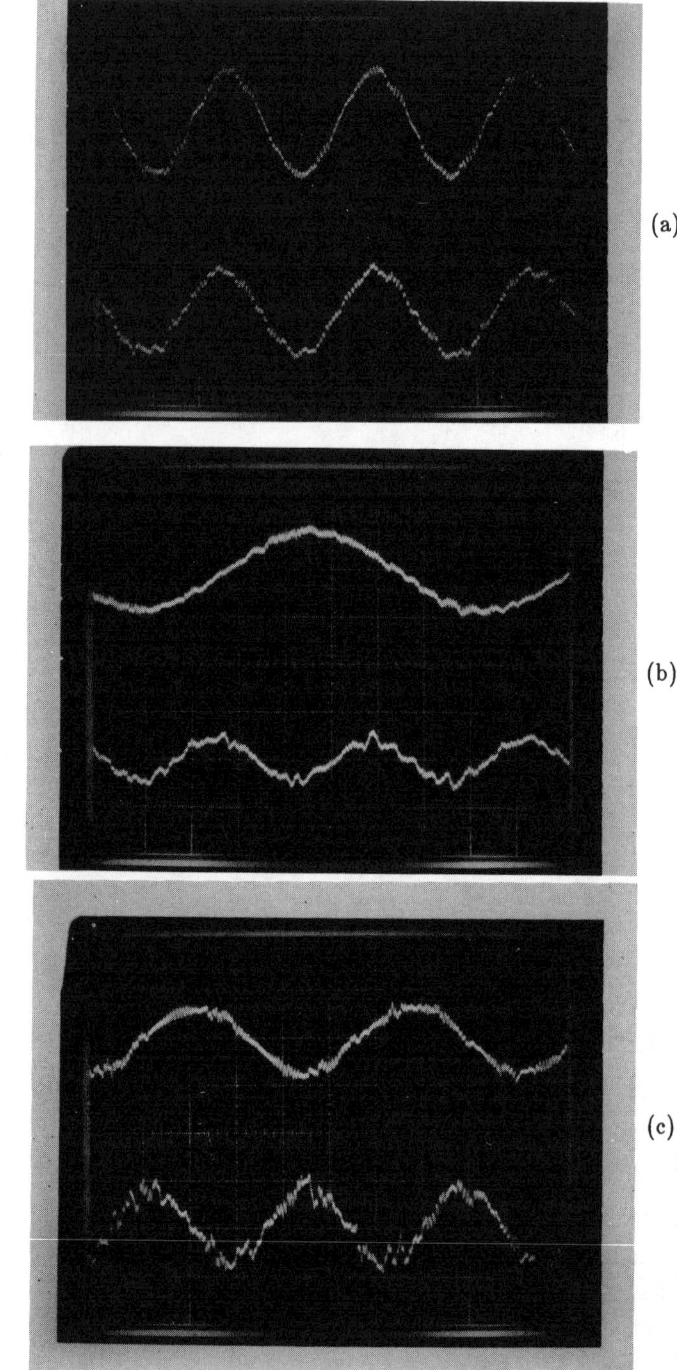

Figure 8: Motor/Line Current Waveforms (a) 55 Hz - Motoring. (b) 30 Hz - Motoring. (c) 40 Hz - Regeneration

Drive Performance

Figure 11 shows the speed and motor current of the drive for a speed reversal for -1200 r/min to 1200 r/min. Figure 12 shows the speed and input current for a step change in speed from 0 to 1200 r/min. This figure shows that although the basis for the control is constant power flow, the quality of the input current waveform is maintained during speed transients, as well.

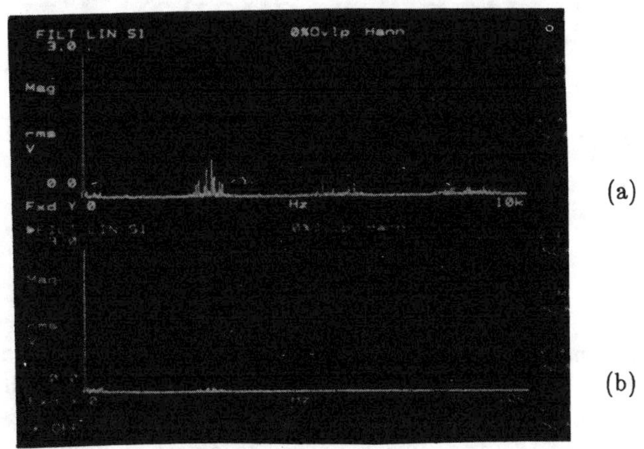

Figure 9: Current Spectrum (a) Unfiltered (b) Filtered

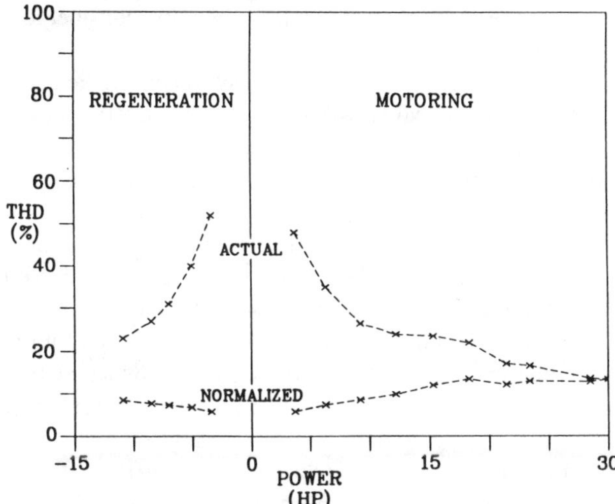

Figure 10: Line Current Distortion

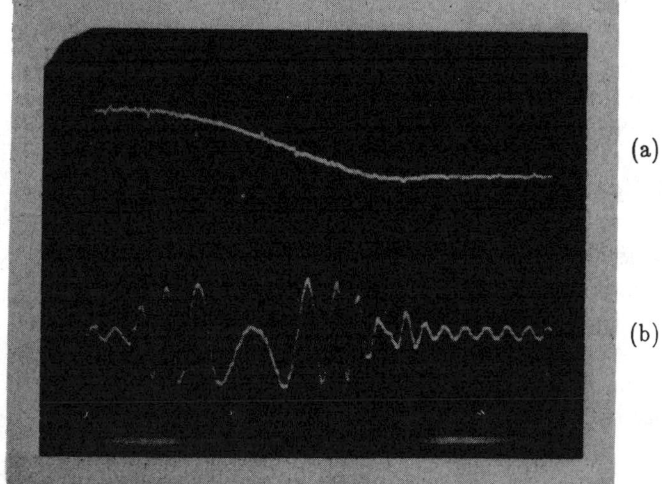

Figure 11: Speed Reversal (a) Speed. (b) Motor Current - 100 A per div.

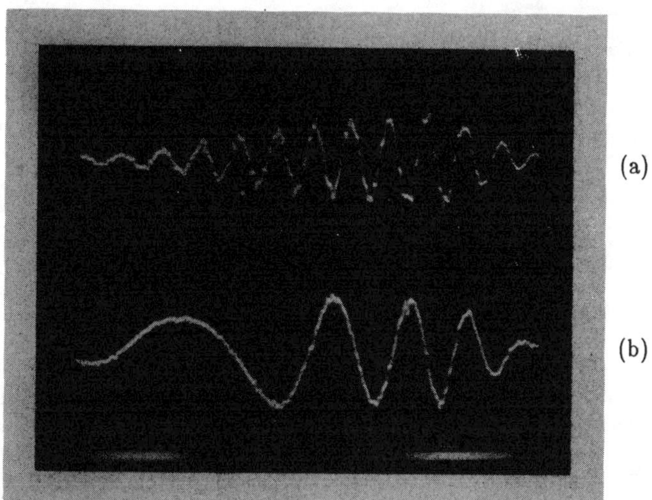

Figure 12: Acceleration (a) Line Current - 100 A per div. (b) Motor Current - 100 A per div.

Conclusion

The design and control strategy of a matrix converter has been described. The converter was applied to a servo-type, 30-hp ac induction motor drive. A new switching technique featuring unity fundamental displacement factor and high quality input current waveform has been presented. The main hardware features include switch interlocking and an energy recovery circuit. The result is an efficient, high performance drive, with a high utilization of devices.

Acknowledgment

Some of the material presented in this paper was developed in cooperation with Mitsubishi Electric Corporation. The authors wish to express their thanks in particular to Dr. H. Sugimoto for his contribution.

References

1. Gyugyi, L. and Pelly, B. R., *Static Power Frequency Changers,* John Wiley & Sons, 1976.

2. Venturini, M., "A New Sine Wave In, Sine Wave Out Conversion Technique Eliminates Reactive Elements," *Proceedings of Powercon 7,* 1980, pp. E3-1 to E3-15.

3. Schauder, C. D., "Hidden Dc-Link Ac/Ac Converter Using Bilateral Power Switches," United States Patent 4,642,751.

4. Ziogas, P. D, Khan, S. I., Rashid, M. H., "Analysis and Design of Forced Commutated Cycloconverter Structures with Improved Transfer Characteristics," *Transactions on Industrial Electronics,* Vol. IE-33, 1986, pp. 271-280.

5. Kastner, G. and Rodriguez, J., "A Forced Commutated Cycloconverter with Control of the Source and Load Currents," *First European Conference on Power Electronics and Applications,* 1985, pp. 1.141-1.146.

Design and Performance of a High-Frequency Link Induction Motor Drive Operating at Unity Power Factor

SEUNG K. SUL, MEMBER, IEEE, AND THOMAS A. LIPO, FELLOW, IEEE

Abstract—**The design and performance of a complete three-phase converter system and field-oriented induction motor drive based upon a 20-kHz ac link is described. By using the same converter for the ac input side as well as the output load side, it is shown that power can be transferred in either direction. It is also shown that, with the use of a current regulator, both power flow on the link and the link voltage amplitude can be regulated. In addition, by suitable feedback control, the power factor at the input to the converter can be adjusted to unity. Both computer and experimental results show unity power factor operation, low harmonic current in both the input and output of the system, and bidirectional power flow capability.**

INTRODUCTION

WITH RECENT advances in power electronics, variable-speed operation of an ac machine by use of frequency changers has become a well-established technology. The most widely used and highly developed frequency changers are the six-step and pulsewidth modulated (PWM) inverters which synthesize variable-frequency and variable-voltage ac output from a dc input. These inverters utilize a dc voltage link obtained by rectifying and filtering the utility source voltages.

An important factor behind the widespread use of the dc voltage link has been the ease and effectiveness by which the energy storage function, essential for decoupling the source from load, can be implemented in a dc link. Electrolytic capacitors provide low-cost high-density energy storage in the dc voltage link of a voltage source inverter. However, this type of dc-link-based power conversion system has several inherent limitations. One important drawback is the excessive switching loss and device stress that occur during switching intervals. As a result, the typical switching frequency in medium size 10–50 kW PWM inverters is, at best, 5 kHz. Because of the relatively low switching frequency, dramatic gains in important system attributes—such as faster system response, increased output frequency, improved power densities, and reduction in audible and electrical noise, particularly when the motor is operating at high speeds—are difficult to realize. Another difficulty worth mentioning is the presence of the rectifier bridge which is used to obtain dc from the ac voltage source. Conventional full-bridge rectifiers inject considerable low-order harmonics into the utility grid. In addition, the power flow is unidirectional, and regenerative operation of the system is possible only with considerable added expense.

Recently, resonant ac or dc links have been studied and suggested as strong candidates for the power conversion link. With the resonant link the switching frequency can be increased with less than proportional increases in losses or device stress by restricting switching time to the instants of zero voltage on the link [1], [2]. By increasing the resonant link frequency to 15–25 kHz, the problems associated with switching limitations can be overcome. In particular, the resonant ac link principle has recently been investigated for the power distribution system of the NASA Orbiting Space Station and as the secondary power system of advanced aircraft [3], [4] and a 20-kHz single-phase resonant voltage link has been developed for this purpose. Suitable control algorithms for an interface converter operating from a 20-kHz ac link have already been developed and verified [5], [6].

In this paper, the design and performance of a complete three-phase-to-three-phase converter system based upon a 20-kHz ac link is described. By using the same converter for the ac input side as well as the output load side, power can be readily transferred in either direction. At present, this type of topology requires 12 bidirectional switches, so that it appears to be a costly system. However, the development of new power devices such as MOS-controlled thyristor it is anticipated that cost-effective bidirectional devices will soon become available. Hence the converter described in this paper holds promise as a means for obtaining unity power factor and low harmonic current on the source side of a frequency converter as well as providing fast response with high efficiency and with no acoustic noise and markedly reduced electrical noise at the output.

OVERALL SYSTEM DESCRIPTION

The overall system described in this paper is shown in Fig. 1 wherein two converters are connected through a 20-kHz resonant link. The link voltage is supported by a parallel resonant tank circuit. Each switch of the converter has the

Paper IPCSD 89-24, approved by the Industrial Drives Committee of the IEEE Industry Applications Society for presentation at the 1988 Industry Applications Society Annual Meeting, Pittsburgh, PA, October 2–7. Manuscript released for publication July 25, 1989. This work was supported in part by the NASA Lewis Research Center, Cleveland, OH, under Contract NAG3-786.

S. K. Sul was with the Department of Electrical and Computer Engineering, University of Wisconsin, Madison, WI. He is now with the Goldstar Industrial Systems Company, Seoul, Korea.

T. A. Lipo is with the Department of Electrical and Computer Engineering, University of Wisconsin, 1415 Johnson Drive, Madison, WI 53706-1691.

IEEE Log Number 9034289.

Reprinted from *IEEE Trans. Ind. Applicat.*, vol. 26, no. 3, pp. 434–440, May/June 1990.

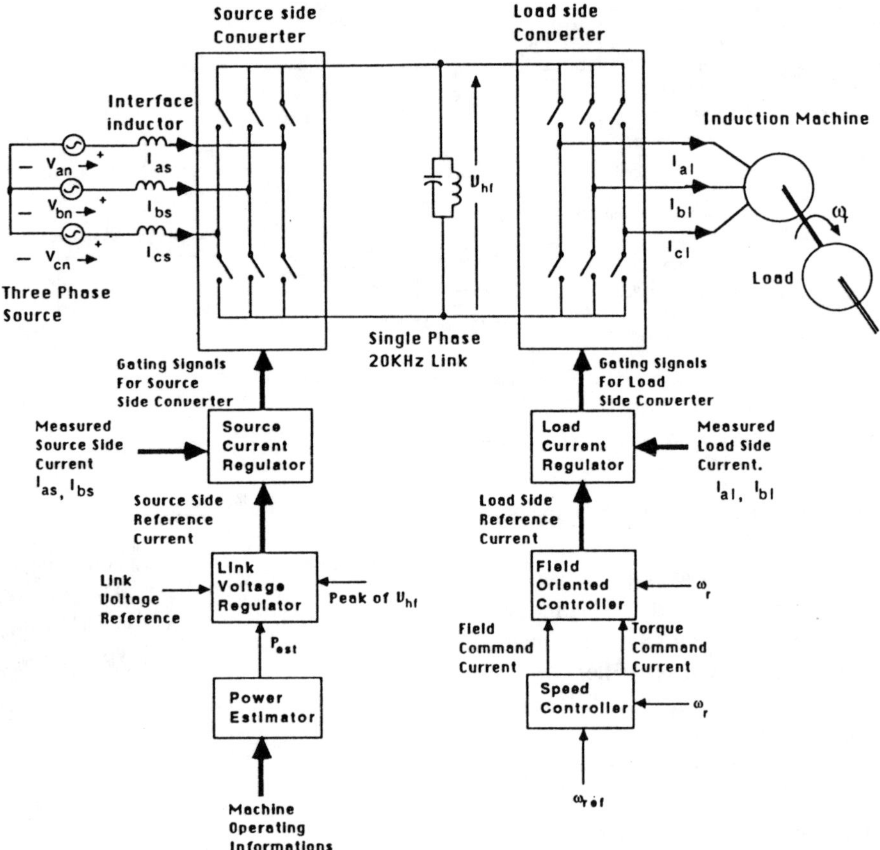

Fig. 1. Power circuit and system control block diagram.

capability of bidirectional current flow and bidirectional voltage blocking. The source side converter is nominally tied to the utility grid through interface inductors, but since these inductors are small they may not be neccessary if sufficient source impedance exists. The load side converter is connected directly to an induction machine without added capacitive filtering. The current of source side converter is controlled by a link voltage regulator which works by balancing the active power flow between the source and load. The current regulator at each converter regulates current in magnitude and phase. The power estimator provides an estimate of the current value of active power to the voltage regulator by calculating the average load power and the system losses based upon measurement of the current operating condition. The induction machine is controlled by a current-regulated field-oriented controller equipped with a speed regulation loop.

Link Voltage Regulation

For cost reasons the energy storage capacity of the link tank circuit must clearly be constructed to be smaller than the dc capacitor in a dc voltage link. To achieve a similar voltage ripple of the link would require an ac capacitor of hundreds of microfarads. Hence power balance between the load and source must be done actively. The ideal method for balancing the power flow between source and load is to measure the instantaneous power delivered to the load and system losses and deliver this exact power to the tank circuit by the source side converter. However, such an instantaneous power matching control appears impossible because of the difference in the source and load frequency and voltage.

The best approach for handling the power balancing problem is to attempt power balance only on an average basis. The instantaneous power unbalance must then be handled by a tank circuit at the cost of link voltage variations. Fortunately, a moderate variation of link voltage is not a severe problem because the power converter connected source or load has the capability of fast regulation and the current in the source and load can be controlled as desired even in the presence of high-frequency link voltage fluctuations. A small or moderate variation will, perhaps, only produce slightly more harmonic content in output current. A large variation of link voltage could, however, create more severe problems. In particular, if the voltage is instantaneously below the minimum voltage needed to synthesize the desired reference command, the actual signal will not be able to follow the reference suggesting the possibility of control instability.

Probably the most elegant approach to measuring power is by means of d, q components. That is, by

$$P=\frac{3}{2}(v_d i_d + v_q i_q).$$

In this case both the voltage and current must be measured. Since the voltage waveform has wide-band harmonics due to the modulation scheme, elimination of the harmonics requires that the cutoff frequency of the filter be set at several hundred hertz. This restriction implies several hundred microseconds of time delay. To suppress the link voltage variation within an

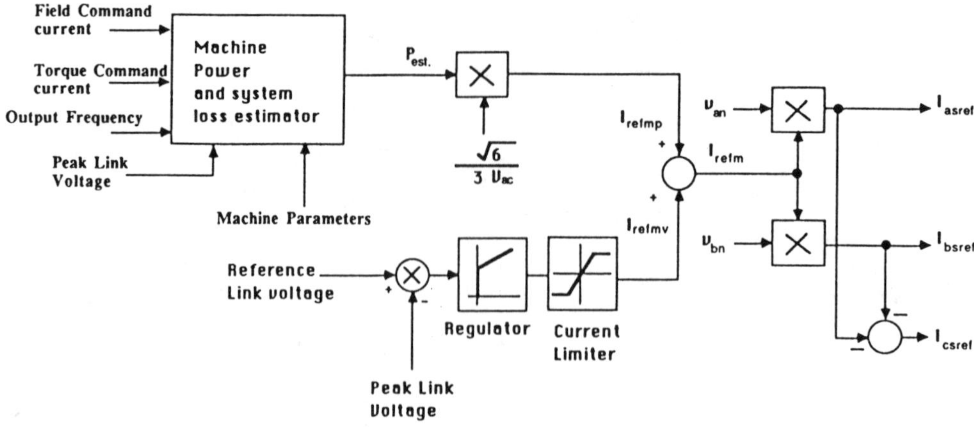

Fig. 2. Block diagram of voltage regulator. v_{ac}: source line-to-line voltage in rms. v_{an}, v_{bn}: instantaneous phase voltage of source.

acceptable level, this time delay is critical lest the capacity of the tank circuit be increased greatly.

The simplest approach for obtaining average power information is to measure the power delivered to the induction machine using a low-pass filter. However, with this method, time delays resulting from the low-pass filter are also inevitable. Thus during the delay time, the difference in average power must be covered by the power capability of the tank circuit. This observation, in turn, implies a degradation in the link voltage regulation.

Another method of obtaining average power is to estimate the power with information derived from the reference currents of the induction machine that are, in turn, available from the field-oriented controller used to control the induction machine. If the current regulation is perfect and if the machine parameters do not change and are known, the average machine power can be estimated without any time delay and without any measurement. In practice, of course, there are always differences between the actual currents and their references. Moreover, the parameters of the machine change according to flux level and operating temperature so that some error between estimated power and the actual power is inevitable. However, these errors can be compensated by using a voltage regulating loop as a minor loop. More detailed descriptions concerning the voltage control loop and power calculator can be found in [6] and [8].

A block diagram of the voltage regulator and power estimator is shown in Fig. 2 in which the source power factor is controlled as unity. The source power factor can be controlled by shifting the phase of the reference current command so long as average power balance is maintained. Hence, the input power factor can be easily programmed to be leading or lagging as desired. In the figure, the magnitude of the reference current is the sum of the value from the power estimator and the value from the link voltage regulator. The phase of the reference current is controlled according to the source voltage.

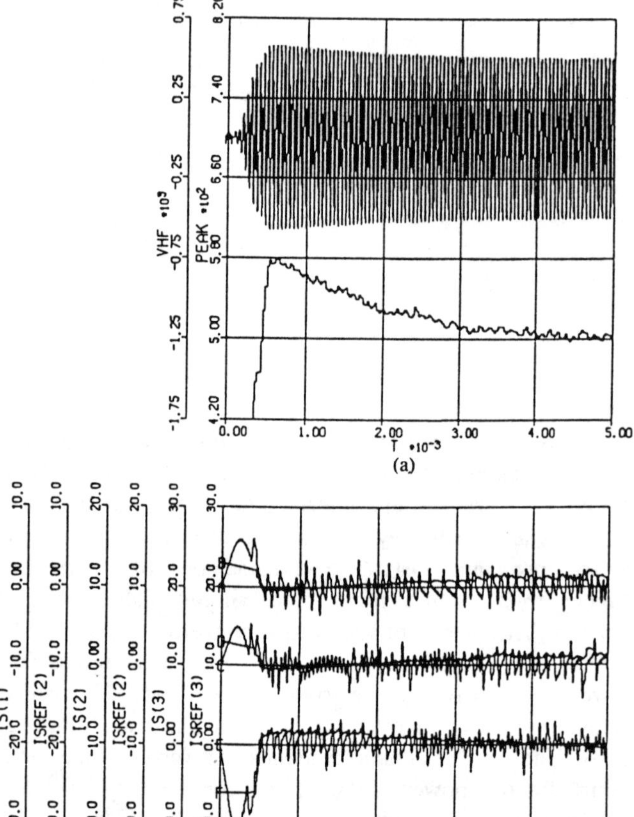

Fig. 3. (a) Simulation result of high-frequency link voltage buildup. Top trace: link voltage in volts. Bottom trace: peak amplitude of link voltage. (b) Simulation result of high-frequency link voltage buildup. From top, *A* is phase source current and its reference, *B* is phase current and its reference, and *C* is phase current and its reference. All traces in amperes.

Transient Behavior of Resonant Link

A computer simulation trace illustrating link voltage buildup is shown in Fig. 3. Note that the energy from the source is pumped to the resonant tank circuit and the tank voltage gradually increases to the given reference value. After overshooting, the voltage settles down to the reference value. In the simulation, the reference voltage is 500 V, and the parameters of the tank circuit are 22.5 μH, 3 μF, and 0.01 Ω. Resistance is incorporated to account for losses in the resonant tank circuit. Note that, after settling down, the source current is almost zero, supplying only the losses of the system.

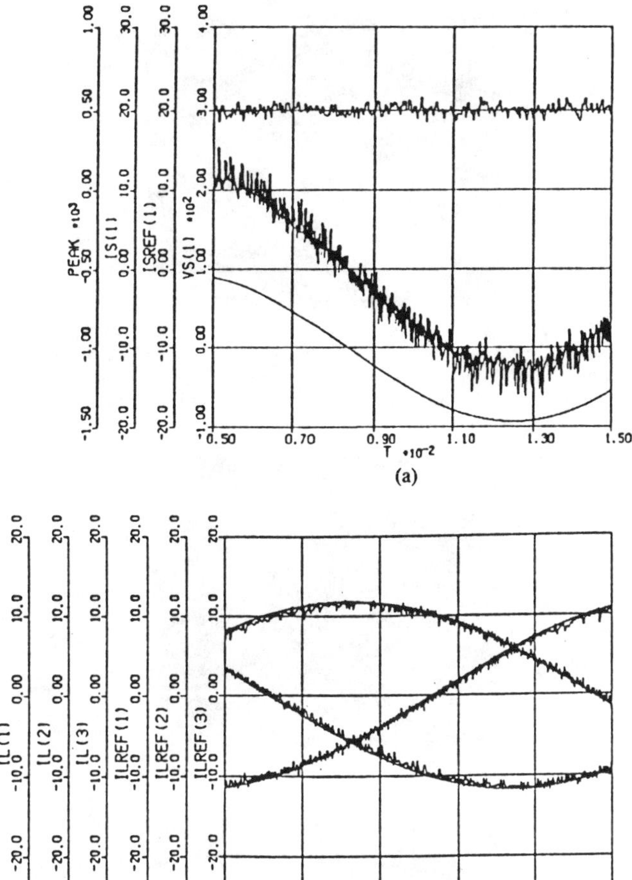

Fig. 4. (a) Simulation result of operating characteristics of system. From top: trace of peak link voltage of volts, A phase source current and its reference (A), and A phase source voltage in (V). (b) Simulation traces showing operating characteristics of system. A, B, and C phase load current and corresponding references. All traces are in amperes.

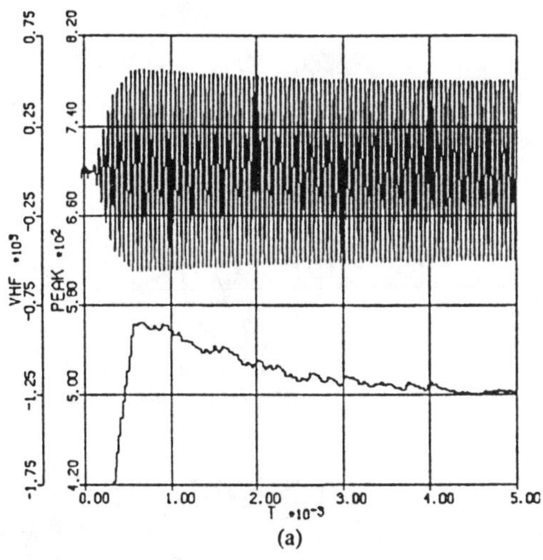

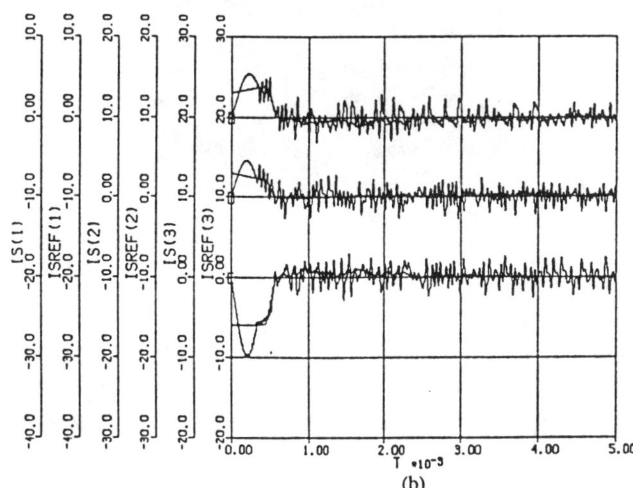

Fig. 5. (a) Simulation result of high-frequency link voltage buildup with mode controller as source current regulator. Top trace: link voltage in volts. Bottom trace: peak amplitude of link voltage. (b) Simulation result of high-frequency link voltage buildup with mode controller as source current regulator. From top: A phase source current and reference, B phase current and its reference, and C phase current and its reference. All traces in amperes.

Another simulation result illustrating the operating characteristics of the system as a whole is shown in Fig. 4. In this simulation it is assumed that a 3-hp induction machine is operating in the steady state at 40 Hz with rated torque. Observe that the link voltage amplitude is reasonably well-regulated. The A phase source current reveals unity power factor operation and indicates only very high-frequency harmonics. The synthesized load current is nearly sinusoidal and has virtually no harmonics less than 40 kHz. Clearly, the parameters of the resonant tank circuit should be traded off with the cost and performance of the system. A larger tank size can clearly provide better voltage regulation at the expense of bulkier components and increased cost.

Current Regulator

In the case of a resonant link system, the current regulators most widely used are the pulse density modulator and the delta modulator [1], [5], [7]. In general, both types of regulators are essentially identical. In the simulation the pulse density modulator was used for the current regulator. Pulse density modulation performs very well in most cases except for cases of low load inductance or when synthesizing fairly high-frequency output. Recently, the authors have reported a new type of current regulator, termed a *mode selection controller* [6], [8]. The mode selection controller operates on-line to select the switching pattern for the next switching mode that will minimize a given error function based on the predicted values of voltage and current at the next switching instant. This type of current regulator can be extended to the control of a complete bidirectional double-bridge system. Mode selection is very effective and easy to apply, especially as a source-side current regulator, where the source voltage and current can be easily measured and independent of system operating conditions. Also, by utilizing mode selection the controller can simultaneously regulate the current as well as the link voltage. In this particular case, the required error function is shown to be simply the sum of the absolute error of each phase current plus that of the link voltage.

The performance of the mode selection controller as a source current regulator is shown in Fig. 5 for the case of link voltage buildup. In these traces all parameters are identical with the case of Fig. 3 except for the current regulator. By

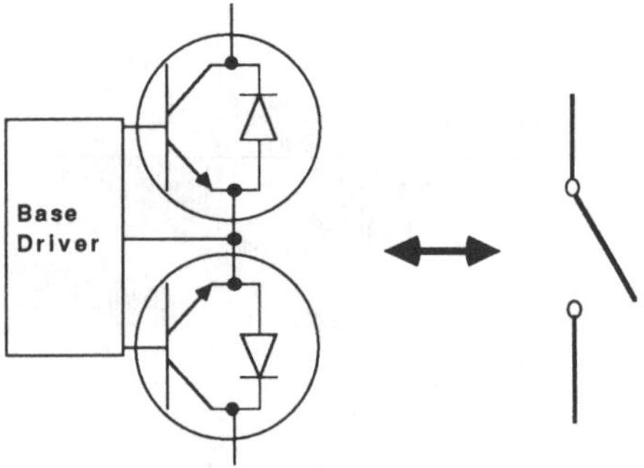

Fig. 6. Implementation of bidirectional switch.

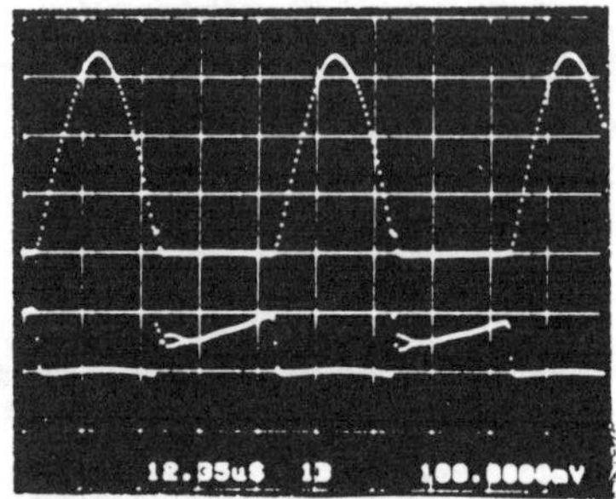

Fig. 7. Voltage and current waveform across a bidirectional switch. Top trace: voltage across switch-130 V/div; ground-4 div from bottom. Bottom trace: current across switch-5 A/div; ground-2 div from bottom. Time scale: 12.35 μs/div.

comparing Fig. 3 and Fig. 5 it can be seen that the voltage overshoot is decreased and the current ripple is also attenuated. Thus the overall performance has clearly been improved.

Experimental Results

The system shown in Fig. 1 has been constructed and thoroughly tested in the laboratory. The speed controller of Fig. 1 is the conventional proportional and integral regulator, and the indirect current regulated field orientation algorithm has been used to implement field-oriented controller. The current regulator of both the line side and load side converters employ the pulse density modulation principle. The link voltage regulator, speed controller, and power estimator were implemented by analog circuits.

The inductors used on the source side are 1.5-mH ferrite-core Litz wire inductors. In the experimental setup, two resonant tank circuits were used. The parameters of each tank are 6 μF and 11.25 μH. Two power transistors were used as a bidirectional power switch and were connected as shown in Fig. 6 [3]. Typical voltage and current wave forms across a switch during normal operation is shown in Fig. 7. As expected, the switching occurs only at the zero crossing points of the link voltage. As a load, a 3-hp 4-pole 60-Hz induction machine was employed, and the machine was mechanically coupled to a 7.5-kW dc machine to apply torque to the induction machine in the positive or negative direction.

Link Voltage Buildup

The experimental result during controlled voltage buildup is shown in Fig. 8. The trace of the peak of the link voltage reveals smooth and well-controlled behavior. Initially, the trace of the A phase current shows a sharp increase to store energy in the inductor. After buildup the current shows a sinusoidal variation in phase with the A phase source voltage. The difference between experimental results and simulation results is due to the difference in the loss of the modeled and actual system. In the simulation the loss component was too small compared to the real system. The real system has some losses associated with the power switch, source side inductor, and resonant tank inductor.

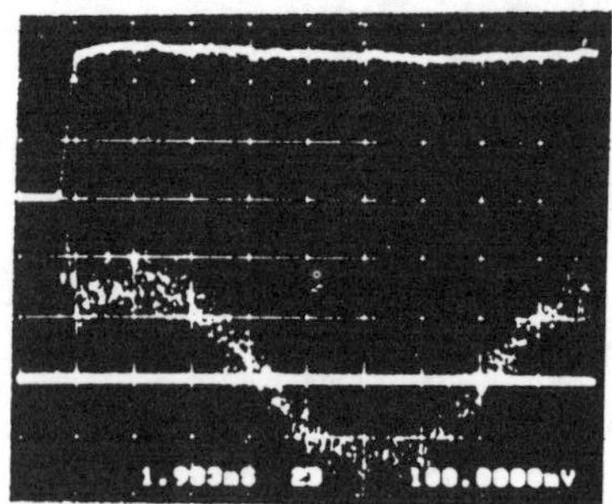

Fig. 8. Peak of high-frequency link voltage and A phase source current waveform during link voltage buildup. Top trace: peak of link voltage-130 V/div; ground-4 div from bottom. Bottom trace: A phase source current-2 A/div; ground-2 div from bottom. Time scale: 1.983 ms/div.

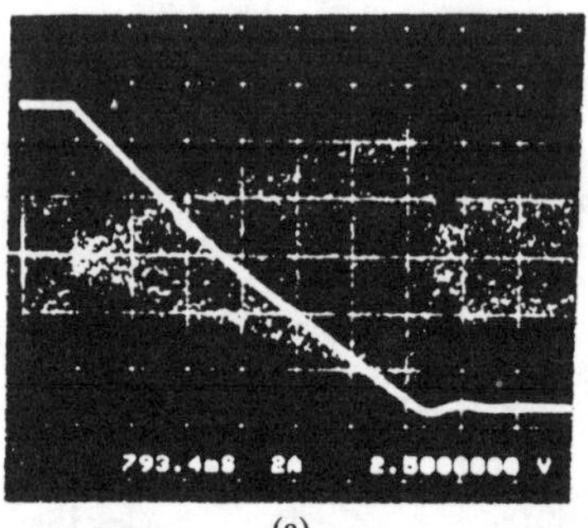

(a)

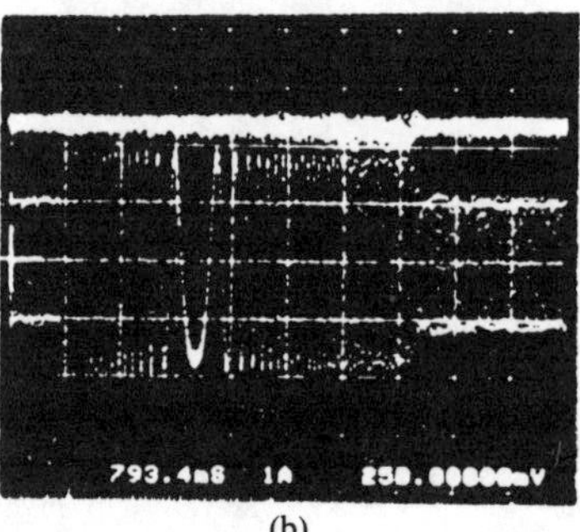

(b)

Fig. 9. (a) Response of field oriented control utilizing high-frequency link power conversion. Mechanical rotational speed-190 r/min/div; ground-4 div from bottom. A phase of source current-5 A/div; ground-4 div from bottom. Time scale: 793.4 ms/div. (b) Response of field oriented control with high-frequency link power conversion. Top trace: peak value of link voltage-130 V/div; ground-4 div from bottom. Bottom trace: induction machine A phase current-5 A/div; ground-4 div. from bottom. Time scale: 793.4 ms/div.

Dynamic Performance of Field Oriented Controller

The test results illustrating the performance of the field-oriented controller is shown in Figs. 9 and 10. In Fig. 9(a), because of large inertia of the dc machine coupled to the induction machine, it takes several seconds to accomplish the

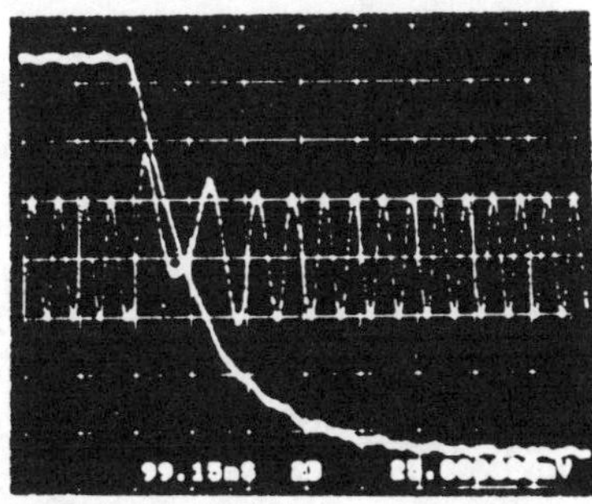

Fig. 10. Response of field-oriented control with high-frequency link power conversion without coupled dc machine. Mechanical rotational speed-190 r/min/div; ground 4 div from bottom. A phase of induction machine current-5 A/div; ground-4 div from bottom. Time scale: 99.15 ms/div.

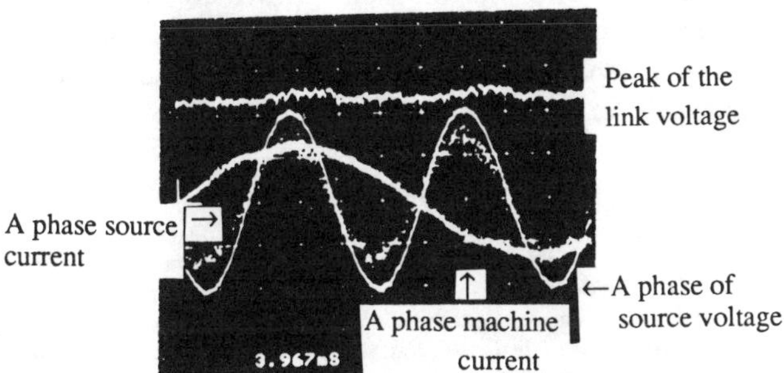

Fig. 11. Waveforms showing unity power factor operation of system during motor operation. Peak of link voltage-130 V/div. A phase of source voltage-40 V/div; A phase source current-5 A/div; A phase induction machine current-5 A/div. All grounds: 4 div from bottom. Time scale: 3.967 ms/div.

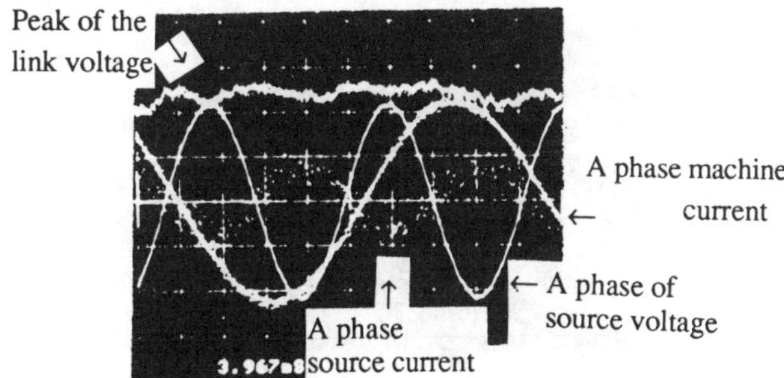

Fig. 12. System traces showing unity power factor operation of system during regeneration. Peak link voltage-130 V/div; A phase of source voltage-40 V/div; A phase of source current-5 A/div. A phase induction machine current-5 A/div. All grounds-4 div from bottom. Time scale: 3.967 ms/div.

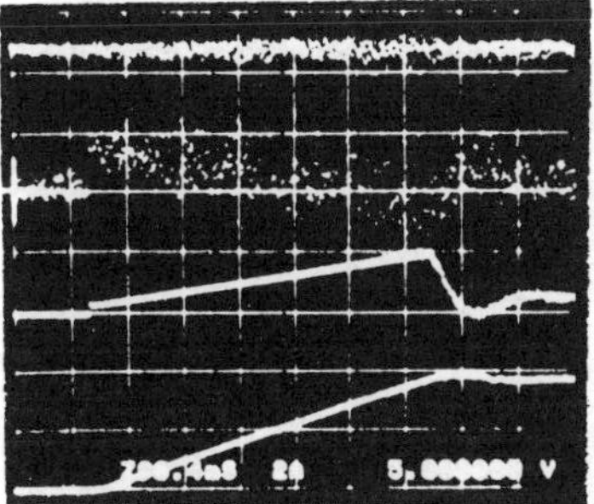

Fig. 13. Operation of power matching controller and voltage regulator. From top: peak value of link voltage-130 V/div; magnitude of reference current from voltage regulator (I_{refmv})-3.5 A/div; magnitude of reference current from power estimator (I_{refmp})-12 A/div; and mechanical rotational speed-190 r/min/div. Grounds located at 5 div, 5 div, 3 div, 0 div from bottom, respectively. Time scale: 793.4 ms/div.

speed change. While not clearly shown due to the large time scale, Fig. 9(a) shows the variation of the power of the system. Before the transient the source supplies only the loss of the system including the mechanical loss. During the deceleration time the mechanical energy is converted to electrical energy. Hence the current of the source rapidly decreases. When the machine begins to accelerate in negative direction, the current increases rapidly to supply the accelerating energy. A trace of the A phase of machine current in Fig. 9(b) clearly shows the change of the frequency as well as the phase. As shown in Fig. 9(b), the link voltage was well-regulated during speed reversal. Fig. 10 shows the system response of the same amount of speed change but this time without the coupled dc machine. The speed reversal was carried out within several tenths of a second. Both test results demonstrate the good dynamic performance of the field-oriented control incorporated with high-frequency link power conversion system.

Unity Power Factor Operation

In Figs. 11 and 12, the steady-state characteristics of the system are shown during motoring and generating operation of the induction machine. In motoring operation, shown in Fig. 11, the source supplies all the losses of the system and the mechanical energy of the induction machine. The trace of the A phase of the source current is in phase with A phase of the source voltage, which clearly demonstrates unity power factor operation. The trace of the peak of the link voltage demonstrates reasonable regulation. During generating operation shown in Fig. 12, the energy generated by the induction machine supplies all losses and the excess energy transfers to the source. Between phase A of the source voltage and the corresponding current there is 180° phase difference. The phase difference means that the source takes the energy from the system with unity power factor. The link voltage regulation for generating operation is poorer than that for motoring operation because of a slight mismatch of the parameters of the power estimator.

Power Matching Controller

As mentioned before, the high-frequency link system has no great reservoir of energy so that the power balance between source and load should be actively controlled. The behavior of the power estimation controller is shown in Fig. 13. During the starting of the induction machine the magnitude of the reference current from estimated power (I_{refmp}) was gradually increased, and after settling of the speed, the magnitude decreased to a small value to supply only the losses of the system. The reference current from voltage regulator, which is a minor loop, deviates around zero. By comparing the magnitude of the current it can be seen that a major part of the magnitude of the source reference current comes from the power estimator. The test result clearly explains the operation of the voltage regulator including the power estimator shown in Fig. 2.

Current Regulation

The characteristics of the current regulator employing pulse density modulation are shown in Figs. 14 and 15. In the case

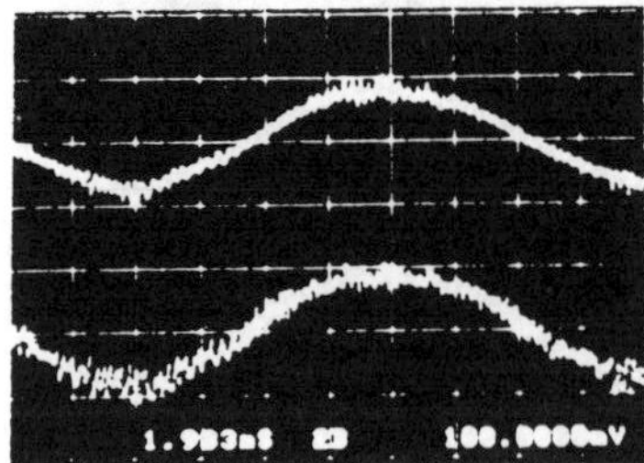

Fig. 14. System performance showing source side current regulation. Top trace: A phase source current-5 A/div; ground-5 div from bottom. Bottom trace: reference of A phase of source current-5 A/div; ground-2 div from bottom. Time scale: 1.983 ms/div.

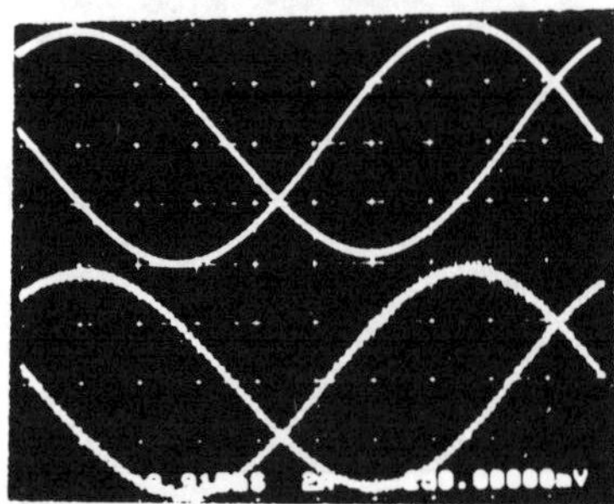

Fig. 15. Oscilloscope traces showing load side current regulation. Top trace: A and B phase induction machine current-5 A/div; ground-6 div from bottom. Bottom trace: references for A and B phase induction machine current-5 A/div; ground-2 div from bottom. Time scale: 9.915 ms/div.

of the source current regulation the reference of the source current itself has some ripples to regulate link voltage and power matching control. The actual current still accurately follows its reference. The load current reference is almost a ripple-free sinusoidal wave during steady-state operation of the induction machine. Hence the actual current shows almost the same trace with its reference. Note that during the operation of the system, no acoustic noise from the power conversion system was present because of its high switching frequency.

Conclusion

In this study a new three-phase-to-three-phase power conversion topology based upon a 20-kHz single-phase voltage link is proposed and tested by computer simulation. To demonstrate the hardware feasibility of the system and to verify the simulation results, an experimental system was built and tested. The simulation results and experimental results agree and exhibit very good load current regulation as well as unity power factor operation of the source side current. Also, the system was shown to have inherent bidirectional power flow capability. The system should prove to be a viable alternative to conventional dc link systems in the near future when bidirectional power semiconductor switches become readily available.

References

[1] P. K. Sood and T.A. Lipo, "Power conversion distribution system using a resonant high-frequency ac link," *IEEE Trans. Ind. Appl. Soc.*, Oct. 1986, pp. 533–541.

[2] D. M. Divan, "The resonant dc link converter—A new concept in static power conversion," in *Conf. Rec. Annu. Meet. IEEE Ind. Appl.*, vol. IA-24, pp. 288–300, Mar./Apr. 1988.

[3] A. C. Hoffman, I. G. Hansen, R. F. Beach *et al.*, "Advanced secondary power system for transport aircraft," NASA Tech. Paper 2463, 1985.

[4] I. G. Hansen and G. R. Sundberg, "Space station 20 khz power management and distribution system," in *Conf. Rec. 1986 Power Electronics Specialist's Conf.*, Vancouver, BC, Canada, June 1986, pp. 676–683.

[5] P. K. Sood, "High frequency link power conversion system," Ph.D. dissertation, Univ. of Wisconsin—Madison, Jan. 1987.

[6] S. K. Sul and T. A. Lipo, "Design and test of bidirectional speed and torque control of induction machines operating from high frequency link converter," NASA Rep. Contract NAG 3-786, Mar. 1988.

[7] M. Kheraluwala and D. M. Divan, "Delta modulation strategies for resonant link inverters," in *Rec. IEEE Power Electronics Specialists Conf.*, Blacksburg, VA, June 1987, pp. 271–278.

[8] S. K. Sul and T. A. Lipo, "Field oriented control of an induction machine in a high frequency link power system," presented at the IEEE Power Electronics Specialists Conf., Kyoto, Japan, Apr. 1988.

Selected Bibliography

[1] S. Doradla and S. K. Mondal, "A three phase ac to dc power transistor converter controlled dc motor drive," *IEEE Trans. Ind. Applicat.*, vol. IA-23, pp. 848–854, Sept./Oct. 1987.

[2] R. J. Hill and F. L. Luo, "Current source optimization in AC/DC GTO thyristor converters," *IEEE Trans. Ind. Electron.*, vol. IE-34, pp. 475–482, Nov. 1987.

[3] M. K. Nalbant et al., "Design of a 1 KW power factor correction circuit," *Proc. Power Conv.*, pp. 121–135, Oct. 1989.

[4] K. K. Sen and A. E. Emanuel, "Unity power factor single phase power conditioning," *IEEE PESC Rec.*, pp. 516–524, 1987.

[5] B. H. Khan, G. K. Dubey, and S. R. Doradla, "An economical four-quadrant GTO converter and its application to dc drive," *IEEE Appl. Power Electron. Conf. Rec.*, pp. 237–243, 1990.

[6] B. H. Khan, S. R. Doradla, and G. K. Dubey, "A new simultaneous gating GTO dual converter fed dc motor drive without circulating current," *IEEE/IAS Ann. Meet. Conf. Rec.*, pp. 520–526, 1988.

[7] M. J. Kocher and R. L. Steigerwald, "An ac to dc converter with high quality input waveforms," *IEEE Trans. Ind. Applicat.*, vol. IA-19, pp. 586–599, July/Aug. 1983.

[8] S. I. Khan, P. D. Ziogas, and M. H. Rashid, "Forced commutated cycloconverters for high-frequency link applications," *IEEE Trans. Ind. Applicat.*, vol. IA-23, pp. 661–672, July/Aug. 1987.

[9] X. Ma, "High performance PWM frequency changers," *IEEE Trans. Ind. Applicat.*, vol. IA-22, pp. 267–280, Mar./Apr. 1986.

[10] M. Braun and K. Hasse, "A direct frequency changer with control of input reactive power," *Third IFAC Symp. Contr. Power Electron. Elec. Drives*, pp. 187–194, 1983.

[11] J. Rodriguez, "A new control technique for ac–ac converters," *Third IFAC Symp. Contr. Power Electron. Elec. Drives*, pp. 203–208, 1983.

[12] P. D. Ziogas, S. I. Khan, and M. H. Rashid, "Some improved forced commutated cycloconverter structures," *IEEE Trans. Ind. Applicat.*, vol. IA-21, pp. 1242–1253, Sept./Oct. 1985.

[13] P. D. Ziogas, S. I. Khan, and M. H. Rashid, "Analysis and design of forced commutated cycloconverter structures with improved transfer characteristics," *IEEE Trans. Ind. Electron.*, vol. IE-33, pp. 271–280, Aug. 1986.

[14] P. D. Ziogas, Y.-G. Kang, and V. R. Stefanović, "Rectifier-inverter frequency changers with suppressed dc link components," *IEEE Trans. Ind. Applicat.*, vol. IA-22, pp. 1027–1036, Nov./Dec. 1986.

[15] M. Venturini, "A new sine wave in, sine wave out, conversion technique eliminates reactive elements," *Proc. Powercon 7*, pp. E3-1–E3-15, 1980.

[16] A. Alesina and M. G. B. Venturini, "Solid-state power conversion: A Fourier analysis approach to generalized transformer synthesis," *IEEE Trans. Circuits Syst.*, vol. CAS-28, pp. 319–330, Apr. 1981.

[17] T. Ohnishi and H. Okitsu, "A novel PWM technique for 3-phase inverter/converter," *Int. Power Electron. Conf. Rec.*, Tokyo, pp. 384–395, 1983.

[18] A. Mozder and B. K. Bose, "Three-phase ac power control using power transistors," *IEEE Trans. Ind. Applicat.*, vol. IA-12, pp. 499–504, Sept./Oct. 1976.

[19] J. B. Klaassens and E. J. F. M. Smits, "Series-resonant AC-power interface with an optimal power factor and enhanced conversion ratio," *IEEE PESC Rec.*, pp. 39–48, 1986.

[20] F. C. Schwarz, "A doublesided cycloconverter," *IEEE Trans. Ind. Electron.*, vol. IECI-28, pp. 282–291, Nov. 1981.

[21] P. M. Espelage and B. K. Bose, "High frequency link power conversion," *IEEE Trans. Ind. Applicat.*, vol. IA-13, pp. 387–394, Sept./Oct. 1977.

[22] L. Gyugyi and F. Cibulka, "The high frequency base converter—A new approach to static high power conversion," *IEEE Trans. Ind. Applicat.*, vol. IA-15, pp. 420–429, July/Aug. 1979.

[23] R. L. Steigerwald and R. E. Tompkins, "A comparison of high frequency link schemes for interfacing a dc source to a utility grid," *IEEE/IAS Ann. Meet. Conf. Rec.*, pp. 759–766, 1982.

[24] W. McMurray, "Frequency converter technology for aircraft power systems," *J. Energy*, vol. 6, pp. 328–333, Sept./Oct. 1982.

Part 5
DC-to-DC Converters

Paper 5.1

BASICS OF SWITCHED-MODE POWER CONVERSION: TOPOLOGIES, MAGNETICS, AND CONTROL

SLOBODAN ĆUK

California Institute of Technology
Pasadena, California

ABSTRACT

Switched-mode power conversion emerged recently as an interdisciplinary field which requires a fundamental knowledge in three areas: power circuit configurations, control systems, and magnetic circuits. A tutorial review of basic switched-mode power conversion topologies, properties, and simple analysis methods is given first. Principles of magnetic circuit analysis treated next, provide better understanding of power inductor and power transformer design requirements. Closing the feedback loop in pulse-width modulated (pwm) systems requires basic understanding of dc-to-dc converter dynamics, and so the accompanying transfer functions and frequency response methods are also reviewed. With these basic building blocks well understood, the sophisticated and complex structures of modern electronic power processing systems may be more easily and reliably designed.

1. INTRODUCTION

The practicing engineers in the Power Electronics field today are faced with an unusual challenge. Their everyday job requires expertise in three fundamental areas of electrical engineering: classical power conversion methods, magnetic circuit designs, and control system techniques. Traditionally, each of those areas might be considered as a specialty in its own right, requiring considerable effort to master it. Thus, this review paper is an attempt to ease these difficulties for novices to the field by introducing them to the fundamentals in each of the three key areas: topologies, magnetics and control. For the reader of this two volume book, the purpose of this paper is to build the bridge toward better understanding of the advanced concepts presented in follow-up scientific papers [1 - 16, 18 - 30] which constitute this two volume book.

This work was sponsored by the Office of Naval Research, Washington DC, under Contract N00014-78-C-0757; and by the International Business Machines Corporation, Kingston NY.

In Section 2, the fundamental reasoning for changing to switching conversion technology from the classical linear (dissipative) power conversion control is presented.

Fundamental conversion topologies reviewed by Section 3 include buck, boost, buck-boost and Ćuk converters. Along the converter topology development many topics are introduced at appropriate places where they can be easily understood: dc analysis through volt-sec balance on inductors, two modes of operation (continuous and discontinuous conduction), efficiency evaluation in presence of component nonidealities, dc isolation and multiple output extensions, two-quadrant (battery charger/discharger) and four-quadrant (switched-mode amplifier and ac uninterruptible power supplies) converter classification.

The Section 4 on magnetics fundamentals reviews the key results pertinent to the understanding and design of inductors and transformers for switching power conversion applications: analogy of magnetic circuits with electric circuits and reluctance concept, effect of the airgap on the inductor flux-current characteristic, inductors with dc bias, transformer operation and modelling, transformer design with no dc bias and some simplified design procedure for inductor and transformer core selection using area product or core geometry [43] approach.

Modelling of switching-mode regulator and its control transfer properties (loop gain) are reviewed in Section 5 on a very fundamental level, which demonstrates very simple models of the nonlinear converter power stage and separately linear modulator transfer properties.

2. POWER CONVERSION ALTERNATIVES

Two alternatives for delivery of electric power from a dc source to a load in a controllable manner are linear and switched-mode power conversion. They are illustrated in Fig. 1, reduced to their simplest forms.

Reprinted with permission from *Powerconversion International*, 32 pp., August, September, October 1981.

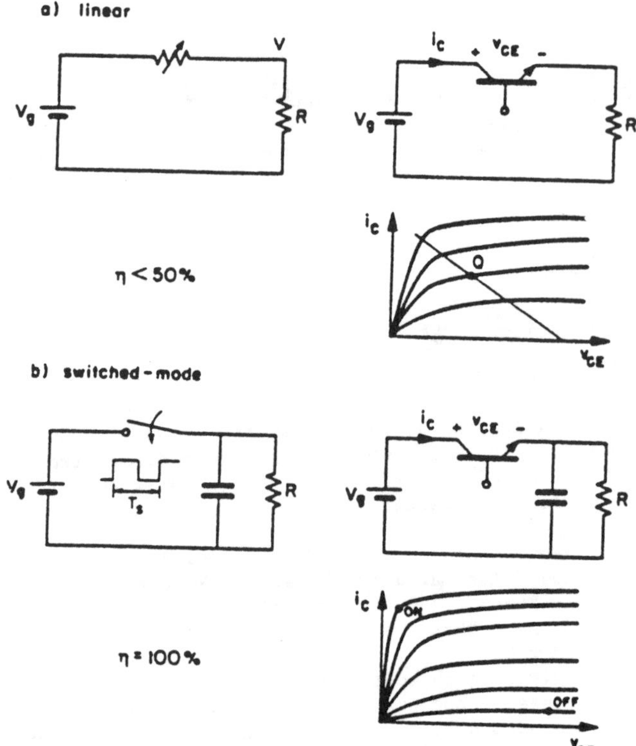

Fig. 1. Comparison of linear (dissipative) (a) and switched-mode (nondissipative) (b) power conversion.

Linear power conversion (Fig. 1a) relies on the presence of a series linear element, either a resistor (mechanical control), or a transistor used in the linear mode, (electronic control) such that the total load current is passed through the series linear element. Therefore, the greater the difference between the input and output voltages (the higher the controlling power range) the more power is lost in the controlling device. Thus, linear power conversion even in its ideal form is dissipative and inefficient, typically in the 30-60% efficiency range.

In switched-mode power conversion, (Fig. 1b) however, the controlling device is an ideal switch, which is either closed or open. Then by controlling the ratio of the time intervals spent in the closed and open position (often defined as duty ratio), the power flow to the load can be controlled in a very efficient way. Namely, ideally it is 100% efficient even for a wide range of power being controlled. However, in practice it is reduced somewhat owing to nonideal realization of the switch. Nevertheless the semiconductor device (bipolar transistor, for example) is clearly used in a much more efficient way. When the device is fully ON it has only a small saturation voltage drop across it (typically 0.3V to 1V). In the OFF condition, the reverse leakage current is usually negligible, so that the power loss is negligible despite the fact that the blocking voltage across it may be high. However, the output voltage is far from being dc as in the linear example, and pulsed power is applied. Although this may be acceptable for some applications such as oven heating, in many other uses a constant dc output voltage is desired. The power flow to the load may be easily smoothed out by the addition of a low-pass LC filter.

We therefore reach two important conclusions: *Efficient electric power conversion and control requires the use of switches as its basic components. The need to generate dc output voltage introduces ideally lossless storage components, inductors, and capacitors whose role is to smooth out the inherent pulsating behavior originating from the switching action.*

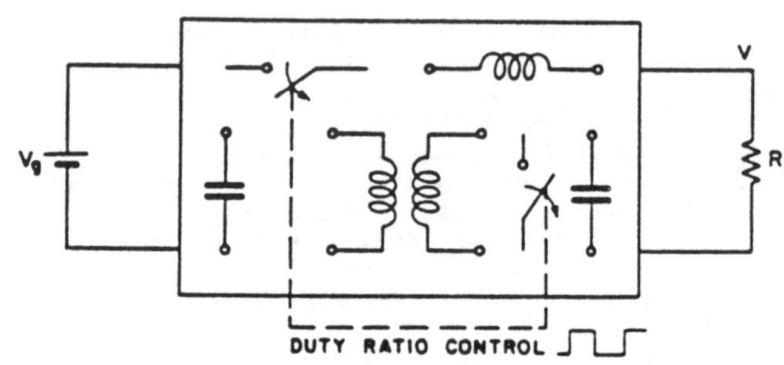

Fig. 2. General switched-mode power conversion consists of storage components and switches arranged in a topology which has effective low-pass filter nature.

Thus, in general, efficient switched-mode power conversion may be postulated as in Fig. 2. Note the addition of the transformer as a component which provides an often very important practical requirement, dc isolation between input and output grounds. In Fig. 2, the storage components and switches are purposely shown disconnected to emphasize a great variety of possible converter topologies, of which only the very few basic ones will be reviewed here.

Converter topology, however, is not random but has to form effectively a low-pass filter in order to achieve the basic dc-to-dc conversion function.

Although the conversion would be 100% efficient in the ideal case of lossless components such as in Fig. 2, in practice each of the components in Fig. 2 is lossy, thus leading to reduced efficiency. For example, a switch implemented by semiconductor devices is lossy, as in the real physical inductor, when its windings resistance and core losses are taken into account. Transformers and capacitors similarly further degrade the efficiency. Therefore, the prime objective in switched-mode power conversion becomes to realize the given conversion function, (such as dc-to-dc conversion) with the least number of components to improve its overall efficiency and reliability.

Let us therefore now take a closer look at some of the simplest ways that dc voltage conversion may be accomplished. In parallel with introduction of the basic switching dc-to-dc converter configurations, some rudimentary methods for their analysis will be explained.

3. DC-TO-DC CONVERTER TOPOLOGY FUNDAMENTALS

The simplest dc-to-dc converter topologies consist of a single switch (single-pole, double-throw ideal switch S in Fig. 3), a single inductor, and a single capacitor. Let us now see how by different arrangement of this limited number of components (Fig. 3) a number of useful and different dc-to-dc conversion functions can be realized.

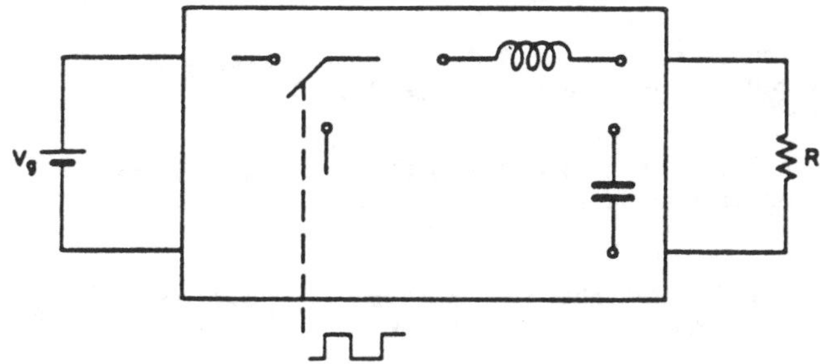

Fig. 3. All three simple dc-to-dc converter topologies: the buck, the boost and the buck-boost can be obtained by simple rearrangement of the three components: ideal switch, inductor and capacitor.

3.1 Buck (Step-Down) Dc-to-Dc Converter

The simplest configuration to understand is the basic buck converter shown conceptually in block diagram form in Fig. 4. The input dc voltage V_g is chopped by the switch S (hence the widely used name "chopper" for this converter type) resulting in an intermediate pulsed waveform v_1. Low-pass filtering of this waveform passes only the average DV_g to form the output dc voltage $V = DV_g$. Here the duty ratio D is defined as the ratio of the on-time interval (switch S in supply V_g position) to the total switching interval T_s. As seen in Fig. 4, by controlling the duty ratio of the switch (dotted line), the output dc voltage is controlled (dotted line).

Frequency Viewpoint (Fourier Analysis)

The output voltage is not ideal as seen in Fig. 4, but in addition to a dc component it consists of a small ripple voltage component at the switching frequency $f_s \triangleq 1/T_s$, as seen in Fig. 5. A frequency viewpoint customary to engineers, becomes very useful here. Namely, the pulse-width-modulated (pwm) voltage waveform at the input of the low-pass LC filter (in Fig. 5, D = 0.5 is illustrated) may be broken down into its dc component

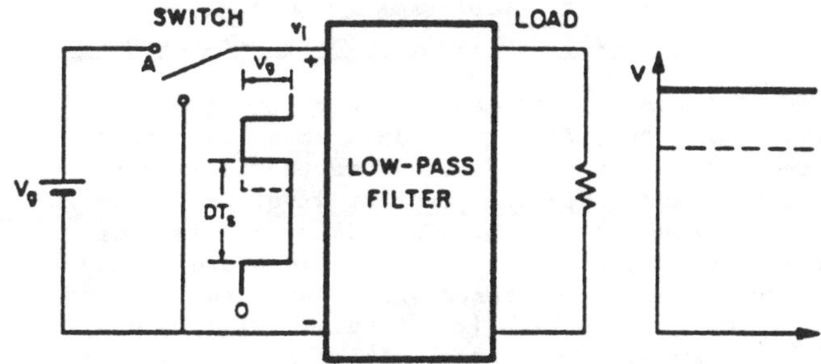

Fig. 4. Controlled dc-to-dc power conversion in a basic buck converter through pulse width modulation.

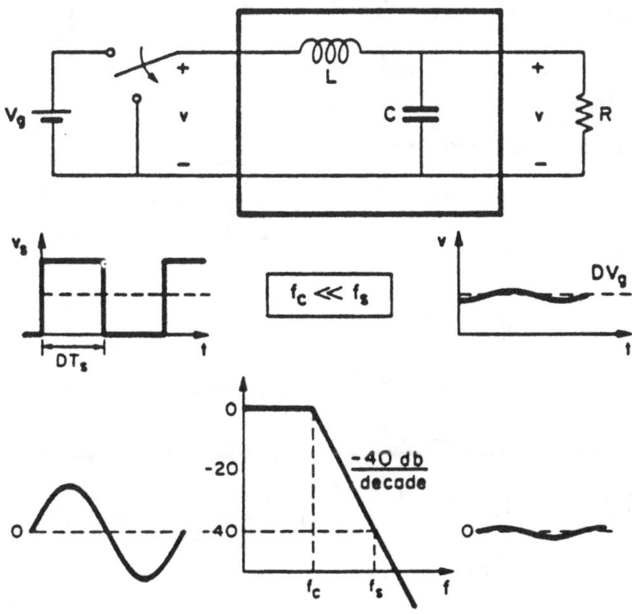

Fig. 5. Frequency viewpoint reveals that for low output switching ripple filter corner frequencies must be well below switching frequency.

and harmonics at the switching frequency f_s and its integer multiples by use of the Fourier series. The dc component passes unattenuated through the filter to generate its primary desirable dc output $V = DV_g$.

Provided that the filter corner frequency $f_c = 1/2\pi\sqrt{LC}$ is significantly lower than the switching frequency (typically at least a decade below f_s), the first and higher order harmonics are substantially attenuated by passing through the LC filter, resulting in an acceptably low switching ripple voltage at the output. A quantitative expression for the switching ripple can be obtained easily by examination of the characteristic waveforms in the switching converter.

Characteristic Waveforms in Switching Converters and Evaluation of Switching Ripple

The small switching ripple of the converter (typically specified to be less than 1%) directly translates into the idealized rectangular voltage waveform and triangular current waveform on the inductors seen in Fig. 6. The rising and falling slopes of the inductor current ripple are easily deduced from the corresponding linear switched network to be $(V_g - V)/L$ (for interval DT_s), and V/L (for interval $D'T_s$), since voltage ripple is being neglected.

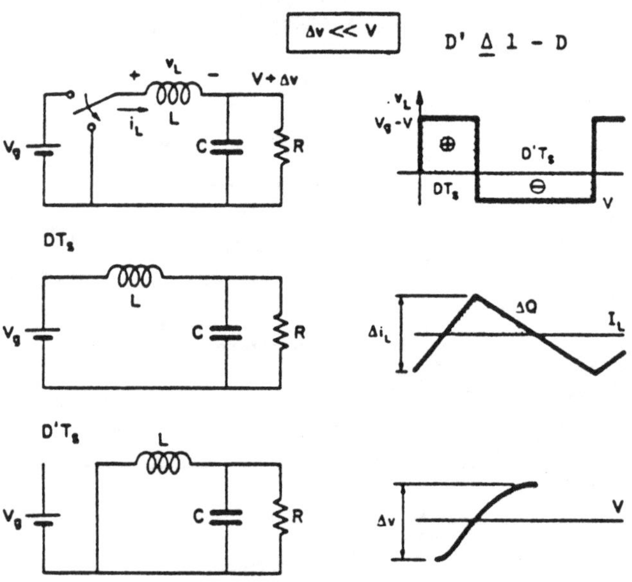

Fig. 6. *Quantitative evaluation of the output voltage switching ripple through characteristic waveforms in switching converters.*

To calculate the switching output voltage ripple Δv, it is assumed that the average inductor current I flows into the load resistance R to generate the dc voltage V = IR, while the inductor current ripple Δi_L flows into the output capacitor to generate the output voltage ripple Δv. This is very good approximation for small switching ripple. Since the capacitance voltage is the integral of its current, $v = \int i dt$, and since the capacitor ripple current is triangular in shape, the voltage ripple typically consists of segments of two parabolas. The total voltage ripple Δv is easily obtained from the stored charge ΔQ, which corresponds to the area under inductor current ripple. Hence

$$\Delta Q = \frac{1}{2}\left(\frac{DT_s}{2} + \frac{D'T_s}{2}\right)\frac{\Delta i_L}{2} = \frac{1}{8} T_s \Delta i_L \tag{1}$$

From the falling slope of the inductor current V/L,

$$\Delta i_L = \frac{V}{L} D'T_s \tag{2}$$

Thus the absolute output voltage ripple is

$$\Delta v = \frac{\Delta Q}{C} = \frac{1}{8}\frac{T_s \Delta i_L}{C} = \frac{1}{8}\frac{D'T_s^{\,2}}{LC} V \tag{3}$$

and the relative voltage ripple Δv/V is

$$\frac{\Delta v}{V} = \frac{1}{8}\frac{D'T_s^{\,2}}{LC} \tag{4}$$

Restated in terms of the corner frequencies,

$$\frac{\Delta v}{V} = \frac{\pi^2 D'}{2}\left(\frac{f_c}{f_s}\right)^2 \quad \text{where } f_c \triangleq \frac{1}{2\pi\sqrt{LC}} \tag{5}$$

For example, for D = 0.5, f_c = 500Hz, f_s = 20kHz, the output voltage ripple is 0.154%.

This result for the buck converter can be generalized for other switching converters:

$$\text{small switching ripple} \Rightarrow \text{natural frequencies} \ll \text{switching frequency} \tag{6}$$

As a consequence of this basic requirement for small switching ripple, the voltage waveforms on the inductors in many converters have the typical rectangular shape. This then serves as a basis for an alternative way of finding steady-state (dc) voltage and current relationships in switching converters.

Steady-State (Dc) Analysis and Volt-Sec Balance on Inductors

In the buck converter, the switching function and filtering function are clearly delineated (cascade connection of the two) such that application of Fourier transform analysis was possible. However, in many more complex switching converters, and even in some simple ones such as the boost and buck-boost, the switching action is buried within the low-pass filter network, and an alternative more general method for finding the dc conditions must be found.

From Faradey's law for the inductor voltage,

$$v_L = L\frac{di_L}{dt} \tag{7}$$

and by integration over the full period T_s, we get

$$\frac{1}{L}\int_0^{T_s} v_L dt = \int_0^{T_s} di_L = i_L(T_s) - i_L(0) = 0 \tag{8}$$

since in the steady state, the initial and final values of the inductor current must be equal. Removal of the finite (nonzero) proportionality constant L in (8) results in a general criterion for the steady-state, the so-called volt-second balance on the inductor, as:

$$\int_0^{T_s} v_L dt = 0 \qquad \text{volt-sec balance on inductors} \qquad (9)$$

or, for the two switched intervals,

$$\int_0^{DT_s} v_L dt = - \int_{DT_s}^{T_s} v_L dt \qquad (10)$$

volt-second stored   volt-second released

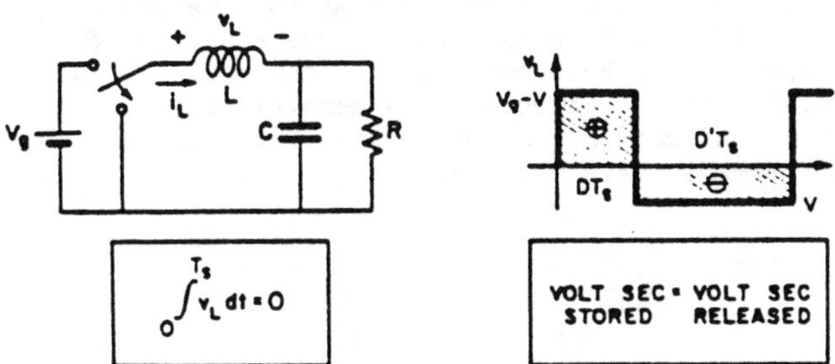

Fig. 7. General method for finding the steady-state conditions in switching converters: Volt second balance on inductors.

The basic requirement for low ouput voltage ripple (6) directly translates into the rectangular voltage waveform on the inductor, since the ripple is neglected as illustrated for the buck converter in Fig. 7. This further simplifies the calculations and reduces them to a simple product of voltages and time intervals. For example, for the buck converter in Fig. 7, the volt-second balance becomes

$$(V_g - V)\, DT_s = VD'T_s \qquad (11)$$

and, after simplification, the stepped-down conversion ratio of the buck converter is obtained as

$$\frac{V}{V_g} = D \qquad (12)$$

Since the converter is ideally 100% efficient (no second-order parasitic elements taken into account), the ratio of the output dc current and average input current is the inverse of (12):

$$\frac{I}{I_g} = \frac{1}{D} \qquad (13)$$

Thus, the buck converter dc conversion function can be modeled by a simple dc-to-dc transformer whose turns ratio is equal to duty ratio D, as shown in Fig. 8. Note, however, that the current conversion ratio (13) is referred to the *average* and *not instantaneous* input and output currents, which as seen from Fig. 8 substantially deviate from the ideal constant (dc) currents. In particular, the input current consists of large pulses, which often cause the so-called *conducted* electromagnetic interference (EMI) on the source lines. This *pulsating* input current causes substantially higher EMI problems than the *nonpulsating* output inductor current (the double-pole inductive filter of Fig. 5 is assumed here).

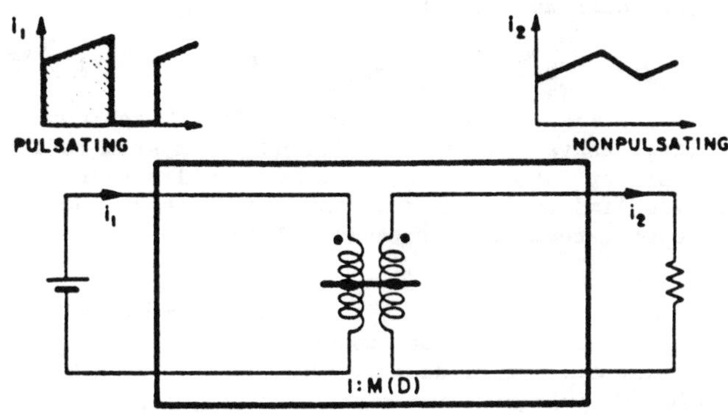

Fig. 8. Input and output currents in the buck converter of Fig. 7 and the definition of pulsating and nonpulsating currents.

Semiconductor Implementation of the Switching Action

To fully gain electronic control of the converter, a semiconductor implementation of the single-pole, double-throw switch is desired. Two alternative implentations, using a diode and a bipolar transistor (either npn or pnp type), are shown in Fig. 9. In either case the diode works in synchronism with the transistor, which is the only controlled device. When the transistor is turned ON, the input dc voltage reverse-biases the diode and turns the diode OFF for interval DT_s. Then, when the transistor turns OFF, the inductor voltage reversal forward biases the diode and turns it ON (inductor current flow cannot be interrupted instantaneously). Note, however, that this semiconductor

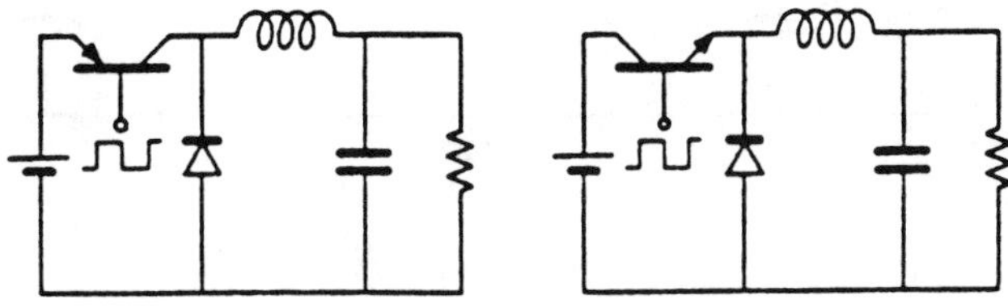

Fig. 9. Semiconductor implementation of the ideal switch with bipolar transistor (npn or pnp) and a diode.

implementation simulates the original ideal switch only in a limited fashion. Namely, while the ideal switch conducts current in either direction and can block voltage of either polarity (hence, it could be termed a *four-quadrant* switch), the shown semiconductor version limits the current flow to only one direction and blocks voltage of only one polarity (hence it could be designated a *single-quadrant* switch). Thus, this implementation by its nature limits the whole converter to *single-quadrant* operation, that is, only one voltage and one current polarity are available at the output. In a later section, it will be shown how the removal of the limitations imposed by the switch implementation may lead to a two-quadrant converter and eventually to a four-quadrant converter.

3.2 How to Create Step-Up (Boost) Function

The simple buck converter of Fig. 5 achieves dc voltage conversion very efficiently compared to its linear regulator counterpart, but still retains some of its limitations: it is capable of only reducing (stepping-down) the input dc voltage.

However, only a very simple step is needed to create a step-up (boost) converter from the original buck converter, as shown in Fig. 10. The buck converter pulsating input current (Fig. 8), often requires an input filter to smooth out large current variations. Hence the buck converter of Fig. 10a has an input capacitance to reduce current ripple returned to the source.

A simple interchange of the source and load (bilateral inversion) generates a boost converter from the original buck converter.

The dc gain of the new boost configuration, due to the nature of source and load interchange, is equal to the reciprocal of the buck converter gain (12), that is, the boost converter gain becomes:

$$\frac{V}{V_g} = \frac{1}{D} \geq 1 \quad \text{for} \quad D \quad [0,1] \tag{14}$$

Practical boost converter implementation by use of an npn bipolar transistor as a controlling device and a diode is shown in Fig. 11, in which the input capacitance is also omitted as nonessential for basic operation of the converter. Hence, again, conversion is realized by the least number of components: a single switch, inductor, and capacitor put together into a different topology. However, this time the low-pass LC filter is "broken" by the switching action, thus mixing the chopping and filtering functions which were easily differentiated in the buck converter. Thus, the volt-sec balance on the inductor as a general criterion, and the boost converter waveforms of Fig. 11, lead to the steady-state (dc) voltage gain as:

$$\frac{V}{V_g} = \frac{1}{1 - D} \tag{15}$$

Note that here the duty cycle D determines interval DT_s during which the transistor is turned ON as is customary in all converters, while expression (14) actually referred to the switch closed during its complementary interval D', and hence the D⇒D' conversion.

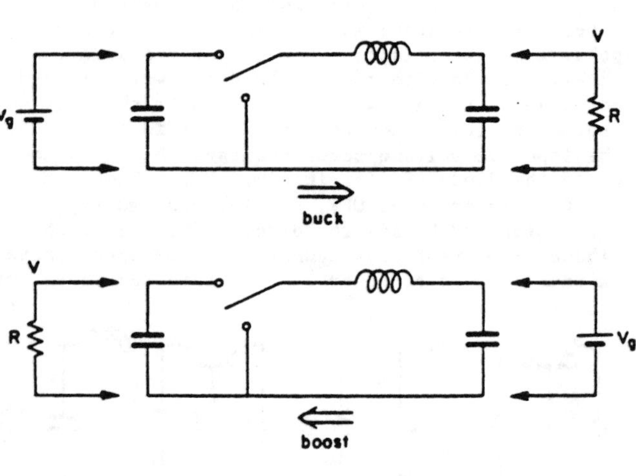

Fig. 10. How to create a step-up (boost) converter from a step-down (buck) converter by a process of bilateral inversion.

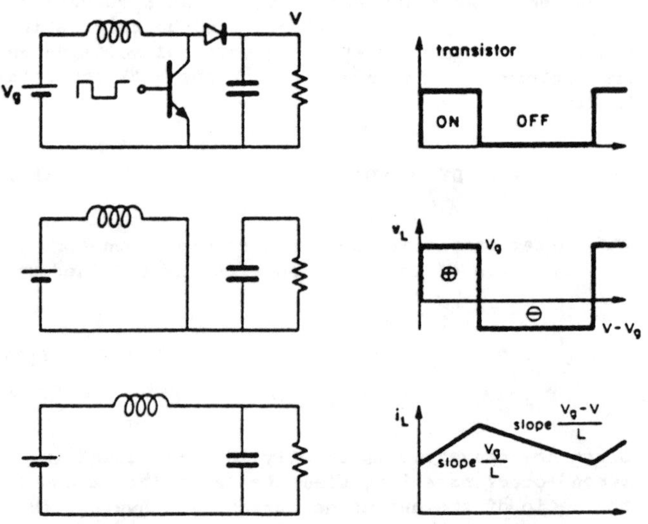

Fig. 11. Analysis and characteristic waveforms in the boost converter.

Effect of Parasitics on Voltage Gain and Efficiency

The importance of including some lossy elements in the converter analysis now becomes quite obvious, since otherwise the obtained results may even be qualitatively misleading. For example, the dc voltage gain of the boost converter (15) becomes infinitely large when the duty ratio D approaches 1, clearly a physically incorrect result. However, the inclusion of some lossy elements, such as the parasitic resistance R_ℓ of the inductor, corrects this problem. The efficiency of course, is now reduced from the original 100%, because of the $I_\ell^2 R_\ell$ loss on the inductor resistance, to:

$$\eta = \frac{P_{out}}{P_{out} + P_{loss}} = \frac{V^2/R}{V^2/R + I_\ell^2 R_\ell} \tag{16}$$

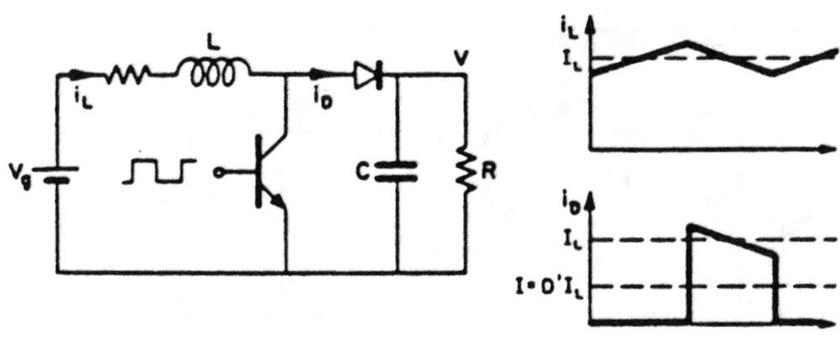

Fig. 12. Pulsating output (diode) current is a source of boost converter inefficiency at high duty ratios.

From the inductor and diode current waveforms in Fig. 12, the ratio of the average inductor I_L and the load current I becomes

$$\frac{I_\ell}{I} = \frac{1}{D'}, \tag{17}$$

and the efficiency becomes

$$\eta = \frac{1}{1 + \alpha/(1-D)^2} \quad \text{where } \alpha \triangleq \frac{R_\ell}{R} \tag{18}$$

By use of this result, and since efficiency is alternatively $\eta = VI/V_g I_L$, the voltage gain becomes:

$$\frac{V}{V_g} = \frac{I_L}{I}\eta = \frac{1}{1-D}\,\frac{1}{1+\alpha/(1-D)^2} = \frac{1-D}{(1-D)^2+\alpha} \tag{19}$$

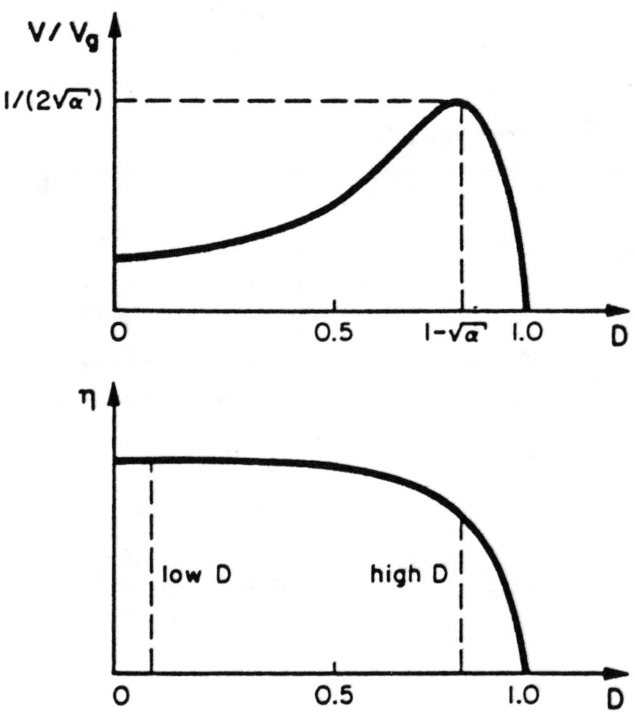

Fig. 13. Voltage gain and efficiency of the boost converter deteriorate significantly at high duty ratios.

As seen in Fig. 13, the voltage dc gain now correctly exhibits a maximum value over the duty ratio D range. Also, the efficiency is seen to decrease significantly for higher duty ratios. Comparison of the inductor and diode current waveforms at low and high duty ratios reveals the source of gross differences in efficiencies at the two extremes (low and high duty cycle), as illustrated in Fig. 14.

For low duty ratio, the average diode current I_D (equal to dc load current I), is almost equal to the average inductor current I_L. Thus, the resistive inductor loss $P_{loss} = I_L^2 R_\ell$ and power delivered to the load I^2R are roughly in the ratio R_ℓ/R. Hence for $R_\ell/R = 1/100$, the efficiency loss is very good, around 1%. However, for the same amount of power delivered to the load at high duty ratio D, the diode current has to be a narrow pulse of high magnitude (Fig. 14), such that its average value over the full cycle is unchanged. But, the height (magnitude) of this pulse also determines the average inductor current, which now becomes several times, or even an order of magnitude, higher than the delivered dc load current. The final consequence is that on the *same* inductor resistance it generates a considerably higher loss. For example for D = 0.8, and $R_\ell/R = 0.01$ as before, the efficiency loss becomes $I_\ell^2 R_\ell/I^2R = 25\%$, or 25 times higher.

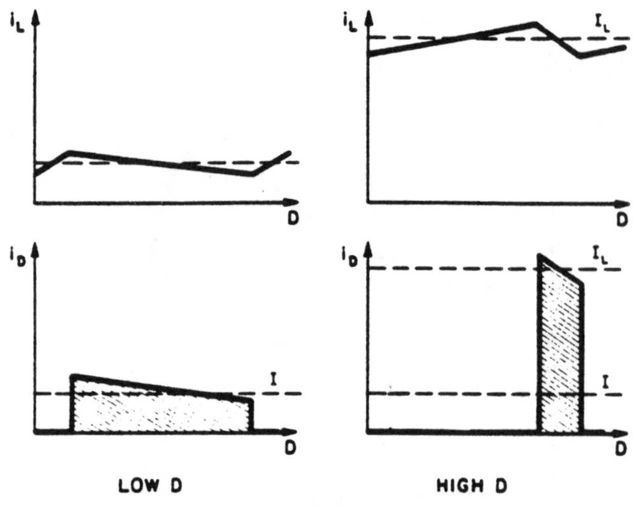

Fig. 14. Inefficiency of boost converter at high duty ratio is attributed to the narrow pulse, high magnitude output diode current.

This example clearly demonstrates the two important facts associated in general with switching converters:

1. The presence of even minute parasitic elements can signficantly alter even the qualitative behavior of switching converters (infinite dc gain vs. finite dc voltage gain, infinite Q factors vs. finite damping factors for dynamic considerations).

2. Pulsating currents in general lead to inefficient use of nonideal physical components (resistive losses in inductors and capacitors etc.), and should be minimized as much as possible.

This last point is further reinforced by consideration of the input current in the buck converter (Fig. 8). Owing to its pulsating nature, discharge of the input dc battery will cause, in its internal source resistance, considerably higher loss than for a smooth (nonpulsating) current. The difference will be higher, the lower the duty ratio of the switch, for the same reason as before — narrow pulse of high magnitude. Thus, pulsating current at either input or output is undesirable for inefficiency as well as high conducted noise reasons. Later (Section 3.4), a converter which meets this criterion will be presented.

The buck converter can only step-down input dc voltage, the boost converter can only step-up dc voltage. Let us now synthesize a converter which can perform either of these two functions.

3.3 How to Create the General Step-Down or Step-Up Function

The previous two converters can now be viewed as emanating from switching the single inductor (inductive energy transfer) between the input (dc source) and the output port (dc load with capacitance across it), as illustrated in Fig. 15a and b. The remaining third possibility, in which the inductor is grounded, results in the buck-boost converter of Fig. 15c.

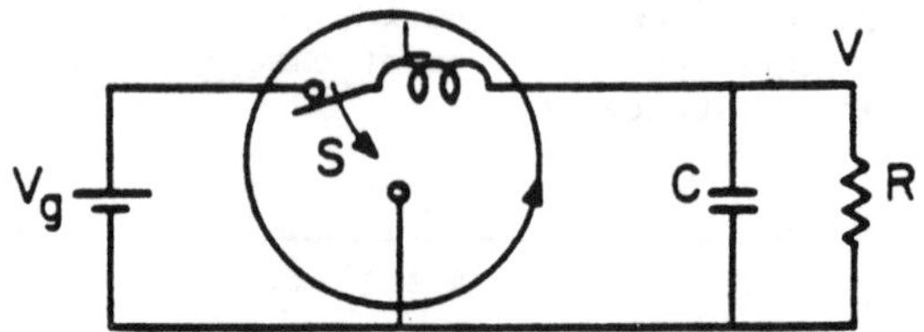

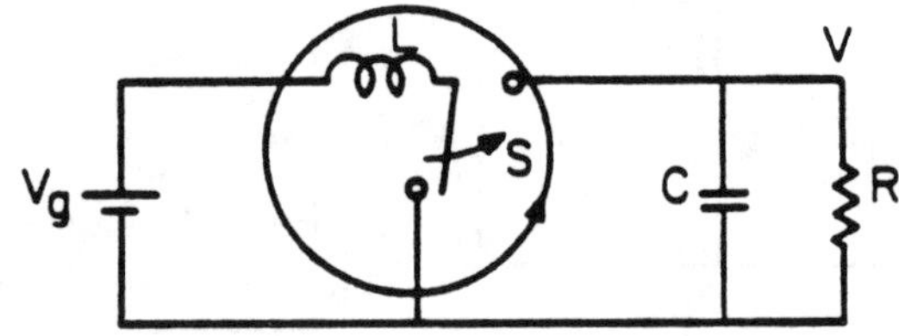

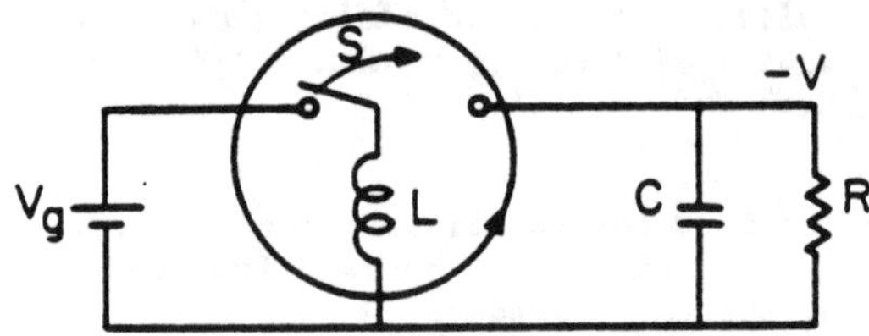

Fig. 15. Generation of three basic inductive energy transfer converters by cyclic rotation of the inductance in series with a switch.

From the usual volt-sec balance in steady-state, the dc voltage gain is

$$\frac{V}{V_g} = \frac{D}{1 - D} \tag{20}$$

Thus either a step-up ($D > 0.5$) or a step-down ($D < 0.5$) function can be achieved in the same converter. As before in the boost converter, inclusion of inductor parasitic resistance results in a finite voltage gain instead of the infinite gain given by (20) for $D = 1.0$.

So far the switch has been considered ideal. However, the semiconductor implementation as shown in Fig. 16 results in additional efficiency loss.

Effect of Switch Nonidealities on Efficiency

The semiconductor switch may well be approximated by two batteries (Fig. 16): one modelling the saturation voltage drop of transistor V_s, and the other the forward voltage drop of the diode V_F. Leakage currents in both devices when they are off can safely be neglected. To simplify derivations and observations, we now assume that the inductors are *ideal* and consider only efficiency loss due to switch nonidealities. From the input and output pulsed current waveforms, the average currents are calculated, and so the efficiency η is

$$\eta = \frac{VD'I_L}{V_g DI_L} = \frac{V/V_g}{D/D'} = \frac{\text{real voltage gain}}{\text{ideal voltage gain}} \tag{21}$$

However in steady-state the volt-sec balance still applies, and results in

$$(V_g - V_s)DT_s = (V + V_F)D'T_s \tag{22}$$

$$\frac{D}{D'} = \frac{V + V_F}{V_g - V_s} \tag{23}$$

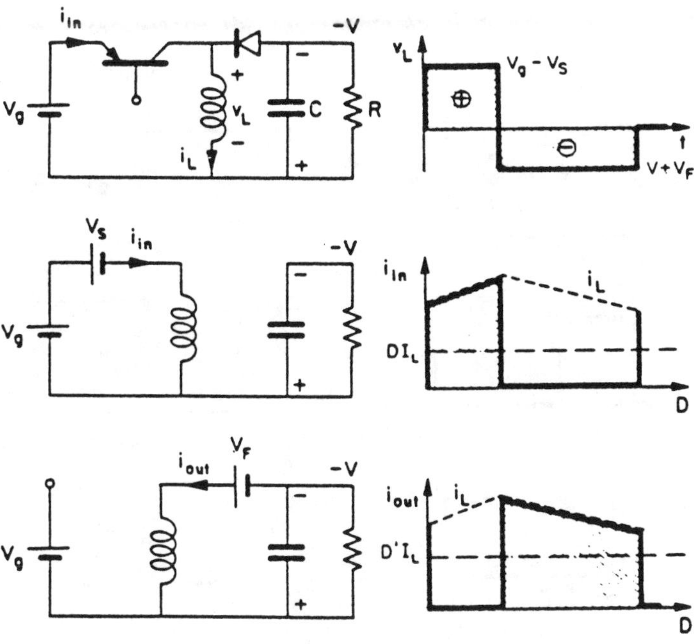

Fig. 16. Converter efficiency in presence of switch nonidealities (nonzero transistor and diode voltage drops).

Substitution of (23) in (21) finally gives

$$\eta = \frac{V_g - V_s}{V_g}\,\frac{V}{V + V_F} \tag{24}$$

In the special case of the buck-boost converter, this result could have been obtained from consideration of "input" and "output" circuit efficiency η_I and η_o, respectively

$$\eta_I = \frac{(V_g - V_s)I_{in}}{V_g I_{in}} = \frac{V_g - V_s}{V_g}$$

$$\eta_o = \frac{VI_{out}}{(V + V_F)I_{out}} = \frac{V}{V + V_F} \tag{25}$$

$$\eta = \eta_I \eta_o$$

The form of the result (24) is very illuminating and leads to a general conclusion:

High efficiency is difficult to obtain even with switching converters when either input or output voltages are low and comparable to transistor and diode drops.

For example, for 3V output, efficiency degradation is 25% due solely to the inclusion of the diode drop $V_F = 1V$. A diode with a lower voltage drop (such as a Schottky diode) would improve efficiency. A transistor with a high saturation voltage causes similar efficiency degradation on the input side for low input voltages. Simultaneous low input and low output voltage conversion is apparently even more inefficient.

However, these dc losses are not the only semiconductor losses since, in addition, switching losses are generated in the semiconductors as well. Namely, during the switching between its ON and OFF states which does not happen instantaneously, the transistor travels through its linear high dissipation region as illustrated in Fig. 17. Integration of the instantaneous power (product of transistor voltage and current) over the transition interval and its averaging over the switching period results in switching losses. New MOSFET power transistors have much shorter switching times (rise and fall times) than comparably rated bipolar transistors, hence reduced switching losses, but their dc losses are higher due to still substantial ON resistance of the device. Note that a power FET is appropriately modelled by its ON resistance (typically 0.3Ω - 3Ω range) rather than the battery V_s as in the bipolar transistor case. Thus, the inclusion of all losses (semiconductor losses, parasitic resistance losses, core losses in magnetic components etc.) may lead to substantial deviation from the ideal 100% efficiency.

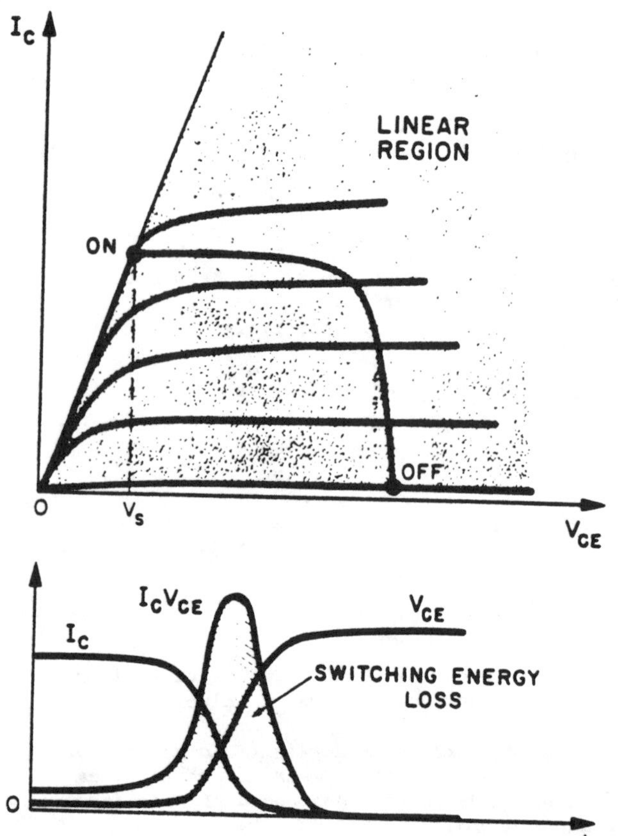

Fig. 17. Finite semiconductor switching times lead to switching losses during transition between the ON and OFF states.

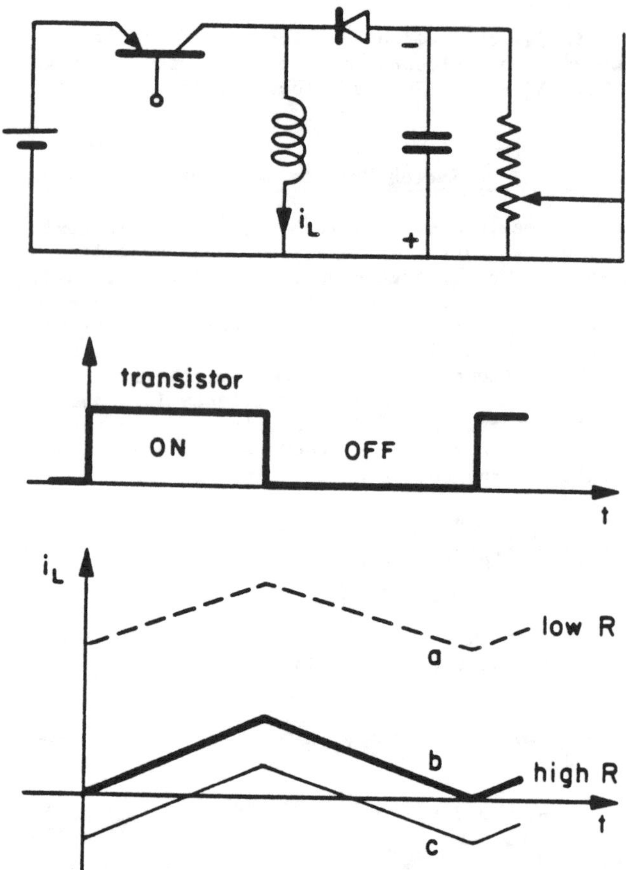

Fig. 18. Decrease of the load current below some critical value (waveform b) leads to a new mode of operation: discontinuous conduction mode.

Discontinuous Conduction Mode

In practice load current may change over a wide range, from no load to full load, and it is desirable that converter operation not be significantly affected. However, this is not so as illustrated in Fig. 18. Namely, increase of load resistance leads to a decrease of load current, hence the average inductor current is continuously reduced from waveform a in Fig. 18 to waveform b. Nevertheless, further decrease of the load current *does not* produce waveform c. The waveform c would require that the inductor current falls to zero and *reverses its direction during* the transistor OFF time. However, the diode is a current unidirectional element and does not conduct current in the opposite direction. Hence at the instant defined by waveform b in Fig. 18, a new mode of converter operation is encountered termed discontinuous conduction mode (DCM). Further decrease of load current beyond that point results in the typical discontinuous inductor current waveform shown in Fig. 19 from which the name originated. The inductor current, after reaching zero level in interval D_2T_s, stays at this level for the remaining part of the $D'T_s$ interval (D_3T_s), thus resulting in a third linear network for which both transistor and diode are OFF.

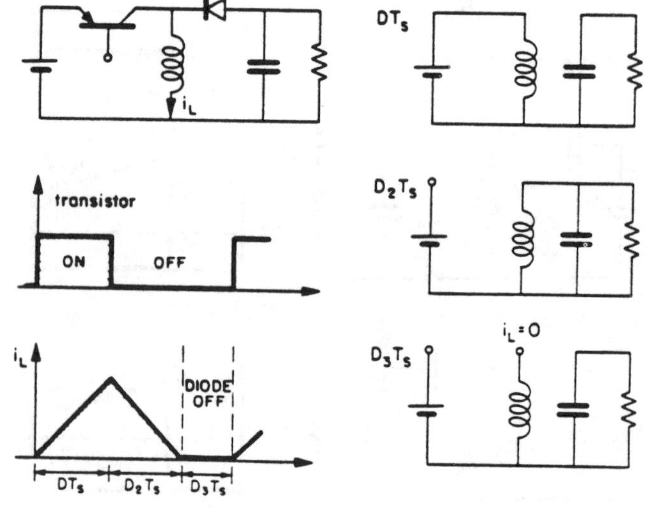

Fig. 19. Salient features of the discontinuous conduction mode illustrated on the buck-boost converter.

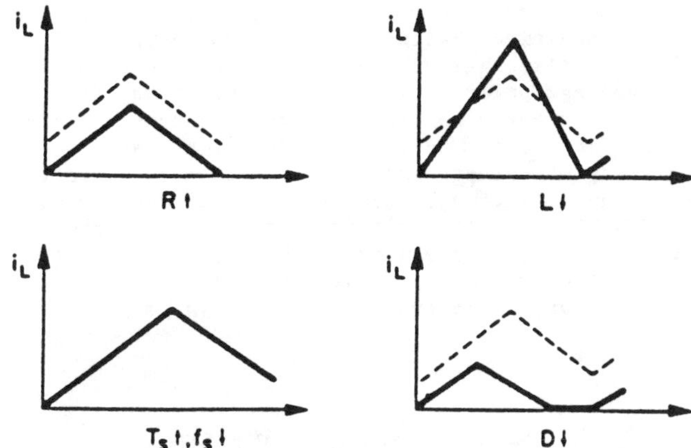

Fig. 20. Four parameters are affecting discontinuous conduction mode: decrease of load current, inductance L, switching frequency f_s and duty cycle D.

As seen from Fig. 20, in addition to increase of load resistance, other parameters are those which affect the inductor current ripple: decrease of inductance value, increase of switching period and decrease of duty ratio. The first three can conveniently be lumped into a single dimensionless parameter K

$$K = \frac{2L}{RT_s} \tag{26}$$

whose reduction in value leads to the discontinuous conduction mode. Note that the decay interval D_2T_s and the voltage gain M are as yet undetermined:

$$\frac{V}{V_g} = f_1(D,K) \tag{27}$$

$$D_2 = f_2(D,K) \tag{28}$$

However, from the volt-sec balance on the inductor (Fig. 21)

$$\frac{V}{V_g} = \frac{D}{D_2} \tag{29}$$

in which the "decay" duty ratio D_2 is still unknown. However, from the instantaneous diode current in Fig. 21 and 100% efficiency assumption,

$$D_2\left(\frac{1}{2}\frac{V}{L}D_2T_s\right) = \frac{V}{R} \tag{30}$$

$$D_2 = \sqrt{K} \quad ; \quad K = \frac{2L}{RT_s} \tag{31}$$

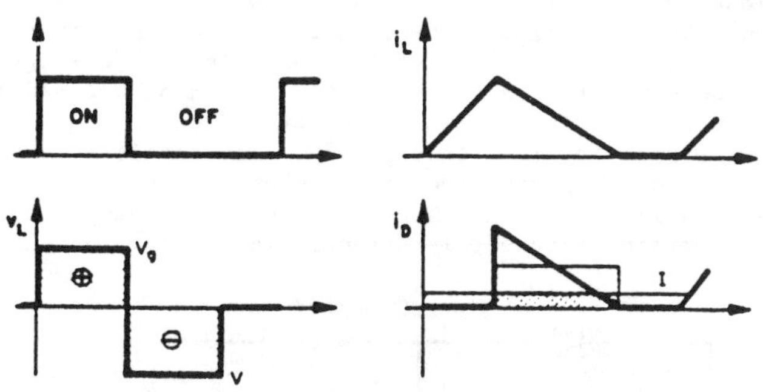

Fig. 21. Evaluation of dc conditions in discontinuous conduction mode (DCM) through waveform observation.

Thus, the solution for (27) and (28) becomes

$$\frac{V}{V_g} = \frac{D}{\sqrt{K}} \tag{32}$$

$$D_2 = \sqrt{K} \tag{33}$$

The converter will then operate in this discontinuous conduction mode whenever:

$$\text{DCM:} \quad D_2 < 1 - D \qquad K < (1 - D)^2 \tag{34}$$

The normal mode of converter operation ($K > (1-D)^2$) is often designated continuous conduction mode (CCM).

Two-Quadrant Converter Concept

The onset of discontinuous conduction mode is triggered by the inability of a diode to conduct current in the reverse direction, that is, because of the *current unidirectional* implementation of the ideal switch. However, if an alternative path is provided for the current to flow in the reverse direction, this mode of operation will be circumvented and continuous conduction mode obtained even in the no-load case. This is shown by addition of another transistor across the diode and another diode across the original transistor, which provide for alternate current flow and realize in hardware a *current bidirectional* switch or, as termed here, a *two-quadrant switch*. The two transistors in Fig. 22 are switched out of phase (when one transistor is ON the other is OFF and vice versa), and the diodes act as synchronous switches. Special precautions usually have to be made (dead time) to guard against their overlapping conduction.

The immediate result of such two-quadrant switch implementation is that the discontinuous conduction mode is completely eliminated, even at no load, as seen in Fig. 22. Note, however, that even though the instantaneous inductor current may become negative, its average current (and also the average diode current) has to be positive, because the power flow is in *average* still from the source to the lead (from left to right in Fig. 22). Nevertheless, the direction of power flow can be changed provided an active load such as a battery or motor turning into a generator is used, as illustrated in Fig. 23.

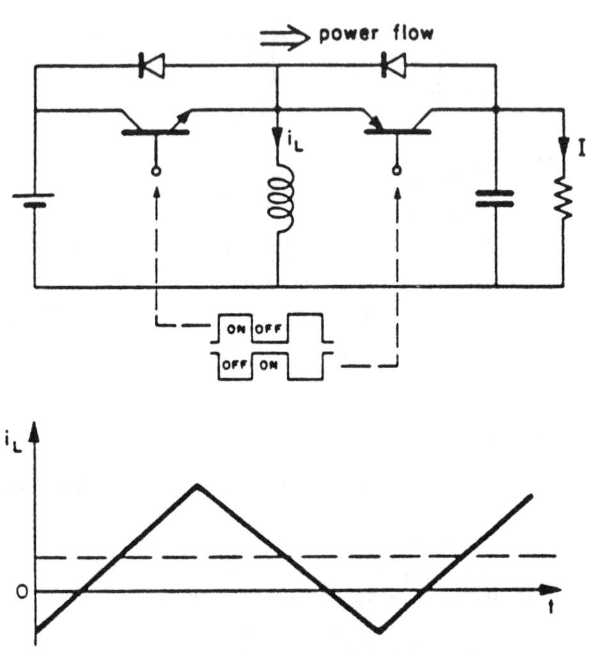

Fig. 22. Bidirectional current implementation of the ideal switch eliminates discontinuous conduction mode even at low load currents.

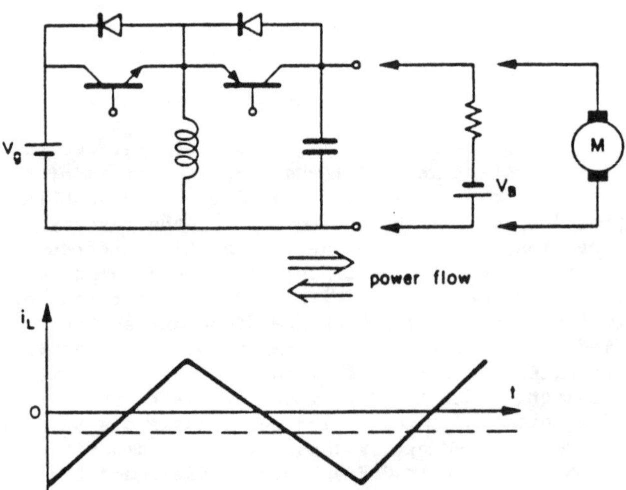

Fig. 23. Bidirectional power flow allows the motor load to become generator, and battery to change from a current sink (charge) to a current source (discharge).

Therefore, the average inductor current can be either positive (battery charging) or negative (battery discharging). Note, however, that the output voltage polarity is the same, negative, for either current direction. Hence, the converter is classified as a *two-quadrant converter:* a single polarity of voltage and two polarities of current, which on voltage vs. current plot would occupy two quadrants. Finally it is apparent that any one-quadrant converter can easily be turned into a two-quadrant converter, provided its switch implementation is current-bidirectional, that is, a two-quadrant switch.

Dc Isolation and Multiple Outputs

For many practical applications dc isolation is required between the input (source) and (load). Besides the main protection reasons and requirement for different output grounds, a number of additional side benefits are achieved, as illustrated on Fig. 24. The dc isolated version of the buck-boost converter (sometimes also referred to as the fly-back converter) is obtained in two simple steps: first, the two winding (bifilar or otherwise) inductor is built (Fig. 24a), and then electrical connection between the two windings is broken, thus resulting in the dc isolated version of Fig. 24b. Note, however, that this process itself suggests that the transformer obtained in such a way must have the same inductive storage capability as the original single inductor. This has a rather serious drawback, as will be discussed later in Section 4 on magnetics design, since such a transformer has to be designed to withstand a dc bias greater than the average input current. Although this may limit its usefulness for higher power designs, the simplicity of the dc isolation generation makes this configuration a viable choice for lower power designs.

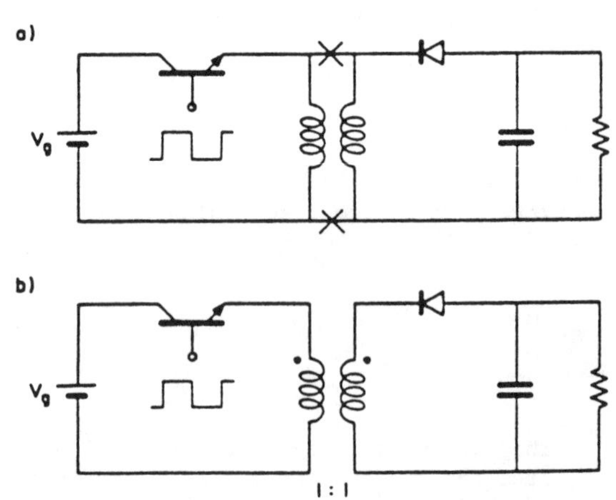

Fig. 24. Simple bifilar windings step (a) leads to a dc isolation in the buck-boost converter (b) through breaking electrical connections.

The isolation feature, brings as a by product some additional benefits (as it does in general for any isolated configuration). A simple change of the isolation transformer turns ratio contributes an additional step-up (or step-down) factor (Fig. 25), which helps alleviate efficiency degradation problems occurring at high duty cycles (as described in Paper 18). Namely, an additional step-up is obtained by the turns ratio without running the converter at an excessively high duty cycle. Finally, the original converter limitation (negative output voltage polarity for positive input voltage polarity) is easily removed by simple interchange of transformer secondary connections (dot polarity marks inverted) and appropriate change of diode direction, as seen in Fig. 25.

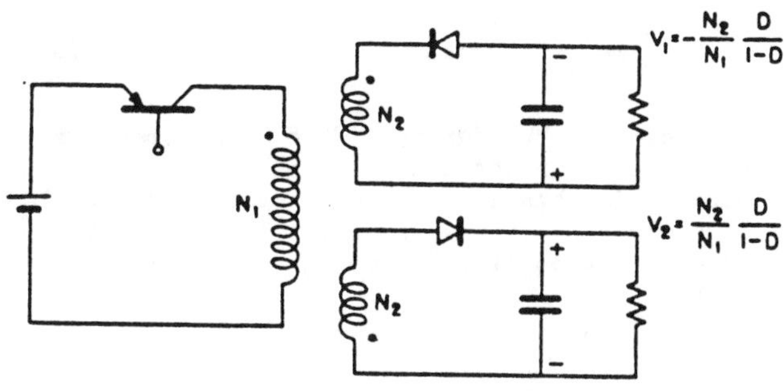

Fig. 25. Multiple outputs and polarity inversion are immediate additional benefits of the dc isolation transformer.

Both nonisolated and isolated versions of the buck-boost converter are clear examples of the converter based on *inductive energy transfer* — the input energy is stored in the inductor (or transformer magnetizing inductance) while the transistor is ON, and released to the load when transistor is OFF. As a consequence both input (transistor) and output (diode) currents come in lumps (pulsating currents), which can cause substantial input and output conducted noise — recognized as a potentially serious problem in switching power supplies.

Until recently it was believed that the buck, the boost, and the buck-boost converters were the simplest and the only conceivable single-switch configurations. However, this was readily disproved by the conception of a new single-switch configuration, which in an elegant and optimum manner resolved deficiencies such as pulsating currents and the far from ideal isolation transformer, such as that in the buck-boost converter.

3.4 One Step Closer to the Ideal Dc-to-Dc Converter (Ćuk converter)

With a clearly defined goal of achieving nonpulsating currents, the desired converter configuration gradually emerges: an inductor is needed in series with both input source and output load for either switch position. Then, energy transfer and level conversion is achieved by use of a single capacitance and a single switch as shown in Fig. 26a, or its bipolar transistor, diode implementation in Fig. 26b. Unlike previous single switch configurations, the Ćuk converter is based on *capacitive energy transfer*. Thus its dc current gain may be easily deduced from the capacitor current waveform using a charge-balance method in steady-state (see waveform in Fig. 26)

$$I_1 D'T_s = I_2 DT_s \tag{35}$$

or, from the 100% efficiency argument, the voltage dc gain is

$$\frac{V}{V_g} = \frac{D}{1 - D} \tag{36}$$

that is, the same as for conventional buck-boost (Fig. 24). Note that for simplicity of argument the inductors were assumed to be large enough such that the slope is negligible and results in rectangular current waveforms. The transistor and diode in Fig. 26b operate in the usual synchronous manner: when the transistor is OFF, the diode is ON and the capacitance is charged with polarity direction shown; when the transistor subsequently turns ON, the capacitance voltage reverse biases the diode and turns it OFF. More details about the Ćuk converter, including the original approach to its discovery, are given in Paper 18.

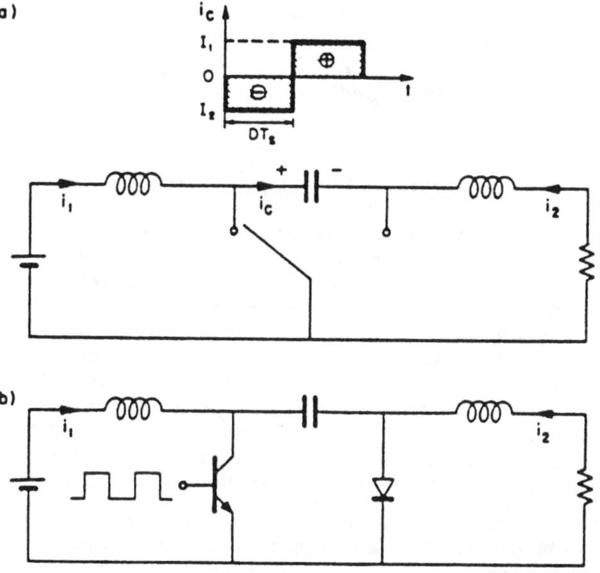

Fig. 26. Basic Ćuk converter is comprised of two inductors, capacitor, and single switch (a) implemented by a transistor and a diode (b).

Ideal Dc Isolation Transformer in the Ćuk Converter

The high efficiency requirement and simplicity lead to the single-ended dc isolated version of the Ćuk converter shown in Fig. 27, and described in more detail later in Paper 22. However, the same charge balance of the nonisolated version (Fig. 26) now has to be present on both energy transferring capacitances C_1 and C_2, as seen in waveforms of Fig. 27. Thus, the transformer average primary current is zero, just as is its average secondary current. Therefore, there is no dc bias on the transformer, as it operates as a true ac transformer. This is unlike the flyback transformer (Fig. 25) which carries a large dc bias current, on the order of its output and input dc current ratings. This has significant penalizing ramifications upon the compactness, size and weight as well as performance (leakage reactances) of the two respective transformers, as will become apparent in Section 4 dealing with magnetic phenomena.

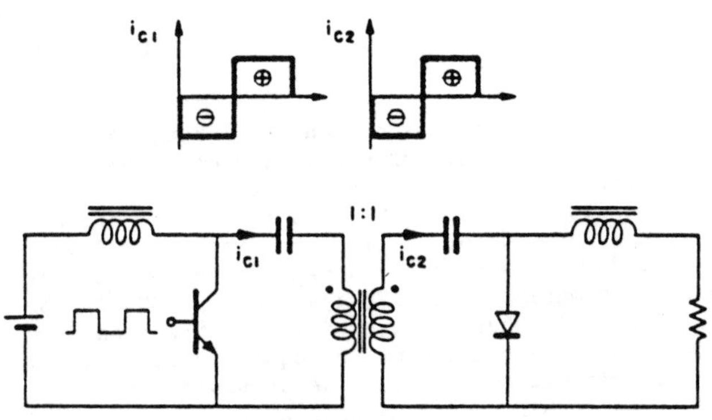

Fig. 27. Dc isolation is obtained in the Ćuk converter at the expense of a single additional component -- a coupling capacitor, besides the obvious isolation transformer addition.

Quadrant Classification of Converters

The topological development of the four single-switch converter types is now completed by their upgrade from a single quadrant dc-to-dc converter first to a two-quadrant converter and then to a four quadrant generalization, as shown in Fig. 28. As seen in Fig. 28b, the two quadrant Ćuk converter is obtained easily by allowing the switch current to be bidirectional through an additional transistor and diode. However, the four-quadrant converter of Fig. 28c, which allows either polarity of output voltage or current (hence it can be used as either a dc-to-ac inverter, for example, or backwards as an ac-to-dc controlled rectifier), requires a new true push-pull amplifier concept as revealed in Paper 24. With this concept any single-quadrant converter can be conveniently made into a four-quadrant converter.

So far, the importance of the topological interconnections has been emphasized in synthesizing useful configurations from the jumble of available components that were illustrated in Fig. 2. However, as seen in Fig. 2 and Fig. 27, magnetic components have the dominant presence in many switching power conversion schemes. Thus, understanding of the flux distribution in magnetic circuits is important not only for optimum design of magnetic components, transformer and inductors, but also for some more advanced magnetic structures introduced later in Paper 28.

4. MAGNETIC FUNDAMENTALS

Two *vector field quantities* are associated with the magnetic field. One, the *field intensity vector H* (sometimes also called the field strength) is directly related to its cause through the electric currents which produce the magnetic field, as given by the Ampere's law in the integral form

$$\oint H d\ell = \iint_S J dS \tag{37}$$

The other, the *flux density* B (sometimes also called magnetic induction) is directly related to the effects (mechanical forces, electric voltages) of the field as given by Faraday's law of electromagnetic induction (rate of change of magnetic flux $\phi = \int_S B dS$)

$$v = \frac{d}{dt} N \int_S B dS \tag{38}$$

For the simple case of the infinite straight conductor in free space carrying current I, the field intensity vector H can be easily found using the symmetry argument (equal tangential vector H at distances of radius r) as seen in Fig. 29. Ampere's circuital law (37) simplifies then to

$$H = \frac{I}{2\pi r} \tag{39}$$

In principle, the magnetic field intensity H caused by the conductor carrying current I can be found for any point in space. Associated with vector H is the flux density vector B, which *in free space* is always parallel in direction and proportional in magnitude, (as seen also in Fig. 29) such that:

$$B = \mu_o H \tag{40}$$

where μ_o is the permeability of free space which characterizes this medium for its magnetic properties, just as conductivity σ_o characterizes it for its electric properties.

Units in Magnetic Circuits

The addition of the fourth electric quantity to the MKS (meter, kilogram, second) system of units results in the MKSA rationalized (or Georgi) system in which the fourth unit is the Ampere (A) for current, which has now obtained wide acceptance since it became a subset of the international standard SI system. In this system, which will be

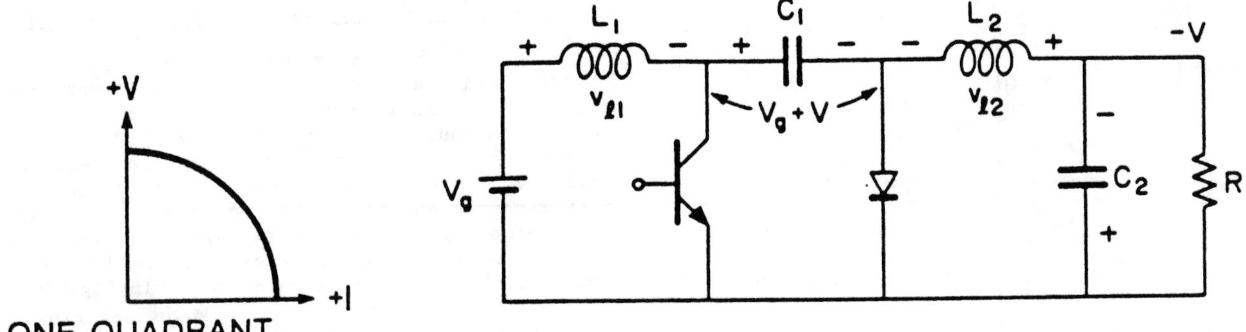

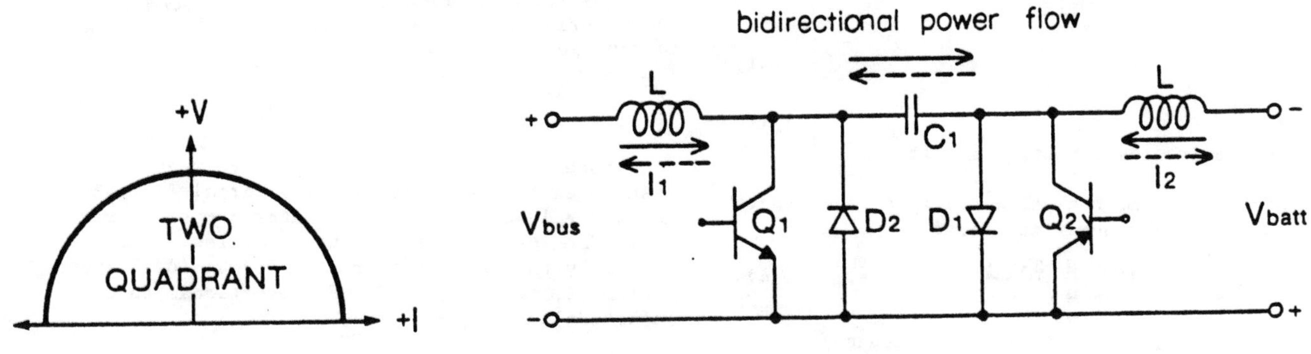

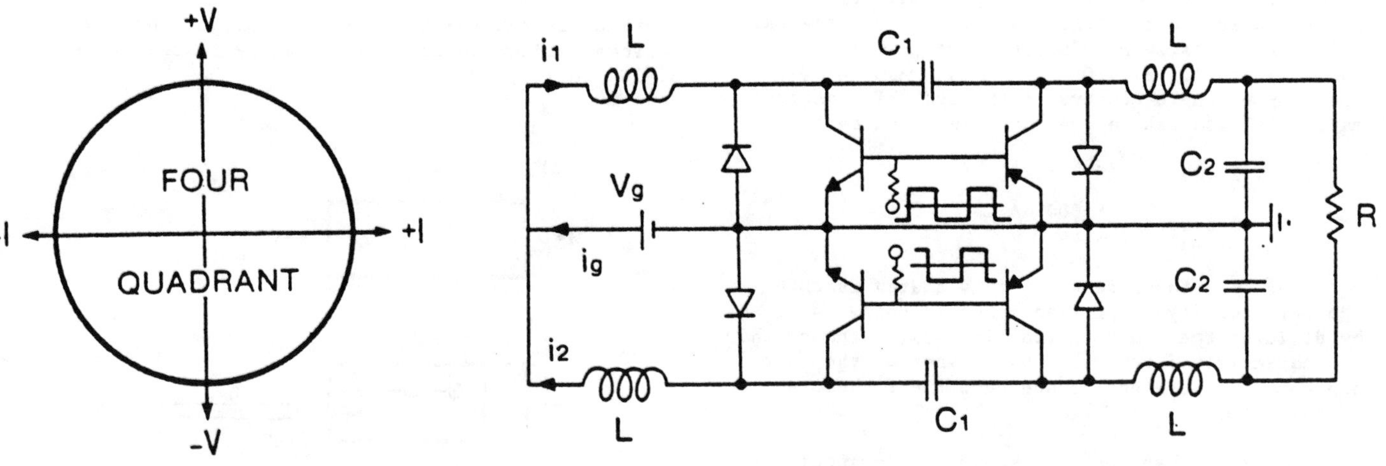

Fig. 28. *Quadrant classification of switching converters: (a) single quadrant (b) two quadrant (c) four quadrant.*

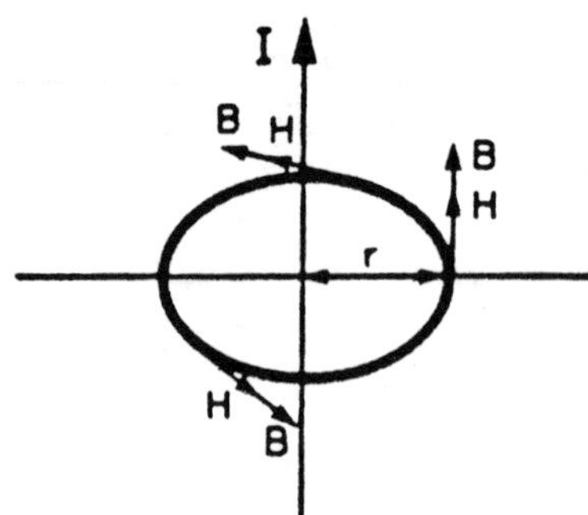

Fig. 29. Application of Ampere's circuital law to a single conductor in free space.

used here, the two field quantities have the following unit dimensions

$$H \; (=) \; \frac{A}{m}\left(\frac{\text{ampere}}{\text{meter}}\right)$$
$$B \; (=) \; T \; (\text{tesla}) \tag{41}$$

where (=) designates dimensional unit.

In this system, the permeability of free space μ_o has a particular numerical value

$$\mu_o = 4\pi \; 10^{-7} \; \frac{H}{m}\left(\frac{\text{henry}}{m}\right) \tag{42}$$

where H (henry) is the unit (for inductance).

It may be visualized how the adoption of the electric current unit (A) in (39) and the process of rationalization (association of 2π constant with permeability μ_o of free space) results in the A/m unit for field intensity vector H.

Unfortunately, the old CGS or Gaussian system is still widely used, especially by magnetic core manufacturers in the U.S. In this system, the unit for flux intensity H is Oersted (Oe), while the unit for flux density B is Gauss (G). Fortunately, there is a simple conversion through which magnetic materials data can be presented in SI units:

$$1 \text{ gauss} = 10^{-4} \text{ tesla}$$
$$1 \text{ oersted} = \frac{1000}{4\pi} \; \frac{A}{m} \tag{43}$$

The only convenience of this system is that the permeability μ_o of free space is unity, as seen by dividing the two equations in (43), although this may cause even further confusion whether the units are gauss or oersteds (since here B = H, because μ_o = 1 G/Oe).

So far we have only looked at the magnetic properties of currents in free space. However, the true importance and practical usefulness lies in the existence of certain materials, such as ferromagnetic materials and iron with permeability μ much larger than that of free space, that can substantially enhance its magnetic properties.

Characteristics of Ferromagnetic Materials

The ability of ferromagnetic materials to produce larger effect (larger B hence larger flux) with smaller means (smaller H hence smaller current) is perhaps easiest to comprehend by visualizing the presence of a great number of magnetized regions, called magnetic domains, such as seen in Fig. 30. Each magnetic domain may be conceptually visualized as originating from a magnetic dipole (small loop of current) which has a random orientation in space for demagnetized materials such as shown in Fig. 30a (current I reduced to zero). Thus the net flux contribution of the elementary magnetic domains on a global scale is zero, although locally it may be fully magnetized. However, even a small current I in the conductor, such as shown in Fig. 30b, may generate sufficient external field strength H to orient the majority of the small magnetic domains in the direction of the external field H. Thus the flux density in free space $\mu_o H$ is augmented many times by the additional intrinsic flux density of the material B_i as seen in Fig. 30b. Stating this in equation form,

$$B = \mu_o H + B_i \tag{44}$$

Note that further increase of current I results in further increase of external field H, and hence leads to an even greater number of magnetic domains oriented in its direction. Mathematically this may be expressed for an ideal linear medium (B_i parallel to H and proportional to its magnitude) as

$$B_i = \mu_o \chi H \tag{45}$$

where χ is magnetic susceptibility.

Combining (44) and (45) we get

$$B = \mu_o (1 + \chi)H = \mu_r \mu_o H = \mu H \tag{46}$$

where μ_r is the relative permeability of the ferromagnetic material, which can be in the range of 100 to 100,000.

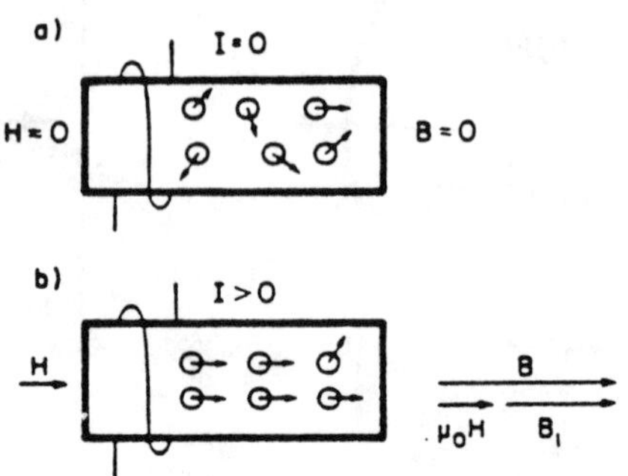

Fig. 30. Random orientation of magnetic domains in demagnetized materials (a) and their orientation in the direction of external field H generated by coil current I.

Comparison of (46) and (40), pictorially represented in Fig. 31a, emphasizes the role of the ferromagnetic material in enhancing its magnetic characteristics through greatly increased slope on the B - H characteristic. However, after a certain point, further increase of field strength H does not lead to as rapid increase of flux density as before (following the dotted line in Fig. 31a), but instead follows the slope of the flux density in free space, as illustrated in Fig. 31b. This is however, easy to understand, bearing in mind the finite number of magnetic domains as in Fig. 30. Thus, when the externally applied field strength H is sufficient to orient *all* magnetic domains in its direction, further increase of H will not produce as rapid increase of flux density. In other words, a phenomenon called saturation of magnetic flux density occurs as illustrated in Fig. 32. This saturation flux density B_{sat} becomes a very important ferromagnetic material parameter since, as will be shown later, it has direct bearing on the size and weight of the magnetic components. It may vary from 0.3 tesla for ferrite materials (mixture of Mn FeO_4 with $ZnFeO_4$) to better than 2T for pure iron. Tne intermediate range is covered by alloys of iron and the other two ferromagnetic materials, nickel and cobalt.

Another important classification of the ferromagnetic materials is also readily visible from Fig. 32. Namely, in some materials such as silicon iron (3% S_i, 97% F_e), Orthonol (50% N_i, 50% F_e), Permendur (50% C_o, 50% F_e), even a very small field strength H (on the order of A/cm) is capable of fully aligning all magnetic domains and results in the square characteristic of Fig. 32a. These materials are often termed square-loop materials. On the other hand, in materials such as Ferrite (MnZn alloy) the flux density variation is gradual, such that a distinct linear region is visible before the saturation point is reached. These materials are ideally categorized as linear materials. They can be approximated by (46) and a constant permeability μ designating the slope of the characteristic. These are, of course, idealizations, since either square or linear materials exhibit a *nonlinear* relationship between magnetic-field intensity and flux density, such that no single value of permeability can be used to characterize it, as seen from the empirically (experimentally) measured B - H characteristic for square and linear materials in Fig. 3. This nonlinear magnetization characteristic is further compounded by the fact that the B - H characteristic is actually not even single-valued but double-valued, exhibiting hysterisis loop behavior (increase of H and subsequent decrease do not result in the same characteristic). The static losses are directly associated with the area of the B - H loop at a given frequency, while the dynamic losses characterize additional core loss owing to the widening of the B - H loop at higher frequencies. Although they can also be appropriately modelled [44], we will limit our discussion here to the linear materials characterized by constant μ in (46) and the idealized B - H characteristic of Fig. 32b. This will enable us to introduce important magnetic circuit concepts and to get a handle on the flux distribution in magnetic circuits, just as easily as finding the current distribution in electric circuits by use of Kirchoff's laws.

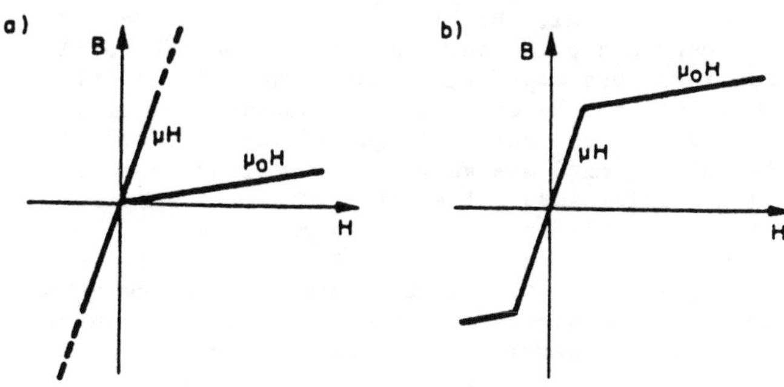

Fig. 31. Two essential features of the ferromagnetic materials: high permeability μ (steep slope on a B - H curve) (a) and saturation (b).

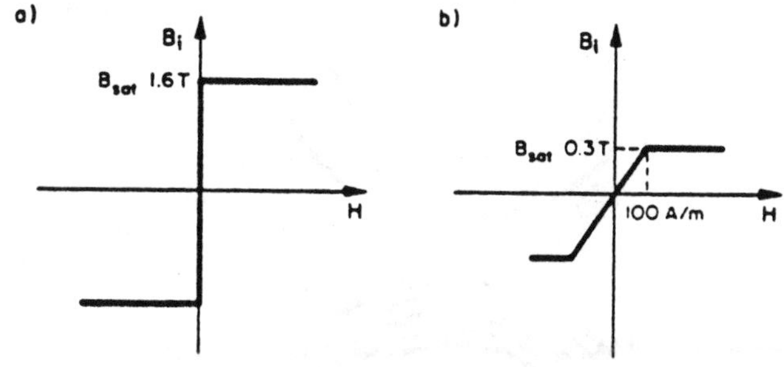

Fig. 32. Square-loop ferromagnetic materials (a) usually exhibit high saturation flux density while the linear ferromagnetic materials (b) have lower saturation flux density.

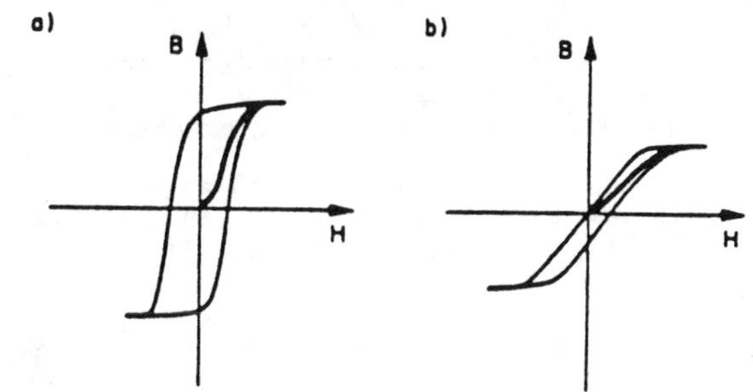

Fig. 33. Third essential feature of ferromagnetic materials: nonlinear, double valued B - H loop characteristic of square (a) and linear (b) materials.

4.1 Magnetic Circuit Concept

Despite all the complications ferromagnetic material introduces (as visible in Fig. 33 in its double-value nonlinear characteristic), its presence actually allows a much simpler practical approach. Namely, owing to the high permeability of the material, the lines of flux are guided into a prescribed path shown in Fig. 34b on the ideal toroidal core *magnetic circuit*. This is exactly analogous to the way the corresponding quantity to flux ϕ, the current I, is guided in the *electric circuit of* Fig. 34a shown for comparison purposes in a similar toroidal shape. While the sustained flow of an electric current is made possible by the presence of the *voltage source* v (Fig. 34a) the analog magnetic flux is maintained in the core because of the presence of the corresponding source, the current-carrying coil, often called magnetomotive force F = Ni (by analogy with electromotive force v).

a)

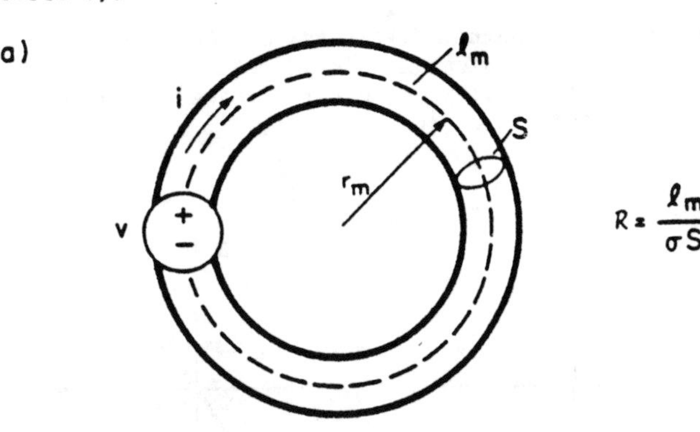

b)

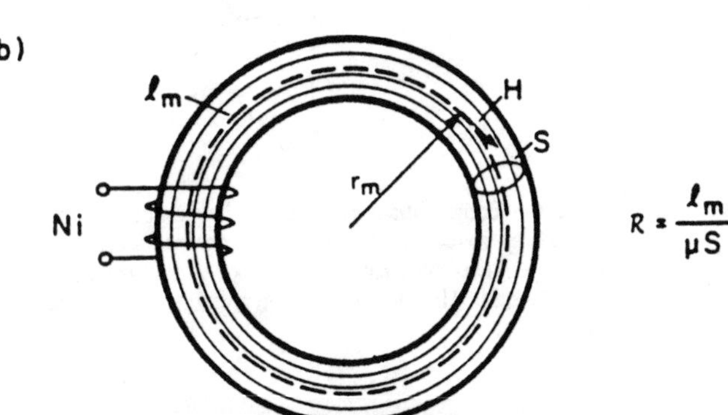

Fig. 34. Analogy between the electric circuits in which current is guided by high conductivity wires (a) and magnetic circuit (b) in which flux is guided through high permeability ferromagnetic material.

The analogy between electric and magnetic circuits is based on the analogy between the equations describing electric and magnetic fields, such as:

$$i = \int_S J dS \qquad \phi = \int_S B dS \tag{47}$$

$$v = \oint E dl \qquad F = Ni = \iint_S H dl \tag{48}$$

$$J = \sigma E \qquad B = \mu H \tag{49}$$

Just as the electric circuits are only the simplification of the general electric field concept (described by electric field vector E and current density vector J) owing to the high conductivity properties of certain materials (copper, aluminum, etc.), the magnetic circuits can be analogously considered as the simplification of the corresponding field concept described by magnetic field intensity vector H and flux density vector B, which is similarly made possible by the existence of ferromagnetic materials with high permeability (high conductivity for the magnetic flux). This is best illustrated now on the example in which the transition from the electric field to the electric circuit of Fig. 34a is done in the same way as the transition from magnetic field to the magnetic circuit of Fig. 34b, thus exposing the *reluctance concept*.

The Reluctance Concept

For a given voltage source v, and assuming uniform cross section and uniform current density, the current i can be found by going through the intermediate steps of calculating field quantities, that is

$$i = JS = \sigma ES = \frac{\sigma S}{\ell_m} v \tag{50}$$

However, the field quantities could have been completely by passed and the current found using Ohm's law:

$$i = \frac{v}{R}; \tag{51}$$

where

$$R = \frac{\ell_m}{\sigma S} \tag{52}$$

However, the same procedure may be applied under the same assumptions of uniform cross section and uniform flux distribution to magnetic circuits. For example, applying Ampere's circuital law (37) to the toroidal core of Fig. 34b, the vector H has constant magnitude at distance r given by

$$H = \frac{Ni}{2\pi r} \tag{53}$$

This equation suggests that field intensity magnitude H, and thus flux density B changes its magnitude along the cross section (varying r) even when a linear medium (constant μ) is assumed. However, for engineering applications, an average quantity H_m given at the mean magnetic path length $\ell_m = 2\pi r_m$ and assumed uniform throughout the cross-section results in a very good approximation, accurate to within 2% of the exact result obtained by integration over the area. This is so because, in many practical applications, the core cross-sectional area width is relatively small compared to the total radius of the toroid, such that the core may be considered quasifilamentary and replaced by this idealization. The remaining procedure completely follows its electric circuit analog, that is, to find the flux ϕ as a result of the magnetomotive force F = Ni in the toroid of Fig. 34b, we use:

$$\phi = B \cdot S = \mu HS = \mu \cdot \frac{Ni}{\ell_m} S \tag{54}$$

However, again the above process of going through the intermediate field quantities can be completely by passed, and flux obtained directly as

$$\phi = \frac{Ni}{R} \tag{55}$$

$$R = \frac{\ell_m}{\mu S} \tag{56}$$

where R is the *reluctance* of the magnetic path.

Although this concept of reluctance is developed here for the special case of linear magnetic circuits, its usefulness extends far beyond, since even in the nonlinear magnetic circuits in which μ is a function of H, it can give helpful qualitative insight into flux distributions as well as quite accurate quantitative results in some cases.

From Material to Device Properties

Another important change has taken place with introduction of the reluctance concept. Reluctance as defined by (56) contains not only magnetic properties (μ) but also all the geometric properties of the magnetic path (cross-section S and magnetic path length ℓ_m). Therefore the original B - H characteristic of Fig. 35a containing only the material property (permeability μ is the slope of the linear part) is now translated into a flux versus ampere-turns characteristic of the toroidal sample of Fig. 34b, which is obtained by scaling the vertical B coordinate by the cross-sectional area of the sample S and the horizontal by its magnetic path length (Fig. 35b). The slope now has the meaning of permeance (inductance per single turn) also defined as

$$P = \frac{1}{R} = \frac{\phi}{i} \tag{57}$$

Finally, by scaling the two coordinates by the number of turns, a curve of the same shape relates flux linkages $\lambda = N\phi$ (total flux seen by the windings) to the current i in the windings. The slope of this characteristic is defined as the inductance of the device

$$L = \frac{\lambda}{i} = \frac{N\phi}{i/N} = N^2 \frac{\phi}{i} = N^2 P \tag{58}$$

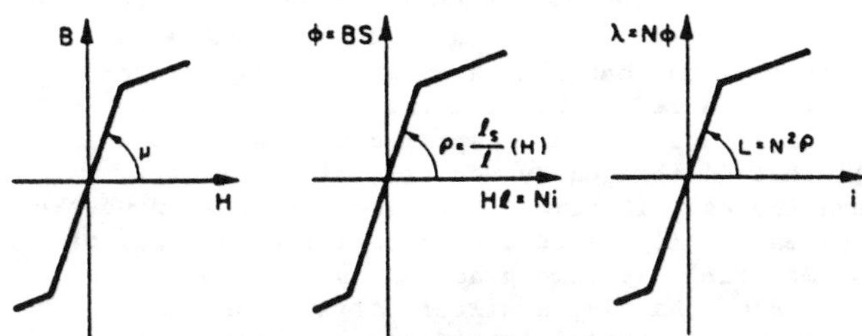

Fig. 35. Change from material properties (a) to device properties involves scaling of the coordinates by geometrical factors (cross-section, magnetic path length) (b) and turns ratios (c).

Thus finally an electric circuit device parameter is directly related to the magnetic properties of the material (μ) and its geometrical configuration.

All three graphs in Fig. 35 are purposely shown the same to emphasize the fact that the salient features of the three characteristics remain intact; only the scales along its coordinates (and of course dimensions) change. In fact, the B - H characteristic for different materials is actually obtained directly from the measurement of the ϕ vs NI characteristic for the particular standard geometry sample.

However, while the material property is fixed for the given mixture of the ferromagnetic materials (alloys), the flux vs. ampere turns characteristic can be greatly influenced both in its shape and scale factors, just by varying the geometry of the magnetic configurations and employing airgaps, as shown next.

4.2 Air Gaps in Magnetic Circuits

Let us now see, by use of the reluctance concept, how the presence of the airgap can profoundly change the magnetic device characteristics (inductance L and its dc bias capability, for example). The introduction of the airgap of length ℓ_g in the toroid of Fig. 34b results in the magnetic circuit of Fig. 36a. Using the reluctance concept we can now define two reluctances, R_m of the core and R_g of the gap, as

$$R_m = \frac{\ell_m}{\mu S} \qquad R_g = \frac{\ell_g}{\mu_o S} \tag{59}$$

since the airgap permeability is μ_o.

Furthermore, it is apparent that the two airgaps are in series with the source of magnetic potential as in the electric circuit analog of Fig. 36b, hence the flux is found as

$$\phi = \frac{Ni}{R_g + R_m} = (P_g + P_m)\ Ni \tag{60}$$

or

$$\lambda = N\phi = N^2(P_g + P_m)i \tag{61}$$

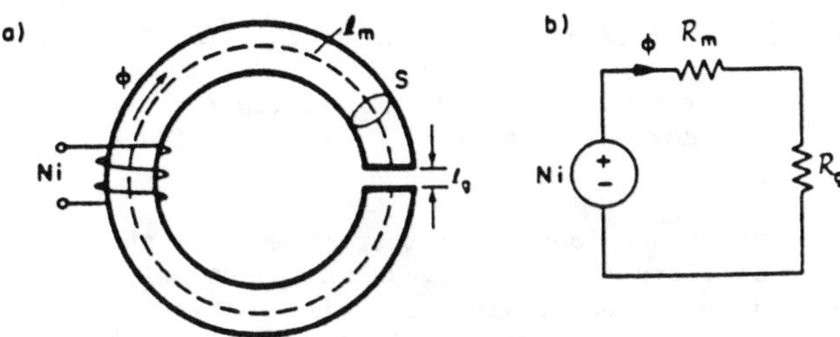

Fig. 36. Magnetic circuit with airgap (a) and its linear reluctance model (b).

In practice the reluctance of the airgap is often much larger than that of the magnetic path even though $\ell_m \gg \ell_g$, since the permeability of airgap is so much smaller, that is, $\mu_o \ll \mu_r\mu_o$ or

$$\frac{R_m}{R_g} = \frac{\ell_m/\ell_g}{\mu_r} \ll 1 \tag{62}$$

For example for $\ell_m/\ell_g = 100$, and $\mu_r = 1{,}000$ (not unusual for ferromagnetic materials), $R_m/R_g = 0.1$. Thus the λ, i characteristic of the device in Fig. 36 is greatly influenced even by a minute airgap, as may be observed from Fig. 37 and equation for its slope:

$$L(\ell_g) = \frac{N^2\mu_o S}{\ell_g} \tag{63}$$

Thus, increase of airgap results in decrease of the slope of the λ - i curve, and hence a higher peak inductor current is allowed before the core saturation point is reached. This has great practical significance for the design of switching converters. For example, the inductor current waveform has a typical triangular waveshape superimposed on the dc current level, as illustrated in Fig. 37 by inclusion of a typical inductor current waveform (heavy line). Higher inductor dc bias currents are possible by increase of the airgap, but at the sacrifice of reducing inductance L value (smaller slope of dotted line in Fig. 37).

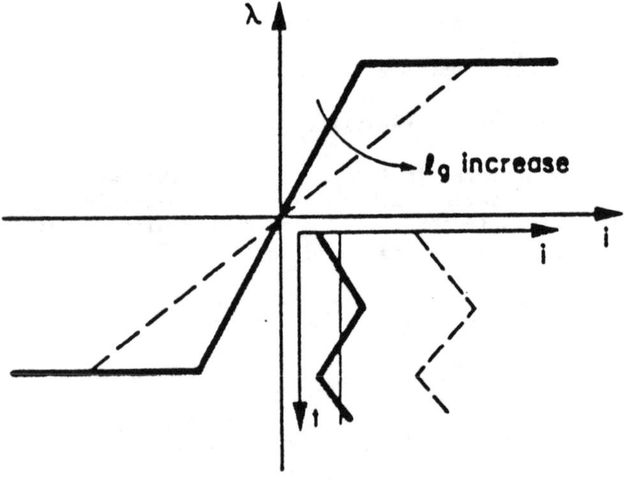

Fig. 37. Effect of the airgap on the flux linkages vs. current characteristic of the inductor: increase of the airgap increases dc current capability of the inductor.

Let us now look at another example of the magnetic circuits with airgap, which not only changes the slope (scale), but also changes the shape of the λ - i characteristic. In Fig. 38a an EI core configuration is used with the airgap ℓ_g in one of the outer legs and the winding on the inner leg. As seen from the electric circuit analog Fig. 38b and d, the flux first follows the ungapped loop for $i < i_1$. However, when this leg saturates when $i > i_1$, the flux has an alternative lower reluctance path through the gapped leg as seen in Fig. 38d. Finally, when that flux saturates for $i > i_2$, the third slope in the composite λ - i characteristic is obtained as shown on Fig. 38c. This composite core structure is useful for prevention of transient saturation of transformers in switching regulators.

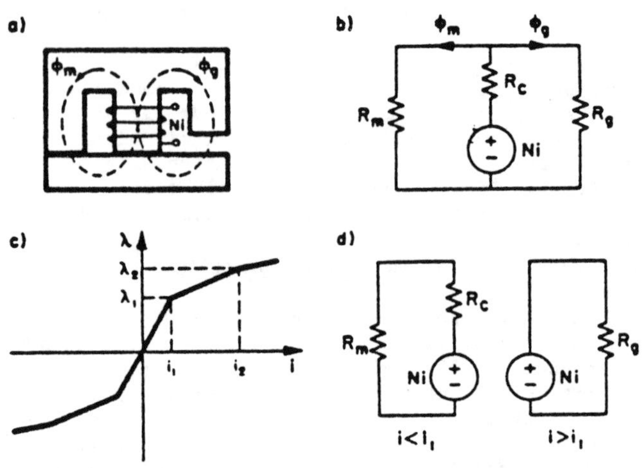

Fig. 38. Single airgap in EI core structure (a) leads to a composite λ - i characteristic (c) which eliminates core saturation problems.

For nominal steady-state operation, the flux excursions are limited below λ_1. During some transient conditions, the flux "overflows" into the next interval ($\lambda < \lambda_2$) which has still sufficient inductive slope to prevent excessively high currents from damaging the converter.

Finally, the introduction of the airgap into the core with a square-loop characteristic material has the similar effect of slanting the λ - i characteristic. In fact, the nonlinear characteristic of the permeability μ becomes greatly diminished because of (62) and (63), and the new composite structure may be well represented by a linear characteristic similar to that in Fig. 37. Unfortunately, it is often referred to as "shearing over" of the square-loop B - H characteristic of Fig. 32a into the linear one of Fig. 32b, although it is quite obvious that the material properties are still unchanged: the flux vs. ampere turns characteristic of the composite core structure is all that is changed by addition of an airgap. Nevertheless, in some other cases, such as powdered iron material, the reference to effective μ_{eff} of the material has some practical significance and advantage. Namely, a mixture of iron and some nonmagnetic material introduces a distributed airgap, which effectively changes the slope of the ϕ - Ni curve and can be traced back on the B - H loop as some equivalent slope μ_{eff} (see Fig. 35), which is usually referred to in manufacturers' data sheets.

4.3 Inductor Design

Magnetic circuits with airgaps constitute a fundamental background on which the inductor design can be built. In switching power converters, the inductor requirements are often specified in terms of three quantities:

(a) desired dc current carrying capability I of the inductor
(b) ripple current i_{ac} as a percentage of dc current
(c) efficiency of the inductor with respect to copper losses

The second requirement translates at a given switching frequency f_s and ac voltage excitation into a corresponding requirement on inductor element value L. The third requirement can be either implicitly assumed, by adopting a particular current density J as a design parameter, or it can be explicitly imposed as a total copper loss on the windings, P_{cu}. Both of these approaches [43] will be outlined here.

With these quantities specified, the inductor design then involves finding the minimum core size which will satisfy the above requirements. The number of turns N, wire size A_w and the airgap ℓ_g are among the other quantities to be determined.

Although in Fig. 39a a toroidal core with core cross-section S and winding (window) area W is chosen as a reference, the following analysis is equally valid for any other core configuration.

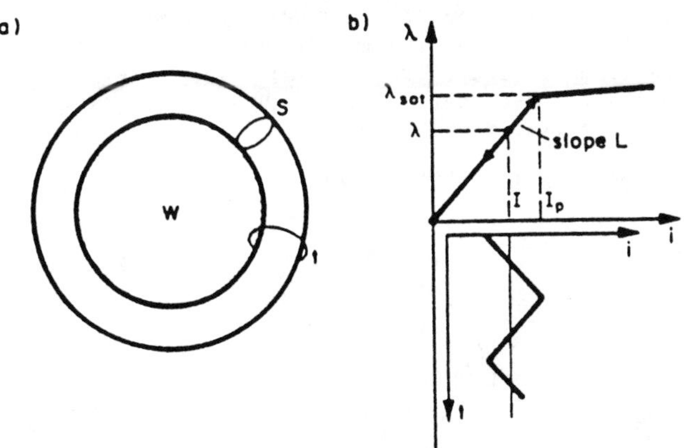

Fig. 39. Definition of the core geometry (a) for the design of inductors carrying dc current (b).

Design via Area Product A_p Approach

Here the current density J is adopted as design parameter. From the linear flux characteristic for inductor in Fig. 39b, and by *fully utilizing* its flux capability (peak current reaching the knee of the saturation characteristic) we have

$$N = \frac{LI}{BS} \tag{64}$$

where B is maximum allowed dc flux density, and S core cross-sectional area.

In order to *fully utilize* the available window area, N number of turns carrying current I and having J current density have to fit into window area W such that

$$kW = \frac{N \cdot I}{J} \tag{65}$$

where k is empirical window utilization factor (usually between 0.3 and 0.6) which shows how closely layers of wire can be packed.

Substitution of (64) in (65) and rearrangement results in

$$A_p = WS = \frac{LI^2}{BJk} \tag{66}$$

where the area product A_p has dimensions m^4 and contains core geometry information, while the right hand side contains the specifications (L, I and J) and core magnetic characteristic (B). All the different core sizes can then be tabulated with increasing value of area product A_p.

The design steps are then the following:

1. Pick the core with the area product closest but higher than the one calculated by use of (66) and record its W and S.
2. Determine the number of turns N by use of (64).
3. Determine the wire cross-section $A_w = I/J$ and wire size.
4. Using mean length per turn data, find the copper losses P_{cu}.
5. Finally, calculate the airgap ℓ_g by use of

$$\ell_g = \frac{\mu_o N^2 S}{L} \tag{67}$$

Design via Core Geometry K_g Approach

Here the total winding losses P_{cu} are adopted as a design parameter in addition to L and I. Let us find first these losses accumulated on winding resistance R_ℓ, assuming *fully utilized* window area W

$$P_{cu} = R_\ell I^2 = \rho \frac{N^2 t I^2}{kW} \tag{68}$$

where t is mean length per turn of the winding, usually specified in the manufacturers' data sheets for the cores and ρ is resistivity of the conductor given for copper at 25°C as

$$\rho = 1.724 \times 10^{-6} \ \Omega\text{cm} \tag{69}$$

To prevent core saturation and yet *fully utilize* the core, the same condition as before (64) applies. Substitution of (64) in (68) and rearrangement results in

$$K_g = k\frac{WS^2}{t} = \frac{\rho(LI^2)^2}{B^2 P_{cu}} \qquad (70)$$

Core geometry parameter K_g again lumps together all the geometrical core parameters, while the right-hand side contains all electrical and magnetic parameters.

Note that in the area product A_p approach one would assume certain current density (say in the range of $J = 250\ A/cm^2 - 1000\ A/cm^2$) and then calculate the copper losses P_{cu}. Sometimes this could result in overly conservative design (losses too small), or just the opposite, too high copper losses, since factor of 4 in current density choice leads to factor of 16 in corresponding copper losses. This is, of course, avoided in this core geometry approach since winding losses P_{cu} are the starting parameter. They would be furthermore chosen as certain percentage α of the total power being processed P, say $\alpha = 1\%$. Thus, 1% efficiency loss could be attributed to the copper loss on inductor. Therefore, this second approach seems to be closer to the engineering judgement and requiring fewer design alterations before the final design is reached.

The design steps are then the following:

1. Pick the core with the core geometry product K_g closest but higher than the one calculated by use of (70) and record the core cross section S, window area W, and mean length per turn t.
2. Determine the number of turns by use of (64).
3. Determine the wire cross-section $A_w = k\frac{W}{N}$ and wire size.
4. Calculate the airgap ℓ_g by use of (67).

4.4 Transformer Operation and Modelling

If another winding is added to the toroidal core of Fig. 34b the two winding *transformer* of Fig. 40 is obtained. The primary N_1 turns are excited by the voltage source v_1, and the secondary N_2 turns are loaded with resistance R across which the output voltage v_2 is obtained. Assuming that the magnetic flux is completely confined to the core, the fundamental voltage step-up or step-down conversion function is easily obtained from Faraday's law:

$$v_1 = N_1\frac{d\phi_m}{dt}$$

$$v_2 = N_2\frac{d\phi_m}{dt} \Rightarrow \frac{v_2}{v_1} = \frac{N_2}{N_1} \qquad (71)$$

where ϕ_m is the mutual flux. One of the advantageous features of transformer operation is that to generate this mutual flux ϕ_m, only a very small fraction of the load current is needed to excite the core. This can easily be seen by applying Ampere's

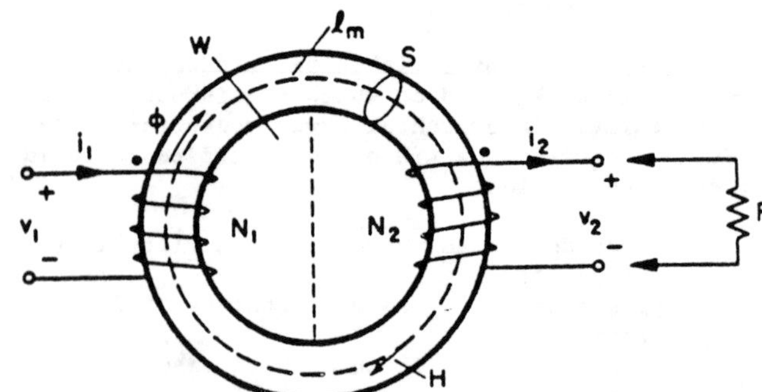

Fig. 40. Two winding isolation transformer shown schematically. In practice windings N_1 and N_2 are distributed around the core to minimize leakage inductance.

circuital law to the toroidal core of Fig. 40 (or using the reluctance concept and electronic circuit analog):

$$H\ell_m = N_1 i_1 - N_2 i_2 \qquad (72)$$

Note that in (72) the Ampere turns $N_2 i_2$ of the secondary winding are *subtracted* from the primary ampere turns and the flux generated by the secondary current is opposing the original primary current flux (Lenz's law).

The mutual flux ϕ_m generates positive voltages at the dot-marked terminals (dot convention) as in Fig. 40. Thus primary excitation current flows *into the dot-marked* terminal, while secondary load current flows *out of the dot-marked* terminal. Note that in the case of the two inductors on the same core (coupled-inductors) the ampere turns would *add* and the secondary current would also flow into the dot-marked end.

Rearranging (72) we get

$$i_1 = \frac{N_2}{N_1} i_2 + i_m \qquad (73)$$

$$i_m = \frac{H\ell_m}{N_1} \qquad (74)$$

The primary current i_1, thus, consists of two parts; a load current component (secondary reflected current) and a much smaller magnetizing current i_m, which is used to excite the core (often less than 1% of load current in an efficient transformer).

In many switching converter applications, saturation of the isolation transformer may lead to catastrophic failure of the converter. To avoid saturation, the transformer has to be ideally excited by equal volt-second excitations in either the positive or negative direction. Thus for the special rectangular voltage waveform, often encountered in switching converters and illustrated in Fig. 41, one gets:

$$V_p DT_s = 2N_1\phi \quad \text{(positive excitation)} \quad (75)$$

and

$$V_s D'T_s = 2N_1\phi \quad \text{(negative excitation)} \quad (76)$$

requiring that the areas under positive and under negative voltage be equal.

Therefore, the excitation voltage has to be a true ac waveform (zero voltage average) if "core creep" and eventual core saturation is to be avoided. Note that because of (71) volt-second balance on the secondary will be ensured, since it is characterized by the same volts/turn quantity which is unique for a given transformer irrespective of how many secondary turns it has.

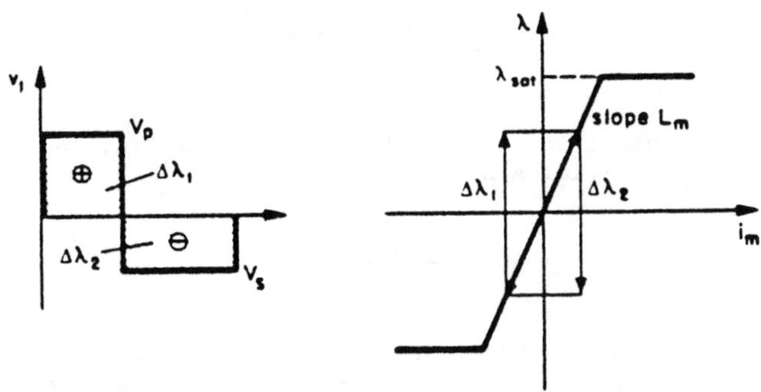

Fig. 41. Zero net average voltage is required for equal core excitation in both directions.

Finally to avoid saturation, that is $\phi \leq \phi$ sat, either (75) or (76) can be used to give

$$N_1 \geq \frac{V_p D}{2B_m S f_s} \quad (77)$$

where B_m is the maximum allowable flux density. Thus, a sufficient number of primary turns have to be used to prevent saturation of the core. Stated in another way, at given operating conditions (duty cycle D and switching frequency f_s), the given core (geometry cross-section S and flux density B_m) can support so many volts/turn without saturating.

Just as shown in (58), the slope of the $\lambda - i_m$ curve in Fig. 41 is the magnetizing inductance L_m given by

$$L_m = N_1^2 P_m = N_1^2 \frac{\mu S}{\ell_m} \quad (78)$$

Thus, the simplest transformer model which accounts for finite magnetizing inductance L_m, and uses ideal N_1: N_2 turns ratio transformer is shown in Fig. 42. This transformer model assumes perfect coupling (all primary flux couples to the secondary and vice versa, hence no leakage inductances).

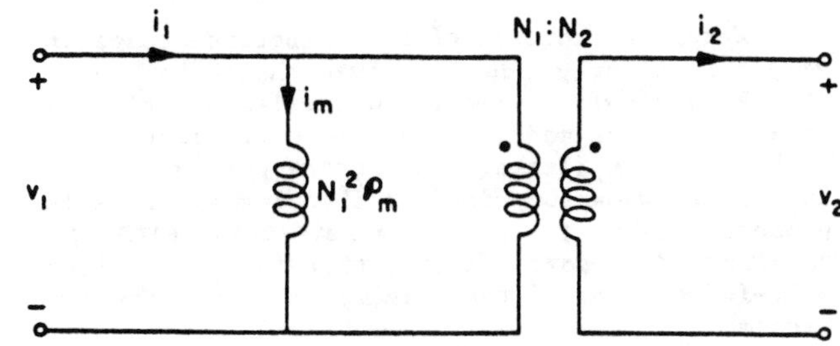

Fig. 42. Transformer model assuming perfect coupling (zero leakage inductances).

However, just as it was shown in the section on converter topologies, even a small amount of parasitics may lead to significant undesirable effects, the second order effects in transformers can likewise seriously affect the converter performance, especially those operating at high switching frequency. Let us therefore refine the model of Fig. 42 to include some of these second order effects. For example, in practice part of the flux generated by the primary flux $\phi_{\ell 1}$ is not coupled to the secondary, as pictorially represented by the dotted lines in Fig. 43a. We may model this by a leakage inductance $L_{\ell 1}$, which is in analogy with (58) given by

$$L_{\ell 1} = N_1^2 P_{\ell 1} \quad (79)$$

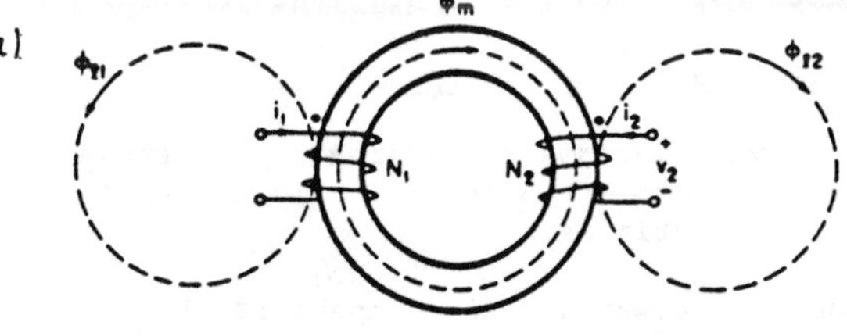

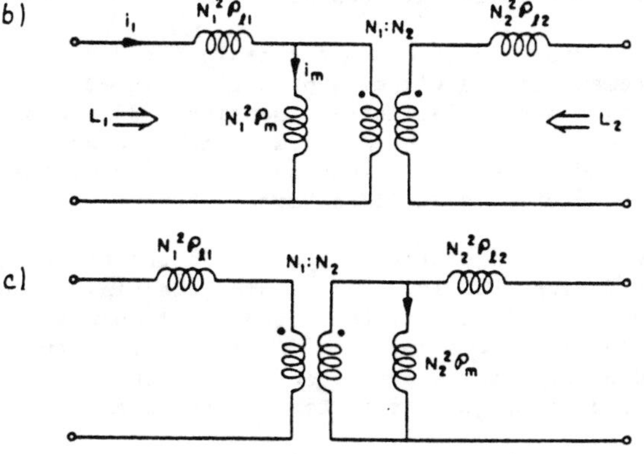

Fig. 43. Physical transformer with leakage fluxes (a) (air fluxes $\phi_{\ell 1}$ and $\phi_{\ell 2}$) and equivalent circuit model representations (b) and (c).

Here, the concept of the reluctance comes in very conveniently. Namely, even though we can not attach particular geometry to the leakage flux path, it still can be modelled by some equivalent flux path permeance (leakage inductance per unit turn). In effect, we assume in (77) that leakage flux is proportional to the primary ampere turns with P_{ℓ_1} constant of proportionality, that is $\phi_{\ell_1} = N_1 i_1 P_{\ell_1}$. Self-inductances of the primary and secondary then become

$$L_1 = N_1^2 (P_{\ell_1} + P_m) \tag{80}$$

$$L_2 = N_2^2 (P_{\ell_2} + P_m) \tag{81}$$

From (80) the input part of equivalent circuit can be easily deduced, as in Fig. 43c, while (81) is analogously easily realized in the output part of the equivalent circuit in Fig. 43c. Putting the two models together with the ideal $N_1 : N_2$ turns ratio transformer, a complete equivalent circuit model is obtained with magnetizing inductance modelled either on the primary side (Fig. 43b) or secondary side (Fig. 43c). The leakage reactances can be minimized from that given by (79) by proper winding techniques such as bifilar winding of primary and secondary, or sandwich winding the layers of primary and secondary windings. The effects of different winding techniques on leakage inductances of the multiple winding transformer are covered in depth in Paper 13.

Let us now turn to the transformer sizing for the given power and efficiency requirements.

4.4 Transformer Design

In switching power converters, the transformer requirements are often specified in terms of the following quantities:

(a) desired power handling capability P
(b) efficiency of the transformer design with respect to copper losses.

As before in the inductor design, the second requirement can be either implicitly assumed by adopting a particular current density J as a design parameter, or it can be explicitly imposed as a total winding power dissipation P_{cu}. Both of these approaches will be outlined here.

With these quantities specified, the transformer design then involves finding the minimum core size which will satisfy the above requirements, and still not go into saturation. The number of turns N_1 and N_2 of primary and secondary and their wire sizes are other quantities to be determined.

Again as before the toroidal core of Fig. 40 is chosen as a reference, although the analysis is equally valid for any other core configuration, provided cross-section S and winding area W are appropriately defined.

Design via Area Product A_p Approach

Here the same current density J is adopted for both primary N_1 turns and secondary N_2 turns. For a square wave -- periodic excitation, the primary voltage V_1 and secondary voltage V_2 which can be supported on a given core are obtained from Faraday's law (71) as:

$$N_1 = \frac{V_1}{4B_m S f_s} \tag{82}$$

$$N_2 = \frac{V_2}{4B_m S f_s} \tag{83}$$

Winding area W is fully utilized when:

$$kW = N_1 A_{w1} + N_2 A_{w2} = N_1 \frac{I_1}{J} + N_2 \frac{I_2}{J} \tag{84}$$

Substitution of N_1 and N_2 from (82) and (83) into (84) yields after rearrangement:

$$A_p = WS = \frac{V_1 I_1 + V_2 I_2}{4B_m k J f_s} \tag{85}$$

Often converter transformer is designed for very high efficiency (on the order of 1%-2% power loss). Thus, $V_1 I_1 \approx V_2 I_2$, and (85) becomes

$$A_p = \frac{P}{2B_m k J f_s} \tag{86}$$

where P is power handling capability of the transformer. Note how in (86) the increase of the switching frequency f_s can lead to the substantially reduced size of the transformer for the given power level, or increasing power throughput for the same core size. Thus, the modern approach of off-line switching power supplies completely eliminates bulky and heavy 60Hz transformer, and replaces it with a switching power supply, whose isolation transformer operates at say, 60kHz, and hence is order of magnitudes lighter and smaller.

The design steps are then the following:

1. Pick the core with the area product A_p closest but higher than the one calculated by use of (86) and record its W and S.
2. Determine the number of primary and secondary turns by use of (82) and (83).
3. Calculate the wire cross-sections A_{w1} and A_{w2} and determine the wire sizes.
4. Using mean length per turn t, calculate the primary and secondary copper losses and evaluate the transformer efficiency.
5. Evaluate the magnetizing inductance by use of (78), and estimate the magnetizing current.

Design via a Core Geometry K_g Approach

Here the design parameters are the total winding losses P_{cu} on both primary and secondary windings. Just as for the inductor design (68) the losses become

$$P_{cu} = R_{\ell 1} I_1^2 + R_{\ell 2} I_2^2 = 2\rho \frac{t}{kW}\left(N_1^2 I_1^2 + N_2^2 I_2^2\right) \tag{87}$$

where again t is mean length per turn, and resistivity ρ as given before in (69).

Substitution of (82) and (83) in (87) and rearrangement yields:

$$K_g = \frac{kWS^2}{t} = \frac{\rho\, P^2}{4\, B_m^2 f_s^2 P_{cu}} \tag{88}$$

where P is as before power handling capability of the core.

The design steps are then the following:

1. Choose the core with the core geometry product K_g closest but higher than the one calculated by use of (88) and record its cross-section S, window W and mean length per turn t. Here parameter P_{cu} was chosen as some percentage (1%-2%) of the total power throughput.
2. Determine the number of turns by use of (82) and (83).
3. Calculate the wire cross-sections A_{w1} and A_{w2} and determine the wire sizes.
4. Evaluate the magnetizing inductance by use of (78) and estimate the magnetizing current.

Note that in both of these approaches a transformer with *no dc bias* is assumed, such as the one in the Ćuk converter. If, however the transformer for the flyback converter of Fig. 18 needs to be designed, the substantial dc bias on the transformer requires use of the *gapped core*. The design procedure then follows the design of the inductors with dc bias, with the only exception that the two windings have to be accounted for.

4.5 Inductor and Transformer Design Example

Let us now apply these magnetics design techniques to the dc isolated Ćuk converter of Fig. 44. Only the core geometry K_g approach will be illustrated, since the design steps are similar to the area product A_p approach.

Problem

Design magnetics for a 150W dc isolated Ćuk converter, which inverts 15V input dc voltage to a -15V at 10A at the output. Thus, a 1 : 1 transformer turns ratio and operation at D = 0.5 duty ratio is assumed as illustrated in Fig. 44. The converter operates at f_s = 100kHz, hence a low-loss ferrite material is used. Standard ferrite pot cores are to be used, hence the maximum flux density

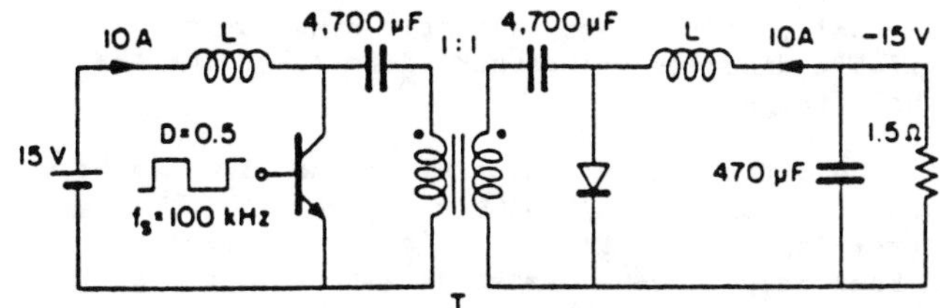

Fig. 44. Design of magnetics components in the dc isolated Ćuk converter.

is B_m = 0.3T, and the fill factor for a ferrite pot core is assumed to be k = 0.3.

Input and output inductor current ripple is limited to 10% of their respective dc value I = 10A. Inductor copper losses are limited to 2W, and the transformer copper losses to 0.5W.

Inductor Design

The ripple current of 10% of the dc current value translates into a Δi = 2A peak-to-peak ripple current. This corresponds from $\Delta i = DV_g/Lf_s$ to an inductance of L = 37.5 μH at f_s = 100kHz, D = 0.5, and V_g = 15V. Assuming maximum flux density of B_m = 0.3T, this leads to a dc flux density B = 0.27T since B_{ac} = 0.03 from Section 4.3. Inductor design steps proceed then as outlined in Section 4.3:

1. For the given parameters: L = 37.5μH, I = 10A, B = 0.27T, P_{cu} = 2W, $\rho = 1.724 \times 10^{-8}\,\Omega m$, the core geometry K_g is calculated from (70) as $K_g = 0.0163\text{cm}^5$. From the ferrite pot core geometrical data one finds for the 2616 pot core size that $K_g = 0{,}0279\,\text{cm}^5$, close enough to the design goal. For the chosen 2616 pot core the geometrical data are

   $$W = 0.53\text{cm}^2 \quad S = 0.94\text{cm}^2 \quad t = 5.2\text{cm}$$

2. Number of turns N are calculated from (64) as

   $$N = 14.8 \approx 15$$

   Thus 15 turns are needed

3. The wire cross-section A_w is calculated from (65)

   $$A_w = \frac{kW}{N} = 0.0106\text{cm}^2$$

   In the wire tables one finds that #17 wire size has bare cross-section $A_{17} = 0.0104\text{cm}^2$ hence 15 turns of #17 wire gauge are chosen for the inductor.

4. The airgap is calculated from (67) as

   $$\ell_g = 1.8\text{mm}$$

Thus, the middle leg of one of the pot core halves would have to be gapped to this length for the core to have I = 10A dc current capability and inductance of L = 37.5μH. In summary, 15T of #17 wire on a 2616 pot core with 1.8mm gap is the design which very closely meets the stated objectives.

It actually differs very slightly since only available discrete values had to be taken for the actual design.

The actual current density in the wire may be calculated as $J = 10A/0.0106cm^2 \approx 950A/cm^2$. It is interesting to note that if this current density had been adopted as a design parameter in the area product approach the same inductor design would result.

Finally from the manufacturer's data sheets for ferrites (magnetic ferrite material) for 100kHz and $B_{ac} = 0.03T$ the core losses are $P_{Fe}/weight = 2.2mW/g$ or for the 2616 pot core $P_{Fe} = 16.3mW$, which is negligible compared to $P_{cu} = 2W$ copper losses.

Transformer Design

Following the steps for core geometry approach we get:

1. For the given parameter values

   $P = 150W,\ P_{cu} = 0.5W,\ B_m = 0.3T,\ f_s = 100kHz,$

   $\rho = 1.724 \times 10^{-8}\ \Omega m$

   the core geometry K_g is caculated from (88) as

   $$K_g = \frac{\rho}{P_{cu}} \left(\frac{P}{2B_m f_s}\right)^2 = 2.152 \times 10^{-3} cm^5$$

   From the geometrical data for a ferrite pot core one finds $K_g = 4.28 \times 10^{-3} cm^5$ for the 1811 pot core (18mm diameter, 11mm height). For the chosen 1811 core the geometrical data are:

   $W = 0.266cm^2 \quad S = 0.43cm^2 \quad t = 3.56cm$

2. Primary and secondary number of turns N (for this 1 : 1 transformer) are obtained from either (82) or (83) for $V_1 = V_2 = 15V$ as

   $$\frac{V_g}{4B_m S f_s} = 2.9$$

   hence 3 turns for both primary and secondary windings are chosen.

3. The wire cross-section A_{w1} is calculated from

   $$A_{w1} = \frac{kW}{2N_1} = 0.0133cm^2$$

   The nearest wire size is #16 with cross-section $A_{16} = 0.0131cm^2$, hence 3 turns of #16 wire gauge are chosen for both primary and secondary.

4. The magnetizing inductance is estimated by use of (78) as

   $$L_m = N_1^2 \frac{\mu S}{\ell_m} = 36\mu H$$

   where $\ell_m = 2.6cm$ for the 1811 core and the effective permeability of ferrite is assumed as $\mu = 1930\mu_o$, where $\mu_o = 4\pi \times 10^{-7} H/m$. This corresponds to a magnetizing current of about 2A or about 20% of full load current. In summary, the dc isolation transformer is built on an 1811 pot core with 3T of #16 for both primary and secondary.

The actual current density in the wire may be calculated as $J = 10A/0.0131 = 763A/cm^2$. It is interesting to note that if this current density had been adopted as a design parameter in the area product approach the same transformer design would result.

Finally from the manufacturer's data sheets for ferrites for 100kHz and $B_{ac} = 0.3T$, the per unit weight core losses are $P_{Fe}/weight = 0.8W/g$ or for 1811 pot core $P_{Fe} = 2W$. Hence the total losses are $P_{cu} + P_{Fe} = 2.5W$.

Summarizing all the losses as a percentage of input power, 1.33% is lost in each inductor and 1.6% in the transformer for a total 4.26% efficiency degradation due to the losses on magnetic components. Of course to this, the semiconductor losses discussed in the Section on converter topologies should be added (both dc and switching losses) as well as losses in capacitive storage components.

Magnetics Redesign for Off-Line Switching Power Supply

The just completed magnetics design may be easily updated for off-line switching power supply applications, in which the input voltage is $V_g = 150V$ obtained by direct line rectification. In comparison with the previous design of Fig. 44, the new design of Fig. 45 calls for a 10 : 1 isolation transformer instead of the original 1 : 1 transformer. However, instead of repeating the whole design, the new design can be obtained very easily by using a simple turns ratio argument to redesign the input induction L_1 and isolation transformer primary of T_1 transformer.

Thus, the input inductor needs to be 10^2 or 100 times larger, that is $L_1 = 3.75mH$. However, input current $I_1 = 1A$ (ten times smaller) such that energy storage $L_1 I_1^2 = LI^2$ and remains unchanged. Hence, from (70) the same core geometry is used, that is 2616 pot core with $\ell_g = 1.8mm$ gap. However, instead of 15T of #17 wire size, now 150T of #27 wire are used which occupy the same window area.

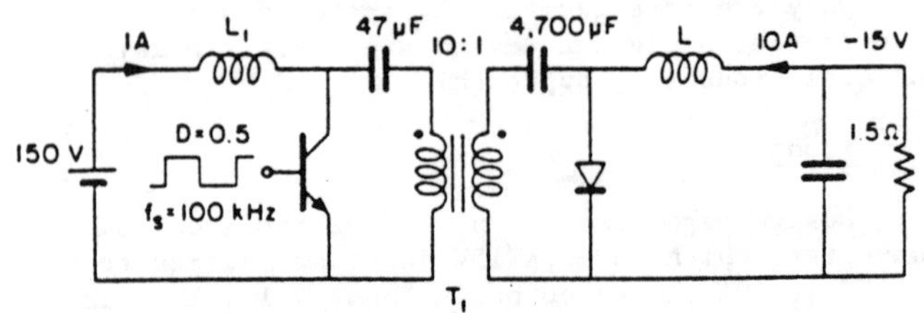

Fig. 45. Upgrade of the converter of Fig. 44 for the off-line (150 V_{dc}) switching power supply applications, involves only simple turns ratio adjustments.

Power throughput of the isolation transformer is still 150W, hence the same 1811 pot core is used. However, instead of 3T of #16 wire size, now 30T of #26 wire size are used for the primary, while the secondary remains the same (3T of #16 wire size). Copper and core loss data remains the same as in the previous design.

It should also be emphasized that in both isolation transformer designs (transformer T and T_1) an *ungapped* ferrite pot core was used, which in some isolation transformer designs would be prohibited, as shown next.

Comparison of the Isolation Transformer Design in the Flyback and Ćuk Converters

It is appropriate to conclude this section on magnetics with a comparison of the ideal properties of the isolation transformer of the Ćuk converter (Fig. 44) and the less desirable properties of the flyback converter (Fig. 16), which are concisely illustrated in Fig. 46.

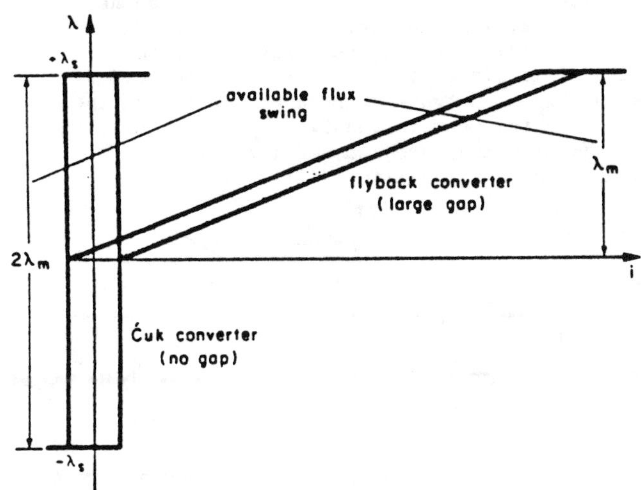

Fig. 46. Comparison of the isolation transformer salient features in the Ćuk and flyback converter.

In the Ćuk converter of Figs. 44 and 45, the isolation transformer has no dc current component in either winding (dc blocked), hence it can be built on an *ungapped* toroid of *square-loop material*, resulting in the square λ - i characteristic of Fig. 46. Furthermore, its very small magnetizing current excites the core in *both directions*, hence the full flux capability of the core is utilized (Fig. 46).

In the flyback converter, on the contrary, the core must be *gapped* very appreciably (the more the larger the dc input current). This is because the transformer is really an inductor with dc bias, as is apparent from its derivation from the nonisolated configuration (Fig. 17). Thus, the transmitted energy is stored in the magnetic field (principally in the airgap) during one interval of the switching cycle, and is released to the output during the other interval. Consequently, the magnetizing current is available in only *one direction*, constituting the *total primary* or secondary current instead of just a small fraction of it. Thus, only *half of the flux capability* of the core is used, as illustrated by the λ - i characteristic. In terms of equations, instead of $2B_m$ only B_m is used in (86) resulting in half the area product requirement and proportionally smaller core geometry.

Overall, therefore, a smaller, ungapped square-loop core can be used in the Ćuk converter than the gapped core in the flyback converter, resulting in lower core loss, lower copper loss and smaller leakage inductances. From a general viewpoint, these benefits all stem from the fact that, in the Ćuk converter, power is transmitted through the transformer from the input to the output during both intervals of the switching cycle and *continuously* (transformer is "transparent" to the power flow with no intermediate storage), whereas in the flyback converter the same power flow has to be first stored during one interval and then released during the other interval (transformer is "nontransparent" to the power flow and is used as an inductive energy storage device).

This comparison thus reveals the sizeable impact that the converter topology can have upon the magnetic content and its limitations. A more detailed and quantitative comparison with flyback and other converters (such as the buck format) can be found in Paper 22.

5. CONTROL FUNDAMENTALS

It was established very early, in Section 3 on converter topologies, that semiconductor implementation of the ideal switch allows electronic control of the power processing through variation of the switch duty cycle (Fig. 4). Electronic control of the conversion ratio, in turn, allows an easy transformation of the converter into a switched-mode regulator as shown in Fig. 47. The output is compared with a reference voltage and the error signal is amplified to provide the control signal. Since the converter transistor (buck converter shown in Fig. 47) is driven by a pulse width modulated (PWM) drive signal, the control signal v_c is transformed into a corresponding PWM signal in a modulator stage which is commonly a simple comparator . A clock ramp waveform of frequency f_s and height V_m is applied to one comparator input, and turns the power switch ON periodically at the beginning of each clock cycle. The switch is turned OFF when the clock ramp overtakes the control signal applied to the other comparator input. The overall feedback then needs to be negative to have desirable correcting features: increase of the output voltage (either due to load current change or source voltage increase) leads to decrease of the control signal and decrease of duty cycle D, which in turn lowers the output voltage to the original regulated value. However, just as in any linear feedback system, closing the loop may lead to oscillation problems, hence the need for better understanding of control properties of switching converters, which is hampered by the nonlinear switching process and lack of a convenient circuit model.

5.1 Problems In Control of Switching Regulators

The complexity of modelling a closed-loop switching regulator system is transparent in Fig. 47. Even a small-signal perturbation of the control signal at a simple frequency f generates an output which contains a multitude of frequencies: the fundamental signal at frequency f and its harmonics 2f, 3f, ect.; the switching ripple at the switching frequency f_s and its harmonics $2f_s$, $3f_s$, etc.; and finally, output at frequencies which are sums and differences, such as $f_s + f$, $f_s - f$ etc. (side-bands). Fortunately the problem is not as severe as it may seem from this. Namely, the basic requirement of low output switching ripple compared to its dc value requires that the low-pass filter corner frequency is well below the switching frequency f_s (actually below $f_s/2$), by at least a decade or two. This then highly accentuates the component of the output at the control fundamental frequency f, and de-emphasizes its harmonics.

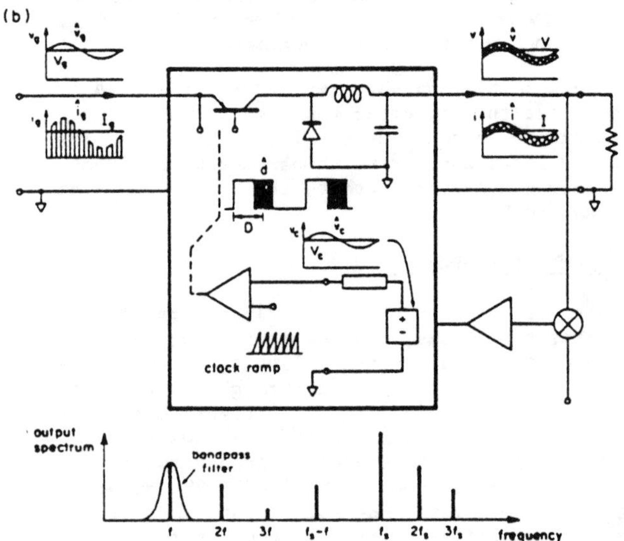

Fig. 47. Switched-mode regulator and complexity of modelling its control properties.

Thus, the linearized part of the transfer properties consists of the output signal (magnitude and phase) at the same frequency as the input control signal $\hat{v}_c$. Hence, a control transfer function for the linearized system can be defined as $\hat{v}/\hat{v}_c$.

Since the objective is to solve for the transfer functions of a dc-to-dc converter, the requirement is for a small-signal ac (dynamic). model linearized around a particular large-signal dc (steady-state) operating point, as suggested in Fig. 48, where the operating point is defined by certain values of steady state input voltage V_g and duty ratio D. In this sense, the line voltage and duty ratio are "inputs" that jointly determine the output voltage and all other internal quantities. Similarly, a model of the modulator is required from which the modulator transfer function, control input voltage to duty ratio output, can be found.

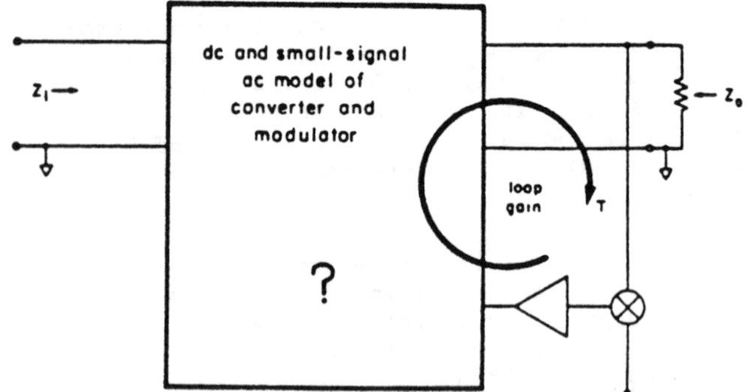

Fig. 48. Objective of modelling switching regulators: dc and ac small signal model of converter and modulator.

5.2 Control and Line Transfer Properties of Switching Converters

The simple buck converter of Fig. 49 is chosen to facilitate explanation. For each position of the switch in Fig. 49a, the linear switched networks of Fig. 49b and Fig. 49c are obtained. Therefore, for modelling purposes, the problem is well defined since it is completely described by the two linear networks. However, it is precisely this switching between the two linear circuits that made the modelling problem nonlinear (piecewise linear), and its modelling difficult.

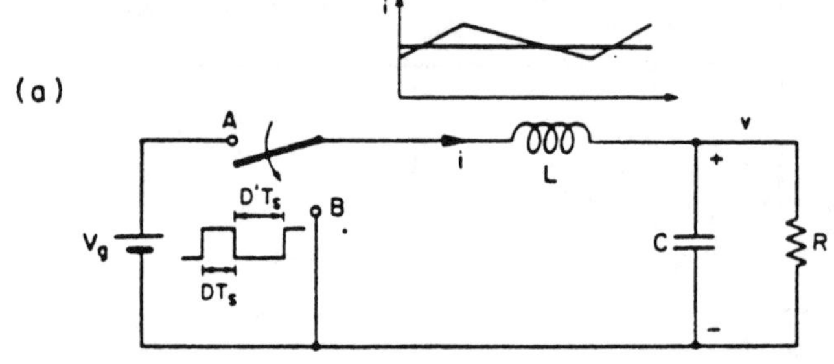

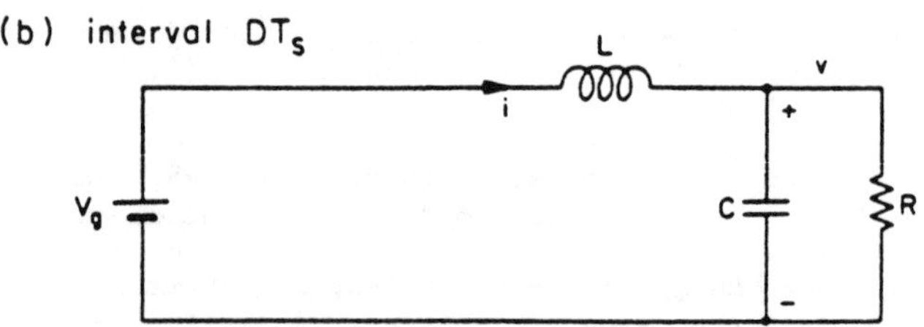

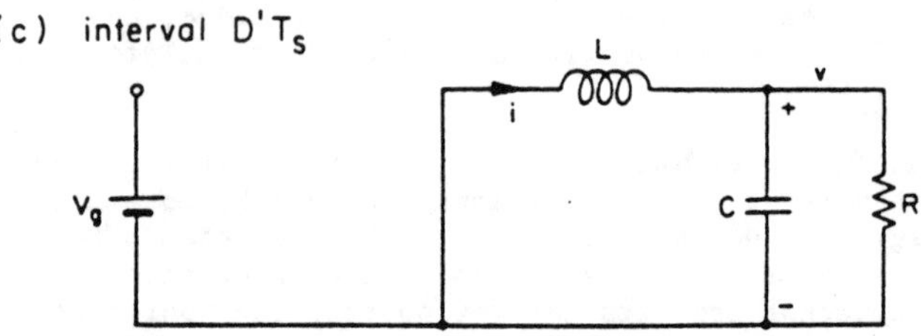

Fig. 49. A simple buck converter (a) and its two linear switched circuit models for interval DT_s (b) and interval $D'T_s$ (c).

Nevertheless it is this switching action which is responsible for dc voltage level change such that $V/V_g = D$ and $I/I_g = 1/D$. Thus, the switching action can be modelled by an ideal transformer whose "turns ratio" is 1 : D and whose frequency range (unlike a "real" transformer) extends down to dc. This is represented by a transformer symbol with a bar across it as shown in Fig. 50a.

It is also apparent that the output LC filter, besides influencing the switching ripple, also has an effect upon a slowly varying input voltage. Hence, an appropriate model for the line to output transfer function is as shown in Fig. 50b, in which the transformer symbol is augmented to indicate that the conversion ratio applies to ac as well as to dc.

Finally, in the case of duty cycle variations, and fixed line voltage, the transformer turns ratio becomes a modulated quantity 1 : $(D + \hat{d})$, as in Fig. 50c. This is translated to a fixed 1 : D turns ratio transformer and two generators controlled by the $\hat{d}$ modulation as shown in Fig. 50d, through the intermediate steps of perturbation and linearization, in which second-order terms $\hat{i}\,\hat{d}$ etc. are neglected. Note that in the model of Fig. 50d, the current source controlled by $\hat{d}$ may at first seem superfluous (ideal voltage source across it). However, it is needed to correctly predict input impedance to the converter as well as to account for any nonidealities in the input (finite source impedance of supply line, input LC filter, etc.).

From the equivalent circuits in Fig. 50, the following dynamic transfer properties can easily be derived:

Control Transfer Function:

$$\left.\frac{\hat{v}}{\hat{d}}\right|_{\hat{v}_g = 0} = V_g \frac{1}{1 + sL/R + s^2LC} \qquad (89)$$

Line Transfer Function:

$$\left.\frac{\hat{v}}{\hat{v}_g}\right|_{\hat{d} = 0} = D \frac{1}{1 + sL/R + s^2LC} \qquad (90)$$

Frequency plots (magnitude and phase) of the control transfer function (89) for some typical converter element values are shown in Fig. 51, exhibiting a two-pole characteristic.

5.3 Modulator Transfer Properties

The "naturally sampled" (simple comparator) modulator is shown in Fig. 52. Assuming that the clock ramp is linear, we have:

$$d = \frac{v_c}{V_m} \qquad (91)$$

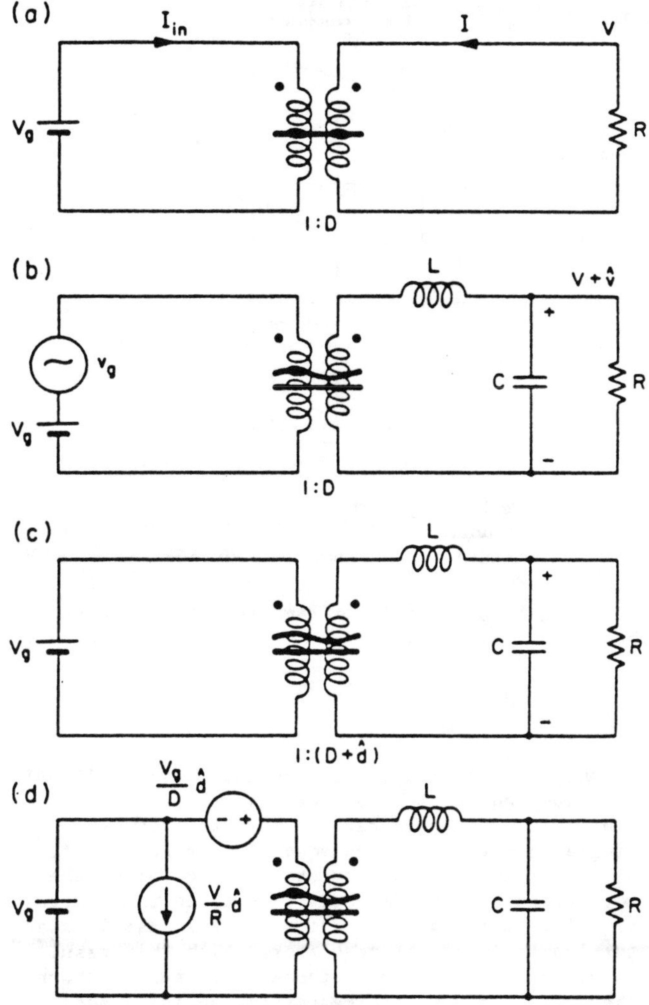

Fig. 50. Simple qualitative arguments lead to the development of the equivalent circuit models for the buck converter of Fig. 3 for: dc (a), ac small signal line variations (b) and control transfer properties (d)

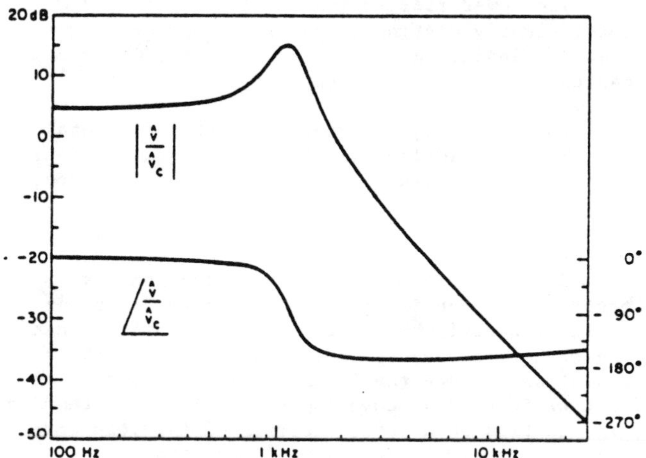

Fig. 51. Control to output transfer function of the buck converter.

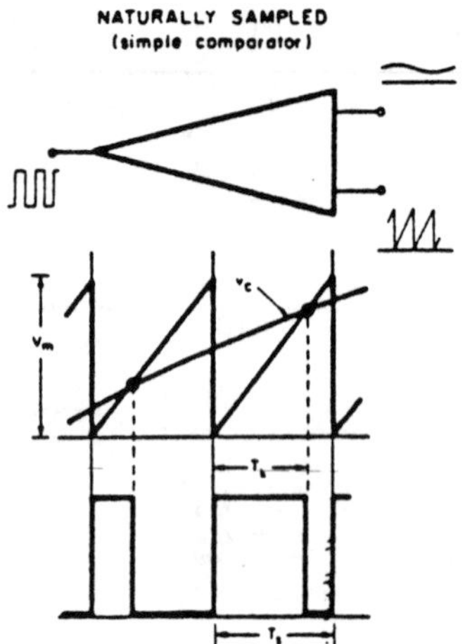

Fig. 52. *Naturally sampled (simple comparator) modulator, and determination of the duty ratio by the input signal and clock ramp.*

where V_m is the modulator ramp amplitude. Perturbation of (91) yields

$$\hat{d} = \frac{\hat{v}_c}{V_m} \tag{92}$$

As shown in Paper 15, this modulator type *does not* introduce any phase lag, nor any frequency dependent term, and hence can be characterized by a single gain factor. Consequently a simple shift of the transfer characteristic in Fig. 51 by the modulation gain in decibels results in the control transfer function $\hat{v}/\hat{v}_c$, which in this case is also the loop-gain of the regulator. With this result obtained, the standard methods of linear feedback theory can be used thereafter for analysis and design of switching regulators.

6. CONCLUSIONS

The Power Electronics field is comprised of three clearly distinguished areas: power conversion topologies, magnetics and control, whose basics are reviewed in Sections 3, 4, and 5.

In Section 3, the review of the fundamental converter topologies also led to the gradual introduction of many basic concepts, analysis methods, and terminology encountered in switched-mode power conversion.

Section 4 on magnetics was intentionally broader in scope in order to fill a void: power conversion designers often voice the opinion that the magnetics area is their weakest of the three key areas. Hence the fundamental and tutorial review of Section 4, covering the basic understanding of magnetism phenomena, analysis of magnetic circuits and their practical implementations, was justified.

Only a broad perspective of control system aspects in power conversion is offered in Section 5, since the application of control systems to switched-mode power conversion is gradually developed in greater detail throughout the book.

This review of basics sets the proper foundation for easier understanding of the advanced concepts presented in other papers [1-16, 18-30] of this two volume book. Furthermore, some of the results presented are covered in more detail in several PhD theses [31-35] of students at the California Institute of Technology since the formation of the Power Electronics Group in 1970.

Additional reading in each of the three key areas is highly recommended. Reference books on switched-mode power conversion [36-40] include many fundamental results, as well as help to broaden the viewpoint. Reference books on magnetics [41-44] give a rather balanced insight into the basic understanding of magnetic circuits, their analysis and practical implementations for inductor and transformer design.

Finally, only a few books on control systems [45-47] are suggested, since almost any book on linear control system theory which includes classical (frequency domain and Laplace transform) and modern (time domain and state-space description) control system theory would be sufficient to provide the needed background.

It is both hoped and believed that the research material presented in this book will stimulate further new advances in the switched-mode power conversion field in the years to come.

REFERENCES

Papers:

[1] R. D. Middlebrook, "Power Electronics: An Emerging Discipline," IEEE International Symposium on Circuits and Systems, 1981 Record, Chicago, IL, April 27-29, 1981.

[2] R. D. Middlebrook, "Power Electronics: Topologies, Modelling, and Measurement," IEEE International Symposium on Circuits and Systems, 1981 Record, Chicago, IL, April 27-29, 1981.

[3] G. W. Wester and R. D. Middlebrook, "Low-Frequency Characterization of Switched Dc-to-Dc Converters," IEEE Power Electronics Specialists Conference, 1972 Record, pp. 9-20, Atlantic City, NJ, May 22-23, 1972.

[4] R. D. Middlebrook, "Describing Function Properties of a Magnetic Pulse-Width Modulator," IEEE Power Electronics Specialists Conference, 1972 Record, pp. 21-35, Atlantic City, NJ, May 22-23, 1972.

[5] R. D. Middlebrook, "A Continuous Model for the Tapped-Inductor Boost Converter," IEEE Power Electronics Sepcialists Conference, 1975 Record, pp. 63-79, Culver City, CA, June 9-11, 1975.

[6] R. D. Middlebrook and Slobodan Ćuk, "A General Unified Approach to Modelling Switching-Converter Power Stages," IEEE Power Electronics Specialists Conference, 1976 Record, pp. 18-34, Cleveland, OH, June 8-10, 1976.

[7] R. D. Middlebrook, "Input Filter Considerations in Design and Application of Switching Regulators," IEEE Industry Applications Society Annual Meeting, 1976 Record, pp. 366-382, Chicago, IL, October 11-14, 1976.

[8] Slobodan Ćuk and R. D. Middlebrook, "A General Unified Approach to Modelling Switching Dc-to-Dc Converters in Discontinuous Conduction Mode," IEEE Power Electronics Specialists Conference, 1977 Record, pp. 36-57, Palo Alto, CA, June 14-16, 1977.

[9] R. D. Middlebrook and Slobodan Ćuk, "Modelling and Analysis Methods for Dc-to-Dc Switching Converters," IEEE International Semiconductor Power Converter Conference, 1977 Record, pp. 90-111, Lake Buena Vista, FL, March 28-31, 1977.

[10] R. D. Middlebrook and Slobodan Ćuk, "Design Techniques for Preventing Input-Filter Oscillations in Switched-Mode Regulators," Powercon 5, the Fifth National Solid-State Power Conversion Conference held May 4-6, 1978 in San Francisco, CA.

[11] Shi-Ping Hsu, Art Brown, Loman Rensink, and R. D. Middlebrook, "Modelling and Analysis of Switching Dc-to-Dc Converters in Constant-Frequency Current-Programmed Mode," IEEE Power Electronics Specialists Conference, 1979 Record, pp. 284-301, San Diego, CA, June 18-22, 1979.

[12] Robert Erickson, Bill Behen, R. D. Middlebrook, and Slobodan Ćuk, "Characterization and Implementation of Power MOSFETS in Switching Converters," Powercon 7, the Seventh National Solid-State Power Conversion Conference held March 24-27, 1980, in San Diego, CA.

[13] Shi-Ping Hsu, R. D. Middlebrook, and Slobodan Ćuk, "Transformer Modelling and Design for Leakage Control."

[14] W. M. Polivka, P. R. K. Chetty, and R. D. Middlebrook, "State-Space Average Modelling of Converters with Parasitics and Storage-Time Modulation," IEEE Power Electronics Specialists Conference, 1980 Record, pp. 119-143, Atlanta, GA, June 16-20, 1980.

[15] R. D. Middlebrook, "Predicting Modulator Phase Lag in PWM Converter Feedback Loops," Powercon 8, the Eighth International Solid-State Power Electronics Conference, held April 27-30, 1981, in Dallas, TX.

[16] Farhad Barzegar, Slobodan Ćuk, and R. D. Middlebrook, "Using Small Computers to Model and Measure Magnitude and Phase of Regulator Transfer Functions and Loop Gain," Powercon 8, the Eighth International Solid-State Power Electronics Conference, held April 27-30, 1981, in Dallas, TX.

[17] Slobodan Ćuk, "Basics of Switched-Mode Power Conversion: Topologies, Magnetics and Control."

[18] Slobodan Ćuk and R. D. Middlebrook, "A New Optimum Topology Switching Dc-to-Dc Converter," IEEE Power Electronics Specialists Conference, 1977 Record, pp. 160-179, Palo Alto, CA, June 14-16, 1977.

[19] Slobodan Ćuk and R. D. Middlebrook, "Coupled-Inductor and Other Extensions of a New Optimum Topology Switching Dc-to-Dc Converter," IEEE Industry Applications Society Annual Meeting, 1977 Record, pp. 1110-1126, Los Angeles, CA, October 2-6, 1977.

[20] Slobodan Ćuk, "Switching Dc-to-Dc Converter with Zero Input or Output Current Ripple," IEEE Industry Applications Society Annual Meeting, 1978 Record, pp. 1131-1146, Toronto, ONT, October 1-5, 1978.

[21] Slobodan Ćuk, "Discontinuous Inductor Current Mode in the Optimum Topology Switching Converter," IEEE Power Electronics Specialists Conference, 1978 Record, pp. 105-123, Syracuse, NY, June 13-15, 1978.

[22] R. D. Middlebrook and Slobodan Ćuk, "Isolation and Multiple Output Extensions of a New Optimum Topology Switching Dc-to-Dc Converter," IEEE Power Electronics Specialists Conference, 1978 Record, pp. 256-264, Syracuse, NY, June 13-15, 1978.

[23] R. D. Middlebrook, Slobodan Ćuk, and Bill Behen, "A New Battery Charger/Discharger Converter," IEEE Power Electronics Specialists Conference, 1978 Record, pp. 251-255, Syracuse, NY, June 13-15, 1978.

[24] Slobodan Ćuk and Robert Erickson, "A Conceptually New High-Frequency Switched-Mode Amplifier Technique Eliminates Current Ripple," Powercon 5, the Fifth National Solid-State Power Conversion Conference held May 4-6, 1978, in San Francisco, CA.

[25] R. D. Middlebrook, "Modelling and Design of the Ćuk Converter," Powercon 6, the Sixth National Solid-State Power Conversion Conference held May 2-4, 1979, in Miami Beach, FL.

[26] Loman Rensink, Art Brown, Shi-Ping Hsu, and Slobodan Ćuk, "Design of a Kilowatt Off-Line Switcher Using a Ćuk Converter," Powercon 6, the Sixth National Solid-State Power Conversion Conference held May 2-4, 1979, in Miami Beach, FL.

[27] Slobodan Ćuk, " General Topological Properties of Switching Structures," IEEE Power Electronics Specialists Conference, 1979 Record, pp. 109-130, San Diego, CA, June 18-22, 1979.

[28] Slobodan Ćuk, "A New Zero-Ripple Switching Dc-to-Dc Converter," IEEE Power Electronics Specialists Conference, 1980 Record, pp. 12-32, Atlanta, GA, June 16-20, 1980.

[29] Slobodan Ćuk and R. D. Middlebrook, "Advances in Switched-Mode Power Conversion, Part 1," Robotics Age, vol. 1, no. 2, pp. 6-19, Winter 1979.

[30] Slobodan Ćuk and R. D. Middlebrook, "Advances in Switched-Mode Power Conversion, Part 2," Robotics Age, vo. 2, no. 2, pp. 28-41, Summer 1980.

PhD Theses:

[31] Gene W. Wester, "Low-Frequency Characterization of Switched Dc-to-Dc Converters," California Institute of Technology, May 1972.

[32] Dennis J. Packard, "Discrete Modeling and Analysis of Switching Regulators," California Institute of Technology, May 1976; also, Report No. M76-43, Hughes Aircraft Co., Aerospace Group, Culver City, California.

[33] Slobodan Ćuk, "Modelling, Analysis and Design of Switching Converters," vol. I and vol. II, California Institute of Technology, November 1976; also NASA Contractor Report CR-135174.

[34] Shi-Ping Hsu, "Problems in Analysis and Design of Switching Regulators," California Institute of Technology, September 1979.

[35] Loman Rensink, "Switching Regulator Configurations and Circuit Realizations," California Institute of Technology, December 1979.

Books on Power Electronics:

[36] B. D. Bedford and R. G. Hoft, Principles of Inverter Circuits, Wiley; 1964.

[37] E. R. Hnatek, Design of Solid-State Power Supplies, Van Nostrand Reinhold; 1971.

[38] J. R. Nowicki, Power Supplies for Electronic Equipment, Leonard Hill, London; 1971.

[39] S. B. Dewan and A. Straughen, Power Semiconductor Circuits, Wiley-Interscience; 1975.

[40] Abraham I. Pressman, Switching and Linear Power Supply, Power Converter Design, vol. I and vol. II, Hayden; 1977.

Books on Magnetics:

[41] MIT Staff, Magnetic Circuits and Transformers, Massachusetts Institute of Technology, 15th printing, 1965.

[42] W. T. Hunt, Jr., and Robert Stein, Static Electromagnetic Devices, Allyn and Bacon; 1964.

[43] Colonel W. T. McLyman, Transformer and Inductor Design Handbook, Marcel Dekker; 1978.

[44] J. K. Watson, Applications of Magnetism, Wiley; 1980.

Books on Control Systems and Electric Circuits:

[45] J. L. Melsa and D. G. Schultz, Linear Control Systems, McGraw Hill; 1969.

[46] C. Desoer and E. Kuh, Basic Circuit Theory, McGraw Hill; 1969.

[47] J. J. D'Azzo and C. H. Houpis, Control Theory, McGraw Hill; 1975.

Paper 5.2

A GENERAL UNIFIED APPROACH TO MODELLING SWITCHING-CONVERTER POWER STAGES

R. D. Middlebrook and Slobodan Cuk

California Institute of Technology
Pasadena, California

ABSTRACT

A method for modelling switching-converter power stages is developed, whose starting point is the unified state-space representation of the switched networks and whose end result is either a complete state-space description or its equivalent small-signal low-frequency linear circuit model.

A new canonical circuit model is proposed, whose fixed topology contains all the essential input-output and control properties of any dc-to-dc switching converter, regardless of its detailed configuration, and by which different converters can be characterized in the form of a table conveniently stored in a computer data bank to provide a useful tool for computer aided design and optimization. The new canonical circuit model predicts that, in general, switching action introduces both zeros and poles into the duty ratio to output transfer function in addition to those from the effective filter network.

1. INTRODUCTION

1.1 Brief Review of Existing Modelling Techniques

In modelling of switching converters in general, and power stages in particular, two main approaches - one based on state-space modelling and the other using an averaging technique - have been developed extensively, but there has been little correlation between them. The first approach remains strictly in the domain of equation manipulations, and hence relies heavily on numerical methods and computerized implementations. Its primary advantage is in the unified description of all power stages regardless of the type (buck, boost, buck-boost or any other variation) through utilization of the exact state-space equations of the two switched models. On the other hand, the approach using an averaging technique is based on equivalent circuit manipulations, resulting in a single equivalent linear circuit model of the power stage. This has the distinct advantage of providing the circuit designer with physical insight into the behaviour of the original switched circuit, and of allowing the powerful tools of linear circuit analysis and synthesis to be used to the fullest extent in design of regulators incorporating switching converters.

1.2 Proposed New State-Space Averaging Approach

The method proposed in this paper bridges the gap earlier considered to exist between the state-space technique and the averaging technique of modelling power stages by introduction of state-space averaged modelling. At the same time it offers the advantages of both existing methods - the general unified treatment of the state-space approach, as well as an equivalent linear circuit model as its final result. Furthermore, it makes certain generalizations possible, which otherwise could not be achieved.

The proposed state-space averaging method, outlined in the Flowchart of Fig. 1, allows a unified treatment of a large variety of power stages currently used, since the averaging step in the state-space domain is very simple and clearly defined (compare blocks 1a and 2a). It merely consists of averaging the two exact state-space descriptions of the switched models over a single cycle T, where $f_s = 1/T$ is the switching frequency (block 2a). Hence there is no need for special "know-how" in massaging the two switched circuit models into topologically equivalent forms in order to apply circuit-oriented procedure directly, as required in [1] (block 1c). Nevertheless, through a hybrid modelling technique (block 2c), the circuit structure of the averaged circuit model (block 2b) can be readily recognized from the averaged state-space model (block 2a). Hence all the benefits of the previous averaging technique are retained. Even though this outlined process might be preferred, one can proceed from blocks 2a and 2b in two parallel but completely equivalent directions: one following path a strictly in terms of state-space equations, and the other along path b in terms of circuit models. In either case, a perturbation and linearization

This work was supported by Subcontract No. A72042-RHBE from TRW Systems Group, under NASA Prime Contract NAS3-19690 "Modeling and Analysis of Power Processing Systems."

Reprinted from *IEEE Power Electron. Specialists Conf. (PESC) Rec.*, pp. 18–34, 1976.

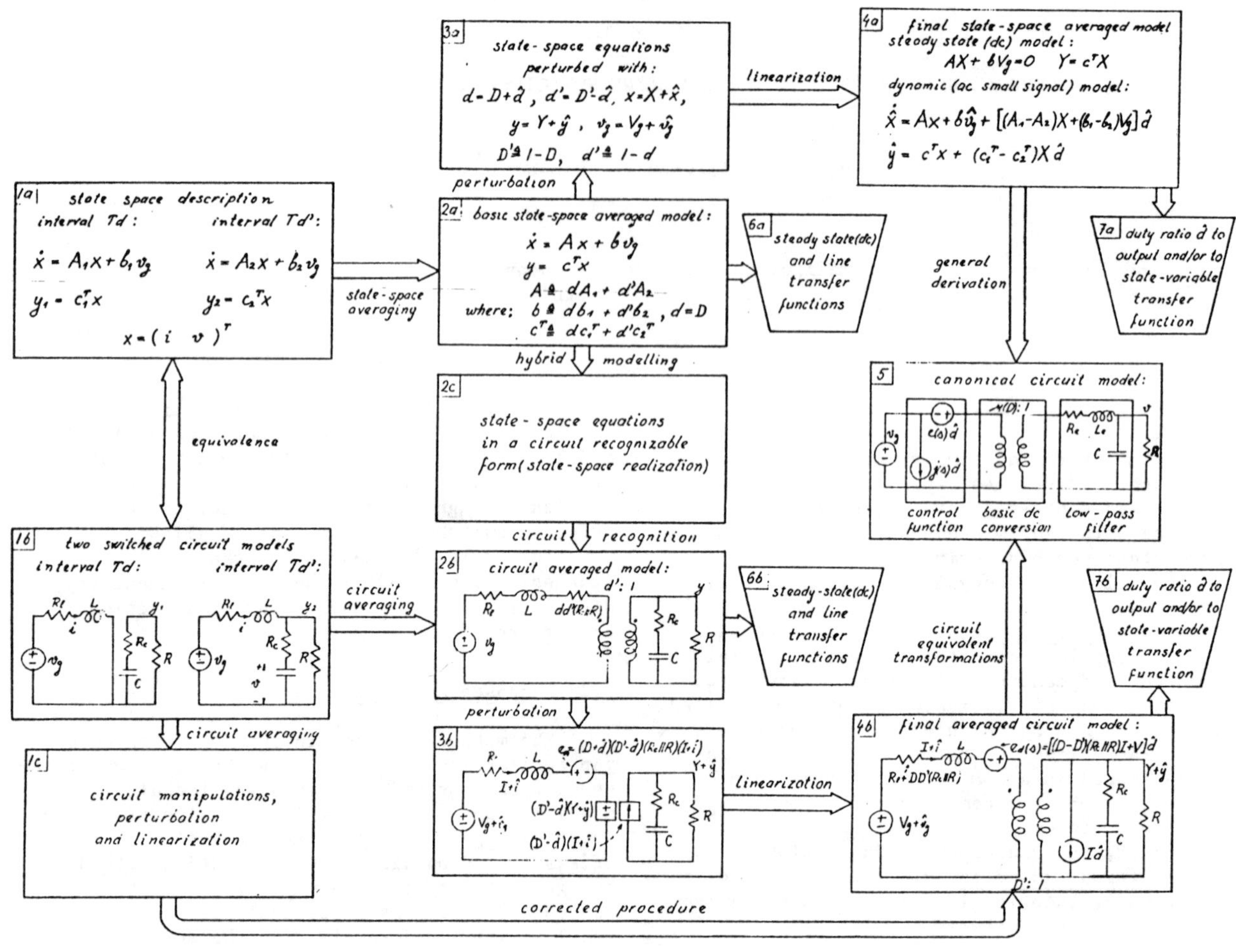

Fig. 1. Flowchart of averaged modelling approaches

process required to include the duty ratio modulation effect proceeds in a very straightforward and formal manner, thus emphasizing the corner-stone character of blocks 2a and 2b. At this stage (block 2a or 2b) the steady-state (dc) and line to output transfer functions are already available, as indicated by blocks 6a and 6b respectively, while the duty ratio to output transfer function is available at the final-stage model (4a or 4b) as indicated by blocks 7a and 7b. The two final stage models (4a and 4b) then give the complete description of the switching converter by inclusion of both independent controls, the line voltage variation and the duty ratio modulation.

Even though the circuit transformation path b might be preferred from the practical design standpoint, the state-space averaging path a is invaluable in reaching some general conclusions about the small-signal low-frequency models of any dc-to-dc switching converter (even those yet to be invented). Whereas, for path b, one has to be presented with the particular circuit in order to proceed with modelling, for path a the final state-space averaged equations (block 4a) give the complete model description through general matrices A_1, A_2 and vectors b_1, b_2, c_1^T, and c_2^T of the two starting switched models (block 1a). This is also why along path b in the Flowchart a particular example of a boost power stage with parasitic effects was chosen, while along path a general equations have been retained. Specifically, for the boost power stage $b_1 = b_2 = b$. This example will be later pursued in detail along both paths.

In addition the state-space averaging approach offers a clear insight into the quantitative nature of the basic averaging approximation, which becomes better the further the effective low-pass filter corner frequency f_c is below the switching frequency f_s, that is, $f_c/f_s \ll 1$. This is, however, shown to be equivalent to the requirement for small output voltage ripple, and hence does not pose any serious restriction or limitation on modelling of practical dc-to-dc converters.

Finally, the state-space averaging approach serves as a basis for derivation of a useful general circuit model that describes the input-output and control properties of any dc-to-dc converter.

1.3 New Canonical Circuit Model

The culmination of any of these derivations along either path a or path b in the Flowchart of Fig. 1 is an equivalent circuit (block 5), valid for small-signal low-frequency variations superimposed upon a dc operating point, that represents the two transfer functions of interest for a switching converter. These are the line voltage to output and duty ratio to output transfer functions.

The equivalent circuit is a canonical model that contains the essential properties of any dc-to-dc switching converter, regardless of the detailed configuration. As seen in block 5 for the general case, the model includes an ideal transformer that describes the basic dc-to-dc transformation ratio from line to output; a low-pass filter whose element values depend upon the dc duty ratio; and a voltage and a current generator proportional to the duty ratio modulation input.

The canonical model in block 5 of the Flowchart can be obtained following either path a or path b, namely from block 4a or 4b, as will be shown later. However, following the general description of the final averaged model in block 4a, certain generalizations about the canonical model are made possible, which are otherwise not achievable. Namely, even though for all currently known switching dc-to-dc converters (such as the buck, boost, buck-boost, Venable [3], Weinberg [4] and a number of others) the frequency dependence appears only in the duty-ratio dependent voltage generator but not in the current generator, and then only as a first-order (single-zero) polynomial in complex frequency s; however, neither circumstance will necessarily occur in some converter yet to be conceived. In general, switching action introduces both zeros and poles into the duty ratio to output transfer function, in addition to the zeros and poles of the effective filter network which essentially constitute the line voltage to output transfer function. Moreover, in general, both duty-ratio dependent generators, voltage and current, are frequency dependent (additional zeros and poles). That in the particular cases of the boost or buck-boost converters this dependence reduces to a first order polynomial results from the fact that the order of the system which is involved in the switching action is only two. Hence from the general result, the order of the polynomial is at most one, though it could reduce to a pure constant, as in the buck or the Venable converter [3].

The significance of the new circuit model is that any switching dc-to-dc converter can be reduced to this canonical fixed topology form, at least as far as its input-output and control properties are concerned, hence it is valuable for comparison of various performance characteristics of different dc-to-dc converters. For example, the effective filter networks could be compared as to their effectiveness throughout the range of dc duty cycle D (in general, the effective filter elements depend on duty ratio D), and the configuration chosen which optimizes the size and weight. Also, comparison of the frequency dependence of the two duty-ratio dependent generators provides insight into the question of stability once a regulator feedback loop is closed.

1.4 Extension to Complete Regulator Treatment

Finally, all the results obtained in modelling the converter or, more accurately, the network which effectively takes part in switching action, can easily be incorporated into more complicated systems containing dc-to-dc converters. For example, by modelling the modulator stage along the same lines, one can obtain a linear circuit model of a closed-loop switching regulator. Standard linear feedback theory can then be used for both analysis and synthesis, stability considerations, and proper design of feedback compensating networks for multiple loop as well as single-loop regulator configurations.

2. STATE-SPACE AVERAGING

In this section the state-space averaging method is developed first in general for any dc-to-dc switching converter, and then demonstrated in detail for the particular case of the boost power stage in which parasitic effects (esr of the capacitor and series resistance of the inductor) are included. General equations for both steady-state (dc) and dynamic performance (ac) are obtained, from which important transfer functions are derived and also applied to the special case of the boost power stage.

2.1 Basic State-Space Averaged Model

The basic dc-to-dc level conversion function of switching converters is achieved by repetitive switching between two linear networks consisting of ideally lossless storage elements, inductances and capacitances. In practice, this function may be obtained by use of transistors and diodes which operate as synchronous switches. On the assumption that the circuit operates in the so-called "continuous conduction" mode in which the instantaneous inductor current does not fall to zero at any point in the cycle, there are only two different "states" of the circuit. Each state, however, can be represented by a linear circuit model (as shown in block 1b of Fig. 1) or by a corresponding set of state-space equations (block 1a). Even though any set of linearly independent variables can be chosen as the state variables, it is customary and convenient in electrical networks to adopt the inductor currents and capacitor voltages. The total number of storage elements thus determines the order of the system. Let us denote such a choice of a vector of state-variables by x.

It then follows that any switching dc-to-dc converter operating in the continuous conduction mode can be described by the state-space equations for the two switched models:

(i) interval Td: (ii) interval Td':

$$\dot{x} = A_1x + b_1v_g \qquad \dot{x} = A_2x + b_2v_g$$
$$y_1 = c_1^Tx \qquad y_2 = c_2^Tx \tag{1}$$

where Td denotes the interval when the switch is in the on state and $T(1-d) \equiv Td'$ is the interval for which it is in the off state, as shown in Fig. 2. The static equations $y_1 = c_1^Tx$ and $y_2 = c_2^Tx$ are necessary in order to account for the case when the output quantity does not

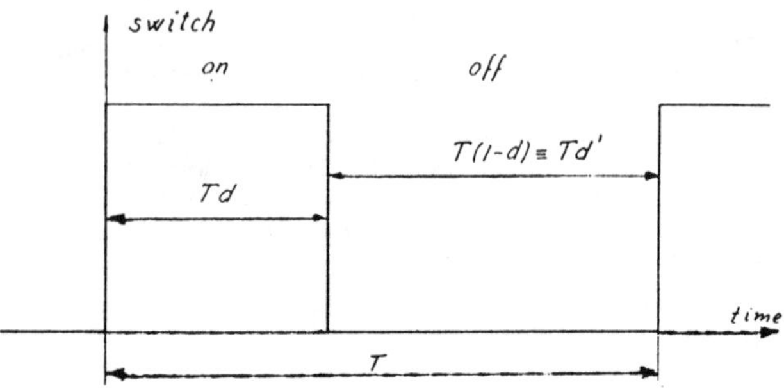

Fig. 2. Definition of the two switched intervals Td and Td'.

coincide with any of the state variables, but is rather a certain linear combination of the state variables.

Our objective now is to replace the state-space description of the two linear circuits emanating from the two successive phases of the switching cycle T by a single state-space description which represents approximately the behaviour of the circuit across the whole period T. We therefore propose the following simple averaging step: take the average of both dynamic and static equations for the two switched intervals (1), by summing the equations for interval Td multiplied by d and the equations for interval Td' multiplied by d'. The following linear continuous system results:

$$\dot{x} = d(A_1x+b_1v_g) + d'(A_2x+b_2v_g)$$
$$y = dy_1 + d'y_2 = (dc_1^T+d'c_2^T)x \tag{2}$$

After rearranging (2) into the standard linear continuous system state-space description, we obtain the basic averaged state-space description (over a single period T):

$$\dot{x} = (dA_1+d'A_2)x + (db_1+d'b_2)v_g$$
$$y = (dc_1^T+d'c_2^T)x \tag{3}$$

This model is the basic averaged model which is the starting model for all other derivations (both state-space and circuit oriented).

Note that in the above equations the duty ratio d is considered constant; it is not a time dependent variable (yet), and particularly not a switched discontinuous variable which changes between 0 and 1 as in [1] and [2], but is merely a fixed number for each cycle. This is evident from the model derivation in Appendix A. In particular, when $d = 1$ (switch constantly on) the averaged model (3) reduces to switched model (ii), and when $d = 0$ (switch off) it reduces to switched model (iii).

In essence, comparison between (3) and (1) shows that the system matrix of the averaged model is obtained by taking the average of two switched model matrices A_1 and A_2, its control is the average of two control vectors b_1 and b_2, and its output is the average of two outputs y_1 and y_2 over a period T.

The justification and the nature of the approximation in substitution for the two switched models of (1) by averaged model (3) is indicated in Appendix A and given in more detail in [6]. The basic approximation made, however, is that of approximation of the fundamental matrix $e^{At} = I + At + \cdots$ by its first-order linear term. This is, in turn, shown in Appendix B to be the same approximation necessary to obtain the dc condition independent of the storage element values (L,C) and dependent on the dc duty ratio only. It also coincides with the requirement for low output voltage ripple, which is shown in Appendix C to be equivalent to $f_c/f_s \ll 1$, namely the effective filter corner frequency much lower than the switching frequency.

The model represented by (3) is an averaged model over a single period T. If we now assume that the duty ratio d is constant from cycle to cycle, namely, $d = D$ (steady state dc duty ratio), we get:

$$\dot{x} = Ax + bv_g$$
$$y = c^Tx \tag{4}$$

where

$$A = DA_1 + D'A_2$$
$$b = Db_1 + D'b_2 \tag{5}$$
$$c^T = Dc_1^T + D'c_2^T$$

Since (4) is a linear system, superposition holds and it can be perturbed by introduction of line voltage variations $\hat{v}_g$ as $v_g = V_g + \hat{v}_g$, where V_g is the dc line input voltage, causing a corresponding perturbation in the state vector $x = X + \hat{x}$, where again X is the dc value of the state vector and $\hat{x}$ the superimposed ac perturbation. Similarly, $y = Y + \hat{y}$, and

$$\dot{\hat{x}} = AX + bV_g + A\hat{x} + b\hat{v}_g$$
$$Y + \hat{y} = c^TX + c^T\hat{x} \tag{6}$$

Separation of the steady-state (dc) part from the dynamic (ac) part then results in the steady state (dc) model

$$AX + bV_g = 0; \; Y = c^T X \Rightarrow Y = -c^T A^{-1} b V_g \tag{7}$$

and the dynamic (ac) model

$$\begin{aligned} \dot{\hat{x}} &= A\hat{x} + b\hat{v}_g \\ \hat{y} &= c^T \hat{x} \end{aligned} \tag{8}$$

It is interesting to note that in (7) the steady state (dc) vector X will in general only depend on the dc duty ratio D and resistances in the original model, but not on the storage element values (L's and C's). This is so because X is the solution of the linear system of equations

$$AX + bV_g = 0 \tag{9}$$

in which L's and C's are proportionality constants. This is in complete agreement with the first-order approximation of the exact dc conditions shown in Appendix B, which coincides with expression (7).

From the dynamic (ac) model, the line voltage to state-vector transfer functions can be easily derived as:

$$\begin{aligned} \frac{\hat{x}(s)}{\hat{v}_g(s)} &= (sI-A)^{-1} b \\ \frac{\hat{y}(s)}{\hat{v}_g(s)} &= c^T (sI-A)^{-1} b \end{aligned} \tag{10}$$

Hence at this stage both steady-state (dc) and line transfer functions are available, as shown by block 6a in the Flowchart of Fig. 1. We now undertake to include the duty ratio modulation effect into the basic averaged model (3).

2.2 Perturbation

Suppose now that the duty ratio changes from cycle to cycle, that is, $d(t) = D + \hat{d}$ where D is the steady-state (dc) duty ratio as before and $\hat{d}$ is a superimposed (ac) variation. With the corresponding perturbation definition $x = X + \hat{x}$, $y = Y + \hat{y}$ and $v_g = V_g + \hat{v}_g$ the basic model (3) becomes:

$$\dot{\hat{x}} = \underbrace{AX+bV_g}_{\text{dc term}} + \underbrace{A\hat{x}+b\hat{v}_g}_{\text{line variation}} + \underbrace{[(A_1-A_2)X + (b_1-b_2)V_g]\hat{d}}_{\text{duty ratio variation}} + \underbrace{[(A_1-A_2)\hat{x} + (b_1-b_2)\hat{v}_g]\hat{d}}_{\text{nonlinear second-order term}} \tag{11}$$

$$Y + \hat{y} = \underbrace{c^T X}_{\text{dc term}} + \underbrace{c^T \hat{x}}_{\text{ac term}} + \underbrace{(c_1^T - c_2^T) X\hat{d}}_{\text{ac term}} + \underbrace{(c_1^T - c_2^T)\hat{x}\hat{d}}_{\text{nonlinear term}}$$

The perturbed state-space description is nonlinear owing to the presence of the product of the two time dependent quantities $\hat{x}$ and $\hat{d}$.

2.3 Linearization and Final State-Space Averaged Model

Let us now make the small-signal approximation, namely that departures from the steady state values are negligible compared to the steady state values themselves:

$$\frac{\hat{v}_g}{V_g} \ll 1, \quad \frac{\hat{d}}{D} \ll 1, \quad \frac{\hat{x}}{X} \ll 1 \tag{12}$$

Then, using approximations (12) we neglect all nonlinear terms such as the second-order terms in (11) and obtain once again a linear system, but including duty-ratio modulation $\hat{d}$. After separating steady-state (dc) and dynamic (ac) parts of this linearized system we arrive at the following results for the final state-space averaged model.

Steady-state (dc) model:

$$X = -A^{-1} b V_g; \quad Y = c^T X = -c^T A^{-1} b V_g \tag{13}$$

Dynamic (ac small-signal) model:

$$\begin{aligned} \dot{\hat{x}} &= A\hat{x} + b\hat{v}_g + [(A_1-A_2)X + (b_1-b_2)V_g]\hat{d} \\ \hat{y} &= c^T \hat{x} + (c_1^T - c_2^T) X\hat{d} \end{aligned} \tag{14}$$

In these results, A, b and c^T are given as before by (5).

Equations (13) and (14) represent the small-signal low-frequency model of any two-state switching dc-to-dc converter working in the continuous conduction mode.

It is important to note that by neglect of the nonlinear term in (11) the source of harmonics is effectively removed. Therefore, the linear description (14) is actually a linearized describing function result that is the limit of the describing function as the amplitude of the input signals $\hat{v}_g$ and/or $\hat{d}$ becomes vanishingly small. The significance of this is that the theoretical frequency response obtained from (14) for line to output and duty ratio to output transfer functions can be compared with experimental describing function measurements as explained in [1], [2], or [8] in which small-signal assumption (12) is preserved. Very good agreement up to close to half the switching frequency has been demonstrated repeatedly ([1], [2], [3], [7]).

2.4 Example: Boost Power Stage with Parasitics

We now illustrate the method for the boost power stage shown in Fig. 3.

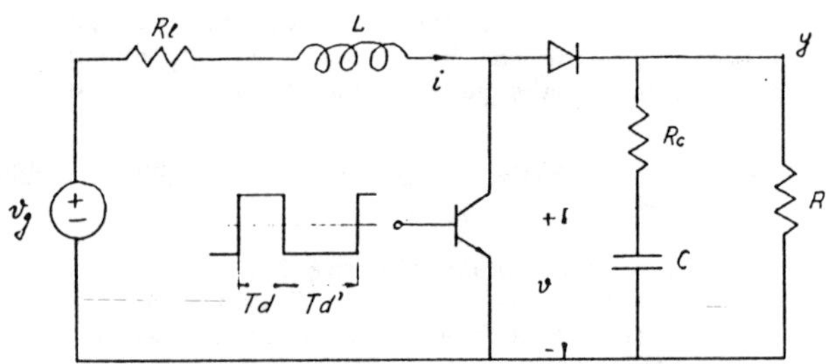

Fig. 3. Example for the state–space averaged modelling: boost power stage with parasitics included.

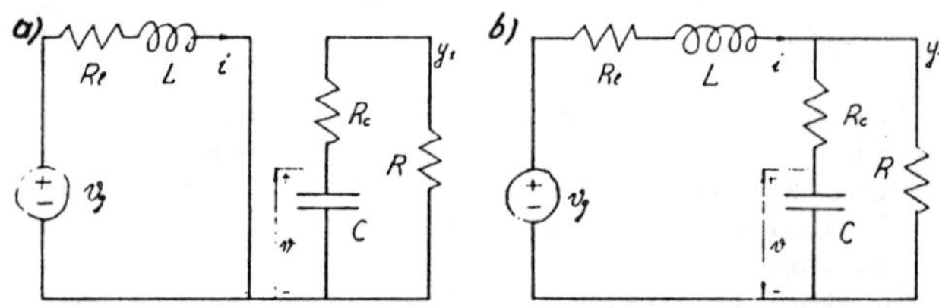

Fig. 4. Two switched circuit models of the circuit in Fig. 3 with assumption of ideal switches. All elements in the final state-space averaged model (13) and (14) are obtained: A_1, b_1, c_1^T from a) for interval Td, and A_2, b_2, c_2^T from b) for interval Td'.

With assumption of ideal switches, the two switched models are as shown in Fig. 4. For choice of state-space vector $x^T = (i \ v)$, the state space equations become:

(i) interval Td: $\dot{x} = A_1 x + b v_g$, $y_1 = c_1^T x$

(ii) interval Td': $\dot{x} = A_2 x + b v_g$, $y_2 = c_2^T x$ (15)

where

$$A_1 = \begin{bmatrix} -\frac{R_\ell}{L} & 0 \\ 0 & -\frac{1}{(R+R_c)C} \end{bmatrix} \qquad A_2 = \begin{bmatrix} -\frac{R_\ell + R_c \| R}{L} & -\frac{R}{L(R+R_c)} \\ \frac{R}{(R+R_c)C} & -\frac{1}{(R+R_c)C} \end{bmatrix}$$

$$c_1^T = \begin{bmatrix} 0 & \frac{R}{R+R_c} \end{bmatrix} \qquad c_2^T = \begin{bmatrix} R \| R_c & \frac{R}{R+R_c} \end{bmatrix} \tag{16}$$

Note that (15) is the special case of (1) in which $b_1 = b_2 = b = [1/L \ \ 0]^T$.

Using (16) and (5) in the general result (13) and (14), we obtain the following final state-space averaged model.

Steady-state (dc) model:

$$X = \begin{bmatrix} I \\ V \end{bmatrix} = \frac{V_g}{R'} \begin{bmatrix} 1 \\ (1-D)R \end{bmatrix}; \quad Y = \frac{V_g (1-D) R}{R'} \tag{17}$$

in which I is the dc inductor current, V is the dc capacitor voltage, and Y is the dc output voltage.

Dynamic (ac small signal) model:

$$\frac{d}{dt}\begin{bmatrix} \hat{i} \\ \hat{v} \end{bmatrix} = \begin{bmatrix} -\frac{R_\ell + (1-D)(R_c \| R)}{L} & -\frac{(1-D)R}{L(R+R_c)} \\ \frac{(1-D)R}{(R+R_c)C} & -\frac{1}{(R+R_c)C} \end{bmatrix} \begin{bmatrix} \hat{i} \\ \hat{v} \end{bmatrix} + \begin{bmatrix} \frac{1}{L} \\ 0 \end{bmatrix} \hat{v}_g + \begin{bmatrix} \frac{R}{L}\,\frac{(D'R+R_c)}{R+R_c} \\ -\frac{R}{(R+R_c)C} \end{bmatrix} \frac{V_g \hat{d}}{R'} \tag{18}$$

$$\hat{y} = \begin{bmatrix} (1-D)(R_c \| R) & \frac{R}{R+R_c} \end{bmatrix} \begin{bmatrix} \hat{i} \\ \hat{v} \end{bmatrix} - V_g \frac{R_c \| R}{R'} \hat{d}$$

in which $R' \triangleq (1-D)^2 R + R_\ell + D(1-D)(R_c \| R)$.

We now look more closely at the dc voltage transformation ratio in (17):

$$\frac{V}{V_g} = \frac{Y}{V_g} = \underbrace{\frac{1}{1-D}}_{\text{ideal dc gain}} \ \underbrace{\frac{(1-D)^2 R}{(1-D)^2 R + R_\ell + D(1-D)(R_c \| R)}}_{\text{correction factor}} \tag{19}$$

This shows that the ideal dc voltage gain is 1/D' when all parasitics are zero ($R_\ell = 0$, $R_c = 0$) and that in their presence it is slightly reduced by a correction factor less than 1. Also we observe that nonzero esr of the capacitance ($R_c \neq 0$) (with consequent discontinuity of the output voltage) affects the dc gain and appears effectively as a resistance $R_1 = DD'(R_c \| R)$ in series with the inductor resistance R_ℓ. This effect due to discontinuity of output voltage was not included in [2], but was correctly accounted for in [1].

From the dynamic model (18) one can find the duty ratio to output and line voltage to output transfer functions, which agree exactly with those obtained in [1] by following a different method of averaged model derivation based on the equivalence of circuit topologies of two switched networks.

The fundamental result of this section is the development of the general state-space averaged model represented by (13) and (14), which can be easily used to find the small-signal low-frequency model of any switching dc-to-dc converter. This was demonstrated for a boost power stage with parasitics resulting in the averaged model (17) and (18). It is important to emphasize that, unlike the transfer function description, the state-space description (13) and (14) gives the complete system behaviour. This is very useful in implementing two-loop and multi-loop feedback when two or more states are used in a feedback path to modulate the duty ratio $\hat{d}$. For example, both output voltage and inductor current may be returned in a feedback loop.

3. HYBRID MODELLING

In this section it will be shown that for any specific converter a useful circuit realization of the basic averaged model given by (3) can always be found. Then, in the following section, the perturbation and linearization steps will be carried out on the circuit model finally to arrive at the circuit model equivalent of (13) and (14).

The circuit realization will be demonstrated for the same boost power stage example, for which the basic state-space averaged model (3) becomes:

$$\begin{bmatrix} \frac{di}{dt} \\ \frac{dv}{dt} \end{bmatrix} = \begin{bmatrix} -\frac{R_\ell + d'(R_c \| R)}{L} & -\frac{d'R}{L(R+R_c)} \\ \frac{d'R}{(R+R_c)C} & -\frac{1}{(R+R_c)C} \end{bmatrix} \begin{bmatrix} i \\ v \end{bmatrix} + \begin{bmatrix} \frac{1}{L} \\ 0 \end{bmatrix} v_g \tag{20}$$

$$y = \begin{bmatrix} d'(R_c \| R) & \frac{R}{R+R_c} \end{bmatrix} \begin{bmatrix} i \\ v \end{bmatrix}$$

In order to "connect" the circuit, we express the capacitor voltage v in terms of the desired output quantity y as:

$$v = \frac{R+R_c}{R} y - (1-d)R_c i \quad .$$

or, in matrix form

$$\begin{bmatrix} i \\ v \end{bmatrix} = \begin{bmatrix} 1 & 0 \\ d'R_c & \frac{R+R_c}{R} \end{bmatrix} \begin{bmatrix} i \\ y \end{bmatrix} \tag{21}$$

Substitution of (21) into (20) gives

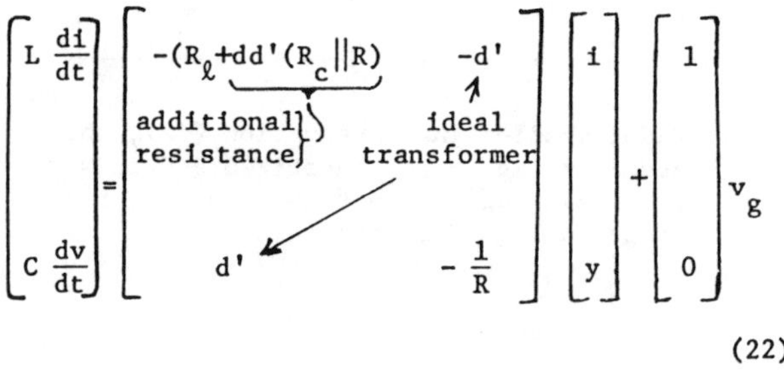

$$\begin{bmatrix} L\frac{di}{dt} \\ C\frac{dv}{dt} \end{bmatrix} = \begin{bmatrix} \underbrace{-(R_\ell + dd'(R_c \| R))}_{\text{additional resistance}} & \underbrace{-d'}_{\text{ideal transformer}} \\ d' & -\frac{1}{R} \end{bmatrix} \begin{bmatrix} i \\ y \end{bmatrix} + \begin{bmatrix} 1 \\ 0 \end{bmatrix} v_g \tag{22}$$

From (22) one can easily reconstruct the circuit representation shown in Fig. 5.

The basic model (22) is valid for the dc regime, and the two dependent generators can be modeled as an ideal d':1 transformer whose range extends down to dc, as shown in Fig. 6.

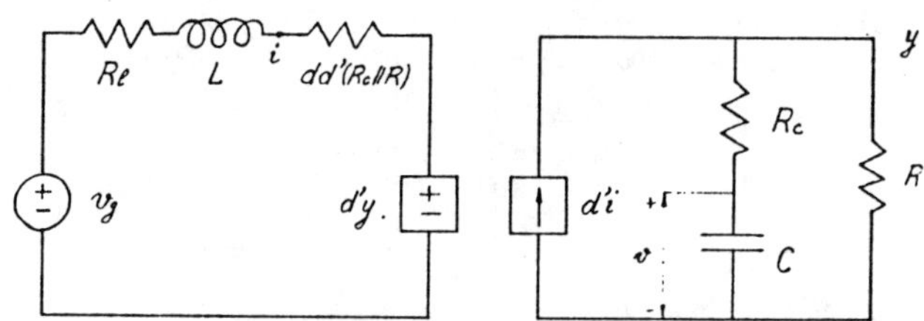

Fig. 5. Circuit realization of the basic state-space averaged model (20) through hybrid modelling.

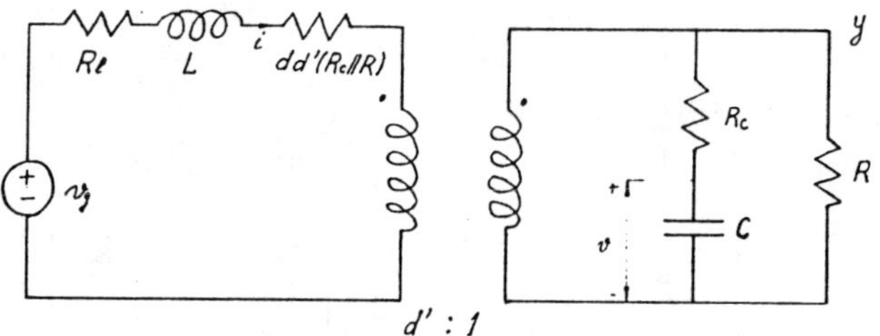

Fig. 6. Basic circuit averaged model for the boost circuit example in Fig. 3. Both dc-to-dc conversion and line variation are modelled when d(t)=D.

As before, we find that the circuit model in Fig. 6 reduces for d = 1 to switched model in Fig. 4a, and for d = 0 to switched model in Fig. 4b. In both cases the additional resistance $R_1 = dd'(R_c \| R)$ disappears, as it should.

If the duty ratio is constant so d = D, the dc regime can be found easily by considering inductance L to be short and capacitance C to be open for dc, and the transformer to have a D':1 ratio. Hence the dc voltage gain (19) can be directly seen from Fig. 6. Similarly, all line transfer functions corresponding to (10) can be easily found from Fig. 6.

It is interesting now to compare this ideal d':1 transformer with the usual ac transformer. While in the latter the turns ratio is fixed, the one employed in our model has a dynamic turns ratio d':1 which changes when the duty ratio is a function of time, d(t). It is through this ideal transformer that the actual controlling function is achieved when the feedback loop is closed. In addition the ideal transformer has a dc transformation ratio d':1, while a real transformer works for ac signals only. Nevertheless, the concept of the ideal transformer in Fig. 6 with such properties is a very useful one, since after all the switching converter has the overall property of a dc-to-dc transformer whose turns ratio can be dynamically adjusted by duty ratio modulation to achieve the controlling function. We will, however, see in the next section how this can be more explicitly modelled in terms of duty-ratio dependent generators only.

Following the procedure outlined in this section one can easily obtain the basic averaged circuit models of three common converter power stages, as shown in the summary of Fig. 7.

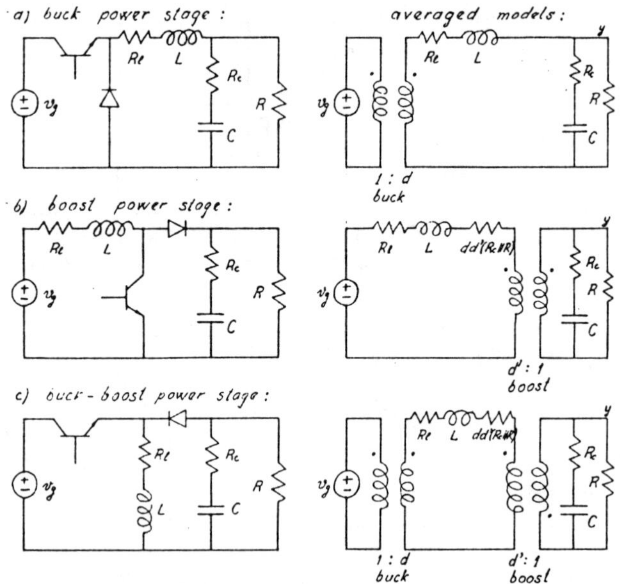

Fig. 7. Summary of basic circuit averaged models for three common power stages: buck, boost, and buck-boost.

The two switched circuit state-space models for the power stages in Fig. 7 are such that the general equations (1) reduce to the special cases $A_1 = A_2 = A$, $b_1 \neq b_2 = 0$ (zero vector) for the buck power stage, and $A_1 \neq A_2$, $b_1 = b_2 = b$ for the boost power stage, whereas for the buck-boost power stage $A_1 \neq A_2$ and $b_1 \neq b_2 = 0$ so that the general case is retained.

4. CIRCUIT AVERAGING

As indicated in the Introduction, in this section the alternative path b in the Flowchart of Fig. 1 will be followed, and equivalence with the previously developed path a firmly established. The final circuit averaged model for the same example of the boost power stage will be arrived at, which is equivalent to its corresponding state-space description given by (17) and (18).

The averaged circuit models shown in Fig. 7 could have been obtained as in [2] by directly averaging the corresponding components of the two switched models. However, even for some simple cases such as the buck-boost or tapped inductor boost [1] this presents some difficulty owing to the requirement of having two switched circuit models topologically equivalent, while there is no such requirement in the outlined procedure.

In this section we proceed with the perturbation and linearization steps applied to the circuit model, continuing with the boost power stage as an example in order to include explicitly the duty ratio modulation effect.

4.1 Perturbation

If the averaged model in Fig. 7b is perturbed according to $v_g = V_g + \hat{v}_g$, $i = I + \hat{i}$, $d = D + \hat{d}$, $d' = D' - \hat{d}$, $v = V + \hat{v}$, $y = Y + \hat{y}$ the nonlinear model in Fig. 8 results.

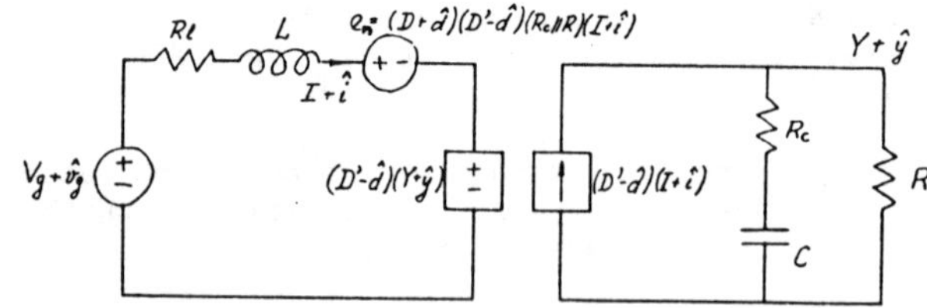

Fig. 8. Perturbation of the basic averaged circuit model in Fig. 6 includes the duty ratio modulation effect $\hat{d}$, but results in this nonlinear circuit model.

4.2 Linearization

Under the small-signal approximation (12), the following linear approximations are obtained:

$$e_n \approx DD'(R_c \| R)(I+\hat{i}) + \hat{d}(D'-D)(R_c \| R)I$$

$$(D'-\hat{d})(Y+\hat{y}) \approx D'(Y+\hat{y}) - \hat{d}Y$$

$$(D'-\hat{d})(I+\hat{i}) \approx D'(I+\hat{i}) - \hat{d}I$$

and the final averaged circuit model of Fig. 9 results. In this circuit model we have finally obtained the controlling function separated in terms of duty ratio $\hat{d}$ dependent generators e_1 and j_1, while the transformer turns ratio is dependent on the dc duty ratio D only. The circuit model obtained in Fig. 9 is equivalent to the state-space description given by (17) and (18).

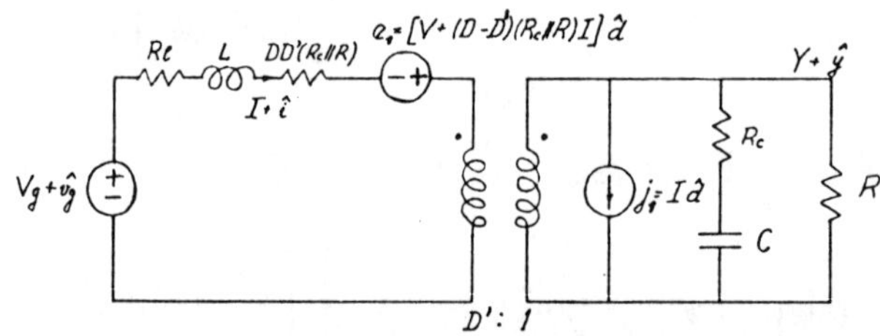

Fig. 9. Under small-signal assumption (12), the model in Fig. 8 is linearized and this final averaged circuit model of the boost stage in Fig. 3 is obtained.

5. THE CANONICAL CIRCUIT MODEL

Even though the general final state-space averaged model in (13) and (14) gives the complete description of the system behaviour, one might still wish to derive a circuit model describing its input-output and control properties as illustrated in Fig. 10.

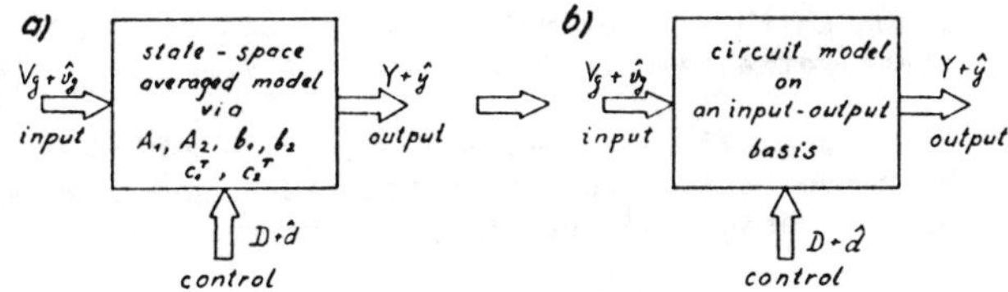

Fig. 10. Definition of the modelling objective: circuit averaged model describing input-output and control properties.

In going from the model of Fig. 10a to that of Fig. 10b some information about the internal behaviour of some of the states will certainly be lost but, on the other hand, important advantages will be gained as were briefly outlined in the Introduction, and as this section will illustrate.

We propose the following fixed topology circuit model, shown in Fig. 11, as a realization

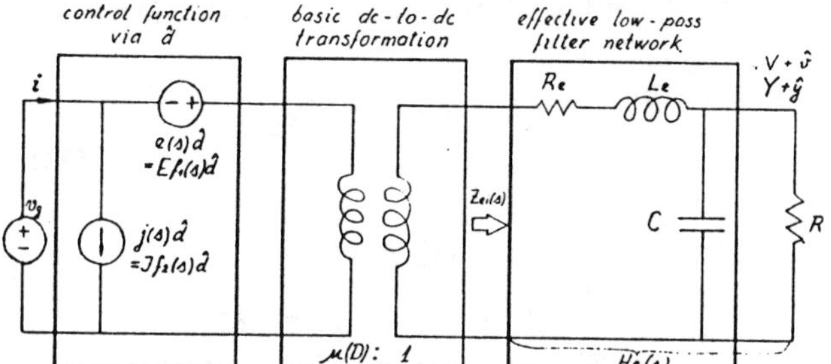

Fig. 11. Canonical circuit model realization of the "black box" in Fig. 10b, modelling the three essential functions of any dc-to-dc converter: control, basic dc conversion, and low-pass filtering.

of the "black box" in Fig. 10b. We call this model the canonical circuit model, because any switching converter input-output model, regardless of its detailed configuration, could be represented in this form. Different converters are represented simply by an appropriate set of formulas for the four elements $e(s)$, $j(s)$, μ, $H_e(s)$ in the general equivalent circuit. The polarity of the ideal μ:1 transformer is determined by whether or not the power stage is polarity inverting. Its turns ratio μ is dependent on the dc duty ratio D, and since for modelling purposes the transformer is assumed to operate down to dc, it provides the basic dc-to-dc level conversion. The single-section low-pass L_eC filter is shown in Fig. 11 only for illustration purposes, because the actual number and configuration of the L's and C's in the effective filter transfer function realization depends on the number of storage elements in the original converter.

The resistance R_e is included in the model of Fig. 11 to represent the damping properties of the effective low-pass filter. It is an "effective" resistance that accounts for various series ohmic resistances in the actual circuit (such as R_ℓ in the boost circuit example), the additional "switching" resistances due to discontinuity of the output voltage (such as $R_1 = DD'(R_c \| R)$ in the boost circuit example),

and also a "modulation" resistance that arises from a modulation of the switching transistor storage time [1].

5.1 Derivation of the Canonical Model through State-Space

From the general state-space averaged model (13) and (14), we obtain directly using the Laplace transform:

$$\hat{x}(s)=(sI-A)^{-1}\hat{v}_g(s)+(sI-A)^{-1}[(A_1-A_2)X+(b_1-b_2)V_g]\hat{d}(s)$$
$$\hat{y}(s)=c^T\hat{x}(s)+(c_1^T-c_2^T)X\hat{d}(s) \qquad (23)$$

Now, from the complete set of transfer functions we single out those which describe the converter input-output properties, namely

$$\hat{y}(s) = G_{vg}\,\hat{v}_g(s) + G_{vd}\,\hat{d}(s)$$
$$\hat{i}(s) = G_{ig}\,\hat{v}_g(s) + G_{id}\,\hat{d}(s) \qquad (24)$$

in which the G's are known explicitly in terms of the matrix and vector elements in (23).

Equations (24) are analogous to the two-port network representation of the terminal properties of the network (output voltage $\hat{y}(s)$ and input current $\hat{i}(s)$). The subscripts designate the corresponding transfer functions. For example G_{vg} is the source voltage $\hat{v}_g$ to output voltage $\hat{y}$ transfer function, G_{id} is the duty ratio $\hat{d}$ to input current $\hat{i}(s)$ transfer function, and so on.

For the proposed canonical circuit model in Fig. 11, we directly get:

$$\hat{y}(s) = (\hat{v}_g+e\hat{d})\,\frac{1}{\mu}\,H_e(s)$$
$$\hat{i}(s) = j\,\hat{d} + (e\hat{d}+\hat{v}_g)\,\frac{1}{\mu^2 Z_{ei}(s)} \qquad (25)$$

or, after rearrangement into the form of (24):

$$\hat{y}(s) = \frac{1}{\mu}\,H_e(s)\,\hat{v}_g(s) + e\,\frac{1}{\mu}\,H_e(s)\hat{d}(s)$$
$$\hat{i}(s) = \frac{1}{\mu^2 Z_{ei}(s)}\,\hat{v}_g(s) + \left[j + \frac{e}{\mu^2 Z_{ei}(s)}\right]\hat{d}(s) \qquad (26)$$

Direct comparison of (24) and (26) provides the solutions for $H_e(s)$, $e(s)$, and $j(s)$ in terms of the known transfer functions G_{vg}, G_{vd}, G_{ig} and G_{id} as:

$$e(s) = \frac{G_{vd}(s)}{G_{vg}(s)}, \qquad j(s) = G_{id}(s) - e(s)G_{ig}(s) \qquad (27)$$

$$H_e(s) = \mu G_{vg}(s)$$

Note that in (27) the parameter $1/\mu$ represents the ideal dc voltage gain when all the parasitics are zero. For the previous boost power stage example, from (19) we get $\mu = 1-D$ and the correction factor in (19) is then associated with the effective filter network $H_e(s)$. However, μ could be found from

$$\frac{Y}{V_g} = -c^T A^{-1} b = \frac{1}{\mu} \times (\text{correction factor}) \qquad (28)$$

by setting all parasitics to zero and reducing the correction factor to 1.

The physical significance of the ideal dc gain μ is that it arises as a consequence of the switching action, so it cannot be associated with the effective filter network which at dc has a gain (actually attenuation) equal to the correction factor.

The procedure for finding the four elements in the canonical model of Fig. 11 is now briefly reviewed. First, from (28) the basic dc-to-dc conversion factor μ is found as a function of dc duty ratio D. Next, from the set of all transfer functions (23) only those defined by (24) are actually calculated. Then, by use of these four transfer functions G_{vd}, G_{vg}, G_{id}, G_{ig} in (27) the frequency dependent generators $e(s)$ and $j(s)$ as well as the low-pass filter transfer function $H_e(s)$ are obtained.

The two generators could be further put into the form

$$e(s) = Ef_1(s)$$

$$j(s) = Jf_2(s)$$

where $f_1(0) = f_2(0) = 1$, such that the parameters E and J could be identified as dc gains of the frequency dependent functions $e(s)$ and $j(s)$.

Finally, a general synthesis procedure [10] for realization of L,C transfer functions terminated in a single load R could be used to obtain a low-pass ladder-network circuit realization of the effective low-pass network $H_e(s)$. Though for the second-order example of $H_e(s)$ this step is trivial and could be done by inspection, for higher-order transfer functions the orderly procedure of the synthesis [10] is almost mandatory.

5.2 Example: Ideal Buck-boost Power Stage

For the buck-boost circuit shown in Fig. 7c with $R_\ell = 0$, $R_c = 0$, the final state-space averaged model is:

$$\begin{bmatrix} \frac{d\hat{i}}{dt} \\ \frac{d\hat{v}}{dt} \end{bmatrix} = \begin{bmatrix} 0 & -\frac{D'}{L} \\ \frac{D'}{C} & -\frac{1}{RC} \end{bmatrix} \begin{bmatrix} \hat{i} \\ \hat{v} \end{bmatrix} + \begin{bmatrix} \frac{D}{L} \\ 0 \end{bmatrix} \hat{v}_g + \begin{bmatrix} \frac{V_g - V}{L} \\ \frac{-V}{D'RC} \end{bmatrix} \hat{d} \qquad (29)$$

in which the output voltage $\hat{y}$ coincides with the state-variable capacitance voltage $\hat{v}$.

From (28) and (29) one obtains $\mu = D'/D$. With use of (29) to derive transfer functions, and upon substitution into (27), there results

$$e(s) = \frac{-V}{D^2}\left(1 - s\frac{DL}{D'^2R}\right), \quad j(s) = \frac{-V}{(1-D)^2R}$$

$$H_e(s) = \frac{1}{1 + s/RC + s^2 L_e C}, \quad \mu = \frac{1-D}{D} \qquad (30)$$

in which V is the dc output voltage.

The effective filter transfer function is easily seen as a low-pass LC filter with $L_e = L/D'^2$ and with load R. The two generators in the canonical model of Fig. 11 are identified by

$$E = \frac{-V}{D^2}, \quad f_1(s) \equiv 1 - s\frac{DL}{D'^2R}$$

$$J = \frac{-V}{(1-D)^2R}, \quad f_2(s) \equiv 1 \qquad (31)$$

We now derive the same model but this time using the equivalent circuit transformations and path b in the Flowchart of Fig. 1.

After perturbation and linearization of the circuit averaged model in Fig. 7c (with $R_\ell = 0$, $R_c = 0$) the series of equivalent circuits of Fig. 12 is obtained.

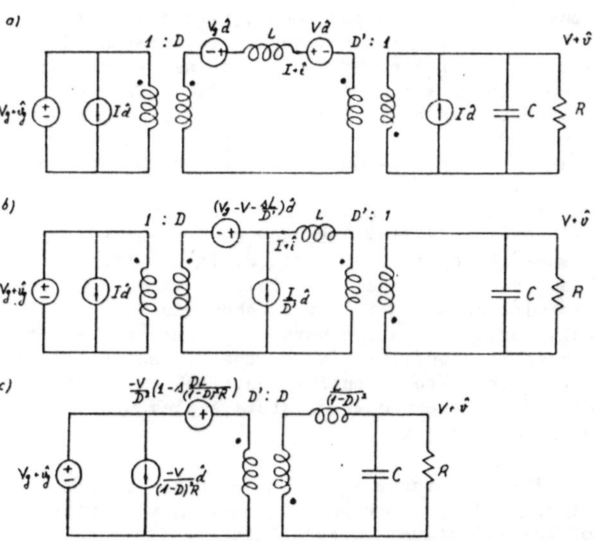

Fig. 12. Equivalent circuit transformations of the final circuit averaged model (a), leading to its canonical circuit realization (c) demonstrated on the buck-boost example of Fig. 7c (with $R_\ell = 0$, $R_c = 0$).

The objective of the transformations is to reduce the original four duty-ratio dependent generators in Fig. 12a to just two generators (voltage and current) in Fig. 12c which are at the input port of the model. As these circuit transformations unfold, one sees how the frequency dependence in the generators arises naturally, as in Fig. 12b. Also, by transfer of the two generators in Fig. 12b from the secondary to the primary of the 1:D transformer, and the inductance L to the secondary of the D':1 transformer, the cascade of two ideal transformers is reduced to the single transformer with equivalent turns ratio D':D. At the same time the effective filter network L_e, C, R is generated.

Expressions for the elements in the canonical equivalent circuit can be found in a similar way for any converter configuration. Results for the three familiar converters, the buck, boost, and buck-boost power stages are summarized in Table I.

	$\mu(D)$	E	$f_1(s)$	J	$f_2(s)$	L_e
buck	$\frac{1}{D}$	$\frac{V}{D^2}$	1	$\frac{V}{R}$	1	L
boost	$1-D$	V	$1-s\frac{L_e}{R}$	$\frac{V}{(1-D)^2R}$	1	$\frac{L}{(1-D)^2}$
buck-boost	$\frac{1-D}{D}$	$\frac{-V}{D^2}$	$1-s\frac{DL_e}{R}$	$\frac{-V}{(1-D)^2R}$	1	$\frac{L}{(1-D)^2}$

Table I Definition of the elements in the canonical circuit model of Fig. 11 for the three common power stages of Fig. 7.

It may be noted in Table I that, for the buck-boost power stage, parameters E and J have negative signs, namely $E = -V/D^2$ and $J = -V/(D'^2R)$. However, as seen from the polarity of the ideal D':D transformer in Fig. 12c this stage is an inverting one. Hence, for positive input dc voltage V_g, the output dc voltage V is negative ($V < 0$) since $V/V_g = -D/D'$. Therefore $E > 0$, $J > 0$ and consequently the polarity of the voltage and current duty-ratio dependent generators is not changed but is as shown in Fig. 12c. Moreover, this is true in general: regardless of any inversion property of the power stage, the polarity of two generators stays the same as in Fig. 11.

5.3 Significance of the Canonical Circuit Model and Related Generalizations

The canonical circuit model of Fig. 11 incorporates all three basic properties of a dc-to-dc converter: the dc-to-dc conversion function (represented by the ideal μ:1 transformer); control (via duty ratio $\hat{d}$ dependent generators); and low-pass filtering (represented by the effective low-pass filter network $H_e(s)$). Note also that the current generator $j(s)\,\hat{d}$ in the canonical circuit model, even though superfluous when the source voltage $v_g(s)$ is ideal, is necessary to reflect the influence of a nonideal source generator (with some internal impedance) or of an input filter [7] upon the behaviour of the converter. Its presence enables one easily to include the linearized circuit model of a switching converter power stage in other linear circuits, as the next section will illustrate.

Another significant feature of the canonical circuit model is that any switching dc-to-dc converter can be reduced by use of (23), (24), (27) and (28) to this fixed topology form, at least as far as its input-output and control properties are concerned. Hence the possibility arises for use of this model to compare in an easy and unique way various performance characteristics of different converters. Some examples of such comparisons are given below.

1. The filter networks can be compared with respect to their effectiveness throughout the dynamic duty cycle D range, because in general the effective filter elements depend on the steady state duty ratio D. Thus, one has the opportunity to choose the configuration and to optimize the size and weight.

2. Basic dc-to-dc conversion factors $\mu_1(D)$ and $\mu_2(D)$ can be compared as to their effective range. For some converters, traversal of the range of duty ratio D from 0 to 1 generates any conversion ratio (as in the ideal buck-boost converter), **while in others** the conversion ratio might be restricted (as in the Weinberg converter [4], for which $\frac{1}{2}<\mu<1$).

3. In the control section of the canonical model one can compare the frequency dependences of the generators e(s) and j(s) for different converters and select the configuration that best facilitates stabilization of a feedback regulator. For example, in the buck-boost converter e(s) is a polynomial, containing actually a real zero in the right half-plane, which undoubtedly causes some stability problems and need for proper compensation.

4. Finally, the canonical model affords a very convenient means to store and file information on various dc-to-dc converters in a computer memory in a form comparable to Table I. Then, thanks to the fixed topology of the canonical circuit model, a single computer program can be used to calculate and plot various quantities as functions of frequency (input and output impedance, audio susceptibility, duty ratio to output transfer response, and so on). Also, various input filters and/or additional output filter networks can easily be added if desired.

We now discuss an important issue which has been intentionally skipped so far. From (27) it is concluded that in general the duty ratio dependent generators e(s) and j(s) are rational functions of complex frequency s. Hence, in general both some new zeros and poles are introduced into the duty ratio to output transfer function owing to the switching action, in addition to the poles and zeros of the effective filter network (or line to output transfer function). However, in special cases, as in all those shown in Table I, the frequency dependence might reduce simply to polynomials, and even further it might show up only in the voltage dependent generators (as in the boost, or buck-boost) and reduce to a constant ($f_2(s) \equiv 1$) for the current generator. Nevertheless, this does not prevent us from modifying any of these circuits in a way that would exhibit the general result -- introduction of both additional zeros as well as poles.

Let us now illustrate this general result on a simple modification of the familiar boost circuit, with a resonant L_1,C_1 circuit in series with the input inductance L, as shown in Fig. 13.

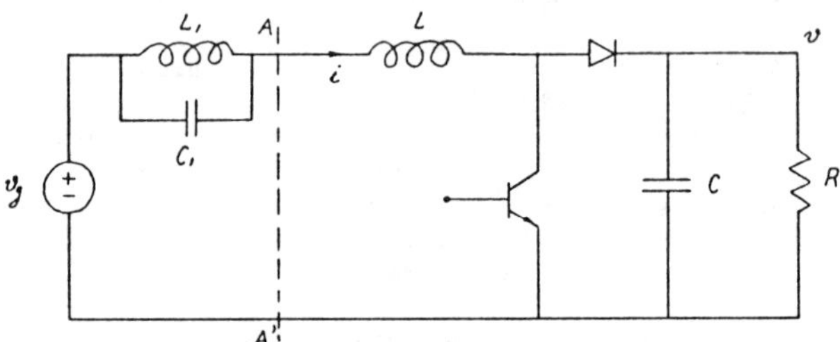

Fig. 13. Modified boost circuit as an illustration of general frequency behaviour of the generators in the canonical circuit model of Fig. 11.

By introduction of the canonical circuit model for the boost power stage (for the circuit to the right of cross section AA') and use of data from Table I, the equivalent averaged circuit model of Fig. 14a is obtained. Then, by application of the equivalent circuit transformation as outlined previously, the averaged model in the canonical circuit form is obtained in Fig. 14b. As can be seen from Fig. 14b, the voltage generator has a double pole at the resonant frequency $\omega_r = 1/\sqrt{L_1C_1}$ of the parallel L_1,C_1 network. However, the effective filter transfer function has a double zero (null in magnitude) at precisely the same location such that the two

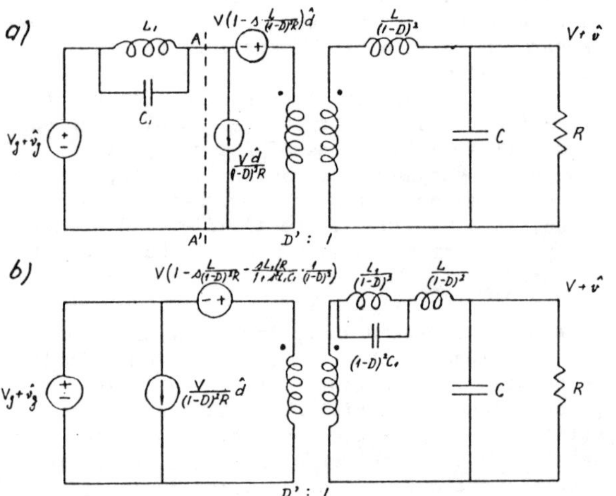

Fig. 14. Equivalent circuit transformation leading to the canonical circuit model (b) of the circuit in Fig. 13.

pairs effectively cancel. Hence, the resonant null in the magnitude response, while present in the line voltage to output transfer function, is not seen in the duty ratio-to output transfer function. Therefore, the positive effect of rejection of certain input frequencies around the resonant frequency ω_r is not accompanied by a detrimental effect on the loop gain, which <u>will not</u> contain a null in the magnitude response.

This example demonstrates yet another important aspect of modelling with use of the averaging technique. Instead of applying it directly to the whole circuit in Fig. 13, we have instead implemented it only with respect to the storage element network which effectively takes part in the switching action, namely L, C, and R. Upon substitution of the switched part of the network by the averaged circuit model, all other linear circuits of the complete model are retained as they appear in the original circuit (such as L_1,C_1 in Fig. 14a). Again, the current generator in Fig. 14a is the one which reflects the effect of the input resonant circuit.

In the next section, the same property is clearly displayed for a closed-loop regulator-converter with or without the input filter.

6. SWITCHING MODE REGULATOR MODELLING

This section demonstrates the ease with which the different converter circuit models developed in previous sections can be incorporated into more complicated systems such as a switching-mode regulator. In addition, a brief discussion of modelling of modulator stages in general is included, and a complete general switching-mode regulator circuit model is given.

A general representation of a switching-mode regulator is shown in Fig. 15. For concreteness, the switching-mode converter is represented by a buck-boost power stage, and the input and possible additional output filter are represented by a

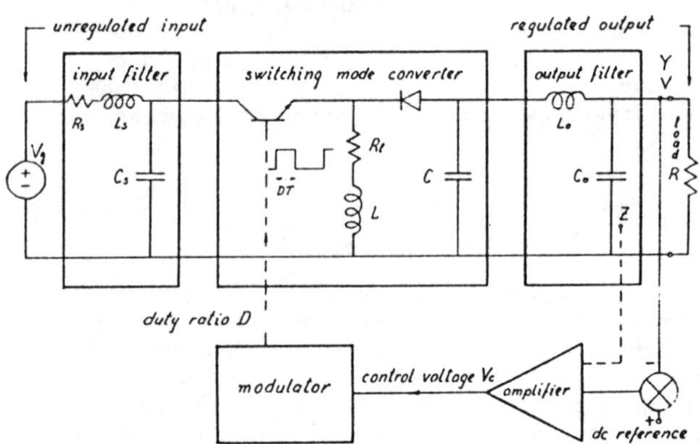

Fig. 15. General switching-mode regulator with input and output filters. The block diagram is general, and single-section LC filters and a buck-boost converter are shown as typical realizations.

single-section low-pass LC configuration, but the discussion applies to any converter and any filter configuration.

The main difficulty in analysing the switching mode regulator lies in the modelling of its nonlinear part, the switching-mode converter. However, we have succeeded in previous sections in obtaining the small-signal low-frequency circuit model of any "two-state" switching dc-to-dc converter, operating in the continuous conduction mode, in the canonical circuit form. The output filter is shown separately, to emphasize the fact that in averaged modelling of the switching-mode converter only the storage elements which are actually involved in the switching action need be taken into account, thus minimizing the effort in its modelling.

The next step in development of the regulator equivalent circuit is to obtain a model for the modulator. This is easily done by writing an expression for the essential function of the modulator, which is to convert an (analog) control voltage V_c to the switch duty ratio D. This expression can be written $D = V_c/V_m$ in which, by definition, V_m is the range of control signal required to sweep the duty ratio over its full range from 0 to 1. A small variation v_c superimposed upon V_c therefore produces a corresponding variation $\hat{d} = \hat{v}_c/V_m$ in D, which can be generalized to account for a nonuniform frequency response as

$$\hat{d} = \frac{f_m(s)}{V_m} \hat{v}_c \qquad (32)$$

in which $f_m(0) = 1$. Thus, the control voltage to duty ratio small-signal transmission characteristic of the modulator can be represented in general by the two parameters V_m and $f_m(s)$, regardless of the detailed mechanism by which the modulation is achieved. Hence, by substitution for $\hat{d}$ from (32) the two generators in the canonical circuit model of the switching converter can be expressed in terms of the ac control voltage $\hat{v}_c$, and the resulting model is then a linear ac equivalent circuit that represents the small-signal transfer properties of the nonlinear processes in the modulator and converter.

It remains simply to add the linear amplifier and the input and output filters to obtain the ac equivalent circuit of the complete closed-loop regulator as shown in Fig. 16.

The modulator transfer function has been incorporated in the generator designations, and the generator symbol has been changed from a circle to a square to emphasize the fact that, in the closed-loop regulator, the generators no longer are independent but are dependent on another signal in the same system. The connection from point Y to the error amplifier, via the reference voltage summing node, represents the basic voltage feedback necessary to establish the system as a voltage regulator. The dashed connection from point Z indicates a possible additional feedback sensing; this second feedback signal may

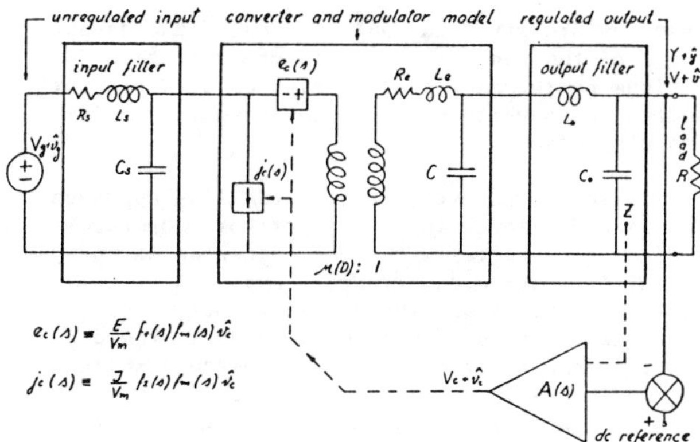

Fig. 16. General small-signal ac equivalent circuit for the switching-mode regulator of Fig. 15.

be derived, for example, from the inductor flux, inductor current, or capacitor current, as in various "two-loop" configurations that are in use [9].

Once again the current generator in Fig. 16 is responsible for the interaction between the switching-mode regulator-converter and the input filter, thus causing performance degradation and/ or stability problems when an arbitrary input filter is added. The problem of how properly to design the input filter is treated in detail in [7].

As shown in Fig. 16 we have succeeded in obtaining the linear circuit model of the complete switching mode-regulator. Hence the well-known body of linear feedback theory can be used for both analysis and design of this type of regulator.

7. CONCLUSIONS

A general method for modelling power stages of any switching dc-to-dc converter has been developed through the state-space approach. The fundamental step is in replacement of the state-space descriptions of the two switched networks by their average over the single switching period T, which results in a single continuous state-space equation description (3) designated the basic averaged state-space model. The essential approximations made are indicated in the Appendices, and are shown to be justified for any practical dc-to-dc switching converter.

The subsequent perturbation and linearization step under the small-signal assumption (12) leads to the final state-space averaged model given by (13) and (14). These equations then serve as the basis for development of the most important qualitative result of this work, the canonical circuit model of Fig. 11. Different converters are represented simply by an appropriate set of formulas ((27) and (28)) for four elements in this general equivalent circuit. Besides its unified description, of which several examples are given in Table I, one of the advantages of the canonical circuit model is that various performance characteristics of different switching converters can be compared in a quick and easy manner.

Although the state-space modelling approach has been developed in this paper for two-state switching converters, the method can be extended to multiple-state converters. Examples of three-state converters are the familiar buck, boost, and buck-boost power stages operated in the discontinuous conduction mode, and dc-to-ac switching inverters in which a specific output waveform is "assembled" from discrete segments are examples of multiple-state converters.

In contrast with the state-space modelling approach, for any particular converter an alternative path via hybrid modelling and circuit transformation could be followed, which also arrives first at the final circuit averaged model equivalent of (13) and (14) and finally, after equivalent circuit transformations, again arrives at the canonical circuit model.

Regardless of the derivation path, the canonical circuit model can easily be incorporated into an equivalent circuit model of a complete switching regulator, as illustrated in Fig. 16.

Perhaps the most important consequence of the canonical circuit model derivation via the general state-space averaged model (13), (14), (23) and (24) is its prediction through (27) of additional zeros as well as poles in the duty ratio to output transfer function. In addition frequency dependence is anticipated in the duty ratio dependent current generator of Fig. 11, even though for particular converters considered in Table I, it reduces merely to a constant. Furthermore for some switching networks which would effectively involve more than two storage elements, higher order polynomials should be expected in $f_1(s)$ and/or $f_2(s)$ of Fig. 11.

The insights that have emerged from the general state-space modelling approach suggest that there is a whole field of new switching dc-to-dc converter power stages yet to be conceived. This encourages a renewed search for innovative circuit designs in a field which is yet young, and promises to yield a significant number of inventions in the stream of its full development. This progress will naturally be fully supported by new technologies coming at an ever increasing pace. However, even though the efficiency and performance of currently existing converters will increase through better, faster transistors, more ideal capacitors (with lower esr) and so on, it will be primarily the responsibility of the circuit designer and inventor to put these components to best use in an optimal topology. Search for new circuit configurations, and how best to use present and future technologies, will be of prime importance in achieving the ultimate goal of near-ideal general switching dc-to-dc converters.

REFERENCES

[1] R. D. Middlebrook, "A Continuous Model for the Tapped-Inductor Boost Converter," IEEE Power Electronics Specialists Conference, 1975 Record, pp. 63-79 (IEEE Publication 75 CHO 965-4-AES).

[2] G. W. Wester and R. D. Middlebrook, "Low-Frequency Characterization of Switched dc-dc Converters," IEEE Trans. on Aerospace and Electronic Systems, Vol. AES-9, No. 3, May 1973, pp. 376-385.

[3] R. Haynes, T. K. Phelps, J. A. Collins, and R. D. Middlebrook, "The Venable Converter: A New Approach to Power Processing," IEEE Power Electronics Specialists Conference, NASA Lewis Research Center, Cleveland, Ohio, June 8-10, 1976.

[4] A. H. Weinberg, "A Boost Regulator with a New Energy-Transfer Principle," Proceedings of Spacecraft Power Conditioning Seminar, pp. 115-122 (ESRO Publication SP-103, Sept. 1974).

[5] H. F. Baker, "On the Integration of Linear Differential Equations," Proc. London Math. Soc., 34, 347-360, 1902; 35, 333-374, 1903; second series, 2, 293-296, 1904.

[6] R. D. Middlebrook and S. Cuk, Final Report, "Modelling and Analysis of Power Processing Systems," NASA Contract NAS3-19690.

[7] R. D. Middlebrook, "Input Filter Considerations in Design and Application of Switching Regulators," IEEE Industry Applications Society Annual Meeting, Chicago, Oct. 11-14, 1976.

[8] R. D. Middlebrook, "Describing Function Properties of a Magnetic Pulsewidth Modulator," IEEE Trans. on Aerospace and Electronic Systems, Vol. AES-9, No. 3, May, 1973, pp. 386-398.

[9] Y. Yu, J. J. Biess, A. D. Schoenfeld and V. R. Lalli, "The Application of Standardized Control and Interface Circuits to Three DC to DC Power Converters," IEEE Power Electronics Specialists Conference, 1973 Record, pp. 237-248 (IEEE Publication 73 CHO 787-2 AES).

[10] F. F. Kuo, "Network Analysis and Synthesis," John Wiley and Sons, Inc.

APPENDICES

In this sequence of Appendices several of the questions related to substitution of the two switched models (1) by the state-space description (3) are discussed.

In Appendix A it is briefly indicated for a simplified autonomous example how the correlation between the state-space averaging step and the linear approximation of the fundamental matrix is established. In Appendix B the exact dc conditions, which are generally dependent on the storage element values, are shown to reduce under the same linear approximation to those obtained from (7). In Appendix C it is demonstrated both analytically and quantitatively (numerically), for a typical set of parameter values for a boost power stage, that the linear approximation of the fundamental matrix is equivalent to $f_c << f_s$, where f_c is the effective corner frequency of the low-pass filter and f_s is the switching frequency. This inequality is in turn connected with the condition for low output voltage ripple, and hence does not impose any significant restriction on the outlined modelling procedure.

APPENDIX A

The fundamental approximation in the state-space averaging approach

Let the two linear systems be described by

(i) interval Td, $0<t<t_o$: ii) interval Td', $t_o<t<T$:

$$\dot{x} = A_1 x \qquad \dot{x} = A_2 x \tag{33}$$

The exact solutions of these state-space equations are:

$$\begin{aligned} x(t) &= e^{A_1 t} x(0), && t \in [0,t_o] \\ x(t) &= e^{A_2(t-t_o)} x(t_o), && t \in [t_o,T] \end{aligned} \tag{34}$$

The state-variable vector x(t) is continuous across the switching instant t_o, and so:

$$x(T) = e^{A_2(T-Td)} x(t_o) = e^{d'A_2T} e^{dA_1T} x(0) \tag{35}$$

Suppose that the following approximation is now introduced into (35):

$$e^{d'A_2T} e^{dA_1T} \approx e^{(dA_1+d'A_2)T} \tag{36}$$

resulting in an approximate solution

$$x(T) \approx e^{(dA_1+d'A_2)T} x(0) \tag{37}$$

However, this is the same as the solution of the following linear system equation for x(T):

$$\dot{x} = (dA_1+d'A_2)x \tag{38}$$

The last model (38) is, therefore, the averaged model obtained from the two switched models given by (33) and is valid provided approximation (36) is well satisfied. This is so if the following linear approximations of the fundamental matrices hold:

$$\begin{aligned} e^{dA_1T} &\approx I + dA_1T \\ e^{d'A_2T} &\approx I + d'A_2T \end{aligned} \tag{39}$$

In essence, (36) is the first approximation to the more general result Baker-Campbell-Hausdorff series [5]:

$$AT = (dA_1+d'A_2)T + dd'(A_1A_2-A_2A_1)T^2 + \cdots \tag{40}$$

where

$$e^{AT} = e^{d'A_2T} e^{dA_1T} \tag{41}$$

Hence, when two matrices are commutative, that is $A_1A_2 = A_2A_1$, then $A = dA_1 + d'A_2$ and (36) becomes an exact result.

APPENDIX B

Derivation of the exact dc conditions and their simplification under linear approximation of the fundamental matrices

We now derive the exact steady-state (dc) condition from the general state-space description of the two switched circuit models. Let $x = x_1$ be the state-variable vector for interval TD $(0<t<t_o)$ and $x = x_2$ that for interval TD' $(t_o<t<T)$.

i) interval TD, $(0<t<t_o)$: ii) interval TD' $(t_o<t<T)$:

$$\dot{x}_1 = A_1x + bv_g \qquad \dot{x}_2 = A_2x + bv_g \tag{42}$$

The respective solutions are:

$$\begin{aligned} x_1(t) &= e^{A_1t} x_1(0) + V_g B_1(t) b \\ x_2(t) &= e^{A_2t} x_2(t_o) + V_g B_2(t-t_o) b \end{aligned} \tag{43}$$

where

$$B_i(t) = \int_0^t e^{A_i\tau} d\tau = A_i^{-1}(e^{A_it} - I) \quad \text{for } i = 1,2 \tag{44}$$

provided inverse matrices A_1^{-1}, A_2^{-1} exist.

Solutions (43) contain two yet undetermined constants, $x_1(0)$ and $x_2(t_o)$. We therefore impose two boundary conditions:

a) the vector of state variables is continuous across the switching instant t_o, since the inductor currents and capacitor voltages cannot change instantaneously. Hence

$$x_1(t_o) = x_2(t_o) \tag{45}$$

b) from the steady state requirement, all the state variables should return after period T to their initial values. Hence:

$$x_1(0) = x_2(T) \tag{46}$$

The boundary conditions (45) and (46) are illustrated in Fig. 17, where v(0) = v(T), i(0) = i(T) and i(t) and v(t) are continuous across the switching instant t_o.

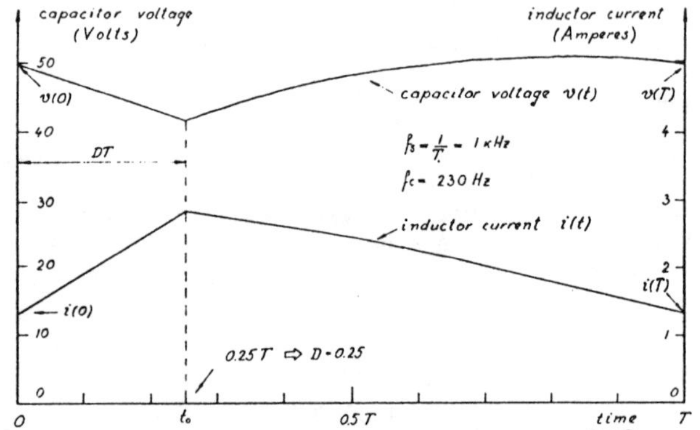

Fig. 17. Typical state-variable time dependence over a single period T in the steady-state, for the boost circuit numerical example with f_s=1kHz.

Insertion of (45) and (46) into (43) results in solution for the initial condition:

$$x_1(0) = V_g(I-e^{D'A_2T}e^{DA_1T})^{-1}(e^{D'A_2T}B_1(DT)+B_2(D'T))b \tag{47}$$

As seen from Fig. 17, the average values of inductor current and capacitor voltage could be found by integration over the period T; in general, the steady-state vector X is found from:

$$X = \frac{1}{T}\left[\int_0^{t_o} x_1(\tau)d\tau + \int_{t_o}^{T} x_2(\tau)d\tau\right] \tag{48}$$

Hence, by use of (43) through (47) in (48), the integration could be carried out and the explicit solution obtained as

$$X(T) = g(A_1,A_2,D,T) \tag{49}$$

in which the actual expression could easily be found [6].

For the boost circuit example of Fig. 3, and with parameter values V_g = 37.5V, D = 0.25, R_ℓ = 0.46Ω, R_c = 0.28Ω, L = 6mH, C = 45μF, and R = 30Ω, the output dc voltage obtained from (49) and the initial inductor current i(0) from (47) are plotted as functions of switching frequency $f_s = 1/T$ in Fig. 18 via a computer program. As seen from Fig. 18, the point where the initial inductor current becomes zero determines the boundary between continuous and discontinuous

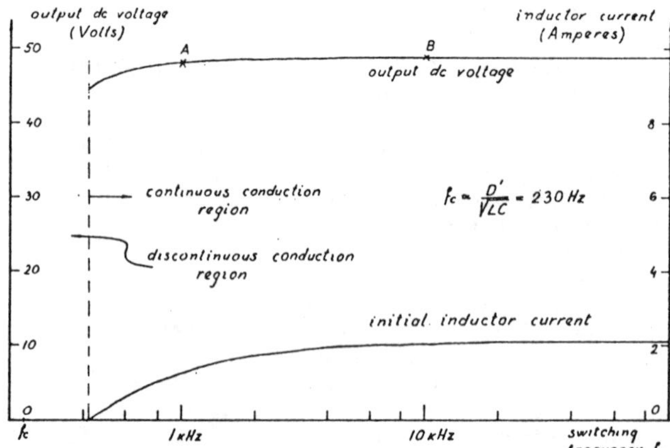

Fig. 18. Typical dependence of the steady-state (dc) conditions (output voltage) on the switching frequency f_s in the continuous conduction region (to the right of the dotted line).

conduction regions. It is also evident from Fig. 18 that the output dc voltage changes with switching frequency f_s, particularly when f_s becomes close to f_c, the effective filter corner frequency.

If the linear approximations (39) are substituted into (49), the first-order approximation of the dc state-vector X becomes independent of T, namely

$$X = -(DA_1+D'A_2)^{-1}b\ V_g \tag{50}$$

which is equivalent to the state-space averaged result (13).

For a given switching frequency, one can find the initial condition $x_1(0)$ and, with use of (43), plot the time dependence of the state variables during a period T to obtain the steady state switching ripple. For the same numerical example for the boost power stage, and with switching frequency f_s = 1 kHz (point A on Fig. 18), substantial ripple in the output voltage and inductor current is observed as demonstrated by Fig. 17. However, if all conditions are retained but the switching frequency is increased to f_s = 10 kHz (point B on Fig. 18), the plot of Fig. 19 is obtained, from which it is evident that the switching ripple is substantially reduced. Moreover the state variables show very strong linearity in the two intervals Td and Td'. This is by no means an accident, but a consequence of the fact that linear approximations (39) are well satisfied at point B since f_s/f_c = 43.5 >> 1, as verified in Appendix C.

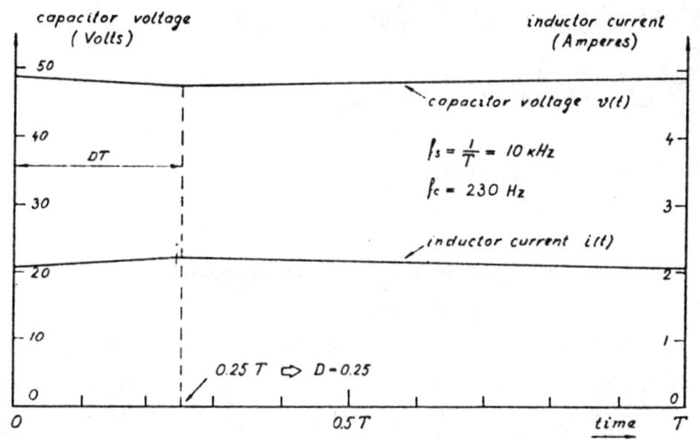

Fig. 19. Same as Fig. 17 but with f_s =10kHz. Strong linearity and small ripple exhibited by the curves are consequences of $e^{AT} \approx I + AT$, since $f_c/f_s \ll 1$.

APPENDIX C

On the linear approximation of the fundamental matrix

We now demonstrate the linear approximations (39) for the boost circuit example (16), in which for simplicity of presentation $R_\ell = 0$ and $R_c = 0$ is assumed. The two exponential (fundamental) matrices are:

$$e^{A_1 DT} = \begin{bmatrix} 1 & 0 \\ 0 & e^{-2\alpha DT} \end{bmatrix}$$

$$e^{A_2 D'T} = e^{-\alpha D'T} \begin{bmatrix} \cos\omega_o D'T + \frac{\alpha}{\omega_o}\sin\omega_o D'T & -\frac{\sin\omega_o D'T}{\omega_o L} \\ \frac{\sin\omega_o D'T}{\omega_o C} & \cos\omega_o D'T - \frac{\alpha}{\omega_o}\sin\omega_o D'T \end{bmatrix} \tag{51}$$

where

$$\alpha = \frac{1}{2RC}, \qquad \omega_o = \sqrt{\frac{1}{LC} - \alpha^2}$$

Suppose now that the switching frequency $f_s = 1/T$ is much greater than the natural frequencies α and ω_o of the converter, such that

$$\omega_o D'T \ll 1 \quad \text{and} \quad \alpha D'T \ll 1 \tag{52}$$

Then, by introduction of the linear approximations

$$e^{-\alpha D'T} \approx 1 - \alpha D'T, \quad \cos\omega_o D'T \approx 1, \quad \sin\omega_o D'T \approx \omega_o D'T \tag{53}$$

equations (51) reduce to:

$$e^{A_1 DT} \approx I + A_1 DT$$
$$e^{A_2 D'T} \approx I + A_2 D'T \tag{54}$$

For the typical numerical values in Appendix B, and for f_s = 10kHz, replacement of the fundamental matrices by their linear approximations introduces insignificant error (less than 2%) since conditions (52) are well satisfied. Furthermore, since usually $\omega_o \gg \alpha$ (as also in this case), condition (52) becomes

$$\omega_c T \ll 1 \tag{55}$$

or, with an even greater degree of inequality,

$$f_c \ll f_s \tag{56}$$

where $2\pi f_c = \omega_c = D'/\sqrt{LC}$ is the effective filter corner frequency.

Paper 5.3

A Two-Quadrant Transistor Chopper for an Electric Vehicle Drive

ROBERT L. STEIGERWALD, MEMBER, IEEE

Abstract—**A two-quadrant dc–dc transistor converter capable of delivering 400 A motoring current and of generating 200 A braking current is described. The chopper operates from a 108-V dc source (54 lead-acid cells) and supplies the armature current of a separately excited dc machine in an electric vehicle application (3000-lb commuter-type vehicle). The chopper employs high-current transistors specifically developed for the application and power diodes packaged together in power module form. Snubber networks which reduce both turn-on and turn-off device stresses are employed. The interaction of the snubber networks for the motoring and braking transistors is described and design considerations presented. It was found that for these snubbers a minimum on-time and a minimum off-time for the transistors must be maintained to ensure that the transistors' dynamic load lines never enter into the region of forward bias or reversed bias second breakdown. A technique is described which instantaneously detects a transistor failure and initiates the appropriate action in order to prevent machine overcurrent and overtorque. Factors are discussed which are crucial to ensure proper transitions from motoring to braking and to inhibit device power dissipation due to parasitic currents. The selection of a variable-frequency/variable-pulsewidth switching strategy and protection and control techniques unique to high-current transistor choppers are discussed.**

INTRODUCTION

IN a separately excited dc motor drive, machine armature current and, hence, torque can be controlled by field current alone once the machine has reached or exceeded base speed. In this case the machine counter electromotive force (CEMF) is approximately equal to the dc source voltage, and the dc source is applied directly across the machine armature. Below base speed the armature current must be controlled and limited by means other than field control. These techniques include contactor switched resistors (sometimes used in combination with stepped battery voltage levels under contactor control) and armature chopper control. The switched resistor scheme tends to be lossy unless a machine of sufficiently low base speed is employed. Such a machine, however, becomes larger and more expensive as the base speed decreases, which is undesirable in an electric vehicle application. Alternately, the switched resistor scheme can be used in conjunction with a shifting transmission which effectively raises the base speed of the machine to more manageable levels. However, the inconvenience and/or additional weight may be unacceptable. In addition, smooth regenerative braking is difficult to obtain with this scheme.

Paper SPCC 79-22, approved by the Static Power Converter Committee of the IEEE Industry Applications Society for presentation at the 1979 Industry Applications Society Annual Meeting, Cleveland, OH, September 30–October 4. Manuscript released for publication March 17, 1980. This work was supported by the U.S. Department of Energy, Washington, DC, under Contract DE-AC03-76CS51294 for Phase II of the Near-Term Electric Vehicle Program.

The author is with the Corporate Research and Development Center, General Electric Company, Schenectady, NY 12301.

In the case of an armature chopper the armature current is controlled and limited in an efficient manner, and the base speed of the machine can be selected at reasonably high values (although the armature chopper rating decreases with lower base motor speeds). A highly efficient smooth lightweight drive system results from this scheme. In addition, by employing a two-quadrant chopper, smooth regenerative braking is easily obtained.

A two-quadrant transistor armature chopper which performs this function is described. By employing transistors, circuit simplification results, and a high chopper frequency can be used compared with more conventional thyristor choppers. By employing a sufficiently high chopping frequency, additional inductance in series with the relatively low inductance armature winding is avoided. The power circuit characteristics as well as snubber circuit selection are discussed. Control and protection schemes unique to this transistor chopper are given, and experimental data are presented to illustrate chopper operation.

DESCRIPTION OF CONTROL SYSTEM

The control system in which the armature chopper is employed is shown in Fig. 1. The approach is based on a scheme which is discussed in [1]. The microcomputer control and additional details of this system are discussed in [2]. The approximate torque-speed envelope for this drive system is shown in Fig. 2. At motor speeds below base speed, the armature chopper supplies an adjustable armature current up to 400 A positive for motoring and up to 200 A negative for generating. The base speed is defined here as that speed at which the counter EMF is approximately equal to the battery voltage (i.e., armature current can be controlled by field control only). The base speed in generating is normally higher than the base speed in motoring because motoring current reduces battery terminal voltage, while braking (charging) current increases the battery voltage. The maximum motor armature current rating is selected such that a vehicle acceleration from 0–30 mi/h can be accomplished in 9 s. The maximum generating current is limited mainly by the maximum battery charging current which can be accepted repeatedly without inhibiting battery life. The corner points (i.e., motor base speed) were selected as the best compromise between the armature chopper rating and the motor size, and commutator design. During the armature control mode the field current is maintained at rated value by a low-current (≅5 A) transistor chopper. In the field control mode the armature chopper is completely bypassed by a contactor, and the armature current is controlled by the field chopper. The overall system is controlled by a microcomputer

Reprinted from *IEEE Trans. Ind. Applicat.*, vol. IA-16, no. 4, pp. 535–541, July/August 1980.

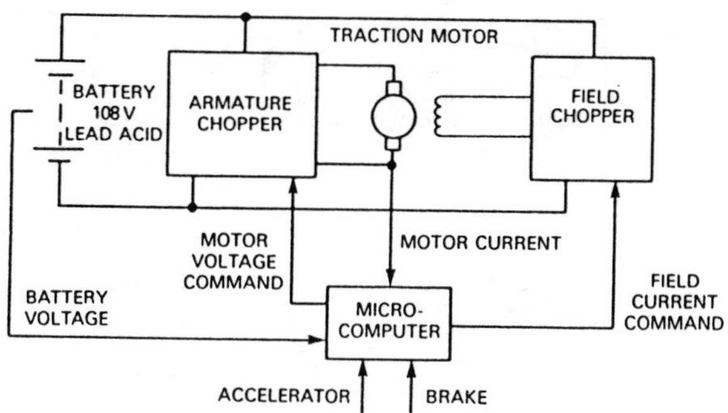

Fig. 1. Electrical drive system block diagram.

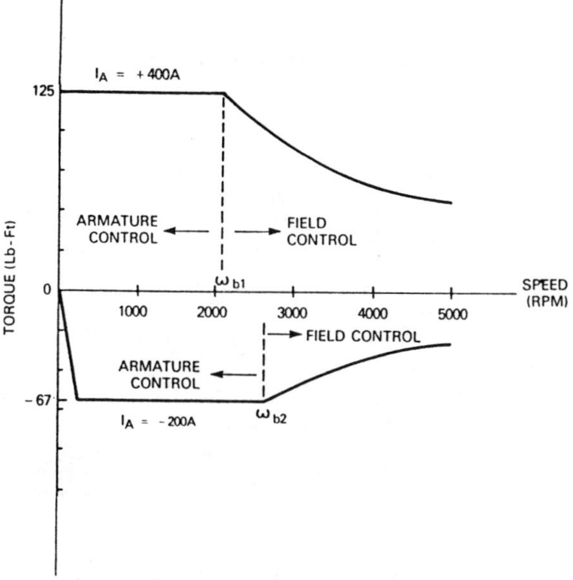

Fig. 2. Torque-speed envelope of drive system.

[2]. Note that the armature control loop is closed through the microcomputer software. This fact creates some interesting and unique interface requirements (such as armature chopper fast-acting current limiting) which will be discussed below.

ARMATURE CHOPPER POWER CIRCUIT

The armature chopper power circuit is shown in Fig. 3. Three power modules (shown within the dotted line) are employed in the circuit. Each power module contains a set of two Darlington power transistors in parallel (only one is shown for simplicity) and a feedback high-speed power diode. Two parallel modules are used to obtain the two parallel transistor sets (Q1 and Q2) needed for the higher motoring current rating (400 A), while only a single module transistor set (Q3) is needed to meet the generating current rating (200 A).

Transistors Q1 and Q2 along with diode D3 comprise the motoring (voltage stepdown) chopper, while transistor Q3 and parallel diodes D1 and D2 comprise the generating (voltage stepup) chopper. A 1200-μF capacitor bank provides a path for the high-frequency current required by the chopper and limits voltage transients each time the transistors turn off, which otherwise would occur due to the energy stored in the battery cable inductance ($\cong$10 μH). A main contactor CC connects the armature circuit to the motor and serves as an emergency disconnect in the event of a fault. A small resistor and relay in parallel with the CC serve to charge the capacitor bank before the CC is allowed to close.

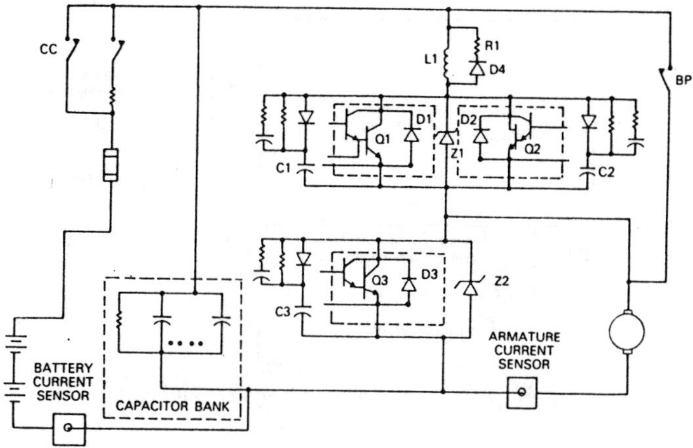

Fig. 3. Armature chopper power circuit.

A magnetically sensitive current sensor measures armature current which is used for system control and for a fast-acting current limit for armature chopper protection. A battery current sensor provides information for fuel gauging, battery charging, and battery fault current which shuts the drive down (i.e., opens the CC).

A turn-off polarized snubber consisting of C1 and C2 in parallel and their series diodes provide turn-off stress reduction for the motoring power transistors, while C3 and its series diode provide turn-off stress reduction for transistor Q3. In parallel with each of these series snubber diodes is a resistor which serves to discharge the snubber capacitors when its appropriate transistor turns on. It was found that an additional small *RC* snubber across each series diode was needed to limit voltage transients each time the diode snapped off at the end of a capacitor charging interval (i.e., after a transistor has turned off). A detailed description of turn-off stress reduction networks can be found in [3]-[8].

A 2-μH inductor, L1, is placed in series with the chopper transistors in order to limit transistor turn-on stress. The inductor serves to limit the magnitude of the reverse recovery current of the feedback diodes as well as the peak snubber capacitor charging current. For example, when Q3 turns on, the reverse recovery current of D1 and D2, as well as the charging current of C1 and C2, is limited by L1. When the diodes have recovered and the snubber capacitors have charged, the current trapped in L1 now circulates and dies out in its parallel connected resistor diode combination.

Zener diode voltage clamps are employed across each transistor to limit the voltage magnitude applied to the transistor after turn-off. The voltage spike is due to parasitic inductances, as will be discussed later. Other investigators have noted the importance of the circuit layout in reducing voltage transients [9] and have employed Zener clamps to limit their magnitude [10].

ARMATURE CHOPPER MICROPROCESSOR INTERFACE

The interface between the microprocessor and the armature chopper is illustrated in Fig. 4. The contactor commands, motor/brake command, and armature chopper malfunction are

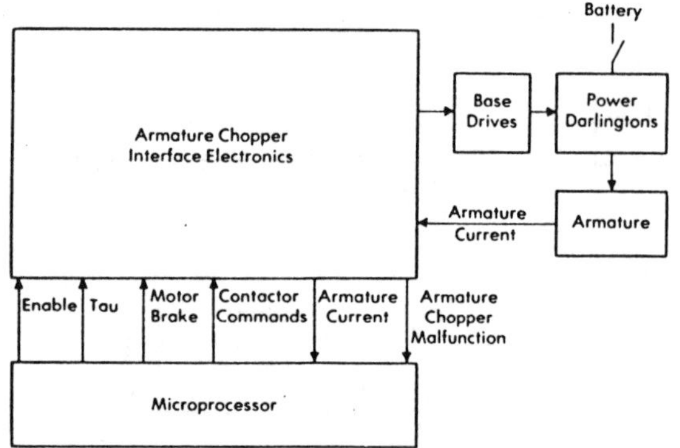

Fig. 4. Armature chopper/mircoprocessor interface.

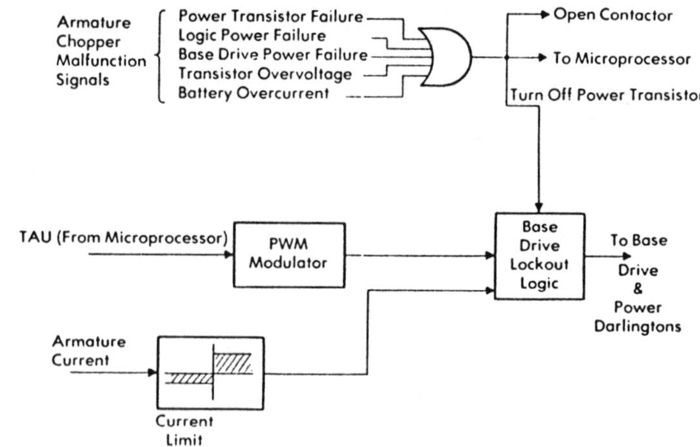

Fig. 5. Interface electronics.

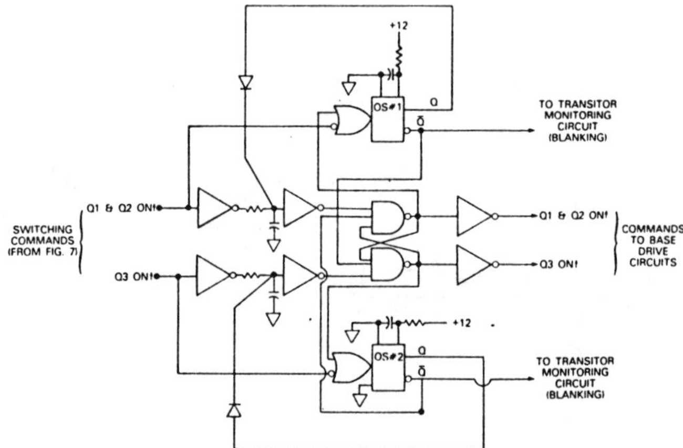

Fig. 6. Base drive lockout and steering logic.

digital signals, while the chopper duty cycle command, τ, and armature current are analog signals. It is the function of the interface electronics to convert these commands into modulated base drive signals, provide a local fast-acting current limit, and provide an analog armature current signal to the microprocessor. In addition, the interface electronics must sense an armature chopper malfunction and notify the microprocessor of such an event.

A more detailed description of the interface electronics is shown in Fig. 5. The pulsewidth modulator (PWM) is of the variable-voltage/variable-frequency type. The modulator frequency as a function of duty cycle, τ, is given by

$$f = \frac{E_d}{2L_a \Delta I_a}(\tau - \tau^2).$$

The frequency is a parabolic function of duty cycle (as shown in Fig. 9). This type of modulator results in constant peak-to-peak ripple current for all motor speeds and armature currents and has the characteristic that the chopping frequency is never higher than necessary for a given condition, and thus average snubber losses are minimized [11]. For the parameters of this system, a 2000-Hz peak frequency was employed which resulted in a peak-to-peak ripple current of approximately 40 A. The motor armature inductance is approximately 250 μH.

A local fast-acting current limit is also provided by the interface electronics. If the current exceeds approximately 440 A motoring or 240 A braking, the power transistors are turned off until the current falls approximately 80 A at which time normal switching is again allowed to occur. The current limit will be discussed in more detail later.

Several parameters are sensed to determine if there is an armature chopper malfunction as seen in Fig. 5. A power transistor failure detection circuit senses the transistor voltage after every transistor turn-off to ensure that the transistor has not failed at turn-off. As will be discussed in more detail below, a transistor failure or any other malfunction causes the contactor CC to be opened, the power transistors to be turned off, and the microprocessor to be notified. Other signals which are sensed include the logic power supply voltage levels, base drive power supply, transistor overvoltage, and battery overcurrent. Any abnormal values of these parameters will cause a malfunction signal to be generated.

Fig. 6 illustrates the circuit which interfaces the PWM to the power transistor base drive circuit. The operation of this circuit is critical. The flip-flop (cross-coupled NAND gate) in the center of Fig. 6 ensures that Q3 and Q1-Q2 never conduct simultaneously, which would short the dc source. However, due to the transistor's storage times, the gating on of a transistor must be delayed until after the command to turn off the opposite transistor in order to allow for the off-going transistor's storage time. This function is accomplished by a simple time delay that is implemented with the two one-shot multivibrators (OS #1 and OS #2), which are cross-coupled to the NAND gate flip-flop. In addition, the one-shots are used for two other functions. First, a constant transistor off-time is accomplished by coupling the one-shot outputs through signal diodes back to the inverted input to the NAND gates. This has the effect of holding a power transistor off for the duration of the one-shot timing interval each time a transistor is turned off. The assurance of a constant off-time is important to allow the current which circulates in L1, D4, and R1 (Fig. 3) to die out before a transistor is again turned on. This is necessary since, if D4 is not cleared of stored charge, the turn-on snubbering effect of L1 will be ineffective which, in turn, causes high transistor turn-on stress. The other function of the one-shots is to provide a blanking signal to the transistor monitoring circuit as discussed below.

Fig. 7 illustrates the armature current switching logic and transistor monitoring circuit, the function of which will now be described. NAND gates 1 and 2 pass the modulator on/off

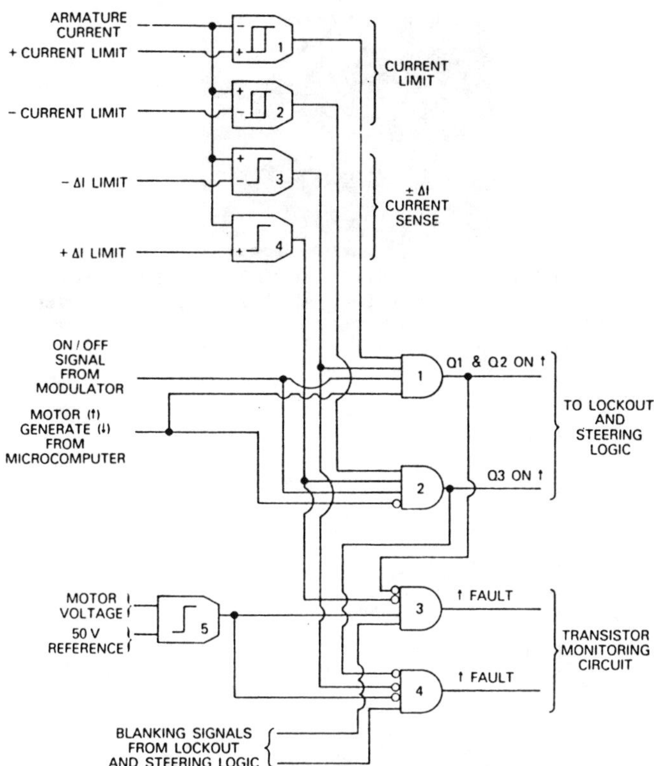

Fig. 7. Transistor monitoring circuit and current logic.

transistor command as determined by the motor/generate command from the microcomputer. Other inputs to gates 1 and 2 may inhibit transistor turn-on commands. Two current limiting comparators with hysteresis (1 and 2) serve as a local fast-acting current limit. The instantaneous armature current is compared against the peak current limit reference values. In the motoring case, if the peak armature current (which is also the peak transistor current) exceeds the current limit value of 420 A, the output of comparator 1 turns off Q1 and Q2 through the action of gate 1, independent of the command from the microprocessor. Q1 and Q2 are held off by comparator 1 until the armature current (and hence the transistor current) falls approximately 80 A, as set by the comparator hysteresis. After that point has been reached, the normal modulator signal is again allowed to pass through gate 1 until the current limit value is again exceeded. The current limit scheme for the generating chopper works in a similar manner, except that the limit value is set at –240 A. Note that with this scheme the transistor collector currents are never allowed to exceed a value beyond which they are rated and can successfully turn off. This limiting scheme is fundamentally different from other schemes [12] which measure the collector-emitter voltage to determine when a transistor is coming out of saturation and turns the transistor off when this condition occurs. With that scheme, however, the transistor peak current limit will be a function of transistor gain, and transistors with higher gain will be required to turn off higher currents. Since the reverse bias second breakdown capability of a power transistor does not normally increase with gain, that scheme may require transistor selection or derating to be practical.

The transistor monitoring circuit senses a transistor failure at turn-off. This operation will be explained by considering the instant a turn-off command has been given to Q1-Q2. In this instance the output of gate 1 would go high, and a fault signal would appear at the output of gate 2, except that a blanking signal is applied to gate 3 from the lockout and steering logic. This blanking signal, which was initiated at the instant a turn-off command was given, prevents a fault signal from being generated for a time which is known to be longer than the transistor storage time. After Q1-Q2's storage time, the motor voltage drops to near zero as D3 comes into conduction. This fact is sensed by comparator 5, which prevents a fault signal from being sent after the blanking signal has timed out. Note that if Q1-Q2 failed to turn off, the motor voltage would not have decreased, and comparator 5 would have allowed a fault signal to be sent and the drive to be shut down as soon as the blanking signal timed out. Thus a transitor failure is detected even if the current is well below the current limited value. It is noted that if the current is low enough to be discontinuous, the motor voltage will be at the counter EMF value after the current has gone to zero (rather than at zero due to diode D3 conducting). This would cause the transistor monitoring circuit to indicate a fault erroneously. To prevent this, the $\pm\Delta I$ current sense comparators prevent a fault signal from being sent if the current has fallen below a sufficiently low value (i.e., if the current is approaching the discontinuous condition). The transistor monitoring circuit for the generating transistor works in an identical manner except that the output of comparator 5 is inverted. The $\pm\Delta I$ current sensing logic serves one other function. If the current is in a module feedback diode, the $\pm\Delta I$ current sense signal prevents the transistor parallel with the feedback diode from being gated on and storing charge and possibly carrying current in the reverse direction. Such an operation can cause transient currents in the transistor when the opposite transistor is again gated. This charge appears as an abnormally long reverse recovery time feedback diode to the transistor being switched on.

ARMATURE CHOPPER PERFORMANCE

The armature chopper is shown in Fig. 8. The hardware on top of the casting comprises the armature chopper. The field chopper/battery charger, logic power supply, logic cards, accessory battery charger, filter capacitors, and contactors are mounted below the casting. In Fig. 9 the chopping frequency and computed losses are shown as a function of the chopper duty cycle. The highest frequency is needed at a duty cycle of 0.5 in order to maintain the constant 40-A peak-to-peak ripple current since at this point the highest fundamental ripple voltage is delivered to the motor. Since the switching losses are proportional to frequency, the highest loss also occurs at this operating point. The chopper efficiency varies between 92 percent at a duty cycle of 0.5 and 98 percent at a duty cycle of 1.0.

In Fig. 10 the transistor collector-emitter voltage and base drive waveform are shown. Note the voltage spike which occurs at transistor turn-off. This spike is due to parasitic inductance caused by the loop (Fig. 3) defined by the capacitor bank, R1, D4, Q1-Q2, D3, and back to the capacitor bank. The parasitic inductance in this case is approximately 0.1 μH. It was

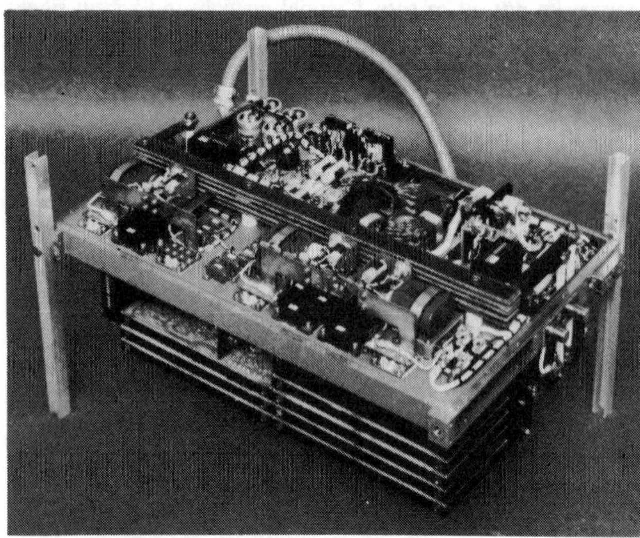

Fig. 8. Armature chopper hardware.

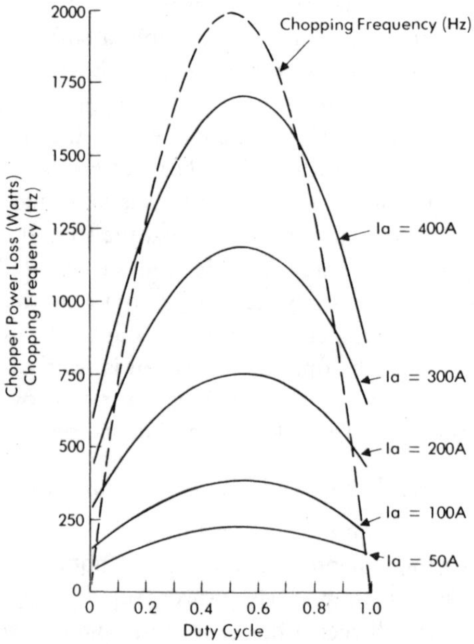

Fig. 9. Frequency and power loss versus duty cycle.

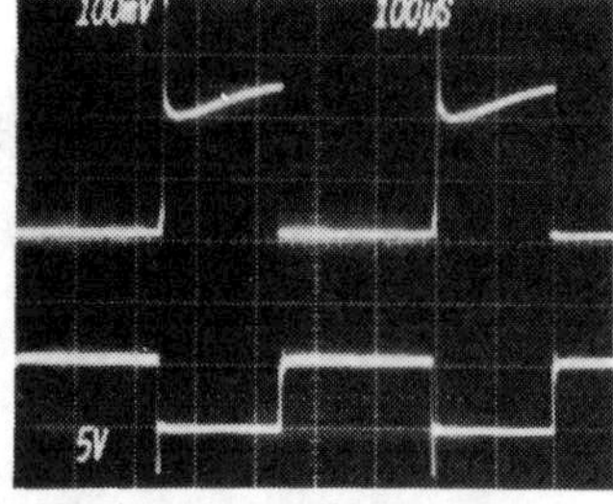

Fig. 10. Darlington collector-emitter voltage and base current versus time. Top: 50 V/cm (zero at center line). Bottom: 2 A/cm (0–1 cm from bottom). Time: 100 μs/cm.

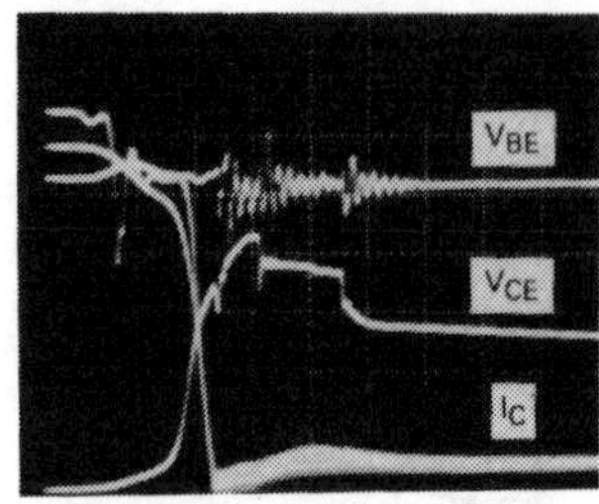

Fig. 11. Darlington waveforms at turn-off base-emitter voltage: 2 V/cm (0–2 cm from top). Collector-emitter voltage: 50 V/cm (zero at bottom line). Darlington collector currents: 40 A/cm (zero at bottom line). Time: 2 μs/cm.

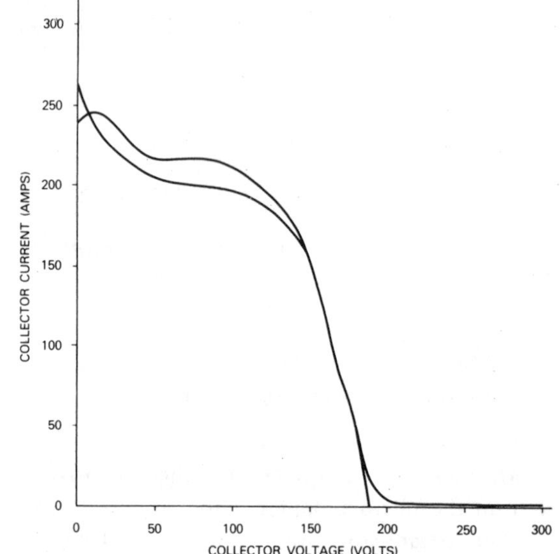

Fig. 12. Darlington transistor through I_C-V_{CE} plane at turn-off.

found that due to the fast transistor switching speed (fall time) of less than 1 μs acting in conjunction with the parasitic inductance, the Zener diode clamps (Z1 and Z2) were needed to limit the transistor voltage both at turn-off and turn-on due to the overcharging of the snubber capacitors. The base circuit employed is similar to that described in [13] and provides a 1.5-A turn-off pulse and maintains a –4-V reverse base bias during the transistor off-time.

In Fig. 11 the transistor turn-off waveforms are shown. The sharing of the two parallel transistors (Q1 and Q2) collector currents is shown. The fall time of less than 1 s is seen as well as the clamping action of Zener diodes which manifests itself as a voltage "backporch" of approximately 180 V immediately after turn-off. The base-emitter voltage is also shown to maintain a negative bias after turn-off. It was found that, for these devices, a negative base voltage was necessary to ensure reliable device turn-off. Fig. 12 shows the transition through the $I_C - V_{CE}$ plane at turn-off for the parallel transistors. From this curve it is seen that the turn-off dissipation is shared approximately equally. The snubber capacitors (C1-C3) were chosen as 1 μF and were judged to be a reasonable compromise between the snubber losses and transistor turn-off dissipation. Note that the snubber capacitors C1-C3 also act as snubbers for diodes D1-D3 and thus limit voltage transients when these diodes turn off.

Fig. 13 shows the detailed base voltage and current at tran-

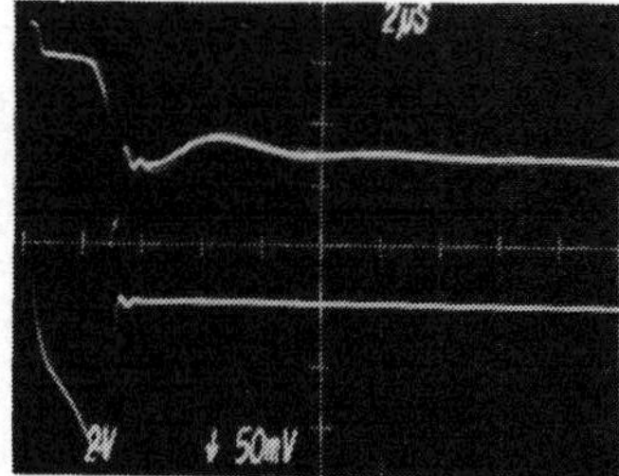

Fig. 13. Darlington base waveforms at turn-off. Top: Base-emitter voltage: 2 V/cm (0–1 cm from top). Bottom: Base current: 1 A/cm (0–3 cm from bottom).

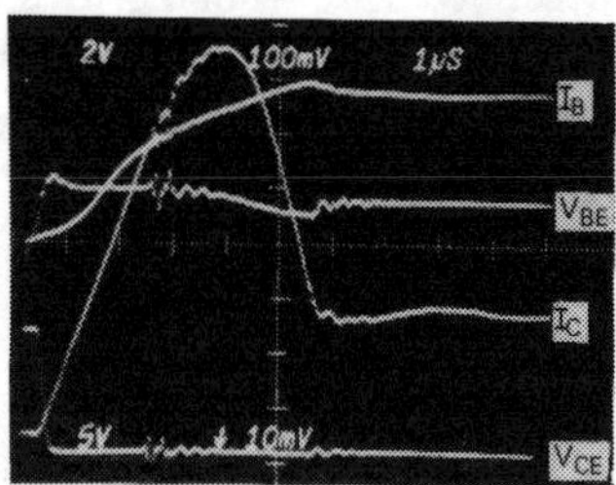

Fig. 14. Darlington waveforms at turn-on. Base current: 1 A/cm (zero at center line). Base-emitter voltage: 1V/cm (zero at center line). Collector current: 20 A/cm (zero at bottom line). Collector-emitter voltage: 50 V/cm (zero at bottom line). Time: 1 µs/cm.

sistor turn-off. As mentioned earlier, maintaining a negative turn-off voltage was important for proper device operation. Fig. 14 shows the transistor waveform at turn-on. As seen, a relatively large pulse of collector current is present at turn-on as the opposite snubber capacitor is charged. For example, when Q1 and Q2 are turned on, capacitor C3 must be charged. Inductor L1 limits the peak magnitude of this charging pulse to

$$I_{CP} = E_d/\sqrt{L1/C3}.$$

This pulse must be added to the motor current at that instant to determine the total transistor current. It may be important that the transistor not try to turn off at the peak of this current pulse since the reverse biased second breakdown rating of the device may be exceeded. Consequently, a minimum turn-on duration circuit can be used. For the equipment described here, it was found that the transistor storage time was sufficiently long to ensure that once the transistor is turned on it cannot turn off again until after the peak of the turn-on current pulse. As seen in Fig. 14, the turn-on dissipation is negligible since the presence of inductor L1 allows the collector voltage to fall to zero before the current has risen substantially.

Fig. 15 shows the Zener diode currents into the two parallel diodes, which comprise Z1, and their relationship to the collector-emitter voltage at transistor turn-off. As seen, the Zener limits the voltage to approximately 200 V. The measured power dissipated in the Zener diodes under the worst operating condition (2000 Hz) is illustrated in Figs. 16 and 17. As seen, the dissipated power increases substantially with current and battery voltage. Under the usual operating conditions, the dissipation of the Zener clamps is small. Only under hard accelerations (>200 A) and high battery voltage, due to high generation into a substantially charged battery, are the Zeners

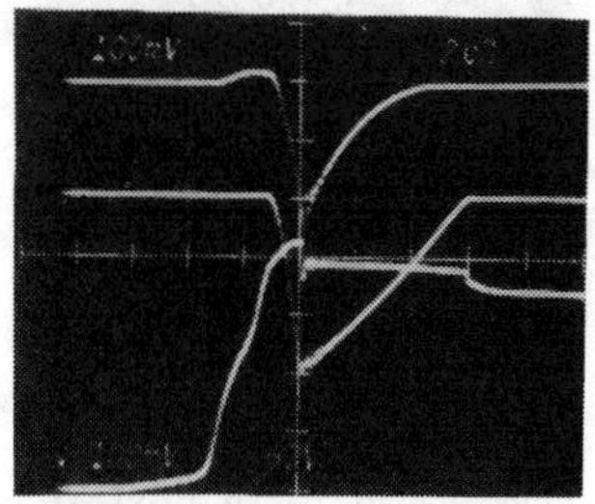

Fig. 15. Zener clamp currents and collector voltage at Darlington turnoff. Top: Zener current: 40 A/cm (0–1 cm from top). Middle: Zener current: 40 A/cm (0–1 cm above center line). Bottom: Collector-emitter voltage: 50 V/cm (zero at bottom line). Time: 2 µs/cm.

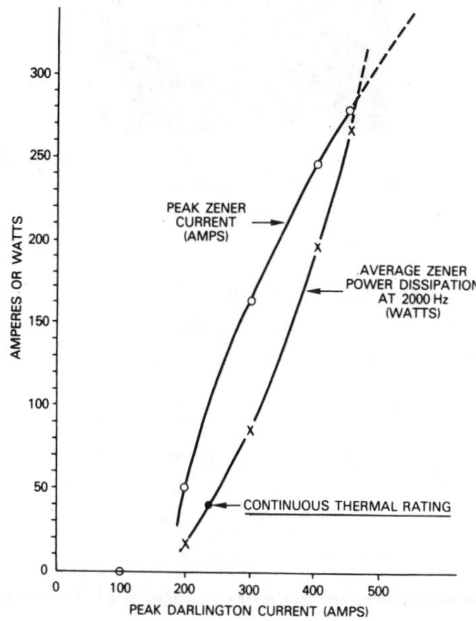

Fig. 16. Measured Zener power dissipation at 2000 Hz and peak Zener current versus peak Darlington current for motoring (Zener Z1).

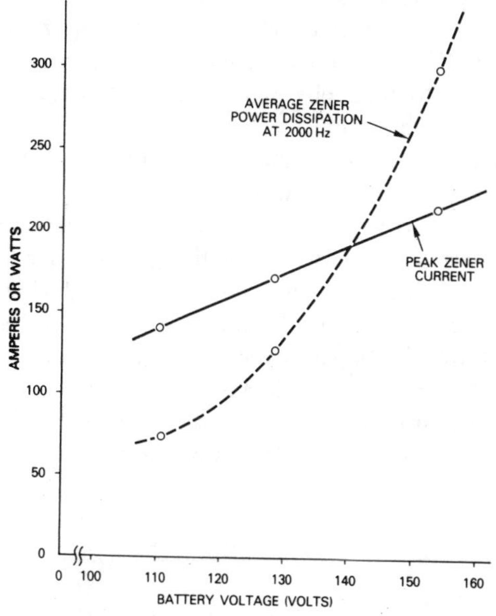

Fig. 17. Measured Zener power dissipation at 2000 Hz and peak Zener current versus battery voltage during regeneration for a 270-A peak transistor current (Zener Z2).

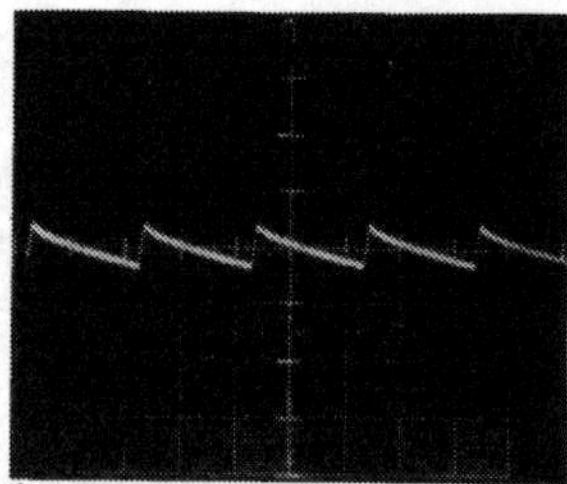

Fig. 18. Current delivered to stalled rotor. Armature current: 50 A/cm (zero at bottom line). Time: 1 μs/cm.

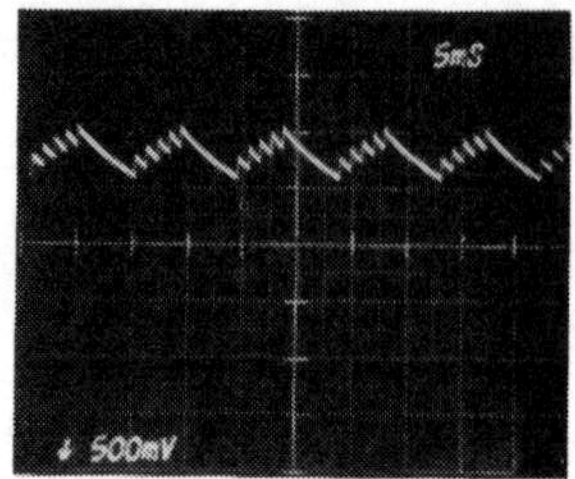

Fig. 19. Motor current during local current limit (stalled rotor). Armature current: 100 A/cm (0–2 cm from bottom). Time: 5 μs/cm.

called upon to dissipate substantial power. Since these are transient conditions, the thermal design and overall drive efficiency are not substantially affected by employing the Zener clamps.

Figs. 18 and 19 show the armature current delivered by the chopper under stalled rotor conditions for the normal and for the local current limited cases. In Fig. 19 it is seen that when the 400-A point is reached, the transistors are turned off (independent of the microprocessor command) until the current drops approximately 80 A, at which point normal chopping is resumed.

CONCLUSION

A two-quadrant transistor chopper with a peak current rating of 400 A motoring and 200 A generating and operating from a 108-V dc source has been described. A peak switching frequency of 2000 Hz obviated the need for a choke in series with the motor armature. For a two-quadrant chopper there is an interaction between the turn-off and turn-on stress reducing networks. The turn-off network, while reducing transistor dissipation at turn-off, causes a transient current pulse in the opposite transistor when it is switched on, thus increasing its turn-on duty. The turn-on snubber, while reducing turn-on losses, causes the transistor voltage to rise above its normal level at turn-off. Proper snubber selection must take these effects into account. A minimum transistor on-time and a minimum transistor off-time are needed to ensure proper snubber operation and minimize transistor stress.

A technique has been described which senses a power transistor failure within approximately 50 μs independent of the current load level. Other interface circuitry between the microcomputer control and the chopper has been described. A unique current control logic scheme, which ensures that the transistor is gated only when it can carry forward current, ensures that a nonconducting transistor does not incur switching losses due to inadvertent charge storage. A local fast-acting current limit which overrides the microcomputer command ensures that the chopper current does not exceed a value which the transistor can successfully turn off.

The chopper described here is being used in a commuter-type electric vehicle developed for the Department of Energy and serves to illustrate the practicality of transistor drives in the 40-kW range.

REFERENCES

[1] B.K. Bose and R.L. Steigerwald, "A DC motor control system for electric vehicle drive," *IEEE Trans. Ind. Appl.*, vol. IA-14, pp. 565–572, Nov./Dec. 1978.

[2] B.K. Bose and H. Sutherland, "A microcomputer based real time feedback controller for an electric vehicle drive system," *IEEE Ind. Appl. Soc. Conf. Rec.*, 1979.

[3] E.T. Calkin and B.H. Hamilton, "A conceptually new approach for regulated DC to DC converters employing transistor switches and pulse width control," *IEEE Trans. Ind. Appl.*, vol. IA-12, No. 4, pp. 368–377, July/Aug. 1976.

[4] E.T. Calkin and B.H. Hamilton, "Circuit techniques for improving the switching loci of transistor switches in switching regulators," *IEEE Ind. Appl. Soc. Conf. Rec.*, pp. 477–484, 1972.

[5] R.L. Steigerwald, "Application techniques for high power gate turn-off thyristors," *IEEE Ind. Appl. Soc. Conf. Rec.*, pp. 165–174, 1975.

[6] T.M. Undeland, "Switching stress reduction in power transistor converters," *IEEE Ind. Appl. Soc. Conf. Rec.*, pp. 383–392, 1976.

[7] PH. Lataire, G. Maggetto, and M. Hendrickx, "Variable speed drives with low and medium power DC motors and transistor choppers," in *Int. Conf. Electrical Machines*, pp. 131-1–31-10, 1976.

[8] R.W. Stokes, "High voltage transistor inverters for AC traction drives," in *Int. Semiconductor Power Converter Conf. Rec.*, pp. 270–294, Mar. 1977.

[9] J.D. van Wyk and J.J. Schoeman, "The application of transistorized switches to DC and AC machines for the control of battery vehicles up to 30 kW," in *Proc. Second IFAC Symp. Control in Power Electronics and Electrical Drives*, pp. 841–852, Oct. 1977.

[10] A.R. Daniels, V.S. Gott, and K.W. Howe, "A transistor controller for a battery driven vehicle," in *Int. Conf. Power Electronics—Power Semiconductors and Their Applications*, pp. 57–62, Dec. 1974.

[11] W. McMurray, "Stepless solid-state controls for battery-powered DC electric vehicles," in *IFAC Symp. Control in Power Electronics and Electrical Drives*, pp. 421–435, 1974.

[12] H. Knoll, "High-current transistor choppers, "in *Pro. Second IFAC Symp. Control in Power Electronics and Electrical Drives*, pp. 307–315, Oct. 1977.

[13] R.L. Steigerwald, "Pulse battery charger employing 1000 A transistor switches," in *IEEE Ind. Appl. Soc. Conf. Rec.*, pp. 1127–1132, 1977.

Paper 5.4

High-Frequency Resonant Transistor DC–DC Converters

ROBERT L. STEIGERWALD, MEMBER, IEEE

Abstract—Transistor dc-dc converters which employ a resonant circuit are described. A resonant circuit is driven with square waves of current or voltage, and by adjusting the frequency around the resonant point, the voltage on the resonant components can be adjusted to any practical voltage level. By rectifying the voltage across the resonant elements, a dc voltage is obtained which can be either higher or lower than the input dc voltage to the converter. Thus, the converter can operate in either the step-up or step-down mode. In addition, the switching losses in the inverter devices and rectifiers are extremely low due to the sine waves that occur from the use of a resonant circuit (as opposed to square waves in a conventional converter); also, easier EMI filtering should result. In the voltage input version, the converter is able to use the parasitic diode associated with an FET or monolithic Darlington, while in the current input version, the converter needs the inverse blocking capability which can be obtained with an IGT or GTO device. A low-power breadboard operating at 200–300 kHz has been built. Two typical application areas are switching power supplies and battery chargers. The converter circuits offer improvements over conventional circuits due to their high efficiency (low switching losses), small reactive components (high-frequency operation), and their step-up/step-down ability.

I. INTRODUCTION

RESONANT CONVERTERS have normally been associated with thyristor converters because the resonant load can be used to commutate the thyristors. To achieve this commutation, the load must be driven at a frequency such that a leading power factor is presented to the inverter. Several schemes have been presented for obtaining dc–dc power conversion using these thyristor resonant converters [1]–[6]. More recently, resonant inverters employing power transistors have appeared in the literature [7]–[10]. Most of these papers have discussed converters in which the load is in series with the resonant components, or single-ended schemes in which one power switch is employed (these schemes are derived from TV horizontal deflection circuits). This report describes several resonant converter topologies, many of which have the load attached in parallel with the resonant components.

A resonant circuit is driven with square waves of current or voltage, and by adjusting the frequency around the resonant point, the voltage on the resonant components can be adjusted to any practical voltage level. By rectifying the voltage across the resonant elements, a dc voltage is obtained which can be either higher or lower than the input dc voltage to the converter. Thus, the converter can operate in either the step-up or step-down mode. In addition, the switching losses in the inverter devices and rectifiers are extremely low due to the sine waves that occur from the use of a resonant circuit (as opposed to square waves in a conventional converter); also, easier EMI filtering should result. In the voltage input version, the converter is able to use the parasitic diode associated with an FET or monolithic Darlington, while in the current input version, the converter needs the inverse blocking capability which can be obtained with an IGT or GTO device. A low-power breadboard operating at 200–300 kHz has been built and results are presented. Results from a digital computer simulation are also presented. The converter circuits offer improvement over conventional circuits due to their high efficiency (low switching losses), small reactive components (high-frequency operation), and their step-up/step-down ability. Two typical application areas are switching power supplies and battery chargers.

Manuscript received May 21, 1983; revised November 7, 1983.

The author is with the Research and Development Center, General Electric Company, Schenectady, NY 12301.

II. DESCRIPTION OF TRANSISTOR RESONANT INVERTERS

Several configurations of resonant converters are described in this section. Fig. 1 shows a full-bridge resonant dc–dc converter. Operation of the converter can be understood by referring to the waveforms of Fig. 2. A series resonant circuit is excited by the full-bridge transistor inverter, and the voltage across the ac capacitor is rectified and filtered directly.

The resonant inverter using gate turn-off devices can be run such that the load appears lagging to the inverter (i.e., the devices are turned off by gate control rather than by anode current commutation). This fact allows the output voltage to be reduced from its peak value (which occurs near resonance) by increasing the inverter frequency above resonance. Thus, an isolating transformer (to be included later) need not be designed for a frequency below which maximum voltage is delivered. Also, relatively large output voltage variations (to be discussed in more detail later) can be obtained with frequency control without increasing the output ripple voltage (since the frequency is increased to reduce voltage).

The switching losses of the resonant inverter of Fig. 1 are inherently low for the following reasons: Since the load can be run at a lagging power factor, current is always in a feedback diode at the instant its parallel connected transistor turns on (see Fig. 2); thus, there are no turn-on switching losses in the power switches. Also, this same phenomenon allows a snubber capacitor C_s to be placed directly across the power switch (no snubber dump is experienced) to reduce turn-off dissipation. Since no resistor is needed in series with the capacitor no snubber dissipation results; that is, a lossless snubber action results, allowing relatively large snubbers to be used, which in turn results in low transistor power dissipation and low voltage overshoots at device turn-off. In addition, the feedback diodes used in the inverter of Fig. 1 can be of medium speed since there is no voltage immediately applied

Reprinted from *IEEE Trans. Ind. Electron.*, vol. IE-31, no. 2, pp. 181–191, May 1984.

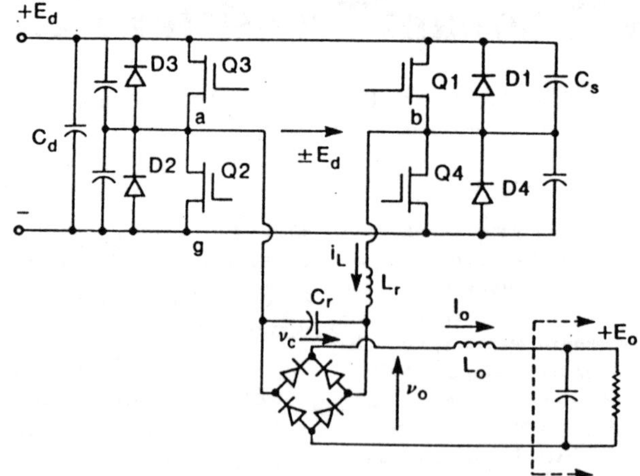

Fig. 1. Voltage input full-bridge resonant dc–dc converter.

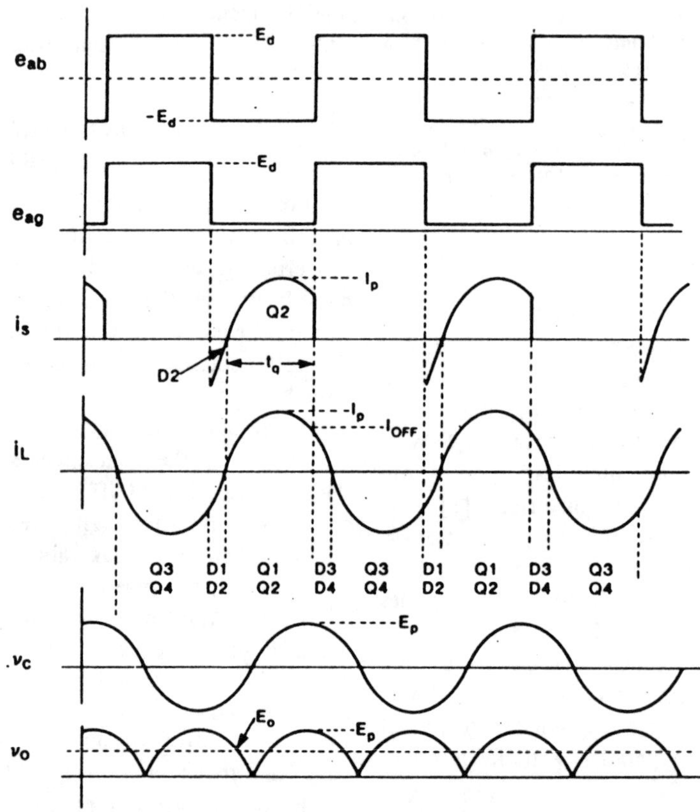

Fig. 2. Waveforms for converter of Fig. 1.

to the diode after it turns off. Rather, the transistor in parallel with the diode conducts, keeping the diode voltage low; only after the transistor turns off is voltage applied to the diode. This turn-off time is shown as t_q in Fig. 2. The parasitic diodes present in many power Darlingtons, and FET's are suitable for this purpose.

It is noted that the diodes in the SCR resonant inverters must be of high speed since the opposite SCR is turned on to commutate the diode, which must immediately turn off and block voltage. In order to protect the SCR and diode from *di/dt*-related problems, small series inductances and lossy device snubbers are needed.

Fig. 3 illustrates a half-bridge version of the transistor resonant converter. The circuit operation is the same as that for the circuit of Fig. 1, except that one-half the dc voltage is applied alternately to the resonant circuit. Fig. 4 shows a push-pull version of the resonant inverter. In this case, the ac inductance in series with the capacitor is achieved by using two windings on a common core. Again, the operation is the same as the circuit of Fig. 1, except that twice the voltage is applied to the switching devices. This circuit has the advantage that all of the FET gate drivers are referenced to a common point.

Fig. 5 shows two methods of obtaining transformer isolation. The points labeled *a* and *b* can be connected to the points *a* and *b* in the previous circuits. Note that the leakage

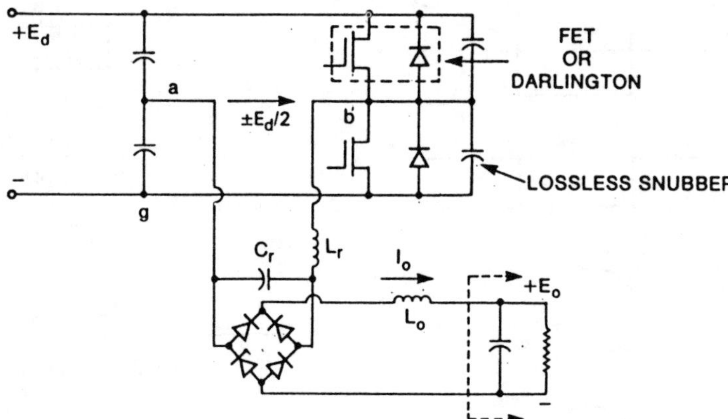

Fig. 3. Voltage input half-bridge.

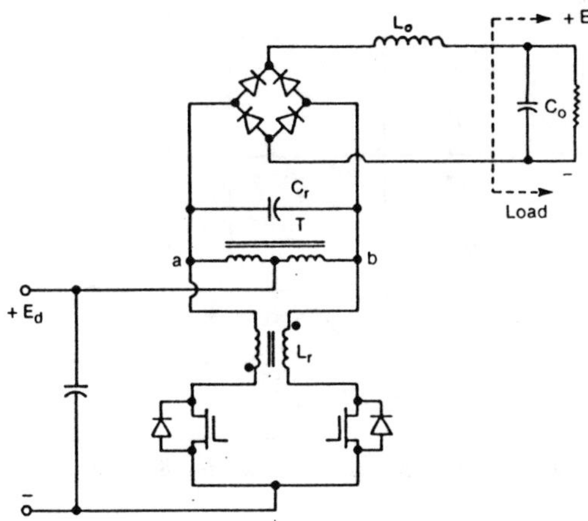

Fig. 4. Voltage input push-pull.

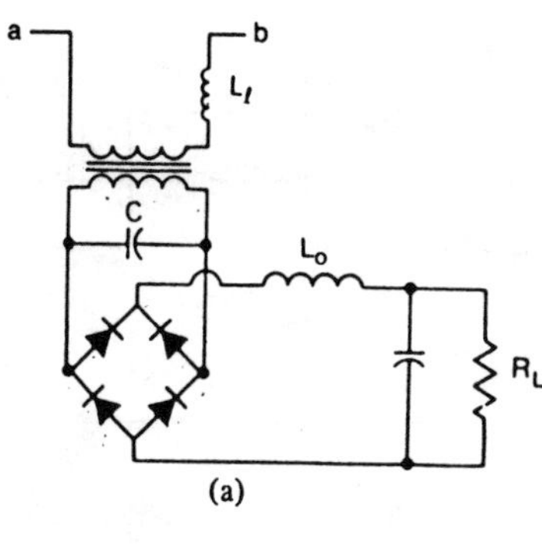

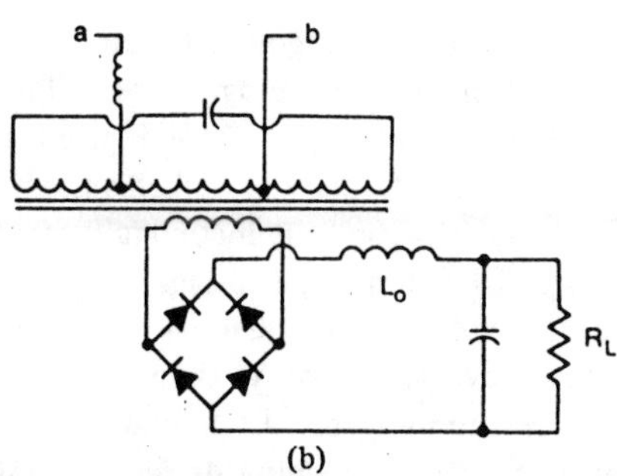

Fig. 5. Two methods of transformer coupling to load for voltage input converters. (a) Resonant capacitor on secondary. (b) Resonant capacitor on extended primary winding.

inductance of the transformer can serve as the resonant inductor, while the resonant capacitor can be placed on the secondary side (as in Fig. 5(a)), or on an extended transformer winding (as in Fig. 5(b)). Of course, the capacitor could also be placed on its own isolation winding.

All of the inverters discussed so far were of the voltage input type. Fig. 6 illustrates a full-bridge current-fed version of a gate turn-off resonant converter. The main difference is that a switching device capable of blocking reverse voltage (rather than passing reverse current as in the voltage-fed case) is needed. Only GTO's are presently available to perform this task, although a diode in series with a transistor could be used. Note that a path exists for instantaneous current transfer as the devices switch through C_r, the diode bridge and C_O. In this case, the rectifier and load is applied directly across the resonant inductor to allow this low-impedance path. Fig. 7 shows waveform sketches illustrating the expected circuit operation. Note that the resonant circuit is still driven at a frequency such that a lagging load is presented to the inverter between points a and b (i.e., the current i_c lags the voltage v_{ab}). This type of operation results in switching device waveforms which are opposite to those normally encountered in thyristor inverters; in this case, the device has negative voltage across it just before it conducts, and blocks voltage immediately when it is turned off by gate control. Also, fast device reverse recovery characteristics are not needed since reverse voltage is not suddenly applied to a device to turn it off as in a thyristor

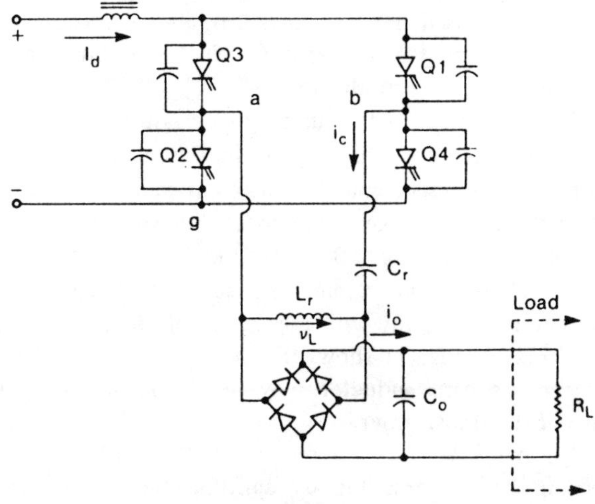

Fig. 6. Current input full-bridge resonant dc-dc converter.

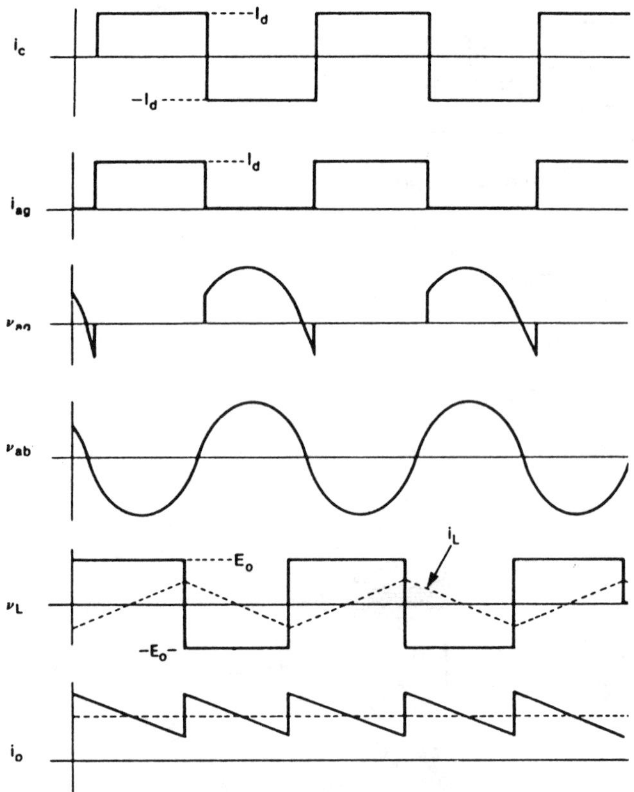

Fig. 7. Waveforms for converter of Fig. 6.

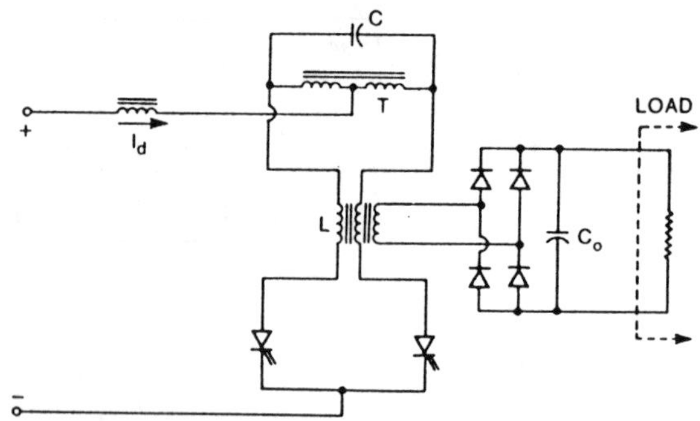

Fig. 8. Current input push-pull.

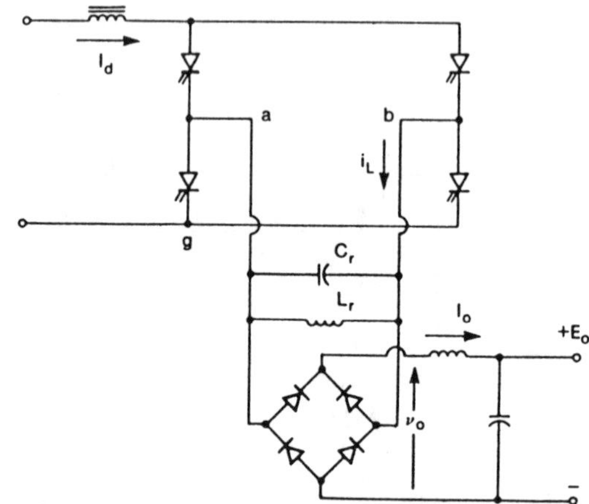

Fig. 9. Current input parallel resonant converter.

circuit. To commutate the inverter, the incoming devices are gated on slightly before the outgoing devices are turned off. During this overlap time, the incoming device will not conduct since it has negative voltage applied (see Fig. 7). Only after the outgoing devices have turned off will this negative voltage attempt to reverse polarity, and the incoming devices conduct. Note that this circuit has similar advantages to those described with regard to the voltage-input resonant inverter. That is, devices with fast reverse recovery times are not needed, and simple lossless snubbing can be employed by placing a small capacitor across each switching device. To obtain transformer isolation, a secondary winding is placed on L_r. Note that, in this case, the transformer magnetizing inductance (not the leakage inductance) forms the resonant inductor. Alternately, a discrete inductor in parallel with the transformer could be used. Fig. 8 shows a push-pull version of a current-input resonant converter in which the output is taken from a winding on the ac inductor.

An alternate version of a current-input gate turn-off resonant converter is shown in Fig. 9. In this case, a parallel resonant circuit is used, and the output is taken by directly rectifying the tank voltage. The expected waveforms for this circuit are shown in Fig. 10. They are similar to those of Fig. 7, and all the same comments made concerning the device switching waveforms with regard to Fig. 6 apply to the circuit of Fig. 9. Fig. 11 shows the push-pull version of this circuit; the resonant inductor may be the magnetizing inductance of the transformer.

Finally, half-bridge arrangements of the current input circuits can be implemented by splitting the dc inductor as shown in Fig. 12.

III. ANALYSIS OF VOLTAGE-INPUT TRANSISTOR RESONANT INVERTERS

A piecewise linear analysis of the full-bridge voltage-input transistor resonant inverter of Fig. 1 will be presented in this section. This analysis will aid in determining waveforms and peak device stresses, and result in design curves. Measured breadboard waveforms will be given in the next section.

Before proceeding with the detailed analysis, it is useful to develop a simple approximate expression for peak device current by considering only the fundamental components of the waveforms. The expression gives surprisingly accurate results due to the resonant nature of the inverter (i.e., considerable harmonic filtering by the resonant components takes place). Since the maximum power will, in many cases, occur when the resonant circuit is driven near its resonant point, the resonant circuit presents a near unity power factor to the inverter. Therefore, the current drawn from the dc bus (and carried by the power switches) will be approximate half sinusoids of current. Therefore, the peak switch current (i.e., the peak of the sinusoid) is given approximately by

$$I_p \cong \frac{\pi}{2} \frac{P}{E_d \eta} \tag{1}$$

where

I_p peak device current (amperes),
P power delivered to load (watts),
E_d dc bus voltage (volts),
η converter efficiency.

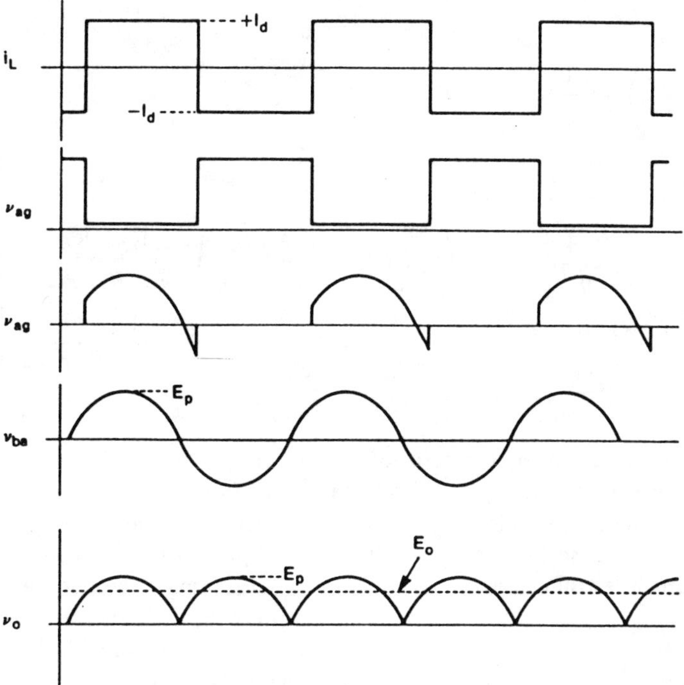

Fig. 10. Waveforms for current input converter of Fig. 9.

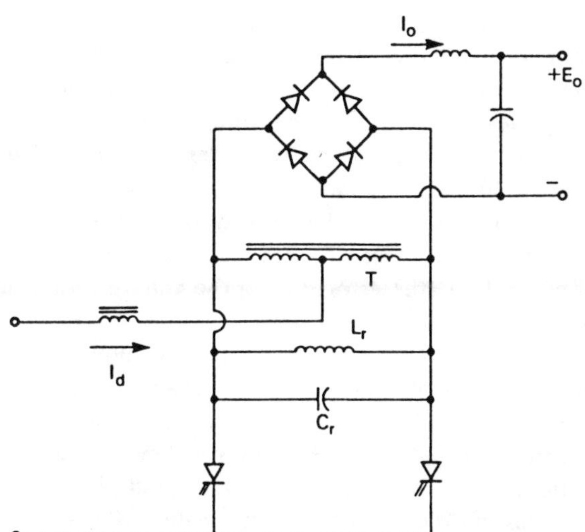

Fig. 11. Push-pull current input parallel resonant converter.

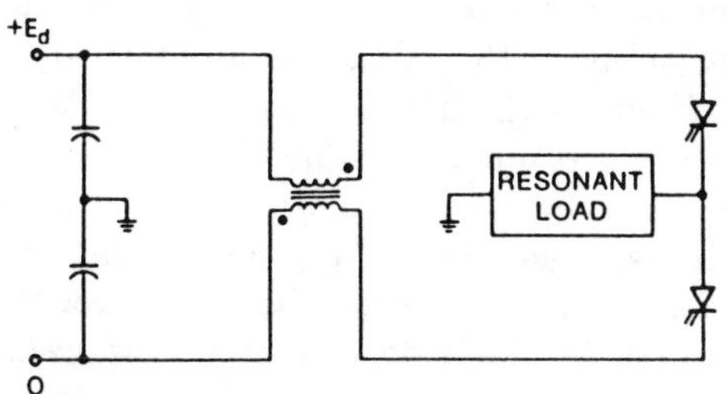

Fig. 12. Half-bridge current input converter.

The device must block the dc bus voltage plus any transient overshoots due to dc link inductance. This fact and (1) allow a quick estimate of the power device rating for a given application. A formal method of selecting the resonant components L_r and C_r will now be developed from a piecewise linear transient circuit analysis.

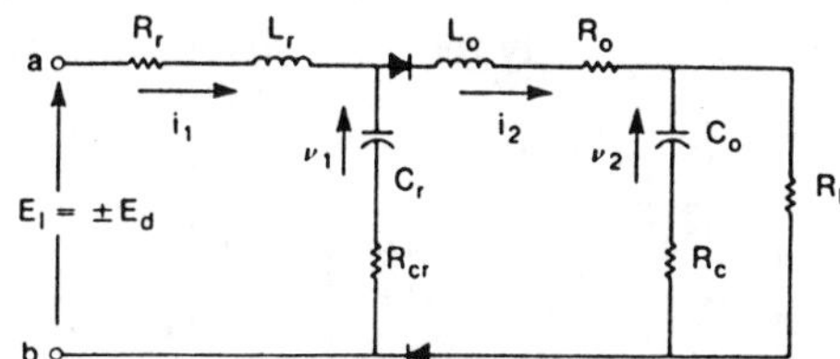

Fig. 13. Equivalent circuit for circuit analysis.

Fig. 13 shows the equivalent circuit of the resonant inductance and capacitance L_r and C_r, and the dc output filter L_o and C_o, assuming the diode bridge is conducting. The equivalent series resistances of the components are also included. The dc load is represented by resistor R_L. The points a and b are fed with a square voltage wave from the bridge inverter (i.e., from points a and b of Fig. 1).

The differential equations describing circuit operation may be written by inspection in state variable form as follows:

$$\frac{di_1}{dt} = \frac{1}{L_r}\,[E_I - i_1 R_r - v_1 - (i_1 - i_2)R_{cr}]$$

$$\frac{dv_1}{dt} = \frac{1}{C_r}\,[i_1 - i_2]$$

$$\frac{di_2}{dt} = \frac{1}{L_o}\left[v_1 + (i_1 - i_2)R_{cr} - i_2 R_o - \left(i_2 - C_o \frac{dv_2}{dt}\right) R_L\right]$$

$$\frac{dv_2}{dt} = \frac{1}{C_o}\left[\frac{R_L}{R_c + R_L}\, i_2 - \frac{v_2}{R_c + R_L}\right]. \tag{2}$$

Substituting the expression for dv_2/dt in the fourth expression into the third expression, the equations may finally be written in the matrix form

$$\frac{d}{dt}\begin{bmatrix} i_1 \\ v_1 \\ i_2 \\ v_2 \end{bmatrix} = \begin{bmatrix} -\left(\frac{R_r}{L_r}+\frac{R_{cr}}{L_r}\right) & -\frac{1}{L_r} & \frac{R_{cr}}{L_r} & 0 \\ \frac{1}{C_r} & 0 & \frac{-1}{C_r} & 0 \\ \frac{R_{cr}}{L_o} & \frac{1}{L_o} & -\frac{1}{L_o}\left(R_{cr}+Ro+\frac{R_cR_L}{R_c+R_L}\right) & \frac{-1}{L_o}\frac{R_L}{R_c+R_L} \\ 0 & 0 & \frac{1}{C_o}\frac{R_L}{R_c+R_L} & -\frac{1}{C_o}\frac{1}{R_c+R_L} \end{bmatrix} \times \begin{bmatrix} i_1 \\ v_1 \\ i_2 \\ v_2 \end{bmatrix} + \begin{bmatrix} \frac{1}{L_r} \\ 0 \\ 0 \\ 0 \end{bmatrix} \times E_I. \quad (3)$$

For the analysis to be presented here, the solution of these equations is simplified by assuming that i_2 and therefore v_2 vary a negligible amount during a half-cycle, i.e., the value of L_o is assumed to be large enough so that negligible ripple occurs at the output. Therefore, it is assumed that

$$i_2(t) = \text{const.} = I_o$$
$$v_2(t) = \text{const.} = E_o. \quad (4)$$

This simplifying assumption has the effect of reducing (3) to second-order (i.e., only the first two quantities are variable):

$$\frac{d}{dt}\begin{bmatrix} i_1 \\ v_1 \end{bmatrix} = \begin{bmatrix} -\frac{R_r+R_{cr}}{L_r} & \frac{-1}{L_r} \\ \frac{1}{C_r} & 0 \end{bmatrix} \times \begin{bmatrix} i_1 \\ v_1 \end{bmatrix} + \begin{bmatrix} \frac{R_{cr}}{L_r} & \frac{1}{L_r} \\ \frac{-1}{C_r} & 0 \end{bmatrix} \times \begin{bmatrix} I_o \\ E_I \end{bmatrix}. \quad (5)$$

These equations are now normalized using the following definitions and base quantities:

$$\omega_o = \frac{1}{\sqrt{L_rC_r}} = \text{undamped resonant frequency}$$

$$Z_o = \sqrt{L_r/C_r} = \text{base impedance}$$

Base Voltage $= E_I$

Base Current $= E_I/Z_o$

Base Time $= 1/\omega_o$.

Equation (5) can then be put into the form

$$\frac{d}{dt'}\begin{bmatrix} i_1' \\ v_1' \end{bmatrix} = \begin{bmatrix} -(R_L'+R_{cr}') & -1 \\ 1 & 0 \end{bmatrix}\begin{bmatrix} i_1' \\ v_1' \end{bmatrix} + \begin{bmatrix} I \\ -I_o' \end{bmatrix} \quad (6)$$

where the primes indicate per-unit quantities.

In arriving at (6), a term $R_{cr}I_o/E_I$ in the first equation was dropped since the equivalent series resistance of the capacitor C_r is small.

Equation (6) can now be solved in piecewise linear fashion by assuming a desired output current I_o', frequency, input voltage $E_I = 1$, and arbitrary initial condition. The equations are integrated numerically (fourth-order Runge-Kutta) until the voltage on capacitor C_r is sensed to reverse. At that point, a new integration is started with the initial conditions equal to their current value but reversed (since current has changed direction due to the rectifier action). The integration is then continued until the end of that half-cycle. These final conditions are used as the initial conditions for the next cycle (except reversed in direction). Integration is continued cycle by cycle until two successive cycles are repeated within a specified tolerance, at which point steady state is assumed. When steady state is reached, the average value of the absolute value of one-half cycle of voltage across C_r is taken as the dc output voltage (the error due to the voltage drop across R_{cr} is neglected).

Several runs were made using this technique to obtain the transistor current waveforms, resonant capacitor voltage waveform, and to obtain the output voltage as a function of frequency. Fig. 14 shows several waveforms for various operating frequencies. The waveforms were multiplied by the base quantities in order to obtain actual values which will be compared to breadboard waveforms in the next section. As seen, the resonant capacitance was chosen as 0.1 μF, while the resonant inductor was chosen as 7.5 μH (an undamped resonant frequency of 184 kHz); the output dc voltage decreases as the frequency is increased from 180 kHz to 300 kHz. (Note: the scales on the various graphs are not identical.) As the frequency is raised, the capacitor voltage is damped to a lower value, and the FET current contains a more negative initial portion (i.e., the power factor is lower and more current is carried by the feedback diodes). The reverse diode current occurring just before turn-off confirms the negligible turn-on switching loss as expected (this diode current is indicated in Fig. 14(a)). As the frequency is raised, the diode conducts for a larger and larger fraction of the half-cycle, while the FET conducts for a smaller and smaller portion of the half-cycle. In the limit, each device conducts for one quarter-cycle. Since the turn-off time for the diode is equal to the FET conduction time, the shortest diode turn-off

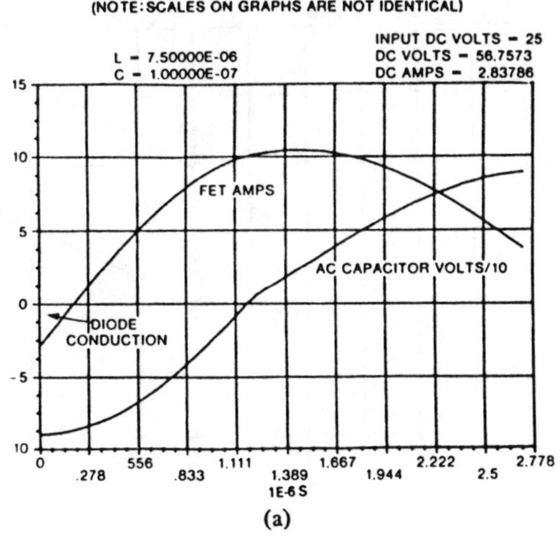

(a)

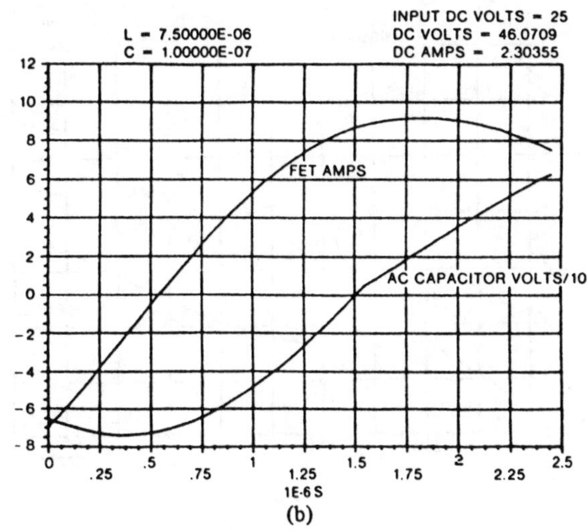

(b)

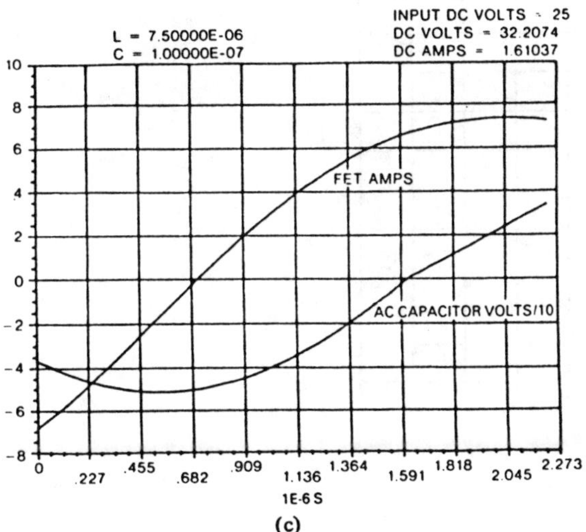

(c)

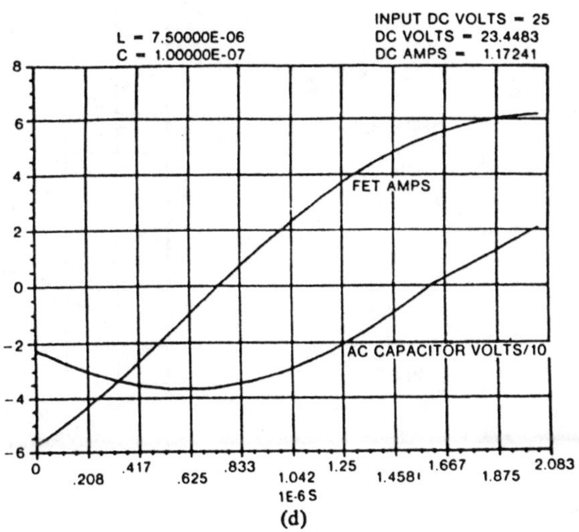

(d)

Fig. 14. Computed waveforms showing one half cycle of operation with operating frequency as a parameter. (Note: Scales on graphs are not identical.) (a) $f = 180$ KHz, (b) $f = 200$ KHz, (c) $f = 220$ KHz, (d) $f = 240$ KHz, (e) $f = 260$ KHz, (f) $f = 280$ KHz, and (g) $f = 300$ KHz.

time t_q ever encountered is known

$$t_q \geqslant \frac{1}{4f_{MAX}}. \tag{7}$$

Even at 300 kHz, a diode turn-off time of approximately 800 ns is encountered. It was found that the FET parasitic diode was adequate even at these high frequencies, as will be explained in the next section.

Fig. 15 shows a plot obtained by making several computer runs similar to those which resulted in the waveforms of Fig. 14. In order to obtain the low switching losses discussed above, the converter is always operated on the right side of the resonant curves (i.e., so that the resonant load presents a lagging power factor to the inverter). From these curves it is seen that the input voltage can be stepped up or down, and that the output voltage is a function of load resistance and frequency. Fig. 15 can be used as a design curve; given any voltage step-up/step-down ratio, desired operating frequency, and desired damping (i.e., value of R_o'), a unique L_r and C_r can be determined. Breadboard results are given in the next section.

IV. EXPERIMENTAL RESULTS

In order to verify the waveforms and the expected behavior of the voltage input resonant inverter, the circuit of Fig. 3 was breadboarded. International Rectifier IRF350's were used as the power devices (the FETs' parasitic diodes were used as the feedback diodes). Output inductor L_o was large enough so that negligible ripple current in the output current (I_o) was present. The half-bridge input capacitors were 1 μF each. The FET's were driven directly from small-pulse transformers (with a dead time during the switching intervals to prevent simultaneous conduction of series devices). Transformer coupling is simple due to the high frequencies involved and the square-wave operation of the inverter (no device conducts for more than a 50-percent duty cycle).

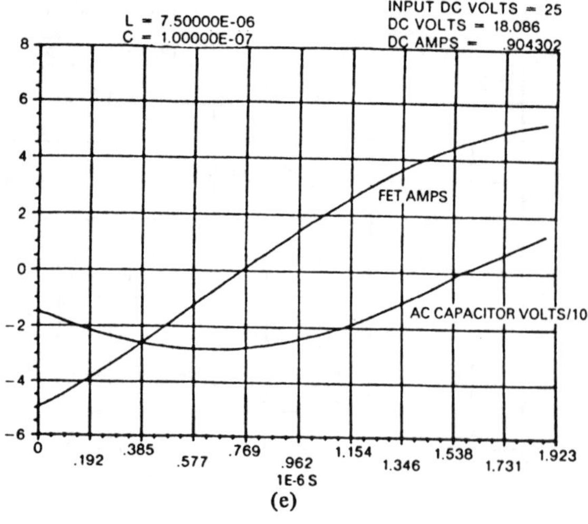

(e)

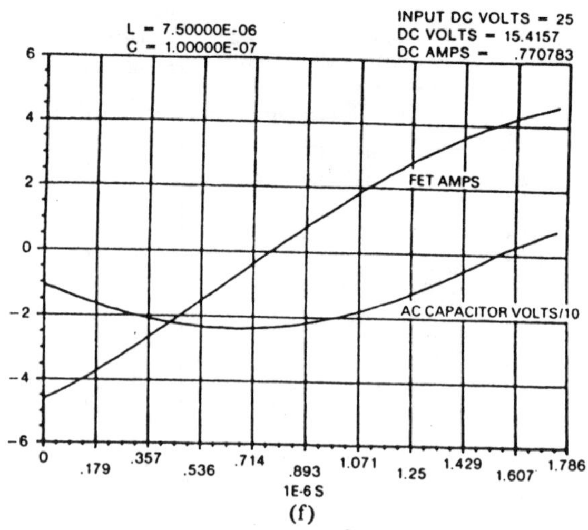

(f)

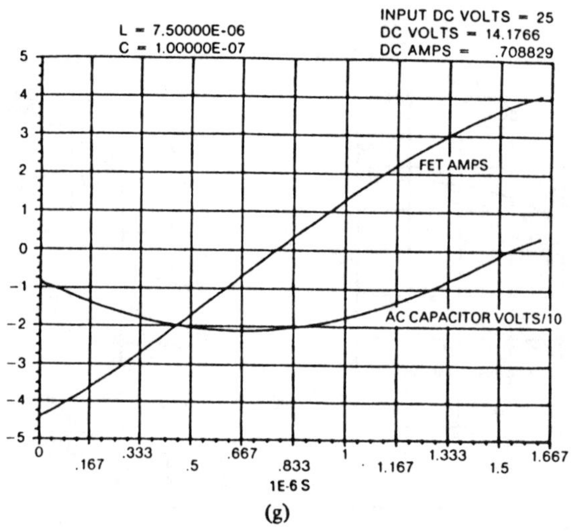

(g)

Fig. 14. (*Continued*).

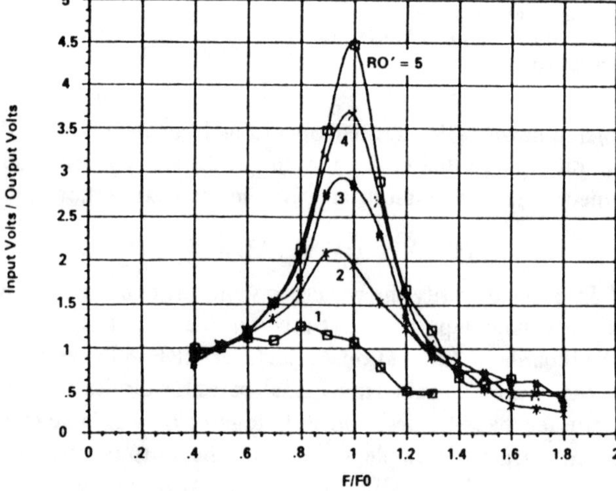

Fig. 15. Voltage ratio versus frequency.

Fig. 16(a)-(c) illustrates waveforms measured from the half-bridge inverter for the same parameters as listed in the computer runs of Fig. 14. As seen, the circuit behavior and waveforms agree well with those predicted. The magnitudes of FET current and output voltages, however, are lower than those predicted; that is, the resonant circuit is more damped than the analysis predicts. This additional damping is presumably due to the semiconductor voltage drops, capacitor and inductor equivalent series resistances, and wiring resistances at the high frequencies of interest. These resistances are included in the analysis ((6)), but the values of the breadboard components are not known.

The question arises as to whether the circuit will operate with no output inductor L_o. In this case, the ac voltage on capacitor C_r is rectified directly into a low impedance load. While this type of operation has not been analyzed to date, experimental waveforms have been obtained. The waveforms with inductor L_o of Fig. 17 may be compared with those of Figs. 18 through 21. For these cases, a resonant inductor of 21.7 μH and a resonant capacitor of 0.0376 μF were used, and a dc link voltage of 100 V was employed ($\cong \pm 50$ V applied to resonant circuit). As seen in Fig. 17, the waveforms with the dc inductor appear as expected. The waveforms of Fig. 18 were obtained by shorting inductor L_o without changing any other circuit parameters. As seen, the ac capacitor voltage is squared off due to the loading of the resonant capacitor by

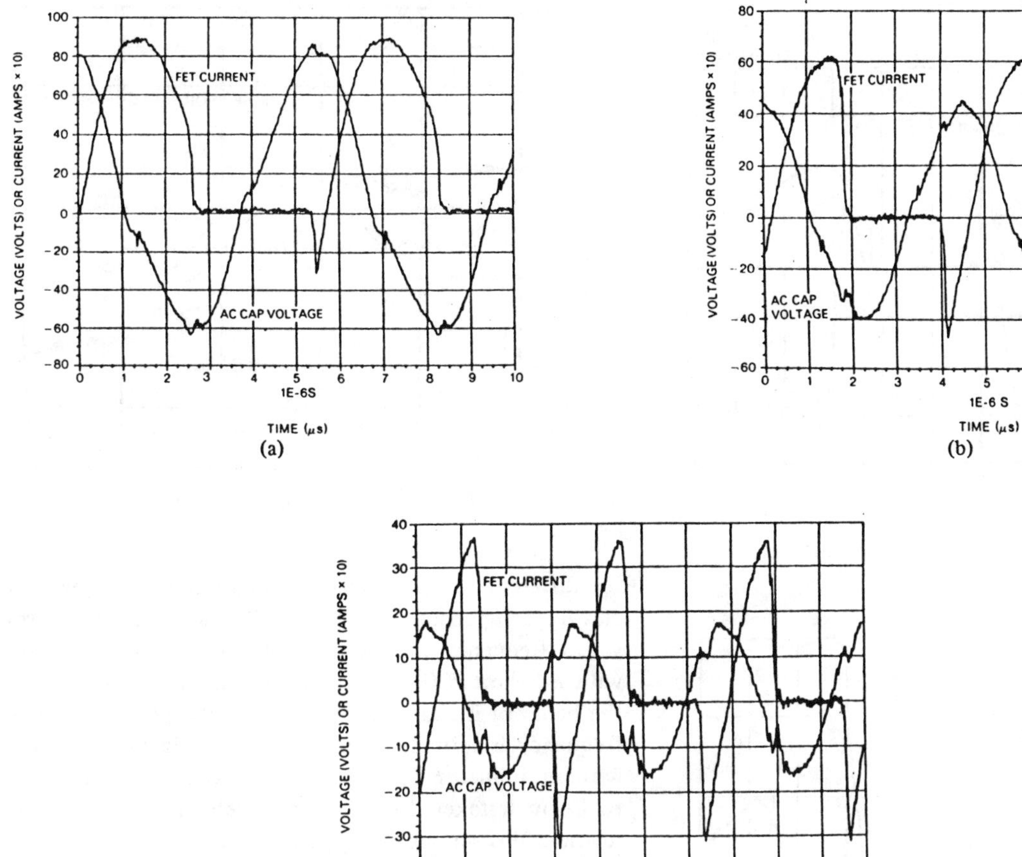

Fig. 16. Measured waveforms. (a) $V_{DC}=53$ V, $f_0=175.4$ KHz, $L=7.5$ μH, $C=.1$ μF, $R_L=20$ Ω; (b) $V_{DC}=53$ V, f=220 KHz, L=7.5 μH, C=0.1 μF, $R_L=20$ Ω; (c) $V_{DC}=53$ V, $f=300$ KHz, $L=7.5$ μH, $C=0.1$ μF, $R_L=20$ Ω.

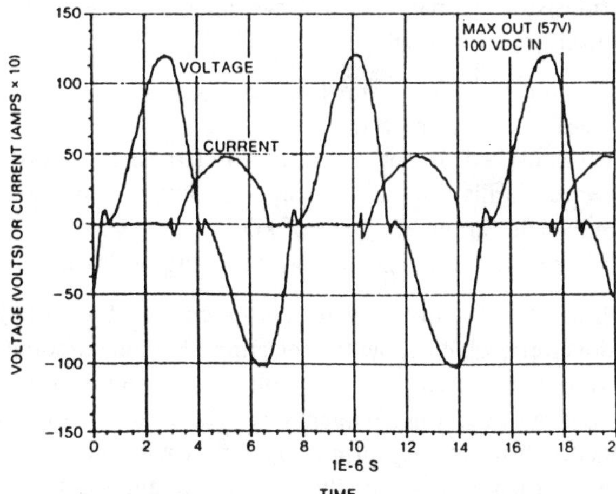

Fig. 17. AC capacitor volts and FET amps with choke.

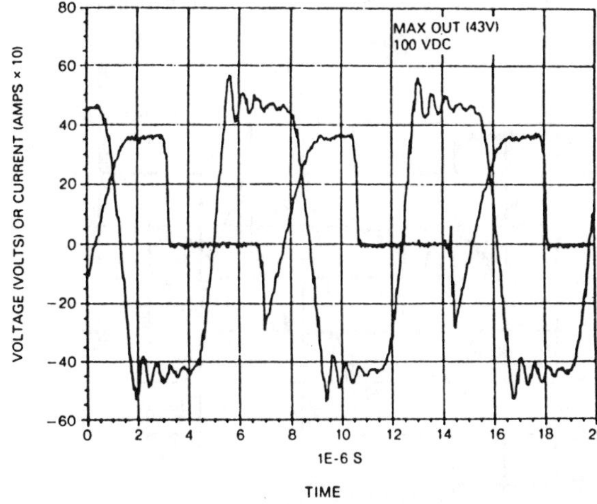

Fig. 18. AC capacitor volts and FET amps with choke shorted.

the dc capacitive filter. Also, the phase-shift between the capacitor voltage and device current has shifted, and more negative device current is present, indicating that the resonant load now appears to have a lower equivalent resonant frequency. This fact is verified by lowering the operating frequency to find the maximum output power frequency. These waveforms are shown in Fig. 19, and occur when the maximum power is being delivered to the load. It appears that the output filter capacitor has the effect of increasing the equivalent resonant capacitor value. Figs. 20 and 21 show waveforms

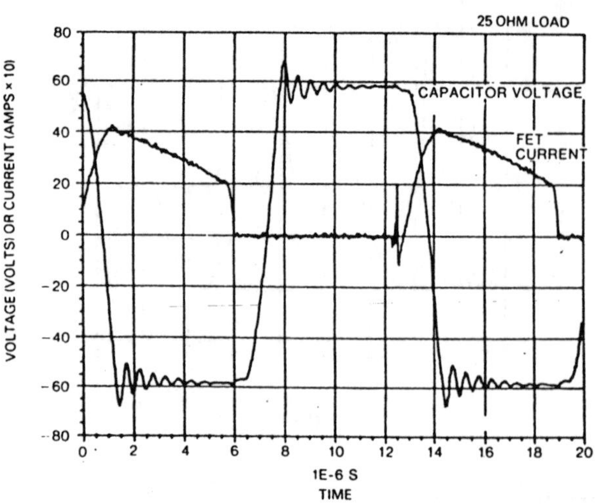

Fig. 19. Experimental waveforms—choke shorted.

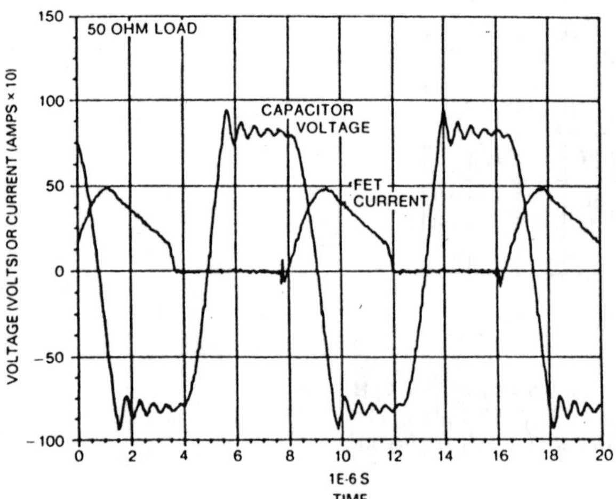

Fig. 20. Experimental waveforms—choke shorted.

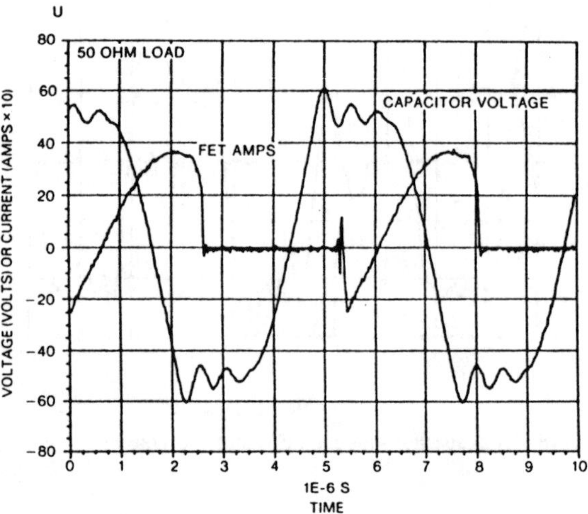

Fig. 21. Experimental waveforms—choke shorted.

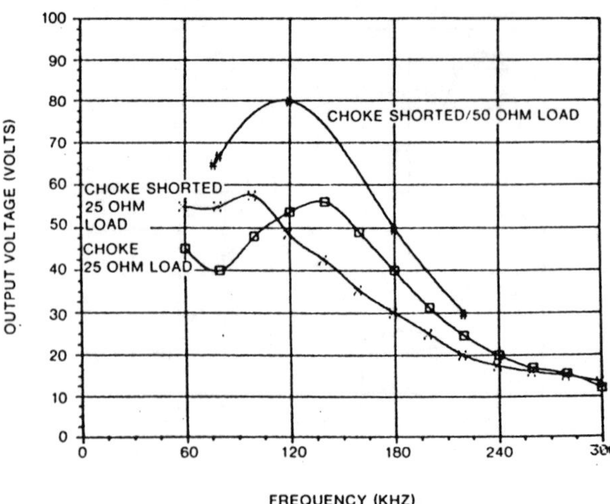

Fig. 22. Output voltage versus frequency.

for different values of load resistance and operating frequencies for comparison. Finally, Fig. 22 shows the output voltage versus frequency for the case with inductor L_o, and the case with L_o shorted (for two different load resistances). As seen, the behavior is similar for both cases, except that the resonant frequency is shifted. In summary, it is evident that operation without inductor L_o is possible; however, an analysis needs to be undertaken to obtain complete understanding of the relationships among component values, to develop a design methodology, as well as to make quantitative comparisons of the two cases.

V. SUMMARY AND CONCLUSIONS

Transistor dc-dc power converters have been described which are capable of operating in the hundreds of kilohertz range, and which employ a resonant circuit. The advantages of the transistor resonant converters which were verified by a low-power breadboard are:

- low switching losses and low transistor stresses due to lossless snubber operation;
- medium-speed diodes are sufficient (transistor parasitic inverse parallel diodes can be used), even for operating frequencies in the hundreds of kilohertz;
- ability to step the input voltage either up or down.

Normalized design curves were presented for the voltage input converters, which allow the selection of resonant components given the output load and voltage, the input voltage, and the desired operating frequency for the case of an inductor-capacitor filter at the output. Operation with a capacitive filter was verified experimentally, although an analysis for this case needs to be completed in order to derive accurate design curves.

A 500-W converter operating up to 300 kHz which employed FET power switches was described. The same circuits can be used with bipolar transistors or gate turn-off SCR's (GTO's) for considerably higher power levels. Several circuit alternatives were proposed. Since the same lossless snubber action will result, it is expected that operation at frequencies considerably higher than normally encountered will be possible, with corresponding energy efficiencies exceeding 90 percent. Future work should include further investigation of the various proposed circuit topologies and investigation of closed-loop feedback controls for the converters. Also, magnetic component design and construction techniques to reduce high-frequency losses should be investigated.

REFERENCES

[1] J. J. Biess, L. Y. Inouye, and J. H. Shank, "High voltage series resonant inverter ion engine screen supply," in *Power Electronics Specialists Conf. Rec.*, 1974, pp. 97-105.

[2] F. C. Schwarz and J. Ben Klaassens, "A controllable multikilowatt dc current source with constant maximum power factor in its three phase supply line," in *Power Electronics Specialists Conf. Rec.*, 1975, pp. 205-215.

[3] F. C. Schwarz, "An improved method of resonant current pulse modulation for power converters," *IEEE Trans. Ind. Electron. Contr. Instrum.*, vol. IECI-23, no. 2, pp. 133-141, May 1976.

[4] K. A. Check, "Designing improved high-frequency dc-dc converters with a new resonant thyristor technique," in *Proc. Power Con 6*, 1979, pp. F3-1-F3-7.

[5] L. Genuit, "Maximizing converter reliability with a thyristor high-frequency resonant technique," in *Proc. Power Con 8*, 1981, A-3, pp. 1-11.

[6] V. T. Ranganathan, P. D. Ziogas, and V. R. Stefanovic, "A regulated dc-dc voltage source converter using a high-frequency link," in *Ind. Appl. Soc. Conf. Rec.*, Oct. 1981, pp. 917-924.

[7] R. King and T. A. Stuart, "A normalized model for the half-bridge series resonant converter," *IEEE Trans. Aerospace Elect. Systs*, vol. AES-17, no. 2, pp. 190-198, Mar. 1981.

[8] E. E. Buchanan and E. J. Miller, "Resonant switching power conversion technique," *Power Electronics Specialists Conf. Rec.*, 1975, pp. 188-193.

[9] E. J. Miller, "Resonant switching power conversion," in *Power Electronics Specialists Conf. Rec.*, 1976, pp. 206-211.

[10] W. Ebbinge, "Designing very high efficiency converters with a new high frequency resonant GTO technique," in *Proc. Power Con 8*, 1981, A-1, pp. 1-7.

Paper 5.5

A Comparison of Half-Bridge Resonant Converter Topologies

ROBERT L. STEIGERWALD, SENIOR MEMBER, IEEE

Abstract—**The half-bridge series-resonant, parallel-resonant, and combination series-parallel resonant converters are compared for use in low output voltage power supply applications. It is shown that the combination series-parallel converter, which takes on the desirable characteristics of the pure series and the pure parallel converter, removes the main disadvantages of those two converters. Analyses and breadboard results show that the combination series-parallel converter can run over a large input voltage range and a large load range (no load to full load) while maintaining excellent efficiency. A useful analysis technique based on classical ac complex analysis is also introduced.**

Introduction

TO REDUCE the size of power supplies intended for use in modern computing systems, it is desirable to raise the operating frequency to reduce the size of reactive components. To reduce the higher switching losses resulting from higher frequency operation, resonant power conversion is receiving renewed interest. This paper will compare the series-resonant topology, parallel-resonant topology, and a combination series-parallel resonant topology for use in low output voltage power supply applications. It is shown that the combination series-parallel converter, which takes on the desirable characteristics of the pure series and the pure parallel converter, removes the main disadvantages of those two converters. In particular, it will be shown by analyses and breadboard results that the combination series-parallel converter can run over a large input voltage range and a large load range (no load to full load) while maintaining excellent efficiency. In addition, a useful analysis technique based on classical ac complex analysis is introduced.

Circuit Descriptions

Fig. 1 illustrates three types of resonant converters which may be used for high-frequency switching power supply applications. In the series-loaded circuit, the two capacitors $C_s/2$ form a series-resonant capacitor of value C_s. In the parallel-loaded converter C_p is the only resonant capacitor, while the capacitors $C_{in}/2$ serve only to split the input dc voltage. The series-parallel loaded converter has both series-resonant and parallel-resonant capacitors. All three of these converters result in low switching losses for the power devices. The circuits may be operated either above or below the resonant frequency of the resonant circuit. It is presently felt by the author that operation above resonance is preferred. This preference is explained by reference to Fig. 2.

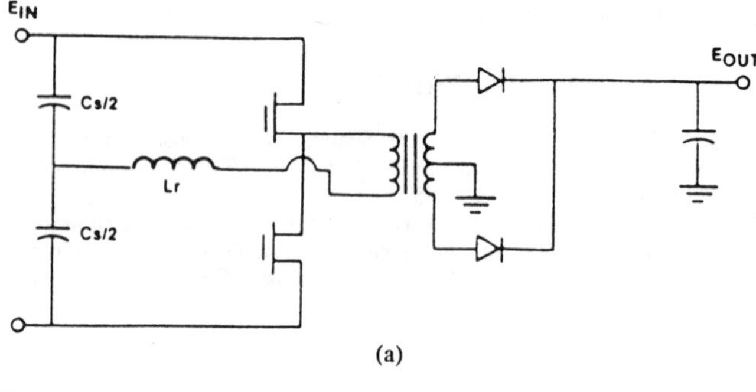

(a)

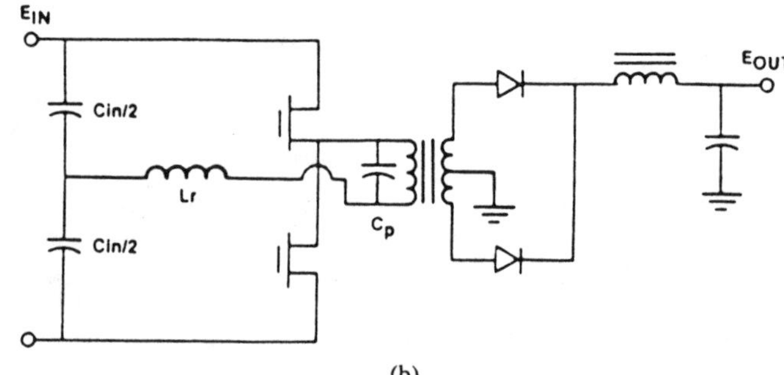

(b)

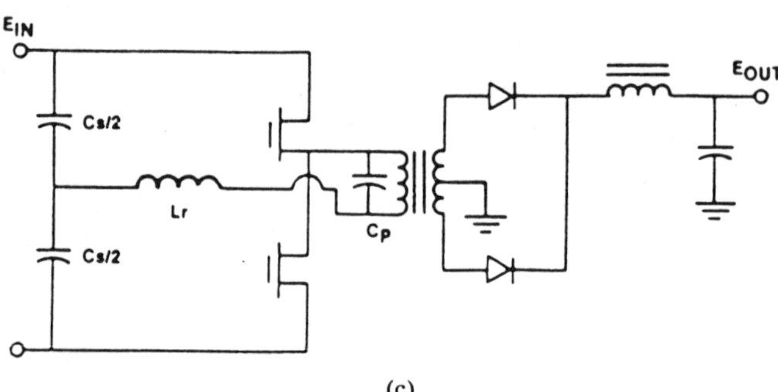

(c)

Fig. 1. Three types of half-bridge resonant converters. (a) Series loaded. (b) Parallel loaded. (c) Series-parallel loaded.

In Fig. 2 waveforms are shown for a resonant converter operating above resonance. In all three converters the half-bridge applies a square wave of voltage to the resonant circuit, and due to the filtering action of the resonant circuit, approximate sine waves of current are present in the resonant inductor L_r. The fact that the circuit is operating

Manuscript received March 10, 1987; revised December 1, 1987. This paper was presented at the 1987 Applied Power Electronics Conference, March 1987.

The author is with General Electric Company, Corporate Research and Development, P.O. Box 43, Building 37-473, Schenectady, NY 12301.

IEEE Log Number 8719321.

Reprinted from *IEEE Trans. Power Electron.*, vol. 3, no. 2, pp. 174–182, April 1988.

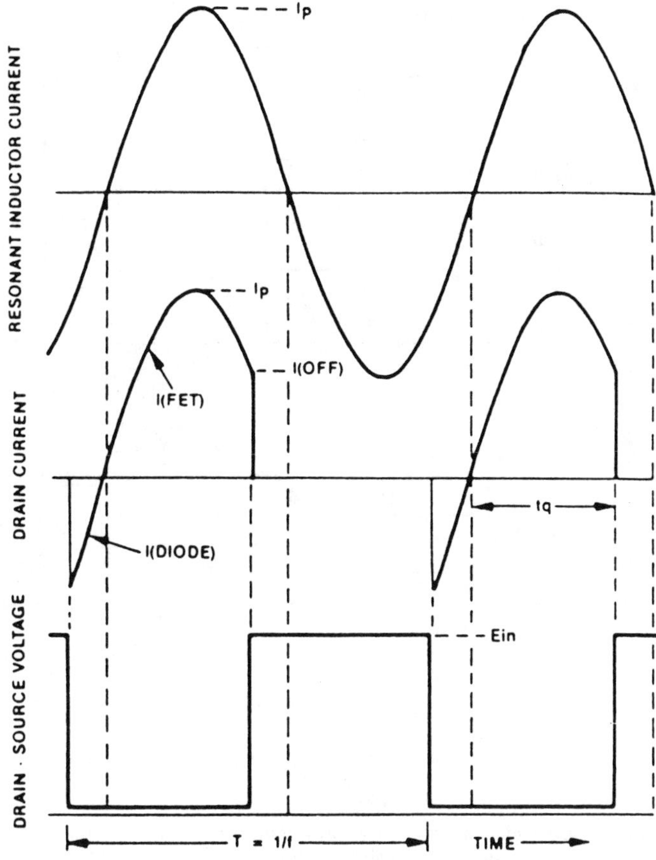

Fig. 2. Ideal resonant converter waveforms.

above resonance can be deduced from the fact that the current delivered to the resonant circuit (that is, the current in L_r) is lagging the voltage applied to the resonant circuit (that is, the fundamental component of the square wave applied by the half-bridge circuit). The current carried by the power FETs is a 180° section of this sine wave of current as illustrated in Fig. 2. From Fig. 2 it is seen that no turn-on switching losses exist in the FET because its inverse diode carries current and the voltage across the FET is zero before the FET conducts forward current. Note that the inverse FET current is caused by the opposite FET turning off. For example, if the bottom FET in the half-bridge turns off, the current that was in this FET is transiently maintained by the inductive action of the resonant inductor, which forces the current to come up through the upper FET in the inverse direction (i.e., through its inverse parasitic diode). Note also that once the current reverses due to the resonant action of the circuit, the inverse diode which was conducting has a turn-off time t_q equal to the forward conduction time of the power FET (see Fig. 2) before forward voltage is applied to the diode. This fact results in no switching stresses being applied to the diode, and, in fact, the inverse parasitic diode associated with power FETs (or bipolar Darlington transistors if used) are of sufficient speed to be useful even at circuit operating frequencies of hundreds of kHz.

Therefore, a main advantage of operating above resonance for the resonant converters is that there are no diode or FET switching losses and the diode can be of medium speed. Note, however, that to achieve those advantages the FETs must switch off current and are therefore subject to turn-off switching losses. However, lossless snubbers can simply be implemented by placing small snubber capacitors directly across the FET devices. No snubber discharge resistors are needed. This can be done because the capacitor is never discharged by turning the FET on but rather is discharged by turning off the opposite FET in the half-bridge. For example, when a bottom FET turns off, a capacitor which is placed directly across the upper FET will be discharged by the load current which will eventually be in the inverse parasitic diode of the upper FET.

Note also that considerable switching losses in power FETs operating at higher frequencies are actually due to storing energy in the FET drain-source and drain-gate capacitances and then discharging these capacitances internally (and losing the associated energy) the next time the FET turns on. This loss can be significant at higher voltages and frequencies. By operating the resonant converters above resonance, this loss is eliminated by the same argument put forth in the previous paragraph concerning lossless snubbers. That is, the energy stored in any capacitance directly across the device is returned to the dc source by virtue of the opposite FET turning off. In addition, the output and input filter sizes are minimized because the frequency is limited to a known lower limit (in operation below resonance the frequency is lowered to control output, and therefore the filters must be designed for the lowest frequencies encountered).

All of the aforementioned advantages are lost if the converter is operated below resonance. That is, below resonance operation results in FET turn-on switching losses, diode switching losses (high-speed diodes are needed), energy stored in device capacitances is discharged and lost internal to the FET's, and the input and output filters must be designed for the minimum switching frequency. FET turn-off does occur in a lossless manner when operating below resonance. However, because turn-off losses can be reduced using the lossless snubber technique when operating above resonance, this is not a major argument for operating the converter below resonance. For all of these reasons, it is felt that operation of resonant converters above resonance is the proper choice for most power supply applications operating at high frequencies. Therefore, the analyses to follow are all done for operation above resonance.

In the following sections an ac analysis technique is described, and the characteristics of each of the three resonant converters when operating above resonance are derived and compared. Further information can be found in [1] and [2], which give a detailed discussion and analysis of the parallel-resonant converter. In [3] a detailed analysis of the series-resonant converter is given. Small-signal stability considerations of resonant converters are given in [4]. The combination series/parallel resonant converter is introduced in [5]. An analysis of the combination series-parallel converter for the case of operation below resonance is given in [6].

Resonant Converter Circuit Analysis

For the three resonant converters considered here, the half-bridge converter applies a square wave of voltage to a resonant network. The resonant network has the effect of filtering the higher harmonic voltages so that, essentially, a sine wave of current appears at the input to the resonant circuit (this is true over most of the load range of interest). This fact allows classical ac analysis techniques to be used. The analysis proceeds as follows. The fundamental component of the square wave input voltage is applied to the resonant network, and the resulting sine waves of current and voltage in the resonant circuit are computed using classical ac analysis. For a rectifier with an inductor output filter, the sine wave voltage at the input to the rectifier is rectified, and the average value taken to arrive at the resulting dc output voltage. For a capacitive output filter, a square wave of voltage appears at the input to the rectifier while a sine wave of current is injected into the rectifier. For this case the fundamental component of the square wave voltage is used in the ac analysis.

It is important to note that the power supply load resistance is not the same load resistance which should be used in the ac analysis. The rectifier with its filter acts as an impedance transformer as far as the resonant circuit is concerned. This is due to the nonlinear nature of the rectifier.

Fig. 3 illustrates the derivation of the equivalent resistance to use in loading the resonant circuit when using an ac analysis. The parallel and series-parallel resonant converters use an inductor output filter and drive the rectifier with an equivalent voltage source (i.e., a low-impedance source provided by the resonant capacitor). A square wave of current is drawn by the rectifier, and its fundamental component must be used in arriving at an equivalent ac resistance. For this case, the equivalent ac resistance is given by

$$R_{ac} = \frac{\pi^2}{8} R_L. \tag{1}$$

Also given in the figure are the formulas for computing the fundamental ac components from the actual circuit values. The series-resonant converter uses a capacitive output filter and therefore drives the rectifier with a current source. A square wave of voltage appears at the input to the rectifier. For this case the equivalent ac resistance is given by

$$R_{ac} = \frac{8}{\pi^2} R_L. \tag{2}$$

Also given in the figure are formulas for computing fundamental ac components from the actual converter waveforms. In summary, classical ac analysis techniques can be used to investigate the characteristics of the three resonant converters by taking the fundamental components

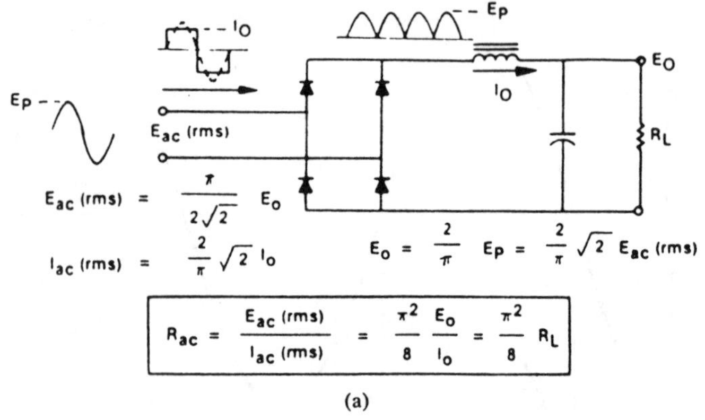

(a)

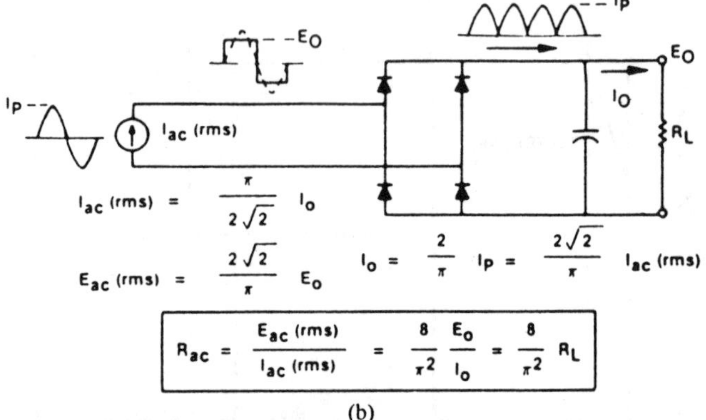

(b)

Fig. 3. Equivalent ac resistors as presented by rectifier loads. (a) Voltage source drive (applies to parallel and series-parallel converters). (b) Current source drive (applies to series converter).

of all the waveforms and by loading the resonant circuits with an equivalent resistance which takes into account the nonlinear behavior of the output rectifiers.

Analysis of Series-Resonant Converter

By using the equivalent load resistance R_{ac} and the ac analysis technique derived earlier, the characteristics of the series-resonant converter will be derived. The equivalent ac circuit of Fig. 4 will be used. The voltages designated by upper-case V's are the ac fundamental components present in the circuits. They will be converted to square waves where appropriate at the end of the analysis. By using the equation for a voltage divider, it is a simple matter to write down the ac gain of the series-resonant circuit (see top of Fig. 4):

$$\frac{V_0}{V_{IN}} = \frac{1}{1 + j\left[\frac{X_L}{R_{ac}} - \frac{X_C}{R_{ac}}\right]} \tag{3}$$

Note that V_{IN} is the fundamental component of the square wave of voltage applied to the resonant circuit by the inverter. This square wave of voltage is, for the half bridge converter, of magnitude $E_{IN}/2$ (see Fig. 1). Because the input to the resonant circuit is a square voltage wave and the output is also a square voltage wave, the converter gain in terms of actual converter values is given by the

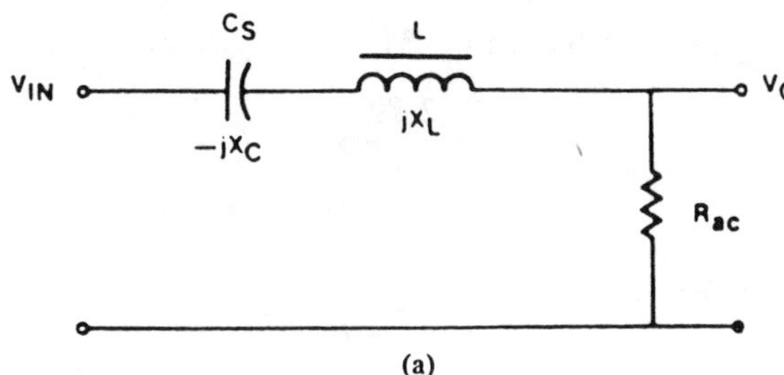

(a)

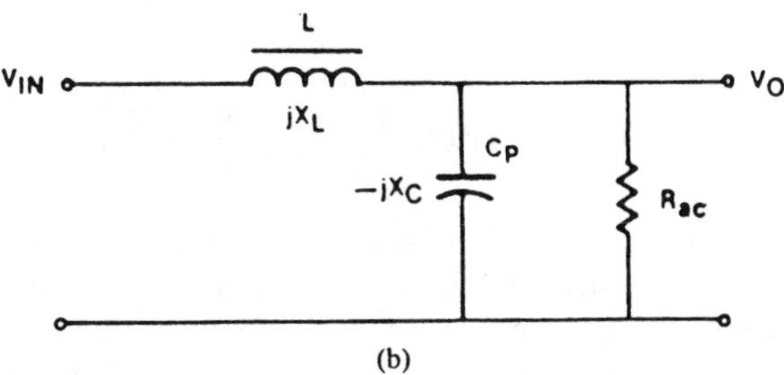

(b)

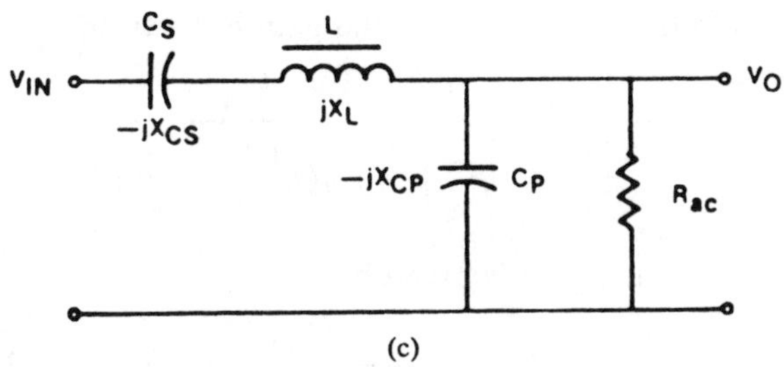

(c)

Fig. 4. AC equivalent circuits for resonant converters. (a) Series loaded. (b) Parallel loaded. (c) Series-parallel loaded.

same expression as before (the factor relating the fundamentals to the square wave magnitudes cancel on the left side of the foregoing equation):

$$\frac{E_0}{E_d} = \frac{1}{1 + j\left[\frac{X_L}{R_{ac}} - \frac{X_C}{R_{ac}}\right]} \tag{4}$$

where

$$E_d = \frac{E_{IN}}{2}. \tag{5}$$

Now substituting the fact that

$$R_{ac} = \frac{8}{\pi^2} R_L \tag{6}$$

and defining

$$Q = \frac{\omega_0 L}{R_L} \tag{7}$$

and

$$\omega_0 = \frac{1}{\sqrt{LC_s}} \tag{8}$$

results in the expression for the converter gain finally being given by

$$\frac{E_0}{E_d} = \frac{1}{1 + j\frac{\pi^2}{8}Q\left[\frac{\omega}{\omega_0} - \frac{\omega_0}{\omega}\right]}. \tag{9}$$

Note that the upper-case E's refer to the dc voltages which actually occur in the converter. E_d is the actual square wave voltage applied to the resonant circuit and for the half-bridge is equal to $E_{IN}/2$.

The previous equation is plotted in Fig. 5 for five values of Q. These curves may be considered accurate above resonance where the filtering action of the resonant circuit is sufficient to allow approximate sine waves of current to be in the circuit even though square waves of voltage excite the circuit.

Analysis of Parallel-Resonant Converter

A similar analysis can be carried out for the parallel-resonant converter. Using the equivalent resistance R_{ac} from Fig. 3 and the second equivalent circuit of Fig. 4, the ac gain of the circuit is given by

$$\frac{V_0}{V_{IN}} = \frac{1}{1 - \frac{X_L}{X_C} + j\frac{X_L}{R_{ac}}}, \tag{10}$$

for this case (see Fig. 3)

$$V_0 = \frac{\pi}{2\sqrt{2}} E_0 \tag{11}$$

and

$$V_{IN} = \frac{2\sqrt{2}}{\pi} E_d \tag{12}$$

where

$$E_d = \frac{V_{IN}}{2}. \tag{13}$$

Defining

$$Q = \frac{R_L}{\omega_0 L} \tag{14}$$

where

$$\omega_0 = \frac{1}{\sqrt{LC_p}}, \tag{15}$$

the dc gain of the parallel resonant converter is finally given by

$$\frac{E_0}{E_d} = \frac{1}{\frac{\pi^2}{8}\left[1 - \left[\frac{\omega}{\omega_0}\right]^2\right] + j\frac{\omega}{\omega_0}\left[\frac{1}{Q}\right]}. \tag{16}$$

This equation is plotted in Fig. 6. Note that the maximum output occurs near resonance for Q's above two or so and that the maximum output voltage can be computed from

$$\left(\frac{E_0}{E_{IN}}\right)_{max} = Q. \tag{17}$$

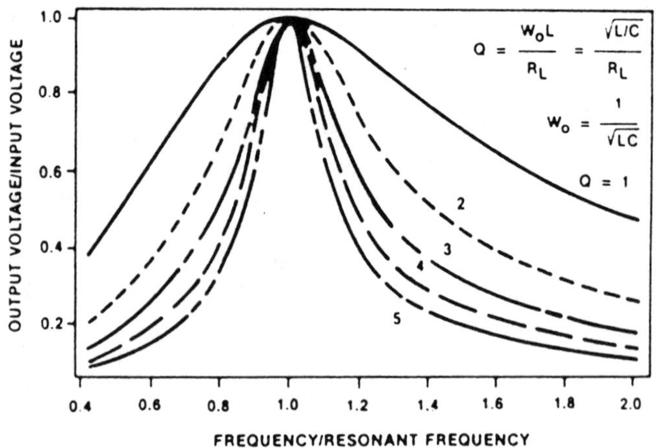

Fig. 5. Series-resonant converter gain (valid for frequencies at or above resonance only).

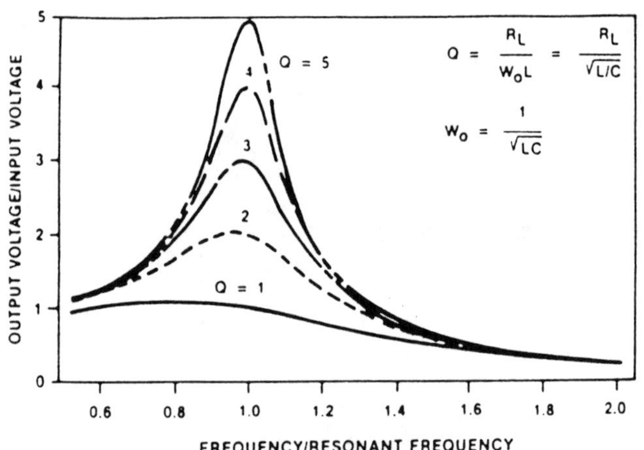

Fig. 6. Parallel-resonant converter gain (valid for frequencies at or above resonance only).

Again, these curves are accurate above resonance where the resonant circuit filters harmonics of the input square waves.

Analysis of Series-Parallel Converter

The analysis of the series-parallel resonant converter proceeds in a manner similar to the earlier ac analyses although more algebra is involved. Using classical ac analysis techniques, it can be shown that the gain of the third circuit of Fig. 4 is (using R_{ac} from Fig. 3)

$$\frac{V_0}{V_{IN}} = \frac{1}{1 + \frac{X_{CS}}{X_{CP}} - \frac{X_L}{X_{CP}} + j\left[\frac{X_L}{R_{ac}} - \frac{X_{CS}}{R_{ac}}\right]}. \tag{18}$$

Defining

$$Q_s = \frac{X_L}{R_L} \tag{19}$$

where

$$\omega_s = \frac{1}{\sqrt{LC_s}}, \tag{20}$$

and using the facts (see Fig. 3)

$$E_0 = \frac{2\sqrt{2}}{\pi} V_0 \tag{21}$$

and

$$V_{IN} = \frac{2\sqrt{2}}{\pi} E_d, \tag{22}$$

the gain of the series-parallel converter may be written as

$$\frac{E_0}{E_d} = \frac{1}{\frac{\pi^2}{8}\left[1 + \frac{C_P}{C_S} - \omega^2 LC_p\right] + jQ_s\left[\frac{\omega}{\omega_s} - \frac{\omega_s}{\omega}\right]}. \tag{23}$$

As seen from the previous expression, the gain will depend on the choice of the ratio of C_P to C_S, which also determines the parallel- or series-resonant characteristics of the circuit. The choice of this ratio will be discussed later. Here, the characteristic gain curves for two cases will be plotted. For $C_P = C_S$, the gain is given by

$$\frac{E_0}{E_d} = \frac{1}{\frac{\pi^2}{8}\left[2 - \left[\frac{\omega}{\omega_s}\right]^2\right] + jQ_s\left[\frac{\omega}{\omega_s} - \frac{\omega_s}{\omega}\right]}. \tag{24}$$

If $C_S = 2C_P$, the gain is given by

$$\frac{E_0}{E_d} = \frac{1}{\frac{\pi^2}{16}\left[3 - \left[\frac{\omega}{\omega_s}\right]^2\right] + jQ_s\left[\frac{\omega}{\omega_s} - \frac{\omega_s}{\omega}\right]}. \tag{25}$$

Figs. 7 and 8 show graphs of the previous two equations. Each curve is for a different value of Q_s, the series Q of the circuit. As seen, for series Q's above three or four, the peak of the resonant curves appear at approximately the same frequency given by the resonant frequency of the series capacitor and the series inductance. In other words, for these values of series Q's, the load resistance is low enough to approximately "short out" the parallel resonant capacitor, which results in the circuit approximating a series-resonant converter. As the converter is unloaded, the series Q expression decreases and the resonant peak moves higher in frequency. This is due to the fact that the equivalent resonant capacitance at light load is given by the parallel combination of the series- and parallel-resonant capacitors (see Fig. 4 for the case when R_{ac} is large). Finally, at light loads and no load, the resonant peak will occur at a frequency given by

$$f_{02} = \frac{1}{2\pi\sqrt{\frac{LC_pC_s}{C_P + C_S}}}. \tag{26}$$

Note that as the series Q expression results in a smaller value, the parallel Q expression (which is equal to the reciprocal of the series Q expression) results in a larger value. That is, as the load resistance goes from a small value to a large value, the circuit characteristics go from

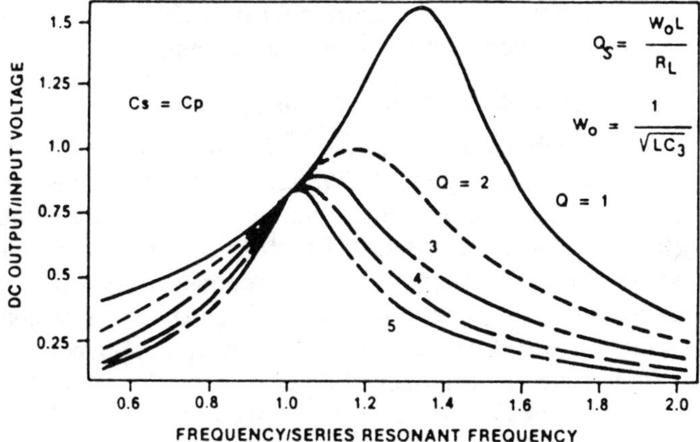

Fig. 7. Combination series-parallel converter gain (valid for frequencies at or above resonant peaks only).

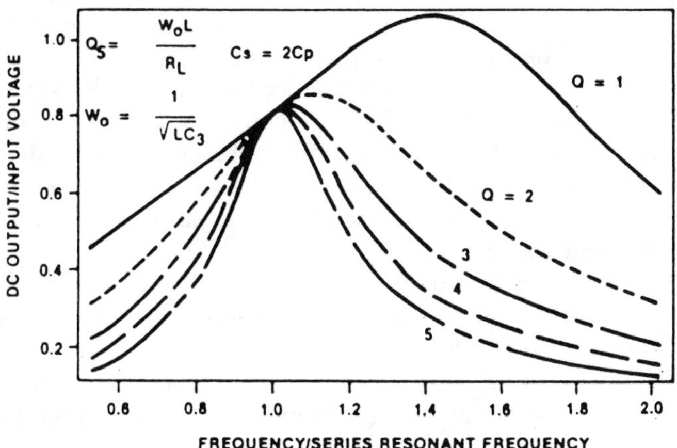

Fig. 8. Combination series-parallel converter gain (valid for frequencies at or above resonant peaks only).

those of a series-resonant to those of a parallel-resonant converter.

Comparison of Resonant Converter Topologies

In the following discussion the characteristics peculiar to each of the three resonant converter topologies analyzed will be discussed with a view toward selecting the proper converter for a given application.

Series-Resonant Converter

The series-resonant converter (top of Fig. 1) has the main disadvantage that the output voltage cannot be regulated for the no-load case. This can be seen from the characteristic resonant curves of Fig. 5. At $Q = 1$, for example, the curves have very little "selectivity," and, in fact, at no load the curve would simply be a horizontal line. This means that this converter would only be used "as is" in applications where no-load regulation was not required. A means of getting some no-load regulation would be to turn the converter on and off in a time ratio control fashion at a frequency much lower than the resonant frequency of the converter.

Another disadvantage of this converter is that the output dc filter capacitor must carry high ripple current (equal in magnitude to 48 percent of the dc output current). This is a significant disadvantage for applications with low output voltage and high current. For this reason the series-resonant converter is not considered suitable for low-output-voltage high-output-current converters but rather is more suitable for high-output-voltage low-output-current converters. For the high-output-voltage case no magnetic components are needed on the high-voltage side of the converter.

The main advantage of the converter is that the series-resonant capacitors on the primary side act as a dc blocking capacitor. Because of this fact the converter can easily be used in full-bridge arrangements without any additional control to control unbalance in the power FET switching times or forward voltage drops (i.e., dc currents are kept out of the transformer). For this reason the series-resonant converter is suitable for high-power applications where a full-bridge converter is desirable.

Another advantage of the series-resonant converter is that the currents in the power devices decrease as the load decreases. This advantage allows the power device conduction losses (as well as other circuit losses) to decrease as the load decreases, thus maintaining high part load efficiency. As will be seen in the next section, this is not the case for the parallel-resonant converter.

Note that if the converter is operating near resonance (i.e., at heavy load) and a short circuit is applied to the converter output, the current will rise to high values. To control the output current under such conditions, the frequency of the converter is raised by the control. Making the converter short circuit proof is relatively easy because it takes a few resonant cycles for the current to rise. This fact allows considerable time for the control circuit to take action.

Parallel-Resonant Converter

The characteristic gain curves for the parallel-resonant converter are given in Fig. 6. From these curves it is seen that, in contrast to the series-resonant converter, the converter is able to control the output voltage at no load by running at a frequency above resonance. Note also that the output voltage at resonance is a function of load and can rise to very high values at no load if the operating frequency is not raised by the regulator.

The main disadvantage of the parallel-resonant converter is that the current carried by the power FETs and resonant components is relatively independent of load. By way of illustration, Fig. 9 shows calculated values of input current to the resonant circuit (i.e., the current in the resonant inductor—which is also in the power FETs) as a function of load resistance. Also shown in the figure is the phase of the current relative to the fundamental of the square wave of voltage applied to the resonant circuit and the frequency of operation. As seen, as the load resistance increases (load decreases), the frequency of operation increases to regulate the output voltage, but the current into the resonant circuit stays relatively constant. The consequence of this behavior is that the conduction losses in

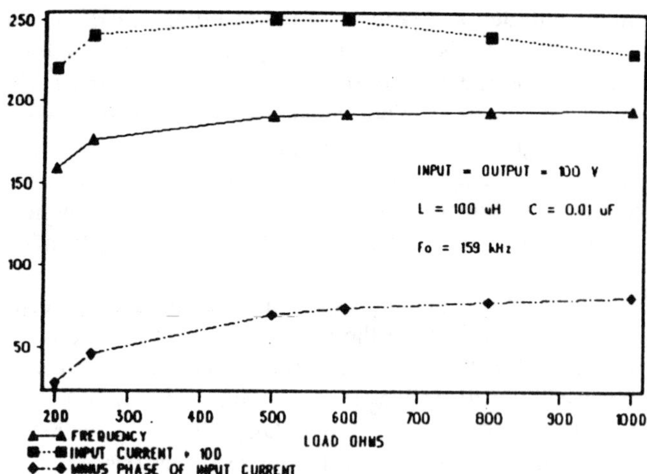

Fig. 9. Characteristics of parallel-resonant converter.

the FETs and the reactive components stay relatively fixed as the load decreases so that the light-load efficiency of the converter suffers. In addition, this circulating current increases as the input dc voltage to the converter increases. Thus this converter is less than ideal for applications which have a large input voltage range and which require it to operate considerably below its maximum design power while maintaining very high efficiency. Conversely, the converter is better suited to applications which run from a relatively narrow input voltage range (e.g., plus or minus 15 percent) and which present a more or less constant load to the converter near the maximum design power (e.g., 75 percent of maximum design power). Of course, the power converter must be designed thermally for the maximum power and, therefore, has no problem running at reduced power thermally—only the part-load efficiency is less than the full-load efficiency.

The parallel-resonant converter is suitable for low-output-voltage high-output-current applications. This is due to the fact that the dc filter on the low-voltage-output side of the transformer is of the inductor input type and, therefore, dc output capacitors capable of carrying very high ripple currents are not needed. The inductor limits the ripple current carried by the output capacitor. Note also that the transformer leakage inductance could be used as the resonant inductance by placing the resonant capacitor across the total span of the secondary winding. This is normally not ideal for low output voltages because the capacitor would have to carry too much ac current. However, for higher output voltage converters this placement of the resonant capacitor may be desirable. Also, the resonant capacitor can be placed on a tertiary transformer winding. These alternate arrangements are discussed more fully in [1].

The parallel-resonant converter is naturally short circuit proof. This property can be seen by applying a short directly across the resonant capacitor. For that case, the entire square wave voltage applied by the inverter is directly across the resonant inductor and, therefore, the current is limited by this impedance. This property makes the parallel-resonant converter extremely desirable for applications with severe short circuit requirements.

Combination Series-Parallel Converter

The combination series-parallel converter attempts to take advantage of the best characteristics of the series and the parallel converter while eliminating their weak points (lack of no-load regulation for the series-resonant converter and circulating current independent of load for the parallel-resonant converter). As will be shown, this goal is met by proper selection of the resonant components but a somewhat wider frequency range of operation is needed.

By viewing the characteristic gain curves of Figs. 7 and 8, it is clear that the converter can operate and regulate at no load provided that the parallel-resonant capacitor C_p is not too small (if C_p is zero, then the circuit reverts to the series-resonant converter). It is seen that the smaller C_p is, the less "selectivity" is available in the resonant curves. That is, the converter resembles a series converter more and more as C_p gets smaller and smaller. However, for reasonable values of C_p the converter will clearly operate with no load, which removes the main disadvantage of the series-resonant converter. In doing this, the converter takes on some of the characteristics of the parallel-resonant converter.

It is desirable that the main disadvantage of the parallel-resonant converter (constant circulating current independent of load) not be present in this converter. This will be true but only for certain component values. This can be seen in the calculated curves of Fig. 10 which give the input current to the resonant circuit (i.e., the current in the resonant inductance) as a function of load resistance. As seen for these sample component values, the input current decreases as the load decreases (resistance increases) as desired. This curve may be compared with that of Fig. 9 for the straight parallel-resonant converter. It was noted that for other values of the circuit components no current decrease was achieved.

The effect of decreasing C_p was shown in Figs. 7 and 8, respectively. As C_p gets smaller relative to C_s, the curves have less "selectivity." For example, if it is desirable to maintain the output voltage at a normalized value of 0.6 at a light load of $Q = 1$, Fig. 7 shows that the frequency of operation needed is approximately 1.7. On the other hand, Fig. 8 shows that a frequency of 2 is needed. In other words, as C_p gets smaller, the upper frequency needed at light loads increases. This is the limiting factor in reducing C_p to reduce circulating current.

To have the circulating current decrease with load to maintain high part-load efficiency, it is desirable to select the converter components so that the full load Q is in the neighborhood of 4 or 5. For these values of Q_s the converter appears essentially as a series-resonant converter and the circulating current will decrease as the load decreases. As the load decreases further, the converter takes on the characteristics of a parallel-resonant converter, and the circulating current no longer decreases with load.

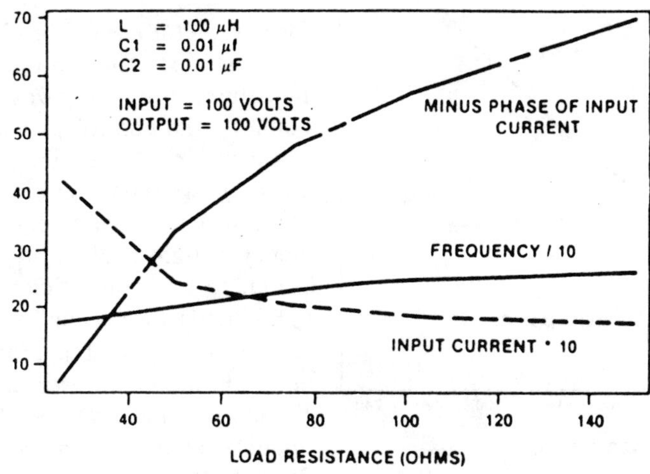

Fig. 10. Characteristics of combination series-parallel converter.

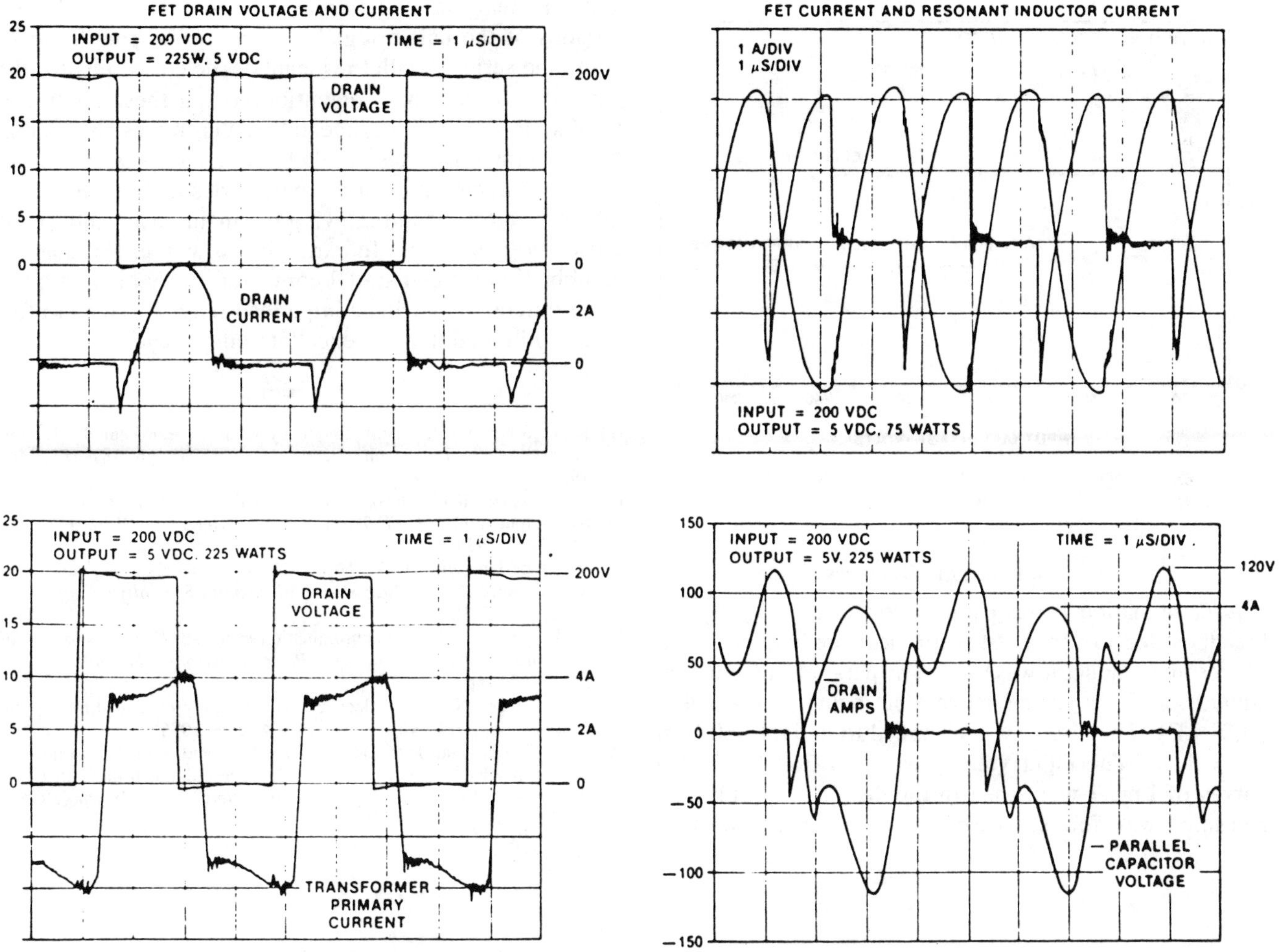

Fig. 11. Breadboard waveforms.

However, for the case of $C_p = C_s$ the circulating current decreases approximately 2 to 1 as the load decreases from its full-load value. Because the losses due to the circulating current are proportional to the square of the current, the conduction losses are decreased 4 to 1 over their full-load value. This decrease is sufficient to maintain good part-load efficiency. Therefore, it is felt that $C_s = C_p$ is a good compromise design which gives good part-load efficiency while allowing regulated operation at no load with a reasonable upper frequency.

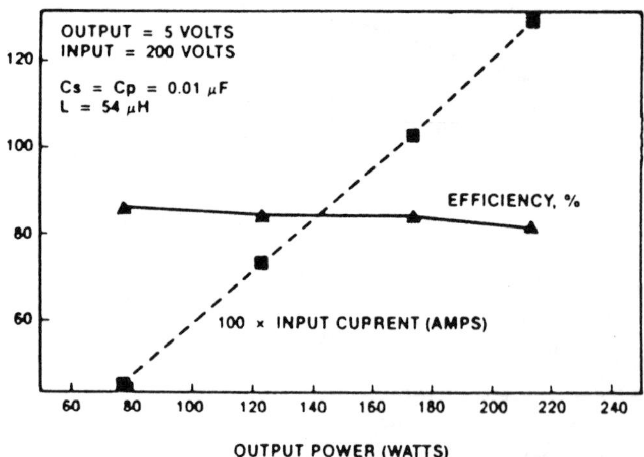

Fig. 12. Performance of combination series-parallel converter breadboard.

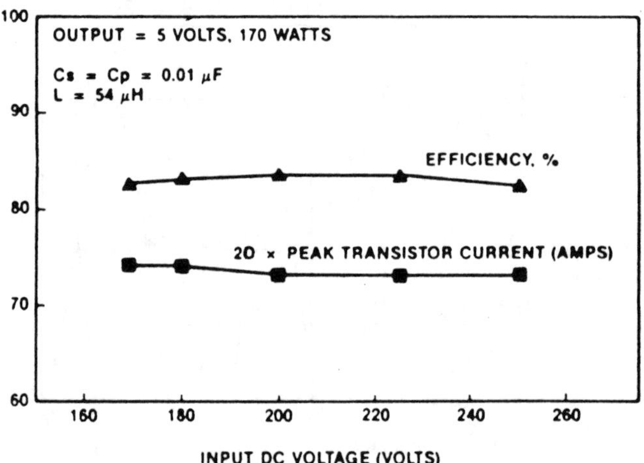

Fig. 13. Performance of combination series-parallel converter breadboard.

Experimental Results

A combination series-parallel converter (Fig. 1) was breadboarded to verify the theoretical predictions. A 48-μH resonant inductor was used. The parallel capacitor and equivalent series capacitor were set equal to each other (0.01 μF). The circuit was designed to deliver 250 W to a 5-V load. The input voltage was 180–360 V dc. The curves of Fig. 7 were used in the design. Fig. 11 gives measured waveforms. These may be compared with the ideal waveforms of Fig. 2. As seen, lossless turn-on is demonstrated, and the current waveforms are sinusoidal in nature. Fig. 12 gives the measured efficiency (not counting the control power) and the peak current to the resonant circuit (i.e., the peak FET current or circulating current). As seen, the circulating current decreases with load, which accounts for the excellent hold-up of efficiency at light load.

Fig. 13 gives the efficiency and peak circulating current (peak transistor current) as a function of input dc voltage to the converter at approximately 70-percent load. As seen, these quantities remain approximately constant as the input voltage varies. The frequency varied between approximately 250 and 380 kHz for a load variation of 75–225-W output and a constant 200-V dc input.

Summary and Conclusion

An ac analysis method was used to derive the characteristics of the half-bridge series-resonant, parallel-resonant, and series-parallel resonant dc-dc converters for the case of super-resonant operation. Using these analytical results, as well as experimental results, it was shown that the combination series-parallel converter takes on the desirable characteristics of the pure series and the pure parallel converter while removing the main disadvantages of those two converters. In particular, it was shown that the combination series-parallel converter can run over a large input voltage range and a large load range (no load to full load) while maintaining excellent efficiency.

References

[1] R. L. Steigerwald, "High frequency resonant transistor dc-dc converters," *IEEE Trans. Ind. Electron.*, vol. IE-31, pp. 181–191, May 1984.

[2] ——, "Analysis of a resonant transistor dc-dc converter with capacitive output filter," *IEEE Trans. Ind. Electron.*, vol. IE-32, pp. 439–444, Nov. 1985.

[3] V. Volperian and S. Cuk, "A complete dc analysis of the series resonant converter," in *IEEE Power Electronics Specialists Conf. Rec.*, 1982, pp. 85–100.

[4] V. Volperian, "High-*Q* approximation in the small-signal analysis of resonance converters," in *IEEE Power Electronics Specialists Conf. Rec.*, 1985, pp. 707–715.

[5] D. V. Jones, "Compact electrical power supply for signal processing applications," US Patent 4,533,986, Aug. 6, 1985.

[6] A. K. S. Bhat and S. B. Dewan, "Analysis and design of a high frequency resonant converter using *LCC* type commutation," in *Conf. Rec. 1986 IEEE Industry Applications Society Annual Meeting*, 1986, pp. 657–663.

Paper 5.6

A Normalized Model for the Half-Bridge Series Resonant Converter

R. KING AND T. A. STUART, SENIOR MEMBER, IEEE
University of Toledo

Abstract

Closed-form steady-state equations are derived for the half-bridge series resonant converter with a rectified (dc) load. Normalized curves for various currents and voltages are then plotted as a function of the circuit parameters. Experimental results based on a 10-kHz converter are presented for comparison with the calculations.

I. Introduction

The need for both higher power and less weight in aerospace power systems presents a continual problem for the power supply designer. As new components are developed, it becomes necessary to reexamine previous design techniques in order to obtain the full benefit of this changing technology. This reevaluation process is obviously enhanced by accurate and easy-to-use models that are readily understood by most power supply engineers. Straightforward models of this type are not always available, however, and this often leads to confusion in evaluating power supply design alternatives.

One of the more prevalent examples of this modeling problem is the series resonant converter, which is widely used for dc-to-dc conversion in aerospace power supplies. The high power/weight ratio and efficiency advantages of this circuit are widely recognized, and it has been analyzed extensively [1-7, 9]. A considerable amount of effort has also been spent on developing computer simulations of this circuit [8, 10], and the accuracy of some of these is quite remarkable. However, in spite of this widespread attention this circuit continues to present formidable design problems, and there is a strong need for more straightforward models. Many of the relationships between the various circuit parameters demand further clarification and engineers are in need of more detailed design tools.

Manuscript received June 13, 1980.

This research was supported by the National Aeronautics and Space Administration Lewis Research Center under Grant NSG-3281.

Authors' address: Department of Electrical Engineering, University of Toledo, 2801 W. Bancroft St., Toledo, OH 43606.

Perhaps the most complete analysis of the series resonant converter to date is that in the paper by Schwarz [6]. For completeness the present paper includes the derivation of many of the equations originally presented in [6]. However the present work includes more details of these derivations, along with several results that apparently have not been discussed in the previous literature. Analyses are included for both continuous and discontinuous load current, and many of the more important results are presented in the form of normalized graphs. These normalized graphs are also compared with experimental data based on a 10-kHz converter.

Nomenclature

A, B	Terms defined by (17) and (18).
C	Capacitance value of resonance capacitors.
E_L	Energy supplied to load.
E_S	Energy obtained from source.
I_{avg}	Half-cycle average output current at primary of transformer.
$I_{D\,avg}$	Average diode current.
I_{L0}, I_{L2}	i_L at $t = 0$ and at $t = t_2$.
I_{peak}	Peak value of output current at primary of transformer.
$I_{Q\,avg}$	Average transistor current.
I_{rms}	RMS output current at primary of transformer.
$i_{1,2,3}$	Loop currents.
i_L	$= i_1 - i_2$, output current at primary of transformer.

Reprinted from *IEEE Trans. Aerosp. Electron. Syst.*, vol. AES-17, no. 2, pp. 190–198, March 1981.

L	Inductance value of resonance inductor.
q	Normalized load voltage defined by (2).
$V_{c\ peak}$	Peak capacitor voltage.
V_{ci}	Voltage across capacitor C_i.
V_{ij}	Voltage across capacitor i at time t_j.
V_0	Amplitude of square-wave output voltage at primary of transformer. V_0 is always considered positive.
V_0'	DC load voltage.
V_s	DC source voltage.
Z_o	Impedance term defined by (2).
α	Delay angle.
β	Transistor conduction angle.
w_o	Resonance frequency (in radians per second) defined by (2).

II. Equations for Continuous Load Currents

The basic schematic and the continuous output current waveform of a half-bridge series resonant converter are shown in Figs. 1 and 2, respectively. Although the circuit diagram indicates bipolar transistors for the switching devices, the analysis is equally valid for other devices such as thyristors or power metal-oxide-semiconductor field-effect transistors (MOSFETs). Additional components such as the snubber circuits and small series inductors commonly used with the thyristor version should not affect the model as long as they do not markedly alter the natural resonant frequency.

This model includes the following approximations:

1) The output voltage V_0' is assumed to be constant. This implies that the transformer primary voltage V_0 can be viewed as a dc source that changes polarity so as to oppose i_1 or i_2.

2) All components are assumed to be ideal, implying that all circuit losses are included with the output power.

We define the following terms:

$$V_{10} \equiv v_{c1}(0), \quad V_{11} \equiv v_{c1}(t_1), \quad V_{12} \equiv v_{c1}(t_2),$$

$$V_{20} \equiv v_{c2}(0) = V_s - V_{10}, \quad V_{21} \equiv v_{c2}(t_1) = V_s - V_{11} \quad (1)$$

$$w_o \equiv 1/\sqrt{2LC}, \quad Z_o \equiv \sqrt{L/2C}, \quad q \equiv 2V_0/V_s \quad (2)$$

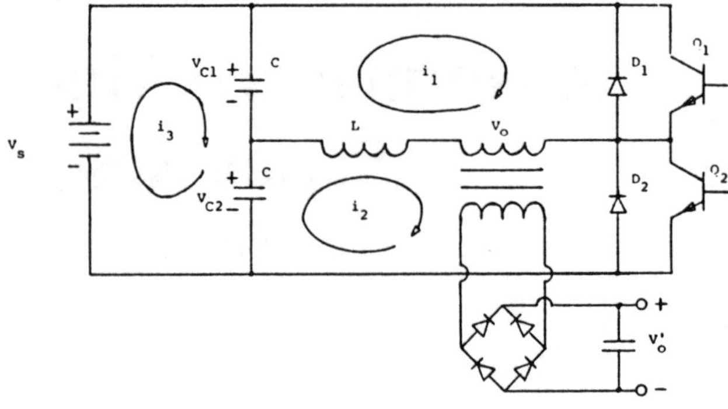

Fig. 1. Basic schematic of half-bridge series resonant converter. The polarity of V_O is always such that it opposes current in transformer primary.

Fig. 2. Typical normalized load current waveform in continuous current operation ($q = 0.7, \alpha = 80^\circ, \beta = 156^\circ$).

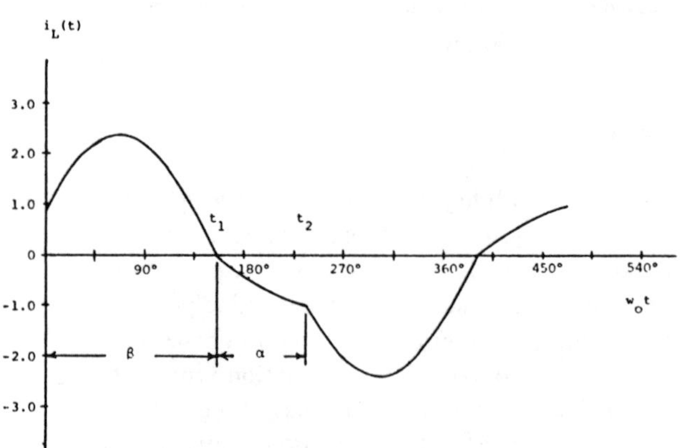

$$\alpha \equiv w_o(t_2 - t_1), \quad \text{where } \alpha \leqslant 180^\circ \text{ for continuous conduction}$$

$$\beta \equiv w_o t_1, \qquad t' \equiv t - t_1 \ . \quad (3)$$

Note that the switching delay angle α and the switch conduction angle β are defined simply as certain time periods multiplied by w_o and that the radian frequency of i_L is always $\leqslant w_o$.

If Q_1 is turned on at $t = 0$ (Q_2 is turned on at t_2) and

$$i_{1(0)} \equiv I_{L0} \quad (4)$$

we have

$$i_1(t) = I_{L0} \cos(w_o t) + [(V_{10} - V_0)/Z_o] \sin(w_o t), \quad 0 \leqslant t \leqslant t_1 \quad (5)$$

$$i_1(t') = [(V_{11} + V_0)/Z_o] \sin(w_o t'), \quad 0 \leqslant t' \leqslant t_2 - t_1 \ . \quad (6)$$

Since $i_1(t) = 0$ at $w_o t = \beta$ and $\beta > 0$, we have

$$\beta \equiv w_o t_1 = \tan^{-1}[(-I_{L0} Z_o / V_{10} - V_0)] + \pi \; . \tag{7}$$

For the i_3 loop,

$$(2/C)\int_0^t i_3(t)\,dt - (1/C)\int_0^t i_1(t)\,dt + V_{10} + V_{20} = V_s, \quad 0 \leqslant t \leqslant t_1 \tag{8}$$

but from (1), $V_s = V_{10} + V_{20}$ and therefore

$$i_3(t) = i_1(t)/2, \quad 0 \leqslant t \leqslant t_1 \tag{9}$$

$$v_{c1}(t) = V_{10} + (1/C)\int_0^t -[i_1(t)/2]\,dt, \quad 0 \leqslant t \leqslant t_1$$

$$= -I_{L0} Z_o \sin(w_o t) + (V_{10} - V_0)\cos(w_o t) + V_0 \tag{10}$$

$$V_{11} = v_{c1}(t_1) = -I_{L0} Z_o \sin\beta + (V_{10} - V_0)\cos\beta + V_0 \; . \tag{11}$$

Likewise,

$$v_{c1}(t') = V_{11} + (1/C)\int_0^{t'} -[i_1(t')/2]\,dt', \quad 0 \leqslant t' \leqslant t_2 - t_1$$

$$= (V_{11} + V_0)\cos(w_o t') - V_0 \tag{12}$$

$$V_{12} = v_{c1}(t' = t_2 - t_1) = (V_{11} + V_0)\cos\alpha - V_0 \; . \tag{13}$$

For cyclic stability, the conditions at t_2 must be symmetric with those at $t = 0$; therefore,

$$V_{12} = V_s - V_{22} = V_s - V_{10} \text{ and } I_{L2} = -I_{L0} \; . \tag{14}$$

The energy into the load during $0 \leqslant t \leqslant t_2$ is given by the following expressions:

$$E_{L1} = |V_0| \int_0^{t_1} i_1(t)\,dt$$

$$= (V_0/w_o)\{I_{L0}\sin\beta - [(V_{10} - V_0)/Z_o](\cos\beta - 1)\} \tag{15}$$

$$E_{L2} = -|V_0| \int_0^{t_2 - t_1} i_1(t')\,dt', \quad \text{(the sign of } V_0 \text{ reverses)}$$

$$= (V_0/w_o)(1 - \cos\alpha)\{I_{L0}\sin\beta - [(V_{10} - V_0)/Z_o] \cdot \cos\beta - (2V_0/Z_o)\} \; . \tag{16}$$

Define the following terms:

$$A \equiv \{I_{L0}\sin\beta - [(V_{10} - V_0)/Z_o](\cos\beta - 1)\} \tag{17}$$

$$B \equiv (1 - \cos\alpha)\{I_{L0}\sin\beta - [(V_{10} - V_0)/Z_o] \cdot \cos\beta - (2V_0/Z_o)\} = (1 - \cos\alpha)[A - (V_{10} + V_0)/Z_o] \; . \tag{18}$$

Therefore the total energy into the load during the interval $0 \leqslant t \leqslant t_2$ is

$$E_L \equiv E_{L1} + E_{L2} = (|V_0|/w_o)(A + B) \; . \tag{19}$$

The energy from the source V_s is given by

$$E_{S1} = V_s \int_0^{t_1} i_3(t)\,dt = (V_s/2)\int_0^{t_1} i_1(t)\,dt$$

$$= V_s A / 2w_o \tag{20}$$

$$E_{S2} = V_s \int_0^{t_2 - t_1} i_3(t')\,dt' = (V_s/2)\int_0^{t_2 - t_1} i_1(t')\,dt'$$

$$= -V_s B / 2w_o \; . \tag{21}$$

Therefore the total energy from V_s during the interval $0 \leqslant t \leqslant t_2$ is

$$E_s = (V_s/2w_o)(A - B) \; . \tag{22}$$

The energy stored in the circuit elements at t_0 is given by

$$E_{STO} = \tfrac{1}{2} L I_{L0}^2 + \tfrac{1}{2} C V_{10}^2 + \tfrac{1}{2} C (V_S - V_{10})^2 \; . \tag{22a}$$

The energy stored in the circuit elements at t_2 is given by

$$E_{ST_2} = \tfrac{1}{2} L I_{L2}^2 + \tfrac{1}{2} C V_{12}^2 + \tfrac{1}{2} C (V_S - V_{12})^2 \; . \tag{22b}$$

Substituting from (14),

$$E_{ST2} = \tfrac{1}{2} L (-I_{L0})^2 + \tfrac{1}{2} C (V_S - V_{10})^2 + \tfrac{1}{2} C (V_{10})^2$$

or

$$E_{STO} = E_{ST2} \; . \tag{22c}$$

Therefore, since the stored energy is the same at t_0 and t_2 and the circuit components were assumed to be ideal,

$$E_S = E_L \tag{23}$$

$$(V_s/2w_o)(A - B) = (V_0/w_o)(A + B) \tag{24}$$

or

$$q \equiv (2V_0/V_s) = (A - B)/(A + B) \tag{25}$$

and

$$(B/A) = (1 - q)/(1 + q) \; . \tag{26}$$

We now want to consider the capacitor voltage relationships. From (11) and (17),

$$V_{11} = V_{10} - A Z_o \; . \tag{27}$$

From (13) and (27),

$$V_{12} = (V_{10} - A Z_o + V_0)\cos\alpha - V_0 = Z_o(1 - \cos\alpha) \cdot [A - (V_{10} + V_0)/Z_o] - Z_o[A - (V_{10} + V_0)/Z_o] - V_0 . \tag{28}$$

From (18) and (28),

$$V_{12} = B Z_o - A Z_o + V_{10} \; . \tag{29}$$

For cyclic stability,

$$V_{12} = V_{20} = V_s - V_{10} \; . \tag{30}$$

From (29) and (30),

$$V_{10} = (V_s/2) + (Z_o/2)(A - B) \; . \tag{31}$$

From (26) and (31),

$$V_{10} = V_s/2 + A Z_o [q/(1+q)] \; . \tag{32}$$

From (27) and (32),

$$V_{11} = (V_s/2) - A Z_o [1/(1+q)] \; . \tag{33}$$

Repeating (18),

$$B = (1 - \cos\alpha)[A - (V_{10} + V_0)/Z_o)] \; . \tag{34}$$

Therefore,

$$\cos\alpha = [A - B - (V_{10} + V_0)/Z_o]/[A - (V_{10} + V_0)/Z_o] \; . \tag{35}$$

From (26), (32), and (35)

$$\cos\alpha = (2Aq/(1+q) - \{V_s/2 + A Z_o[q/(1+q)] + V_0\} \cdot (1/Z_o))/(A - \{V_s/2 + A Z_o [q/(1+q)] + V_0\}(1/Z_o)) \; . \tag{36}$$

Substituting $V_0 = V_s q/2$ gives

$$\cos\alpha = [Aq - (V_s/2 Z_o)(1+q)^2]/[A - (V_s/2 Z_o)(1+q)^2] \qquad \text{or} \tag{37}$$

$$A = (V_s/2 Z_o)\,[(1+q)^2(1 - \cos\alpha)/(q - \cos\alpha)] \; . \tag{38}$$

Substituting (38) into (32) and (33) produces

$$V_{10} = (V_s/2)\{[q^2 + 2q - (q^2 + q + 1)\cos\alpha]/[q - \cos\alpha]\} \tag{39}$$

$$V_{11} = (V_s/2)[(q\cos\alpha - 1)/(q - \cos\alpha)] \; . \tag{40}$$

For cyclic stability

$$I_{L0} = -I_{L2} \; . \tag{41}$$

Therefore from (4), (6), and (41),

$$-I_{L0} = [(V_{11} + V_0)/Z_o] \sin w_o(t_2 - t_1) \; . \tag{42}$$

Substituting for V_{11} from (40),

$$I_{L0} = (V_s/2 Z_o)\{(1 - q^2)\sin\alpha/(q - \cos\alpha)\} \; . \tag{43}$$

From (2), (7), (39), and (43),

$$\beta = \pi + \tan^{-1}\{(q^2 - 1)\sin\alpha/[2q - (1 + q^2)\cos\alpha]\} \; . \tag{44}$$

We can now determine the average rectified value of $i_L(t)$:

$$\begin{aligned} I_{avg} &= (1/t_2)\Big(\int_0^{t_1} \{I_{L0}\cos(w_o t) + [(V_{10} - V_0)/Z_o] \cdot \sin(w_o t)\}\,dt - \int_0^{t_2 - t_1} [(V_{11} + V_0)/Z_o]\sin(w_o t')\,dt'\Big) \\ &= (1/t_2)\big((I_{L0}/w_o)\sin(w_o t_1) - [(V_{10} - V_0)/w_o Z_o] \cdot (\cos w_o t_1 - 1) + [(V_{11} + V_0)/w_o Z_o] \cdot [\cos w_o(t_2 - t_1) - 1]\big) \\ &= (1/w_o t_2)\{I_{L0}\sin\beta - [(V_{10} - V_0)/Z_o](\cos\beta - 1) + [(V_{11} + V_0)/Z_o](\cos\alpha - 1)\} \; . \end{aligned} \tag{45}$$

Substituting the value of V_{11} from (11) into (45) yields

$$I_{avg} = (1/w_o t_2)\big(I_{L0}\sin\beta - [(V_{10} - V_0)/Z_o](\cos\beta - 1) + (1 - \cos\alpha)\{-(2V_0/Z_o) + I_{L0}\sin\beta - [(V_{10} - V_0)/Z_o]\cos\beta\}\big) \; . \tag{46}$$

Comparing (46) with (17) and (18) we have

$$I_{avg} = (A + B)/w_o t_2 \; . \tag{47}$$

From (26) we have

$$B = A[(1-q)/(1+q)] \tag{48}$$

$$I_{avg} = 2A/(\alpha+\beta)(1+q) \;. \tag{49}$$

From (38) and (49) we have

$$I_{avg} = (V_s/2Z_o)[2(1+q)(1-\cos\alpha)/(\alpha+\beta)(q-\cos\alpha)] \tag{50}$$

And from (44) and (50) we have

$$I_{avg} = (V_s/2Z_o)\,\{2(1+q)(1-\cos\alpha)/ [(q-\cos\alpha)(\alpha+\tan^{-1}\{(q^2-1)\sin\alpha/ [2q-(1+q^2)\cos\alpha]\}+\pi)]\} \;. \tag{51}$$

To determine the peak value of $i_1(t)$, we differentiate (5) and set the result = 0:

$$d\,i_1(t)/dt = -w_o I_{L0}\sin(w_o t) + w_o[(V_{10}-V_0)/Z_o]\cos(w_o t) = 0 \;. \tag{52}$$

Therefore,

$$I_{peak} \text{ occurs at } w_o t_{max} = \tan^{-1}[(V_{10}-V_0)/I_{L0}Z_o] \tag{53}$$

but from (7),

$$\beta-\pi = \tan^{-1}[-I_{L0}Z_o/(V_{10}-V_0)] \;. \tag{54}$$

Therefore,

$$w_o t_{max} = \beta-\pi/2 \tag{55}$$

$$I_{peak} = I_{L0}\sin\beta - [(V_{10}-V_0)/Z_o]\cos\beta \;. \tag{56}$$

Comparing (17) and (56),

$$I_{peak} = A-(V_{10}-V_0)/Z_o \;. \tag{57}$$

Substituting (38), (39), and $V_0 = qV_s/2$ into (57) gives

$$I_{peak} = (V_s/2Z_o)[(1+q^2-2q\cos\alpha)/(q-\cos\alpha)] \;. \tag{58}$$

For the rms value of $i_1(t)$ we have

$$I_{rms} = [(1/t_2)(\int_0^{t_1}\{I_{L0}\cos w_o t + [(V_{10}-V_0)/Z_o] \cdot \sin w_o t\}^2\,dt + \int_0^{t_2-t_1}\{[(V_{11}+V_0)/Z_o] \cdot \sin w_o t'\}^2\,dt')]^{1/2} \;. \tag{59}$$

$$I_{rms} = ([1/(\alpha+\beta)]\,\{I_{L0}^2(\beta/2+\sin 2\beta/4) + [(V_{10}-V_0)/Z_o]^2(\beta/2-\sin 2\beta/4) + [I_{L0}(V_{10}-V_0)/Z_o]\sin^2\beta + [(V_{11}+V_0)/Z_o]^2(\alpha/2-\sin 2\alpha/4)\})^{1/2} \;. \tag{60}$$

Substitutions could be made to eliminate I_{L0}, β, V_{10}, and V_{11} to produce an expression for I_{rms} as a function of Z_o, q, and α. This step will be omitted however since the resulting equation is relatively complex.

By integrating and substituting as in (45) and (46) we can also obtain the average transistor current $I_{Q\,avg}$ and the average diode current $I_{D\,avg}$:

$$I_{Q\,avg} = [A/2(\alpha+\beta)] \tag{61}$$

$$I_{D\,avg} = [B/2(\alpha+\beta)] \;. \tag{62}$$

Substituting (38) for A, (44) for β, and (48) for B gives

$$I_{Q\,avg} = (V_s/2Z_o)\{((1+q)^2(1-\cos\alpha)/ [2(q-\cos\alpha)[\pi+\tan^{-1}\{-(1-q^2)\sin\alpha/ [2q-(1+q^2)\cos\alpha]\}+\alpha)]\} \tag{63}$$

$$I_{D\,avg} = (V_s/2Z_o)[(1-q^2)(1-\cos\alpha)/ 2(q-\cos\alpha)(\pi+\tan^{-1}\{-(1-q^2)\sin\alpha/ [2q-(1+q^2)\cos\alpha]\}+\alpha)] \;. \tag{64}$$

Another variable of interest is the peak voltage across each capacitor. From Figs. 1 and 2 it can be seen that the peak negative voltage across C_1 will occur at $t = t_1$ where $i_1(t)$ reverses. This also corresponds to the peak positive voltage across C_2 since

$$V_{C\,peak} = V_{21} = V_s - V_{11}, \quad V_{11} \text{ is negative} \;. \tag{65}$$

Substituting (40) into (65) yields

$$V_{C\,peak} = (V_s/2)\{[1+2q-(q+2)\cos\alpha]/[q-\cos\alpha]\} \;. \tag{66}$$

One more important observation can be obtained from any of several of these equations, one of these being (66). Equation (66) indicates that if $q = \cos\alpha$, $V_{C\,peak}$ becomes unbounded, implying that

$$q > \cos\alpha \;. \tag{67}$$

Therefore the range of α for continuous conduction is

$$\cos^{-1} q < \alpha \leqslant 180° \;. \tag{68}$$

As yet nothing has been established about the upper limit of q. Suppose $q > 1$. If this is true it must hold for any $\alpha, 0° \leqslant \alpha \leqslant 180°$. Therefore it must hold for $\alpha = 0°$; if this is the case, then from (18), (19), and (22)

$$B = 0$$

$$E_L = (V_0/w_o) A$$

$$E_S = (V_0/q\, w_o) A$$

and since it was assumed that $q > 1$,

$$E_L > E_S$$

which does not allow cyclic stability. Therefore the assumption that $q > 1$ is false and we have the limits

$$1 \geqslant q > \cos\alpha \ . \tag{69}$$

III. Equations for Discontinuous Load Current

The discontinuous output current waveform for some $\alpha > 180°$ is shown in Fig. 3. All approximations are identical to the continuous current analysis.

If Q_1 is turned on at $t = 0$,

$$i_1(t) = [(V_{10} - V_0)/Z_o] \sin(w_o t), \quad 0 \leqslant t \leqslant t_1 \tag{70}$$

$$i_1(t') = [(V_{11} + V_0)/Z_o] \sin(w_o t'), \quad 0 \leqslant t' \leqslant t_2 - t_1 \tag{71}$$

$$i_1(t) = 0, \quad t_2 \leqslant t \leqslant t_2' \tag{72}$$

where in this case we have

$$I_{L0} = 0 \tag{73}$$

$$w_o t_1 = w_o(t_2 - t_1) = \pi \tag{74}$$

$$\alpha \equiv w_o(t_2' - t_1), \quad \beta = \pi \ . \tag{75}$$

By comparison with the continuous current analysis, we see that all calculations will be virtually the same except that different time intervals will be used for the average and rms currents. Therefore most of these calculations can be extended to the discontinuous case.

From (17) and (18), replacing the α in these expressions with π,

$$A = 2(V_{10} - V_0)/Z_o \tag{76}$$

$$B = 2(V_{10} - 3V_0)/Z_o \ . \tag{77}$$

From (39) and (40), replacing the α is these expressions with π,

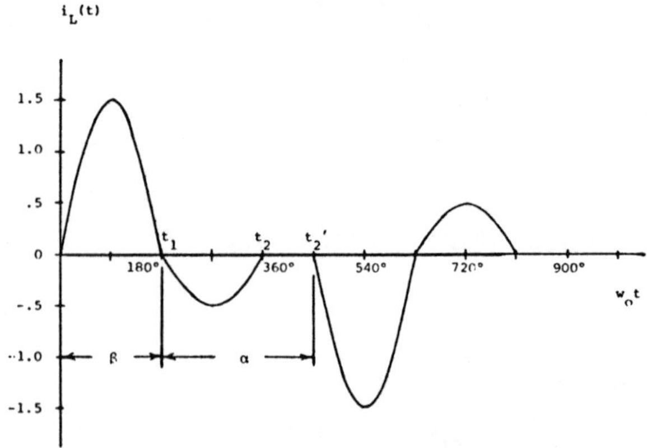

Fig. 3. Typical normalized load current waveform in discontinuous current operation ($q = 0.5, \alpha = 270°, \beta = 180°$).

$$V_{10} = (V_s/2)(1 + 2q) \tag{78}$$

$$V_{11} = -V_s/2 \ . \tag{79}$$

Using an approach similar to (45),

$$I_{avg} = (1/w_o t_2')[(2V_{10} - 2V_{11} - 4V_0)/Z_o]$$

$$= (V_s/2Z_o)\,[4/(\alpha + \pi)] \ . \tag{80}$$

From (58),

$$I_{peak} = [V_s(1 + q)/2Z_o] \ . \tag{81}$$

Using an approach similar to (59) and (60),

$$I_{rms} = ((1/w_o t_2')\{[(V_{10} - V_0)/Z_o]^2 (\pi/2)$$

$$+ [(V_{11} + V_0)/Z_o]^2 (\pi/2)\})^{1/2}$$

$$= (V_s/2Z_o)\,[(1 + q^2)\,\pi/(\alpha + \pi)]^{1/2} \ . \tag{82}$$

From (61) and (62),

$$I_{Q\,avg} = V_s(1 + q)/2Z_o(\alpha + \pi) \tag{83}$$

$$I_{D\,avg} = V_s(1 - q)/2Z_o(\alpha + \pi) \tag{84}$$

and from (65),

$$V_{c\,peak} = 1.5\, V_s \ . \tag{85}$$

IV. Experimental Results

Some of the more important equations can be summarized as follows.

Continuous Case

$$\cos^{-1} q < \alpha \leqslant 180°, \ \beta = \pi + \tan^{-1}$$

$$\cdot \{(q^2 - 1)\sin\alpha/[2q - (1 + q^2)\cos\alpha]\}$$

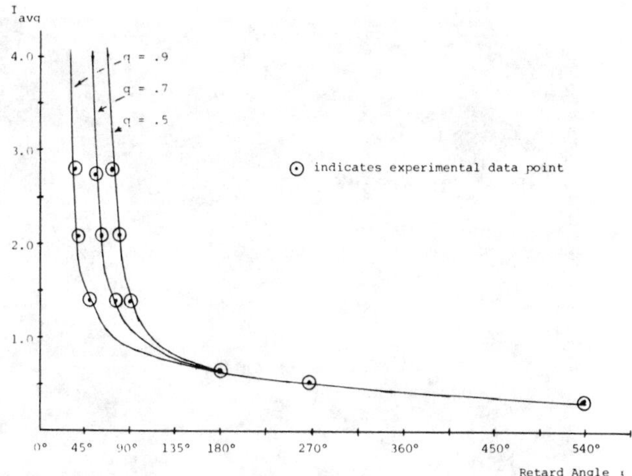

Fig. 4. Normalized average load current versus retard angle α with normalized load voltage as parameter.

Fig. 5. Normalized peak load current versus retard angle α with normalized load voltage as parameter.

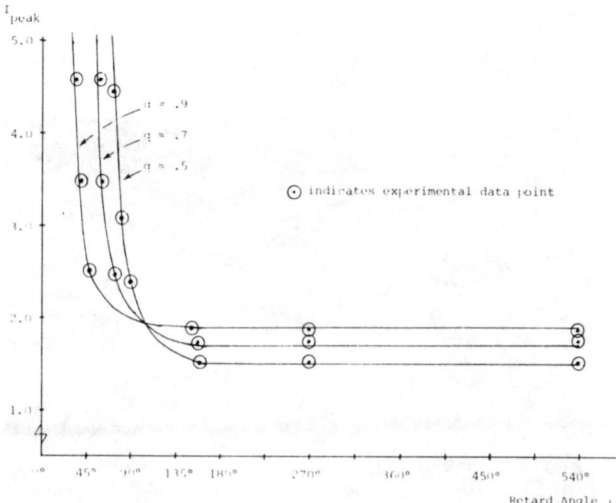

$$V_{10} = (V_s/2)\{[q^2 + 2q - (q^2 + q + 1)\cos\alpha]/[q - \cos\alpha]\}$$

$$V_{11} = [V_s(q\cos\alpha - 1)/2(q - \cos\alpha)]$$

$$I_{L0} = (V_s/2Z_o)\,[(1 - q^2)\sin\alpha/(q - \cos\alpha)]$$

$$I_{avg} = (V_s/2Z_o)\,[2(1 + q)(1 - \cos\alpha)/(\alpha + \beta)(q - \cos\alpha)]$$

$$I_{peak} = (V_s/2Z_o)\,[(1 + q^2 - 2q\cos\alpha)/(q - \cos\alpha)]$$

$$I_{rms} = ([1/(\alpha + \beta)]\,\{I_{L0}^2\,[\beta/2 + \sin 2\beta/4]$$

$$+ [(V_{10} - V_0)/Z_o]^2\,(\beta/2 - \sin 2\beta/4)$$

$$+ [I_{L0}(V_{10} - V_0)/Z_o]\sin^2\beta$$

$$+ [(V_{11} + V_0)/Z_o]^2(\alpha/2 - \sin 2\alpha/4)\})^{1/2}$$

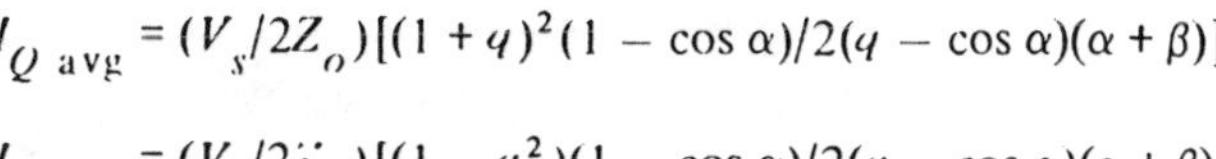

$$I_{Q\,avg} = (V_s/2Z_o)[(1 + q)^2(1 - \cos\alpha)/2(q - \cos\alpha)(\alpha + \beta)]$$

$$I_{D\,avg} = (V_s/2Z_o)[(1 - q^2)(1 - \cos\alpha)/2(q - \cos\alpha)(\alpha + \beta)]$$

$$V_{c\,peak} = (V_s/2)\{[1 + 2q - (q + 2)\cos\alpha]/(q - \cos\alpha)\}$$

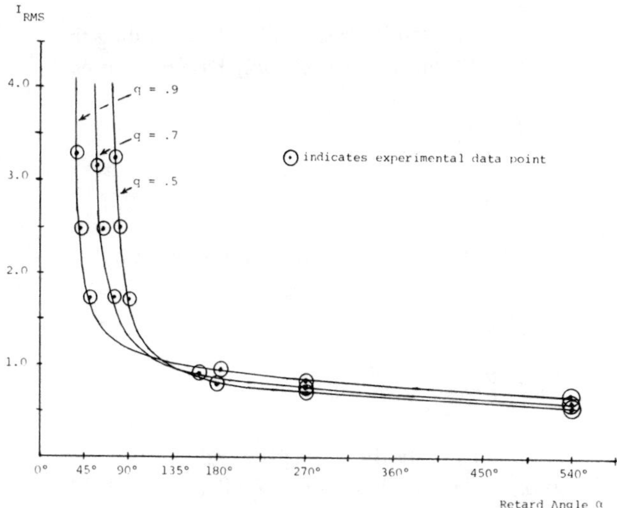

Fig. 6. Normalized rms load current versus retard angle α with normalized load voltage as parameter.

Fig. 7. Normalized peak capacitor voltage versus retard angle α with normalized load voltage as parameter.

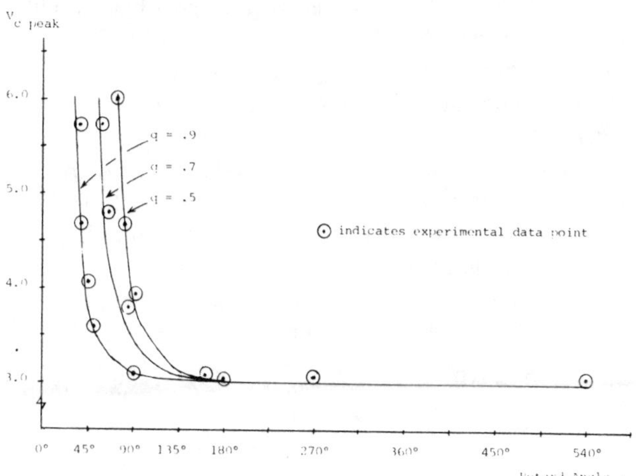

Discontinuous Case

$\alpha \geqslant 180°$, $\beta = \pi$, $V_{10} = (V_s/2)(1 + 2q)$, $V_{11} = -V_s/2$, $I_{L0} = 0$, $I_{avg} = (V_s/2Z_o)[4/(\alpha + \pi)]$, $I_{peak} = V_s(1 + q)/2Z_o$, $I_{rms} = (V_s/2Z_o)[(1 + q^2)\,\pi/(\alpha + \pi)]^{1/2}$, $I_{Q\,avg} = V_s(1 + q)/2Z_o(\alpha + \pi)$, $I_{D\,avg} = V_s(1 - q)/2Z_o(\alpha + \pi)$, $V_{c\,peak} = 1.5\,V_s$.

From the above equations, those variables of most interest from a design standpoint might be I_{avg}, I_{peak}, I_{rms}, $I_{Q\,avg}$, $I_{D\,avg}$, and $V_{c\,peak}$. To check the accuracy of these equations, tests were performed on a amall half bridge converter with the following ratings and parameters: $V_s = 150$ V dc, $w_o = 2\pi \times 10^4$ rad/s, $Z_o = 52\Omega$, $P_{out} = 150$ W (max).

Experimental and calculated curves for I_{avg}, I_{peak}, I_{rms}, and $V_{c\,peak}$ are shown in Figs. 4 through 7 for various values of q. These results indicate very good agreement between the calculated and experimental data. Plots for $I_{Q\,avg}$ and $I_{D\,avg}$ were not included since these variables can be determined from I_{avg} using q. Note that Figs. 4 through 7 are normalized by dividing the actual value by one of the following base quantities

$$I_{base} = V_s/2Z_o$$

$$V_{base} = V_s/2 \ .$$

Thus the actual current I or voltage V is given by

$$I = I_n \times I_{base}$$

$$V = V_n \times V_{base}$$

where I_n and V_n are the normalized values. By using this approach the curves may be applied to any half-bridge circuit once q, α, and the base quantities are known.

In designing these circuits it is advantageous to select q as high as possible when V_s is at its lower limit, e.g., $q = 0.9$ or 0.95. However when V_s goes high, q will obviously decrease, and thus q may vary considerably over the normal range of V_s. For this reason it is useful to include curves for lower values of q such as those for $q = 0.5$ and 0.7.

A few comments are in order as to how the experimental measurements were performed. The first of these is in regard to the original approximation of lumping all circuit losses with the output power (i.e., assume lossless components). This was approximated experimentally in the following manner:

1) At a given q, α, and R_L, measure I_{avg}, and $P_{loss} = P_{in} - P_{out}$.

2) Since the output voltage is dc, define $\Delta V_0 = P_{loss}/I_{avg}$.

3) While holding I_{avg} constant, readjust α and R_L to obtain $V_{om} = (qV_s/2) - \Delta V_0$, where V_{om} is the actual measured primary output voltage, i.e., the voltage used to determine q is the measured value plus an additional amount to compensate for the circuit losses, i.e.,

$$V_o = V_{om} + \Delta V_o .$$

The output transformer was omitted in the actual experimental circuit in order to reduce losses and simplify the control circuitry.

The output current waveforms for the continuous and discontinuous cases are shown in Figs. 8 and 9, respectively. If α is measured on an oscilloscope (as in these experiments), some care must be taken to insure that α is measured exactly from the zero current crossing. This becomes especially important in the continuous current case as α approaches the limiting value of $\cos^{-1} q$.

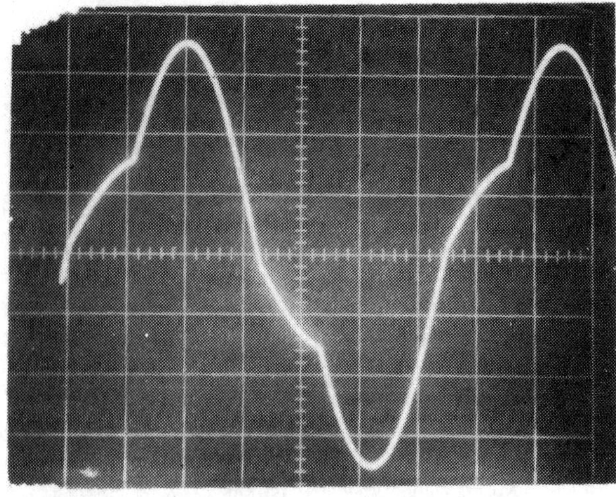

Fig. 8. Typical load current waveform in continuous current operation with $\alpha = 80^\circ$, $q = 0.7$ (corrected for losses). Vertical: 1 A/div; horizontal: 20 µs/div.

Fig. 9 Typical load current waveform in discontinuous current operation with $\alpha = 270^\circ$, $q = 0.5$ (corrected for losses). Vertical: 1 A/div; horizontal: 50 µs/div.

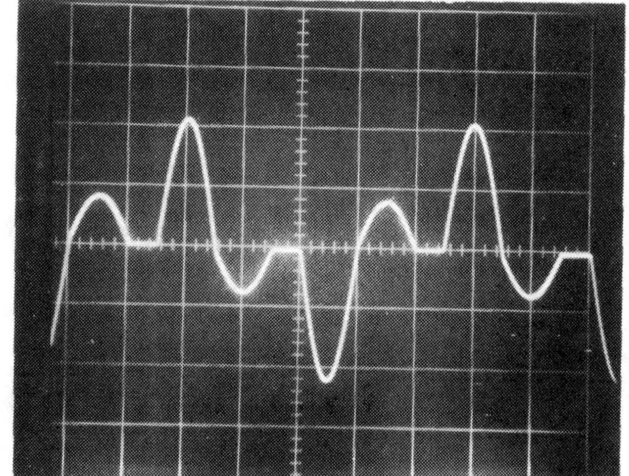

V. Summary

This set of equations and normalized curves provides a straightforward model that appears to be quite useful in the design and analysis of series resonant converters. Parametric curves of this type quickly indicate how changes in α, q, and Z_o will affect circuit performance. Since this analysis assumes ideal components, all circuit losses must be lumped with the output power to obtain the greatest accuracy. However, when the losses are handled in this manner, there appears to be very good agreement between the calculated and experimental results.

References

[1] F.C. Schwarz, "A method of resonant current pulse modulation for power converters," *IEEE Trans. Ind. Electron. Contr. Instrum.*, vol. IECI-17, pp. 209-221, May 1970.

[2] J. Biess, L. Inouye, and J.H. Shank, "High voltage series resonant inverter ion engine screen supply, *Proc. 1974 IEEE Power Electronics Specialists Conf.*, pp. 97-105.

[3] M. Nakaoka, Y. Murakami, and M. Nishimura, "A time-sharing, high frequency series capacitor-commutated inverter circuit and its performance analysis," *Elec. Eng. Japan*, vol. 94, no. 2, pp. 36-44, 1974.

[4] F.C. Schwarz and J.B. Klaasens, "A controllable secondary multikilowatt dc current source with constant maximum power factor in its 3 phase supply line," *Proc. 1975 IEEE Power Electronics Specialists Conf.*, pp. 205-215.

[5] R. Kasturi, "An analysis of series inverter circuits," *IEEE Trans. Ind. Electron. Contr. Instrum.*, vol. IECI-22, pp. 515-519, Nov. 1975.

[6] F.C. Schwarz, "An improved method of resonant current pulse modulation for power converters," *IEEE Trans. Ind. Electron. Contr. Instrum.*, vol. IECI-23, pp. 133-141, May 1976.

[7] M. Shioya, "Operating characteristics of the current-feed time-sharing inverter consisting of series inverter units," *Elec. Eng. Japan*, vol. 96, no. 3, pp. 65-72, 1976.

[8] E. Kittl, "Transient waveform analysis of switching converter," DRSEL-TL-PE, Tech. Rep., ECOM-4493, U.S. Army Electronics Command, Fort Monmouth, NJ, Apr. 1977.

[9] F.C. Schwarz and J.B. Klaasens, "A 95-percent efficient 1-KW converter with an internal frequency of 50 KHz," *IEEE Trans, Ind. Electron. Contr. Instrum.*, vol. IECI-25, pp. 326-333, Nov. 1978.

[10] M.P. Dougherty, "A series resonant inverter simulation using super-sceptre," *Proc. 1979 Nat. Aerospace and Electronics Conf.*, pp. 517-524.

Paper 5.7

STATE-PLANE ANALYSIS OF PARALLEL RESONANT CONVERTER*

Ramesh Oruganti   Fred C. Lee

Electrical Engineering Department
Virginia Polytechnic Institute &
State University
Blacksburg, Va - 24061

ABSTRACT

A method for analyzing the complex operation of a parallel resonant converter is developed, utilizing graphical state-plane techniques. The comprehensive mode analysis uncovers, for the first time, the presence of other complex modes besides the continuous conduction mode and the the discontinuous conduction mode and determines their theoretical boundaries. Based on the insight gained from the analysis, a novel, high-frequency resonant buck converter is proposed. The voltage conversion ratio of the new converter is almost independent of load.

1.0 INTRODUCTION

The ever-increasing demand for smaller and lighter power processing equipment has been the main motivating factor behind the use of progressively higher internal conversion frequencies. In this context, resonant converters have emerged as being superior to conventional PWM converters due to the following reason. Depending on the configuration and the operating modes, resonant converters can eliminate either the turn-on loss [1,2], the turn-off loss [3,4] or both [5,6] of the power switches, thereby enabling the converter to operate at higher frequencies.

Two popular types of resonant converters for high-power , high-frequency applications are 1) the series resonant converter (SRC)[3] and 2) the parallel (load-capacitor link) resonant converter (PRC)[4]. Generally, at operating frequencies sufficiently less than the tank resonant frequency, the SRC behaves as a current source, whereas the PRC acts as a voltage source. Thus in voltage regulator applications, PRC would require much less operating frequency range than the SRC to compensate for load variations and is the superior configuration.

While the steady-state and the dynamic properties of SRC have been analyzed in many recent literature[7,8,9,10,11], the analysis of PRC is scarce and is limited to only continuous conduction mode of operation[4,11]. The various modes of operation that occur when load current and operating frequency are changed have not been understood owing to the complexity of PRC operation and to the lack of an appropriate analytical tool to tackle the problem.

Graphical state-plane technique has been previously used effectively in the analysis and control of inverter and converter circuits[12,13,14]. More recently, this technique has been applied successfully to SRCs for analyzing their steady-state and transient behavior and for assessing the merits and demerits of various control methods[9,10].

In this paper, a detailed graphical state-plane analysis of PRC is carried out. The analysis reveals for the first time the presence of a variety of modes of operation including some hitherto unknown and establishes the boundaries between them. Using the state-plane diagrams the operation of the converter in the different regions are fully explored.

A novel resonant converter circuit, named **resonant buck converter** is derived from the state-plane analysis of PRC. This circuit may be viewed as a resonant analog of the buck-type converter. It possesses many desirable properties. For example, the voltage transfer ratio varies almost linearly with the control frequency and is almost load-independent, unlike most resonant converters. Since both turn-on and turn-off losses are eliminated, the new converter circuit can operate at very high frequencies. Based on this novel circuit and the concept of "resonant switch" developed in [5], a host of practical resonant power processing circuits have been proposed and analyzed in Ref.[6].

2.0 STATE-PLANE ANALYSIS

Fig. 1 shows the circuit diagram of a half-bridge version of PRC. The state-plane analysis is simplified by assuming that 1) output filter inductor current, I_o, is constant and 2) circuit losses are negligible. The first assumption is justifiable since the operating frequency of the inverter is usually much higher than the corner frequency of the output filter. Thus in one switching cycle, I_o is essentially constant. Since a high Q tank circuit is desirable in practical design, the second assumption also is generally reasonable. However, under certain operating conditions, such as when the oper-

---

* The work was supported under NASA grant "Control Analysis and Design of Resonant Converters" NAG 3-551 from NASA Lewis Research Center, Cleveland, OH.

Reprinted from *IEEE Power Electron. Specialists Conf. (PESC) Rec.*, pp. 56–73, 1985.

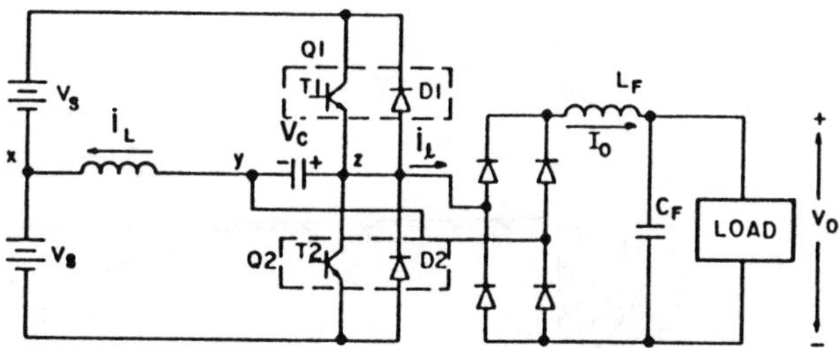

Fig. 1. A half-bridge parallel resonant converter(PRC)

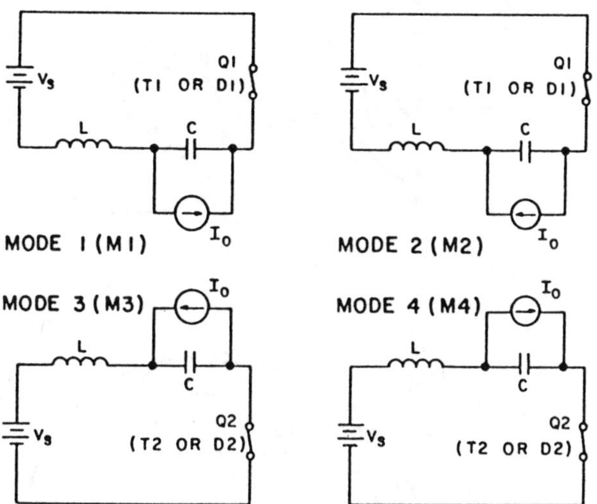

Fig. 2. Resonant topological modes of PRC

ating frequency is close to the resonant frequency, the effect of parasitic losses tend to be more pronounced and the analysis will only be approximately correct.

2.1 Resonant Topological Modes

In this paper, the term **mode**, when used alone, refers to the circuit mode of operation under steady-state, such as continuous conduction mode or discontinuous conduction mode. The term **topological mode**, on the other hand, refers to a particular equivalent circuit assumed by the converter during certain interval of operation.

The transistor, T1, and its antiparallel diode, D1, (Fig. 1) together act as a bidirectional switch, termed Q1. Likewise, T2 and D2 act as another bidirectional switch, Q2. Depending on whether Q1 is on or Q2 is on, the voltage across **zx** in the circuit is either $+V_s$ or $-V_s$. Also, depending on the polarity of v_C, the link current, i_ℓ, is either $+I_o$ or $-I_o$.

The resulting four **resonant topological modes** (M1 thru M4), are shown in Fig. 2. Fig. 3 shows a common equivalent circuit for these four topological modes along with the values of the equivalent source voltage, V_E, and the equivalent load current, I_E.

TOPOLOGICAL MODE	UNDER CONDITIONS	V_E	I_E
M1	Q1'ON' & Vc–ve	V_s	$-I_o$
M2	Q1'ON' & Vc+ve	V_s	$+I_o$
M3	Q2'ON' & Vc+ve	$-V_s$	$+I_o$
M4	Q2'ON' & Vc–ve	$-V_s$	$-I_o$

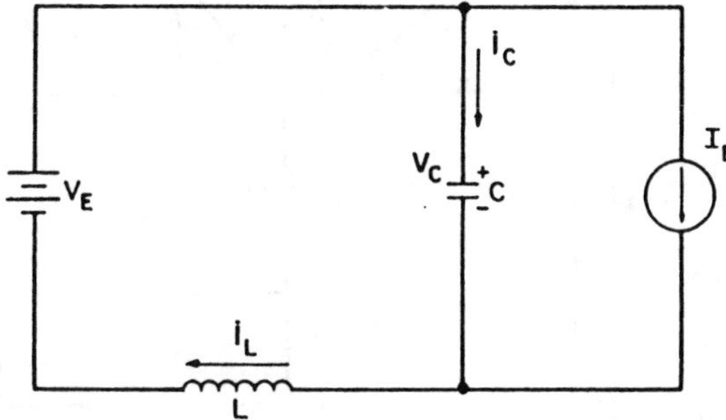

Fig. 3. Common equivalent circuit for different conduction intervals

Fig. 4 shows the circuit waveforms under continuous conduction mode of operation (CCM) to illustrate the occurrence of these topological modes. In Fig. 4, during the interval (0,t1') a single device T1 conducts. However, two topological modes, M1 and M2, occur. On the contrary, interval (t1,'t2) is associated with a single topological mode, M2, though two devices, T1 and D1, conduct. Thus, in PRC, the topological modes and the device conduction intervals do not uniquely correspond to each other, unlike in SRC [9]. These four topological modes are adequate to describe the operation in CCM mode. Five additional, non-resonant, topological modes exist under other operating conditions and will be discussed in Section 2.5.

2.2 State Portrait

The solution to the network in Fig. 3 is given by,

$$i_L = \frac{V_E - V_{C0}}{Z_0} \mathrm{Sin}\{\omega_0(t-t_0)\} + (I_{L0} - I_E) \mathrm{Cos}\{\omega_0(t-t_0)\} + I_E \qquad (1)$$

$$v_C = (I_{L0} - I_E) Z_0 \mathrm{Sin}\{\omega_0(t-t_0)\} - (V_E - V_{C0}) \mathrm{Cos}\{\omega_0(t-t_0)\} + V_E \qquad (2)$$

where V_{C0} and I_{L0} are initial conditions at $t = t_0$.

$$Z_0 \stackrel{\Delta}{=} \sqrt{L/C} = \text{Characteristic Impedance (ohms)}$$

$$\omega_0 \stackrel{\Delta}{=} 1/\sqrt{LC} = \text{Resonant Frequency (rad/sec)}$$

$$\theta \stackrel{\Delta}{=} \omega_0(t-t_0) \qquad (3)$$

Normalizing all currents and voltages with V_s/Z_0 and V_s respectively, the following equations for the state trajectory are derived from Eqs. (1) and (2).

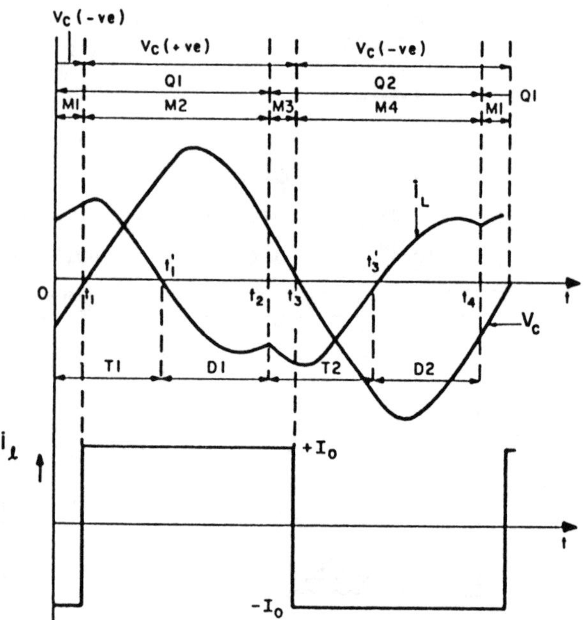

Fig. 4. CCM mode waveforms ($I_{oN} < 1$, $\omega_N < 1$)

$$(i_{LN}-I_{EN})^2 + (v_{CN}-V_{EN})^2$$

$$= (I_{LON}-I_{EN})^2 + (V_{CON}-V_{EN})^2 \overset{\Delta}{=} \rho^2 \qquad (4)$$

$$\theta = \text{ARCTAN}\left[\frac{-(i_{LN}-I_{EN})}{v_{CN}-V_{EN}}\right] - \theta_0, \text{ where} \qquad (5)$$

$$\theta_0 = \text{ARCTAN}\left[\frac{-(I_{LON}-I_{EN})}{V_{CON}-V_{EN}}\right]$$

The subscript "N" in Eqs. (4) and (5) refers to normalized circuit variables.

The state trajectories are circles with radius ρ, which depends on the initial conditions, and with center located at (V_{EN}, I_{EN}). The time elapsed between two points on the circular trajectory is proportional to the angle subtended at its center.

Based on Eq. (4), four sets of state trajectories, one for each of the four topological modes, are shown in Figs. 5(a)-(d), along with their corresponding mode centers. Since each topological mode corresponds to only one polarity of v_C, the corresponding set of trajectories extends to only one half of the v_{CN} - i_{LN} plane. By combining these sets of trajectories, a composite state portrait, which completely characterizes the PRC at a given load current, can be constructed as in Fig. 5(e). As shown in Ref.[9], the instantaneous energy of the resonant tank is proportional to d^2, where "d" is the distance between the current state of the tank and the origin. Thus, the size of the trajectory directly indicates the tank energy level.

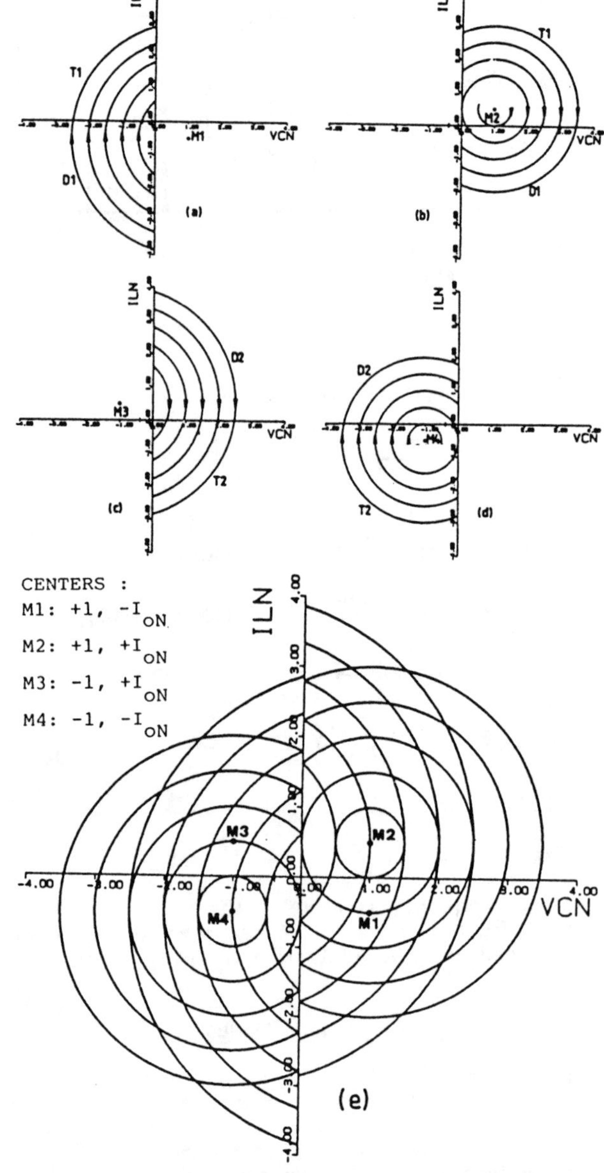

Fig. 5. State portrait of PRC for $I_{oN} = 0.5$

a) M1 trajectories b) M2 trajectories
b) M3 trajectories d) M4 trajectories
e) The composite state portrait

2.3 Equilibrium Trajectories

For a given operating frequency, ω, and load, a closed equilibrium trajectory curve that corresponds to the steady-state waveforms can be drawn on the state-plane. Figs. 6(a) and 6(b) are examples of equilibrium trajectories in the CCM mode when $I_{oN} < 1.0$. Fig. 6(a) is applicable when $\omega_N < 1.0$ and Fig. 6(b) when $\omega_N > 1.0$, where $\omega_N = \omega/\omega_0$. Waveforms corresponding to Fig. 6(a) and Fig. 6(b) are shown in Fig. 4 and Fig. 7, respectively.

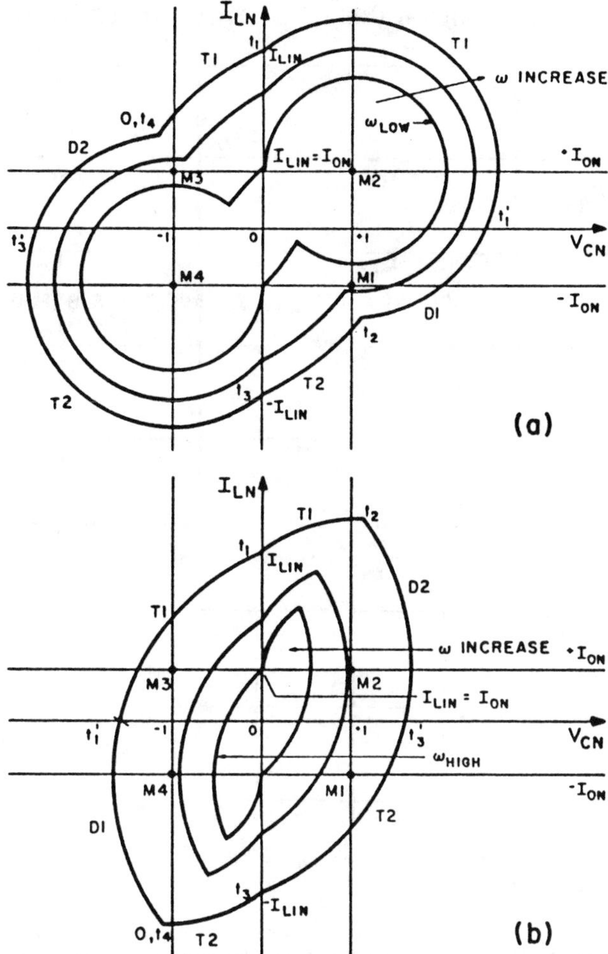

Fig. 6. CCM equilibrium trajectories for $I_{oN} < 1$ and a) $\omega_N < 1$ b) $\omega_N > 1$

The topological mode sequence in Fig. 6(a) and Fig. 6(b), in fact for all CCM operations, is M1-M2-M3-M4-M1- . However, the device sequence is T1-D1-T2-D2-T1- in Fig. 6(a) while it is T1-D2-T2-D1-T1- in Fig 6(b). In Fig. 6(a) the transistors are naturally commutated and the diodes are force commutated. In Fig. 6(b) it is the diodes which are self-commutated and the transistors are force commutated. In general, the larger trajectories correspond to higher tank energy levels and larger output voltages. In Fig. 6(a) the trajectory size increases with frequency, whereas in Fig. 6(b) the trajectory size decreases with frequency. In both diagrams, the trajectory size ideally approaches infinite proportions when the operating frequency approaches the resonant frequency.

2.4 Forced Commutation Trap Zones

Fig. 8 shows a set of equilibrium trajectories, similar to that in Fig. 6(a), in which the power switch is naturally commutated. The circular areas (radius = I_{oN}), marked around centers M2 and M4, are called the **forced commutation trap zones** . As il-

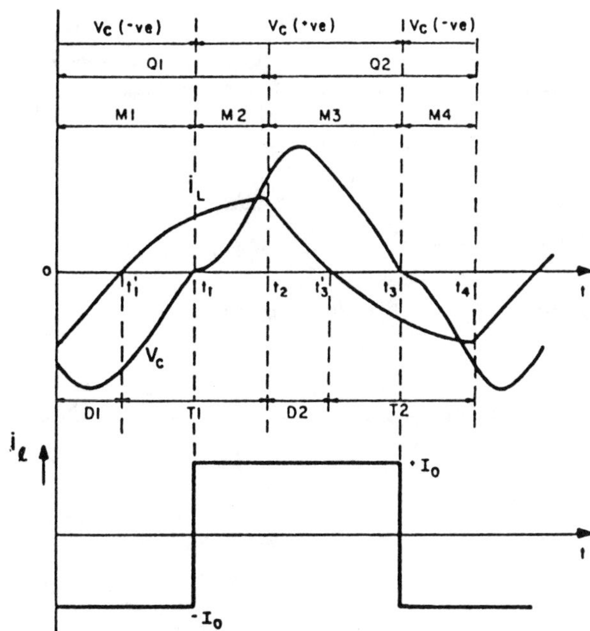

Fig. 7. CCM mode waveforms for Fig. 6(b)

lustrated by the transient trajectory, "S", in Fig. 8, if under transient conditions T1 is switched on while in TRAP1 zone , it will no longer be naturally commutated. This is because the dc offset in current, I_{oN}, is more than the oscillatory peak current amplitude. If the converter is designed for natural commutation only, switching in the trap zone should be avoided.

2.5 Non-Resonant Topological Modes

2.5.1 Inductor Charging Intervals: In Fig. 6(a) and (b), $I_{L1N}(-I_{L1N})$ is the normalized inductor current at the instant, t1(t3), when the M1(M3) trajectory reaches the vertical axis. If $I_{L1N}(-I_{L1N})$ happens to be between $-I_{oN}$ and $+I_{oN}$, a careful examination

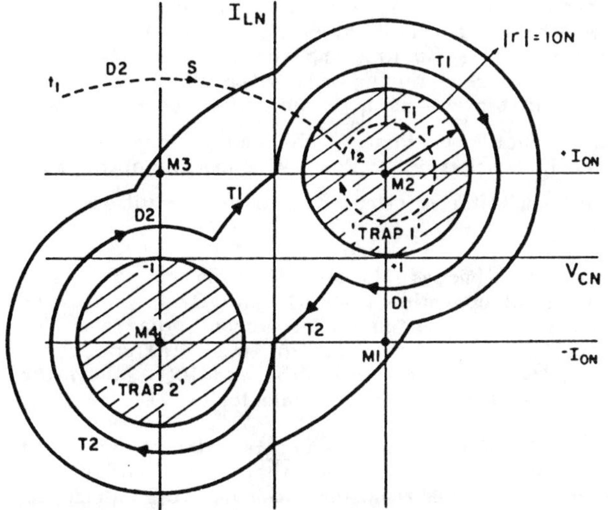

Fig. 8. Forced commutation trap zones

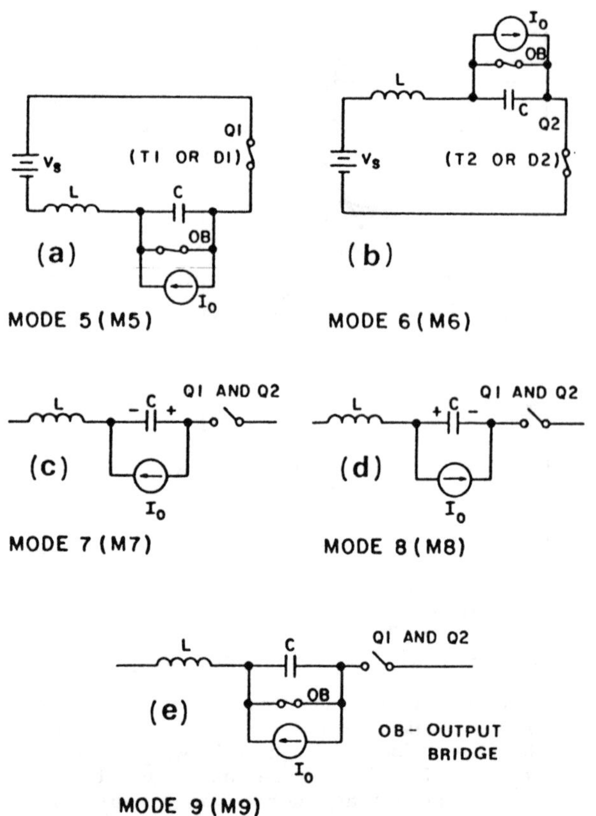

Fig. 9. Non-resonant topological modes
- equivalent circuit diagrams

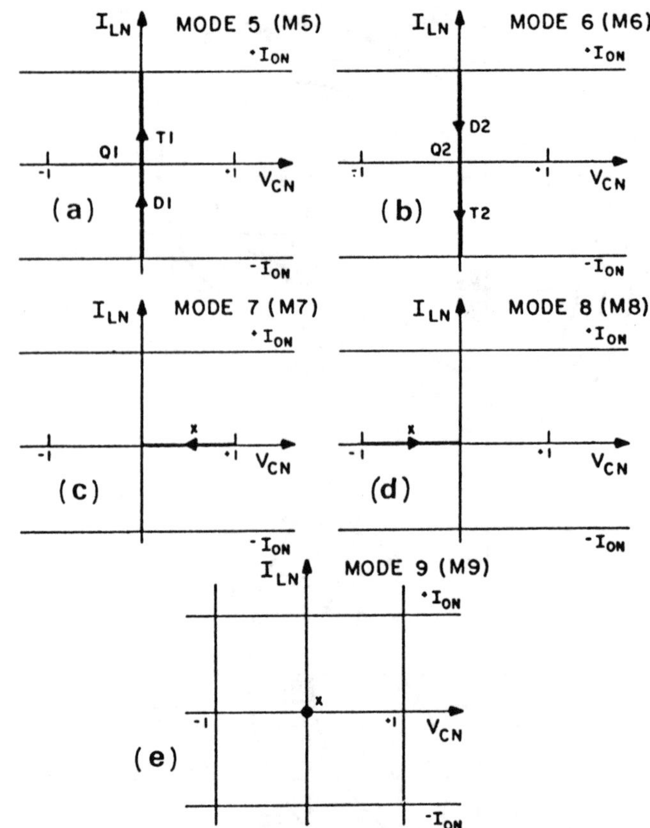

Fig.10. Non-resonant topological modes
- state-plane trajectories

of the state portrait in Fig. 5(e) reveals that there is no available trajectory on which the system could proceed further. Following is an explanation of further circuit operation for the case when Q1(T1 or D1) is kept "on", once the system reaches the vertical axis.

Since $|I_{L1N}|$ is less than $|I_{oN}|$, the excess load current over the resonant inductor current free-wheels through the diodes of the output bridge. This would clamp the resonant capacitor voltage to zero during this interval. T1 (or D1, if the instantaneous i_L is negative) conducts and the inductor is linearly charged to load current. Once i_L reaches I_o value, the clamp on the resonant capacitor is released, and the circuit operates in M2.

Topological modes M5 and M6 correspond to this interval of operation when Q1 and Q2 is "on", respectively. The equivalent circuit diagrams for these two modes are shown in Figs. 9(a) and 9(b), respectively, while Figs. 10(a) and 10(b) show the corresponding state-plane trajectories.

2.5.2 Capacitor Discharge Intervals: A study of Figs. 5(a) and 5(b) shows that at the end of D1 conduction, the trajectory reaches the horizontal axis. If at this instant v_{CN} is between -1 and +1 and if T1 is not re-switched on, once again none of the four resonant topological modes can follow. During this interval Q1 and Q2 are 'off' and the residual resonant capacitor voltage is linearly discharged by the load current. The equivalent circuit diagrams for the resulting topological modes M7 (for positive v_C's) and M8 (for negative v_C's) are shown in Figs. 9(c) and 9(d) respectively. Figs. 10(c) and 10(d) show the corresponding state-plane trajectories.

2.5.3 Discontinuous Operation Interval: If inductor current and capacitor voltage are both zero and if T1 and T2 are both "off", the system can remain at the origin for an indefinite interval with the load current freewheeling through the output rectifier. Fig. 9(e) shows the circuit diagram and Fig 10(e) the state trajectory (just a point) corresponding to this topological mode, called M9.

3.0 COMPLETE MODE ANALYSIS

3.1 Construction of CCM Equilibrium Trajectories

Given the load current, the construction o. steady-state CCM equilibrium trajectories is illustrated in Fig. 11. The steps are as follows: 1) Locate the mode centers M1, M2, M3 and M4. 2) With centers at M2 and M4, draw arcs ABCD and EFGH, respectively, with a fixed radius R. 3) With M1 as center, draw arc AHIF of radius R'(= M1A). This intersects arc EFGH at H & F. 4) Do likewise

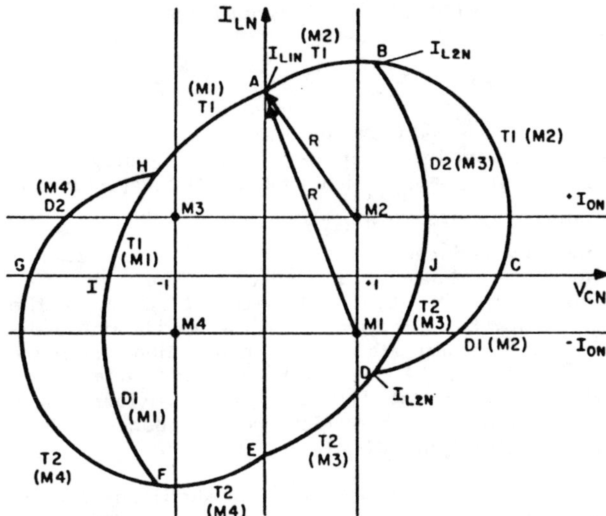

Fig.11. Construction of CCM trajectories

with M3 as center. The intersection points are D & B. 5) ABCDEFGH is one equilibrium trajectory due to one set of intersection points, called **Intersection-1**. 6)ABJDEFIH is another equilibrium trajectory due to the other set of intersection points, called **Intersection-2**.

A study of the angles subtended by the trajectories shows that an Intersection-1 trajectory with greater radius, R, corresponds to a higher operating frequency than the one with smaller R. Thus, as the operating frequency is increased, Intersection-1 trajectory increases in size (see Fig. 6(a)), while. Intersection-2 trajectory decreases in size (see Fig. 6(b)). In general, as the frequency is increased the circuit follows initially Intersection-1 trajectories and the tank energy and the output voltage increases. At a certain boundary frequency ($\omega_N=\omega_{max}$), the trajectory reaches a maximum size. Beyond ω_{max}, the circuit follows Intersection-2 trajectories and the tank energy and output voltage decreases.

3.2 Method of Mode Analysis

For an assumed load current, equilibrium trajectories of Intersections - 1 & 2 are established. The operating frequency is then varied in order to establish the different modes occurring in PRC and the boundaries between them. The above process is repeated for different load currents. In this manner, the operation of PRC is studied for the entire useful range of frequency and load current.

3.3 Mode Definitions

1. CCM - Neither v_C nor i_L stays at zero for any interval
2. DCM - v_C and i_L stay at zero for some duration together

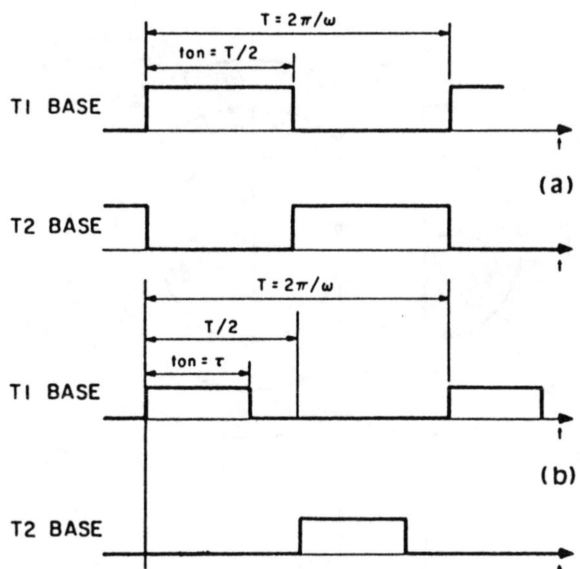

Fig.12. Base-drive strategies
a) Strategy-1 b) Strategy-2

3. TM1(Transition Mode 1) - v_C alone stays at zero for some interval. This mode may also be called the Discontinuous Capacitor Voltage Mode.
4. TM2(Transition Mode 2) - v_C and i_L stay at zero for some interval, but not together
5. LIMIT(Current Limit Mode) - v_C is always zero
6. MULTIPLE(Multiple Conduction-Cycle Modes) - Modes in which a topological mode (M1 thru M4) occurs for more than a resonant period in a switching cycle. Many modes of operation are actually included in this definition.

3.4 PRC Base-Drive Strategies

Two base-drive schemes for the power transistors are possible. In the first method, called **Strategy-1**, the transistors are always switched on alternatively for half-cycle as shown in Fig. 12(a). In the second method, called **Strategy-2**, the transistors are switched on, as shown in Fig. 12(b), for an interval $t_{ON} = \tau < T/2$, where T is the period of one switching cycle. τ is set in such a way that the same transistor is not re-switched on after its antiparallel diode conducts. When T/2 is less than τ, then t_{ON} is set equal to T/2 and Strategies 1 & 2 are identical. The above classification is necessary since the converter operation depends on the type of base-drive strategy adopted under certain operating frequencies and load currents. In such cases, the analysis is separately carried out for the two strategies.

3.5 Load $I_{oN} = 0$

In this limiting case, the centers for M1 and M2 coincide at (1,0) and those for M3 and M4 at (-1,0).

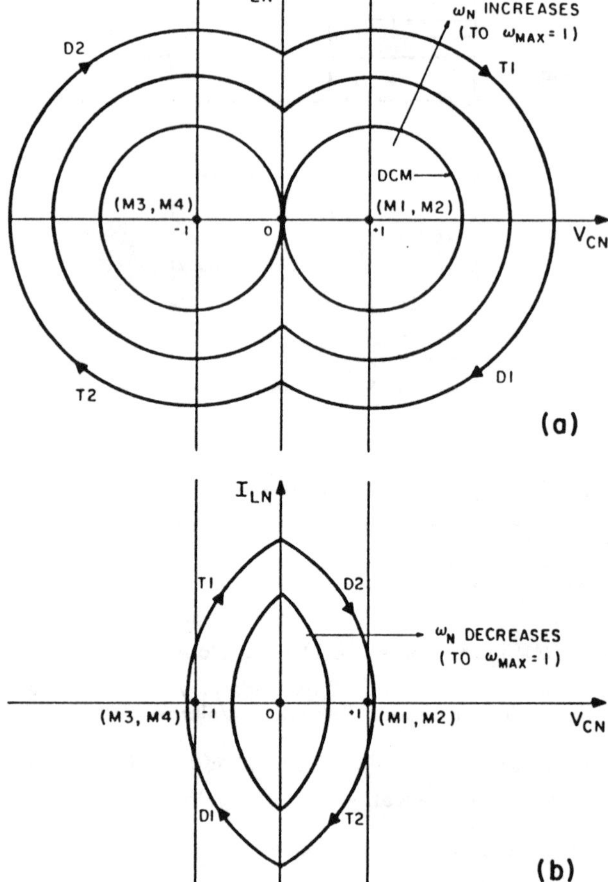

Fig.13. Equilibrium trajectories for I_{oN} = 0
a) $\omega_N < 1$ b) $\omega_N > 1$

Intersection-1 equilibrium trajectories, when $\omega_N < \omega_{max}$ (=1.0), are shown in Fig. 13(a). As ω is increased, the trajectory size increases and is ideally infinite in size at ω_{max}. As ω is increased beyond ω_{max}, the trajectory size begins to decrease following Intersection-2 trajectories (Fig.13(b)), and will shrink, ideally, to the origin as frequency approaches infinity. In Fig. 13(a) the transistors are naturally commutated whereas in Fig. 13(b) they must be force commutated.

In Fig. 13(a), when frequency is decreased, the trajectory marked DCM, which is the lower limit of CCM mode , is reached. Each of the two transistors and two diodes conduct for half a resonant period. This boundary occurs when the operating frequency equals half the resonant frequency. Let us assume that Strategy-2 is adopted for the base-drive at a switching frequency below this boundary frequency. This implies that after T1 and D1 conduct, T1 is not re-switched on. Instead, the system remains at the origin till T2 is switched on. Thus the trajectory marked DCM in Fig. 13(a) represents not only the boundary between CCM and DCM but also all the DCM trajectories. The different DCM trajectories are characterized by different dwell times at the origin.

3.6. Load Range $0 < I_{oN} < 1$

Fig. 6(a) shows CCM equilibrium trajectories corresponding to Intersection-1. As frequency is increased, at $\omega_N = \omega_{max}$ (=1.0) the trajectory reaches, ideally, infinite proportions. Beyond ω_{max}, the trajectory reduces in size, following Intersection-2 trajectories shown in Fig. 6(b). The conduction sequence in Fig. 6(a) is T1-D1-T2-D2, with the transistors being naturally commutated and the diodes force commutated. The conduction sequence in Fig. 6(b) is T1-D2-T2-D1, with the diodes being naturally commutated and the transistors force commutated. The topological mode sequence in both cases is M1-M2-M3-M4-M1- .

In the next two sub-sections, we shall consider the non-CCM operation of the circuit for this load range.

3.6.1 Non-CCM Operation when $\omega_N < \omega_{max}$: In Fig. 6(a), when switching frequency is reduced, I_{L1N} (defined in Sec. 2.5.1), progressively decreases until it equals I_{oN} at $\omega_N = \omega_{low}$, which is the lower limit of CCM. When ω is less than ω_{low} either base drive Strategy-1 or Strategy-2 may be adopted.

a) Operation Under Base-Drive Strategy-1

Fig. 14 shows the sequence of state plane diagrams when ω_N is progressively decreased below ω_{low} under Strategy-1. Fig.14(a) shows the trajectory corresponding to ω_{low}. In Fig. 14(b) the operating frequency is less than ω_{low}. Here the triggering of T1 is delayed and this results in $I_{L1N} < I_{oN}$ at the end of M1 interval. The resonant inductor, then, linearly charges up to I_o (M5) and the topological mode M2 follows, with T1 first conducting followed by D1. At the end of the half-cycle, T2 is triggered and the second half-cycle proceeds in a similar way. This mode of operation is named **Transition Mode 1 (TM1)** and the topological mode sequence for this is M1-M5-M2-M3-M6-M4-M1-. This mode may also be appropriately called the **Discontinuous Capacitor Voltage Mode.**

Fig. 14(c) shows the operation of the converter when ω is further reduced. The converter is still in TM1 mode since the topological mode sequence is unaltered. However, the device conduction sequence is quite different from that in Fig. 14(b). Also, the transistors are no longer naturally commutated, which is a disadvantage of using the Base-Drive Strategy-1.

In Fig. 14(d), ω is reduced still further such that topological mode M2 (and likewise M4) occurs exactly for one resonant cycle - as represented by the circles on the trajectory. The frequency corresponding to this boundary is called ω_{mul}. At even

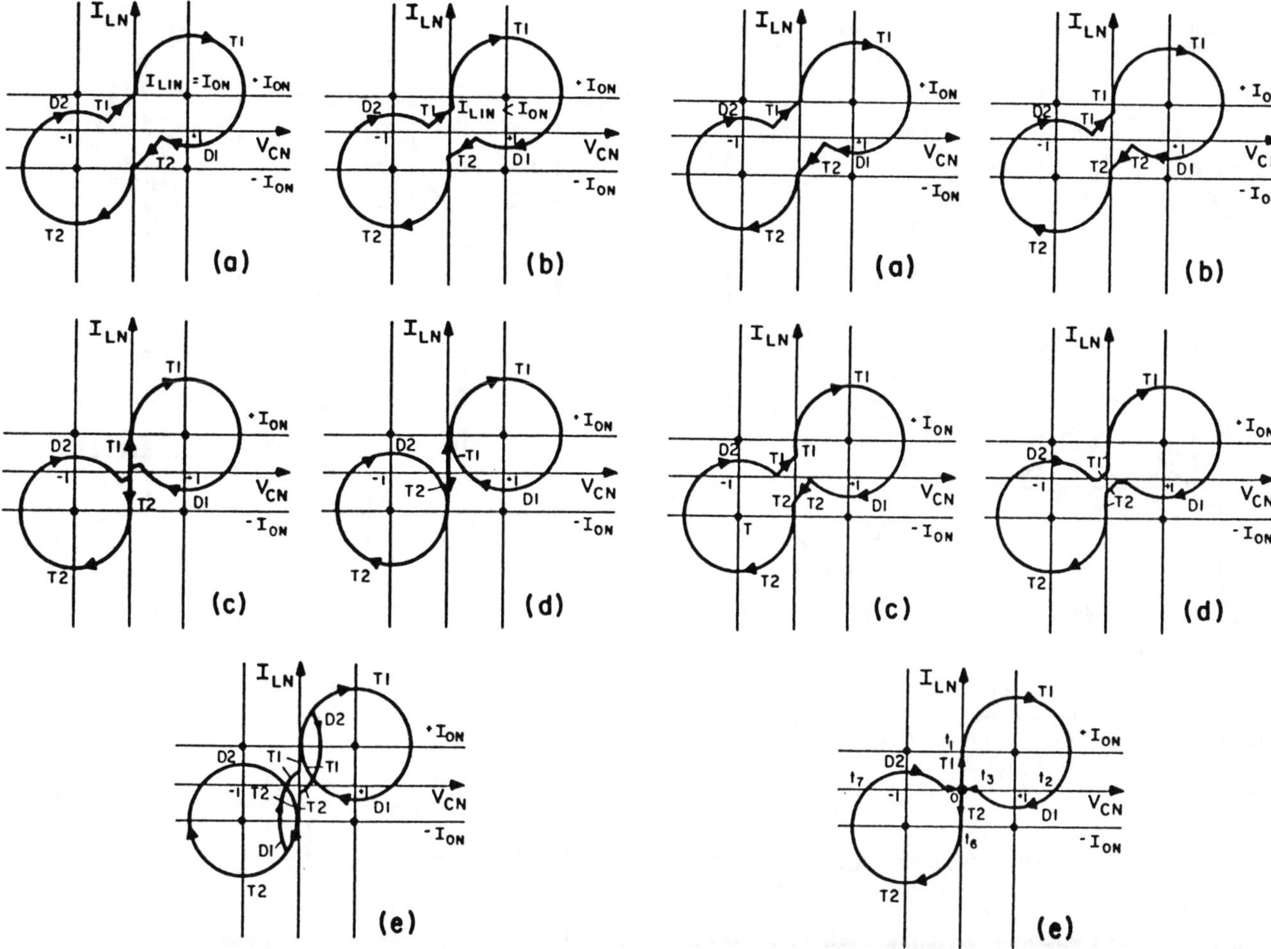

Fig.14. Non-CCM operation for $I_{oN} < 1$ under Strategy-1, as ω_N is decreased below ω_{low}
a)ω_{low}: CCM/TM1 boundary b) & c)TM1 mode
d)ω_{mul}: TM1/MULTIPLE boundary e)MULTIPLE region

Fig.15. Non-CCM operation for $I_{oN} < 1$ under Strategy-2, as ω_N is decreased below ω_{low}
a)ω_{low} : CCM/TM1 boundary b)TM1 mode
c)ω_{tran}: TM1/TM2 boundary d)TM2 mode
e)ω_{disc}: TM2/DCM boundary and DCM mode

lower operating frequencies, multiple resonant cycles occur as illustrated in Fig. 14(e). Fig. 14(e) shows only one of the many possible operating modes in this region, which is named the MULTIPLE modes region. The many operating modes in the MULTIPLE region are similar in nature to those discussed in [7] for series resonant converters. This region occurs under Strategy-1 for all load current ranges. The main disadvantage of operating the converter in this region is as follows:

In Fig. 6(a) and Figs. 14(a) to 14(d), as operating frequency is decreased, the trajectory size progressively decreases. A study of the dc characteristics shows that the output voltage also continuously decreases with frequency[15]. This no longer holds true once MULTIPLE modes region is entered. The circuit exhibits many resonant peaks in this region. This would make the control extremely difficult and impractical. Due to this reason, the present paper does not carry out a detailed analysis of the converter operation in this region.

b) Operation Under Base-Drive Strategy-2

Fig. 15 shows the corresponding sequence of state plane diagrams. Figs. 15(a) and 15(b) are identical to Figs. 14(a) and 14(b). As ω is further reduced below that of Fig. 15(b), the lower boundary for the TM1 mode is reached when $\omega_N = \omega_{tran}$(Fig. 15(c)), below which the circuit operates in another mode named **Transition Mode 2 (TM2)**. When $\omega_N < \omega_{tran}$, as shown in Fig. 15(d), the diodes also are naturally commutated. Here, after T1 and D1 conduct, T1 can not conduct again under this base-drive strategy. The residual capacitor voltage at the end of diode conduction is discharged linearly (M7) till T2 is switched on again. T2 conducts now in topological mode M3 till the trajectory reaches the vertical axis. Then, T2 will linearly charge the inductor (M6) till the current reaches the load current magnitude, I_o. At this instant the clamp

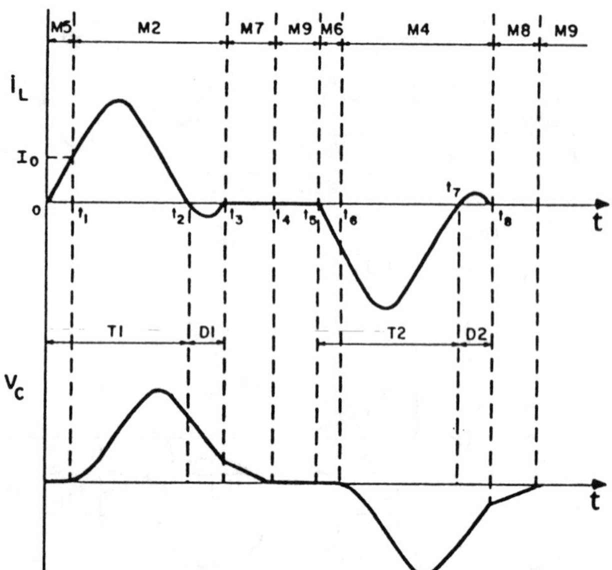

Fig.16. DCM mode waveforms for Fig. 15((e)

on the resonant capacitor is released and T2 will conduct in M4 topological mode. The operation of the circuit in the second half of the cycle follows in a similar fashion. This is the mode of operation named Transition Mode 2 (TM2). The topological mode sequence for TM2 is M1-M5-M2-M7-M3-M6-M4-M8-M1-.

When ω is further reduced, the capacitor discharge interval progressively increases until at a boundary frequency, ω_{disc}, the capacitor fully discharges to zero before T2 (or T1) is switched on (Fig. 15(e)). As ω is reduced below ω_{disc}, the trajectory remains the same with only the dwell time at the origin increasing. The topological mode sequence under this DCM mode is M9-M5-M2-M7-M9-M6-M4-M8-M9-. The resonant tank waveforms under DCM mode of operation are shown in Fig.16 with the time instants corresponding to those in Fig. 15(e).

In all the trajectories of Fig. 15, the transistors are naturally commutated due to the base-drive strategy. The undesirable MULTIPLE region encountered with Strategy-1 is also avoided.

3.6.2 Non-CCM Operation when $\omega_N > \omega_{max}$: In Fig. 6(b), as ω is increased, a boundary is reached at ω_{high}, at which $I_{L1N} = I_{oN}$. The circuit can not operate in CCM beyond this frequency. Fig.17 shows a series of diagrams for the case when $\omega_N > \omega_{high}$. Fig. 17(a) shows the trajectory for the boundary, ω_{high}. When ω is increased beyond ω_{high} as shown in Fig. 17(b), the current I_{L1N} is less than I_{oN} (time instant 0). Hence, following conduction in M1 topological mode, T1 will continue to conduct in M5, linearly charging the inductor. When the inductor current reaches I_o, the circuit switches to M2. The rest of the operation is

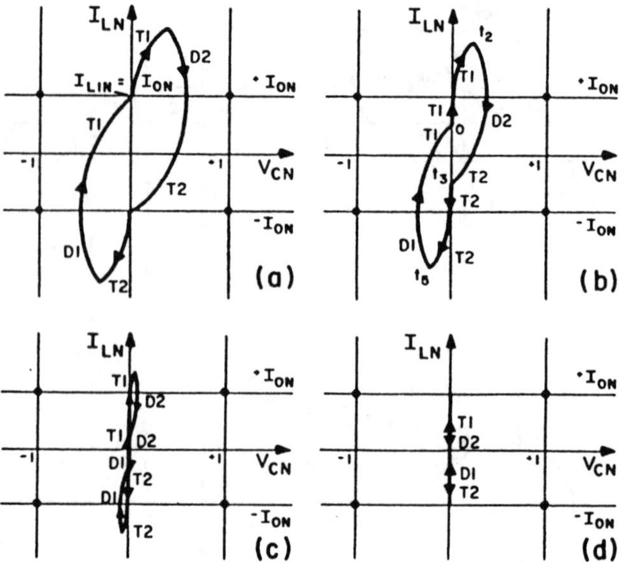

Fig.17. Non-CCM operation for $I_{oN} < 1$, as ω_N is increased above ω_{high}
a) ω_{high} : CCM/TM1 boundary b) & c) TM1 mode
d) ω_{limit}: TM1/LIMIT boundary

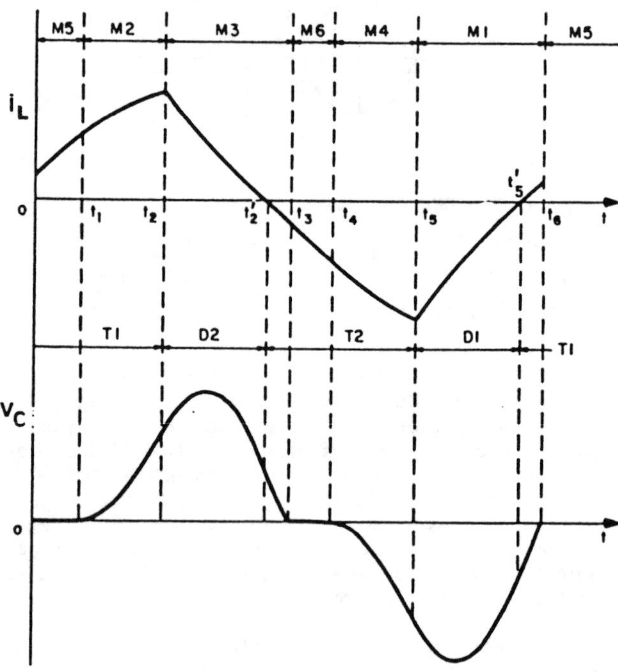

Fig.18. TM1 mode waveforms for Fig. 17(b)

self-explanatory. The resulting mode of operation is the Transition Mode 1 introduced earlier.

Fig.17(c) shows the operation of the circuit at a still higher frequency. The circuit operating mode and the device conduction sequence are unaltered. However, the waveforms are shared by the power devices differently. For example in Fig. 17(b),

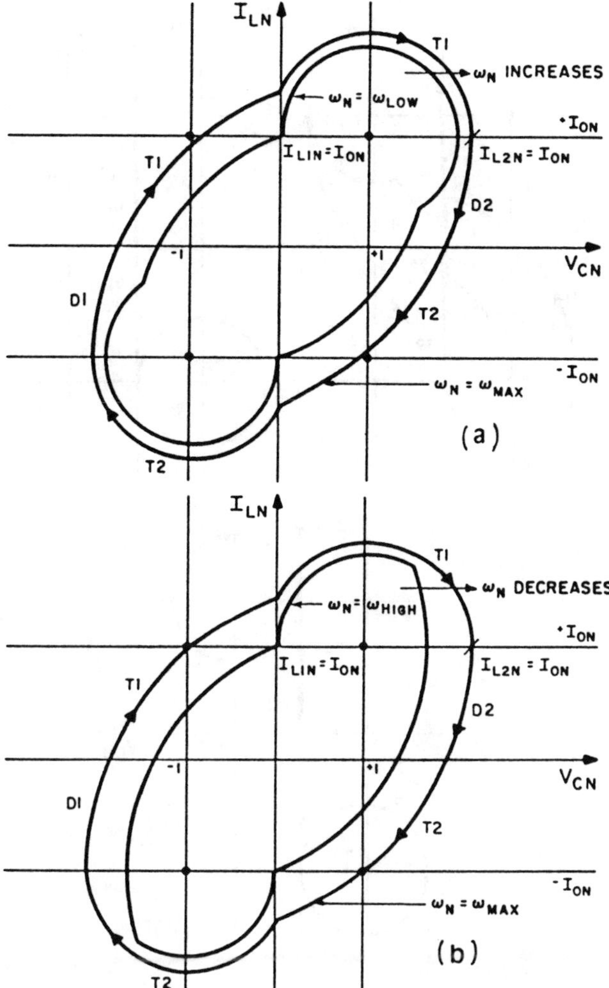

Fig.19. CCM trajectories for $0 < I_{oN} < \sqrt{2}$ and

a)$\omega_{low} < \omega_N < \omega_{max}$ b)$\omega_{max} < \omega_N < \omega_{high}$

T1 alone charges up the inductor in M5 interval, whereas in Fig. 17(c) D1 followed by T1 carry out this function.

As ω is increased, a further limit is reached in Fig. 17(d). Here, the durations of topological modes M1,M2,M3 and M4 in TM1 have shrunk to zero. The resonant inductor is merely charged up and down linearly, with resonant capacitor clamped at zero volt permanently. Thus the output voltage will be zero. As ω is further increased the trajectory stays on the vertical axis. This mode of operation is named the LIMIT mode and would occur, ideally, when the output is short circuited. The topological mode sequence under LIMIT mode is M5-M6-M5-. It is interesting to note that although PRC acts as a voltage-fed converter normally, it has the current limiting capability under short circuit conditions due to the series inductor of the tank circuit. Also, since output power is zero under short circuit, the input voltage source, V_s, supplies only the parasitic losses. Hence, the dc average current drawn from the source would be quite small, ideally zero.

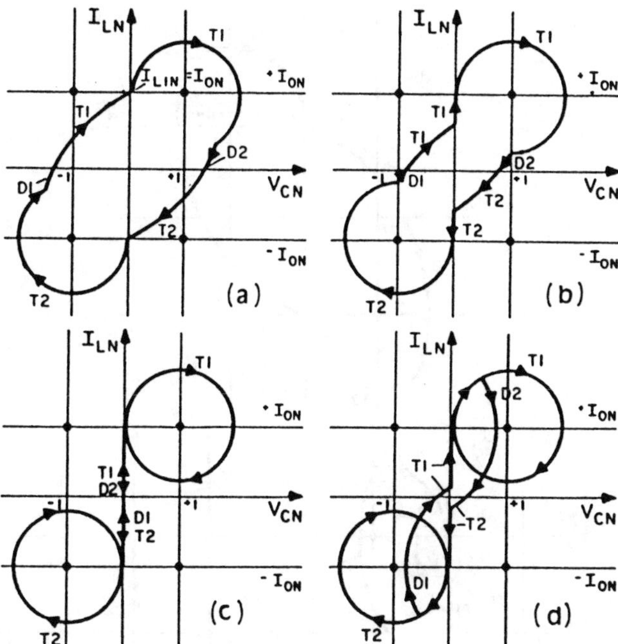

Fig.20. Non-CCM operation for $1 < I_{oN} < \sqrt{2}$,

as ω_N is decreased below ω_{low}

a)ω_{low}: CCM/TM1 boundary b)TM1 mode

c)ω_{mul}: TM1/MULTIPLE boundary d)MULTIPLE region

However, when output is shorted at a low ω, the peak source current can still be considerably large and could be a limiting factor.

The devices are force commutated in all the cases shown in Fig. 17. Fig. 18 shows the tank waveforms corresponding to the transition mode, TM1, in Fig. 17(b).

3.7 Load Range $1 < I_{oN} \leq \sqrt{2}$

Fig. 19 shows the CCM equilibrium trajectories for this range of load current. Fig. 19(a) corresponds to Intersection-1 ($\omega_N < \omega_{max}$) and Fig. 19(b) to Intersection-2 ($\omega_N > \omega_{max}$). In Fig. 19(a), as frequency is decreased, a lower bound, ω_{low}, is reached, when I_{L1N} equals I_{oN}. As frequency is increased, Intersection- 1 & 2 trajectories merge at $\omega_N = \omega_{max}$. A study of the angles subtended at the topological mode centers, shows that ω_{max} in this case is less than 1. Thus, when I_{oN} is more than 1, the maximum trajectory size occurs at an operating frequency less than the resonant frequency. I_{L2N} is defined as the normalized inductor current at the instant when the topological mode change from M2 to M3 occurs. The trajectory corresponding to ω_{max} occurs when I_{L2N} equals I_{oN}. Also, ω_{max} trajectory has finite dimensions, unlike the earlier case when I_{oN} was less than 1 (Fig. 6). This implies that, if I_{oN} is greater than 1, the output

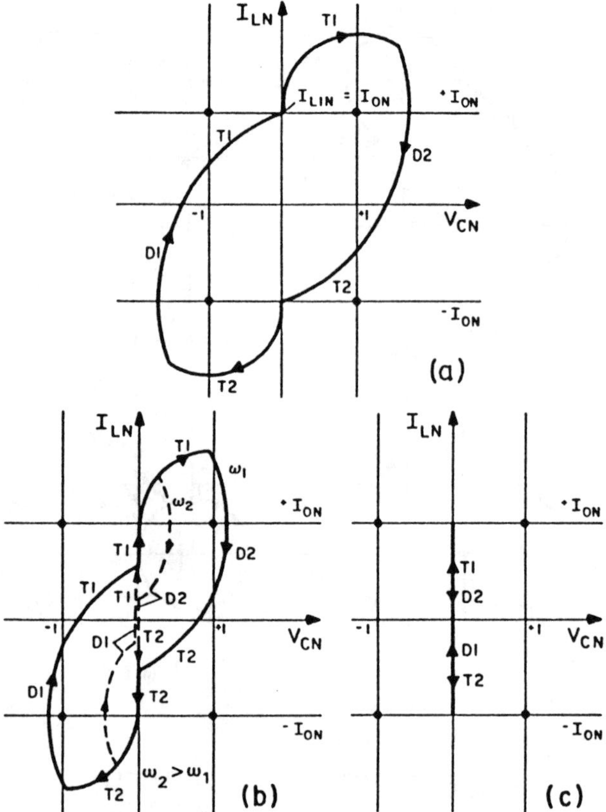

Fig.21. Non-CCM operation for $1 < I_{oN} < \sqrt{2}$, as ω_N is increased above ω_{high}
a) ω_{high}: CCM/TM1 boundary b) TM1 mode
c) ω_{limit}: TM1/LIMIT boundary

voltage is bounded even if losses are neglected. As ω is increased above ω_{max}, Intersection-2 trajectories in Fig. 19(b) follow till the upper CCM boundary, ω_{high}, is reached when $I_{L1N} = I_{oN}$

Another major difference in this load current range is that the transistors are no longer naturally commutated, even when $\omega_N < \omega_{max}$, as shown in Fig. 19(a). This can be explained in the following manner. When T1 conducts in M2, even though the tank current, i_L, varies in a resonant manner, the dc offset in i_L, I_o, is so large that i_L always remains positive. Hence, if natural commutation of transistors is desired, the normalized load current, I_{oN}, must be kept less than 1.

As frequency is decreased below ω_{low}, the series of trajectories in Fig. 20 apply. Since the transistor does not naturally commutate at all, base drive Strategy-2 can no longer be used and only Strategy-1 is applicable. Though Fig. 20 is similar to Fig. 14, the device sequences in these load ranges are not identical. Fig. 20(a) corresponds to ω_{low}, the boundary between CCM and TM1 mode. Fig. 20(b) shows a trajectory in TM1 mode of operation. Fig. 20(c) shows the boundary, ω_{mul}, below which multiple cycle conduction occurs. Fig. 20(d) shows one possible trajectory in MULTIPLE region.

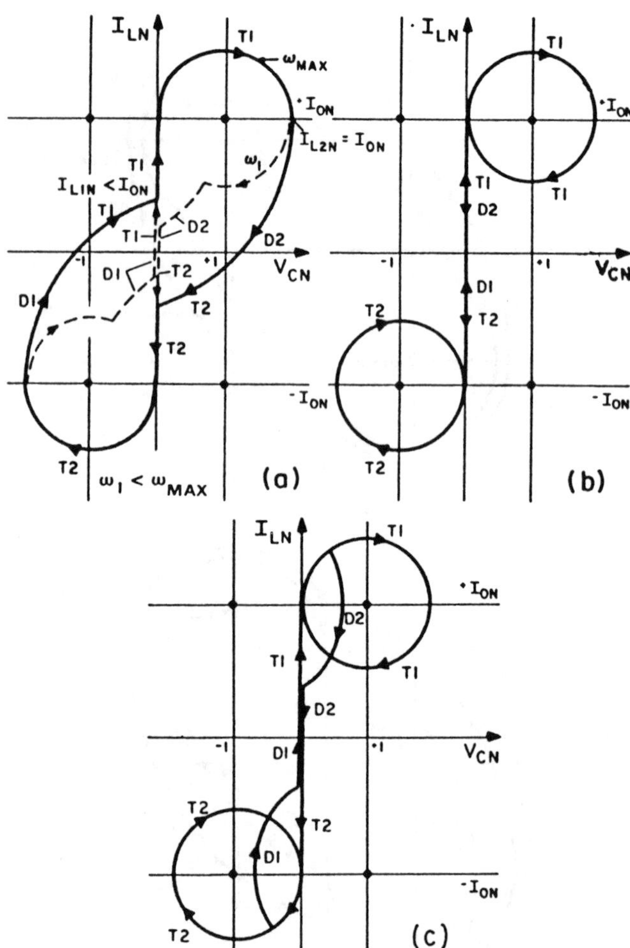

Fig.22. Equilibrium trajectories for $I_{oN} > \sqrt{2}$, as ω_N is decreased below ω_{max}
a) ω_{max} & ω_1: TM1 mode b) ω_{mul}: TM1/MULTIPLE boundary
c) MULTIPLE region

The resulting sequence of trajectories, when ω is increased beyond ω_{high}, is shown in Fig. 21.

3.8 Load Range $I_{oN} > \sqrt{2}$

Figs. 22 and 23 show the equilibrium trajectories. In this range of current, it is not possible to construct CCM Intersection 1 & 2 trajectories at all. The maximum trajectory size, at $\omega_N = \omega_{max}$, occurs, when I_{L2N} (see sec. 3.7) equals I_{oN}, in the TM1 mode itself. A study of the state-plane diagrams shows that for load currents above $I_{oN} = \sqrt{2}$, CCM mode of operation is not possible.

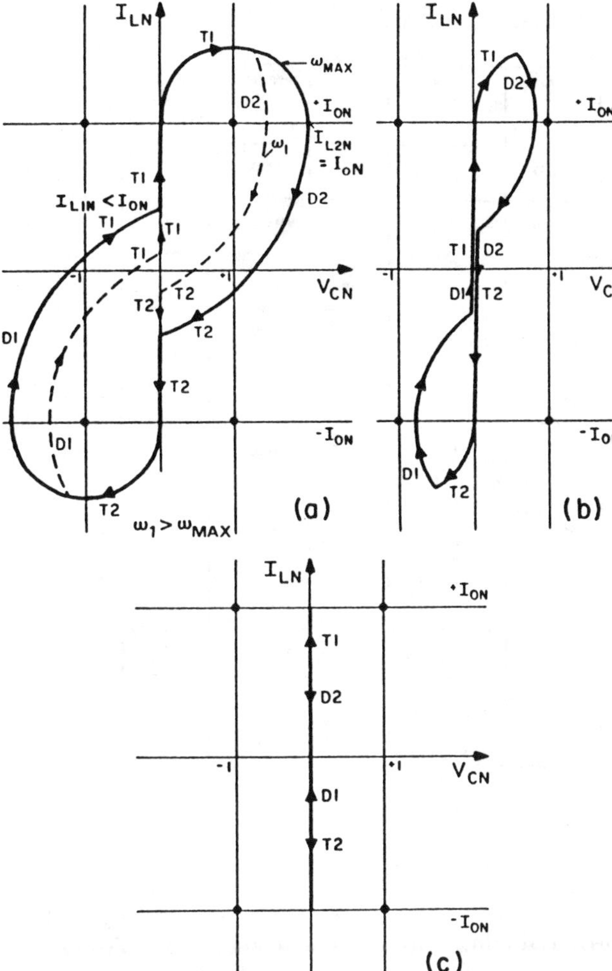

Fig.23. Equilibrium trajectories for $I_{oN} > \sqrt{2}$, as ω_N is increased above ω_{max}
a) ω_{max} & ω_1: TM1 mode b) TM1 mode
c) ω_{limit}: TM1/LIMIT boundary

3.9 Results of Mode Analysis

Table-1 summarizes the different possible converter modes along with their unique topological mode sequences. The Multiple Resonant Cycle Region, MULTIPLE, contains actually many converter modes of operation. For the reason explained in Sec. 3.6.1.a, a detailed analysis of these modes is omitted in this paper.

The Appendix illustrates the method of deriving equations for the boundary frequencies, such as ω_{low}, ω_{max} and ω_{limit}, directly from the state-plane diagrams. Table-A1 in the Appendix contains the equations for all the relevant boundary frequencies in terms of normalized load current, I_{oN}. These are plotted in Figs. 24(a) and 24(b). The boundaries between the regions are marked in Fig. 24(a), while Fig. 24(b) shows the different regions. Table-2 shows the features of the different regions marked in Fig. 24(b). Given load current and operating frequency, we can determine the PRC region of operation from Fig. 24(b).

TABLE 1: CONVERTER MODES IN PRC

CONVERTER MODE	TOPOLOGICAL MODE SEQUENCE
DCM	M9-M5-M2-M7-M9-M6-M4-M8-M9-
MULTIPLE	MANY SEQUENCES POSSIBLE
LIMIT	M5-M6-M5-
TM1	M1-M5-M2-M3-M6-M4-M1-
TM2	M1-M5-M2-M7-M3-M6-M4-M8-M1-
CCM	M1-M2-M3-M4-M1-

Fig. 25 is used to highlight certain features of Fig. 24. The three major regions of PRC are shown in Fig. 25(a). The area under the bell-shaped curve defines the CCM region. Operation in the (current) LIMIT mode is not possible in practice as it implies ideal short circuit. For a particular ω_N, the value of I_{oN} as given by boundary b7 in Fig. 24(a) can be considered as the ideal short circuit current. The area marked "Multiple Modes" in Fig. 25(a) indicates the MULTIPLE region of operation under Strategy-1. As explained in sec. 3.6.1.a, operation in this region can pose control problems and hence ω_{mul} (boundary b1 in Fig. 24(a)) can be treated as the lower limit on the operating frequency under Strategy-1. However, when I_{oN} is less than 1, by adopting base-drive Strategy-2, the MULTIPLE region can be avoided altogether. As operating frequency is reduced below ω_{max}, the non-CCM mode sequence (Fig.24(b)) would then be TM1(Region 5A), TM2(Region 4) DCM(Region 1).

Fig. 25(b) divides the I_{oN} - ω_N plane as per the nature of commutation of the power switches. By restricting the operation to $I_{oN} < 1$ and $\omega_N < 1$ and using base-drive Strategy-2, the PRC can be operated entirely with natural commutation.

Due to lack of space, a complete DC analysis that was performed with the aid of the state-plane diagrams in each of the different regions is not included in this paper. Fig. 26 shows a plot of the normalized output voltage, V_{oN}, as a function of normalized frequency, ω_N, for different normalized load currents, I_{oN}, obtained as a result of this analysis. The plot includes all the different regions of Fig. 24, except the MULTIPLE region. From Fig. 26, we note that when ω_N is approximately less than 0.5, the dc characteristic is almost linear and almost load independent. Also, at operating frequencies above resonance, the output voltage falls quite rapidly with load. In fact, for load I_{oN} greater than 1, no significant output voltage is developed at above resonant frequencies. The complete dc analysis will be included in Ref [15].

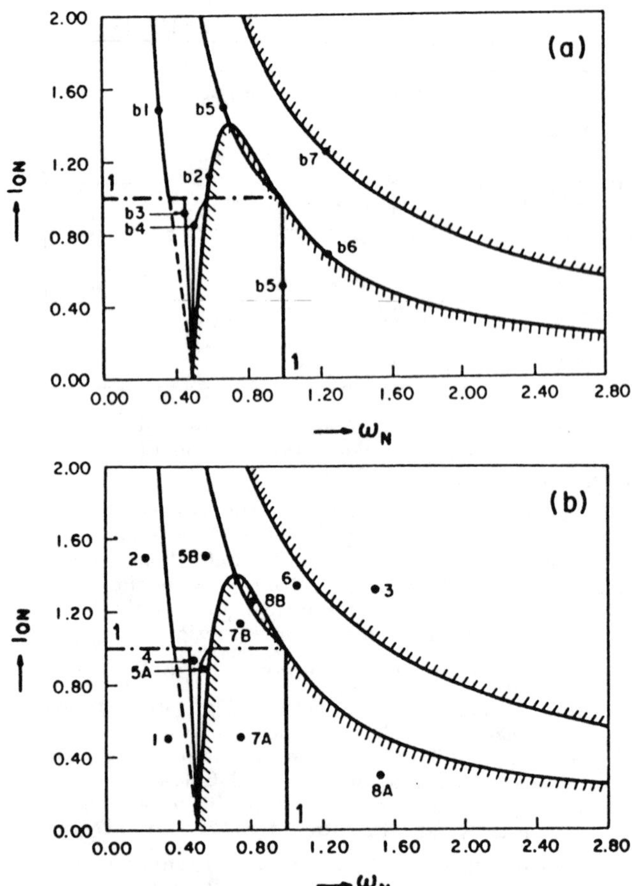

Fig.24. Operating regions of PRC
a)Boundaries - b1: ω_{mul}, b2: ω_{low}, b3: ω_{disc}, b4: ω_{tran}, b5: ω_{max}, b6: ω_{high}, b7: ω_{limit}
b)Regions - see Table-2 for the characteristics

TABLE 2: PRC REGIONS OF OPERATION

REGION #	I_{ON} RANGE	ω_N RANGE	MODE	COMMUTATION	DERIVED FROM INTERSECTION TRAJECTORY #	BASE DRIVE STRATEGY #
1	$I_{ON} < 1$	$\omega_N < \omega_{DISC}$	DCM	NATURAL	1	2
2	I_{ON} ANY	$\omega_N < \omega_{MUL}$	MULTIPLE	NATURAL/ FORCED	1	1
3	I_{ON} ANY	$\omega_N > \omega_{LIMIT}$	LIMIT	FORCED	2	1 or 2
4	$I_{ON} < 1$	$\omega_{DISC} < \omega_N < \omega_{TRAN}$	TM2	NATURAL	1	2
5A	$I_{ON} < 1$	$\omega_{TRAN} < \omega_N < \omega_{LOW}$	TM1	NATURAL	1	1 or 2
5B	$1 < I_{ON} < \sqrt{2}$	$\omega_{MUL} < \omega_N < \omega_{LOW}$	TM1	FORCED	1	1
	$I_{ON} > \sqrt{2}$	$\omega_{MUL} < \omega_N < \omega_{MAX}$				
6	$I_{ON} < \sqrt{2}$	$\omega_{HIGH} < \omega_N < \omega_{LIMIT}$	TM1	FORCED	2	1 or 2
	$I_{ON} > \sqrt{2}$	$\omega_{MAX} < \omega_N < \omega_{LIMIT}$				
7A	$I_{ON} < 1$	$\omega_{LOW} < \omega_N < \omega_{MAX}$	CCM	NATURAL	1	1 or 2
7B	$I_{ON} > 1$	$\omega_{LOW} < \omega_N < \omega_{HIGH}$	CCM	FORCED	1	1 or 2
8A	$I_{ON} < 1$	$\omega_{MAX} < \omega_N < \omega_{HIGH}$	CCM	FORCED	2	1 or 2
8B	$I_{ON} > 1$	$\omega_{MAX} < \omega_N < \omega_{HIGH}$	CCM	FORCED	2	1 or 2

4.0 EXPERIMENTAL RESULTS

Fig. 27 shows the experimental PRC circuit. The diodes DT1 and DT2 are included in order to block the resonant current from flowing through the slow, built-in, anti-parallel diode of the MOSFET. A small snubber circuit across the power switch is found desirable due to the presence of source lead inductances.

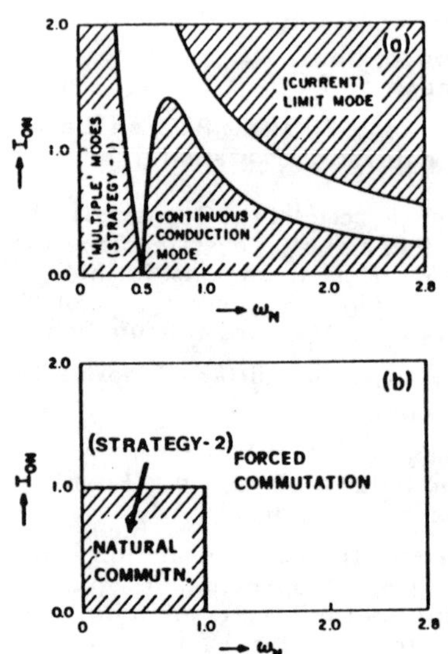

Fig.25. Features of PRC operating regions

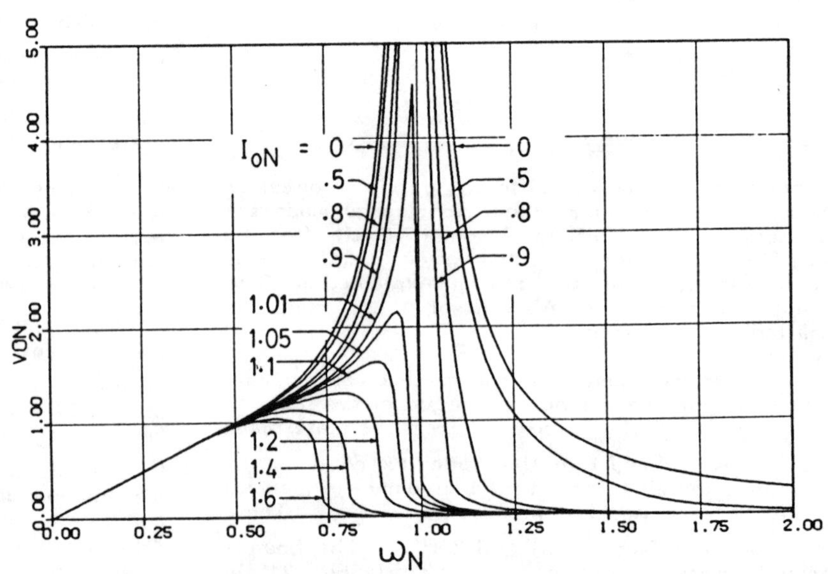

Fig.26. Theoretical DC characteristics of PRC

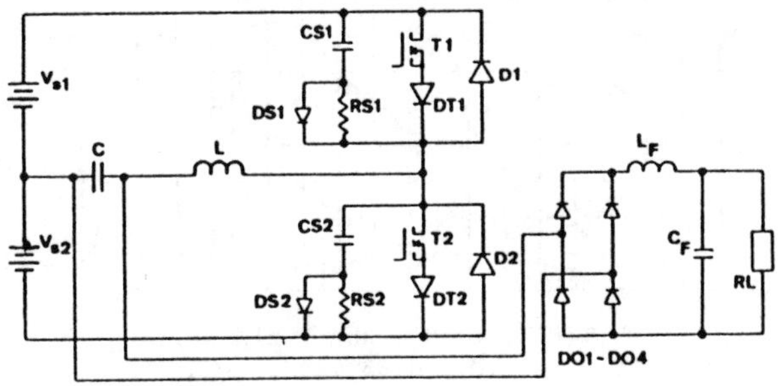

Fig.27. Experimental PRC circuit

VS1,VS2: 25V, T1,T2: 2SK325, DT1,DT2: A115E,
D1,D2: 12FL60S02, DO1~DO4: 40HFL60S02
L: 81.8 μH, C: 0.125 μF, CF: 18.5 μF,
LF: 85.66 mH, CS1,CS2: 1.0nF, RS1,RS2: 470 Ω,
DS1,DS2: A115E,
f_0(measured) = 50.275 kHZ, Z_0 = 25.847 Ω

Two sets of oscillograms are presented to demonstrate the variety of modes that exist in the PRC.

First, let us examine Fig. 24. If I_{oN} is kept constant at a value less than 1 and the frequency is continuously increased, the mode sequence under Strategy-2 will be, DCM, TM2, TM1, CCM($\omega_N < 1$), CCM($\omega_N > 1$), TM1 and LIMIT. The observed sequence of trajectories, for I_o = 0.5A (I_{oN} = 0.517), is shown in Fig. 28, which follows the prediction quite well. It was, however, difficult to observe the TM1 mode between CCM and DCM modes(Fig. 15(b)), due to the effect of parasitics. The waveforms corresponding to the trajectories in Fig. 28 are shown in Fig. 29.

The effect of parasitics due to circuit layout and non-ideal components are clearly observable in these oscillograms. The trajectory segments are not strictly circular, but somewhat spiral inwards, due to the effect of circuit damping. In the DCM and TM2 modes(Figs. 28(a), 28(b), 29(a) and 29(b)), during the capacitor discharge period, the resonant inductor current oscillates, instead of remaining at zero. This is probably due to the interaction of device junction capacitances, snubber capacitances and the parasitic inductances in the circuit. In addition, since an ideal short circuit is not realizable in practice, the trajectory in Fig. 28(h) does not quite stay on the vertical axis, as predicted in Fig. 17(d). The parasitic elements in the circuit also caused some deviations from the predicted mode boundaries, shown in Fig. 24(a). The authors are currently investigating the effect of parasitics on the performance of resonant converters and the results will be published later.

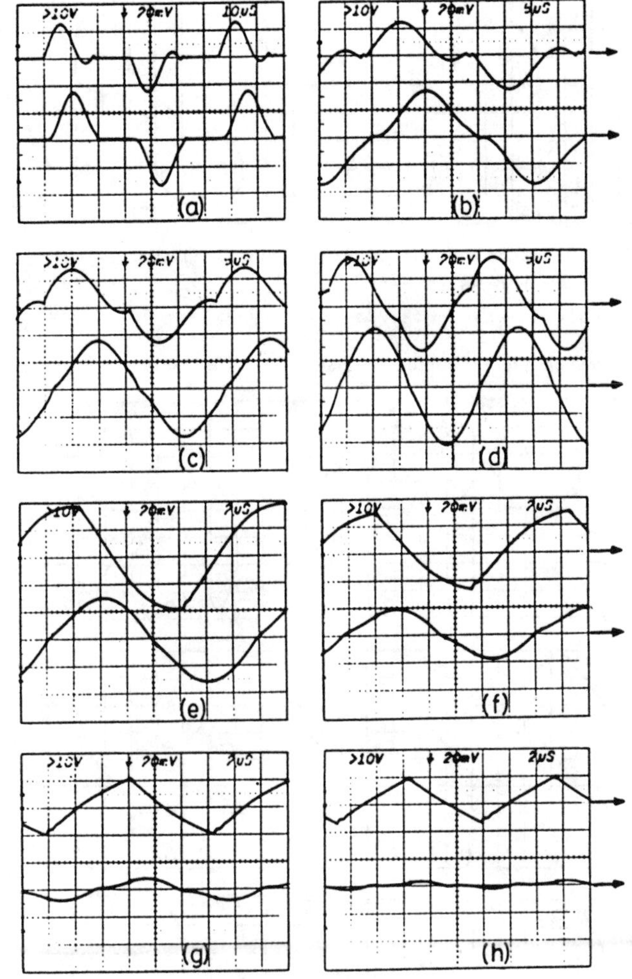

Fig.29. Waveforms corresponding to Fig. 28
Top trace: tank inductor current-1 A/div
Bottom trace: tank capacitor voltage-25.85 V/div

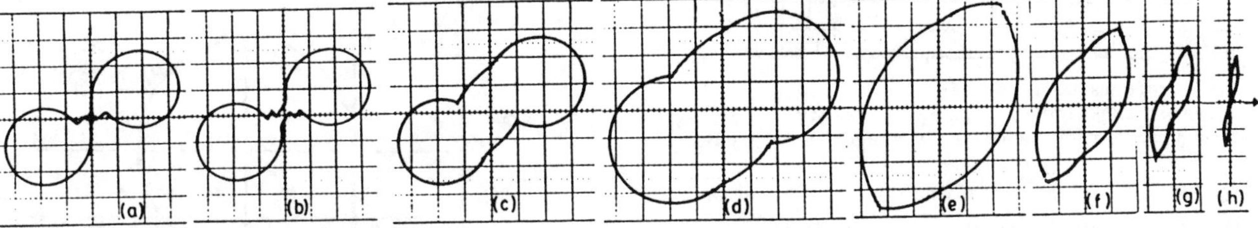

Fig.28. Oscillograms of experimental trajectories under Strategy-2 with I_o = 0.5 A (I_{oN} = 0.517)
Scale: x-axis - 12.925 V/div, y-axis - 0.5 A/div

Switching frequencies and operating modes:

a)15.05kHZ: DCM, b)24.63kHZ: TM2, c)30.73kHZ: CCM (ω_N<1), d)36.78kHz: CCM(ω_N<1), e)63.06kHz: CCM (ω_N>1), f)68.59kHz: CCM(ω_N>1), g)78.70kHz: TM1 h)90.60kHz: near LIMIT mode

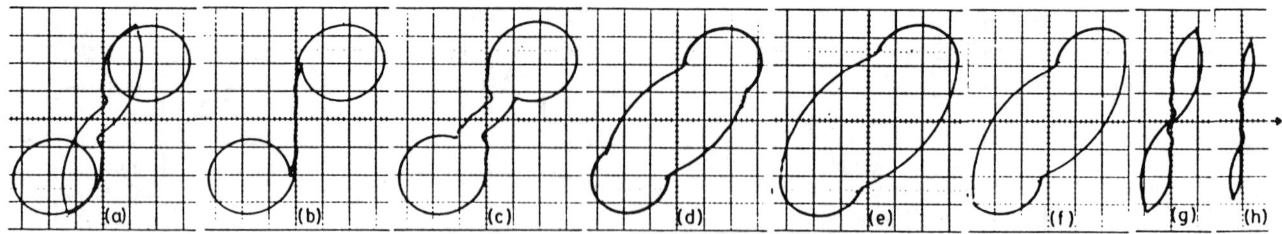

Fig.30. Oscillograms of experimental trajectories under Strategy-1 with I_o = 1.0 A (I_{oN} = 1.034)

Scale: x-axis - 12.925 V/div, y-axis - 0.5 A/div

Switching frequencies and operating modes:

a)17.32kHz: MULTIPLE, b)19.92kHz: TM1/MULTIPLE boundary, c)26.0kHz: TM1, d)33.62kHz: CCM ($\omega_N < \omega_{max}$), e)40.92kHz: CCM($\omega_N = \omega_{max}$), f)44.48 kHz: CCM($\omega_N > \omega_{max}$), g)48.00kHz: TM1, h)52.27kHz: near LIMIT mode

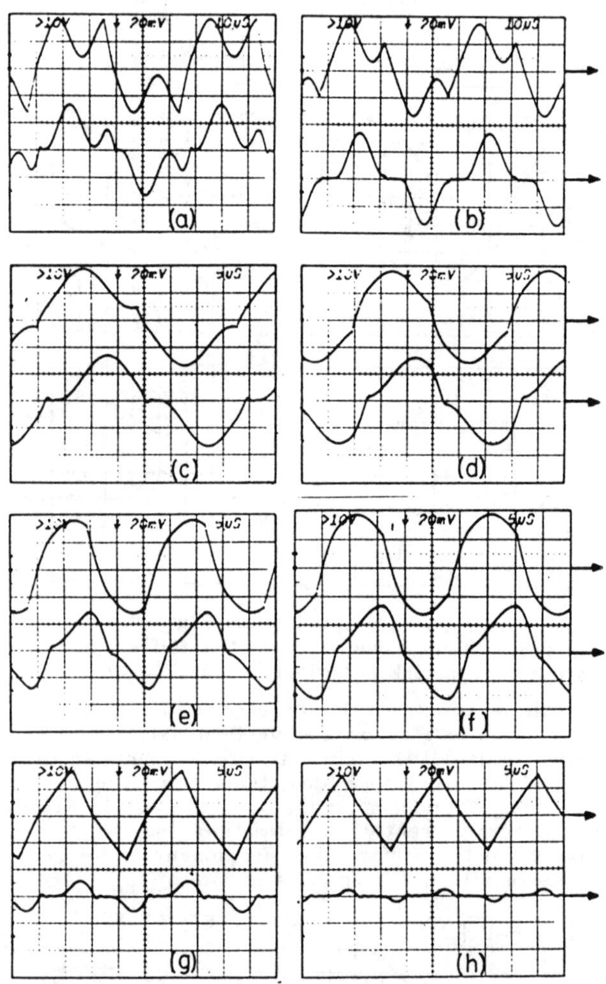

Fig.31. Waveforms corresponding to Fig. 30
Top trace: tank inductor current-1 A/div
Bottom trace: tank capacitor voltage-25.85 V/div

In Fig. 24(b), if I_{oN} is between 1 and $\sqrt{2}$ and operating frequency is continuously increased, the sequence of modes will be MULTIPLE, TM1, CCM($\omega_N < \omega_{max}$), CCM($\omega_N > \omega_{max}$) TM1 and LIMIT modes. Fig. 30 shows the experimental trajectories for I_o = 1.0A (I_{oN} = 1.034), which confirm the prediction.

The corresponding tank waveforms are shown in Fig. 31. The effect of parasitics is again responsible for the trajectory to cross the vertical axis prior to mode change (see Figs. 30(c) and 30(d)), while the mode change occurs exactly at the vertical axis, ideally.

5.0 NOVEL RESONANT BUCK CONVERTER

5.1 Circuit Derivation

In Fig. 26, when ω_N is less than 0.5, the dc conversion ratio is almost a linear function of ω_N, and is almost independent of load. Fig. 32(a) shows the state-plane diagram of PRC operating in the DCM mode. In this mode, after T1 and D1 conduct and

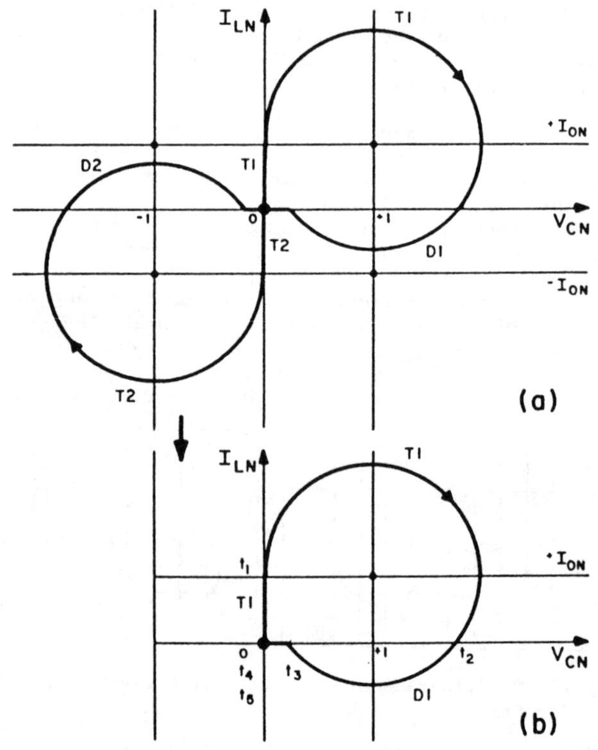

Fig.32. State-plane derivation of the resonant buck converter

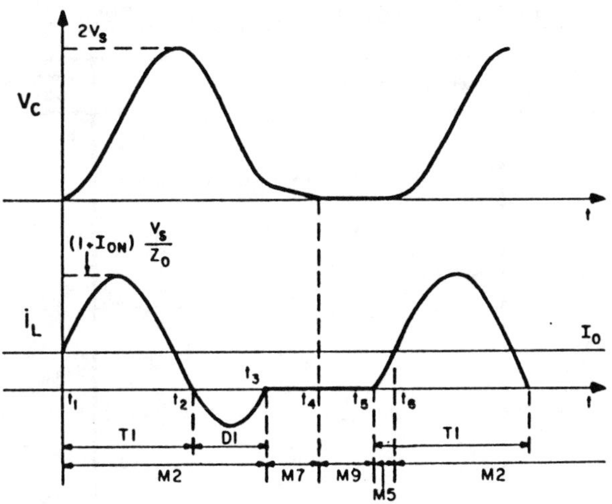

Fig. 33. Waveforms for Fig. 32(b)

after the discharge period of the resonant capacitor, the circuit comes to rest at the origin. Instead of triggering T2 as in normal PRC operation, T1 can be again switched on, thus repeating the previous half-cycle. The resulting equilibrium trajectory is shown in Fig. 32(b). In Fig. 32(b), T1 is triggered at t = 0. The inductor current is linearly charged (topological mode M5) till it equals I_o. At t1, the clamp on the resonant capacitor is released and the circuit continues in topological mode M2 with T1 conducting. At t2, T1 naturally commutates and D1 starts to conduct with the topological mode still remaining at M2. At t3, D1 commutates naturally leaving a residual capacitor voltage. The resonant capacitor now discharges through the load linearly(M7) and the system reaches origin at t4. The circuit stays at origin(M9) till t5, when T1 is switched on again. Fig. 33 shows the corresponding tank waveforms.

Fig. 34 shows a circuit realization of such an operation. In Fig. 34(b), the devices T2 and D2 of the PRC in Fig. 34(a) have been removed. From Fig. 32(b), we note that the resonant capacitor voltage does not reach negative values at all. Hence, the output bridge rectifier no longer performs any rectifying function. It is needed only to provide freewheeling path for the load current during the discontinuous conduction interval(t4-t5) and during the inductor charging interval(t5-t6). Due to this, the output circuit can be further simplified with a freewheel diode(Fig. 34(c)). The derivation is now complete and Fig. 34(c) shows the circuit diagram of the proposed Resonant Buck Converter. Fig. 35 shows the dc characteristics of this converter, normalized output voltage versus normalized frequency, obtained from a detailed state-plane analysis.

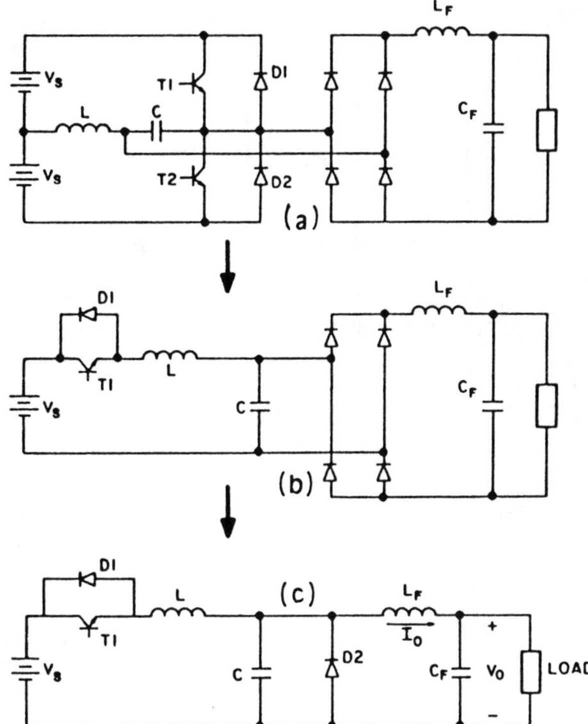

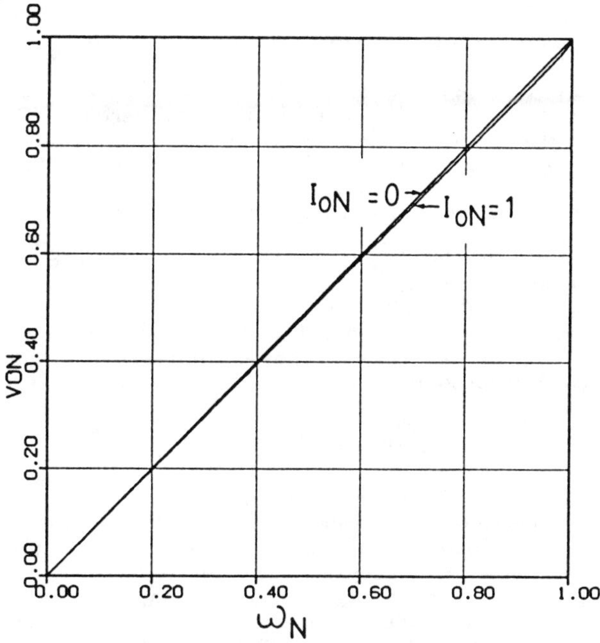

Fig.34. Circuit derivation of the resonant buck converter

Fig.35. DC characteristics of the resonant buck converter

5.2 Features of Resonant Buck Converter

The proposed circuit has certain attractive features, which are stated below.

1) The circuit requires only one power switch to implement the resonant converter concept. 2) Both the transistor and the diode are naturally commutated thus virtually eliminating all switching losses. Due to this, the circuit shows potential for very high frequency applications [6]. 3) Since the operation is mostly similar to the DCM mode of PRC,

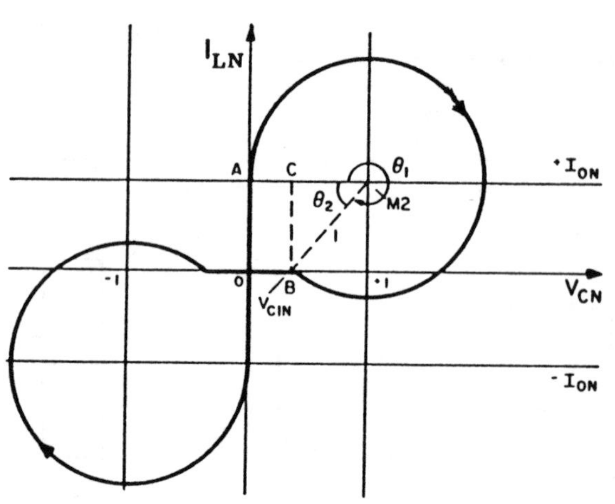

Fig.A1. State trajectory for $\omega_N = \omega_{disc}$

TABLE A1: PRC BOUNDARY FREQUENCIES

#	BOUNDARY FREQUENCY	NORMALIZED BOUNDARY FREQUENCY = π/ϕ — ϕ	APPLICABLE LOAD RANGE
b1	ω_{MUL}	$2(\pi + I_{ON})$	ANY
b2	ω_{LOW}	$2\pi - \cos^{-1} K1 + \cos^{-1}(1/K2) - \cos^{-1} K3$	$I_{ON} < \sqrt{2}$
b3	ω_{DISC}	$2\pi - \cos^{-1} K4 + (1-K4)/I_{ON} + I_{ON}$	$I_{ON} < 1$
b4	ω_{TRAN}	$2\pi - \cos^{-1} K4 + \cos^{-1}(1/K6)$ $- \cos^{-1}[(2-K4)/K6] + 2 I_{ON} - 2\sqrt{1 - K4}$	$I_{ON} < 1$
b5	ω_{MAX}	π	$0 < I_{ON} < 1$
		$\pi - \cos^{-1}[K5/(I_{ON}^2 - K5)] + \cos^{-1}[K5/(I_{ON}^2 + K5)]$	$1 < I_{ON} < \sqrt{2}$
		$\pi + \cos^{-1}(1/3) + 2(I_{ON} - \sqrt{2})$	$I_{ON} > \sqrt{2}$
b6	ω_{HIGH}	$\cos^{-1} K1 + \cos^{-1}(1/K2) + \cos^{-1} K3$	$I_{ON} > \sqrt{2}$
b7	ω_{LIMIT}	$2 I_{ON}$	ANY

$K1 \triangleq (1 - I_{ON}^2)$ $\quad K3 \triangleq (1 + I_{ON}^2)/K2$ $\quad K5 \triangleq \sqrt{I_{ON}^2 - 1}$

$K2 \triangleq \sqrt{1 + 4 I_{ON}^2}$ $\quad K4 \triangleq \sqrt{K1}$, $\quad K6 \triangleq \sqrt{5 - 4 K4}$

the output voltage varies almost linearly with frequency. The output voltage is also almost independent of load current(Fig. 35), unlike most resonant converters . This is an important feature, since the switching frequency can be maintained essentially constant for a varying load.

On the negative side, the circuit requires more components than a normal buck converter. The device rms currents will be somewhat higher. Since, the no-load tank current is high, larger idling losses will be present and this may be undesirable in certain applications.

On the whole, however, it is felt that this circuit is an important addition to the family of power processing circuits. Based on this circuit idea and the concept of "resonant switch" developed in [5], a host of new resonant power processing circuits is introduced [6].

6.0 CONCLUSIONS

The paper presents a method for analyzing the comple operating modes of a parallel resonant converter, using graphical state-plane techniques. The analysis uncovers, for the first time, the presence of many modes of operation, besides the continuous conduction mode(CCM) and the discontinuous conduction mode(DCM), and determines the theoretical boundaries between these modes. The different modes of operation are clearly portrayed by closed equilibrium trajectories on the state-plane. Employing state portrayals, different regions of operation, such as, CCM region, Transition regions, DCM region, Natural Commutation region, Short-Circuit Current Limit region and Multiple Conduction-Cycle region, are clearly defined. Two base-drive strategies for the power switches are also identified and their relative merits discussed.

The insight gained from the analysis has led to the proposal of a novel resonant buck converter having the combined property of the PRC and the conventional buck converter. A desirable feature of the converter is that the voltage conversion ratio is almost independent of load. Furthermore, since the power switch and its anti-parallel diode are both naturally commutated, all switching losses and stresses are virtually eliminated. This enables the new converter to operate at very high frequencies.

APPENDIX

Table-A1 gives the equations for the various boundary frequencies of PRC as functions of the normalized load current, I_{oN}, together with their applicable range of I_{oN}. These equations were derived by utilizing the equilibrium trajectories corresponding to the boundary frequencies. The derivation utilizes the following equations, which can be shown easily, for the normalized time intervals, $\omega_0 \Delta t$, for the different trajectory segments.

1) Inductor linear charging interval

$$\omega_0 \Delta t = \Delta i_{LN}, \qquad \text{(A1)}$$

where Δi_{LN} = Normalized change in inductor current.

2) Resonant Interval

$$\omega_0 \Delta t = \Delta\theta, \qquad (A2)$$

where $\Delta\theta$ = Change in the angle subtended at the center.

3) Capacitor linear discharge interval

$$\omega_0 \Delta t = \Delta v_{CN}/I_{oN}, \qquad (A3)$$

where Δv_{CN} = Normalized change in capacitor voltage.

The derivation of the boundary equation for ω_{disc} is now presented to illustrate the geometrical method adopted in deriving the equations of Table-A1.

Fig. A-1 shows the boundary equilibrium trajectory between TM2 and DCM modes(see Sec. 3.6.1.b and Fig. 15(e)). Since the waveform is symmetrical,

$$T = \text{Switching period}$$

$$= 2\,(t_{OA} + t_{AB} + t_{BO})$$

From Eqs. (A1), (A2) and(A3),

$$T = \frac{2}{\omega_0}\left(I_{oN} + \theta_1 + \frac{V_{C1N}}{I_{oN}}\right).$$

From Fig. A-1,

$$\theta_1 = 2\pi - \theta_2 = 2\pi - \mathrm{Cos}^{-1}\sqrt{1-\overline{BC}^2}$$

$$= 2\pi - \mathrm{Cos}^{-1}\sqrt{1-I_{oN}^2}$$

$$V_{C1N} = \overline{OB} = 1 - \sqrt{1-I_{oN}^2}$$

So, $\omega_{disc} = \omega/\omega_0 = 2\pi/\omega_0 T$

$$= \frac{\pi}{2\pi - \cos^{-1}\sqrt{1-I_{oN}^2} + \dfrac{1-\sqrt{1-I_{oN}^2}}{I_{oN}} + I_{oN}} \qquad (A4)$$

REFERENCES

1. R. L. Steigerwald, "High-Frequency Resonant Transistor DC-DC Converters." IEEE Transactions on Industrial Electronics, Vol. IE-31, No. 2, pp. 181-191, May 1984.

2. R. Redl, B. Molnar and N. O. Sokal, "Class-E Resonant Regulated DC/DC Power Converters: Analysis of Operation, and Experimental Results at 1.5 MHZ"". IEEE Power Electronics Specialists Conference, Record, 1983, pp. 50-60.

3. F. C. Schwarz, "An Improved Method of Resonant Current Pulse Modulation for Power Converters". IEEE Power Electronics Specialists Conference, Record, 1975, pp. 194-204.

4. V. T. Ranganathan, P. D. Ziogas and V. R. Stefanovic, " A Regulated DC-DC Voltage Source Converter Using a High Frequency Link". IEEE Transactions on Industry Applications, Vol. IA-18, No. 3, pp. 279-287, May/June 1982.

5. K. H. Liu and F. C. Lee, "Resonant Switches - A Unified Approach to Improve Performances of Switching Converters". IEEE INTELEC Conference Record, 1984, pp. 344-351.

6. K. H. Liu, R. Oruganti and F. C. Lee, "Resonant switches - Topologies and Characteristics" to be published in IEEE Power Electronics Specialists Conference, Record, 1985.

7. V. Vorperian and S. Cuk, "A Complete DC Analysis of the Series Resonant Converter". IEEE Power Electronics Specialists Conference, Record, 1982, pp. 85-100.

8. R. J. King and T. A. Stuart, "A Normalized Model for the Half-Bridge Series Resonant Converter". IEEE Transactions on Aerospace and Electronic Systems, AES-19, No. 6. pp. 820-830, November 1983.

9. R. Oruganti and F. C. Lee, "Resonant Power Processors: Part I - State Plane Analysis". IEEE-IAS-1984 Annual Meeting, Conference Record, 1984, pp. 860-867.

10. R. Oruganti and F. C. Lee, "Resonant Power Processors: Part II - Methods of Control". IEEE-IAS-1984 Annual Meeting, Conference Record, 1984, pp. 868-878.

11. V. Vorperian and S. Cuk, "Small Signal Analysis of Resonant Converters". IEEE Power Electronics Specialists Conference, Record, 1983, pp. 269-282.

12. F. C. Lee and T. G. Wilson, "Modeling and Analysis of Several Classes of Self-Oscillating Inverters: Part I - State Plane Representations". IEEE Transactions on Circuits and Systems,CAS-29, No.6, pp.355-365, June 1982.

13. F. C. Lee and T. G. Wilson, "Modeling and Analysis of Several Classes of Self-Oscillating Inverters: Part II - Model Extension, Classification and Duality Relationship" IEEE Transactions on Circuits and Systems CAS-29, No. 6, pp. 366-374, June 1982.

14. W. W. Burns and T. G. Wilson, "State-Plane Trajectories Used to Observe and Control the Behavior of a Voltage Step-Up DC-to-DC Converter". IEEE Power Electronics Specialists Conference, Record, 1976, pp. 212-222.

15. R.Oruganti, "State-Plane Analysis of Resonant Converters", Ph.d dissertation, to be submitted to Virginia Polytechnic Institute & State University.

Paper 5.8

Aachen 1989

RECENT DEVELOPMENTS IN HIGH-FREQUENCY QUASI-RESONANT AND MULTI-RESONANT CONVERTER TECHNOLOGIES

Fred C. Lee, Wojciech A. Tabisz and Milan M. Jovanović, Virginia Power Electronics Center, The Bradley Department of Electrical Engineering, Virginia Polytechnic Institute & State University, Blacksburg, Virginia 24061

ABSTRACT

Resonant-switch topologies operating under the principle of zero-current switching and zero-voltage switching are introduced to minimize switching losses, stresses and noises. Employing the resonant-switch concept, the family of quasi-resonant converters (QRCs) and the family of multi-resonant converters (MRCs) are derived from the conventional PWM converters. They are capable of operating in megahertz range, with a significant improvement in performance and power density. Characteristics of these QRCs and MRCs are reviewed and their relative merits and limitations are assessed.

I. INTRODUCTION

Electronic power processing technology has evolved around two fundamentally different circuit schemes: duty-cycle modulation, commonly known as Pulse-Width Modulation (PWM), and resonance. The PWM technique processes power by interrupting the power flow and controlling the duty cycle, which results in pulsating currents and voltages. The resonant technique processes power in a sinusoidal form. The power switches are often commutated under zero current *("soft"* turn-off), but turned on with an abrupt increase of device current *("hard"* turn-on). In cases when resonant converters operate above the resonant frequency, the switches are turned off abruptly (forced or hard turn-off) but turned on softly. Compared with PWM converters, the switching losses and stresses of resonant converters are reduced; however, the conduction losses are generally increased, since sinusoidal currents produce higher rms currents. Due to circuit simplicity and ease of control, the PWM technique has been used predominantly in today's power electronics industry, particularly in low-power applications. Resonant technology, although well-established in high-power SCR motor drives and uninterrupted power supplies, has not been widely used in low-power dc-dc converter applications, due to its circuit complexity.

With available devices and circuit technologies, PWM converters have been designed to operate generally with a 50-200 kHz switching frequency. In this frequency range, the equipment is deemed optimal in weight, size, efficiency, reliability and cost. In certain applications, where high-power density is of primary concern, the conversion frequency has been chosen as high as several hundred kilohertz. With the advent of power MOSFETs, switching frequencies of tens of megahertz are now possible. However, increased switching stresses and losses accompany the higher switching frequency. Furthermore, the leakage inductances in the transformer and junction capacitances in the semiconductor devices cause the power devices to inductively turn-off and capacitively turn-on. As the semiconductor device turns off, voltage spikes are induced by the sharp di/dt across the leakage inductances. On the other hand, when the switch turns on at a high voltage level, the energy stored in the device's output capacitance is dissipated internally in the switching device. Also, turn-on at high voltage levels induces a severe switching noise coupled through the Miller capacitance into the drive circuit. The detrimental effects of the parasitic elements become more pronounced as the switching frequency is increased.

To improve switching conditions for semiconductor devices in power processing circuits, two quasi-resonant techniques were proposed. The first is the **zero-current-switching** technique [1-14]. By incorporating an LC resonant circuit, the current waveform of the switching device is forced to oscillate in a quasi-sinusoidal manner, creating zero-current-switching conditions during both turn-on and turn-off. By simply replacing the power switch(es) in PWM converters with the resonant switch, a family of zero-current-switched (ZCS) quasi-resonant converters (QRCs) has been derived [5-12]. This new family of circuits can be viewed as a hybrid of PWM and resonant converters. QRCs utilize the principle of inductive or capacitive energy storage and transfer in a manner similar to PWM converters, and their circuit topologies also resemble those of PWM converters. However, an LC tank circuit is always present near the power switch and is used not only to shape the current and voltage waveforms of the power switch, but also to store and transfer energy from the input to the output in a manner similar to the conventional resonant converters. For off-line as well as dc-dc converter applications, the zero-current-switching technique is very effective up to 1-2 MHz, since it can eliminate turn-off switching loss and switching stresses. Employing the zero-current-switching technique, several dc-dc and off-line converter topologies have been successfully implemented [15-21], some of them achieving a power density greater than 30 W/in^3 [18]. However, when the semiconductor switches are operated above approximately one megahertz, the capacitive turn-on loss associated with the discharging of energy stored in the parasitic junction capacitance of the MOSFET becomes the primary limiting factor. Furthermore, the Miller effect related to turn-on of the transistor at non-zero voltage and parasitic oscillations, caused by the transistor's output capacitance and circuit inductance, often results in uncontrolled noise and EMI.

* The work was supported by the Virginia Power Electronics Center (VPEC) Industry Partnership Program and Virginia Center for Innovative Technology (CIT).

The second quasi-resonant technique is the **zero-voltage-switching** technique [6, 22-24]. By using an LC resonant network, the voltage waveform of the switching device can be shaped into a quasi-sine wave, such that zero-voltage condition is created for the switch to turn on and turn off without incurring any switching loss. This technique eliminates the turn-on loss associated with the parasitic output capacitance of the active switch(es). Practical quasi-resonant-converter circuits operating at frequencies up to 10 MHz have been implemented [16, 25, 26]. However, zero-voltage-switched (ZVS) QRCs have two major limitations. One problem is an excessive voltage stress to the switching transistor. This stress is proportional to the load range [25, 27] and makes it difficult to implement ZVS-QRCs with wide load variations. Another problem is caused by the junction capacitance of the rectifying diode, which oscillates with the resonant inductance. If damped, this oscillation causes significant power dissipation at high frequencies, while, if undapmed, it adversely affects the voltage gain of the converter and, thus, the stability of the closed loop system [28-31].

A **multi-resonant** switch concept was proposed [30, 31] to overcome the problems of QRCs. In multi-resonant converters [16, 30-36], the zero-voltage switching is achieved by using a resonant network with two resonant capacitors and a resonant inductor. The unique arrangement of multi-resonant network results in absorption of all major parasitic components, including transistor output capacitance, diode junction capacitance and transformer leakage inductances in the resonant circuit. This allows the multi-resonant converters to operate at high frequencies with favorable switching conditions for all semiconductor devices. Constant-frequency operation is also possible if the rectifying diode(s) is replaced with an active switch(es) [37-39].

Quasi-resonant and multi-resonant techniques represent only two of the technologies recently proposed for improving switching conditions and high-frequency operation. Other techniques include class E converters [40-44], resonant and pseudo-resonant converters [45]-[50], resonant forward converter [29], and resonant transition (quasi-square wave) converters [51-54]. This paper concentrates only on the quasi-resonant and multi-resonant technologies.

II. RESONANT SWITCHES

A resonant switch represents a subcircuit consisting of semiconductor switches and resonant LC elements. Depending on the arrangement of the resonant elements with respect to the switches, either zero-current or zero-voltage switching conditions can be created for the switches. The basic quasi-resonant and multi-resonant switches are shown in Fig.1.

The concept of a resonant switch can be directly applied to a large number of conventional PWM converters. Simply by replacing the power switches of a PWM converter with a resonant switch, a new family of ZCS-QRCs [5,6], ZVS-QRCs [6,22-24], or MRCs [30-32] can be derived.

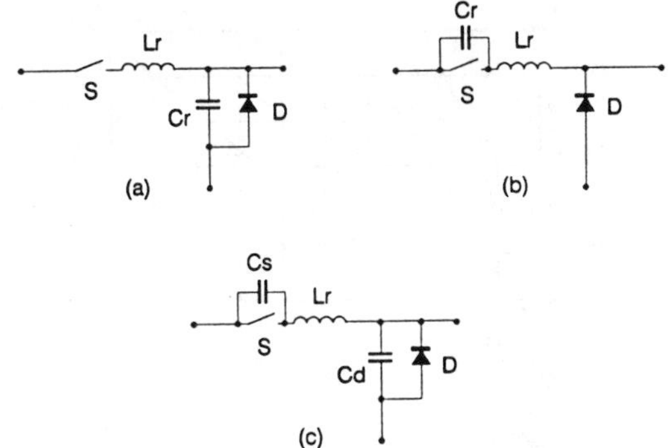

Fig. 1. Resonant switches. (a) Zero-Current Quasi-Resonant. (b) Zero-Voltage Quasi-Resonant. (c) Zero-Voltage Multi-Resonant.

Many topological variations of QRCs can be derived [8-12] using the basic concept of ZC and ZV resonant switches described above.

A. ZC Quasi-Resonant Switch

In a zero-current quasi-resonant switch, the resonant capacitor is in parallel with the rectifying diode and the resonant inductor is in series with the active switch, as shown in Fig. 1(a). The active switch operates with zero-current turn-on and turn-off, whereas the rectifier operates with zero-voltage turn-on and turn-off. If the ideal switch, S, is implemented by a unidirectional switch, the resonant switch is confined to operate in *half-wave mode*, in the sense that the switch current is permitted to resonate only in the positive half cycle. On the other hand, if the switch is bidirectional (with an antiparallel diode) the resonant switch operates in *full-wave mode*.

In essence, the resonant LC circuit is used to shape the current waveform through switch S. At turn-on, the switching transistor can be driven into saturation before the current slowly rises. Due to the resonance between L_r and C_r, current through the active switch oscillates and returns to zero, thus resulting in a natural commutation and improved switching conditions compared to "hard-switched" PWM converters.

The load-line trajectory of PWM switching behavior, shown as trajectory A in Fig. 2, traverses across the high-stress region in which the device is subjected to simultaneous high voltage and high current; whereas the load line trajectory of a resonant switch, shown as trajectory B, moves along the axes. Since high voltage and high current are not exerted simultaneously on the switching device, the switching stresses and losses are minimal.

B. ZV Quasi-Resonant Switch

In the ZV quasi-resonant switch, shown in Fig. 1(b), the resonant capacitance is in parallel with the active switch and the resonant inductance is in series with the rectifying diode. As a result, the active switch operates with zero-voltage turn-on and turn-off, while the diode operates with zero-current turn-on and turn-off. As in the case of a ZC resonant switch, the structure of the active switch determines the operation mode of the resonant switch. If the switch is bidirectional (with an antiparallel diode), voltage across the resonant capacitor is clamped at zero during the negative portion of the resonant cycle and the resonant switch operates in half-wave mode. On the other hand, if the active switch is unidirectional (with a series diode), it can block a negative voltage and the resonant switch operates in a full-wave mode.

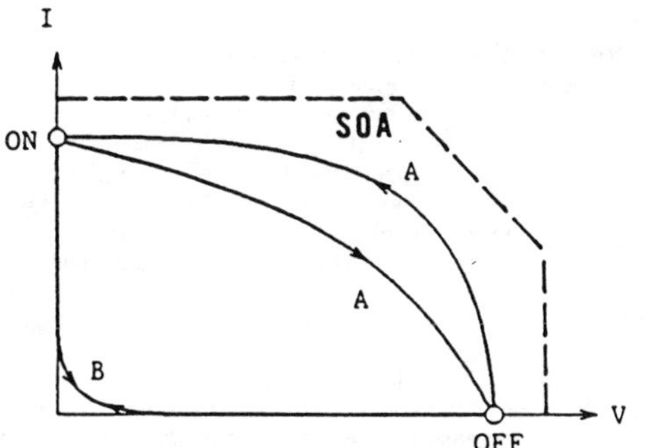

Fig. 2. Switching load line trajectory for PWM converters (trajectory A), and quasi-resonant converters (trajectory B).

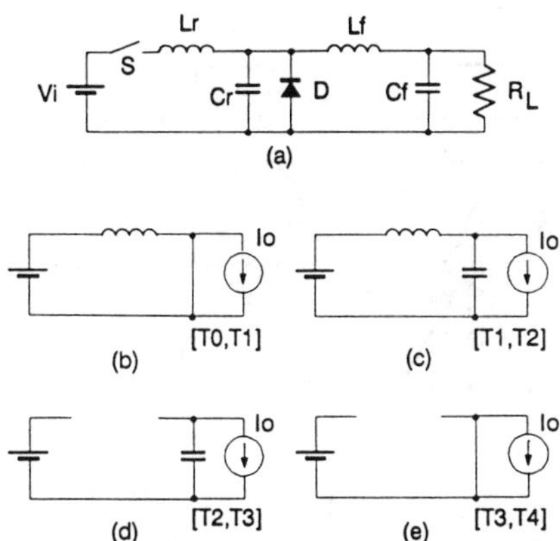

Fig. 3. Buck ZCS-QRC and its equivalent circuits during four topological stages.

C. ZV Multi-Resonant Switch

In the ZV multi-resonant switch, shown in Fig. 1(c), the first resonant capacitor is in parallel with the active switch, the second resonant capacitor is in parallel with the rectifying diode, and the resonant inductor is in series with both the switch and the diode. This arrangement of the resonant network results in operation of both the active switch and rectifying diode with zero-voltage turn-on and turn-off, thus producing the most desirable switching conditions.

III. ZERO-CURRENT-SWITCHED QUASI-RESONANT CONVERTERS

Application of the zero-current quasi-resonant switch results in dc/dc converter topologies with reduced switching loss at turn-off. The switch current is quasi-sine wave and is reduced to zero at turn-off. The principle of operation of ZCS-QRCs is illustrated using the buck topology.

A. Principle of Operation

The buck ZCS-QRC, shown in Fig. 3(a), is obtained from the PWM buck converter by replacing the PWM switch with the ZC resonant switch of Fig. 1(a). To analyze the steady-state circuit behavior, it is assumed that all components are ideal and that $L_f >> L_r$, so that output filter $L_f - C_f$ and the load can be treated as a constant current sink.

A switching cycle can be divided into four stages; their equivalent circuits are shown in Figs. 3(b)-3(e). Before S is turned on, diode D carries the output current I_0, and the capacitor voltage, V_{cr}, is clamped at zero.
1) Inductor-charging stage [T_0, T_1]. At the beginning of a switching cycle, $t = T_0$, S is turned on and the resonant current, I_{Lr}, rises linearly. The stage terminates at $t = T_1$, when I_{Lr} becomes equal to I_0.
2) Resonant stage [T_1,T_2]. At T_1, D turns off, and current $I_{Lr} - I_0$ starts charging C_r. If a half-wave resonant switch is used, switch S will be naturally commutated at time T_a, when the resonating current, I_{Lr}, reduces to zero, as shown in Fig. 4(a). On the other hand, if a full-wave resonant switch is used, current I_{Lr} will continue to oscillate and feed energy back to source V_i through the antiparallel diode D_1, as shown in Fig. 4(b). Current through S again oscillates to zero at time T_b.
3) Capacitor-discharging stage [T_2,T_3]. Since switch S is off at T_2, C_r begins to discharge through the output and V_{cr} decreases linearly. The stage terminates at T_3, when V_{Cr} discharges to zero.
4) Freewheeling stage [T_3,T_4]. This stage occurs after the charge stored in C_r is depleted and the output current begins flowing through diode D. The stage duration is determined by the control, which initiates the next conversion cycle by turning S on.

Typical circuit waveforms, shown in Figs. 4(a) and 4(b), clearly demonstrate the zero-current switching property.

B. DC Voltage-Conversion Ratio

Voltage-conversion ratios for the buck resonant converter are plotted in Figs. 5(a) and 5(b) for the half-wave mode and full-wave mode, respectively. It can be seen that the voltage-conversion ratio in the half-wave mode is very sensitive to load variation, while in the full-wave mode, the voltage-conversion ratio is almost independent of load variation. In full-wave mode converters, when the power switch is turned on, energy is transferred from the source to the resonant tank. When the load demand is low, a large portion of the tank energy is returned to the source. When the load is heavy, most of the tank energy is transferred to the load and only a small portion of that tank energy is returned to the source. Con-

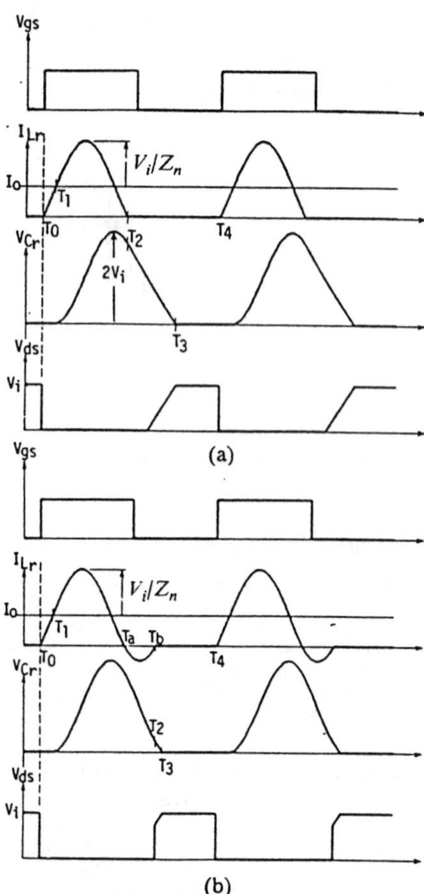

Fig. 4. Waveforms of the buck ZCS-QRC. (a) Half-wave mode. (b) Full-wave mode. From top to bottom: gate-to-source voltage (V_{GS}), resonant inductor current (I_{Lr}), resonant capacitor voltage (V_{Cr}), and drain-to-source voltage (V_{DS}). $Z_n = \sqrt{L_r/C_r}$ is the characteristic impedance of the resonant tank circuit.

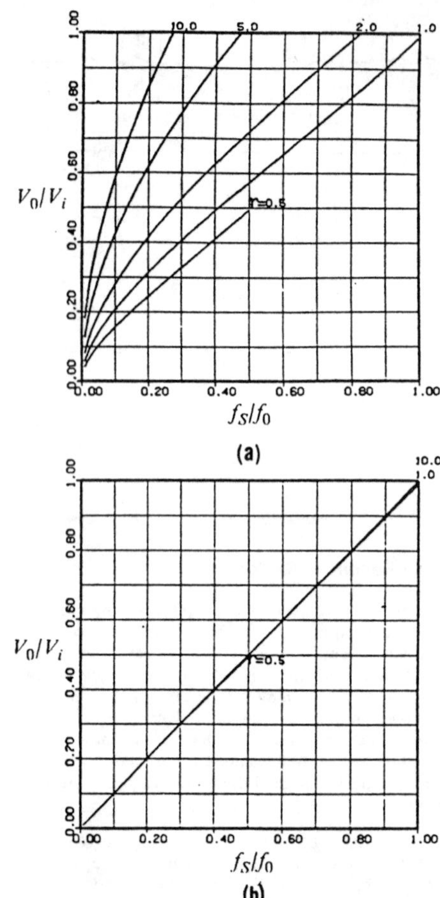

Fig. 5. DC voltage-conversion ratio (V_O/V_i) of buck ZCS-QRC as a function of the normalized switching frequency (f_S/f_0). (a) Half-wave mode. (b) Full-wave mode. Normalized load resistance $r = R_L/\sqrt{L_r/C_r}$ is a parameter.

sequently, the bidirectional switch regulates the tank energy so that the voltage-conversion ratio remains constant as the load is varying. For the half-wave mode, the excessive tank energy cannot be returned to the source when the load demand is reduced. Consequently, the operating frequency has to be reduced to regulate the output voltage. A more rigorous discussion of this subject is given in [12].

It should be noted that the characteristic shown in Fig. 5(b) is exactly the same as that of the PWM buck converter, provided that the horizontal axis is replaced by the duty-cycle ratio. This conclusion can be extended to other converter topologies as well. This simply implies that the QRCs operating in full-wave mode have the same desired dc conversion characteristics and small-signal transfer function [10] as their PWM counterparts.

C. Merits and Limitations

The major advantage of ZCS-QRCs is reduction of the switching loss at turn off. Due to the arrangement of the resonant network, the ZCS-QRCs are insensitive to the leakage inductance of the transformer and the junction capacitance of the rectifier [7]. The price paid for the zero-current switching is an increase in conduction losses, caused by higher rms and peak currents in the active switch. Also, currents circulating in the resonant circuit cause additional conduction losses.

One of the fundamental limitations of ZCS-QRCs for high-frequency operation is the capacitive turn-on loss. This problem is similar to that in PWM converters. The energy stored in the switching transistor's output capacitance during the off-state is dissipated inside the device when the device is switched on. This produces switching loss proportional to the switching frequency and reduces efficiency at high frequencies. In addition, the dv/dt during turn-on is coupled to the gate-drive circuit through the Miller capacitance, causing switching loss and noise in the gate drive.

IV. ZERO-VOLTAGE-SWITCHED QUASI-RESONANT CONVERTERS

The problem of capacitive turn-on, encountered in both PWM and ZCS-QRCs, can be alleviated by shaping the voltage across the switching device so that it reduces to zero prior to turn-on. The ZVS-QRCs are generated by replacing the switches in PWM topologies with the ZV resonant switch of Fig. 1(b). The resonant network shapes the voltage across the transistor for zero-voltage turn-on.

A. Principle of Operation

To illustrate the circuit operation, the buck ZVS-QRC topology, shown in Fig. 6, is used. For simplicity of analysis, the output filter and load are treated as a constant current sink carrying output current I_O. In a steady-state operation, a complete switching cycle can be divided into four stages, starting from the moment S turns off. Before S is turned off, diode D is off, and S carries current I_{Lr} equal to output current I_O.

1) Capacitor-charging stage [T_0, T_1]. At time T_0, S turns off and input current I_{Lr} is diverted into capacitor C_r, causing the voltage across C_r, V_{Cr}, to rise linearly. The stage ends at time T_1 when V_{Cr} reaches V_i and diode D begins conducting.

2) Resonant stage [T_1, T_2]. When D turns on at T_1, resonant capacitor C_r and resonant inductor L_r start resonating. In the half-wave mode of operation, when resonant voltage V_{Cr} decreases to zero at T_2 (Fig. 7(a)), it is clamped at zero by the antiparallel diode of switch S, which carries the reverse current. In full-wave mode, V_{Cr} continues to oscillate to a negative value and again returns to zero at time T_2 (Fig. 7(b)).

3) Inductor-charging stage [T_2, T_3]. After T_2, current I_{Lr} increases linearly and reaches I_0 at time T_3. Normally, in the half-wave mode of operation, S should turn on after V_{Cr} discharges to zero at T_2 and before the resonant current becomes positive (Fig. 7(a)). Otherwise, C_r will begin to charge and S will lose the opportunity to turn on under the zero-voltage condition. In the full-wave mode of operation, S should turn on during the time period when the switch voltage is negative (Fig. 7(b)).

4) Constant-current stage [T_3, T_4]. At T_3, the entire output current I_0 flows through S . The current through S remains constant until S is turned off again at T_4.

It can be seen, from Fig. 7, that the peak voltage across the switch is $V_i + Z_n I_O$. Therefore, when V_i is fixed, the peak value of V_{Cr} increases as the load current is increased. Furthermore, to maintain the ac component larger than the dc component, which is the necessary condition for zero-voltage switching, a lower bound on the load current exists. The waveform of the current through S is quasi square, and its peak value is

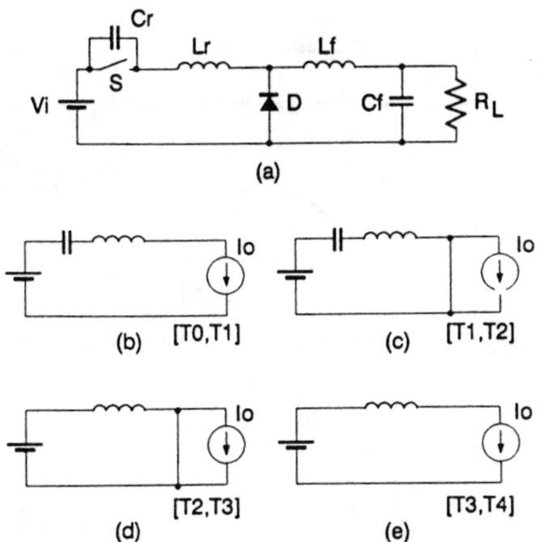

Fig. 6. Buck ZVS-QRC and its equivalent circuits during four topological stages.

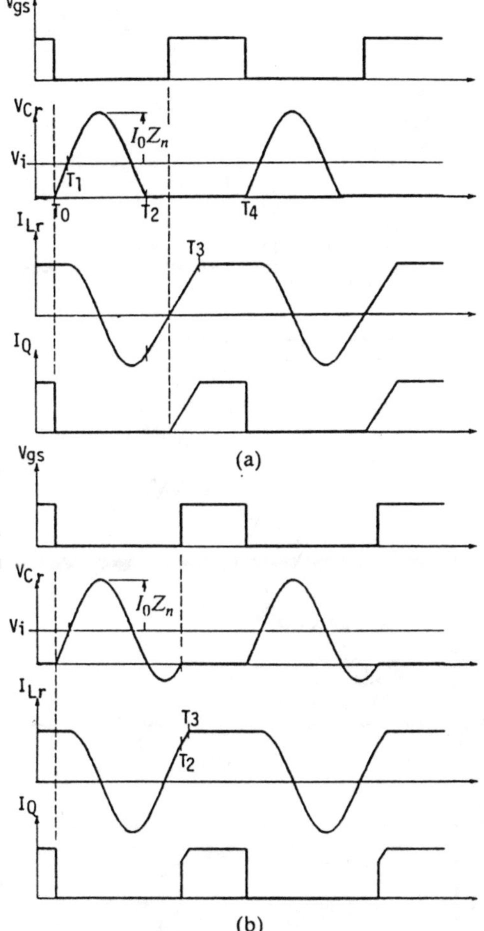

Fig. 7. Waveforms of the buck ZVS-QRC. (a) Half-wave mode. (b) Full-wave mode. From top to bottom: gate-to-source voltage (V_{GS}), resonant capacitor voltage (V_{Cr}), resonant inductor current (I_{Lr}), and transistor current (I_Q). $Z_n = \sqrt{L_r/C_r}$ is the characteristic impedance of the resonant tank circuit.

I_0, thus the rms value of the switch current and the conduction losses are kept minimal.

B. DC Voltage-Conversion Ratio

The dc voltage-conversion ratio of the buck ZVS-QRC is plotted as a function of load resistance and switching frequency in Figs. 8(a) and 8(b) for half-wave mode and full-wave mode, respectively. It can be seen that the voltage-conversion ratio in full-wave mode is insensitive to load variation and is certainly more desirable. However, to achieve full-wave mode operation, a diode in series with the active switch is required to provide a reverse-voltage blocking capability. This diode will prevent discharging of the transistor output capacitance during the resonance. Consequently, the energy stored in the junction capacitances of the semiconductor switch is trapped during off-time and is dissipated internally after the

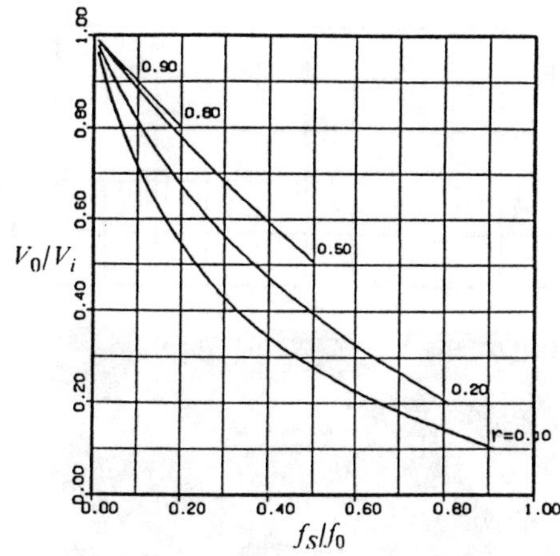

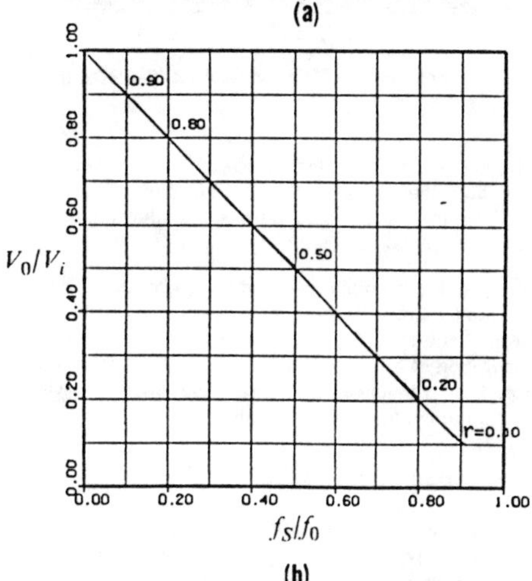

Fig. 8. DC voltage-conversion ratio (V_O/V_i) of buck ZVS-QRC as a function of the normalized switching frequency (f_S/f_0). (a) Half-wave mode. (b) Full-wave mode. Normalized load resistance $r = R_L/\sqrt{L_r/C_r}$ is a parameter.

switch turns on. Therefore, the full-wave mode ZVS-QRCs suffer from capacitive turn-on losses and dv/dt noise, as do ZCS-QRCs and PWM converters.

C. Merits and Limitations

The arrangement of the resonant network in the ZVS-QRCs results in operation of the active switch with zero-voltage turn-on and turn-off. The output capacitance of the transistor and leakage inductance of the transformer are absorbed into the resonant circuit. The improved switching conditions for the active switch allow the ZVS-QRCs to operate at 10 MHz [25, 26].

The operation of ZVS-QRCs is adversely affected by the parasitic junction capacitance of the rectifying diode. This is caused by undesirable switching conditions created for the diode. When the diode current reduces to zero during the linear stage (see Fig. 7), the diode turns off and the voltage applied to the diode theoretically changes abruptly from zero to V_i, as shown in Fig. 9(a). In practice, such an abrupt voltage change is not possible because of the diode junction capacitance. As a result, parasitic oscillations between the resonant inductance and the diode junction capacitance occur in the circuit, as shown in Fig. 9(b). If damped, these oscillations will cause energy dissipation. Undamped, they adversely affect the conversion-ratio characteristics and may cause poor closed-loop performance of the converter [29-31].

Another important concern of ZVS-QRCs is an extensive voltage stress on the switching transistor. Typically, this stress is proportional to the load range in single-ended ZVS-QRCs. Therefore, the single-ended ZVS-QRCs are not practical for applications with a wide load range and/or a high input voltage.

V. MULTI-RESONANT CONVERTERS

The zero-current and zero-voltage resonant switch concepts were originally developed to provide improved switching conditions for the *active* switch. However, it can be seen, from Figs. 1(a) and 1(b), that the zero-current configuration for the active switch is a zero-voltage configuration

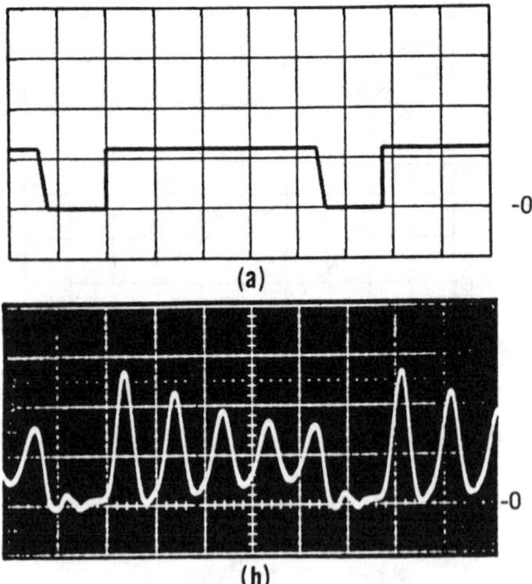

Fig. 9. Voltage across the rectifying diode in ZVS-QRCs. (a) Theoretical. (b) Experimental.

for the diode, and *vice versa* Since zero-voltage switching is a preferred operation for both the active switch and the diode, the quasi-resonant switches optimize the switching conditions for either the active switch or the diode, but not both simultaneously.

The basic idea behind the multi-resonant switch concept is to combine the zero-current and zero-voltage quasi-resonant switches in a multi-resonant switch, shown in Fig. 1(c), and achieve desirable zero-voltage-switching operation of both switching devices. Multi-resonant topologies are generated by replacing the active and passive switch in PWM topologies with the multi-resonant switch.

A. Principle of operation.

A circuit diagram of a buck ZVS-MRC is shown in Fig. 10(a). The four topological stages are shown in Figs. 10(b)-(e). Operating waveforms during a typical topological mode sequence are shown in Fig. 11. The output filter and load are modeled by a constant current sink. It is assumed that the switch is bidirectional. The switching cycle begins at t_0, when the voltage across the active switch reduces to zero and switch S turns on.

1) Linear stage [t_0, t_1]. During this stage, both switches are on and the inductor current increases linearly.

2) First resonant stage [t_1, t_2]. This stage begins when the resonant inductor current becomes equal to the output current and the rectifying diode turns off. During this stage, the resonant circuit is formed by the resonant inductor and capacitance in parallel with the rectifier. This stage is similar to the resonant stage in ZCS-QRCs.

3) Second resonant stage [t_2, t_3]. This stage begins when the active switch is turned off. The resonant circuit is formed then by all three resonant components.

4) Third resonant stage [t_3, t_4]. This stage begins when the voltage across the rectifying diode reduces to zero and the diode turns on. The resonant circuit is formed by the resonant inductor and the capacitance across the active switch. This stage is similar to the resonant stage in ZVS-QRCs. The cycle is completed when the voltage across the active switch reduces to zero and the switch turns on.

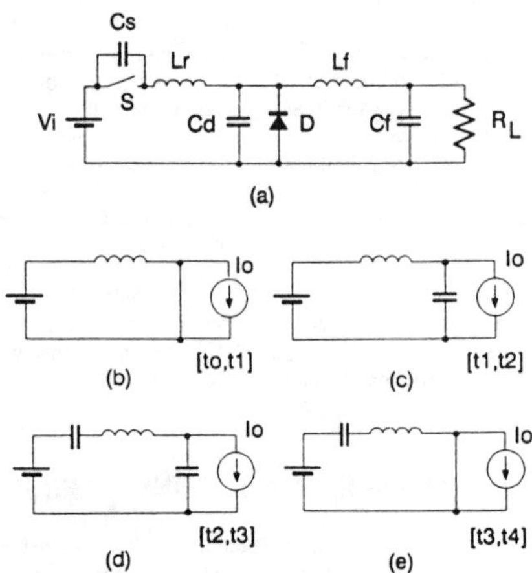

Fig. 10 Buck ZVS-MRC and its equivalent circuits during four topological stages.

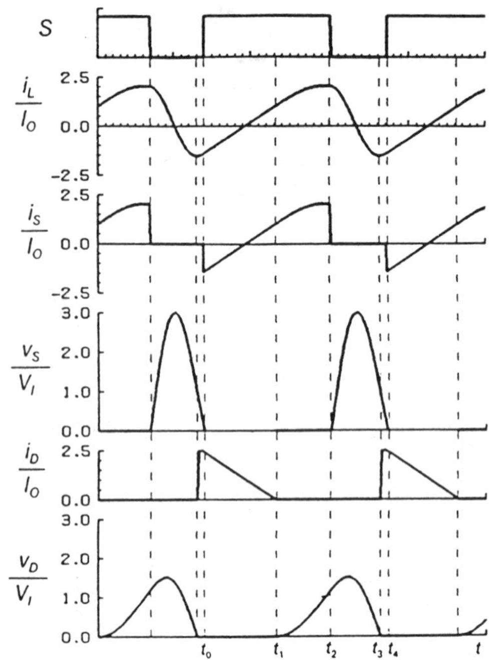

Fig. 11. Normalized waveforms of buck ZVS-MRC. From top to bottom: gate-to-source voltage (S), resonant inductor current (i_L), transistor current (i_S), transistor voltage (V_S), rectifying diode current (i_D), and rectifying diode voltage (v_D).

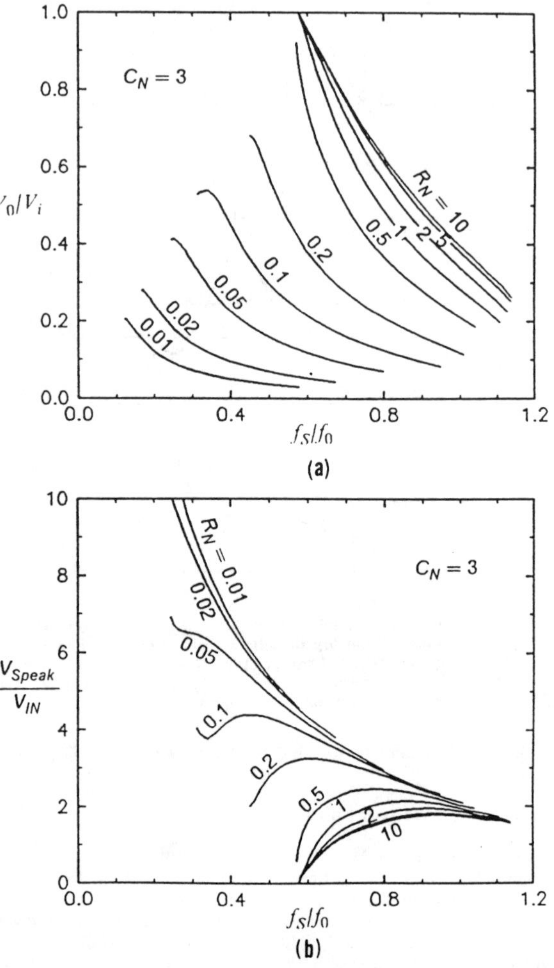

Fig. 12. DC characteristics of buck ZVS-MRC at $C_N = 3$ as functions of the normalized switching frequency (f_S/f_0). (a) DC voltage-conversion ratio V_0/V_i. (b) Transistor voltage stress V_S/V_i. Normalized load resistance $R_N = R_L/\sqrt{L_r/C_s}$ is a parameter.

B. DC Voltage-Conversion Ratio

An important parameter of a ZVS-MRC is the normalized ratio of the resonant capacitances, $C_N = C_d/C_s$. A practical operation can be achieved for $C_N > 1$ [31]. The dc conversion-ratio characteristics and the normalized transistor voltage stress for buck ZVS-MRC with $C_N = 3$ [32] are shown in Fig. 12. It can be seen, from Fig. 12(a), that the conversion ratio is load sensitive, similar to the half-wave ZVS-QRCs. The output-voltage regulation is obtained by varying the switching frequency, similar to ZVS-QRCs. The switching frequency range, however, is narrower for ZVS-MRCs, for a given load/line range [31].

The voltage stress in ZVS-MRCs can be kept within reasonable limits if the normalized load resistance at full load is not chosen to be too small. For example, it can be seen, from Fig. 12(b), that if the normalized load resistance at full load is 0.1, the peak voltage stress on the transistor will be approximately 4 times the input voltage [33]. Since the ZVS-MRCs can operate with a virtually infinite load range, this stress is substantially lower than that of ZVS-QRCs (for example, in a buck ZVS-QRC with a 10 to 1 load range, the transistor voltage stress is 11 times V_i [25]). Detailed design guidelines for ZVS-MRCs are given in [33].

C. Merits and Limitations

The major advantage of ZVS-MRCs is the absorption of all major parasitic reactances of the power circuit: transistor output capacitance, rectifying diode junction capacitance, and transformer leakage inductance. The multi-resonant circuit provides optimum zero-voltage-switching conditions for all semiconductor devices.

The main limitation of ZVS-MRCs is that the current and voltage stresses are higher than those in PWM converters. Typical values of the stresses for a buck converter operating from no load to full load are: transistor current stress, 2 times the output current; transistor voltage stress, 4 times the input voltage; diode current stress, 2 times the output current; diode voltage stress, 2 times the input voltage [30]. The transistor voltage stress, although much higher than that of a PWM converter, is reduced compared to ZVS-QRCs.

VI. PERFORMANCE COMPARISONS OF EXPERIMENTAL CONVERTERS

A number of quasi-resonant and multi-resonant circuits have been built for various off-line power supplies, as well as dc-dc converter applications. In this section, experimental results for several of those circuits are presented.

A. Half-Bridge ZCS-QRCs

A 100 W, half-bridge (HB), off-line ZCS-QRC, shown in Fig. 13, was designed and fabricated using the thick-film hybrid technique [18]. The converter utilizes the leakage inductance of the transformer as a resonant inductance. A complete, step-by-step design procedure of the power stage and the voltage-feedback control is described in [19]. The measured efficiency of the power stage at a 5-V output and the nominal dc input voltage of 300 V, as a function of the output power, is shown in Fig. 14. The efficiency at the maximum power is 78%, whereas the maximum efficiency of approximately 79% occurs at one-half the maximum power (50 W). To maintain the constant output voltage, for a load-current range from full load (20 A) down to 10% of full load (2 A), it is necessary to vary the conversion frequency from 1.5 MHz to 250 kHz. The hybridized converter is shown in Fig. 15. Its power density, including heatsink, is approximately 35 W/in³.

The full-wave ZCS-QRCs are preferred over the half-wave ZCS-QRCs, since their output voltage is less sensitive to load variations. As a result, these converters can be designed with a higher corner frequency of the output filter and a larger bandwidth. However, in the full-wave mode operation, the diode reverse-recovery current causes excessive switching

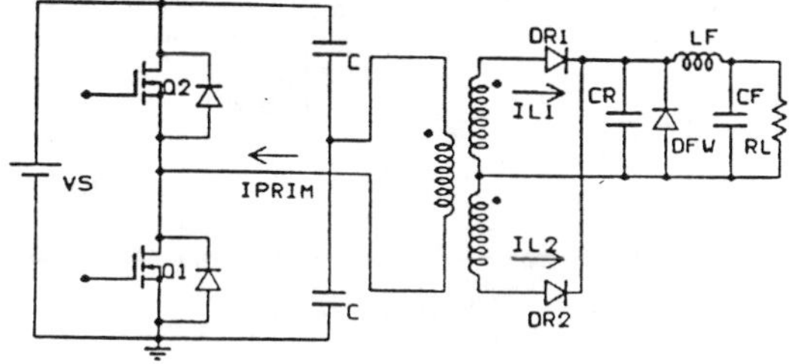

Fig. 13. Half-wave, secondary-side resonant, half-bridge ZCS-QRC. The circuit uses the leakage inductance of the transformer as a resonant element.

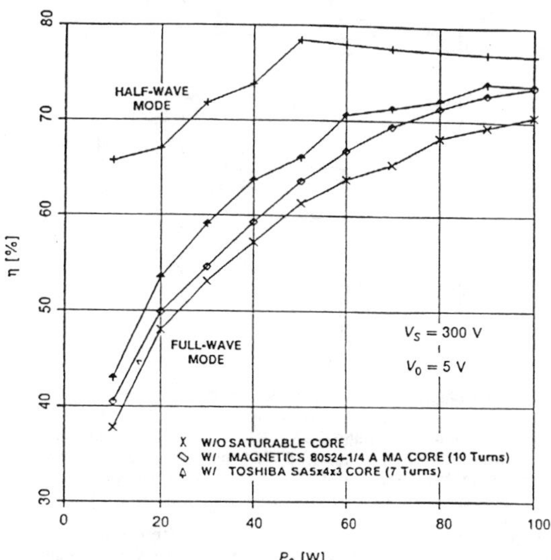

Fig. 14. Measured efficiencies of the 100 W, 300 V, experimental half-wave and full-wave half-bridge ZCS-QRCs as functions of the output power. The data for the full-wave converter are given for a design without saturable cores and for two designs with saturable cores with different core materials. For the converter without saturable cores, stable closed-loop control could not be implemented, due to the excessive noise.

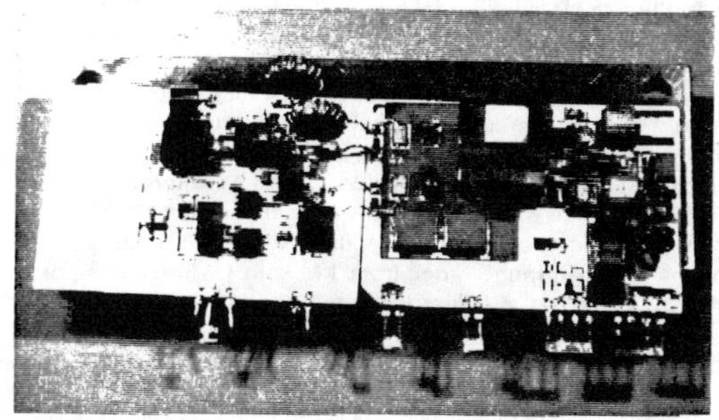

Fig. 15. Photograph of the 100 W, 300 V, hybridized half-bridge ZCS-QRC.

losses and parasitic oscillations, making the converter impractical for off-line applications in the megahertz range [20]. One way to implement the full-wave HB ZCS-QRC is to use a saturable inductor in series with the antiparallel diode to suppress the undesired high-frequency oscillations, as shown in Fig. 16 [20].

The design of a full-wave HB ZCS-QRC operating from a 300 V input and delivering 100 W at 5 V is described in [20]. The measured efficiency of the converter as a function of the output power is shown in Fig. 14. The efficiency of the full-wave converter is lower than that of the half-wave converter. At full-load, the efficiency was 74% and it decreases as the load decreases. The rate of the efficiency decrease is faster than for the half-wave converter. However, the converter has a much reduced frequency range, 750 kHz to 1.4MHz for a 10 % to 100 % load range, and superior transient responses compared to the corresponding half-wave converter [20].

B. Half-Bridge ZVS-QRC

The inherent capacitive turn-on switching loss due to the discharge of the output capacitance of the MOSFET switch limits the maximum operating frequency of the off-line ZCS-QRCs to 1-2 MHz [3, 15-20]. The zero-voltage-switching technique eliminates the turn-on switching loss and

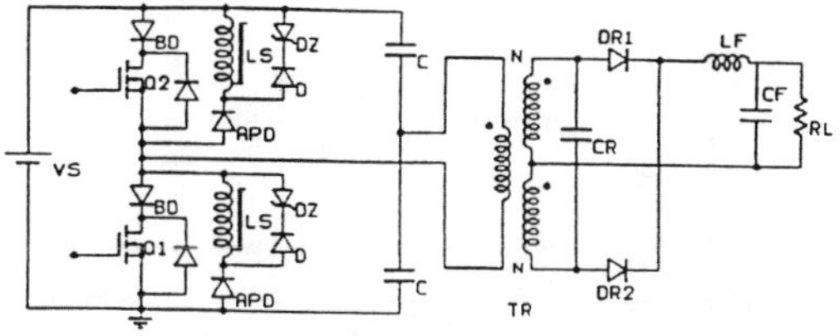

Fig. 16. Full-wave, secondary-side resonant, half-bridge ZCS-QRC with saturable inductors in series with antiparallel diodes. The circuit uses the leakage inductance of the transformer as a resonant element.

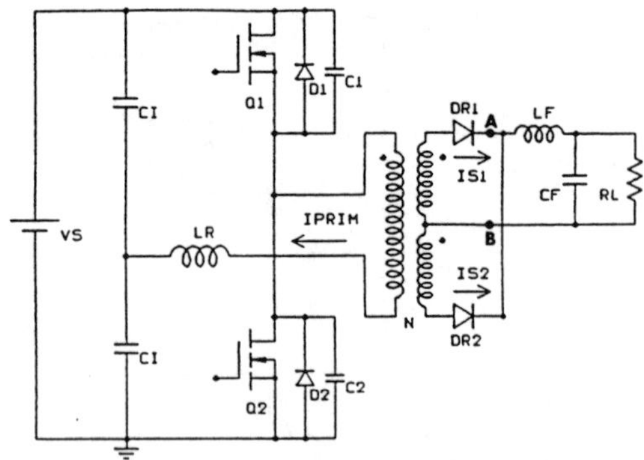

Fig. 17. Circuit diagram of the half-bridge ZVS-QRC. By adding external resonant capacitors in parallel with the rectifiers, the circuit becomes the half-bridge ZVS-MRC. Adding an extra MOSFET switch in the half-bridge ZVS-MRC between points A and B, the constant-frequency half-bridge ZVS-MRC is obtained.

noise. As a result, the ZVS-QRCs are capable of operating at much higher frequencies than the ZCS-QRCs. One common drawback of the ZVS technique, when applied to single-ended converter topologies, is the inherent high voltage stress across the switching transistor. Therefore, practical converter topologies for off-line applications are those that employ multiple switches, such as push-pull and bridge-type topologies, where the voltage across the off switch is automatically clamped by the conduction of its complementary switch.

An experimental 75 W HB ZVS-QRC operating from 300 $\pm$50 V input and with a 5 V output is presented in [26]. The circuit diagram of this converter is shown in Fig. 17. The measured efficiency of the converter, as a function of the output power for different input voltages, is shown in Fig. 18. The peak efficiency of the converter was 83.5% at full load (15 A) and low line (250 V). However, the load range of the converter was very limited. For high line (350 V), the converter operated with zero-voltage switching from full load (15 A) down to 70% of full load (10.5 A), whereas, at low line (250 V), the load range was extended down to 40 % of full load (6 A). The conversion frequency necessary to regulate the output voltage in this input-voltage and load range varied from 1 MHz to 4.2 MHz. It is possible to operate the converter at lighter loads but without zero-voltage switching and, consequently, with lower efficiency and excessive noise. The main reason for the narrow load range of the converter is a relatively high value of the output capacitances of the MOSFET switches, which limit the minimum value of resonant capacitance [26]. A smaller resonant capacitance would extend the load range. However, the minimum capacitance value is limited by the availability of MOSFETs with the desired current and voltage ratings. Additional load limitations come from the parasitic oscillations due to the interaction of the junction capacitance of the rectifiers (D_{R1}, D_{R2} in Fig. 17) and the resonant inductor [26]. As a result, certain trade-offs have to be made regarding conversion frequency, load range, and efficiency.

C. Half-Bridge ZVS-MRC

The performance of the HB ZVS-QRCs can be drastically improved by implementing the multi-resonant technique. The HB ZVS-MRC has the same circuit diagram as the HB ZVS-QRC shown in Fig. 17, except that

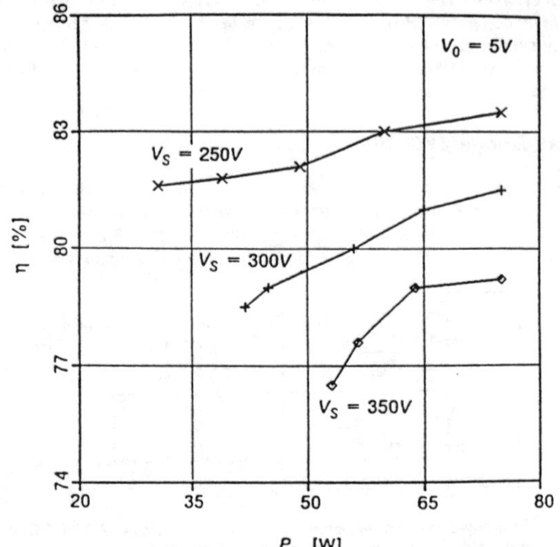

Fig. 18. Measured efficiency of the experimental half-bridge ZVS-QRC as a function of the output power.

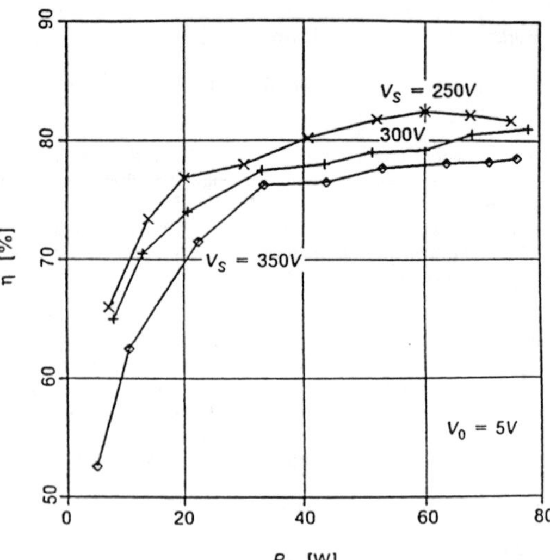

Fig. 19. Measured efficiency of the experimental half-bridge ZVS-MRC as a function of the output power.

external resonant capacitors are added in parallel with the rectifiers [26]. These capacitors are used to resonate the rectifiers' voltages to achieve a "soft" turn-off of the rectifiers. As a result, this technique minimizes parasitic oscillations of all forms and is capable of achieving zero-voltage switching even at no load [31].

The measured efficiency of the breadboarded HB ZVS-MRC, with the same specifications as for the HB ZVS-QRC discussed above, is shown in Fig. 19. The efficiency of the HB ZVS-MRC, 81.7% at full load (15 A) and low line (250 V) and 78.5% at full load and high line (350 V), is slightly lower than that of the HB ZVS-QRC. However, the converter can be operated from full load down to 10% of full load, with a conversion frequency from 1.5 MHz to 8 MHz. It is also possible to operate the converter at no load. Even though, for this particular design, zero-voltage switching is lost, the switches are turned on at a relatively low drain-to-source voltage [26].

The efficiency of the HB ZVS-MRC is always maximum at low line and decreases as the input voltage increases. As a result, the efficiency of the HB ZVS-MRC can be significantly lower at a nominal operating voltage if the input-voltage range is wide. On the other hand, the efficiency of the HB ZCS-QRC can be maximized at any desired input voltage and is not sensitive to the input-voltage range [34]. To illustrate this, Fig. 20 shows the measured efficiencies of the HB ZVS-MRC and HB ZCS-QRC as functions of the input voltages for designs with wide (150-350 V) and narrow (250-350 V) input-voltage ranges [34]. The HB ZVS-MRC is most suitable for off-line applications, where the input-voltage range is relatively narrow. With a narrow input-voltage range, all positive attributes

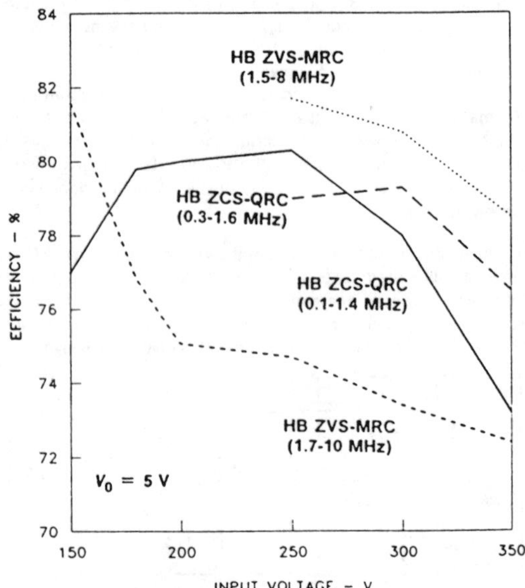

Fig. 20. Measured efficiencies at full power (5 V / 20 A) of the experimental half-bridge ZCS-QRC and ZVS-MRC designed for two input-voltage ranges (150-350 V and 250-350 V) as functions of the input voltage.

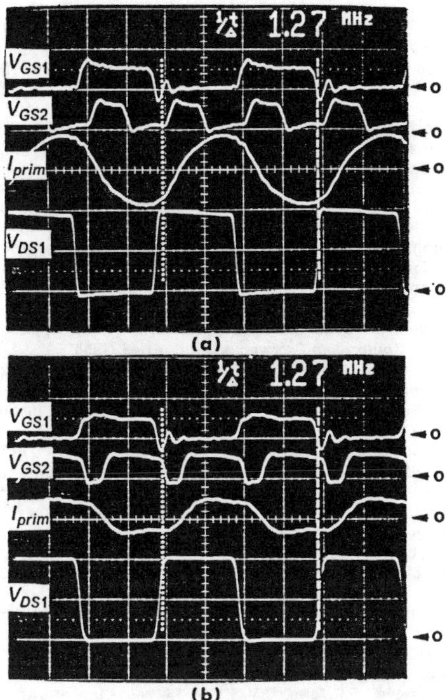

Fig. 21. Oscillograms of the experimental constant-frequency, half-bridge ZVS-MRC for different loads. (a) Full load (5 V / 10 A). (b) No load (5 V / 0 A). Shown from top to bottom are: gate-to-source voltages of the bottom primary switch (V_{GS1}) and the switch on the secondary side (V_{GS2}), primary current (I_{prim}) and drain-to-source voltage of the bottom primary switch (V_{DS1}). Input voltage V_S=120 V.

associated with the multi-resonant operation, such as high efficiency, inherent current limiting, high power density and multiple outputs can be utilized to their fullest extent.

By adding an extra MOSFET switch on the secondary side (between points A and B in Fig. 17) of the HB ZVS-MRC, it is possible to operate the converter at a constant frequency [39]. Figure 21 shows the typical waveforms of a 50 W constant-frequency HB ZVS-MRC at full load and no load. The measured efficiency of the converter (power stage only) at full load (10 A) and with an input voltage of 119 V was 80.3%.

D. Forward ZVS-MRC

A forward ZVS-MRC topology was proposed for on-board power supply applications [32]. The forward topology is relatively simple because only one controlled switch is used. In addition, unlike in a PWM forward converter, no resetting winding is necessary on the power transformer. The resetting mechanism is provided by the secondary-side resonant capacitor [7, 32].

A 50 W forward ZVS-MRC was designed for an on-board power supply application [36]. Figure 22 shows the circuit diagram of the power stage with a resonant gate drive. The gate drive uses an experimental GaAs BJT for fast turn-off. During the off time of the power MOSFET, Q1 is on and current in gate inductor L_g increases linearly. When Q1 is turned off, L_g resonates with the input capacitance of Q2, and Q2 is turned on.

The converter operated at frequencies from 1.87 MHz at I_O = 10 A and V_{IN} = 40 V, to 3.58 MHz at I_O = 0.4 A and V_{IN} = 60 V. The measured efficiency of a complete, self-contained, breadborded power supply (including gate drive, control, protection, and self-bias circuits) is shown in Fig. 23. Gate-to-source and drain-to-source voltage waveforms of the power MOSFET at V_{IN} = 50 V, and output current I_O = 10 A, are shown in Fig. 24. The voltage stress on the power MOSFET was less than $4V_{IN}$ for all load/line conditions. A hybridized version of the power stage is shown in Fig. 25. The finalized power supply will have power density of approximately 45 W/in³.

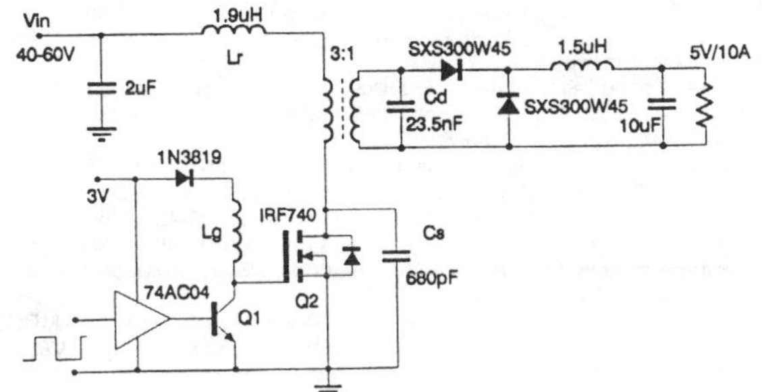

Fig. 22. Circuit diagram of the power stage of the 2 MHz forward ZVS-MRC.

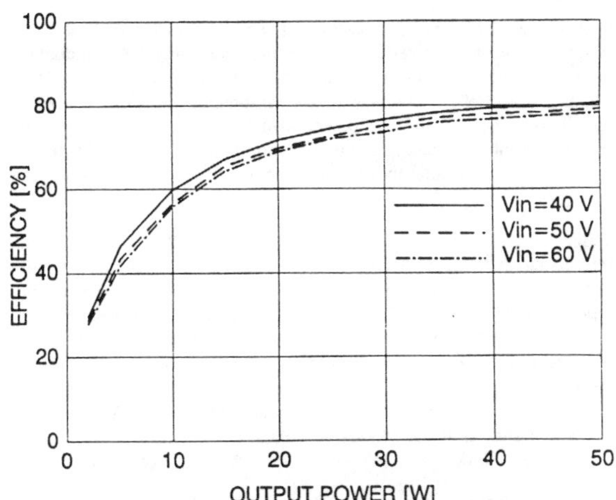

Fig. 23. Efficiency of the forward ZVS-MRC.

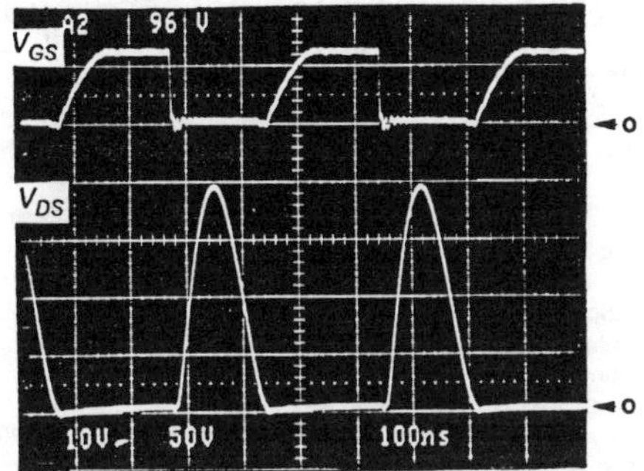

Fig. 24. Gate-to-source and drain-to-source voltage waveforms of the power MOSFET in the forward ZVS-MRC.

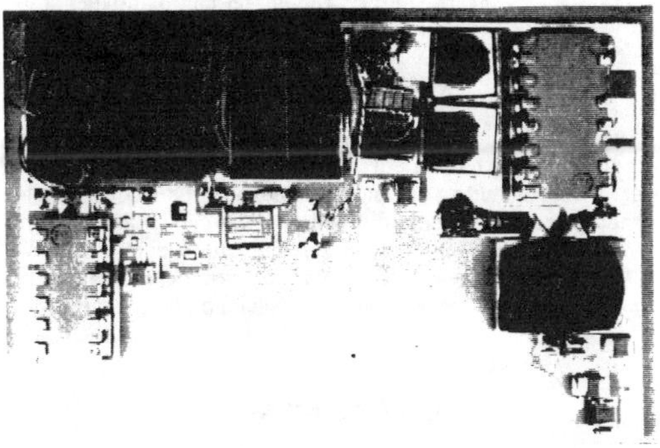

Fig. 25. Photograph of the hybridized power stage of the forward ZVS-MRC. Circuit dimensions: 2.85 x 1.85 x 0.17 in.

VII. SUMMARY

As the switching frequency is boosted into the megahertz range, the abrupt switching approach used in the conventional PWM converters encounters formidable difficulties. In particular, the switching stresses and losses, which are suppressed by means of snubber circuits or are ignored at lower frequencies, become intolerable at higher frequencies.

To alleviate the switching stresses and losses, the concept of the resonant switch was introduced and implemented in the forms of zero-current switching (ZCS) and zero-voltage switching (ZVS). By direct application of the resonant switch(es) into PWM converters, new families of quasi-resonant converters (QRCs) and multi-resonant converters (MRCs) have been discovered. These new families of converters, with literally hundreds of topological variations, can be viewed as hybrids of PWM and conventional resonant converters. They utilize the principles of inductive or capacitive energy storage and transfer for power conversion in a fashion similar to PWM converters. However, an LC tank circuit is always present in conjunction with the power switch and is used not only to shape the current and voltage waveforms but, also, to store and transfer energy from input to output in a manner similar to the conventional resonant converters.

The family of QRCs can be divided into two classes. One class which is referred to as ZCS-QRCs, employs the zero-current-switching concept. The other, referred to as ZVS-QRCs, employs the zero-voltage-switching concept. ZCS-QRCs and ZVS-QRCs can be subdivided into two categories: full-wave (FW) mode and half-wave (HW) mode, depending upon whether the power switch is unidirectional or bidirectional. It has been shown that the FW-QRCs are load insensitive. Therefore, the switching frequency is maintained constant as the load varies. The HW-QRCs are load sensitive and, as the load varies, the switching frequency has to be modulated over a wide range to maintain output-voltage regulation.

For off-line applications and for switching frequencies up to 1MHz, the ZCS technique is effective since it eliminates the switching stresses and turn-off losses. This technique results in a quasi-sinusoidal switch current waveform and a quasi-square switch voltage waveform. The device's voltage stress is minimum, but its conduction loss is higher than that of PWM converters. To operate the semiconductor switches at a higher frequency, the capacitive turn-on loss associated with ZCS must be avoided.

To minimize the capacitive turn-on loss, the ZVS technique was proposed. This technique allows the power switches to turn on under zero-voltage condition and, therefore, eliminate the turn-on loss associated with the parasitic junction capacitances. Since the power switch is always turned on at zero voltage, a simple capacitor snubber can be used to minimize turn-off loss and, thus, reduce the turn-off switching loss.

However, ZVS-QRCs suffer from two major limitations. One limitation is an extensive voltage stress in single-ended configurations with wide load variations. Another difficulty is related to the junction capacitance of the rectifying diode. This capacitance causes undesirable oscillation with the resonant inductance. The oscillation generates considerable EMI noise and adversely affects the converter's regulation characteristics and stability.

A multi-resonant switch concept was proposed to overcome the limitations of the high-frequency QRCs. A new family of ZVS-MRCs was generated. The ZVS-MRCs operate with favorable zero-voltage-switching of all semiconductor devices and are insensitive to the major reactances of the power circuit, including transformer leakage inductance, transistor output capacitance, and rectifying diode junction capacitance. Constant frequency operation of ZVS-MRCs is feasible with a controlled rectifier. The ZVS-MRCs seem to be well suited for on-board dc/dc converters and off-line power supplies operating at switching frequencies in the megahertz range.

REFERENCES

[1] E. Buchanan, E.J. Miller, "Resonant switching power conversion technique," *IEEE Power Electronics Specialists' Conference Record*, pp. 188-193, 1975.

[2] E.J. Miller, "Resonant switching power conversion," *IEEE Power Electronics Specialists' Conference Record*, pp. 206-122, 1976.

[3] P. Vinciarelli, "Forward converter switching at zero current," *U.S. Patent*, 4,415,959, Nov. 15, 1983.

[4] P. Vinciarelli, "Optimal resetting of the transformer's core in single-ended forward converters," *U.S. Patent*, 4,441,146, April 1984.

[5] K. Liu, F.C Lee, "Resonant switches - A unified approach to improve performances of switching converters," *IEEE International Telecommunications Energy Conference Proceedings*, pp. 334-341, 1984.

[6] K. Liu, "High frequency quasi-resonant converter techniques," *Ph.D. Dissertation*, Electrical Engineering Department, Virginia Polytechnic Institute and State University, Oct. 1986.

[7] K. Liu, F.C. Lee, "Secondary-side resonance for high-frequency power conversion," *IEEE Applied Power Electronics Conference Proceedings*, pp. 83-89, 1986.

[8] T. Zheng, D. Chen, F.C. Lee, "Variations of quasi-resonant dc-dc converter topologies," *IEEE Power Electronics Specialists' Conference Record*, pp. 381-392, 1986.

[9] V. Vorpérian, R. Tymerski, K.H. Liu, F.C. Lee, "Generalized resonant switches part 1: Topologies," *VPEC (Virginia Power Electronics Center) Power Electronics Seminar Proceedings*, Virginia Polytechnic Institute and State University, Blacksburg, Virginia, pp. 116-122, 1986.

[10] V. Vorpérian, R. Tymerski, K.H. Liu, F.C. Lee, "Generalized resonant switches part 2: Analysis and circuit models," *VPEC (Virginia Power Electronics Center) Power Electronics Seminar Proceedings*, Virginia Polytechnic Institute and State University, Blacksburg, Virginia, pp. 124-131, 1986.

[11] S. Freeland, R.D. Middlebrook, "A unified analysis of converters with resonant switches," *IEEE Power Electronics Specialists' Conference Record*, pp. 20-30, 1987.

[12] K. Liu, R. Oruganti, F.C. Lee, "Resonant switches - topologies and characteristics," *IEEE Trans. Power Electronics*, vol. 2, no. 1, pp. 106-116, Jan. 1987.

[13] M.M. Jovanović, K. Liu, R. Oruganti, F.C. Lee, "State-plane analysis of quasi-resonant converters," *IEEE Trans. Power Electronics*, vol. 2, no. 1, pp. 36-44, Jan. 1987.

[14] R. Oruganti, "State-plane analysis of resonant converters," *Ph.D. Dissertation*, Electrical Engineering Department, Virginia Polytechnic Institute and State University, Mar. 1987.

[15] R.B. Ridley, A. Lotfi, V. Vorpérian, F.C Lee, "Design and control of a full-wave quasi-resonant flyback converter," *IEEE Applied Power Electronics Conference Proceedings*, pp. 41-49, 1988.

[16] M.M. Jovanović, "High-frequency, off-line power conversion using quasi-resonant and multi-resonant techniques," *Ph.D. Dissertation*, Electrical Engineering Department, Virginia Polytechnic Institute and State University, Sept. 1988.

[17] D.C. Hopkins, M.M. Jovanović, F.C. Lee, F.W. Stephenson, "Hybridized off-line 2-MHz zero-current-switched quasi-resonant converter," *IEEE Trans. Power Electronics*, vol. 4, no. 1, pp. 147-154, Jan. 1989.

[18] D.C. Hopkins, M.M. Jovanović, F.C. Lee, F.W. Stephenson, M. Hayes, "Power-hybrid design of a high-frequency ZCS-QRC," *High Frequency Power Conversion Conference Proceedings*, pp. 304-317, 1989.

[19] M.M. Jovanović, D.C. Hopkins, F.C. Lee, "Evaluation and design of megahertz-frequency off-line zero-current-switched quasi-resonant converters," *IEEE Trans. Power Electronics*, vol. 4, no. 1, pp. 136-146, Jan. 1989.

[20] M.M. Jovanović, F.C. Lee, D.Y. Chen, "A zero-current-switched off-line quasi-resonant converter with reduced frequency range: Analysis, design, and experimental results," *IEEE Trans. Power Electronics*, vol. 3, no. 2, Apr. 1989.

[21] M.M. Jovanović, F.C. Lee, "DC characteristics and stability of push-pull and bridge-type zero-current-switched quasi-resonant converters," *IEEE Trans. Power Electronics*, vol. 4, no. 3, July 1989.

[22] P.C. Todd, R.W. Lutz, "Practical resonant power converters - Theory and application: Part II - The resonant switch concept," *Powertech. Mag.*, May 1986.

[23] K. Liu, F.C. Lee, "Zero-voltage switching technique in dc/dc converters," *IEEE Power Electronics Specialists' Conference Record*, pp. 58-70, 1986.

[24] M.K. Kazimierczuk, J. Jóźwik, "New topologies of of high-efficiency high-frequency zero-voltage-switching resonant dc/dc converters," *29th Midwest Symp. Circuits and Systems Proceedings*, pp. 474-477, 1986.

[25] W.A. Tabisz, P. Gradzki, F.C. Lee, "Zero-voltage-switched quasi-resonant buck and flyback converters -- Experimental results at 10 MHz," *IEEE Power Electronics Specialists' Conference Record*, pp. 404-413, 1987.

[26] M.M. Jovanović, W.A. Tabisz, F.C. Lee, "Zero-voltage-switching technique in high frequency off-line converters," *IEEE Applied Power Electronics Conference Proceedings*, pp. 23-32, 1988.

[27] A. Lotfi, V. Vorpérian, F.C Lee, "Comparison of stresses in quasi-resonant and pulse-width-modulated converters," *IEEE Power Electronics Specialists' Conference Record*, pp. 591-598, 1988.

[28] M.F. Schlecht, L.F. Casey, "Comparison of the square-wave and quasi-resonant topologies," *IEEE Trans. Power Electronics*, vol. 3, no. 1, pp. 83-92, Jan. 1988.

[29] L.F. Casey, M.F. Schlecht, "A high-frequency, low-volume, point-of-load power supply for distributed power systems," *IEEE Trans. Power Electronics*, vol. 3, no. 1, pp. 72-82, Jan. 1988.

[30] W.A. Tabisz, F.C Lee, "Application of a novel, multi-resonant switch in high-frequency dc/dc converters," *VPEC (Virginia Power Electronics Center) Power Electronics Seminar Proceedings*, Virginia Polytechnic Institute and State University, Blacksburg, Virginia, pp. 65-71, 1987.

[31] W.A. Tabisz, F.C Lee, "Zero-voltage-switching multi-resonant technique - A novel approach to improve performance of high-frequency quasi-resonant converters," *IEEE Power Electronics Specialists' Conference Record*, pp. 9-17, 1988.

[32] W.A. Tabisz, F.C Lee, "A novel zero-voltage-switched multi-resonant forward converter," *High Frequency Power Conversion Conference Proceedings*, pp. 309-318, 1988.

[33] W. A. Tabisz, F. C. Lee, "DC analysis and design of zero-voltage-switched multi-resonant converters," *IEEE Power Electronics Specialists' Conference Record*, 1989.

[34] M.M. Jovanović, R. Farrington, F.C. Lee, "Comparison of half-bridge, ZCS-QRC and ZVS-MRC for off-line applications," *IEEE Applied Power Electronics Conference Proceedings*, pp. 445-453, 1989.

[35] M.M. Jovanović, F.C. Lee, "Mode analysis of half-bridge zero-voltage-switched multi-resonant converter," *IEEE Power Electronics Specialists' Conference Record*, 1989.

[36] W.A. Tabisz, R.T. Gean, F.C. Lee, "High-frequency forward ZVS-MRC for a low-profile high-density on-board power supply," *VPEC (Virginia Power Electronics Center) Power Electronics Seminar Proceedings*, Virginia Polytechnic Institute and State University, Blacksburg, Virginia, 1989.

[37] I. Barbi, J. C. Bolacell, D. C. Martins, F. B. Libano, "Buck quasi-resonant converter operating at constant frequency - Analysis, design and experimentation," *IEEE Power Electronics Specialists' Conference Record*, 1989.

[38] D. Maksimović, S. Ćuk, "Constant-frequency control of quasi-resonant converters," *High Frequency Power Conversion Conference Proceedings*, pp. 241-253, 1989.

[39] M.M. Jovanović, R. Farrington, F.C. Lee, "Constant-frequency multi-resonant converters," *VPEC (Virginia Power Electronics Center) Power Electronics Seminar Proceedings*, Virginia Polytechnic Institute and State University, Blacksburg, Virginia, 1989.

[40] R. J. Gutmann, "Application of RF circuit design principles to distributed power converters," *IEEE Trans. Ind. Electron. Contr. Instrum.*, vol. 27, no. 3, pp.156-164, Aug. 80.

[41] R. Redl, B. Molnár, N.O. Sokal "Class E resonant regulated dc/dc power converters: Analysis of operation and experimental results at 1.5 MHz," *IEEE Trans. Power Electronics*, vol. 1, no. 2, pp. 111-120, April 1986.

[42] K. Harada, W. Gu, "Controlled resonant converter with switching frequency fixed," *IEEE Power Electronics Specialists' Conference Record*, pp. 431-438, 1989.

[43] W.C. Bowman, J.F. Balicki, F.T. Dickens, R.M. Honeycutt, W.A. Nitz, W. Strauss, W.B. Suiter, N.G. Ziesse, "A resonant dc-dc converter operating at 22 MHz," *IEEE Applied Power Electronics Conference Proceedings*, pp. 3-11, 1988.

[44] W.A. Nitz, W.C. Bowman, F.T. Dickens, F.M. Magalhaes, W. Strauss, W.B. Suiter, N.G. Ziesse, "A new family of resonant rectifier circuits for high frequency dc-dc converter applications," *IEEE Applied Power Electronics Conference Proceedings*, pp. 12-22, 1988.

[45] J.G. Kassakian, "A new current mode sine wave inverter," *IEEE Trans. Industry Applications*, vol. 18, no. 3, May/June 1982.

[46] O. D. Patterson, D. M. Divan, "Pseudo-resonant full bridge dc/dc converter," *IEEE Power Electronics Specialists' Conference Record*, pp. 424-430, 1987.

[47] A.F. Goldberg, J.G. Kassakian, "The application of power MOSFETs at 10 MHz," *IEEE Power Electronics Specialists' Conference Record*, pp. 91-100, 1985.

[48] B. Carsten, "A hybrid series-parallel resonant converter for high-frequencies and power levels," *High Frequency Power Conversion Conference Proceedings*, pp. 41-47, 1989.

[49] R. L. Steigerwald, "A comparison of half-bridge resonant converter topologies," *IEEE Applied Power Electronics Conference Proceedings*, pp. 135-144, 1987.

[50] J.A. Sabaté, F.C. Lee, "Off-line application of the fixed frequency clamped mode series-resonant converter," *IEEE Applied Power Electronics Conference Proceedings*, pp. 213-220, 1989.

[51] K.D.T. Ngo, "Generalization of resonant switches and quasi-resonant dc-dc converters," *IEEE Power Electronics Specialists' Conference Record*, pp. 395-403, 1987.

[52] V. Vorpérian, "Quasi-Square Wave Converters: Topologies and Analysis," *IEEE Trans. Power Electronics*, vol. 3, no. 2, pp. 183-191, April 1988.

[53] C.P. Henze, H.C. Martin, D.W. Parsley, "Zero-voltage switching in high frequency power converters using pulse width modulation," *IEEE Applied Power Electronics Conference Proceedings*, pp. 33-40, 1988.

[54] D.M. Divan, "Diodes as pseudo active elements in high frequency dc/dc converters," *IEEE Power Electronics Specialists' Conference Record*, pp. 1024-1030, 1988.

High-Frequency High-Density Converters for Distributed Power Supply Systems

JOHN G. KASSAKIAN, SENIOR MEMBER, IEEE, AND MARTIN F. SCHLECHT, MEMBER, IEEE

Invited Paper

An introduction to the technical challenges of developing very high power density power supplies operating at switching frequencies in the vicinity of 10 MHz is given. Primary applications are in the computer, telecommunications, and automotive industries. It is shown that a successful development requires simultaneous considerations of topologies, materials, devices, control, EMI, manufacturing, and packaging. Some results of work being done at MIT are presented, including a new integrated power MOSFET/driver, high-field high-frequency magnetic material characterizations, and high-frequency synchronous rectifiers. The design and performance of a 50-W 3.5-MHz converter is described.

Introduction

This paper discusses the challenges related to increasing the density of power supplies for low-voltage electronic applications. The issues are illustrated by the approaches and results of a research program in this area at MIT.

Power supplies have traditionally been viewed as a peripheral, rather than an integral, part of a system design. But as semiconductor devices with more functions per unit area are produced, and as electronics assumes a larger role in the control of physical systems, the power supply is becoming a critical element because of its size. Computer, automotive, and telecommunications systems are examples of where this is happening today. Unless the power supply benefits from a comparable improvement in power density (output power per unit volume or area), the advantages of denser electronics may be lost in many applications. Also, the trend toward lower voltage logic for VHSIC and other computer applications has produced power supply ripple, regulation, and efficiency specifications that are difficult and expensive to meet with today's technology.

Progress in the development of very high frequency (1–10 MHz) switching converters shows promise of achieving a considerable increase of power density [1]–[6], and in creating standard physical forms for them [7]. These standard forms are expected to be compatible with those of existing integrated circuit packages, making the power supply a component that can be designed into the system at an early stage.

The automobile electrical system is another application for this new breed of supply. In the future, electrical power may very well be distributed throughout the car at high voltage (e.g., 36 or 48 V), and then be converted to lower voltages at such loads as the headlamps and electronic modules. Many of these loads are going to require a tightly regulated voltage, a requirement that will be challenging to meet during cranking and charging. Weight will also continue to be an important issue. Above all, however, a standard, inexpensive, and mass-producible design is required.

Both the computer and automotive applications will use what has come to be known as a *distributed* power supply architecture. In this architecture, power is distributed to the points of load at a relatively high voltage, perhaps 36–48 V. This reduces the weight and the size of the distribution bus that might otherwise dictate the physical configuration of the system, especially in the case of computers. The distribution voltage is then converted to the value required at the load by local converters identical in design and manufacture for each application. Fig. 1(a) illustrates the distributed power supply concept, and Fig. 1(b) shows a physical prototype of a 50-W 10-MHz converter being developed at MIT. The promise is that through manufacturing efficiencies made possible by small size, large numbers, and new fabrication methods, the cost of these converters will be less than the cost, in dollars/watt, of present power supplies. We also expect that because of automated manufacturing techniques, the reliability of these components will be superior to that of conventional supplies, for which automation is generally inapplicable.

Challenges of Very High Frequency Conversion

"Frequency goes up, size comes down" is a belief that has been the single most influential factor motivating the desire for higher switching frequencies in power supplies. To frequencies of about 500 kHz, this relationship between frequency and size is approximately true. However, beyond

Manuscript received August 7, 1987; revised November 24, 1987. This work was supported by the Digital Equipment Corporation, the General Electric Company, Prime Computer, and the MIT/Industry Power Electronics Collegium (a group of companies providing unrestricted support to the academic and research programs in power electronics at MIT).

The authors are with the Laboratory for Electromagnetic and Electronic Systems, The Massachusetts Institute of Technology, Cambridge, MA 02139, USA.

IEEE Log Number 8719365.

Reprinted from *Proc. IEEE*, vol. 76, no. 4, pp. 362–376, April 1988.

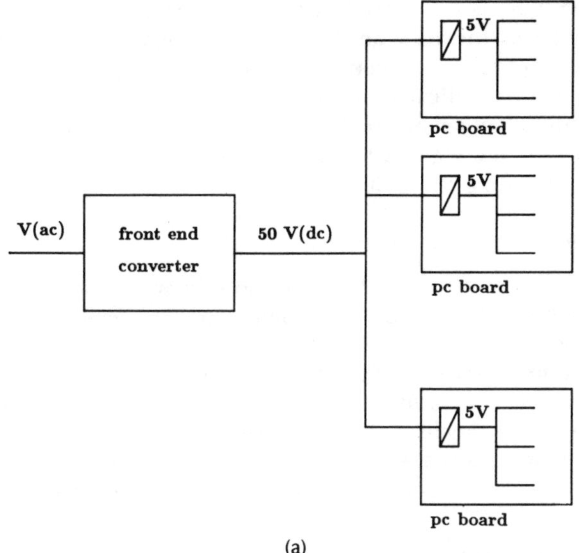

(a)

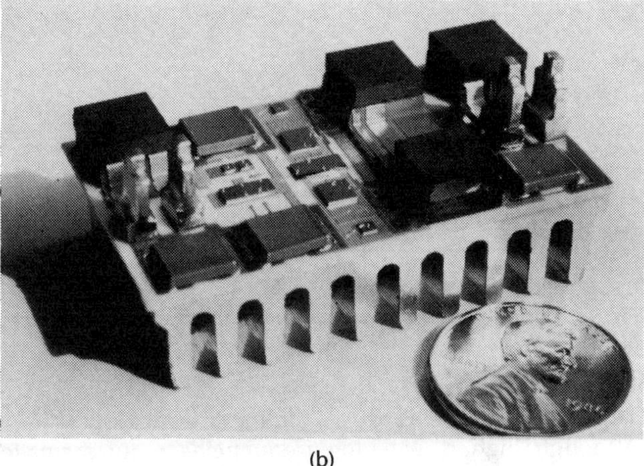

(b)

Fig. 1. (a) Block diagram illustrating the concept of a distributed power supply for a mainframe computer. (b) Physical prototype of the 10 MHz, 50 W, converter being developed at MIT for use in distributed power supplies.

this frequency, phenomena not previously important become so, and size may very well begin to increase. For instance, while the required value of capacitors goes down with increasing frequency, the ability of these smaller capacitors to handle ac current also goes down, often resulting in a net increase in physical size. At some frequency the loss density in magnetic materials increases faster than inductance decreases, requiring larger cores to reduce flux density and loss. Skin and proximity effects at high frequencies require that more space-inefficient winding techniques be used. Even majority carrier semiconductor devices, such as the power metal-oxide-semiconductor field-effect transistor (MOSFET), begin to exhibit significant switching losses when operated above a few megahertz.

All of the above effects result in increased losses. But if the size of the power supply is to be reduced, it must operate at a *higher* efficiency because the heat sink already dominates the size of power supplies operating at frequencies above about 500 kHz. By using new materials, processes, and devices, we can anticipate size reduction while maintaining or improving efficiency. Furthermore, these new materials and processes can result in manufacturing techniques that are reliable, efficient, and mass production oriented.

In this section we will give a brief overview of several important areas that must be addressed in the design of very high frequency converters, that is, converters operating at frequencies in excess of 1 MHz. These areas are:

- topology and parasitics,
- energy storage components,
- semiconductor devices,
- electromagnetic interference,
- packaging and thermal management,
- control.

Our intent in this section is to identify those ways in which the influence of these issues differ in degree or effect from those at low frequencies (<500 kHz). More detailed discussions of many of these issues are given later in the paper.

Topology and Parasitics

The primary topological considerations at high frequencies is to make explicit use of parasitic elements that result from device or construction imperfections. Most important among these are the semiconductor device capacitances, the leakage inductance of transformers, and the inductance of component interconnections.

The input capacitance of a MOSFET (which is the switching device of choice at the frequencies of interest), while of little consequence at low frequencies, has a major effect on overall circuit efficiency at frequencies above about 3 MHz. Not only does this capacitance increase switching time, but twice its stored energy is lost every cycle, unless a resonating gate drive can be developed. Such a lossless drive for a MOSFET used as a synchronous rectifier will be described later. The MOSFET's drain-source capacitance can also be the cause of significant losses as it charges and discharges each cycle. A circuit that employs this capacitance in a ringing tank, recovering rather than dissipating its energy, will also be described. And lastly, the drain-gate capacitance provides negative feedback to the gate that lengthens the device's switching times.

One of the advantages of high-frequency switching is that galvanic isolation can be achieved with a relatively small transformer, so transformers are frequently included in these power supplies. While transformer inter- and intra-winding capacitances can be important, leakage inductance is the biggest problem. The circuit chosen must accommodate this parasitic element, which has the potential to cause a level of dissipation that could dominate the total power supply loss.

Since parasitics must be explicitly incorporated in the design of very high frequency converters, the values of these parasitics must be *predictable*. Therefore the processes used to manufacture components exhibiting important parasitics have to yield consistent values of the parasitic parameters.

Energy Storage

The most volume-intensive components in power suplies are those that store energy: inductors and capacitors. The basic issue here is the electric and magnetic behavior of the materials used in making these components.

At frequencies below those of interest, commonly used magnetic core materials are powdered iron, the Mo-Ni-Co ferrous alloy laminates, and the Mn-Zn ferrite ceramics, such as the 3CX compounds. At frequencies between about 3 and 15 MHz, however, the choice of core material is tightly constrained to the Ni-Zn ferrites by several considerations to be discussed later. Given the magnetic material, then, the remaining challenges are determining the best Ni-Zn ferrite "recipe," and designing the structure of the inductor and transformer windings. The consequence of skin effect for conductor losses is aggravated at high frequency, and the importance of the proximity effect is much greater. Both of these issues will be discussed in some detail.

Capacitors in power supplies are either ac types (in a resonating tank, for example) or dc types (an input or output filter). Even in dc applications, however, capacitors are often subjected to substantial ac currents. Thus the ac behavior of the dielectric used is important in either application. Higher frequencies make it easier to use the low loss, high current, but relatively low value ceramic chip capacitors. But the significant difference is that at very high frequencies, many of the capacitance values required can be obtained using semiconductor junction capacitances. This greatly influences the power supply manufacturing process.

Semiconductor Devices

Semiconductor power devices perform two functions in a dc/dc converter: chopping and rectifying. Conventional circuits employ an active switch for the former, either a power bipolar junction transistor (BJT) or a MOSFET, and passive diodes for the latter, either bipolar junction or Schottky. The BJT is generally inapplicable at the frequencies of interest here because of its relatively slow minority carrier dynamics. The bipolar junction diode is also inapplicable, not only because of reverse recovery problems, but also because its forward drop is too large to permit the converter to achieve the requisite efficiency.

The power MOSFET and Schottky rectifier present their own unique problems, however. Chief among these is capacitance. As already mentioned, the MOSFET input and output capacitances result in losses that cannot be ignored. And even the use of Schottkys does not eliminate the substantial contribution to total losses made by the forward drop of the rectifier. An additional disadvantage of Schottkys is that their large capacitance can cause severe regulation problems at the frequencies of interest [4].

New devices must be designed and built to overcome these problems. As will be shown later, an additional FET monolithically integrated between the main device's gate and source can eliminate the negative feedback problem. Synchronous rectifiers, which are essentially active device replacements for the diode rectifiers, can be designed to reduce the effects of both the capacitance and drop of the diode rectifiers.

Control

There are two principal control challenges in building very high frequency converters. The first is sensing the controlled or controlling variables. The use of conventional current or voltage sensing techniques introduces parasitic inductance, resistance, or capacitance to the circuit. The problem is aggravated by the frequent need for isolation between the input and output of the sensor. Semiconductor magnetic and electric field sensors show promise of providing a practical solution to this problem. The second challenge is achieving a high enough control bandwidth to fully exploit the high switching frequency in the design of the input and output filters.

Electromagnetic Interference

Many power supply applications require conformance with MIL STD 461B (or its commercial equivalent), a standard with two unusual features. The first is that the maximum permissible amplitude of conducted harmonics is expressed in terms of absolute values of current, independent of power level. The second is that this value drops with frequency at a rate of 30 dB/decade at first, but above 2 MHz it is constant. These constraints are summarized in Fig. 2.

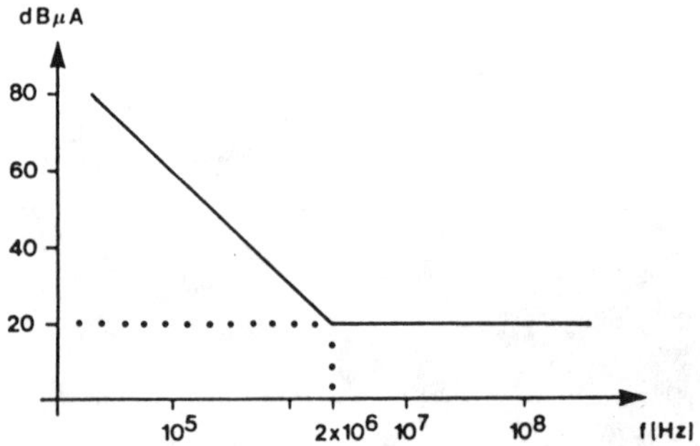

Fig. 2. Conducted current versus frequency as specified by MIL STD 461B.

The vertical scale is dBμA, defined as 20 log $(I/10^{-6})$. Although higher switching frequencies require smaller components to achieve a given attenuation, the implication of this standard is that so much more attenuation is necessary to meet the absolute current requirement that component size cannot be significantly reduced. An active circuit solution to this problem is discussed later.

Packaging and Thermal Management

An increase in the power density of a converter must be accompanied by either an improvement in efficiency or a better heat transfer system. Using technology presently available or anticipated, it is unlikely that the efficiency of a converter operating between 50 and 5 V will exceed 90 percent. And even at this efficiency, the dissipation is high enough so that the package design must produce relatively uniform volumetric dissipation to prevent hot-spots.

For distributed power supply architectures in computers and similar equipment, it is important that the converter package be compatible with the generally efficient heat transfer system used to cool the other board mounted components. This usually means that the package dimensions must conform with those of packages used for these other components, and a single heat transfer system must be used for the whole converter. For example, a 1-in square ECL package can dissipate 5–7 W in many computers. Using the same package and heat transfer system, it would be possible to build a 50-W converter operating at 90 percent efficiency. The resulting power density is about 75 W/in^2. The challenge, then, is to build a 90-percent efficient converter in a package of this size.

Topological Issues

While there are no "magic" power circuit topologies that suddenly make 1–10 MHz operation possible, the topology is important in achieving efficient operation in this frequency range. There are two general classes of dc/dc converters, referred to as *square-wave* converters and *resonant* converters. The square-wave converter impresses square waves of current and voltage on the semiconductor switching elements. This usually leads to switching losses that increase proportionally with frequency. Resonant converters, on the other hand, employ *L-C* circuits to limit the rates of rise of switch voltage or current, often reducing switching losses to negligible values. These two classes of circuits are discussed in more detail in what follows, with the intent of illustrating their relative strengths and weaknesses when applied at high frequencies.

Square-Wave Converters

All square-wave dc-dc converters are composed of semiconductor switches (transistors and diodes) and filter elements (inductors and capacitors). Although there are several topological variations, they are all based on the arrangement of components shown in Fig. 3(a). The inductor L_0 is assumed large enough so that the current I_0 is constant ($L_0 \rightarrow \infty$). Similarly, the voltage V_i is assumed constant ($C_i \rightarrow \infty$). The ideal operation of this circuit can be explained as follows:

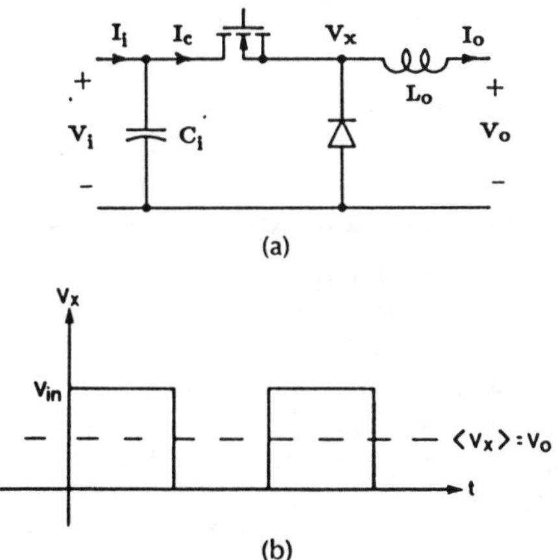

Fig. 3. (a) A square-wave dc/dc converter. (b) Voltage at node $X(\langle V_x \rangle = V_0)$.

• The transistor is turned on for a fraction (called the duty cycle) of the switching period, during which time $V_x = V_i$. The transistor is then turned off and the diode carries the inductor current.

• Since the inductor voltage cannot contain a dc component, the average value of V_x appears across the load. Because this value depends on the duty cycle, it is easily controlled. The voltage V_x and its average value $\langle V_x \rangle$ are shown in Fig. 3(b).

• The inductor and capacitor are made large enough to exclude the ac components in I_c and V_x from the input current I_i and output voltage V_0.

In this manner, the converter passes dc power from one port to another with a controllable voltage ratio. If the switches, inductors, and capacitors were ideal, the efficiency would be 100 percent.

If the switching frequency is raised, L_0 and C_i can be made smaller, resulting in a reduction in the volume of the power circuit. What keeps us from raising the switching frequency indefinitely is that the converter is not ideal. Switching losses are present and proportional to switching frequency. Even if we are not concerned about efficiency from an economic point of view, we are concerned about its effect on physical size. At some point, the reduction in filter size gained by raising the switching frequency is more than offset by the required increase in heatsink volume.

To understand how these switching losses arise, we need to add the parasitic energy storage elements to the ideal circuit topology. For operation in the 1–10 MHz range, the transistor will be a power MOSFET, and the diode a Schottky rectifier. Although both components switch very fast, they have junction capacitances that are influential at this frequency. In addition, the inductance of the loop formed by the filter capacitor, the transistor, and the diode has an important effect upon circuit behavior. Fig. 4(a) shows the dc-dc converter with these parasitic elements included [8].

Ignoring the parasitic inductance for now, we can easily explain the ways in which the parasitic capacitors C_t and C_d affect the switch transitions. If the MOSFET is turned off very quickly, the current I_0 that had been flowing through the channel of the MOSFET will immediately commutate to C_t and C_d in proportion to their relative values. The capacitor C_t will be charged as C_d is discharged, until the voltage V_x reaches zero and the diode turns on. During this interval there is a change in the energy stored in the parasitic capacitors, but there is no dissipation.

When the MOSFET is turned on, however, energy will be lost to three causes. First, the MOSFET must pick up all of the load current before the diode can turn off, and while the diode remains on, the MOSFET continues to support a high voltage. The waveforms of Fig. 4(b) depict this sit-

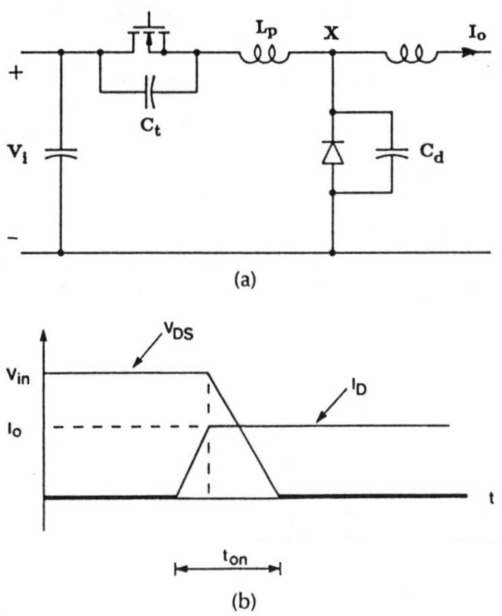

Fig. 4. (a) DC/DC converter with parasitic elements shown. (b) MOSFET waveforms at turn-on showing rise of current before voltage falls.

uation in which both the voltage and the current of the transistor are high at the same time. Second, as the voltage across the MOSFET collapses, the energy stored in its own junction capacitance is discharged through the channel resistance. Finally, the diode capacitance charges as V_x rises. The source of this charge is the input filter capacitor, which delivers an energy equal to QV_i. This energy is greater than the energy finally stored in the diode's capacitor, $\frac{1}{2}QV_i$, the difference being lost in circuit resistance. These loss mechanisms show the importance of designing MOSFETs and Schottky diodes that have as small a capacitance as possible, and for providing high-speed gate drive circuits.

With regard to the parasitic inductance, if care is taken to reduce its value to about 30 nH, it will have a negligible effect on the turn-on transition in systems where $V_i >$ 30 V. The rate at which the MOSFET voltage collapses is typically slow enough to prevent this inductance from impeding the charging of the diode junction capacitance. However, during the turn-off transition, even a small inductance has two important and detrimental effects. First, when the voltage V_x finally reaches zero and the diode turns on, the current still flowing through the parasitic inductance continues to charge the MOSFET's capacitor to a voltage higher than V_i. The MOSFET must be rated for this peak voltage, which, if the inductance is not kept small, could be much larger than V_i. Second, as the oscillation between the inductor and the MOSFET's capacitor decays, an energy equal to $\frac{1}{2}L_p I_0^2$ is lost.

To see how these parasitic elements limit the switching frequency, assume the converter of Fig. 4(a) has an input voltage of 100 V, an output voltage of 50 V (duty cycle = 50 percent), and an output current of 10 A. Typical semiconductor devices chosen for this application would have parasitic capacitances of 300 pF each. With very careful fabrication techniques, the parasitic inductance might be limited to 30 nH, and with a good gate drive circuit, the turn-on transition might be 10 ns. If this 500-W converter were switching at 2 MHz, the total switching losses would be equal to about 25 W, or 5 percent of the output. When the conduction and control circuit losses are added, the total power consumption is high enough to discourage increasing the switching frequency.

When the converter's input-to-output voltage ratio is high (e.g., 50/5), or when electrical isolation between the two external systems is required, a transformer is added to the circuit. Semiconductor devices are used to create an ac waveform by alternately switching the input voltage positively and negatively across the primary winding. Diodes are then used to rectify the secondary voltage. Fig. 5 shows one possible topology in which power flows through the

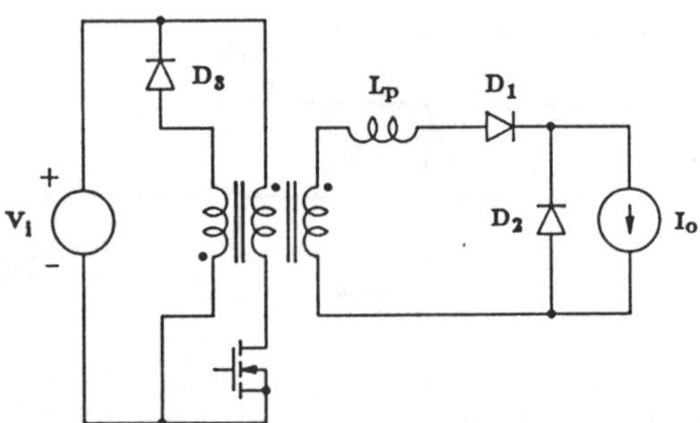

Fig. 5. A single ended, isolated square-wave converter.

transformer for only half of the cycle (when the transistor and diode D_1 are on). During the other half of the cycle the load current free-wheels through diode D_2, while the transformer flux is reset through diode D_3. Converters of this type, in which energy is not first stored in the magnetizing inductance of the transformer before it is transferred to the output, are known as *forward* converters. (Those which do store energy first are of a class called *flyback*.)

The transistor in the circuit of Fig. 5 sees twice the input voltage when it is off. The energy lost at turn-on is therefore much higher than for the nonisolated topology discussed above. In addition, since the transformer coupling is not perfect, the parasitic inductance between the MOSFET and diode is much larger in this converter. This, too, results in increased losses. These two effects combine to limit the practical switching frequency to about 500 kHz for the circuit of Fig. 5. Although there are many other transformer topologies we could try, all impose higher stresses than a circuit without a transformer.

Component improvements could raise the practical switching frequency of a transformer isolated square-wave converter to the 1-2 MHz range, but if the 5-10 MHz range is to be reached, additional means to reduce the switching losses must be employed. Such means are found in another class of power circuit, the resonant topologies discussed next.

Resonant Converters

To avoid the switching losses associated with parasitics, a topology must be chosen that:

- makes use of the parasitics,
- recovers the energy stored in the parasitic elements,
- has switch transitions during which either the voltage or the current is nearly zero.

A class of circuits that approximately satisfies these goals is the resonant converter [2]-[4], [6]. Resonant coverters use second order *L-C* tank circuits to control the rates of rise of switch voltages and/or currents. Ideally, the circuit parasitics are incorporated as part of the tank elements, and at high enough frequencies, the circuit parasitics *are* the tank elements.

Fig. 6(a) shows a simple resonant dc-ac converter using switches to produce a square-wave voltage across a series *L-C-R* network in which the resistor represents the load. If the switching frequency is equal to the resonant frequency of the tank, and if the Q is high enough, the full fundamental component of the square-wave will appear across the resistor while the harmonics will appear across the inductor. The current that flows will then be approximately sinusoidal, and in phase with the square wave of voltage, as shown in Fig. 6(b). The switch current is zero just before and just after the switch transitions, producing nearly zero switching losses. Switching at points of zero voltage can be obtained by using the dual of this circuit [9]. The zero current or voltage switch transition is the strength of the resonant converter. In exchange for this advantage, both the peak and rms values of the current flowing through, or the voltage across, the switches are higher than in a square-wave converter, producing higher on-state losses.

Power flow in a resonant converter can be controlled by varying the switching frequency. The impedance of the tank

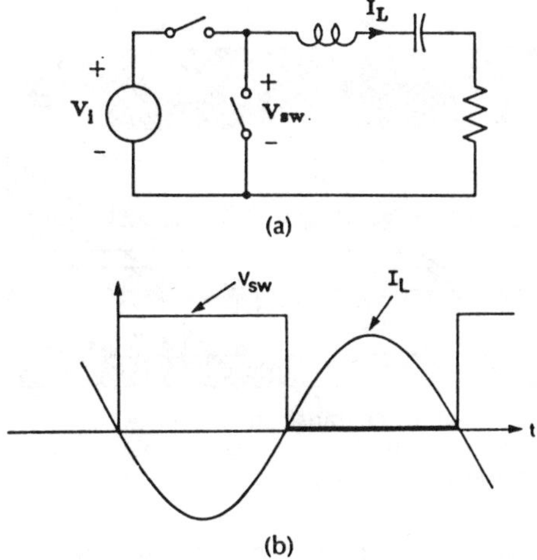

Fig. 6. (a) A voltage source, series resonant converter. (b) Switch waveforms showing zero current transitions.

in Fig. 6 increases as the frequency is moved away from resonance, reducing the load current. The farther away from resonance the switching frequency is moved, the lower the power delivered to the load. Unfortunately, the load current is no longer in phase with the voltage square wave, so switching no longer occurs at zero current. To remedy this, we could use a discontinuous mode of operation, one in which a transistor is turned on, the current rings through a half cycle, and then the switch is turned off at current zero. (In the zero-voltage topology, the switch is turned *off* for the half cycle ring.) By varying the delay between the start of one ring and the next, the average power delivered to the load can be controlled. Topologies that operate in this manner with rectified loads have come to be called "quasi-resonant converters" [10], [11]. They are discussed elsewhere in this issue of the PROCEEDINGS. An alternative is to use a considerably more complex full bridge circuit which allows a form of duty-cycle control at constant frequency.

MAGNETIC COMPONENTS

The design of high-frequency magnetic components is complicated by several considerations not important at low frequencies. Chief among these is the requisite use of ferrite cores at very low flux levels, and the dominating contribution to copper loss of skin and proximity effects. Also, the parasitics of a magnetic component must be reliably predictable and the same from piece to piece. This is because, as mentioned earlier, parasitics have a significant influence on circuit behavior.

The choice of core material for applications between about 3 and 15 MHz is tightly constrained to the Ni-Zn ferrites by several considerations. One is that powdered cores must be powdered so finely to reduce eddy-current losses that their effective permeability is very low, typically less than 30 μ_0 [12]. Another is that in the vicinity of 2 MHz, the Mn-Zn ferrites begin to exhibit a domain wall resonance that is reflected in hysteresis loss increasing rapidly with frequency [13]. Also, the Mn-Zn ferrites are conductive, resulting in high eddy-current losses, and exhibit a permittivity on the order of $10^4\epsilon_0$, which when combined with their high permeability results in wavelengths on the order of a few centimeters, leading to loss producing dimensional resonances.

In this section of the paper we discuss some of the geometrical issues related to copper loss, and present experimentally determined core loss data for several Ni-Zn ferrite materials. The predicted and experimentally determined performance of a prototype 10-MHz transformer is also presented.

Proximity Effects at High Frequency

The term "proximity effect" refers to the influence of a magnetic field caused by current in one conductor on the current distribution in another [14]–[16]. The essential features of this effect can be understood by referring to Fig. 7, which shows a conductor immersed in a uniform mag-

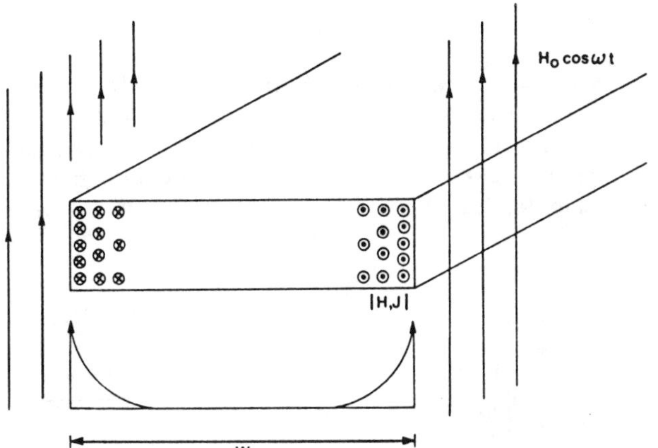

Fig. 7. A conductor immersed in a time varying but uniform magnetic field. The magnitudes of H and J in the conductor are shown for the case of finite, but nonzero, conductivity.

netic field of amplitude H_0 and frequency ω. The current induced in the conductor by the magnetic field is given by Ampere's Law. If the conductor were perfect, then a surface current density of amplitude $K_0 = H_0$ A/m would flow out of the conductor on the right-hand edge, and into the conductor on the left-hand edge. The net induced current in the conductor is zero. On the other hand, if the conductivity of the conductor is finite, and the frequency is such that the skin depth is much greater than the conductor width w then there will be no current induced in the conductor. If the conductor is neither of infinite conductivity, nor narrow compared to a skin depth, then the fields and current density in the conductor will fall off exponentially from each edge, as shown in Fig. 7. The resulting induced current, which can be viewed as circulating up one side and down the other, has a net value of zero but generates loss. In the absence of tangential fields at the top and bottom surfaces of the conductor, these currents will flow only in proximity to the edges, and the loss will therefore be independent of the conductor width, as long as w is greater than a few skin depths.

We can get a quantitative appreciation for the problem created by proximity effects in an inductor by considering the geometry of Fig. 8. This is a "sandwich" inductor, made by laying a spiral of copper between two ferrite plates. A planar geometry such as this has a good aspect ratio for our application. If H_z is uniform between turns, then the z-directed field between the nth and $(n - 1)$th turns can be

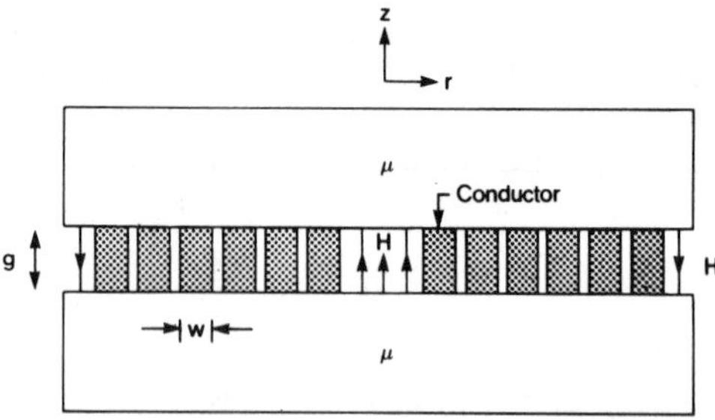

Fig. 8. A "sandwich" inductor made by placing a copper spiral between two plates of ferrite. It is assumed that the ferrite has a high permeability so the field between the plates is only z-directed.

expressed as

$$H_{zn} = H_0(N + 2(1 - n))$$

where $n = 1$ represents the innermost turn and N is the total number of turns. Assuming an inductance of 2 μH, a net current of 1 A, and a frequency of 10 MHz, the calculated copper loss as a function of the ratio of conductor width to skin depth is shown in Fig. 9 [17]. Although the param-

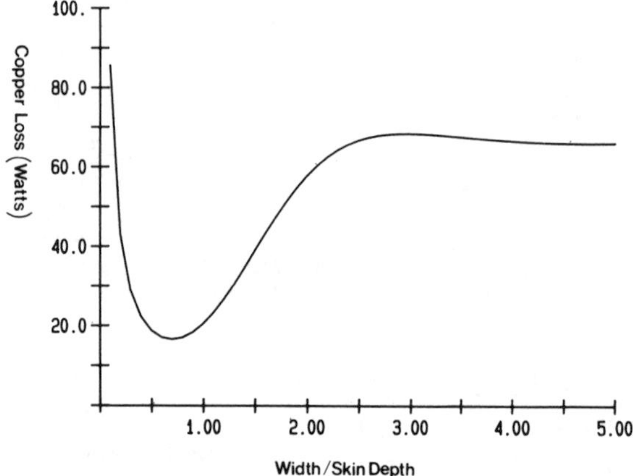

Fig. 9. Copper loss versus the ratio of conductor width w to skin depth for the inductor of Fig. 8. The gap length, $g = 100$ μm.

eters of this inductor are typical of what might be required in a 50-W converter operating at 10 MHz, it is clear that even the minimum loss achievable is well above an acceptable level.

If we consider a transformer instead of an inductor, the distribution of current in the conductors becomes more complex. The proximity effect as described above applies only to the magnetizing current. The distribution of load current is governed by the leakage fields Fig. 10 shows the leakage field H and load current distribution in a 6:1 sandwich transformer with planar windings, assuming a conductor thickness on the order of a skin depth. The primary and secondary currents flow on adjacent surfaces of the conductors because of the tangential boundary condition imposed by the leakage flux between the windings, making it possible to reduce load current losses by making the conductors wider.

We see, then, that once the frequency is high enough for copper dimensions to be on the order of a skin depth, losses in the sandwich inductor are difficult to reduce by increasing the volume of copper. Only the load current losses in a sandwich transformer respond to increasing conductor width, and this reduction is at the expense of an increase in transformer size.

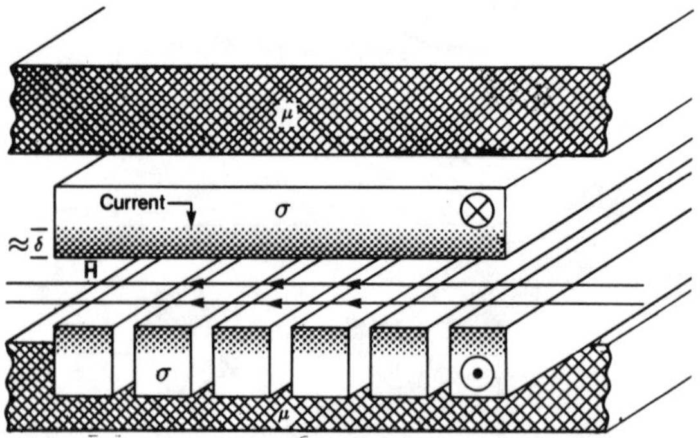

Fig. 10. A 6:1 sandwich transformer leakage field and load current distribution in the windings. Conductor thickness is on the order of a skin depth.

But the magnetizing current can be made to flow on the upper and/or lower surfaces of the conductors if a tangential $\vec{H}$ due to magnetizing current appears at these boundaries. This can be done by sinking the windings into a slot, as shown in Fig. 11(a). Fig. 11(b) shows the field lines as

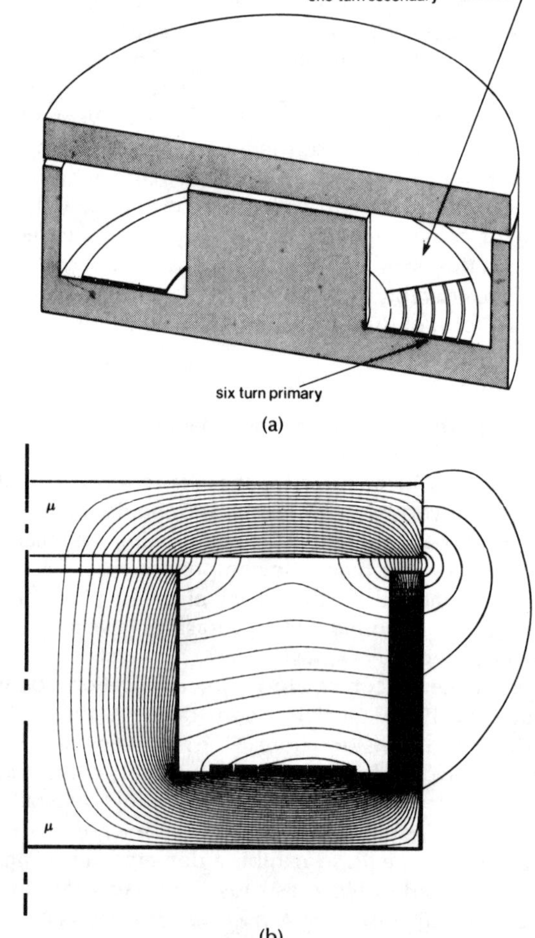

Fig. 11. (a) Cylindrically symmetric slotted core with a planar winding in the bottom of the slot. (b) A plot of magnetic field lines obtained from a finite element analysis. The leakage flux in the slot has a component tangential to the top surface of the conductor.

obtained from a finite element analysis. The flux fringing across the slot has a component tangential to the upper surface of the conductors, creating a boundary condition that distributes the magnetizing current over this surface. That is, the magnetizing current is no longer constrained to flow on adjacent conductor edges as for the sandwich inductor.

A finite element analysis was done to determine how slot depth affects copper loss. The net winding current was constrained to be 1 A at a frequency of 4 MHz, and a permeability of 125 μ_0 was assumed for the ferrite. This value is typical for the 4CX class of material. The copper loss was then calculated for several values of slot depth. Table 1 shows the inductance, series resistance and Q for three values of slot depth. The first entry corresponds to the sandwich inductor, that is, a slot depth of zero. The second two entries are for slot depths equal to half the slot width, and the total slot width, respectively. The results of these calculations clearly show that embedding the windings in a slot reduces considerably the losses due to the proximity effect [17].

Table 1 Effect of Slot of Width *w*

Slot Depth	$L(\mu H)$	$R(\Omega)$	$\omega L/R$
0	3.0	4.4	17
$w/2$	2.5	0.55	110
w	2.7	0.51	130

Magnetic Material Properties

As we previously discussed, Ni-Zn ferrite is the material of choice at the frequencies of interest. Even this material, however, exhibits domain wall resonances at frequencies not much above 10 MHz, so small increases in frequency around 10 MHz can cause large changes in hysteresis loss. Furthermore, loss data from manufacturers is virtually nonexistent for flux levels above a few gauss in this frequency range. For these reasons, we have experimentally measured the permeability and loss of several commercially available Ni-Zn ferrites at 5 and 10 MHz, and at flux levels up to 200 G. A description of the experimental apparatus used to obtain the data, and the analysis program used to extract permeability and loss from these data are given in [19].

Fig. 12 shows the experimental loss and permeability data at 5 and 10 MHz for Ni-Zn ferrites manufactured by three different companies, and intended for application between 1 and 10 MHz. The three materials are C2025 (Ceramic Magnetics), 4C4 (Ferroxcube), and Ferramic Q1 (Indiana General). Note that slightly higher permeability is accompanied by significantly larger hysteresis loss, and that the permeability and loss of each material increase with frequency. These data suggest that of the three materials, Ferramic Q1,

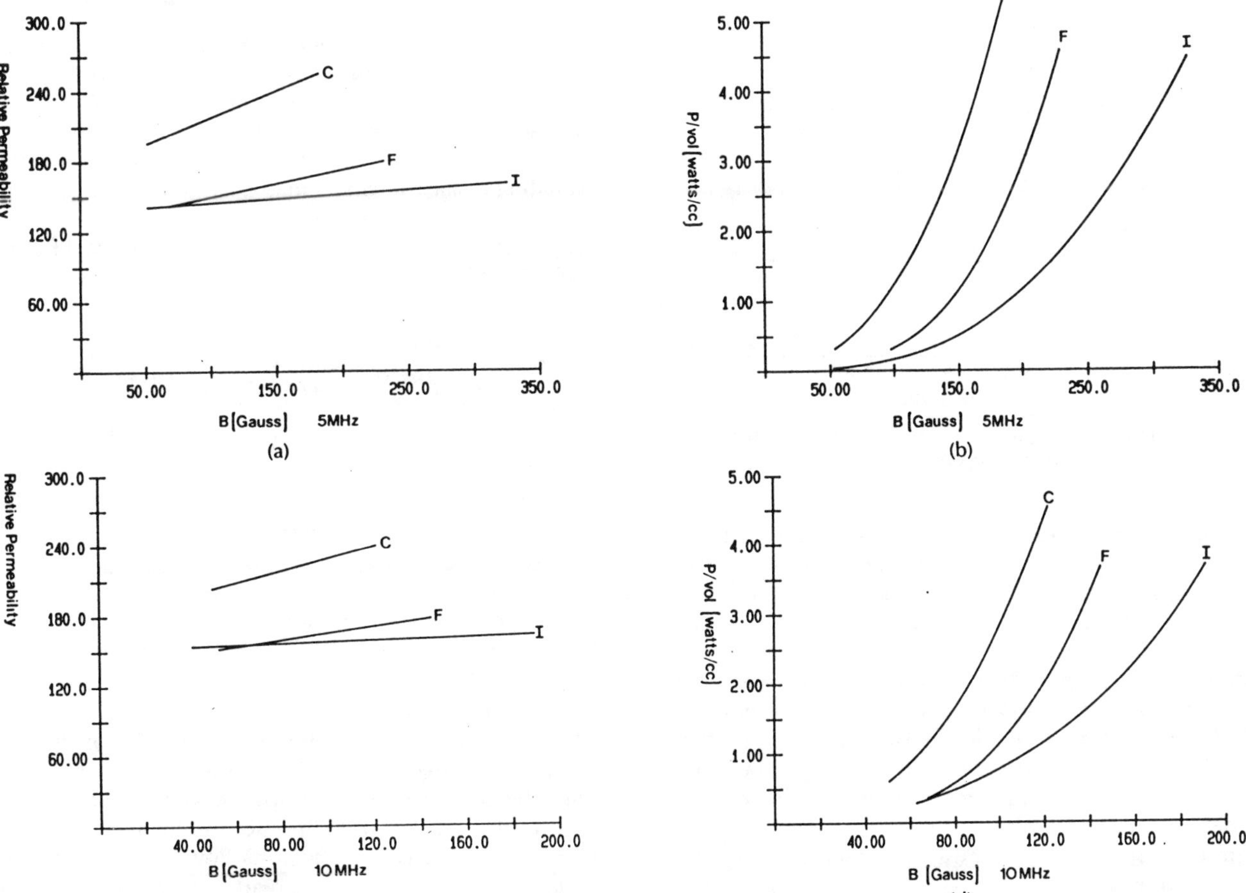

Fig. 12. Experimentally determined characteristics of three commercially available Ni-Zn ferrite materials designed for application between 1 and 10 MHz. (a) Permeability at 5 MHz. (b) Core loss at 5 MHz. (c) Permeability at 10 MHz. (d) Core loss at 10 MHz. (Legend: C = Ceramic Magnetics C2025, *F* = Ferroxcube 4C4, *I* = Indiana General Q1.)

with its lower hysteresis loss, would be the best choice. Although the properties of the materials vary with temperature, these data at 25°C are believed to represent the worst case, since there is evidence that permeability increases and loss decreases with temperature [18].

The experimentally determined characteristics shown in Fig. 12 represent only a single sample of each material. As with most magnetic materials, ferrites display a variation in their properties from batch to batch. Because core loss will generally be a substantial fraction of total converter loss, it is important that this parameter be well controlled. We do not yet have the data necessary to predict the variance of this parameter for presently available commercial materials, but generating this data is an important task.

Design and Performance of an Experimental Transformer

A computer design analysis was performed to determine transformer size as a function of frequency and loss. The program input parameters are the total power dissipation and the frequency. The program generates a design by determining the ratio of copper to hysteresis loss that results in a transformer occupying the minimum area. Results are the dimensions, maximum flux density, and leakage inductance.

Fig. 13 shows some results of this study on a transformer

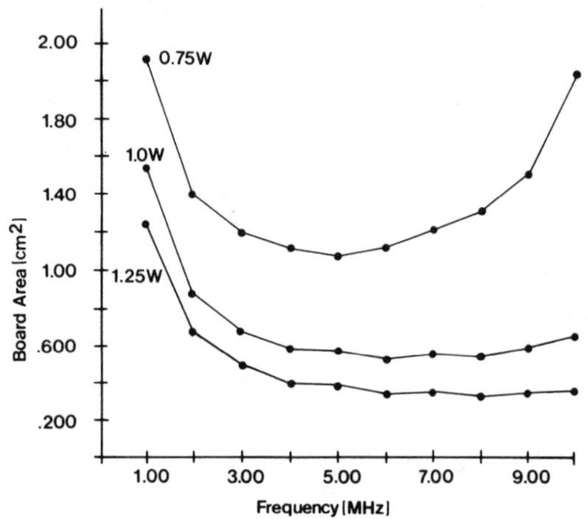

Fig. 13. Minimum area versus frequency for a transformer with single spiral primary and secondary windings.

whose magnetizing inductance, turns ratio, and load current were fixed by the requirements of the prototype converter described later in this paper. Each curve represents a different, but fixed, total allowable dissipation. In each case, the design is such that the loss is dominated by dissipation in the copper. Because the windings were not interleaved to reduce copper loss due to load current, the 0.75-W curve shows a minimum area at about 5 MHz. Studies on designs using two interleaved layers of primary (primary-secondary-primary) show an insignificant increase in size between 5 and 10 MHz.

A prototype 6:1 transformer was constructed with planar spiral windings and no interleaving. The design was not optimized with respect to board area because of the size constraint imposed by commercially available cores. The primary and secondary windings were photolithographed and etched on two sides of a flexible polyimide/copper laminate. The six primary turns were 325 μm wide and separated by 20 μm. The winding structure was placed around the center post of a Ferroxcube 1107PL00-4C4 core. A ferrite plate covered the core with a gap of 110 μm. Calculated, finite element derived, and measured parameters for this transformer are presented in Table 2. The calculated parameters were obtained using approximate formulas derived and presented in [17].

Table 2 Calculated and Measured Parameters

Parameter	Calculated	Finite Element	Measured
L_m	3 μH	3.4 μH	3.6 μH
R_w	0.5 Ω	0.52 Ω	0.52 Ω
L_l	44 nH	48 nH	44 nH
Core loss	0.19 W	—	—
Copper loss	—	0.064 W	—
Total loss	0.25 W	—	0.25 W

Power Semiconductor Components

Efficient conversion using switching frequencies in the 5–10 MHz range require power devices designed for this application rather than for general purpose use. Following is a summary of the major issues in this area, and a description of the work being done on them at MIT.

A Low Capacitance MOSFET With an Integral Driver

As described in the section on topologies, the junction capacitance of power devices must be minimized if switching losses in square-wave converters are to be small. Even in a resonant converter, where these losses are small, the switching frequency is ultimately limited by how small the resonating capacitor can be made, and this, in turn, is limited by the minimum junction capacitance.

Fig. 14 shows a cross-sectional view of a vertical diffused MOS (DMOS) power transistor. This structure is conventional except that the gate electrode has been *lifted* as it passes over the n- region. The reason for this is explained below. The entire bottom surface of the die is the drain, and when the device is off, the space-charge region grows downward from the p-wells in which the channel is formed. When the device is on, electrons flow from the source, through the channel, and spread out as they progress through the n- drift region. The resistance of this drift region dominates the on-state resistance of conventional power MOSFETs, and its length and doping are fixed by the required V_{DS} rating. The area available for conduction is

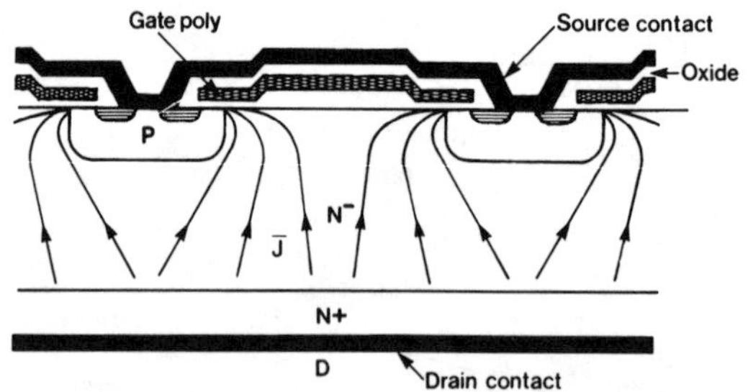

Fig. 14. Cross-sectional view of a vertical DMOS power field effect transistor with lifted gate structure to reduce C_{dg}.

somewhat less than the total area of the device because the current does not fully spread out underneath the p-wells. Unfortunately, the capacitance of the device depends on the full device area, so the product of on-state resistance and capacitance is always higher than its theoretical minimum.

To reduce the MOSFET's *RC* product, it is necessary to make the p-well widths as small as possible. In today's typical devices this width is around 30 μm. However, with the lithographic capabilities used for integrated circuits this distance can be reduced to approximately 10 μm. Fortunately, the power device industry is already heading in this direction to reduce die size (and therefore cost) for a particular one-state resistance.

As we will discuss later, negative feedback through the drain-gate capacitance (C_{dg}) can produce significant switching loss. At high voltages this capacitance is dominated by the space-charge layer, but at low voltages it is dominated by the capacitance of the gate oxide between the p-wells. It is possible to reduce this capacitance by making the gate oxide thicker in this region and lifting the gate electrode. Doing so results in less accumulation underneath the oxide, reducing current spreading, and increasing on-state resistance. But this price is small. By lifting the gate electrode (the polysilicon layer) as it passes over the n-region, we have found through PISCES simulations that the drain-gate capacitance can be reduced by a factor of two while increasing the on-state resistance by only 5 percent.

Besides reducing capacitance, it is also important to improve the MOSFET's switching speed. In our discussion of topologies, we assumed that the channel could be turned on and off very fast compared to the switching period. At conventional frequencies this is true, but at high frequencies the impedance of the drive circuit may cause the transition time to become very long due to negative feedback through C_{dg}. In this case, the rate at which the drain-source voltage can change is limited by the amount of current that the drive circuit can supply to charge (or discharge) the gate-drain capacitance. As seen from the gate terminal, C_{dg} is multiplied by the voltage gain of the circuit (the Miller effect).

The effect of this feedback during the turn-off transition is shown in Fig. 15. When the gate voltage is discharged to its threshold and the channel begins to turn off, the load current, I_0, commutates to C_{dg} and C_{ds}. The current flowing into the drain-gate capacitor also flows through the gate-drive resistance, R_g, raising the gate voltage and keeping the channel on. The result is that some part of the total current, I_0, continues to flow through the channel and dissipates energy during the entire transition. The drive impedance must be made small enough to eliminate this problem.

If the circuit is built of discrete components, it is virtually impossible to make the turn-off gate drive impedance small enough to avoid losses. Although the resistance of the driver can be made small enough, the parasitic inductance of the interconnection between the driver and the MOSFET (about 10 nH) will give too much impedance for the 1–2 ns transition times required. One solution is to monolithically integrate a turn-off drive transistor on the same die as the power device [20]. The electrical and physical configurations of this device are shown in Fig. 16. The turn-off drive transistor is a lateral MOSFET constructed in an extended p-well, as shown in Fig. 16(b). Fig. 16(c) is a photograph of this device

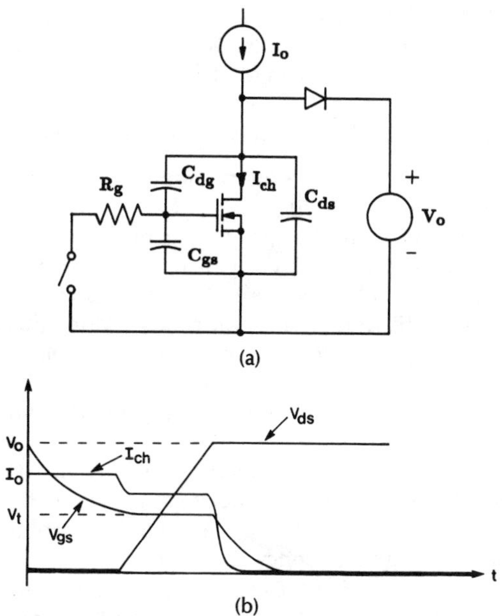

Fig. 15. (a) Schematic of MOSFET showing parasitic capacitances. (b) Waveforms showing the effect of negative feedback during the turn-off transition.

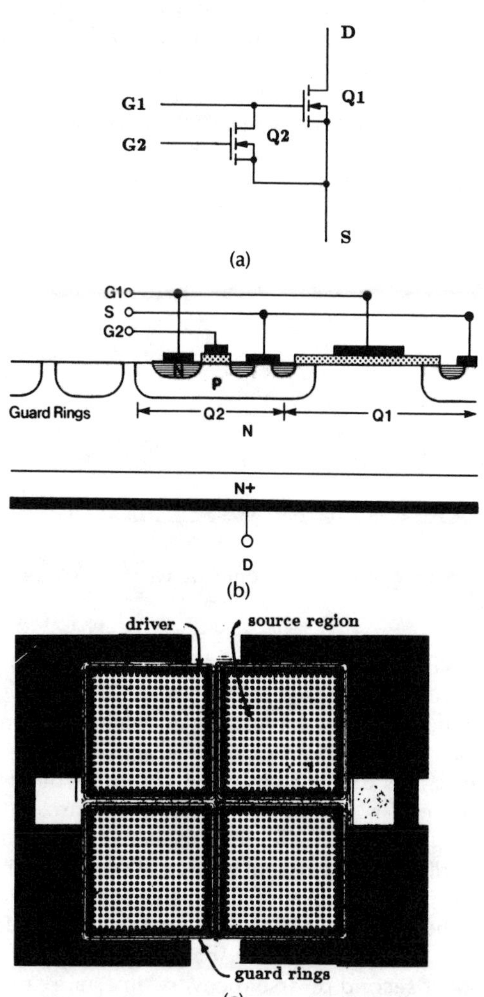

Fig. 16. (a) Schematic representation of MOSFET with integral turn-off driver. (b) Cross-sectional view showing lateral MOSFET in extended p-well. (c) Top view of fabricated device showing interdigitation pattern.

(fabricated in the MIT Microsystems Technology Laboratories) that shows how the integral driver is interdigitated around the cells of the main MOSFET.

A Low Capacitance, Fast-Recovery Synchronous Rectifier

With regard to the secondary side devices, the most important development required is that of a synchronous rectifier. Even though a Schottky diode may have a voltage drop of only 0.4 V when it is carrying the load current, if the output voltage is 5 V, 8 percent of the load power will be dissipated in this diode. To significantly reduce this loss, the diode needs to be replaced by a MOSFET whose resistance is so low that its on-state voltage is less than 0.2 V. This MOSFET is driven with an appropriately timed ("synchronous") gate drive.

Synchronous rectification is not a new idea, but it is seldom used because of the complexity of providing the synchronous gate drive. This implementation problem is aggravated in high-frequency converters where the cycle period is on the order of 100 ns. Furthermore, the large die area required for low on-state resistance results in very large gate and drain capacitances.

To meet the need for low capacitance and a short diode recovery, a special synchronous rectifier is being developed at MIT. This device is designed without a lightly doped drain region because of the low off-state voltage requirement (25 V). The space-charge layer instead grows into the p-region that forms the channel. To minimize the resistance per unit die area, a vertical gate structure is used. Although a U-groove would provide the highest packing density, a V-groove structure as shown in Fig. 17 is used because it

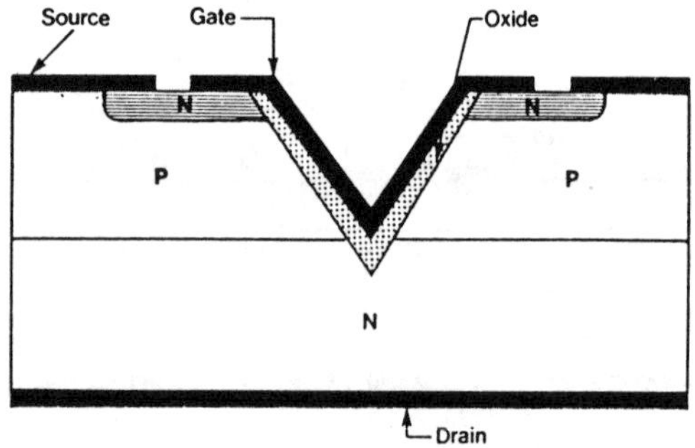

Fig. 17. Cross-sectional view of V-groove synchronous rectifier MOSFET.

gives a smaller C_{dg}. Preliminary designs studied through numerical simulations suggest that an on-state resistance of 1 mΩ/cm^2, an output capacitance of 8.5 nF/cm^2, and an input capacitance of 21 nF/cm^2 can be achieved.

Unique to this device's structure is a short base body diode, rather than the p-i-n diode normally present in a higher voltage MOSFET. The reverse recovery time of the short base diode is dependent on transit time, rather than on lifetime. Since the transit time is proportional to the square of the off-state voltage, it is very short for a device that must only withstand 25 V. Analytic calculations show that sub-nanosecond reverse recovery times are possible, so efficient operation at 10 MHz should be achievable. We have used two-dimensional numerical semiconductor simulations to verify this result. In these simulations, the diode was subjected to a step change of current from +10 A to

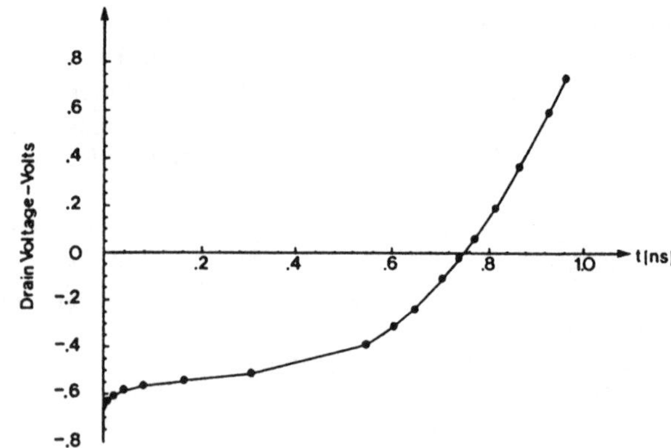

Fig. 18. Voltage across integral MOSFET diode after its current is stepped to a negative value. The diode has recovered its blocking ability, allowing V_{DS} to increase, after 0.8 ns.

−10 A, and the time required for the diode's voltage to drop below zero was observed (see Fig. 18). This time (which also coincides with the complete removal of minority charge in the diode) is very close to the theoretical minimum predicted by dividing the stored charge by the reverse current.

Electromagnetic Interference

Power circuits must limit the amount of switching frequency ripple seen by their source and load in order to avoid EMI. This is particularly important for ripple components in the RF band. As a result, there are strict commercial and military standards for allowable ripple. As an example, the standard summarized in Fig. 2, MIL STD 461B, allows the ripple to fall off at 30 dB/decade until 2 MHz. A second-order filter that meets this specification at 100 kHz would only exceed it by 10 dB at 1 MHz. Increasing the switching frequency from 100 kHz to 1 MHz would therefore permit the energy storage component size to be reduced by only a factor of 1.8 instead of the factor of 10 that was anticipated. Furthermore, since the specification is in terms of absolute ripple, a 40 V, 50 W, converter operating above 2 MHz would have to attenuate its input current ripple by approximately 100 dB.

Rather than provide this attenuation with fourth-order L-C filters that are large and that make the control of the power circuit complex, a combined passive and active filter technique can be used [21]. With this scheme, shown in Fig. 19(a), a second-order filter is used to reduce the input ripple current to the 1-mA level. A linear amplifier controlled with a feedback loop then shunts the remaining ripple. If the gain of this amplifier is high enough, the ripple that still flows in the source can be reduced to the 10-μA level. The power dissipated by this amplifier is small because its currents are so low, and the volume required for the circuitry is much less than the volume of the inductors and capacitors that would be needed if a high order passive filter were used.

For the active approach to work, it is necessary to make an amplifier with high gain at high frequency, gain being defined as the ratio of the input ripple current without the filter to that with the active filter network. We have achieved gains as high as 500 at 1 MHz (50 at 10 MHz) with experimental circuits. Fig. 19(b) gives the schematic of this experimental active filter, and Fig. 19(c) shows the experimentally measured before and after ripple current levels.

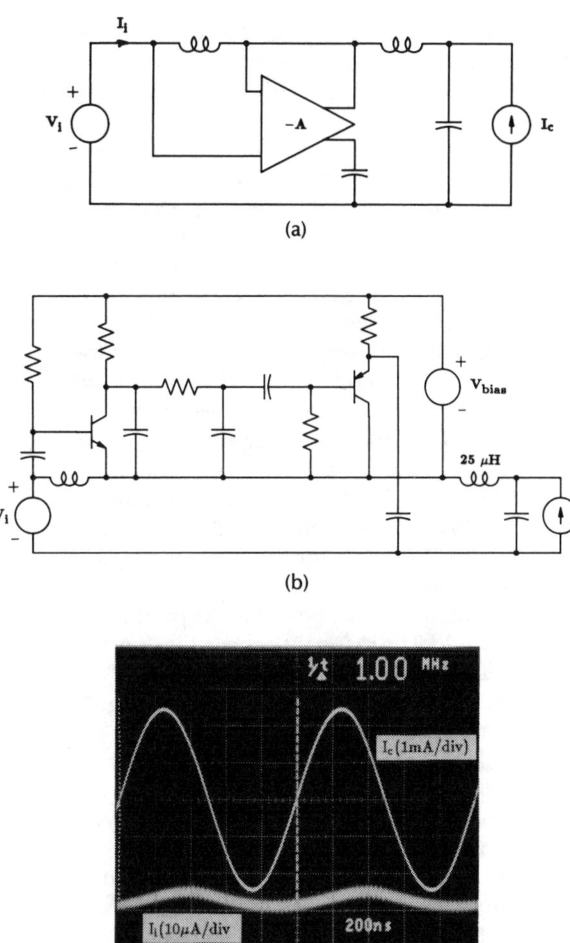

Fig. 19. (a) Active filter imbedded in the input filter to meet strict attenuation requirements. (b) Schematic of active filter designed for 1–10 MHz applications. (c) Waveforms showing before and after ripple currents.

A 5–10 MHz Point of Load Power Supply

This section presents the design and experimental results for a point of load converter being developed at MIT. The purpose of this supply is to convert 40 V to 5 V at 50 W, and it must be small and efficient enough to be mounted directly on the logic boards of a computer. To achieve the small size required, the converter operates in the 5–10 MHz range. A resonant topology with a transformer is used.

The need for high efficiency makes the use of synchronous rectifiers almost necessary. These are low resistance MOSFETs placed in parallel with the secondary side diodes to reduce conduction losses. They have a relatively large junction capacitance whose stored energy, if dissipated, would contribute significantly to circuit losses. A similar problem exists for the primary side MOSFETs. Therefore, these capacitances are included in the circuit as resonating elements.

The input voltage is low enough to avoid the UL, CSA, and VDE recommended practices for safety isolation in the transformer, allowing construction that minimizes leakage inductance. Of the three parasitic elements outlined in the section on square-wave converters, the inductance is the least troublesome in this case.

The Resonant Forward Converter

Since all the semiconductor devices must have zero-voltage switching transitions during which their capacitive energy is recovered, we have developed a resonant version of the forward converter. It is shown in Fig. 20(a) [22]. The

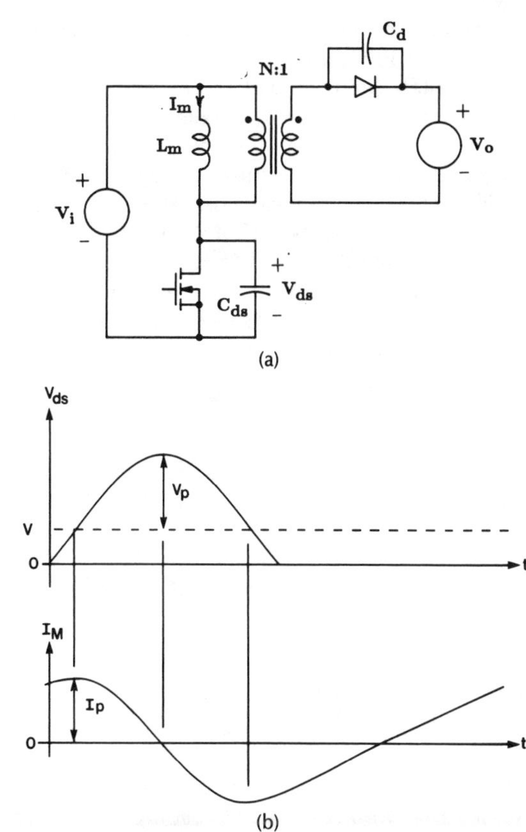

Fig. 20. (a) A resonant forward converter that recovers energy stored in the device capacitances. (b) Waveforms showing off-state ringing.

capacitors C_d and C_{ds} are the diode and MOSFET junction capacitances, respectively, and L_m is the transformer magnetizing inductance. The addition of the synchronous rectifier is discussed later. In this circuit, the MOSFET and the diode conduct simultaneously. When they are both on, operation is identical to that of a normal forward converter. The output capacitor is charged to the input voltage with a current that is limited by the circuit's series impedance, and the current in the magnetizing inductance increases linearly.

The ringing transient that recovers the stored energy occurs when the MOSFET is turned off. The current flowing through the channel first commutates to C_{ds}. As the voltage across this capacitor begins to rise, the transformer voltage falls, and the output diode becomes reverse biased. The magnetizing current continues to flow into both C_{ds}, and through the transformer into C_d. These two capacitors, incrementally in parallel during this part of the cycle, ring with the magnetizing inductor, as shown in Fig. 20(b). Their voltage reaches a peak value of approximately $3.5V_i$ and returns to zero as it heads for a negative value. The output diode and the MOSFET's drain-source diode clamp the voltage to zero, at which point the MOSFET can be turned on with negligible switching loss to begin the new cycle.

Because the ringing inductor L_m never carries the load current, the character of the ring is independent of load. The frequency of the ring is limited by the size of the junction capacitors, so it is important to make them as small as possible. The effect of the leakage inductance, while not discussed in detail here, is negligible if its value can be kept below about 3 percent of the magnetizing inductance. Special care with the secondary side interconnects is necessary to achieve this low value.

The complete point of load power supply uses two resonant forward converters in parallel, each operated 180° out of phase. Since power then flows from input to output at all times during the cycle, the size of the input and output filter elements are much smaller than they would be if power were transferred for only half of the cycle.

Since the resonant forward converter does not have the ability to regulate the output voltage, a preregulator scheme has been devised to compensate for changes in the input voltage and output current levels. This preregulator, shown in Fig. 21, is a square-wave dc-dc converter whose output

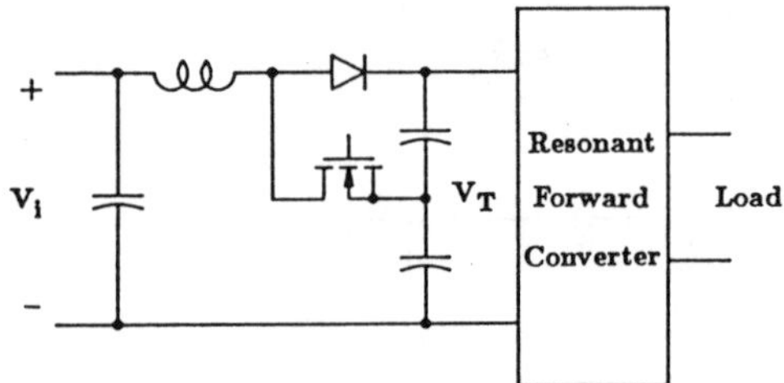

Fig. 21. Low loss preregulator used with the resonant forward converter of Fig. 20.

is higher than its input (an *up*, or *boost* converter). To avoid the losses that would normally accompany square-wave operation above 3 MHz, the normal up-converter topology has been modified by connecting the source of the transistor to a midpoint voltage, V_T, obtained by tapping the transformer, instead of to ground. Both the switching and conduction losses of this transistor are small because, since V_{DS} is low, a very low resistance device can be used. As long as this midpoint voltage is lower than the lowest input voltage anticipated (e.g., 28 V), the output voltage is controllable.

The advantage of this special arrangement is that the voltage rating of the pre-regulator switch must be only as high as the variation in the input voltage (14 V if the input range is 28–42 V). Such a low rating means that a desired on-state voltage can be achieved with a very small die area, which in turn means that the parasitic capacitances of the device will be small. Since the voltage to which these capacitances are charged is also very small, the energy lost during a square-wave switching cycle is minimized, and efficient preregulator operation in the 3–5 MHz range is possible.

Finally, an important advantage of using the square-wave preregulator is that all power circuit switches operate at a constant frequency, no matter how the input voltage or output current varies. This is important because it makes it easier to design EMI filters for the electronic system in which the supply is used.

Fig. 22 gives the full schematic of the prototype 50 W point-of-load supply. The resonant converters operate at 3.6 MHz (the ripple frequency seen by the filters is 7.2 MHz) and the preregulator at 2 MHz. The waveforms in Fig. 23 are of the MOSFET and diode voltages, and they show the zero-voltage switching transitions of both devices. An efficiency of 80–85 percent was achieved in this converter, although we feel that both the efficiency and the frequency can be raised by using specially designed components.

The circuit of Fig. 22 is uniquely suited to the application of synchronous rectifiers as replacements for D_4 and D_5. These rectifiers can be simply and accurately driven by cross coupling their gates to the opposite transformers, as shown in Fig. 24(a). During the off period of each resonant forward converter, the transformer automatically drives the gate of the opposite rectifier, as shown in the waveforms of Fig. 24(b). Most important, this drive scheme uses the rectifier's input capacitance as part of the total resonant capacitance, and the energy stored in it is recovered.

One problem with this drive scheme is that it turns on

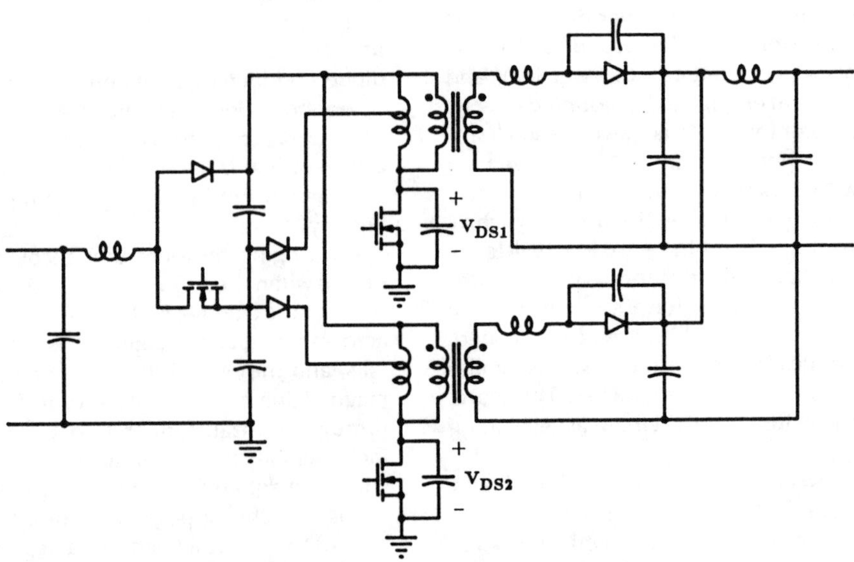

Fig. 22. Schematic of prototype 50 W point-of-load power supply. The tapped inductors represent the magnetizing inductances of T_1 and T_2. The diodes D_2 and D_3 maintain a constant voltage on C_2 and C_3.

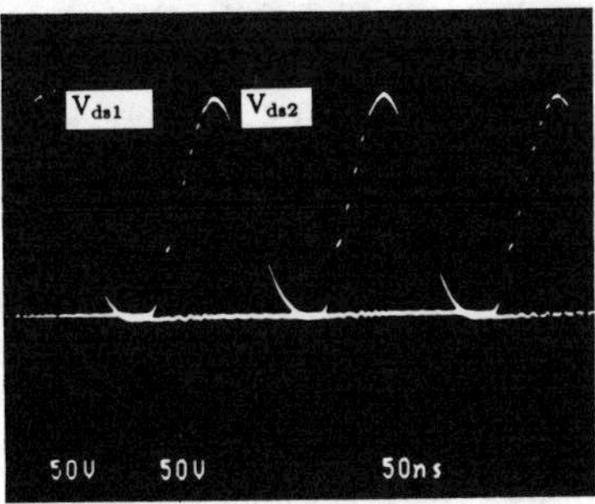

Fig. 23. Waveforms of the MOSFET and diode voltages in the circuit of Fig. 22. The waveforms are sinusoidal pulses displaced by 180°.

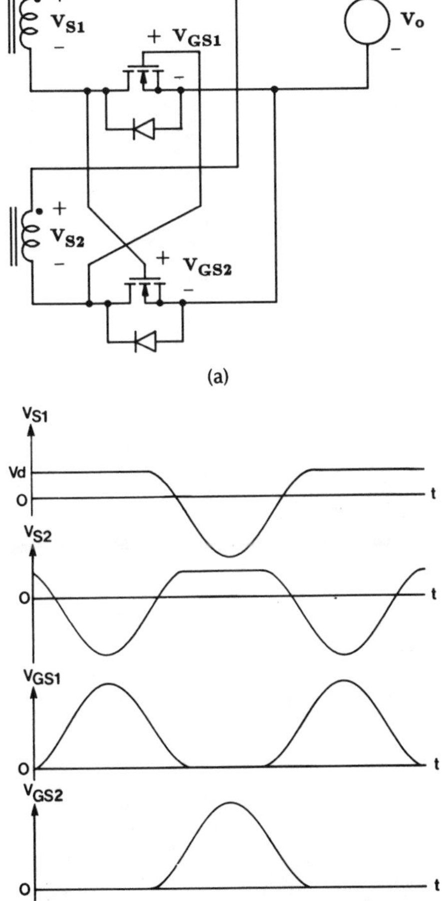

Fig. 24. (a) Cross coupling the gates of synchronous rectifiers in the dual resonant forward converter. (b) Waveforms showing lossless drive of rectifier gates.

the MOSFET only for the time when the gate voltage is above threshold. Therefore, a parallel diode must be present to carry the load current at the beginning and end of the combined rectifier's conduction period. The MOSFET body diode may be used if its recovery time is short enough.

Conclusion

Power supplies for electronic systems are changing dramatically because their switching frequencies are being raised from the 100 kHz range to the 1 MHz, and soon the 10 MHz range. Although this change started with the quest for smaller volumes and the challenges of low voltage logic, the implications are far more broad. The small size of the energy storage components (and, in some cases, the use of parasitics for these components), new materials, and new construction techniques are leading to mass-production oriented manufacturing technologies. Their intended application in distributed power systems will result in these supplies of the future being treated as components. Continued progress in this area requires a multidisciplinary approach to design. Issues of topology, components, control, fabrication, and packaging must be addressed simultaneously.

Acknowledgment

The authors wish to thank the following students in the MIT Laboratory for Electromagnetic and Electronic Systems who contributed to the work reported in this paper: V. Ali, S. Bahl, J. Bernstein, L. Casey, A. Ferencz, A. Goldberg, M. Hakkarainen, L. LaWhite, B. Miwa, L. Pitzele (now with AT&T Bell Laboratories), D. Richards, G. Rittenhouse, and C. Wright.

References

[1] N. O. Sokal and A. D. Sokal, "Class E—A new class of high efficiency tuned single-ended switching power amplifiers," *IEEE J. Solid-State Circuits*, pp. 168–176, June 1975.

[2] R. J. Gutmann, "Application of RF Circuit Design Principles to Distributed Power Converters," *IEEE Trans. Indust. Electron.*, vol. 27, no. 3, pp. 156–164, Aug. 1980.

[3] K. Harada *et al.*, "Megahertz DC-to-DC converters controlled by an amorphous core," *IEEE Trans. Magn.*, vol. 19, no. 5, pp. 2082–2084, Sept. 1983.

[4] A. F. Goldberg and J. G. Kassakian, "The application of power MOSFETs at 10 MHz," in *Power Electronics Specialists Conf. Record*, pp. 91–100, 1985.

[5] C. B. Jones and J. P. Vergez, "Application of PWM techniques to realize a 2 MHz off-line switching regulator, with hybrid implementation," in *Proc. IEEE Applied Power Electronics Conf.*, New Orleans, LA, pp. 221–227, 1986.

[6] T. Ninomiya, T. Higashi, and K. Harada, "Voltage-mode resonant push-pull converter with magnetic power controllers," in *IEEE Power Electronics Specialists Conf.*, (Blacksburg, VA), pp. 339–347, 1987.

[7] P. Vinciarelli, "Forward converter switching at zero current," U. S. Patent 4415959, Nov. 15, 1983.

[8] M. F. Schlecht and L. F. Casey, "Comparison of the square-wave and quasi-resonant topologies," in *Proc. IEEE Applied Power Electronics Conf.*, (San Diego, CA), pp. 124–134, 1987.

[9] J. G. Kassakian, "A new current mode sine wave inverter," *IEEE Trans. Ind. Appl.*, vol. IA-18, no. 3, pp. 273–278, May/June 1982.

[10] K. Liu, R. Oruganti, and F. C. Lee, "Resonant switches—topologies and characteristics," in *IEEE Power Electronics Specialists Conf. Record*, (Toulouse, FR), pp. 106–116, 1985.

[11] K. Liu and F. C. Lee, "Zero-voltage switching technique in DC/DC converters," in *IEEE Power Electronics Specialists Conf.*, (Vancouver, BC), pp. 58–70, 1986.

[12] Micrometals, Inc., *Catalog of Toroidal Cores for RF Applications*, no. 3, issue B, Anaheim, CA, 1984.

[13] J. Smit and H. Wijn, "Physical Properties of Ferrites," in *Advances in Electronics and Electron Physics*, vol. vi, L. Marton, Ed. New York, NY: Academic Press, 1954, pp. 105–110.

[14] H. H. Woodson and J. R. Melcher, *Electromechanical Dynamics*, vol. ii. New York, NY: Wiley, 1968, ch. 7.

[15] B. Carsten, "High frequency conductor losses in switchmode magnetics," *Power Conversion and Intelligent Motion*, pp. 34–36, Nov. 1986.

[16] P. L. Dowell, "Effects of eddy currents in transformer windings," *Proc. Inst. Elec. Eng.*, vol. 113, no. 8, pp. 1387–1394, 1966.

[17] A. F. Goldberg, J. G. Kassakian, and M. F. Schlecht, "Issues related to 1-10 MHz transformer design," *IEEE Power Electronics Specialists Conf. Record*, (Blacksburg, VA), pp. 379–386, 1987.
[18] A. F. Goldberg, "High field properties of Nickel-zinc ferrites at 1-10 MHz," in *Proc. IEEE Applied Power Electronics Conf.*, New Orleans, LA, 1988.
[19] Phillips Electronic Components and Materials Division, *Components and Materials Book C4: Ferroxcube Potcores, Square Cores, and Cross Cores*. The Netherlands, Eindhoven 1984, pp. 33, 40.
[20] J. B. Bernstein, S. Bahl, and M. F. Schlecht, "A low capacitance power MOSFET with an integral gate driver," in *IEEE Power Electronics Specialists Conf.*, (Blacksburg, VA), pp. 61–68, 1987.
[21] L. E. LaWhite and M. F. Schlecht, "Design of active ripple filters for power circuits operating in the 1-10 MHz range," in *IEEE Power Electronics Specialists Conf.*, (Blacksburg, VA), pp. 195–203, 1987.
[22] L. F. Casey and M. F. Schlecht, "A high frequency, low volume, point-of-load power supply for distributed power systems," in *IEEE Power Electronics Specialists Conf.*, (Blacksburg, VA), pp. 439–450, 1987.

Selected Bibliography

[1] R. D. Middlebrook, "Power electronics: Topologies, modelling, and measurement," *Proc. IEEE Int. Symp. Circuits Syst.*, vol. 1, pp. 230–238, 1981.

[2] S. Ćuk and R. D. Middlebrook, "A general unified approach to modelling switching dc-to-dc converters in discontinuous conduction mode," *IEEE PESC Rec.* (Abstract), 1977; *IEEE Trans. Aerosp. Electron. Syst.*, vol. AES-13, pp. 574–575, Sept. 1977.

[3] R. Erickson, B. Behen, R. D. Middlebrook, and S. Ćuk, "Characterization and implementation of power MOSFETs in switching converters," *Proc. POWERCON 7*, 1980.

[4] S. Ćuk and R. D. Middlebrook, "A new optimum topology switching dc-to-dc converter," *IEEE PESC Rec.* (Abstract), 1977; *IEEE Trans. Aerosp. Electron. Syst.*, vol. AES-13, pp. 575–576, Sept. 1977.

[5] S. Ćuk and R. D. Middlebrook, "Advances in switched mode power conversion, Part I," *Robotics Age*, vol. 1, pp. 6–19, Winter 1979.

[6] S. Ćuk and R. D. Middlebrook, "Advances in switched mode power conversion, Part II," *Robotics Age*, vol. 2, pp. 28–41, Summer 1980.

[7] R. D. Middlebrook, "Transformerless dc-to-dc converters with large conversion ratios," *IEEE Trans. Power Electron.*, vol. 3, pp. 484–488, Oct. 1988.

[8] S. Ćuk and R. D. Middlebrook, "Advances in switched mode power conversion (Parts I and II)," *IEEE Trans. Ind. Electron.*, vol. IE-30, pp. 10–29, Feb. 1983.

[9] J. Allen et al., "A gate turn-off thyristor chopper for traction drive," *Proc. IEE*, vol. 132, Pt. B, pp. 93–100, Mar. 1985.

[10] S. B. Dewan and A. Mirbod, "A microprocessor-based optimal control for four quadrant chopper," *IEEE Trans. Ind. Applicat.*, vol. IA-17, pp. 34–40, Jan./Feb. 1981.

[11] B. Holland, "Modeling, analysis and compensation of the current mode converter," *Proc. Powercon II*, pp. 1-2-1–1-2-6, 1984.

[12] B. Brakus, "100 amp switched mode charging rectifier for three-phase mains," *IEEE/INTLEC 1984*, pp. 72–78, 1984.

[13] D. M. Divan, "Design considerations for very high frequency resonant mode dc/dc converters," *IEEE Trans. Power Electron.*, vol. PE-2, pp. 45–54, Jan. 1987.

[14] N. O. Sokal and A. D. Sokal, "Class E—A new class of high efficiency tuned single ended switching power amplifier," *IEEE J. Solid-State Circuits*, vol. SC-10, pp. 168–176, June 1975.

[15] K.-H. Liu and F. C. Lee, "Zero voltage switching technique in dc/dc converters," *IEEE PESC Rec.*, pp. 58–70, 1986.

[16] K.-H. Liu, R. Oruganti, and F. C. Lee, "Resonant switches—Topologies and characteristics," *IEEE PESC Rec.*, pp. 106–116, 1985.

[17] A. K. S. Bhatt and S. B. Dewan, "Analysis and design of a high frequency resonant converter using LCC-type commutation," *IEEE Trans. Power Electron.*, vol. PE-2, pp. 291–301, Oct. 1987.

[18] V. Vorperian, R. Tymerski, and F. C. Lee, "Equivalent circuit models for resonant and PWM switches," *IEEE Trans. Power Electron.*, vol. 4, pp. 205–214, Apr. 1989.

[19] A. Capel, D. O'Sullivan, and J. Marpinard, "High power conditioning for space applications," *Proc. IEEE*, vol. 76, pp. 391–408, Apr. 1988.

[20] K. Harada and T. Nabeshima, "Applications of magnetic amplifiers to high frequency dc-to-dc converters," *Proc. IEEE*, vol. 76, pp. 355–361, Apr. 1988.

[21] F. Kurokawa and H. Matsuo, "A new multiple output hybrid power supply," *IEEE Trans. Power Electron.*, vol. 3, pp. 412–419, Oct. 1988.

[22] W. A. Tabisz, P. M. Gradzki, and F. C. Lee, "Zero voltage switched quasi-resonant buck and flyback converters—Experimental results at 10 MHz," *IEEE Trans. Power Electron.*, vol. 4, pp. 194–204, Apr. 1989.

[23] K. Al-Haddad, T. Krishnan, and V. Rajagopalan, "DC to dc converters with high frequency ac link," *IEEE Trans. Ind. Applicat.*, vol. IA-22, pp. 244–254, Mar./Apr. 1986.

[24] V. T. Ranganathan, P. D. Ziogas, and V. R. Stefanović, "A regulated dc–dc voltage source converter using a high frequency link," *IEEE Trans. Ind. Applicat.*, vol. IA-18, pp. 279–287, May/June 1982.

[25] K.-H. Liu, R. Oruganti, and F. C. Y. Lee, "Quasi-resonant converters—Topologies and characteristics," *IEEE Trans. Power Electron.*, vol. PE-2, pp. 62–71, Jan. 1987.

[26] F. C. Lee, "High frequency quasi-resonant converter technologies," *Proc. IEEE*, vol. 76, pp. 377–390, Apr. 1988.

[27] W. A. Tabisz and F. C. Lee, "Zero voltage switching multiresonant technique—A novel approach to improved performance of high frequency quasi-resonant converters," *IEEE Trans. Power Electron.*, vol. 4, pp. 450–458, Oct. 1989.

[28] W. A. Tabisz, M. M. Jovanović, and F. C. Lee, "High frequency multi-resonant converter technology and its applications," *IEE Conf. Rec.*, July 1990.

[29] E. Buchanan and E. J. Miller, "Resonant switching power conversion technique," *IEEE PESC Rec.*, pp. 188–193, 1975.

[30] D. C. Hopkins, M. M. Jovanović, F. C. Lee, F. W. Stephenson, "Hybridized off-line 2-MHz zero-current-switched quasi-resonant converter," *IEEE Trans. Power Electron.*, vol. 4, pp. 147–154, Jan. 1989.

[31] M. F. Schlecht and L. F. Casey, "Comparison of the square wave and quasi-resonant topologies," *IEEE Trans. Power Electron.*, vol. 3, pp. 83–92, Jan. 1988.

[32] F. C. Schwarz, "An improved method of resonant current pulse modulation for power converters," *IEEE PESC Rec.*, pp. 194–204, 1975.

[33] V. Vorperian and S. Ćuk, "A complete dc analysis of the series resonant converter," *IEEE PESC Rec.*, pp. 85–100, 1982.

[34] L. F. Casey and M. F. Schlecht, "A high frequency low volume point of load power supply for distributed power systems," *IEEE PESC Rec.*, pp. 439–450, 1987.

[35] K. D. T. Ngo, "Generalization of resonant switches and quasi-resonant dc–dc converters," *IEEE PESC Rec.*, pp. 395–403, 1987.

[36] R. A. Fisher, K. D. T. Ngo, and M. H. Kuo, "A 500 kHz, 250 W dc–dc converter with multiple outputs controlled by phase shifted PWM and magnetic amplifiers," *Proc. High Freq. Power Conf.*, pp. 100–110, 1988.

[37] M. M. Jovanović, K.-H. Liu, R. Oruganti, and F. C. Lee, "State plane analysis of quasi-resonant converters," *IEEE Trans. Power Electron.*, vol. PE-2, pp. 56–73, Jan. 1987.

[38] M. M. Jovanović, D. C. Hopkins, and F. C. Lee, "Design

aspects for high frequency off line quasi-resonant converters," *High Freq. Power Conv. Conf. Rec.*, 1987.

[39] M. M. Jovanović, W. A. Tabisz, and F. C. Lee, "Zero-voltage-switching technique in high-frequency off-line converters," *IEEE Appl. Power Electron. Conf. Rec.*, pp. 23-32, 1988.

[40] R. B. Ridley, A. Lotfi, V. Vorperian, and F. C. Lee, "Design and control of a fullwave quasi-resonant flyback converter," *IEEE Appl. Power Electron. Conf. Rec.*, pp. 41-49, 1988.

[41] W. A. Tabisz and F. C. Lee, "A novel zero voltage switched multi-resonant forward converter," *High Freq. Power Conv. Conf. Rec.*, 1988.

[42] J. J. Yang and F. C. Lee, "Computer-aided design and analysis of series resonant converters," *IEEE/IAS Ann. Meet. Conf. Rec.*, vol. 1, pp. 954-959, 1987.

[43] F. S. Tsai and F. C. Lee, "Constant frequency phase controlled resonant power processor," *IEEE/IAS Ann. Meet. Conf. Rec.*, pp. 617-622, 1986.

[44] Y. Chin and F. C. Lee, "Constant frequency parallel resonant converters," *IEEE/IAS Ann. Meet. Conf. Rec.*, pp. 705-710, 1987.

[45] R. J. King and T. A. Stuart, "Modelling the full bridge series resonant power converter," *IEEE Trans. Aerosp. Electron. Syst.*, vol. AES-18, pp. 449-459, July 1982.

[46] A. F. Witulski and R. W. Erickson, "Design of the series resonant converter for minimum component stress," *IEEE Trans. Aerosp. Electron. Syst.*, vol. AES-22, pp. 356-363, July 1986.

[47] Y. G. Kang and A. K. Upadhyay, "Analysis and design of a half-bridge parallel resonant converter," *IEEE PESC Rec.*, pp. 231-243, 1987.

[48] F. C. Raab, "Idealized operation of class-E power converters," *IEEE Trans. Circuits Syst.*, vol. CAS-24, pp. 725-735, Dec. 1977.

[49] K. Harada and W. Gu, "Steady state analysis of class E resonant dc-dc converter regulated under fixed switching frequency," *IEEE PESC Rec.*, pp. 3-8, 1989.

[50] K. Karube, T. Nomura, and T. Nakano, "High frequency resonant MOSFET dc-dc converter," *IEEE PESC Rec.*, pp. 26-32, 1989.

[51] K. Kuwabara, J. Chida, and E. Miyachika, "A constant frequency series resonant dc-dc converter with PWM controlled output," *IEEE PESC Rec.*, pp. 563-566, 1989.

[52] I. Barbi, J. B. Vieria, and J. C. Bolacell, "A forward pulsewidth modulated quasi-resonant converters: Analysis, design and experimental results," *Proc. IECON'89*, pp. 27-32, 1989.

[53] I. Barbi, J. B. Vieria, and H. L. Hey, "A pulsewidth-modulated zero-voltage zero-current-switched half-bridge quasi-resonant converter," *Proc. IECON'89*, pp. 42-47, 1989.

[54] O. D. Patterson and D. M. Divan, "Pseudo-resonant dc/dc converter," *IEEE PESC Rec.*, pp. 424-430, 1987.

[55] V. Vorperian and S. Ćuk, "Small signal analysis of resonant converters," *IEEE PESC Rec.*, pp. 269-282, 1983.

[56] R. Oruganti and F. C. Lee, "Resonant power processors. Part I: State plane analysis," *IEEE Trans. Ind. Applicat.*, vol. IA-21, pp. 1453-1460, Nov./Dec. 1985.

[57] R. Oruganti and F. C. Lee, "Resonant power processors. Part II: Method of control," *IEEE Trans. Ind. Applicat.*, vol. IA-21, pp. 1461-1470, Nov./Dec. 1985.

[58] S. Freeland and R. D. Middlebrook, "A unified analysis of converters with resonant switches," *IEEE PESC Rec.*, pp. 20-30, 1987.

Part 6
DC-to-AC Converters

Paper 6.1

RESONANT SNUBBERS WITH AUXILIARY SWITCHES

William McMurray, Fellow, IEEE

Consulting Engineer
P.O. Box 741, Schenectady, NY 12301

This work was done at Corporate Research and Development,
General Electric Company, Schenectady, NY

Abstract- A resonant snubber is described for voltage-source inverters, current-source inverters, and self-commutated frequency changers. The main self-turnoff devices have shunt capacitors directly across them. A temporary parallel path through a small ordinary thyristor and inductance takes over high-stress turn-on duty from the main device, in a manner that leaves no energy trapped after switching.

INTRODUCTION

In general, a self-turnoff power device such as a gate turn-off thyristor (GTO) or a power transistor requires both a series inductive snubber to limit di/dt when turning on and a shunt capacitive snubber to limit dv/dt when turning off. Unfortunately, the series inductance becomes a hindrance when turning off and the shunt capacitance becomes a burden when turning on, so that auxiliary diodes are necessary to polarize the charge/discharge action of the snubbers [1]. A further consequence is that, after switching, energy remains trapped in the reactive snubber elements. Usually, this energy must be dissipated in resistors. Some circuits can be adapted to recover energy trapped in both the series and shunt snubbers [2-5].

If a converter circuit can be operated in a mode where the switching device is subject to high dynamic stress only at turn-on, then only a series inductance need be provided and no energy is trapped. Similarly, if the circuit can be operated in a mode where the only high dynamic stress occurs at turn-off, then only a shunt capacitance is necessary and, again, no energy is trapped. Such modes of operation can be achieved with resonant circuits. Snubbers that do not trap energy can be termed "lossless" though, of course, there will be some loss because the components are not ideal.

The lossless resonant snubber described here avoids trapping energy in a converter circuit where high dynamic stresses at both turn-on and turn-off are normally encountered. This is achieved by providing a temporary parallel path through a small ordinary thyristor (or other device operating in a similar mode) to take over the high-stress turn-on duty from the main GTO or power transistor, in a manner that leaves no energy trapped after switching.

Since one of the main advantages of GTOs over ordinary thyristors is the elimination of commutating circuits, often including auxiliary thyristors, any proposal to re-introduce auxiliary thyristors might be regarded as regressive. However, the scheme to be presented is not unduly complex and offers some compensating advantages. The arrangement can be adapted for use with either voltage-source or current-source inverters, which will be described and analyzed in that order. Extension of the technique to self-commutated frequency changers is then proposed.

VOLTAGE-SOURCE INVERTERS

The arrangement of a phase leg is shown in Fig. 1. Each main switching branch consists of a GTO G, an anti-parallel diode D, and a snubber capacitor C_s. There is no series impedance between the p and n branches which are directly across the dc voltage source E_d. An auxiliary switching branch connects the ac load terminal via a snubber inductance L_s and a pair of anti-parallel ordinary thyristors S_p and S_n to the juncture of a pair of equal capacitors C_{op}, C_{on} which are connected in series across the dc source. These capacitors may be a center-tapped dc filter capacitor. Since high-voltage capacitors often consist of low-voltage sections internally connected in series, it may only be necessary to bring out a tap. Seen from the auxiliary branch, the arrangement is equivalent to a single capacitance $C_o = 2C_o$ connected to the midpoint $E_d/2$ of the dc source. A similar arrangement using power transistors for the main switching devices has been proposed [6]. Note that series strings of devices may be used in the switching branches for high-voltage operation, with no special difficulty.

Operation of the snubber is shown in Fig. 2, depicting commutation of the load terminal from the positive rail p to the negative rail n under varying load conditions. The positive direction of load current I_L is defined in Fig. 1, and it will be considered as a constant-current source throughout any given commutating interval. Ideal switching of the GTOs and thyristors is assumed (negligible rise and fall times) and stray inductances will be neglected. The load terminal voltage with respect to the negative rail is e.

With the load current I_L maximum and negative, Fig. 2(a), the GTO G_p is initially conducting. When G_p is turned off by a reverse gate pulse, the current is transferred to the snubber capacitors and shared equally while charging C_{sp} and discharging C_{sn} at the same rate. Thus, the total effective snubber capacitance is $C_S = 2C_s$ and the switching time from the positive rail $(e=E_d)$ to the negative rail (e=0) is

$$T_{OFF} = \frac{C_S E_d}{I_{OFF}}$$

Diode D_n now conducts and takes over the load current from the snubber capacitors. This turn-off switching mode traps no energy and is, ideally, lossless. While thyristor S_n receives a firing pulse some time T_Δ after GTO G_p is turned off, it is reverse biased at this time and does not conduct. For the maximum load condition, $T_{OFF} \approx T_\Delta$ may be typical, as indicated in Fig. 2.

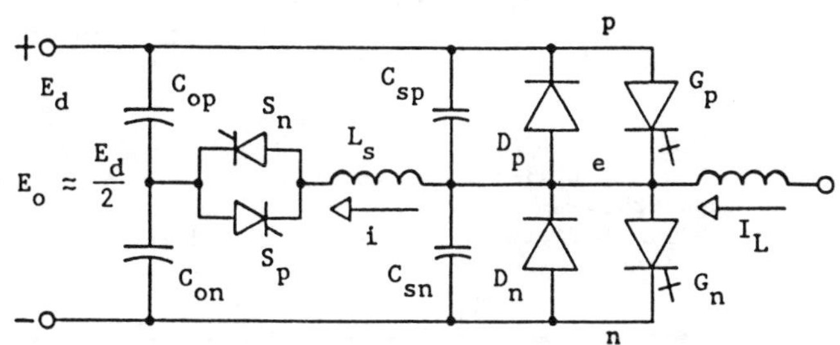

Fig. 1 Voltage-source inverter leg with resonant snubber

Reprinted from *IEEE/IAS Ann. Meet. Conf. Rec.*, pp. 829–834, 1989.

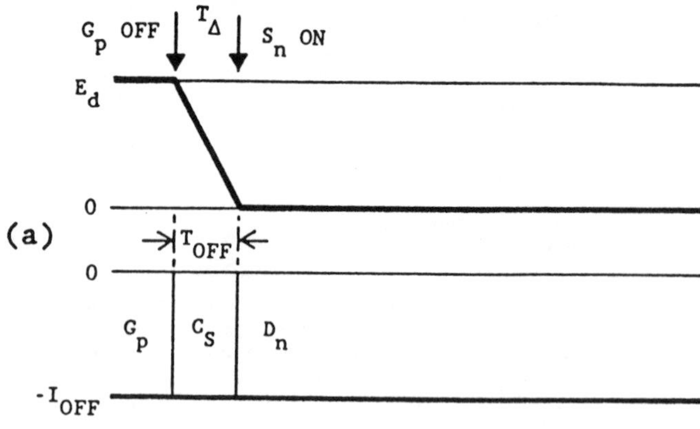

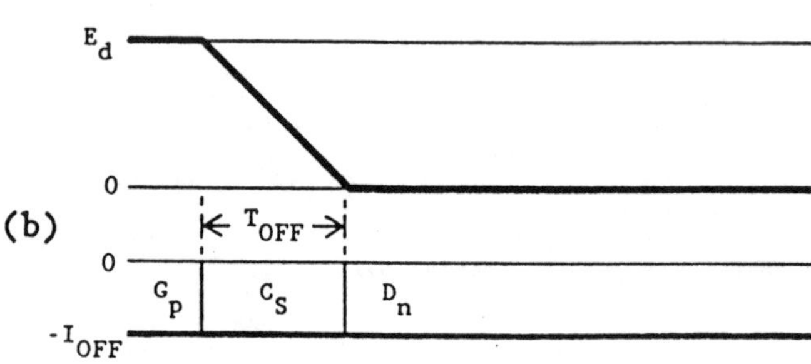

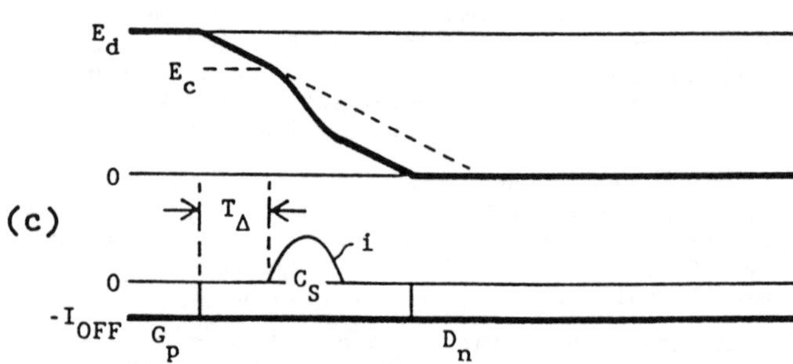

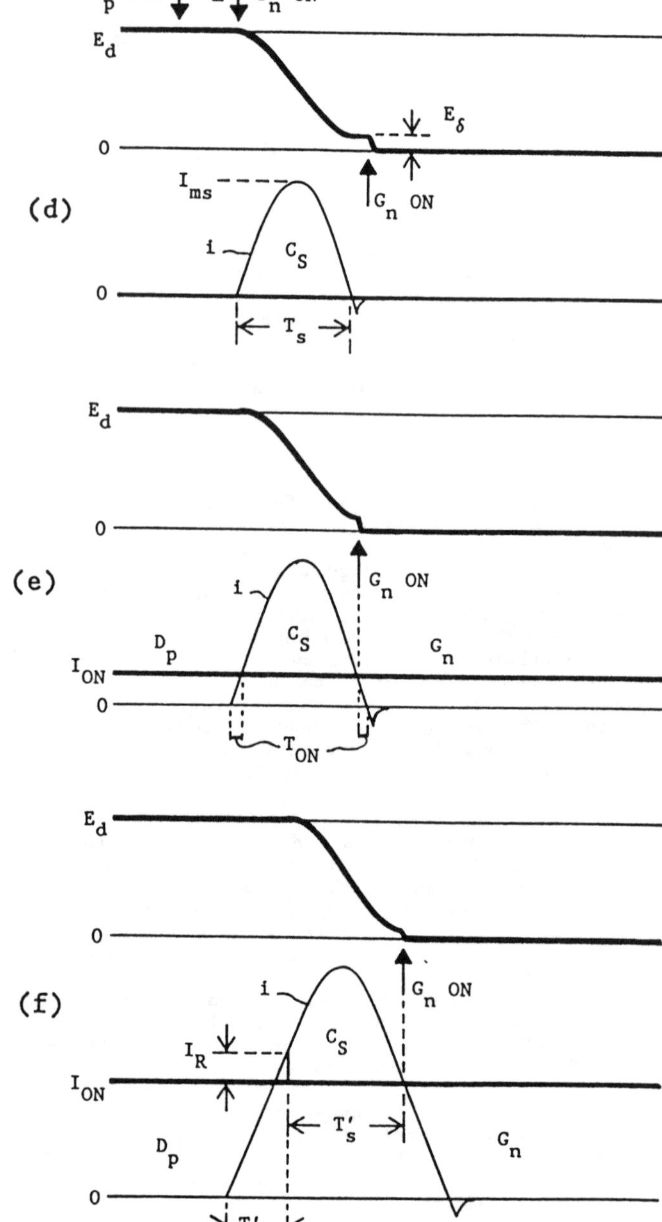

Fig. 2 Waveforms of load terminal voltage (top), load current and snubber current (bottom)
(a) Large negative load current
(b) Intermediate negative load current
(c) Small negative load current
(d) Zero load current
(e) Small positive load current
(f) Large positive load current

At half-load, shown in Fig. 2(b), T_{OFF} is doubled and the voltage on thyristor S_n is zero at the time it is fired, so it still does not conduct. This assumes that the midpoint voltage E_o of the capacitors C_{op}, C_{on} is exactly $E_d/2$. At lighter loads, Fig. 2(c), thyristor S_n becomes forward biased and conducts when it is fired. Analysis of operation in this range will be deferred.

At no load ($I_L=0$), Fig. 2(d), the terminal voltage is held at the positive rail by the charge on the snubber capacitors after G_p is turned off. Discharge begins when thyristor S_n turns on and, ideally, follows the equations

$$e = \frac{E_d}{2} (1 + \cos \omega t)$$

$$i = \frac{E_d}{2} \sqrt{\frac{C_S}{L_S}} \sin \omega t$$

where $\omega = 1/\sqrt{L_S C_S}$ and it is assumed that $C_O >> C_S$.

Switching is completed at time $T_S = \pi \sqrt{L_S C_S}$ where $e = 0$ and GTO G_n can be turned on with no loss. Thus, this mode of switching is also lossless and traps no energy under ideal conditions.

However, imperfections arise because of ohmic losses in the components and because the voltage E_o may not exactly equal $E_d/2$. More exact equations are

$$e = E_d - (E_d - E_o) \frac{C'_S}{C_S} \left[1 - \exp\left(-\frac{\omega' t}{2Q_s}\right) \cos \omega' t\right] \qquad (1)$$

$$i = (E_d - E_o) \sqrt{\frac{C'_S}{L_S}} \exp\left(-\frac{\omega' t}{2Q_s}\right) \sin \omega' t \qquad (2)$$

where Q_s = quality factor of ringing snubber circuit,

$$C'_S = \frac{C_S C_O}{C_S + C_O} \quad \text{and} \quad \omega' = \sqrt{\frac{1-1/(2Q_s)^2}{L_S C'_S}}$$

At time $\omega' t = \pi$, the current i returns to zero and thyristor S_n blocks. The voltage $e = E_\delta$ at this time is

$$E_\delta = E_d - (E_d - E_o) \frac{C'_S}{C_S} \left[1 + \exp\left(- \frac{\pi}{2Q_s} \right) \right]$$

The value of E_δ may be positive or negative, depending upon E_o, C_O and Q_s. If $E_o = E_d/2$ and $C_O >> C_S$, then the effect of losses alone results in

$$E_\delta \approx \frac{E_d}{2} \left[1 - \exp\left(- \frac{\pi}{2Q_s} \right) \right] \approx \frac{\pi E_d}{4Q_s} \quad \text{if } Q_s >> \frac{\pi}{2}$$

which is always positive. Discharge of the snubber capacitors is completed when GTO G_n is turned on and involves a turn-on switching loss W_{ON} absorbed by the GTO

$$W_{ON} = \frac{1}{2} C_S E_\delta^2 = \frac{1}{2} C_S \left(\frac{E_d}{2} \right)^2 \left(\frac{\pi}{Q_s} \right)^2$$

There may be some additional GTO losses due to the reverse recovery charge of thyristor S_n and its snubber. For $Q_s = 20$, the loss due to the residual capacitor discharge is about 2.5% of the stored energy. If $E_o > E_d/2$, the values of E_δ and W_{ON} will be greater. However, if $E_o < E_d/2$, the value of E_δ may be negative, in which case the diode D_n will have conducted before $\omega' t = \pi$ and terminated discharge with $E_\delta \approx 0$, so there will be no GTO turn-on loss.

For the cases $I_L > 0$, Fig. 2(e) and (f), the diode D_p will be conducting initially and must be extinguished before the snubber capacitors begin to discharge. When thyristor S_n turns on, the current $I_L = I_{ON}$ transfers from D_p to S_n, L_S and C_O in a time

$$T_{ON} = \frac{2L_S I_{ON}}{E_d}$$

If the recovery of diode D_p is neglected, as in Fig. 2(e), then the capacitor discharge follows according to (1) with the current i in inductance L_S increased above the level I_{ON} by the sine pulse (2).

However, if diode D_p is assumed to have a peak reverse recovery current I_R, the time to blocking is increased to

$$T'_{ON} = \frac{2L_S(I_{ON} + I_R)}{E_d}$$

as shown in Fig. 2(f) and the subsequent capacitor discharge equations are modified to include terms involving I_R. The terminal voltage e now reaches a minimum when the current falls back below the level I_{ON} at time T'_S found by solving

$$\tan \omega' T'_S = - \frac{I_R}{E_d - E_o} \sqrt{\frac{L_S}{C'_S}}$$

where the angle is slightly less than π. Again assuming $E_o = E_d/2$ and $C_O >> C_S$, the minimum voltage E_δ becomes

$$E_\delta \approx \frac{E_d}{2} - \sqrt{\left(\frac{E_d}{2} \right)^2 + I_R^2 \frac{L_S}{C'_S}} \exp\left(- \frac{\pi}{2Q_s} \right)$$

The effect of the extra initial energy $\frac{1}{2} L_S I_R^2$ due to the diode recovery current trapped in the inductance will be to offset the subsequent discharge losses and reduce the value of E_δ, relieving the turn-on duty of GTO G_n if it is gated at the proper time.

It can be seen from Fig. 2(d)-(f) that the optimum time for turning on the GTO varies with the load current I_{ON} and is best determined by monitoring the current in the snubber capacitors for a zero crossing. The gate turn-on pulse should be locked out until such a zero crossing is detected, or the voltage has been reduced to zero under conditions where $I_L < 0$, Fig. 2(a)-(c). After the GTO G_n turns on, the current I_{ON} is transferred from the auxiliary path S_n-L_S-C_O to the GTO at the same di/dt rate and in the same time T_{ON} as before. The reverse recovery current of thyristor S_n causes a small overshoot in the turn-on current.

The charge ΔQ that must be absorbed by the auxiliary capacitors C_o during this switching process is, neglecting second-order effects,

$$\Delta Q = I_{ON}(T_{ON} + T_S) + C_S E_d$$

The resultant change $\Delta E_o = \Delta Q / C_O$ in the midpoint voltage should be very much smaller than the nominal value $E_o = E_d/2$, or

$$\frac{I_{ON}}{C_O} \left(\frac{2L_S I_{ON}}{E_d} + \pi \sqrt{L_S C_S} \right) + \frac{C_S E_d}{C_O} << \frac{E_d}{2}$$

This is a basic criterion for selecting the value of auxiliary capacitance C_O. In a square-wave inverter, charge pulses to C_O will alternate with discharge pulses of the same magnitude (in steady-state operation), so C_O can be relatively small. However, in each phase leg of a PWM inverter, successive commutations are often of the opposite type (i.e., GTO-to-diode followed by diode-to-GTO) so that there will be many charge pulses before the output polarity reverses to start a compensating train of discharge pulses. In a half-bridge circuit, this will probably restrict usage to the arrangement where the main filter capacitor is center-tapped. In bridge circuits, the several phase legs will be in different phases of the output cycle, tending to balance the charge/discharge action, so smaller auxiliary capacitors may be used to establish a dc midpoint.

Returning to the light-load condition Fig. 2(c), with I_L negative ($I_{OFF} = -I_L$) in the approximate range

$$0 < I_{OFF} < \frac{C_S E_d}{2T_\Delta} ,$$

the snubber capacitor/load terminal voltage e will have reached a value E_c at the time thyristor S_n is fired:

$$E_c = E_d - \frac{I_{OFF} T_\Delta}{C_S}$$

With $E_o < E_c < E_d$, the equations for the discharge pulse through S_n and L_S are, assuming $C_O >> C_S$ and neglecting losses,

$$e = E_o + (E_c - E_o) \cos \omega t - I_{OFF} \sqrt{\frac{L_S}{C_S}} \sin \omega t$$

$$i = (E_c - E_o) \sqrt{\frac{C_S}{L_S}} \sin \omega t - I_{OFF}(1 - \cos \omega t)$$

As shown in Fig. 2(c), the current pulse is the peak of a sine wave that swings e from $E_o + (E_c - E_o)$ to $E_o - (E_c - E_o)$ in less than π radians. Thyristor S_n then blocks and the voltage transition is completed at the original rate $de/dt = -I_{OFF}/C_S$.

CURRENT-SOURCE INVERTERS

A single-phase current-source inverter using symmetrical reverse blocking GTOs G_a and G_b with this same type of resonant snubber is shown in Fig. 3. It requires a center-tap on the ac side for connection of the auxiliary thyristor S with series snubber inductance L_S, as well as for coupling to the ac system or load. This is the dual of a half-bridge voltage source

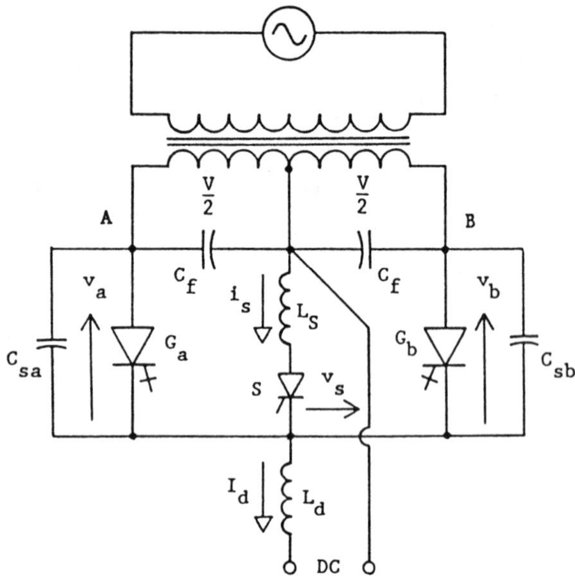

Fig. 3 Current-source inverter with resonant snubber

inverter (Fig. 1), where a center-tap on the dc side is needed for the auxiliary branch, as well as for the return terminal of a single-phase ac load. Again, this lossless snubber scheme can easily be incorporated into a high-voltage circuit using series strings of devices.

The terms "voltage source" and "current source" describe the nature of the dc side, including the dc filter, and the load or system on the ac side should be a "source" of the opposite type. That is, the load on a current-source inverter should be an ac voltage source, as indicated in Fig. 3 by the sine-wave generator $V_m \sin \omega t$. However, the leakage inductance of the transformer renders the voltage source imperfect, as seen at the inverter output terminals, and filter capacitors C_f will generally be required. The interaction between these capacitors and the system inductance is not in the scope of this study.

To simplify the description and analysis of snubber action, it will be assumed that the commutating time is very much shorter than the ac period so that the ac side can be represented by ideal constant voltage sources V/2. If α is the switching angle of the GTOs, or the time is t_α, then

$$V = V_m \sin \omega t_\alpha = V_m \sin \alpha.$$

For natural commutation with ordinary thyristors, α is the firing (turn-on) angle and restricted to the range 0°-180°, but self turn-off with GTOs allows the range 180°-360° to be covered as well. The mode of operation of the snubber depends on the range of α.

For commutation from GTO G_a to G_b in the self-turnoff range $180° < \alpha < 360°$, terminal A is positive with respect to B. The polarity of source voltage V is such that the incoming GTO G_b is initially reverse biased and cannot turn on. The auxiliary thyristor S is also reverse biased. Hence, commutation is accomplished by turning off the outgoing GTO G_a, and the load current I_d is temporarily shared by the snubber capacitors: the capacitor across G_a charges while the capacitor across G_b discharges. When the voltage across G_b becomes zero, it is turned on and carries the full current I_d. The rate of current transfer is limited by stray inductance in the snubber capacitor/GTO loops, which is neglected here. Ideally, there is no energy lost or trapped during commutation. The voltage and current waveforms during this commutation process are shown in Fig. 4. The commutating time T_{OFF} is simply given by

$$T_{OFF} = \frac{2C_s\,|V|}{I_d} = \frac{2C_s V_m\,|\sin \alpha|}{I_d}$$

In the external-turnoff range $0° < \alpha < 180°$, terminal B is positive with respect to A. The incoming GTO G_b is initially forward biased and, ordinarily, thyristor turn-on will produce natural commutation, with the leakage inductance of the transformer and other ac source impedance providing a "free" series snubber for limiting di/dt. However, with a large ac filter capacitance to negate the effect of source inductance and large snubber capacitors directly across the GTOs to ease their turn-off duty, there is no di/dt limit in effect for GTO turn-on. If the outgoing GTO were turned off by gate action, the voltage across the incoming GTO would be increased, making matters worse.

The purpose of the auxiliary branch with thyristor S and inductance L_S is to provide a means of accomplishing the desired commutation without undue stress or losses in any component. The action is illustrated by the waveforms shown in Fig. 5. When thyristor S is turned on, the load current I_d transfers from GTO G_n to S by action of the left-half voltage source at the rate

$$\frac{di}{dt} = \frac{V}{2L_S} = \frac{V_m \sin \alpha}{2L_S} \tag{3}$$

and transfer is completed in the time

$$T_{ON} = \frac{2L_S I_d}{V} \tag{4}$$

The time T'_{ON} in Fig. 5 allows for a reverse recovery current I_R in GTO G_a, which is turned off in the manner of an ordinary thyristor. Application of reverse gate current to G_a should be delayed until after this time.

When G_a blocks, the snubber capacitor across G_a charges while the capacitor across G_b discharges as the total capacitance $2C_s$ rings with inductance L_S, producing a peak pulse current

$$I_{ms} = \frac{V}{2}\sqrt{\frac{2C_s}{L_S}}$$

that is imposed over the load current I_d in thyristor S. After a half cycle, time $T_S = \pi\sqrt{2C_s L_S}$, the state of the capacitors is, ideally, reversed. Even though a

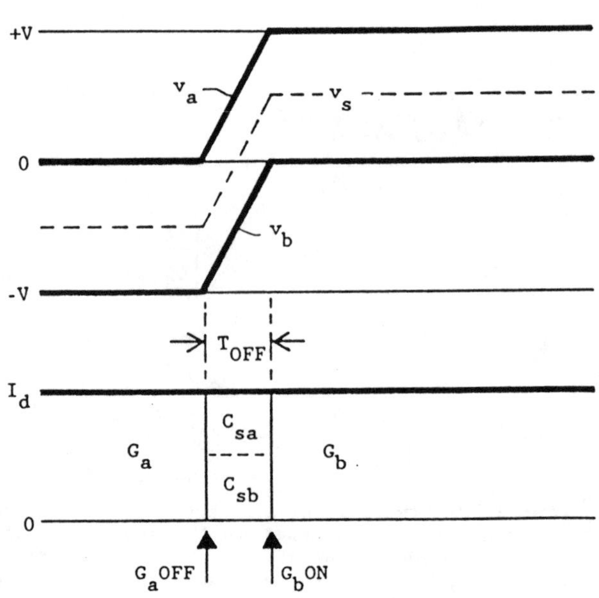

Fig. 4 Waveforms during commutation when action of auxiliary switch is unnecessary: voltages (top), currents (bottom)

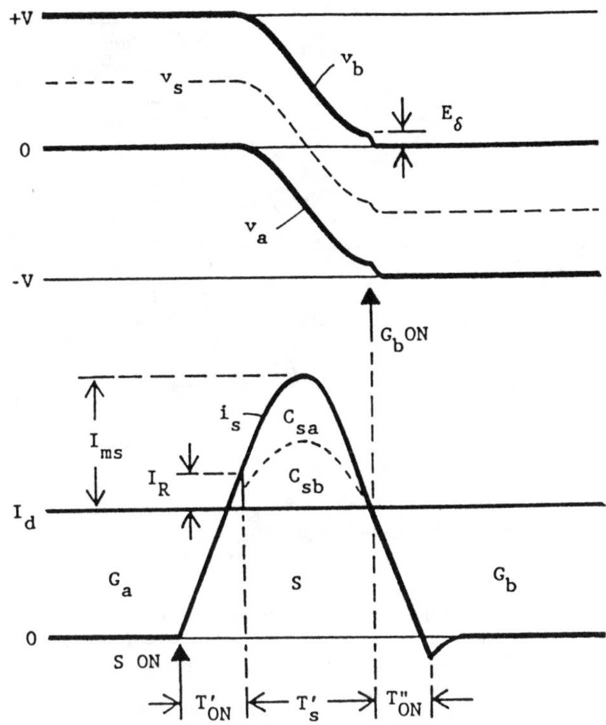

Fig. 5 Waveforms during commutation when action of auxiliary switch is necessary: voltages (top), currents (bottom)

small positive voltage E_δ may remain across GTO G_b, it can now be turned on with low loss and the load current I_d will transfer from the auxiliary branch S to GTO G_b under the action of the right-half voltage source. The rate and time of transfer are approximately the same as those given by (3) and (4), respectively. In Fig. 5, the time T''_{ON} allows for reverse recovery current in thyristor S, which then blocks to complete the commutation.

A three-phase bridge current-source converter operates as two 3-pulse commutating groups, one at each pole of the dc side. The commutating voltages are the line-to-line voltages, and midpoints are required for connection of auxiliary resonant snubber branches. If ac transformers are employed, then the converter-side windings can be connected in delta and center-tapped for the snubber branches. The leakage inductance between the two halves of the windings may suffice as the snubber inductance L_S, and a single set of ac filter capacitors can be connected in delta (or wye).

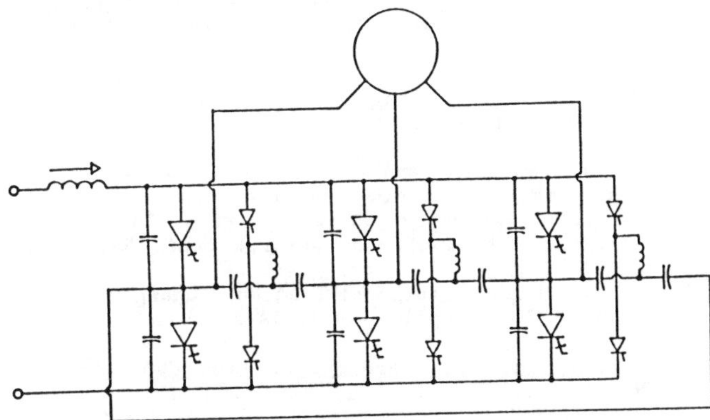

Fig. 6 Three-phase current-source inverter with center-tapped filter capacitors for connection of resonant snubbers

When no transformer is employed, as in the motor drive depicted in Fig. 6, then the ac delta filter capacitors can be center-tapped. The snubber inductors may be shared by the two commutating groups, as indicated. A commutation between two phases involves the snubber capacitors across the pair of commutating GTOs and also the capacitor across the third GTO in the same commutating group. However, the snubber capacitors in the other commutating group do not change their charge, assuming that successive commutations do not overlap. Therefore, the equations given previously for the single-phase case should be modified by substituting $3C_s$ for $2C_s$.

It can be seen that the action of this lossless snubber for a current-source inverter is quite similar to that for a voltage-source inverter. However, if the exact state of the circuit is not known, then an attempt to turn on the auxiliary thyristor should be made before (instead of after) turning off the outgoing GTO. In both cases, turning on the incoming GTO must be carefully timed and controlled as a function of load conditions.

SELF-COMMUTATED FREQUENCY CHANGERS

In converters where only one direction of current is controlled, polarized snubbers can be employed effectively. However, where both polarities of current are controlled by anti-parallel switching devices or their functional equivalent, the snubbers cannot be polarized. With conventional lossy non-polarized snubbing methods, the necessary limiting resistors impede the action of both the shunt capacitors and the series inductors. This introduces problems of snubber size and efficiency which need a solution for applications such as self-commutated frequency changers. Because the advantages of this type of converter are best achieved with high-frequency operation, switching and snubber losses must be minimized.

Since the proposed resonant snubber is non-polarized, it overcomes the problem of high switching loss in this type of application. A three-phase to single-phase self-commutated frequency changer of the cycloconverter type is derived by connecting similar anti-parallel devices across all the GTOs and thyristors in Fig. 6. The concepts of this resonant snubber can be extended to a direct 3-phase to 3-phase pulsewidth-modulated (PWM) frequency changer, operating at a frequency considerably higher than either the input or output frequencies. In the ideal minimum circuit topology, each phase of the input is connected directly to each phase of the output via a pair of anti-parallel reverse-blocking devices such as GTOs. There are a total of 18 GTOs or 9 bidirectional switches of some type in the circuit. The switches are controlled in the manner proposed by Venturini [7-8], or some similar mode [9].

Operation of the switches requires that one side (either input or output) be inductively filtered so that it appears to be a current source during the commutation interval. The other side must be capacitively filtered so that it appears to be a voltage source during this interval. Over a PWM switching cycle, these filters limit the deviation or ripple of the current or voltage, respectively, from an "average" value that varies at the input or output frequency. In a motor drive system, the machine inductance will be sufficient to provide voltage-averaging at the output and a set of relatively small filter capacitors can provide current-averaging at the input. This reduces the number of filters required in the system to an absolute minimum.

At low-to-medium power levels, it might be possible to switch efficiently enough without snubbers. However, at medium-to-high power levels, it is expected that snubbers will become necessary. In operation of a direct PWM frequency changer between commutations, each inductively filtered terminal must be connected to one and only one of the capacitively filtered terminals by a closed switch (turned-on device). Commutation involves turning off this switch and turning on another, to connect the inductively filtered terminal to another one of the capacitively filtered terminals. The lossless snubber switch needed to assist this commutation in certain modes must be connected to a node midway in potential between the pair of capacitively filtered terminals.

These midway nodes are conveniently obtained by splitting at least part of the filter capacitance into series-connected pairs C_f across each pair of lines, as shown in Fig. 7. The snubber switches are connected to these midpoint nodes via series snubber inductances. The main power links between the inductively filtered terminals **a**,**b**,**c** and the capacitively filtered terminals **A**,**B**,**C** are shown by heavy lines in Fig. 7, while the lossless snubber links between the terminals **a**,**b**,**c** and the midpoint terminals **AB**,**BC**,**CA** are shown by light lines. For clarity, Fig. 7 shows only one main power switch, including a snubber capacitance C_s connected directly across its terminals, and only one snubber switch with series inductance L_s.

Two modes of commutation occur in this frequency changer. For illustration, it is assumed that the PWM control requests terminal **b** to switch from terminal **A** to terminal **B** at a time when terminal **A** is more positive than terminal **B** in voltage potential. In the first mode, the current I_b flows from terminal **b** into its filter inductance L_F. In this case, it is only necessary to turn off the conducting device in the link **bA** to start commutation and to turn on the device in the link **bB** to complete commutation after the current I_b has charged the snubber capacitor in the link **bA** and has discharged the snubber capacitor in the link **bB**. The relative voltage and current polarities allow this to happen, and no action of a snubber link is required.

In the second mode, the current I_b has the opposite polarity at the time of commutation. In this case, turning off the conducting device in the link **bA** would cause the current I_b to charge the snubber capacitors in both the link **bA** and the link **bB** such that the potential of terminal **b** would be driven higher than terminal **A**. To turn on, the device in the link **bB** would first have to discharge these snubber capacitors and absorb their stored energy as losses. The difficulty is avoided by first turning on the snubber switch in the link **b-AB**, beginning an intermediate stage of commutation. This turns off the conducting device in the link **bA** by external commutation, and then properly discharges the snubber capacitors to drive the potential of terminal **b** towards the level of terminal **B**. When the potential difference between these terminals is a minimum, it becomes possible to turn on the device in the link **bB** to complete commutation with very low loss.

CONCLUSION

While resonant snubbers introduce considerable complexity, including auxiliary active devices and their controls, the proposed arrangement is not unreasonable if care is taken in design. It should be emphasized that the snubber switches are very much smaller in current rating than the main power switches, and are also much smaller than the auxiliary commutating switches used to turn off conventional thyristors in many present applications. The snubber switches are comparable in size to the snubber diodes used to polarize conventional snubbers.

Resonant snubbers with individual auxiliary switches in each phase have the same advantages as the

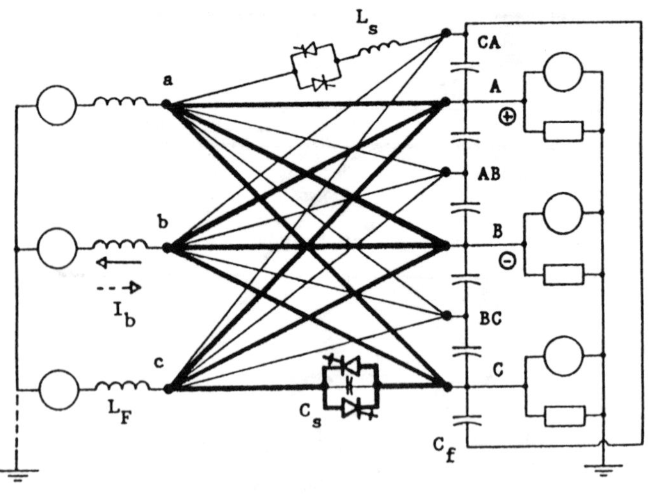

Fig. 7 Self-commutated PWM direct frequency changer with resonant snubbers

so-called "resonant dc link converter" [10], while avoiding its disadvantages such as voltage overshoots, complex controls to regulate the link voltage, continuous oscillation of the dc link voltage, and restriction of switching to discrete intervals. The expense of split filter capacitors and auxiliary thyristors, with more complex firing arrangements for both the thyristors and the main switching devices (GTOs or transistors), is offset by a number of advantages.

REFERENCES

[1] W. McMurray, "Selection of Snubbers and Clamps to Optimize the Design of Transistor Switching Converters," IEEE Trans. Ind. Appl., Vol. IA-16, No. 4, 1980, pp. 513-523.

[2] W. McMurray, "Efficient Snubbers for Voltage Source GTO Inverters," IEEE Trans. Power Electronics, Vol. PE-2, No. 3, July 1987, pp. 264-272.

[3] G. Fregien, H.G. Langer, H-C. Skudelny, "A Regenerative Snubber for a 200 kVA GTO-Inverter," Conf. Rec. IEEE-PESC, 1988, pp. 498-505.

[4] J. Holtz, S.F. Salama, and K-H. Werner, "A Nondissipative Snubber Circuit for High-Power GTO-Inverters," Conf. Rec. IEEE-IAS Ann. Meeting, 1987, pp. 613-618.

[5] J.C. Bendien, H.V.D. Broeck, G. Fregien, "Recovery Circuit for Snubber Energy in Power Electronic Applications with High Switching Frequencies," IEEE Trans. Power Electronics, Vol. PE-3, No. 1, January 1988, pp. 26-30.

[6] G. Bingen, "Utilisation de Transistors a Fort Courant et Tension Elevee," Proc. First European Conference on Power Electronics and Applications, 1985, Vol. 1, pp. 1.15-1.20.

[7] M. Venturini, "A New Sine Wave In, Sine Wave Out, Conversion Technique Eliminates Reactive Elements," Proc. Powercon 7, 1980, pp. E3-1 - E3-15.

[8] M.G.B. Venturini and A. Alesina, "The Generalized Transformer: A New Bidirectional Sinusoidal Waveform Frequency Converter with Continuously Adjustable Input Power Factor," Conf. Rec. IEEE-PESC, 1980, pp. 242-252.

[9] X. Ma, "High-Performance Frequency Changers," IEEE Trans. Ind. Appl., Vol. IA-22, No. 2, 1986, pp. 267-280.

[10] D.M. Divan, "The Resonant DC Link Converter - A New Concept in Static Power Conversion," Conf. Rec. IEEE-IAS Ann. Meeting, 1986, pp. 648-656.

[11] G.L. Skibinski and D.M. Divan, "Characterization of Power Transistors under Zero Voltage Switching," Conf. Rec. IEEE-IAS Ann. Meeting, 1987, pp. 493-503.

Paper 6.2

A New Current Source GTO Inverter with Sinusoidal Output Voltage and Current

MITSUYUKI HOMBU, SENIOR MEMBER, IEEE, SHIGETA UEDA, AKITERU UEDA, MEMBER, IEEE, AND YASUO MATSUDA

Abstract—**A new current source inverter with sinusoidal output voltage and current is presented. Gate turn-off thyristors (GTO's) and pulsewidth modulation (PWM) control techniques are used in the current source inverter to produce the sinusoidal output voltage and current. Three capacitors are connected to the ac output terminals to absorb overvoltages which occur when the GTO current is cut off and to provide a filter function for reducing harmonics in the output current. Voltage spikes, which have been a serious problem in the practical application of this inverter, are suppressed by adding gate pulses which force the inverter into a state of shoot-through. Moreover, this inverter permits the capacitance of an ac output terminal capacitor for absorbing overvoltages to be reduced to one-tenth or less of that of a commutating capacitor in a conventional thyristor type current source inverter. A 3.7-kW induction motor is driven by the inverter. The motor efficiency and noise level are measured and compared with those obtained when the motor is driven by a conventional voltage source PWM inverter. An operating efficiency five or six percent higher and noise level 10 dB lower are obtained for the former. Therefore, this current source GTO inverter is very suitable for ac motor variable speed drives.**

I. INTRODUCTION

VOLTAGE-SOURCE PWM inverters and thyristor type current source inverters have been widely used to drive ac motors. The output voltage of the former is pulse trains and contains many higher order harmonics as does the output current also. On the other hand, output current of the thyristor type current source inverter is a six-stepped square wave and contains many lower order harmonics, such as fifth and seventh orders. In both cases, motor losses and noise level are increased due to these harmonics which are contained in output voltages and currents. In addition, torque pulsations are produced by harmonic voltages and currents [1]–[4]. To eliminate these problems, it is necessary to reduce the harmonics contained in the output voltages and currents significantly and then to produce sinusoidal waveforms.

Recently, self-extinguishing devices, such as GTO's and transistors, have made rapid progress in their applications to voltage source inverters [5]–[7]. In the case of voltage source inverters, the commutating circuit can be omitted by using self-extinguishing devices, and the main circuit configuration can be simplified. Therefore, voltage source PWM inverters using those devices have been used because they offer energy saving operation in pumps or fans, and easy maintenance in rolling mills or transit cars [8], [9].

In the case of current source inverters, an overvoltage absorption capacitor is required even if thyristors are exchanged for self-extinguishing devices, because of the overvoltage which occurs when a current is cut off. Therefore, it appeared that there were no advantages in applying self-extinguishing devices to current source inverters.

If the overvoltage which occurs when a current is cut off can be efficiently absorbed in a simple circuit, however, advantages in applying the self-extinguishing devices to the current source inverters can be realized. A new current source inverter is presented here with sinusoidal output voltage and current. Six GTO's are used to form a three-phase bridge circuit, and overvoltage absorption capacitors are connected to ac output terminals. The PWM control which positively employs the high-speed switching performance of GTO's is introduced. In addition, the PWM control principles are studied, with the intent of reducing the harmonics contained in the output currents. As a result, the GTO can be applied to the current source inverter. Moreover, both output voltage and current can be made almost sinusoidal by a very simple circuit configuration.

In this paper, first of all, the main circuit configuration and the basic operation of this new current source GTO inverter and the PWM control principles are described. Next, the mechanism for the occurrence of voltage spikes contained in the output voltage and their suppression method are explained. Finally, the performance of an induction motor driven by this inverter is shown.

II. MAIN CIRCUIT AND CONTROL CIRCUIT CONFIGURATIONS

A. Main Circuit Configuration and Its Basic Operation

Fig. 1 shows the main circuit configuration of the current source GTO inverter with sinusoidal output and current. This inverter comprises a converter section to convert the constant-frequency ac power from the commercial power source to dc power, a reactor to smooth the dc current and an inverter section to convert the dc power to the variable-voltage variable-frequency ac power. In the inverter section, GTO's are used as switching devices to form a three-phase bridge circuit. Moreover, three capacitors are connected to the ac output terminals to absorb the overvoltages which occur when the GTO current is cut off.

Paper IPCSD 85-13, approved by the Static Power Converter Committee of the IEEE Industry Applications Society for presentation at the 1984 Industry Applications Society Annual Meeting, Chicago, IL, September 30–October 4. Manuscript released for publication February 21, 1985.

M. Hombu, S. Ueda, and A. Ueda are with the Hitachi Research Laboratory, Hitachi Ltd., 1-1, Saiwaicho 3 chome, Hitachi-shi, Ibaraki-ken, 317 Japan.

Y. Matsuda is with the Research and Development Promotion Center, Hitachi Ltd., 5-1, Marunouchi 1 chome, Chiyoda-ku, Tokyo, 100 Japan.

Reprinted from *IEEE Trans. Ind. Applicat.*, vol. IA-21, no. 5, pp. 1192–1198, September/October 1985.

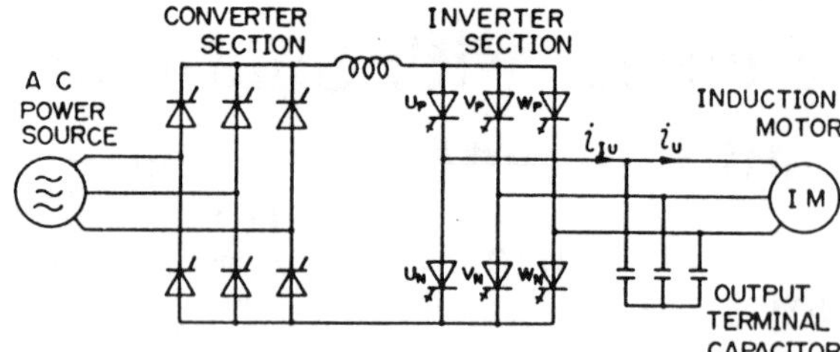

Fig. 1. Main circuit configuration.

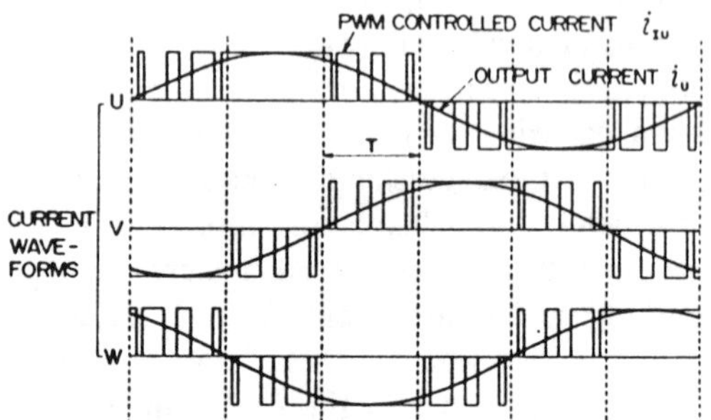

Fig. 2. Basic operation waveforms.

Fig. 2 shows the basic operation waveforms of this inverter. The sinusoidally modulated current i_{IU} is produced in the three-phase bridge circuit composed of GTO's. The overvoltage absorption capacitors which are connected to the ac output terminals function as a filter, so the output current i_U has a sinusoidal waveform. Since this inverter is a current source type, it is capable of easily producing a sinusoidal output voltage if the output current waveform can be made sinusoidal. The commutating behavior of this inverter is such that the current is gradually transferred from phase U to phase V, for example, in period T, while GTO_{UP} and GTO_{VP} are alternately repeating on–off states.

B. Generation Method of PWM Controlled Current Pattern

Fig. 3 shows the generation method of the PWM controlled current pattern. A signal is so produced as to be one when $e_m \geq e_c$ and zero when $e_m < e_c$, where e_m is a trapezoidal modulating wave and e_c is a triangular carrier wave. Thus the PWM controlled current pattern can be obtained. There are two factors to change the pattern: one is the modulation index B/A which is the ratio of modulating wave amplitude to carrier wave amplitude, and the other is pulse number M in a half-cycle of inverter operation. The harmonics in the output current vary by changing these factors. Fig. 4 shows calculated results for the relation between modulation index and harmonics in the PWM controlled current at $M = 83$. In general, the higher the modulation index is, the fewer the harmonics that will be contained. Based on Fig. 4, a current pattern of $B/A = 0.82$ is selected so that the PWM controlled current will contain the least number possible of harmonics, including fifth- and seventh-order harmonics.

C. Block Diagram of Control Circuit

Fig. 5 shows a block diagram of control circuit which generates the PWM controlled current pattern shown in Fig. 3.

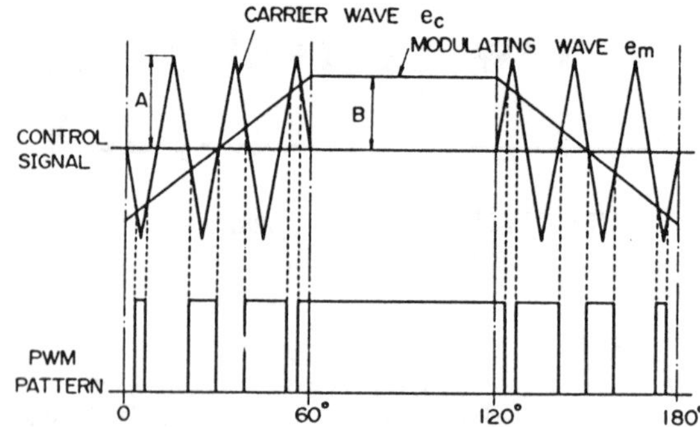

Fig. 3. PWM waveform generation method.

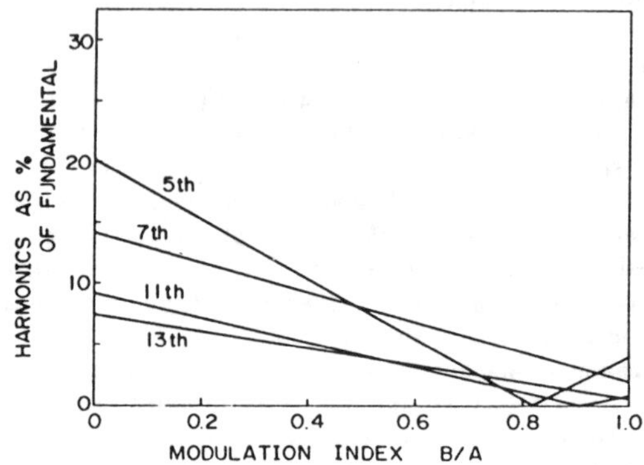

Fig. 4. Harmonics in PWM controlled current (PWM pulse number M = 83).

The control circuit is mainly composed of clock generator, counter, PWM pattern storage memory, ring counter, and PWM waveform synthesizer. In the clock generator, a clock pulse with a frequency proportional to an inverter frequency command is generated. This clock pulse is counted in the counter. Its counted value is used as the address signal for the PWM pattern storage memory composed of ROM's. In the PWM pattern storage memory, several current patterns are stored. These patterns are the sinusoidally distributed pulse trains as shown in Fig. 3. The PWM waveform synthesizer is used to synthesize the output signals of the ring counter, PWM pattern storage memory, and shoot-through pulse generator so as to obtain the gate pulses of the GTO's. The pattern selector chooses an appropriate pattern from those stored in the PWM pattern storage memory so that the GTO switching frequency will be kept nearly constant and independent of the inverter frequency. To suppress the voltage spikes in the output voltage, moreover, the shoot-through pulse generator produces gate pulses (shoot-through gate pulses) which force the inverter section into a state of shoot-through. Suppression of voltage spikes by the shoot-through gate pulses is detailed later. In the experimental equipment, two 2-kbyte ROM's are used and 16 types of current patterns are stored in the PWM pattern storage memory. The PWM current pattern is so selected as to keep GTO switching frequency at nearly 4 kHz.

III. OCCURRENCE MECHANISM AND SUPPRESSION METHOD OF VOLTAGE SPIKES

A. Occurrence Mechanism of Voltage Spikes

Fig. 6 shows the output voltage and current waveforms of this current source GTO inverter driving an induction motor in

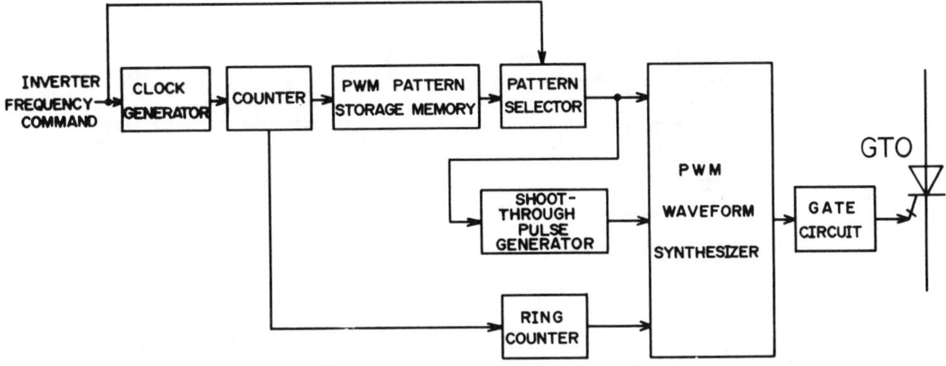

Fig. 5. Block diagram of control circuit.

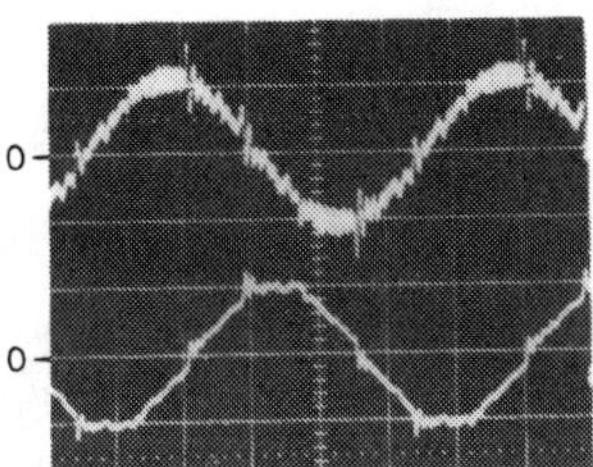

Fig. 6. Output waveforms (inverter frequency f_I = 20 Hz, capacitance of output terminal capacitor C = 5 μF). Upper: output voltage 200 V/div. Lower: output current 10A/div. Horizontal: 10 ms/div.

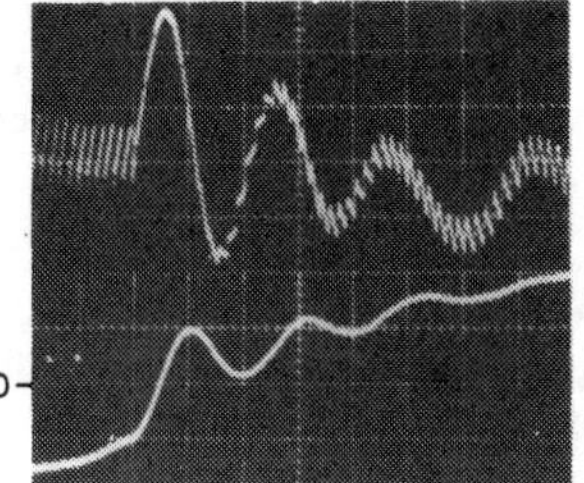

Fig. 7. Expanded waveform of voltage spike. Upper: output voltage 50 V/div. Lower: output current: 2 A/div. Horizontal: 500 μs/div.

the no-load condition. The capacity of the inverter is 15 kVA, its rated output voltage is 400 V, and rated output current is 21.6 A. From this figure, it can be seen that both output voltage and current waveforms closely approximate sine waves. Voltage spikes, however, occur when the output current polarity is changed from negative to positive or vice versa.

Fig. 7 shows an expanded waveform of the voltage spike. The peak value of this voltage spike is 340 V, which is approximately 1.5 times the crest value of the fundamental voltage. When voltage spikes occur, high-voltage GTO's are required. Under some output capacitance or PWM controlled pattern conditions, voltage spikes that would break down the GTO's will occur. Voltage spikes, therefore, are a very serious problem in practical applications of this inverter.

Fig. 8 shows the gate pulses and main circuit conditions which are used to explain the mechanism by which voltage spikes occur. At time t_0, the polarity of PWM controlled current i_{IU} changes from negative to positive. Prior to t_0, the PWM controlled current is gradually transferred from phase U to phase V while GTO_{UN} and GTO_{VN} are alternately repeating on–off states. After t_0, the PWM controlled current is gradually transferred from phase W to phase U while GTO_{WP} and GTO_{UP} are alternately repeating on–off states. Fig. 8(b) shows the circuit conditions under which both GTO_{WP} and GTO_{VN} are on states. During this period, two current-paths are dominant: one is the path along which the current from the dc circuit flows through GTO_{WP}, motor phase W, motor phase V, GTO_{VN} and back to the dc circuit. This current path is referred to as loop 1 hereinafter. The other is the path along which the current circulates through the capacitor of phase U, capacitor of phase V, motor phase V and motor phase U. This path is referred to as loop 2. The current in loop 2 is relatively small as compared with that in loop 1. When GTO_{UP} is turned on and GTO_{WP} is turned off at time t_1, the circuit has the condition shown in Fig. 8(c). The current from the dc circuit is transferred from loop 1 to loop 3. Loop 3 is the path along which the current flows through GTO_{UP}, capacitor of phase U, capacitor of phase W, motor phase W, motor phase V, GTO_{VN}, and back to the dc circuit. Since the current in loop 2 is flowing from motor phase U to the inverter as illustrated at t_1, the current from the dc circuit flows into the capacitor of phase U more easily than into the motor phase U. This is the reason why the current is transferred from loop 1 and loop 3. In loop 3, the energy from the dc circuit flows into and overcharges the capacitor of phase U. This phenomenon functions as a trigger, and the current in loop 2 resonates. The voltage spikes are caused by this resonance. After t_2, operations shown in Fig. 8(b) and (c) are repeated and the capacitor of phase U is charged every time when GTO_{UP} is turned on. As a result, the voltage between phase U and V rises gradually. While such operations are continuing, the current in loop 2 is reduced and its polarity is inverted. At this moment, the voltage spike has a maximum value. Since the current in loop 2 flows so as to discharge the capacitor of phase U after its polarity is inverted, the dc current flows easily into the motor phase U. After that, the oscillation of the current in loop 2 continues for a while, and it gradually decays. The occurrence mechanism for the voltage spikes can be summarized as follows. The energy from the dc circuit flows into the output terminal capacitors when the polarity of

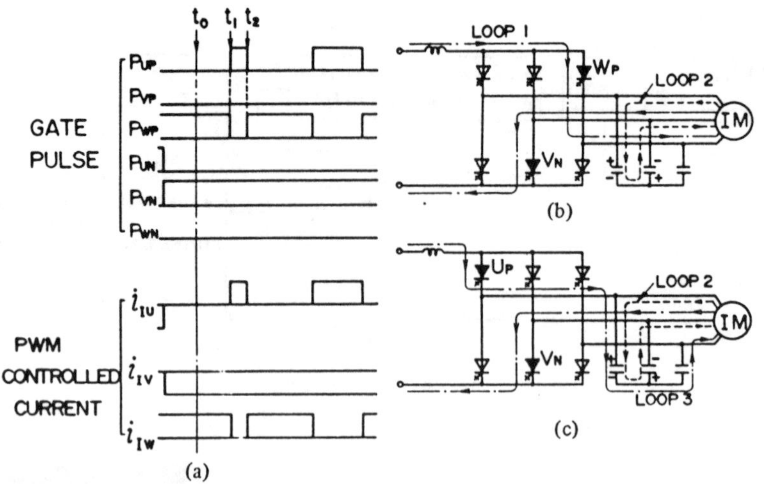

Fig. 8. Occurrence mechanism of voltage spikes. (a) Gate pulses and PWM controlled current waveforms. (b), (c) Conditions in main circuit. (b) $t_0 \leq t < t_1$. (c) $t_1 \leq t < t_2$.

the PWM controlled current is inverted and the resonance between the capacitors and induction motor is excited. As a result, the voltage spikes occur.

B. Suppression Method of Voltage Spikes

As can be seen from the aforementioned mechanism, it is necessary to suppress voltage spikes so that the output capacitor is prevented from overcharging when the polarity of the PWM controlled current is inverted. In a current source inverter, dc power source is regarded as the current source. Therefore, the shoot-through state in which both positive and negative arm GTO's in the inverter are switched on at the same time is quite allowable in main circuit operations if its period is short enough, while shoot-through state is prohibited in the voltage source inverter. Fig. 9 shows the suppression method of voltage spikes. This method effectively uses the phenomenon that the three-phase bridge circuit consisting of GTO's is separated from the motor containing the output terminal capacitors during the shoot-through state mentioned earlier. Pulses S_1–S_5 (dark lines shown in Fig. 9(a)) are the gate pulses which simultaneously turn on both positive and negative arm GTO's so that the inverter is forced into the shoot-through state. The polarity of the PWM controlled current i_{IU} is inverted at t_0. The main circuit operation during the period of $t_0 \leq t < t_1$ is the same as that of Fig. 8(b).

In the case of Fig. 9, the shoot-through gate pulse S_2 is supplied to GTO_{UN} at t_1. This point is different from that in Fig. 8. As shown in Fig. 9(c), therefore, GTO_{UP} and GTO_{UN} are turned on at the same time so that the inverter is put into a shoot-through state. This state continues until t_1'. During the period of $t_1 \leq t < t_1'$, the current from the dc circuit flows through GTO_{UP}, GTO_{UN}, and back to the dc circuit. This current path is referred to as loop 4. In addition, loop 5 is also formed, providing the path along which the current circulates through the capacitor of phase V, capacitor of phase W, motor phase W, and motor phase V. Since the inverter is put into the shoot-through state during the period of $t_1 \leq t < t_1'$, the current which flows through motor phase V and W cannot flow through the GTO's for this period. As a result, this current

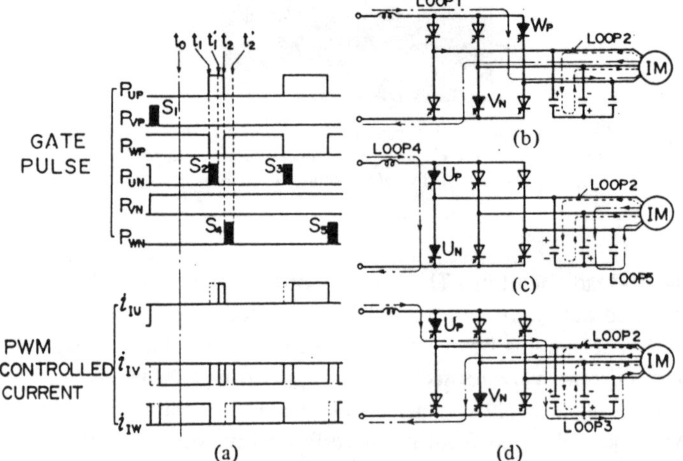

Fig. 9. Suppression method of voltage spikes. (a) Gate pulses and PWM controlled current waveforms. (b)–(d) Conditions in main circuit. (b) $t_0 \leq t < t_1$. (c) $t_1 \leq t < t_1'$. (d) $t_1' \leq t < t_2$.

flows into the output capacitors. This current path is loop 5. In the shoot-through mode shown in Fig. 9(c), the current from the dc circuit flows so as to bypass the output capacitors. Therefore, the capacitors are not overcharged. At t_1', shoot-through gate pulse disappears, and GTO_{UN} is turned off while GTO_{VN} is turned on. Then the main circuit has the condition as shown in Fig. 9(d), which is the same as Fig. 8(c). During the period of $t_1' \leq t < t_2$, the dc current overcharges the output capacitor as already mentioned. When GTO_{WP} and GTO_{WN} are turned on at t_2, the inverter is put into the shoot-through state again, the same as in Fig. 9(c). The inverter is put into the shoot-through state in phase U as shown in Fig. 9(c) during the period of $t_1 \leq t < t_1'$, while the inverter is put into the shoot-through in phase W during the period of $t_2 \leq t < t_2'$. At t_2', the current flows again through GTO_{WP} and GTO_{VN}, and the inverter is put into the same state as that of Fig 9(b). Subsequently, similar operations are repeated. Unless shoot-through gate pulses are added, the main circuit is transferred from the condition of Fig. 9(b) directly to Fig. 9(d) in which the output capacitor is overcharged. When shoot-through gate pulses are added, on the other hand, the main circuit is transferred to the condition Fig. 9(d) after having a period of shoot-through mode. So, the period of Fig. 9(d) during which the output capacitor is overcharged can be shortened by the time corresponding to the shoot-through gate pulsewidth. Moreover, the current in loop 5, which is formed in the shoot-through mode, charges the capacitor of phase V in the direction opposite to that of the current in loop 2 so that it functions to lower the voltage between phases U and V. In other words, adding the shoot-through gate pulses shortens the period during which the output capacitor is overcharged. Another current loop is formed in the direction of cancelling the overcharge. The voltage spikes are suppressed by these two effects.

Fig. 10 shows the gate pulses and current waveforms in one cycle of the inverter operations. During the period for which shoot-through gate pulses are added, the PWM controlled current becomes zero. Therefore, this current waveform is pulsewidth modulated for the period of 360°, while in the case of Fig. 2 the current is not pulsewidth modulated during 60°.

Fig. 11 shows the effect of shoot-through gate pulses for voltage spikes suppression. As shown there, voltage spikes are evaluated in the overshoot voltage ΔV, which is proportional to dc current I_D. The overshoot voltage ΔV is greatly decreased by adding the shoot-through gate pulses. If the output capacitor has a capacitance of 5 μF, ΔV decreases by half or less in comparison with the case without shoot-through gate pulses. For I_D = 10 A and C = 5 μF, for instance, overshoot voltage ΔV reaches 676 V in the case of a conventional thyristor type current source inverter. By using shoot-through gate pulses, ΔV is only 50 V from Fig. 11. This is less than one-tenth of the overshoot voltage in the conventional type. From these, it can be seen that the capacitance of an overvoltage absorption capacitor is reduced remarkably as compared with the capacitance of a commutating capacitor in a thyristor type current source inverter. In the 15 kVA equipment used for the experiments, the capacitance of the capacitor is reduced to one-tenth or less of that for a conventional type inverter.

Fig. 12 shows one example of the output voltage and current waveforms in the cases with shoot-through gate pulses. The voltage spikes are suppressed, and both voltage and current waveforms are very nearly sinusoidal in comparison with those shown in Fig. 6. Fig. 13 shows expanded waveform of the voltage spike. From the figure, it is obvious that the oscillation of output current is remarkably reduced as compared with Fig. 7, resulting in voltage spike suppression.

IV. OUTPUT VOLTAGE AND CURRENT WAVEFORMS

As the voltage spikes which appeared in the output voltage can be suppressed by adding the shoot-through gate pulses, the inverter is used to drive an induction motor. Fig. 14 shows the waveforms obtained when the inverter frequency is changed. In this case, the capacitance of the output capacitor is 5 μF. Over a wide range of inverter frequencies, voltage spikes can be suppressed by the effect of the shoot-through gate pulses, and both output voltage and current waveforms are nearly

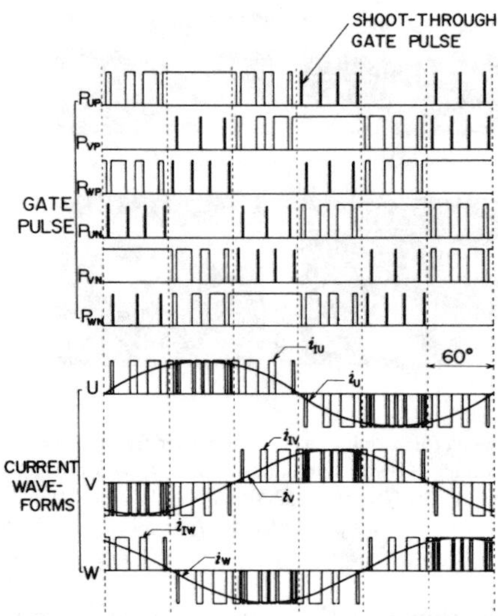

Fig. 10. Gate pulses and current waveforms with shoot-through gate pulses.

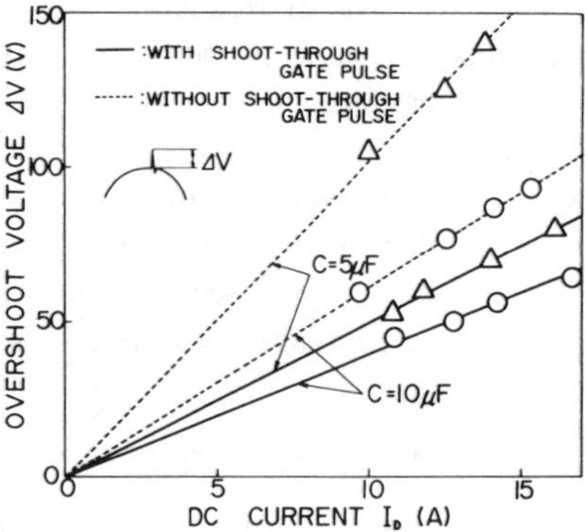

Fig. 11. Characteristics of overshoot voltage.

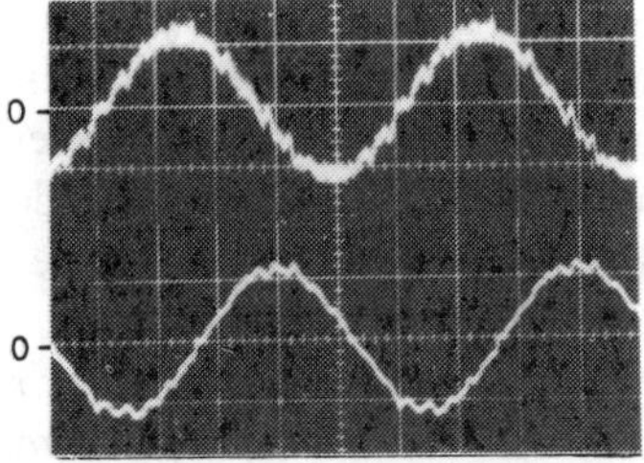

Fig. 12. Output waveforms with shoot-through gate pulses (f_I = 20 Hz, C = 5 μF). Upper: output voltage 200 V/div. Lower: output current 10 A/div. Horizontal: 10 ms/div.

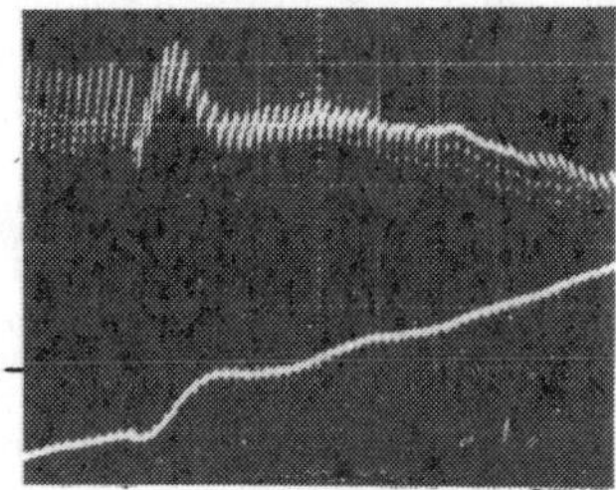

Fig. 13. Expanded waveform of voltage spike with shoot-through gate pulses (f_I = 20 Hz, C = 5 μF). Upper: Output voltage 50 V/div. Lower: output current 2 A/div. Horizontal: 500 μs/div.

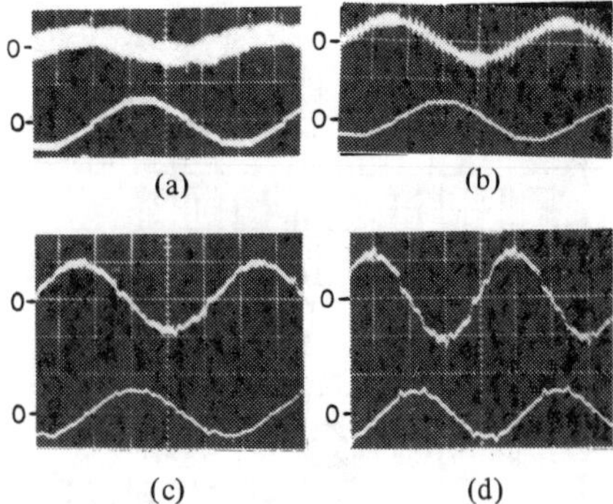

Fig. 14. Output waveforms with changing inverter frequency ($C = 5\ \mu F$). Upper: output voltage. Lower: output current. (a) $f_I = 3.8$ Hz, 100 V/div, 20 A/div, 50 ms/div. (b) $f_I = 10$ Hz, 200 V/div, 20 A/div, 20 ms/div. (c) $f_I = 40$ Hz, 500 V/div, 20 A/div, 5 ms/div. (d) $f_I = 50$ Hz, 500 V/div, 20 A/div, 5 ms/div.

sinusoidal. The ripple of the output voltage is very small, except when the inverter frequency is 3.8 Hz.

Fig. 15 shows the output voltage and current waveforms obtained when the capacitance of the output capacitor is changed. In this case, the inverter frequency is set at 20 Hz. Even if the output capacitance is 5 μF, both output voltage and current waveforms are very close to sinusoidal. The larger the capacitance is, the larger the ripple of output current is, though slight. As long as sinusoidal waveforms are produced, a larger capacitance is not desirable from the viewpoint of cost and size of the inverter. From this, it may be seen that an overvoltage absorption capacitance of 5 μF is sufficient for a 15-kVA class inverter.

V. PERFORMANCE OF INDUCTION MOTOR

As mentioned earlier, this new current source GTO inverter is capable of producing sinusoidal voltage and current waveforms. So, a 3.7-kW induction motor is driven by the inverter and its efficiency and noise level are measured to investigate the effect of waveform improvement. Fig. 16 shows these results, and for comparison, also those results obtained when a conventional type voltage source PWM inverter and a commercial power source are used to drive the induction motor. As compared with the case driven by the voltage source PWM inverter, the motor efficiency increases by five or six percent. On the other hand, the noise level is reduced by nearly 10 dB. In comparison with the case driven by commercial power source, these values are almost the same. That is to say, the effects of producing the sinusoidal output and current are significant. As it obvious from the figure, this new current source GTO inverter is capable of driving an induction motor with high efficiency and low noise level. Therefore, this inverter is very suitable for ac motor variable speed drives.

VI. CONCLUSION

The new current source inverter to which GTO and PWM control techniques were applied was developed. The main points are summarized as follows.

1) Both output voltage and current waveforms could be made to be very closely sinusoidal, with the PWM controlled current pattern selected so as to minimize harmonics.

2) The voltage spikes in the output voltage could be suppressed by adding shoot-through gate pulses which force the inverter into a shoot-through state.

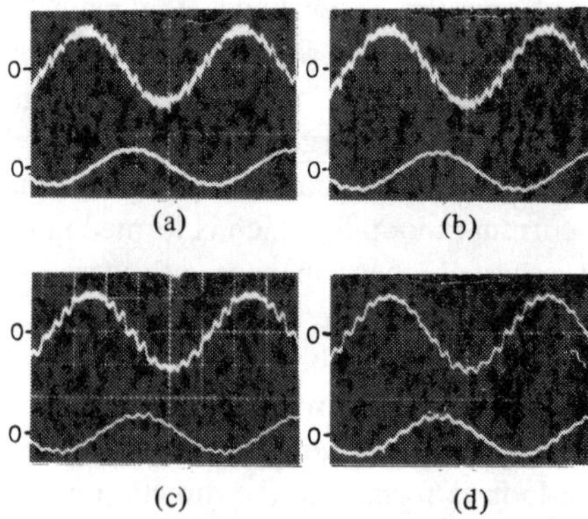

Fig. 15. Output waveforms with changing capacitance of output terminal capacitor ($f_I = 20$ Hz, $M = 199$). Upper: output voltage 200 V/div. Lower: output current 20 A/div. Horizontal: 10 ms/div. (a) $C = 5\ \mu F$. (b) $C = 10\ \mu F$. (c) $C = 20\ \mu F$. (d) $C = 40\ \mu F$.

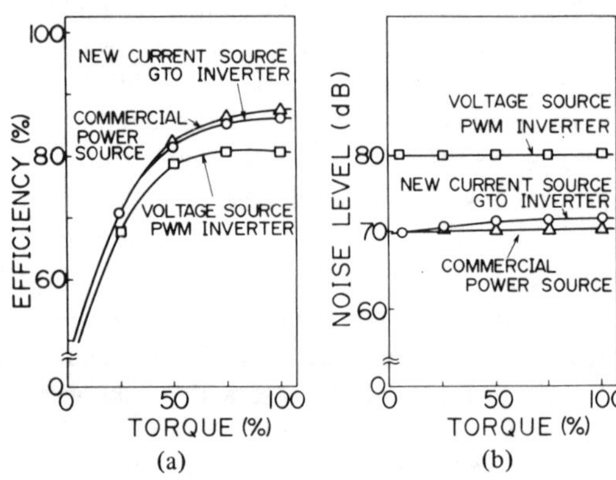

Fig. 16. Comparison of induction motor performance. (a) Motor efficiency. (b) Motor noise level.

3) This inverter was used to drive a 3.7-kW induction motor. In comparison tests with a voltage source PWM inverter, the motor efficiency was seen to increase by five or six percent, and the noise level to be reduced by nearly 10 dB for the former.

4) For the 15-kVA inverter used in the experiments, the capacitance of an overvoltge absorption capacitor could be reduced to one-tenth or less of that of the commutating capacitor in a conventional thyristor type current source inverter.

From the results mentioned, it can be seen that this new current source GTO inverter is very suitable for ac motor variable-speed drives.

REFERENCES

[1] E. A. Klingshirn and H. E. Jordan, "Polyphase induction motor performance and losses on nonsinusoidal voltage source," *IEEE Trans. Power App. Syst.*, vol. PAS-87, pp. 624–631, Mar. 1968.

[2] T. A. Lipo and E. P. Cornell, "State-variable steady-state analysis of a controlled current induction motor drive," *IEEE Trans. Ind. Appl.*, vol. IA-11, pp. 707–712, Nov./Dec. 1975.

[3] J. M. D. Murphy and M. G. Egan, "A comparison of PWM strategies for inverter-fed induction motors," *IEEE Trans. Ind. Appl.*, vol. IA-19, pp. 363–369, May/June 1983.

[4] H. Nagase, Y. Matsuda, K. Ohnishi, H. Ninomiya, and T. Koike, "High performance induction motor drive system using a PWM

inverter," in *Conf. Rec. 1983 Annu. Meet. IEEE Ind. Appl. Soc.*, pp. 596-603.

[5] M. Honbu, Y. Matsuda, K. Miyazaki, and Y. Jifuku, "Parallel operation techniques of GTO inverter sets for large ac motor drives," *IEEE Trans. Ind. Appl.*, vol. IA-19, pp. 198-205, Mar./Apr. 1983.

[6] Y. Matsuda, H. Fukui, H. Amano, H. Okuda, S. Watanabe, and A. Ishibashi, "Development of PWM inverter employing GTO," *IEEE Trans. Ind. Appl.*, vol. IA-19, pp. 335-342, May/June 1983.

[7] S. C. Peak and A. B. Plunkett, "Transistorized PWM inverter induction motor drive system," *IEEE Trans. Ind. Appl.*, vol. IA-19, pp. 379-387, May/June 1983.

[8] Y. Jifuku, K. Miyazaki, M. Honbu, T. Yoshioka, and A. Ishibashi, "GTO inverter for adjustable speed ac motor drive system," in *Conf. Rec. IPEC-Tokyo,* Mar. 1983, pp. 418-425.

[9] A. Ueda, M. Ibamoto, H. Narita, T. Hori, T. Tsuboi, and Y. Yamada, "GTO inverter for ac traction drives," *IEEE Trans. Ind. Appl.*, vol. IA-19, pp. 343-348, May/June 1983.

Paper 6.3

A Current Source GTO Inverter with Sinusoidal Inputs and Outputs

MITSUYUKI HOMBU, SENIOR MEMBER, IEEE, SHIGETA UEDA, AND AKITERU UEDA, MEMBER, IEEE

Abstract—**With the application of gate turn-off thyristors (GTO's) and PWM control techniques, a current source inverter capable of producing sinusoidal input/output (I/O) voltages and currents has been developed. The sinusoidally modulated current is fed to the GTO's in the rectifier and inverter sections. The overvoltage-absorption capacitors connected to the ac input and output terminals function as a filter and, consequently, the waveforms of the input/output voltages and currents become sinusoidal. Because the PWM control utilizes the high-speed switching characteristics of the GTO's, the dc link current smoothing reactor and the overvoltage absorption capacitors are greatly reduced. The dc link voltage in the rectifier section is controlled to adjust the ac motor current. This is accomplished by using the firing angle shift method in conjunction with the method involving varying the width of the bypass gate pulses, which put the rectifier section into a bypass state. The current source GTO inverter is used to drive an 11-kW induction motor. As a result, excellent acceleration and deceleration characteristics are obtained, which verifies that the new current source inverter is quite suitable for driving an ac motor at variable speeds.**

I. Introduction

VOLTAGE SOURCE PWM inverters and current source inverters are widely used for ac motor drive control [1]–[3]. The former use self-extinction devices such as transistors, gate turn-off thyristors (GTO's) etc., and the latter, thyristors. The input/output voltages and currents of these inverters, however, have numerous harmonics. As a result, ac motor losses and noise are increased and torque pulsations are produced [4], [5]. In addition, a problem of harmonic interference with commercial power source also arises. To solve these problems it is necessary to significantly reduce the harmonics in the I/O voltages and currents and to make their final waveforms sinusoidal. To produce the sinusoidal input and output waveforms, research has been undertaken on a current source inverter to which self-extinction devices and PWM control techniques have been applied [6]–[8]. This paper also deals with a current source inverter that can produce sinusoidal input and output waveforms by PWM control through advantageously using the high-speed switching characteristics of the GTO as a switching device in the inverter.

This current source inverter is composed of a rectifier section to convert ac power to dc power, a dc reactor to smooth the dc link current, and an inverter section to convert the dc power to variable-voltage and variable-frequency ac power. Both the rectifier and inverter sections are three-phase bridge circuits, each composed of six GTO's. To absorb overvoltages produced when the GTO current is cut off, three capacitors each are connected to the ac input and output terminals. A sinusoidally pulsewidth modulated current flows in each GTO. The overvoltage absorption capacitors connected to the ac input and output terminals also function as filters so that the input and output currents become sinosoidal.

In the inverter section the PWM control method is applied to produce the sinusoidal output voltage/current waveforms and to suppress the voltage spikes in the output voltages. The results demonstrate that the inverter is very suitable for induction motor drives [6].

The present paper deals mainly with the method for controlling the rectifier section and its operation. First the main and control circuit configurations of the current source GTO inverter are described briefly. Then the PWM control method in the rectifier section, which makes the input current waveforms sinusoidal and regulates a wide range of dc link voltages, is described. Subsequently the waveforms, such as the input current, output voltage, output current, and dc link current when an induction motor is driven by the inverter, are discussed. At the same time, acceleration/deceleration characteristics of an induction motor are shown. Moreover, the experimental frequency spectra of the input current and output voltage/current are described.

II. Main and Control Circuit Configurations

A. Main Circuit Configuration and Its Basic Operation

Fig. 1 shows the main circuit configuration of a current source GTO inverter with sinusoidal inputs and outputs. This inverter is composed of a rectifier section, a dc reactor, and an inverter section, and it supplies power to an induction motor as its load. The rectifier section converts the constant-frequency ac power to dc power. The dc reactor smooths the dc link current, and the inverter section converts dc power to variable-voltage and variable-frequency ac power. Both the rectifier and the inverter sections employ GTO's as switching devices and have capacitors connected to their respective ac terminals to absorb the overvoltages produced when the GTO current is cut off.

Fig. 2 shows the basic operation waveforms of the inverter. Basic operation principles for the rectifier and inverter sections are almost identical. The sinusoidal pulsewidth modulated currents i_{CR}, i_{IU} are made to flow through three-

Paper IPCSD 86-28, approved by the Static Power Converter Committee of the IEEE Industry Applications Society for presentation at the 1985 Industry Applications Society Annual Meeting, Toronto, ON, Canada, October 6–11. Manuscript released for publication September 2, 1986.

M. Hombu, S. Ueda, and A. Ueda are with the Hitachi Research Laboratory, Hitachi Ltd., 1-1, Saiwaicho 3 Chome, Hitachi-shi, Ibaraki-ken, 317 Japan.

IEEE Log Number 8612442.

Reprinted from *IEEE Trans. Ind. Applicat.*, vol. IA-23, no. 2, pp. 247–255, March/April 1987.

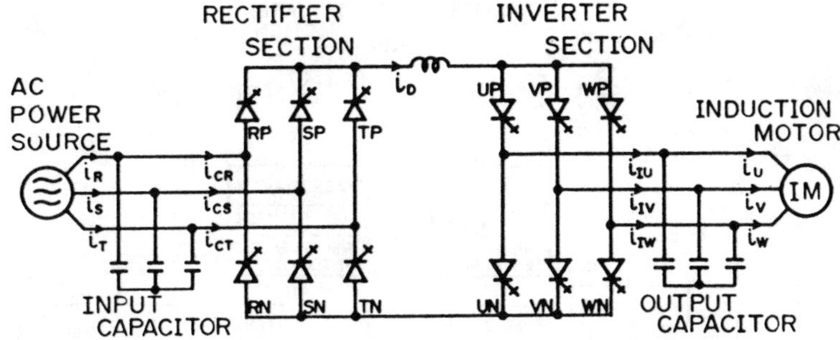

Fig. 1. Main circuit configuration.

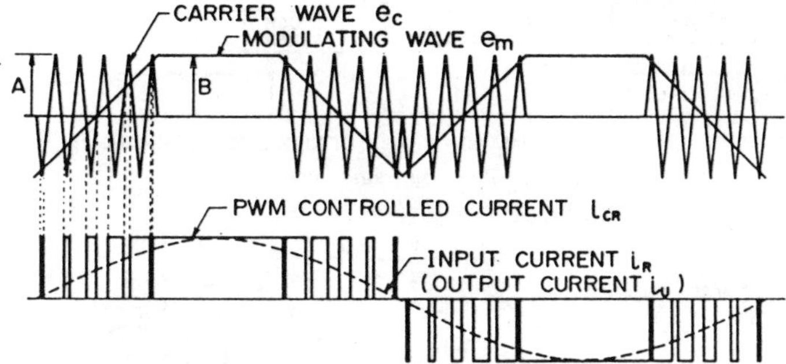

Fig. 2. Basic operation waveforms.

phase bridge circuits composed of the GTO's. Those overvoltage absorption capacitors connected to the ac input and output terminals act as filters so that input and output current i_R, i_U may have sinusoidal waveforms. The inverter of current source type can easily achieve a sinusoidal voltage as long as the current can be made sinusoidal. The figure also shows the method for generating a PWM controlled current pattern by comparing the trapezoidal modulating wave e_m with the triangular carrier wave e_c. The two factors that change this pattern are the modulation index B/A (amplitude ration of e_m to e_c) and the number of pulses M per half-cycle of rectifier or inverter operation. Changing these values will change the harmonics in the input or output current. To make the input or output waveforms sinusoidal, both modulation index and number of pulses must be selected to minimize the harmonics. In determining these values, however, consideration must be given to GTO switching characteristics such as the turn-on/off time, the turn-on/off loss, etc.

B. Control Circuit Block Diagram

Basically both rectifier and inverter sections require PWM control to produce the sinusoidal voltages and currents. In addition, the rectifier section uses the dc link voltage control to regulate the amplitude of the motor currents while the inverter section utilizes the frequency control corresponding to the motor speed. Fig. 3 is a block diagram of the control circuit.

First the rectifier section control circuit is discussed. The PLL circuit produces a clock pulse with a frequency N times that of the ac power source frequency. This clock pulse is counted with counter 1 and the counted value is used as the address signal for the PWM pattern and carrier waveform storage memory. Stored in this memory are the pulse pattern, which serves as the base for controlling the flow of a PWM controlled current to each GTO, and the carrier wave (triangular wave) to control the dc link voltage. The comparator compares the dc voltage command v_{DP} with the carrier wave in the storage memory and produces the bypass gate pulses, which force the rectifier section into the bypass state. Changing the bypass gate pulsewidth serves to control the dc link voltage. Details are given later. The phase-shifter is a circuit to change the firing angle of the rectifier section at a low dc link voltage. The PWM waveform synthesizer 1 synthesizes the output signals of ring counter 1, the PWM pattern and carrier waveform storage memory, and the comparator to provide the gate signals for the rectifier GTO's. In the experimental equipment a 2-kbyte read-only memory (ROM) is employed as the PWM pattern and carrier waveform storage memory, with the basic PWM pattern stored in the most significant bit and the carrier waveform data in the other seven bits.

The main blocks in the inverter section control circuit are the clock generator, the PWM pattern storage memory, ring counter 2, and PWM waveform synthesizer 2. The clock generator generates the clock pulse with a frequency proportional to the inverter frequency command f_p. This clock pulse is counted and the counted value is used as the address signal for the PWM pattern storage memory. Several current patterns are stored in the PWM pattern storage memory. These current patterns, shown in Fig. 2, form a sinusoidally distributed train of pulses. The PWM waveform synthesizer 2 synthesizes the output signals of ring counter 2 and the PWM pattern storage memory, thus providing the gate signals for GTO's in the inverter section. The inverter output frequency can be controlled by changing the inverter output frequency command f_p. The pattern selector is used to select an appropriate current pattern from those stored in the PWM pattern storage memory

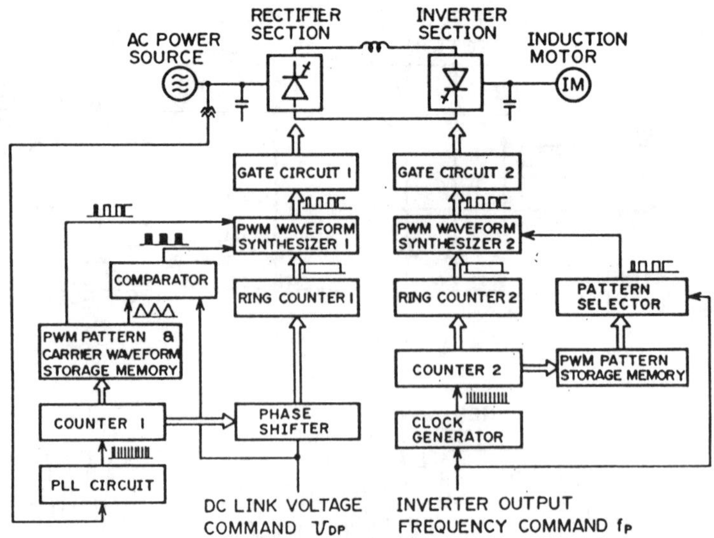

Fig. 3. Block diagram of control circuit.

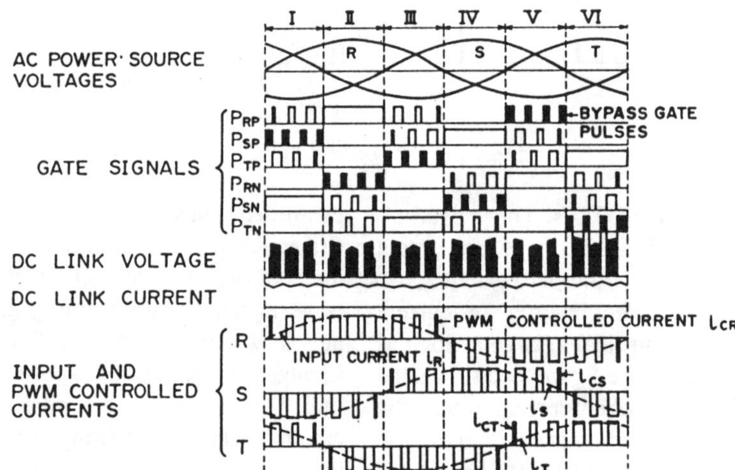

Fig. 4. Gate signals and current waveforms in rectifier section.

so that the GTO switching frequency is kept nearly constant, however much the inverter output frequency is varied.

III. Control Methods

A. Rectifier Section Control Method

The rectifier section requires functions to make the input current, or ac power source current, sinosoidal and to control the dc link voltage. The latter is done by varying the width of the bypass gate pulse, which puts the rectifier into the bypass state. To produce sinusoidal input currents, the sinusoidally distributed basic PWM pulses are combined with the bypass gate pulses.

Fig. 4 shows the waveforms of gate signals, input currents, dc link voltage, and current in the rectifier section during one cycle of the ac power source voltage. The gate signals contain the bypass gate pulses in black. During the period *V*, in which the bypass gate pulses are applied to the GTO_{RP}, for example, the gate signal is also applied to GTO_{RN}. As a result, GTO_{RP} and GTO_{RN} are turned on at the same time so that the rectifier section is put into the bypass state. All other periods are the same as period *V*. As long as bypass gate pulses are supplied, a dc link current will flow, bypassing the ac power source. During this period the PWM controlled current becomes zero. Consequently the PWM controlled currents i_{CR}, i_{CS}, and i_{CT} become sinusoidally pulsewidth-modulated waveforms, as shown in the figure. The capacitors connected to the ac input terminals act as a filter so that the input currents will be nearly sinusoidal waveforms. The gate signals shown in the figure were obtained by combining the bypass gate pulses for controlling the dc link voltage with the basic PWM pulse pattern selected to minimize harmonics. Therefore, the pulsewidths in the gate signals can be distributed sinusoidally and the input currents become sinusoidal waveforms, even if the bypass gate pulsewidth is changed.

As shown in Fig. 4 the dc link voltage is produced by chopping ac power source voltage waveforms. As long as the bypass gate pulses are supplied, the dc link voltage will remain zero. The rectifier section can increase the number of pulses in the dc link voltage waveform, compared with a conventional thyristor-type rectifier, so that the dc current pulsation can be significantly reduced. If the number of pulses in the gate signal, or GTO swithcing frequency, is increased, the pulsation of dc link current can be reduced remarkably, and the

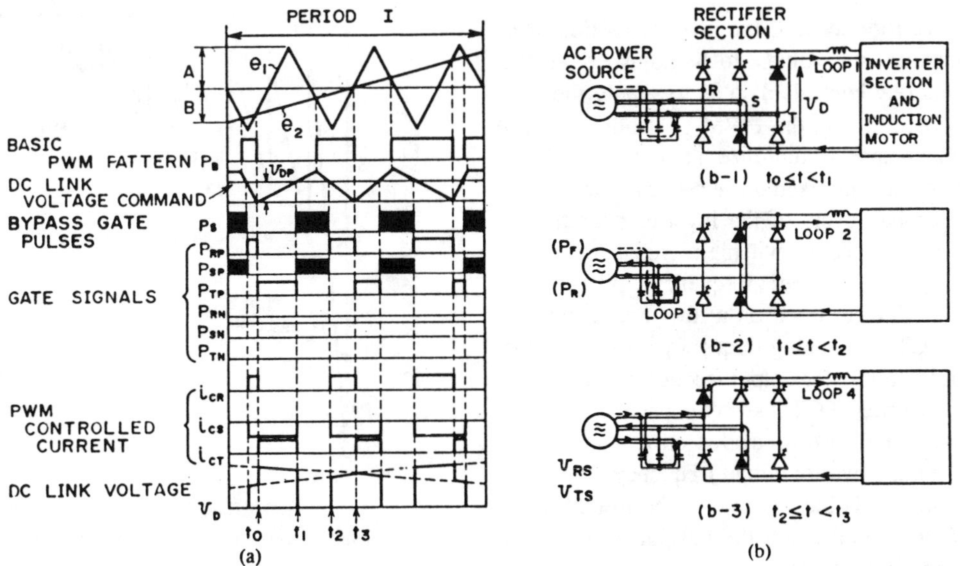

Fig. 5. Method for controlling dc link voltage. (a) Gate signals and dc link voltage. (b) Conditions of main circuit.

input currents can be made more sinusoidal in shape. In the experimental equipment the number of pulses was set at 41 and a switching frequency of 2.05 kHz was selected, considering the control range of the dc link voltage and the GTO switching characteristics.

Fig. 5 shows the method for controlling the dc link voltage, representing the gate signals, dc link voltage, and conditions in the main circuit during period I shown in Fig. 4. Triangular wave e_1 with amplitude A is compared with sawtooth wave e_2 with amplitude B to produce basic PWM pulse pattern P_B while taking "1" with $e_2 \geqq e_1$ and "0" with $e_2 < e_1$. Values of amplitudes A and B are selected to minimize the harmonics in the basic PWM pulse pattern. Triangular carrier wave e_c, synchronized with the basic PWM pattern, is compared with the dc link voltage command v_{DP} to produce the bypass gate pulse P_s. Pulses P_F and P_R, which are obtained as logical products of $\bar{P}_s$ and P_B and $\bar{P}_s$ and $\bar{P}_B$, respectively, are supplied to GTO_{RP} and GTO_{TP} as gate signals during period I. During this period the bypass gate pulse P_s is applied to GTO_{SP} as the gate signal, while that of GTO_{SN} is "1". No gate signals are supplied to GTO_{RN} and GTO_{TN}. During the period $t_0 \leqq t < t_1$, gate signals are supplied to GTO_{TP} and GTO_{SN} so that the circuit has the status shown in (b-1) of Fig. 5(b). Thus the current flows mainly from phase T of the ac power source through GTO_{TP}, dc circuit, and GTO_{SN} and back to phase S in the ac power source. This current path is referred to as "loop 1." During this period the dc link voltage v_D equals voltage v_{TS} between phases T and S in the ac power source.

When GTO_{SP} is turned on and GTO_{TP} is turned off at t_1, the rectifier section is put into a bypass state, shown in (b-2) of Fig. 5(b), while the dc link voltage becomes zero. This condition continues until t_2, when the bypass gate pulse P_s disappears. During the period $t_1 \leqq t < t_2$ the current flows in loops 2 and 3. Loop 2 is the path along which the current flows through the GTO_{SP}, the dc circuit, the inverter section, and the GTO_{SN} while loop 3 is the path along which the current flows through phase T of the ac power source, capacitors in phases T and S, and phase S of the ac power source. Loop 3 is the current path formed because the current which has been flowing in phases S and T of the ac power source during the period $t_0 \leqq t < t_1$ cannot flow through GTO's during the period $t_1 \leqq t < t_2$ in which the rectifier section is put into the bypass state. At t_2 the bypass gate pulse disappears while GTO_{RP} is turned on and GTO_{SP} off. Then the circuit has the status shown in (b-3) of Fig. 5(b). During the period $t_2 \leqq t < t_3$, the current path is loop 4 in which the current flows from phase T of the ac power source through capacitors in phases T and R, GTO_{RP}, DC circuit, GTO_{SN} and back to phase S of the ac power source. The dc link voltage v_D equals the voltage v_{RS} between phases R and S of the ac power source. During this period a small current also flows from phase R of the ac power source. After t_3, operations of (b-1) of Fig. 5(b) through (b-3) of Fig. 5(b) are repeated while the ac power source current is gradually commutated from phase T to phase R. As long as bypass gate pulse exists, the dc link voltage remains zero. If this pulsewidth is widened, the period during which the voltage equals zero is extended while the mean dc link voltage is decreased. If this pulsewidth is narrowed, however, the period during which the voltage remains zero is shortened while the mean dc link voltage is increased. Thus the dc link voltage can be controlled by varying the bypass gate pulsewidth.

As shown in Fig. 5(a), dc link voltage command v_{DP} is compared with a carrier wave e_c so that the bypass gate pulses are produced with $e_c \geqq v_{DP}$. If v_{DP} is decreased, the bypass gate pulsewidth is widened. If v_{DP} is increased, on the other side, the pulsewidth is narrowed. Thus the mean dc link voltage is proportional to the command value v_{DP}. An operation similar to the above is repeated during periods II through VI in Fig. 4.

B. Inverter Section Control Method

The inverter section requires PWM control to produce sinusoidal output voltages and currents and frequency control corresponding to the speed of the induction motor. The output frequency can be controlled easily by changing the inverter output frequency command f_p in the control circuit shown in

Fig. 3. Unlike the rectifier section, the inverter section does not require the mean dc link voltage to be adjusted. So the inverter section is merely controlled so as to supply the gate signals to each GTO following the PWM controlled current patterns prepared in advance to minimize the harmanics. With the PWM controlled current fixed in a certain pattern, the number of pulses per half-cycle of the inverter operation is constant. Therefore the GTO switching frequency is in proportion to the inverter output frequency. If a PWM controlled pattern is selected based on a low inverter output frequency range, the GTO switching frequency is located quite high in the range of high inverter output frequency, exceeding the allowable value in terms of GTO switching characteristics. If, on the other hand, a PWM controlled current pattern is selected based on the high inverter output frequency range, the GTO switching frequency is located low in the low inverter output frequency range. As a result the pulsations of output voltages and currents are increased.

It is necessary, therefore, to select an appropriate PWM controlled current pattern for the inverter output frequency so that the GTO switching frequency is nearly constant. In the control circuit diagram shown in Fig. 3, the pattern selector provides that function. Fig. 6 shows the relation between the inverter output frequency and the GTO switching frequency in the experimental equipment. A PWM controlled current pattern is selected to keep the GTO switching frequency at approximately 4 kHz. In the figure, the numbers represent the number of pulses per half-cycle of inverter operation.

IV. Experimental Results

For experiments, a 15-kVA current source GTO inverter employing 1200-V 90-A GTO was developed. The following describes the experimental results obtained when an 11-kW induction motor was driven by the inverter. The inverter output voltage was 400 V and output current 21.6 A; the output frequency was varied between 2 and 60 Hz. The 11-kW induction motor had a rated voltage of 400 V, a rated current of 21 A, and four poles.

A. Rectifier Section Waveforms

Fig. 7 shows the waveforms of input voltage and current and dc link voltage and current, etc. From the figure it can be seen that the input current waveform, or the ac power source current, is almost sinusoidal. The input capacitor current is the difference between the input current and the PWM controlled current; its waveform can be obtained by subtracting the PWM waveform from the sinusoidal waveform. Since the induction motor can be under no load, the dc input voltage of the inverter section was low and the rectifier section operates in the phase-shift control range. Therefore the dc link voltage of the rectifier section is equivalent to that which would be obtained by chopping the dc link voltage waveform generated when the firing angle in the conventional thyristor-type rectifier is large. The pulsating component in the dc link current, which is defined as the difference between the maximum and minimun values, is 3.5 A, or 12 percent with respect to the rated dc link current of 30 A. In this case the inductance of the dc reactor is 22 mH.

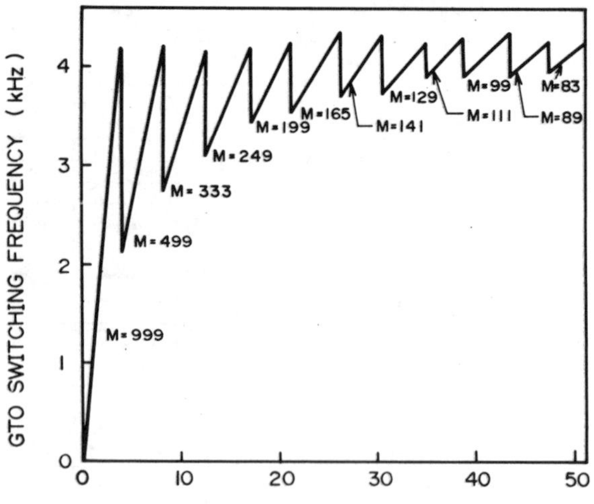

Fig. 6. Relation between inverter output frequency and GTO switching frequency.

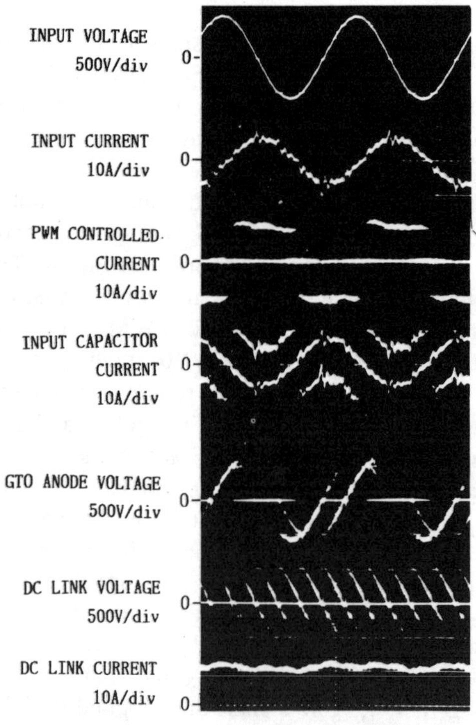

Fig. 7. Voltages and currents waveforms in rectifier section. (Input capacitance C_i: 10 μF; input inductance L_i: 3 mH.)

As described above, the dc link voltage is controlled by varying the width of the bypass gate pulse. Fig. 8 shows the relation between the bypass gate pulsewidth and the dc link voltage, based on actual measurements. The dc link voltage diminishes in proportion to the pulsewidth. As the bypass gate pulsewidth was increased, the pulsewidth of the gate signal, P_{RP} or P_{TP}, shown in Fig. 5, was below the minimum pulsewidth required to operate the GTO's safely. For this reason the bypass gate pulsewidth could not be increased without restrictions. When the bypass gate pulsewidth was reduced, its width became less than the minimum pulsewidth and, in Fig. 5, the GTO_{SP} could not operate normally. For experimental equipment, minimum and maximum bypass gate

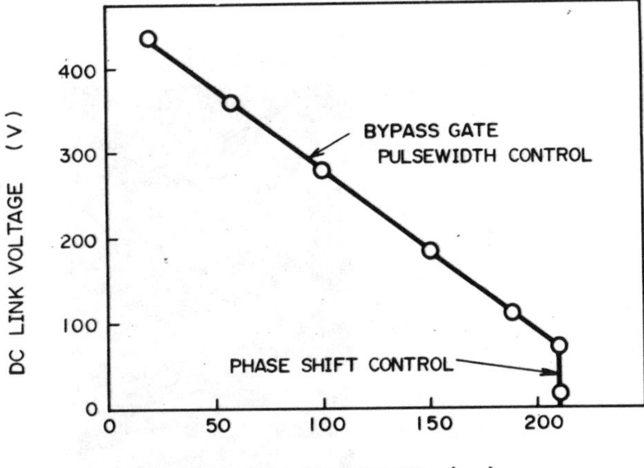

Fig. 8. Characteristics of dc link voltage.

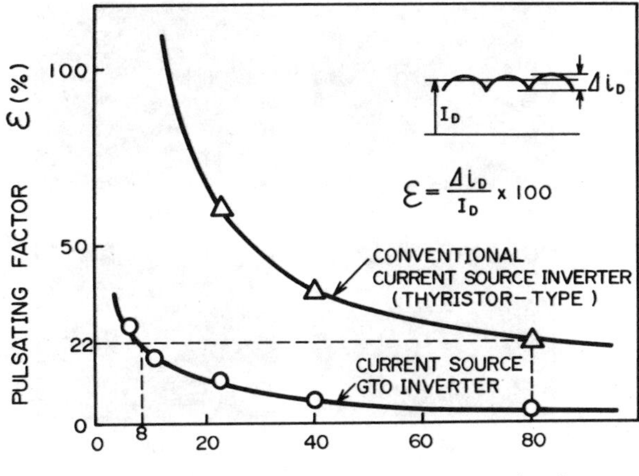

Fig. 9. Pulsating factor of dc link current.

pulsewidths of 20 and 220 μs were selected considering the GTO turn-on and turn-off times, the time constant of the snubber circuit, and the margin. From Fig. 8, the dc link voltage control range by the bypass gate pulse is from 70 to 460 V. Below 70 V the dc link voltage is adjusted by the phase shift control.

In the current source GTO inverter, the waveform on the dc link voltage is equivalent to that obtained by chopping the ac power source voltage at high frequency, shown in Fig. 5, so that the inductance of the dc reactor used to smooth the dc link current can be greatly reduced. Fig. 9 shows the relation between the dc reactor inductance and the dc output current pulsating factor. For purposes of comparison, data on the conventional thyristor-type current source inverter are also given. The pulsating factor is the ratio of the pulsating component to the rated 30-A dc link current. The figure shows that the pulsating factor of the new inverter is much smaller than that of the conventional inverter. Generally the current source inverter has a dc link current pulsating factor of about 20 percent. In the conventional inverter, the pulsating factor is 22 percent when the dc reactor inductance is 80 mH. The new inverter can achieve the same pulsating factor when the dc reactor inductance is only 8 mH. From this it is seen that the new inverter can operate with the inductance of the dc reactor reduced to about 10 percent of that for a conventional inverter.

Because the rectifier section is composed of the GTO's, its firing angle can be set wherever necessary. Fig. 10 shows the input voltage and current waveforms when the firing angle is changed. In this figure the bypass gate pulsewidth is constant. The firing angle lags in (a), is zero in (b), and leads in (c) and (d). In all cases, the input current waveform is nearly sinusoidal. The figure indicates that the rectifier section can operate not only in the lag state, but in the lead state with respect to the ac power source voltage. Using this feature the current source GTO inverter can vary the speed of the induction motor while controlling the reactive power of the ac power source with the input current waveforms kept almost sinusoidal. The rectifier section and dc reactor can be used as a reactive power compensator.

The ac power source which supplies the constant-frequency ac power to the rectifier section has an inductance component corresponding to its capacity. For overcurrent protection, ac

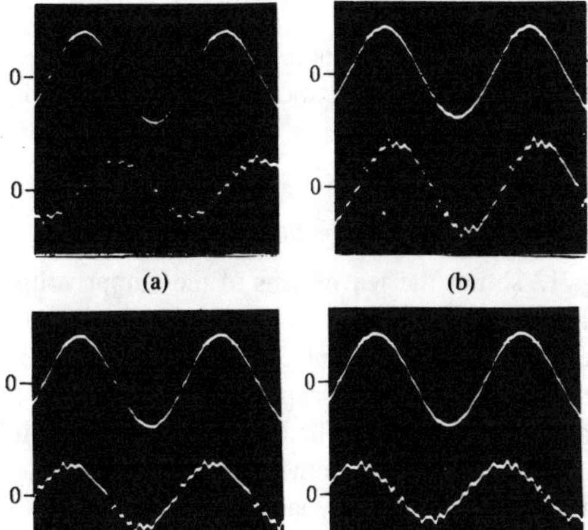

Fig. 10. Input waveforms with changing firing angle. (a) $\alpha = 60°$, lag. (b) $\alpha = 0°$. (c) $\alpha = 60°$, lead. (d) $\alpha = 80°$, lead. (Input capacitance C_i: 10 μF; input inductance L_i: 3 mH.) Upper: voltage 500 V/div. Lower: current 20 A/div. Horizontal: 5 ms/div. α: firing angle.

reactors may be connected to the ac power-source side. The input inductance is defined as the sum of these inductance components.

Fig. 11 illustrates the input voltage and input current waveforms obtained when the input inductance and the capacitance of the input capacitor are changed. In the experimental equipment the internal inductance of the ac power source was 1 mH. Therefore, if the input inductance is 3 mH, it means that 2-mH ac reactors are connected between the ac power source and rectifier section. The input voltage waveform shown in this figure is that of the ac power source, not the ac terminal voltage waveform in the rectifier section. However, if the inductance of the ac power source is 1 mH, the input-voltage waveform, in this case, is equivalent to the ac input terminal-voltage waveform because no ac reactors are connected. The input current is almost sinusoidal, except when the input inductance is 1 mH and the capacitance of the input capacitor is 10 μF. From the waveform shown in this figure, it is seen that the appropriate input inductance is 3 mH and the appropriate capacitance of the input capacitor is 10 μF. The

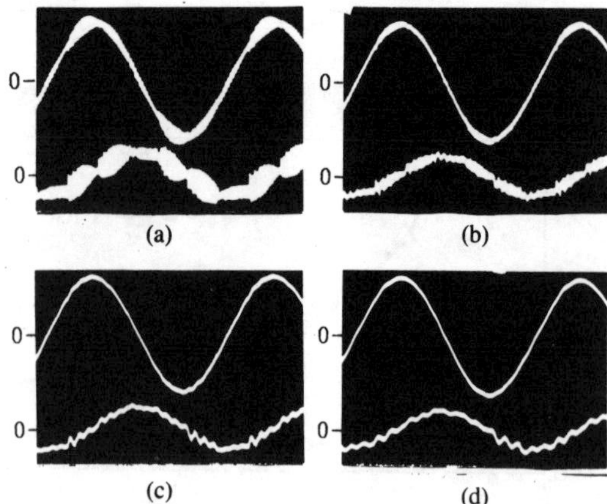

Fig. 11. Input waveforms with changing input capacitance and inductance. (a) C_i = 10 μF, L_i = 1 mH (b) C_i = 20 μF, L_i = 1 mH (c) C_i = 10 μF, L_i = 3 mH (d) C_i = 20 μF, L_i = 3 mH (Pulse number: 41. C_i: input capacitance. L_i: input inductance.) Upper: voltage 500 V/div. Lower: current 20 A/div. Horizontal: 5 ms/div.

value of 3 mH is equivalent to an 8.8 percent impedance drop of the experimental equipment for which capacity was 15 kVA. The value of 10 μF is equivalent to 3.4 percent of its capacity.

B. Inverter Section Waveforms

Fig. 12 shows the waveforms of the output voltage, output current, dc link voltage, etc., in the inverter section. In this figure the inverter output frequency is 20 Hz and the capacitance of the output capacitor is 5 μF. The number of pulses in the PWM controlled current is 199 and the modulation index B/A is 1.0. Both the output voltage and current waveforms are very nearly sinusoidal.

In Fig. 2 which showed the basic operating waveforms, it was indicated that the factors which change the PWM controlled current pattern were the modulation index B/A and the number of pulses M. Fig. 13 shows the output voltage and current waveforms obtained when the modulation index B/A is changed from 0.0 to 1.0. In the cases of (a) and (b), large voltage spikes occur in the output voltage so that the output voltage waveform contains many harmonics. The output current has a quasi-square waveform containing many harmonics like the output voltage. In the cases of (c) and (d), the output voltage and current waveforms are almost sinusoidal. In the case of (d), the waveforms more closely approximate the sinusoidal waveforms than those of (c). It is seen from this figure that it is desirable to select a modulation index of more than 0.8.

In the inverter section the capacitance of the overvoltage absorption capacitor is 5 μF. This is equivalent to 1.7 percent of the capacity of the experimental equipment. The capacitance of the overvoltage absorption capacitor, including the converter section, is only 5 percent.

C. Experimental Frequency Spectra of Input/Output Waveforms

It has been mentioned above that the waveforms of the input/output voltages and currents are almost sinusoidal in the current source GTO inverter. To see how harmonics are contained, the frequency spectra of those waveforms were

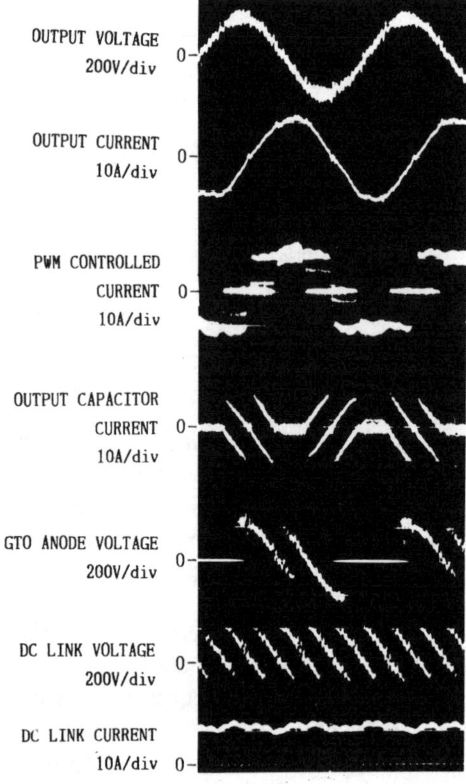

Fig. 12. Voltages and currents waveforms in inverter section. (Inverter output frequency: 20 Hz. Output capacitance: 5 μF. Pulse number: 199. Modulation index: 1.0.)

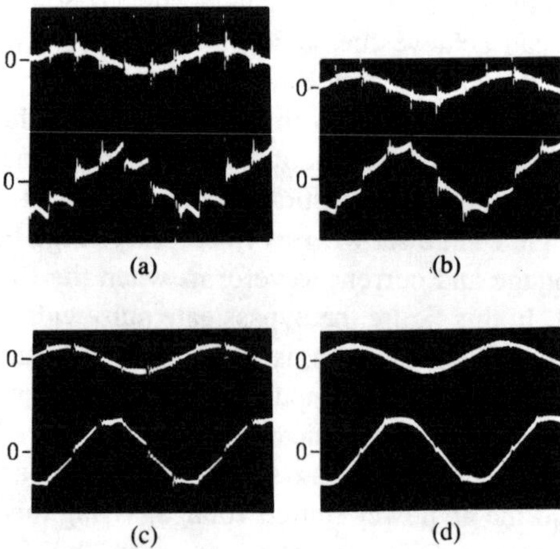

Fig. 13. Output waveforms with changing modulation index. (a) B/A = 0.0. (b) B/A = 0.5. (c) B/A = 0.8. (d) B/A = 1.0. (Output capacitance: 5 μF. Inverter output frequency: 20 Hz. Pulse number: 199. B/A: modulation index.) Upper: voltage 500 V/div. Lower: current 10 A/div. Horizontal: 10 ms/div.

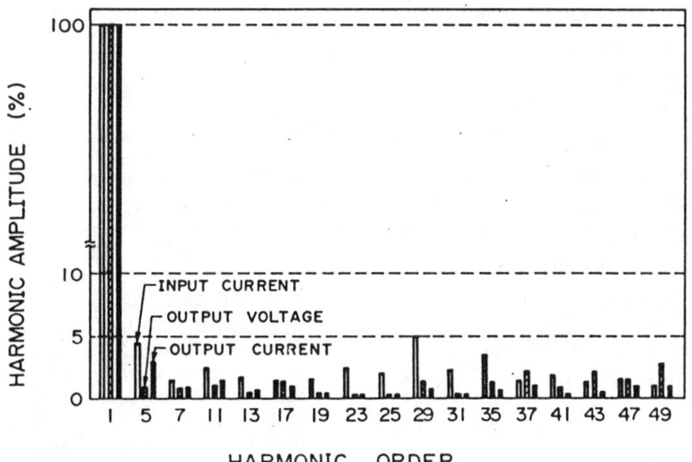

Fig. 14. Frequency spectra of input current and output voltage and current.

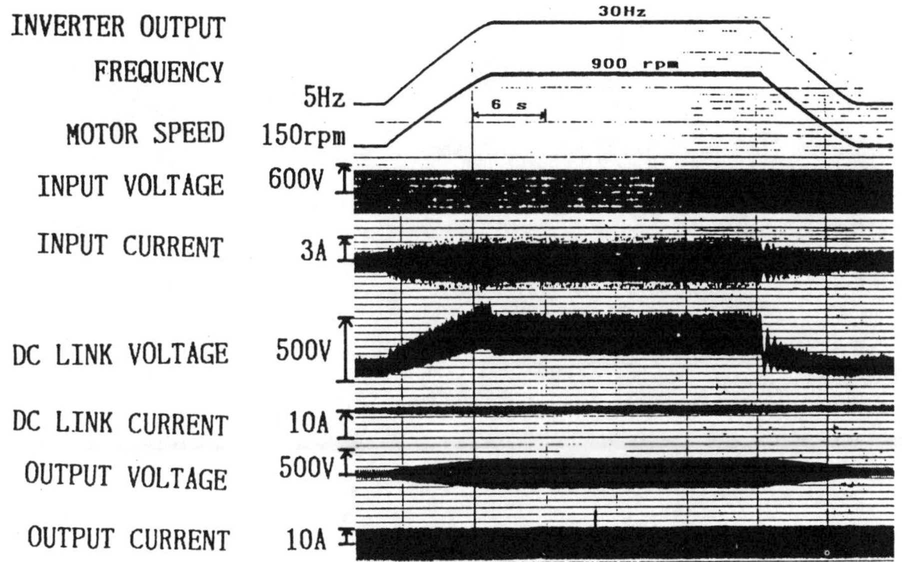

Fig. 15. Acceleration and deceleration characteristics of the 11-kW induction motor.

measured. Fig. 14 shows the experimental frequency spectra of the input current and the output voltage and current shown in Figs. 7 and 12. The waveform of the input current has a 29th-order harmonic of 5 percent, but all the other harmonics in the input current waveform are 4 percent or less. The 49th-order harmonic is largest in the output voltage waveform, although it accounts for only 2.6 percent. The waveform of the output current contains a 5th-order harmonic of 3 percent, but all the other harmonics are 1.5 percent or less. Fig. 14 shows that the input/output voltages and currents in this current source GTO inverter contain only a few harmonics.

D. Induction Motor Acceleration and Deceleration Characteristics

Fig. 15 shows the oscillogram obtained when the speed of the 11-kW induction motor was varied by the current source GTO inverter. The induction motor was accelerated and decelerated following the inverter output frequency. Thus, smooth acceleration and deceleration characteristics were obtained.

V. Conclusion

A current source inverter using GTO's and PWM control techniques was developed. The main points are summarized as follows.

1) Waveforms of input/output voltages and currents are made to be almost sinusoidal.
2) A combination of the phase shift control method and the method in which the width of the bypass gate pulse, which puts the rectifier section into bypass state, is varied has enabled dc link voltage control over a wide range.
3) The inductance of the dc reactor used for smoothing the dc link current has been reduced to about one-tenth of that of the conventional thyristor-type current source inverter.

4) In the experimental 15-kVA equipment, the capacitance of the overvoltage absorption capacitors is as small as 5 percent of the equipment capacity.
5) The rectifier section can be operated in either lag or lead states with respect to the ac power source voltage so that the rectifier section can be used as a reactive power compensator for the ac power source.
6) In tests using the current source GTO inverter to drive an 11-kW induction motor, smooth acceleration and deceleration characteristics are obtained.

From the above it is concluded that the current source GTO inverter is quite suitable for ac motor variable-speed drives.

References

[1] Y. Jifuku, *et al.*, "GTO inverter for adjustable speed ac motor drive system," in *Conf. Rec. IPEC-Tokyo 1983*, pp. 418–425.

[2] M. Hombu, *et al.*, "Parallel operation techniques of GTO inverter sets for large ac motor drives," *IEEE Trans. Ind. Appl.*, vol. IA-19, pp. 198–205, Mar./Apr. 1983.

[3] T. Iiyoshi, *et al.*, "Controls and drives for a modern electrolytic galvanizing line," in *Conf. Rec. 1984 Annu. Meet. IEEE Ind. Appl. Soc.*, pp. 58–63.

[4] J. M. D. Murphy and M. G. Egan, "A comparison of PWM strategies for inverter-fed induction motors," *IEEE Trans. Ind. Appl.*, vol. IA-19, pp. 363–369, May/June 1983.

[5] T. A. Lipo and E. P. Cornell, "State-variable steady-state analysis of a controlled current induction motor drive," *IEEE Trans. Ind. Appl.*, vol. IA-11, pp. 704–712, Nov./Dec. 1975.

[6] M. Hombu, *et al.*, "A new current soruce GTO inverter with sinusoidal output voltage and current," in *Conf. Rec. 1984 Annu. Meet. IEEE Ind. Appl. Soc.*, pp. 807–812.

[7] E. P. Wiechmann, P. D. Ziogas, and V. R. Stefanovic, "A novel bilateral power conversion scheme for variable frequency static power supplies," in *Conf. Rec. IEEE PESC 1984*, pp. 388–395.

[8] K. D. T. Ngo, S. Cuk, and R. D. Middlebrook, "A new flyback dc-to-three-phase converter with sinusoidal outputs," in *Conf. Rec. IEEE PESC 1983*, pp. 377–388.

Paper 6.4

The Resonant DC Link Converter–A New Concept in Static Power Conversion

DEEPAKRAJ M. DIVAN, MEMBER, IEEE

Abstract—**A new approach to realizing efficient high-performance power converters is presented. The concept of a resonant dc link inverter has been proposed and realized with the addition of only one small inductor and capacitor to a conventional voltage source inverter circuit. The new topology is capable of switching almost an order of magnitude faster than state-of-the-art voltage source inverters at significantly improved efficiencies using the same family of devices. The topology is especially suitable for high-power applications using gate turn-off devices.**

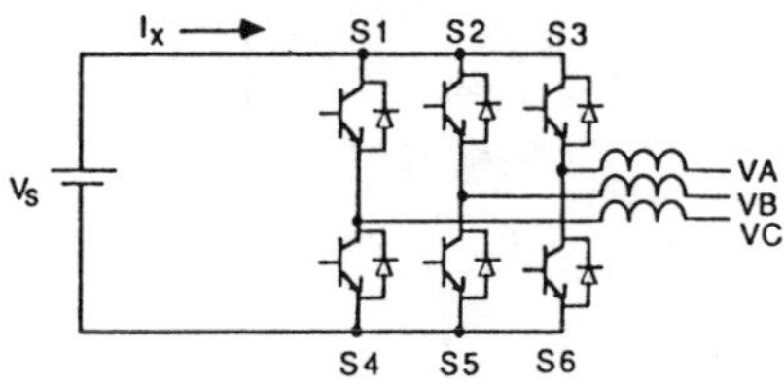

Fig. 1. Schematic of conventional voltage source inverter typically used in PWM applications.

Introduction

THE EMERGENCE of a mature gate turn-off (GTO) device technology over the last ten years has revolutionized the power conversion industry. It has meant a virtual disappearance of the thyristor in force-commutated applications. The autosequentially commutated current source inverter, once a promising and widely used circuit topology, has been almost completely replaced by GTO and transistor voltage source inverters (VSI's) at power ratings up to 1 MW. In fact, the pulsewidth-modulated (PMW) voltage source inverter is probably the most widely used configuration for dc/ac inverter applications in the 10 W–500 kW power range.

The attractiveness of the VSI topology stems from its extremely simple power structure and the need for only six unidirectional gate turn-off devices (Fig. 1). The antiparallel diodes required are typically mounted in the same device package for minimum lead inductance and ease of assembly. The control strategy is reasonably simple and provides a fully regenerative interface between the dc source and the ac load. However, given the limitations on the characteristics of available gate turn-off devices, the following problems can also be identified with the topology.

- Low switching frequencies result from high switching losses. This also results in low-amplifier bandwidth and poor load-current waveform fidelity (harmonics).
- High dv/dt on the output generates interference due to capacitive coupling.
- Diode reverse recovery and snubber interactions cause high device stresses under regeneration conditions.
- Device stresses require large SOA specifications and compromise reliability.
- Acoustic noise at the inverter switching frequency can be very objectionable.
- The generation capability into the ac line is poor.
- The input ac line harmonics are poor.
- The dc link and ac side filters are large.
- The fault recovery characteristics are poor.

An optimum power converter, on the other hand, would be designed with zero switching losses, a switching frequency greater than 18 kHz, small reactive components, and multiquadrant operation capability. The system would also be insensitive to second-order parameters such as diode recovery, device turn-off, and parasitic LC elements. Obviously, the voltage source inverter does not satisfy the requirements for an optimal converter.

This paper presents a new approach to gate-turn-off device switching. It is easily shown that maximum device stresses and switching losses occur when switching off a stiff dc bus. In the concept presented here, the dc bus is made to oscillate at a high frequency so that the bus voltage goes through periodic zero crossings, thus setting up ideal switching conditions for all devices connected across the bus. The resulting topology is seen to require minimum number of devices and moderately sized reactive elements, and it can easily switch at frequencies in excess of 18 kHz at multikilowatt power levels.

Conventional DC/AC Inverter Topologies

As has long been recognized, a substantial increase in inverter switching frequency is required to be able to minimize the lower order harmonics in PWM-type applications. Higher switching frequencies have the concomitant advantages of higher current regulator bandwidth, smaller reactive component size, and for frequencies above 18 kHz, acoustic noise which is above the threshold of human perception. Increases in PWM inverter switching frequency over the last decade (from around 500 Hz to 2 kHz for supplies rated 1–25 kW) have

Paper IPCSD 88-26, approved by the Static Power Converter Committee of the IEEE Industry Applications Society for presentation at the 1986 Industry Applications Society Annual Meeting, Denver, CO, September 28–October 3. This work was supported in part by the Wisconsin Electric Machines and Power Electronics Consortium. Manuscript released for publication July 14, 1988.

The author is with the Department of Electrical and Computer Engineering, University of Wisconsin, 1415 Johnson Drive, Madison, WI 53706- 1691.

IEEE Log Number 8825313.

Reprinted from *IEEE Trans. Ind. Applicat.*, vol. 25, no. 2, pp. 317–325, March/April 1989.

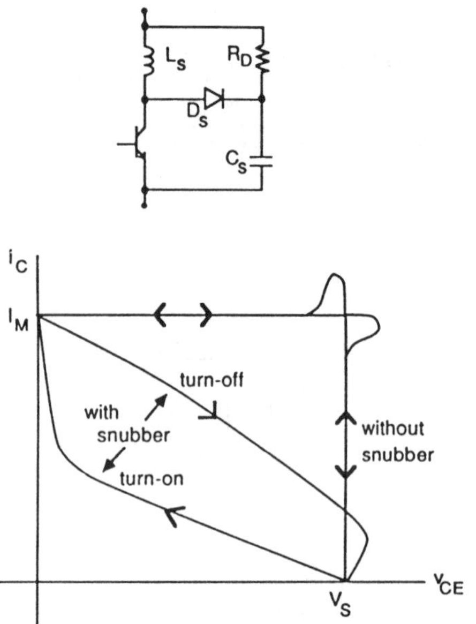

Fig. 2. Typical snubber used with BJT's. (a) Circuit diagram. (b) Switching loci for transistor operating into clamped inductive load, both with and without snubber.

typically been as a result of improvements in device speed and SOA ratings. An equally important approach, topological in nature, explores the possibility of modifying the switching environment to maximize device utilization.

The best known example of such an approach is the perennial search for the quintessential snubber. The elegant concept of controlling the device switching trajectory was first discussed by Calkin and Hamilton [1], and subsequently by McMurray [2], [3], Undeland [4], Zach *et al.* [5], and many others. The snubber network protects the devices by diverting switching losses away from the device itself. A survey of the literature indicates that the simple snubbers of the past have evolved into increasingly complex networks, often to a point where the snubber itself can be called a power-converter topology [5]! Notwithstanding the level of "sophistication" attainable, the most popular snubber configuration is also the simplest and is shown in Fig. 2(a). L_s provides turn-on protection while C_S and D_S constitute a polarized turn-off snubber. R_D provides a dissipative snubber discharge path. Fig. 2(b) shows typical switching loci for a bipolar junction transistor (BJT) operating into an inductive load, both with and without the snubber network. Even though the advantages of using snubbers in BJT inverters are well known, packaging problems and the cost of additional components make their use by industry infrequent. For GTO inverters, on the other hand, the snubber is absolutely essential for device protection and is often the key to a reliable and successful inverter design. While snubbers perform admirably in alleviating device switching losses, the total switching losses do not change appreciably and can actually increase for given operating conditions. Consequently, increases in inverter switching frequency continue to exact a heavy penalty in terms of system efficiency.

Another interesting alternative is the use of resonant mode converters employing a high-frequency resonant LC circuit in the power transfer path. A substantial amount of interest exists in the area, as can be seen from the proliferation of papers on the subject [6]–[13]. Two distinctly identifiable categories

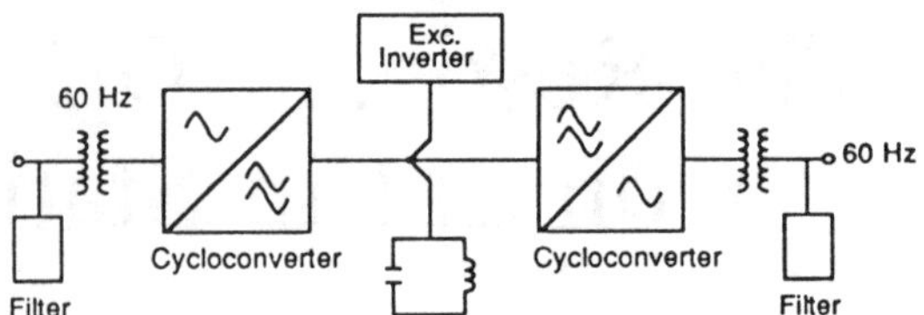

Fig. 3. Block schematic of three-phase-ac-to-three-phase-ac HF link converter [11].

of resonant converter seem to have emerged over the years. Converters of the first category, of which induction heating inverters and dc/dc converters are examples, accomplish control through a modulation of the inverter switching frequency. For these circuits, the frequency-sensitive impedance of the resonant tank is the key to a variable output [6]–[8]. While it is also possible to synthesize low-frequency ac waveforms using such frequency modulation principles, the complexity of control, large number of switching devices, and oversized resonant components makes it an unattractive proposition [9].

The second type of resonant converter, commonly referred to as a high-frequency (HF) link converter, was proposed by Bedford in 1973 [14] and was enhanced in scope by Gyugui [15], and then by Pelly and Gyugyi [16]. The first discussion in the literature was by Espelage and Bose [10], followed by Gyugyi and Cibulka [11]. Most of these realizations use naturally commutated converters and cycloconverters with a high-frequency ac link formed out of resonant LC tank circuits. The HF link converters are capable of ac/ac or dc/ac conversion with bidirectional power flow and can present any desired power factor to the ac supply. Fig. 3 shows the schematic for an ac/ac HF link converter [11]. In contrast with the frequency-modulation scheme used earlier, the link frequency is not very important, and output ac waveform synthesis is done through modulation of the output stage. For natural commutation, phase angle control is the obvious choice.

To obtain the benefits of higher switching frequencies, Schwarz raised the internal resonant frequency to 20 kHz and achieved forced commutation of the thyristors with a series LC circuit, as opposed to a parallel tank [13]. Huisman and deHaan proposed a dc-to-three-phase ac resonant link converter using thyristors [12]. They also proposed integral cycle modulation as a viable control strategy for low-frequency ac waveform synthesis. Sood and Lipo have recently examined the viability of a high-frequency link power distribution system using bidirectional GTO devices in the resonant converters [17].

The HF link converter is a viable topology and is the focus of continuing research. The system is capable of switching at frequencies greater than 18 kHz using available devices at the multikolowatt power level. However, the technology is not economically competitive and has not gained much favor in industry for variable-speed drive applications. This can be attributed to a wide variety of reasons.

- The large number of bidirectional high-speed high-power switches required are realized from available unidirectional devices. Gyugyi's system needs 36 thyristors in addition to an excitation inverter [11].

- The recovery characteristics of the devices/diodes used often necessitate the use of snubber networks.
- The LC resonant circuit handles the full-load power and has large circulating currents, up to six times the load current. Consequently, even though energy stored in the system is small, the VA rating of the resonant elements is substantial.
- Control is extremely complex given the simultaneous tasks of input and output control, HF bus regulation, and thyristor commutation (where applicable).

Basic Principles of the Resonant DC Link Converter

From the foregoing discussion, it is obvious that whereas the dc link system requires the minimum number of devices, it is the resonant converter which is capable of switching at the high-frequencies of interest. It is extremely important to realize that if the switching environment could be modified to ensure zero switching losses, the dc link converter switching frequency would then be restricted only by device turn-on, storage, and turn-off times. Zero switching losses could be obtained by holding the dc bus voltage at zero volts for the duration of the switching transient. An elegant method for attaining the desired objective is to make the dc bus oscillatory, ensuring that the voltage remains at zero for sufficient time to allow lossless switching to take place.

Fig. 4 shows a current-fed resonant converter circuit which can oscillate at or below the tank resonant frequency [18]. Assuming excitation of the H-bridge at the system natural frequency, the tank voltage is seen to be a pure sinusoid, and the average curent in the dc link inductor is just sufficient to compensate for losses in the circuit. It can also be observed that all devices S_1–S_4 switch with zero voltage across them. The zero-switching-loss condition is also seen to hold for switching frequencies below the natural resonant frequency. Further, the dc bus voltage at V_0 is seen to be a rectified sinusoid which goes through two zero crossings per cycle of the switching frequency. If dc power is now delivered to L_L and R_L, as shown in Fig. 4, it is apparent that the resonant circuit damping is independent of the power delivered, provided $L_L \gg L_{dc} > L$. Consequently, the tank continues to oscillate and does not handle any of the power delivered to R_L in the steady state.

Of even greater importance is the conclusion that if V_0 is used as a resonant dc bus, then additional devices connected across that bus could also be operated with zero switching loss provided they were switched at the zero voltage crossings of the bus. Fig. 5 shows the schematic of a dc-to-three-phase resonant dc link inverter. Fig. 6 shows a technique for synthesizing low-frequency ac waveforms using integral cycles of the resonant dc link. With commercially available BJT's and GTO's in this topology, tank resonant frequencies of 20 kHz are easily attainable. This permits the six-transistor inverter stage to switch at up to 40 kHz, giving sufficient resolution to realize control in drive-type applications through an appropriate integral pulsewidth modulation (IPWM) strategy.

The concept is easily extended to a three-phase-ac-to-three-phase-ac converter by the addition of six input devices, as

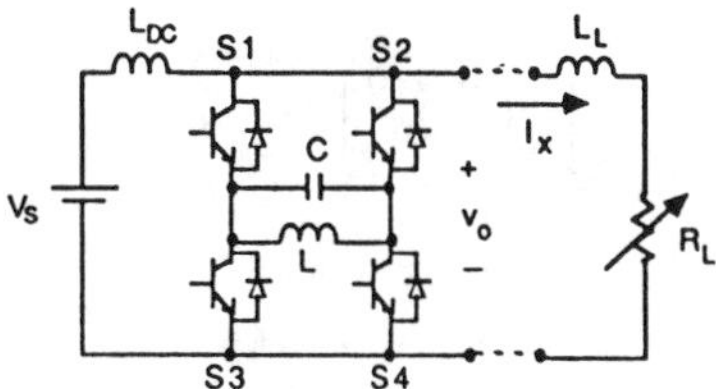

Fig. 4. Current-fed resonance dc link converter using H-bridge.

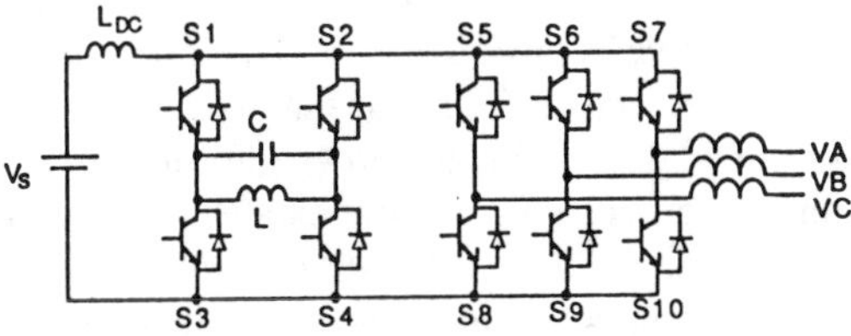

Fig. 5. DC-to-three-phase-ac resonant dc link inverter using H-bridge.

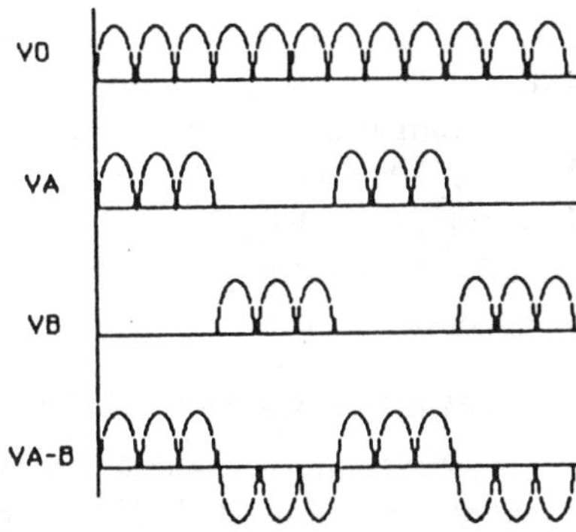

Fig. 6. Synthesis of low-frequency ac waveform fron integral pulses of resonant dc link using DPM.

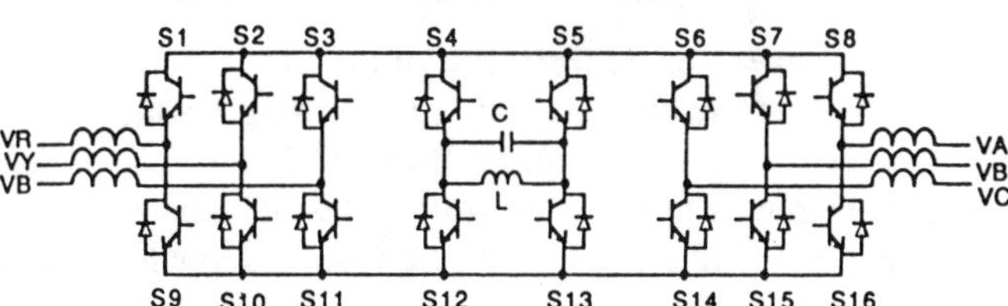

Fig. 7. Three-phase-ac-to-three-phase-resonant dc link power converter topology using H-bridge to resonant dc link.

shown in Fig. 7. All 16 GTO devices can now be switched on the zero crossings of the dc bus, eliminating switching losses in the entire system. The circuit is also seen to be completely symmetric, fully regenerative, has zero switching losses and low energy storage. There is no snubber network, although it is tempting to consider the resonant dc link to be a lossless rotating snubber. The configuration is extremely insensitive to factors such as diode recovery and variations in device storage or turn-off times. During the switching transient, the dc bus voltage automatically continues to be at zero until the last device has recovered its blocking characteristic.

In spite of all the apparent advantages, the circuit in Fig. 5 (or Fig. 7) is far from ideal in its performance. As mentioned earlier, when the current in L_{dc} equals the inverter current, the resonant tank is minimally involved in the power flow. However, the use of a PWM-type modulation strategy causes

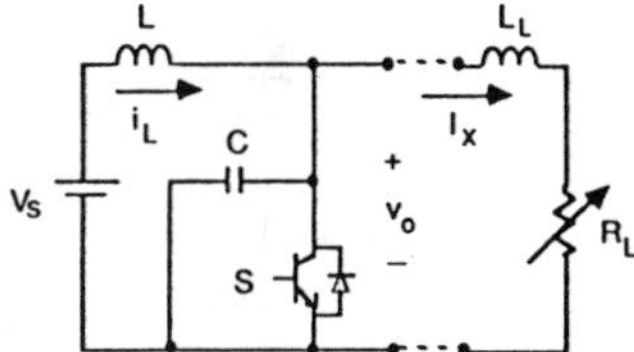

Fig. 8. Basic circuit of single-transistor resonant dc link.

very rapid changes in the dc link current drawn by the inverter stage. In a conventional voltage source inverter, this dc current ripple is absorbed in a large electrolytic capacitor with few deleterious effects. For the resonant dc link inverter, the current in L_{dc} no longer flows into the inverter, and the resulting difference current now excites the tank, causing an undesirable modulation of the dc bus voltage (Fig. 12). The depth of this modulation is proportional to the ratio of the peak load current I_x to the peak capacitor current I_{cp}. Consequently, meeting the desired objective of low energy storage results in high modulation depth of the dc bus voltage. This, in turn, can cause objectionable low-frequency torque pulsations in the load. Increasing the peak capacitor current requires higher device ratings and results in higher dissipation in the tank circuit. In addition to operating problems, four additional devices and a fairly large resonant tank add a cost burden which is difficult to justify. A simpler version of the resonant dc link is considered next.

Single-Transistor Resonant DC Link

Given that the objective is to generate a resonant dc link, consider the circuit shown in Fig. 8. If V_s is applied to the system with the device S off, for lossless L and C, v_0 will be given by

$$v_0(t) = V_s(1 - \cos \omega t) \tag{1}$$

where ω is the resonant frequency of the LC circuit. At $\omega t = 2\pi$, v_0 will return to zero volts, thus setting up the desired lossless switching condition. For finite Q factors, the voltage will never return to zero and will finally stabilize at V_s. On the other hand, if S is maintained on while applying V_s, the current in L is seen to increase linearly. S is then turned off when sufficient energy is stored in the inductor L to ensure that v_0 returns to zero. This then allows S to be turned on once again so as to repeat the process and establish a single transistor resonant dc link.

Having established the desired resonant dc link, Fig. 9(a) shows the obvious extension of the concept to a dc-to-three-phase ac inverter. As in the previous case, the dc link voltage is required to go through zero periodically, thus setting up conditions for the lossless switching of all devices connected across it. To accomplish that objective, it is now necessary to monitor $(i_L - I_x)$ to ascertain that sufficient excess energy is stored in L to ensure that V_0 returns to zero. It is also interesting to note that the oscillator device S is in parallel with the inverter per-phase device pairs. Consequently, S is redundant and the resonant dc link inverter topology reduces to the circuit shown in Fig. 9(b). It is obvious that control of the six devices will now need modification to include action of switch S. The three-phase-ac-to-three-phase-ac converter is also easily derived from the basic circuit and is shown in

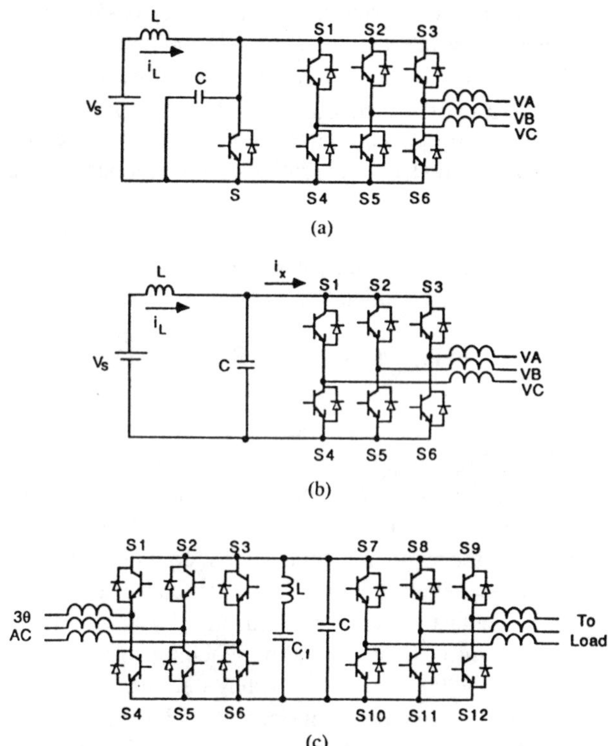

Fig. 9. Variations of single resonant transistor resonant dc link inverters. (a) DC-to-three-phase inverter with seven devices. (b) Resonant dc link inverter using only six devices. (c) Three-phase-ac-to-three-phase ac resonant dc link inverter.

Fig. 9(c). L and C are the resonant elements, and C_f is an electrolytic capacitor which establishes the dc voltage required for resonant dc link operation. Once again, the circuit is completely symmetric, fully regenerative, and without switching losses.

Many significant advantages can be seen to characterize this topology. The addition of one small inductor and one capacitor to a conventional VSI eliminates all switching losses and results in a substantial increase in the inverter efficiency and the switching frequency. Active control of the current $(i_L - I_x)$ ensures that each resonant cycle starts with the same initial conditions. Thus the resonant cycle is controlled in a deadbeat manner, independent of the actual value of dc link current I_x. This results in a virtual elimination of the sustained dc bus modulation encountered in the previous resonant dc link case and also results in a reduction in the size of the resonant elements required. Resonant dc link inverter operation will be analyzed next.

Analysis and Design

Assuming that the load inductance is much greater than the resonant inductor L, the equivalent circuit of the system for the duration of each resonant cycle reduces to that shown in Fig. 10. The value of the link current I_x depends on the individual phase currents and the switching functions for the six inverter devices. Given a PWM-type strategy, I_x can vary by a large amount from one switching cycle to the next. However, during the resonant cycle itself, I_x remains virtually constant. If switch S is turned off when the inductor current is at $I_{L\phi}$,

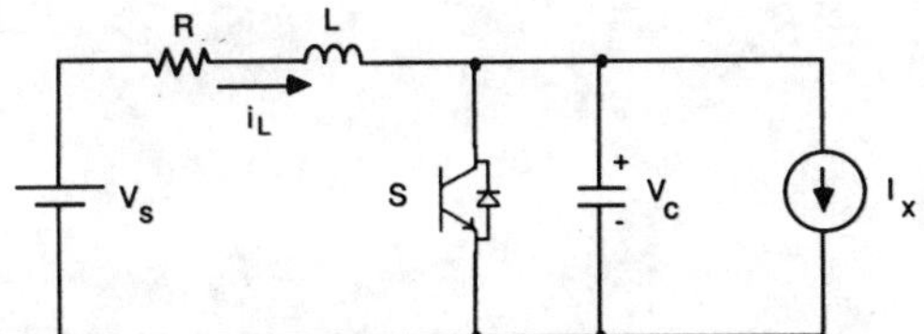

Fig. 10. Equivalent circuit of system during each resonant pulse.

the capacitor voltage and the inductor current can be found to be

$$v_c(t) = V_s - I_xR + e^{-\alpha t}\Bigg[(I_xR - V_s)\cos\omega t + \left(\frac{R}{2\omega \cdot L} \cdot \left(V_s - \frac{R}{2}(I_{L\phi} + I_x)\right) + \omega L(I_{L\phi} - I_x)\right) \cdot \sin \omega t\Bigg] \quad (2)$$

$$i_L(t) = I_x + e^{\alpha t} \cdot \Bigg[(I_{L\phi} - I_x) \cdot \cos \omega t + \left(\frac{2V_s - R(I_{L\phi} + I_x)}{2\omega L}\right) \cdot \sin \omega t\Bigg] \quad (3)$$

for the duration of the resonant cycle. The constants α and ω are given by

$$\alpha = R/2L$$

$$\omega_0 = (L \cdot C)^{-1/2}$$

$$\omega = (\omega_0^2 - \alpha^2)^{1/2}.$$

The preceding equations are valid until V_c returns to zero, at which instant the diode in antiparallel with the switch S conducts and clamps V_c to zero. S can then be turned on to allow i_L to build up to $I_{L\phi}$ once again.

To minimize system losses, R is made as small as feasible. Consequently, assuming that the system is highly underdamped, i.e., $R \ll \omega L$, (2) and (3) reduce to the following form:

$$V_c(t) \simeq V_s + e^{-\alpha t}[-V_s \cdot \cos \omega t + \omega L \cdot I_M \cdot \sin \omega t] \quad (4)$$

$$i_L(t) \simeq I_x + e^{-\alpha t}\left[I_m \cdot \cos \omega t + \frac{V_s}{\omega_L} \cdot \sin \omega t\right] \quad (5)$$

where

$$I_M = I_{L\phi} - I_x. \quad (6)$$

It can be seen that (4), which determines whether V_c will return to zero, is essentially independent of I_x and depends strongly on $(I_{L\phi} - I_x)$. Thus an appropriate control strategy requires that $(i_L - I_x)$ be monitored when S is conducting and that S be turned off when $(i_L - I_x)$ equals the desired value of I_M. This also gives insight into the deadbeat response anticipated. Starting the system with the foregoing initial condition implies that $v_c(t)$ is independent of the load current I_x.

Fig. 11(a) shows a simulated plot of relevant waveforms for the resonant dc link. To illustrate the effect of change in I_x

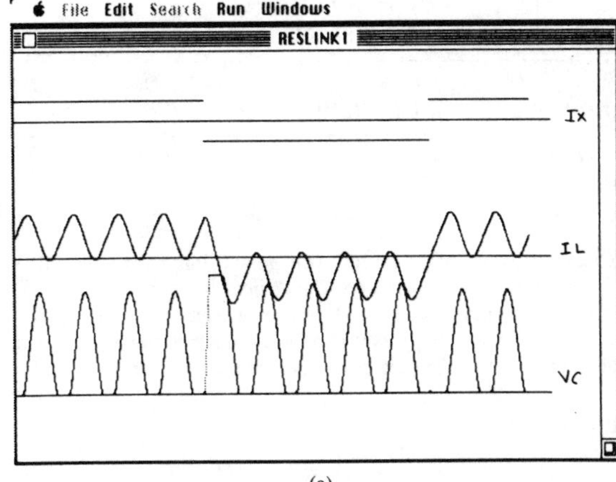

(a)

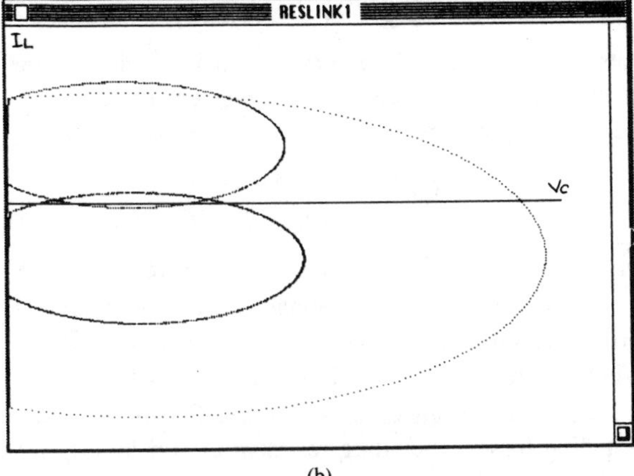

(b)

Fig. 11. Operation of resonant dc link. (a) Computed waveforms for resonant dc link operation. Top trace: dc link current into inverter I_x. Center trace: inductor current i_L. Lower trace: resonant dc link voltage v_c. (b) Phase plane plot of v_c and i_L for waveforms shown in (a).

on operating conditions, I_x is varied from its rated value of +30 A to −30 and back. During the transition from the motoring to the regenerating mode, a large overshoot is observed in $V_c(t)$ for one resonant cycle. The second transition, i.e., from regenerating to motoring, is seen to possess the deadbeat characteristic mentioned earlier. The voltage overshoot is easily contained by a voltage-clamping-type energy-recovery circuit without affecting the superior transient performance of the system. Fig. 11(b) shows a phase plane plot of $v_c(t)$ versus $i_L(t)$ for the waveforms shown in Fig. 11(a).

An optimum design can be formulated for the resonant dc link converter by minimizing the dissipation in the resonant elements. Using the circuit in Fig. 10, the dissipation in the inductor effective series resistance (ESR) is approximately given by

$$P_d = I_a^2 R + \frac{V_S^2}{2Z_0^2} \cdot R \cdot S_k \quad (7)$$

where V_s is the supply voltage, $z_0 = (L/C)^{1/2}$ is the characteristic impedance, I_a is the dc current for rated power output, and S_k is a multiplying factor which includes skin effect, proximity effect, etc. As the switching frequency is assumed by specification, S_k is taken to be a constant. For an inductor wound with N turns of wire, we can write the following

TABLE I[a]
CALCULATED SWITCHING LOSSES

Inverter type	C_s (μH)	L_s (μH)	Q	P_{sw} Device (W)	$P_{inductor}$ (W)
Hard-switching	—	—	—	180	—
H-bridge	3.2	19.8	50	8.4	202
Single-transistor	0.75	85	50	4	45

[a] Calculations are based on link voltage and link current of 150 V, 30 A, giving apparent power of 4.5 kW. The device used has $t_r = 2\ \mu s$, $t_f = 2\ \mu s$. Switching frequency is 20 kHz. This comparison only looks at the trade-off between device switching losses and losses in the additional LC tank circuit. Detailed trade-off studies are currently under examination.

relationships:

$$L = A_L \cdot N^2 \tag{8}$$

$$R = A_R \cdot N = A_R(L/A_L)^{1/2}. \tag{9}$$

Substituting (9) into (7), and minimizing P_d with respect to the resonant circuit characteristic impedance, the optimum value of Z_0 is Z_{0m}, where

$$Z_{0m} = \frac{V_s}{I_a}\left(\frac{3 \cdot S_k}{2}\right)^{1/2}. \tag{10}$$

A comparison is made between a conventional PWM inverter and both types of resonant dc link inverters. The inverters are rated at 4.5 kW with V_s volts, $I_a = 30$ A, and a switching frequency $f_s = 20$ kHz. The transistor rise time t_r is 1 μs, and the fall time t_f is 2 μs. Component values and switching losses, including resonant circuit losses, are calculated for the three configurations and are listed in Table I. Conduction losses are almost the same for all three circuits. It can be seen that the switching losses for the single transistor case are substantially lower than for the other two. Comparing the two resonant dc link inverters, the LC component values and the peak capacitor currents are also seen to be significantly lower for the single-transistor link. The biggest penalty for the new topology is in terms of the device voltage ratings required, i.e., $\geqslant 2 \cdot V_s$.

EXPERIMENTAL RESULTS

A 4.5-kW inverter was designed and fabricated using Fuji 450-V 50-A Darlington transistors to verify the concepts proposed for resonant dc link inverters. The parallel resonant tank topology was tested first and demonstrated severe modulation of the dc bus, as shown in Fig. 12(a). By way of contrast, the single-transistor resonant dc link circuit had a reasonably stable dc bus waveform, even in the presence of substantial modulation of the inductor current i_L (as shown in Figs. 12(b) and 13).

The inverter switched at 18 kHz under no-load conditions, with $L = 65\ \mu$H and $C = 1\ \mu$F and no snubber networks. The losses in the resonant circuit were predominantly in the Litz wire inductor and totaled 35 W at 100 V dc. Device switching losses were nonexistent, as can be ascertained from the $V_{CE} - I_C$ switching locus for the resonant transitor (Fig. 14). This resulted in a substantial reduction in the size of the inverter transistor heat sinks.

The inverter was controlled via a delta-modulation-type controller which was synchronized to the resonant link frequency f_{synch}. A block schematic of the controller is shown in Fig. 15. Control strategies for inverters with regularly sampled data system characteristics raise interesting questions, which are the focus of current investigations. Fig. 16 shows line–line voltage and line–current waveforms while operating with an induction motor load. The line–line voltage consists of a three-level waveform with discrete resonant pulses of zero positive or negativ epolarity and represents an discrete pulse modulation (DPM) pattern (Fig. 12(b)).

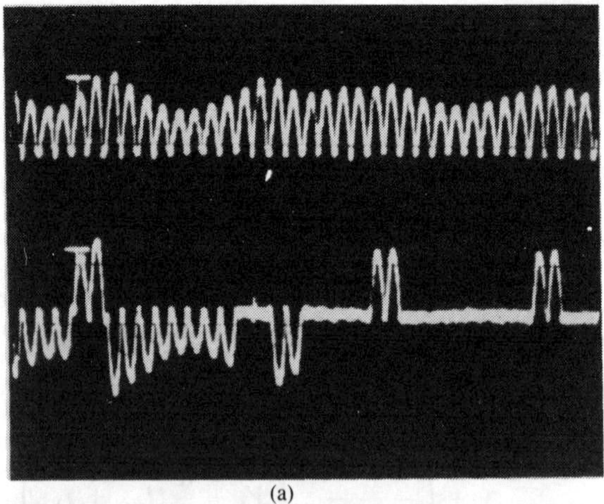

(a)

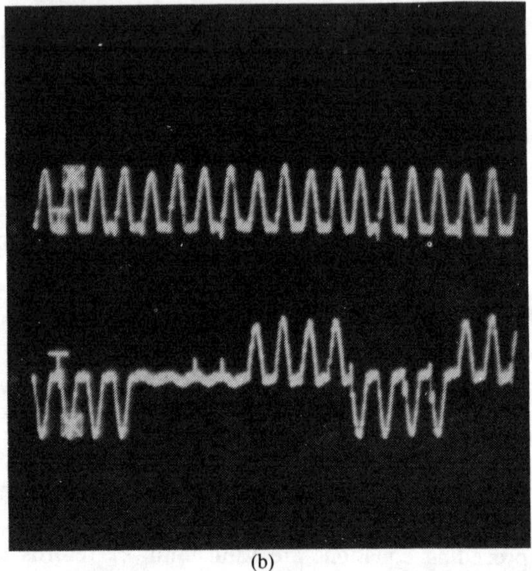

(b)

Fig. 12. Oscillograms of dc bus modulation in presence of DPM switching. (a) For H-bridge resonant dc link inverter. Top trace: dc bus voltage. Lower trace: line–line voltage. (b) Same traces as in (a) but for single-transistor resonant dc link.

Fig. 17(a) shows the frequency spectrum of the line–line voltage demonstrating an almost total absence of any objectionable harmonics. The major spectral component, besides the fundamental, is centered around the carrier frequency of 18 · 1 kHz and possesses the characteristic double peak of carrier-modulated systems. Fig. 17(b) shows the spectrum of the average energy contained in the line–line voltage over a wide bandwidth of 20 kHz. The response is symmetrial around 9 kHz, a consequence of the 18-kHz sampling frequency. It also demonstrates the absence of any dominant frequency components in the audible range and has a spectral response which is reminiscent of colored noise, a result of the nonintegral and

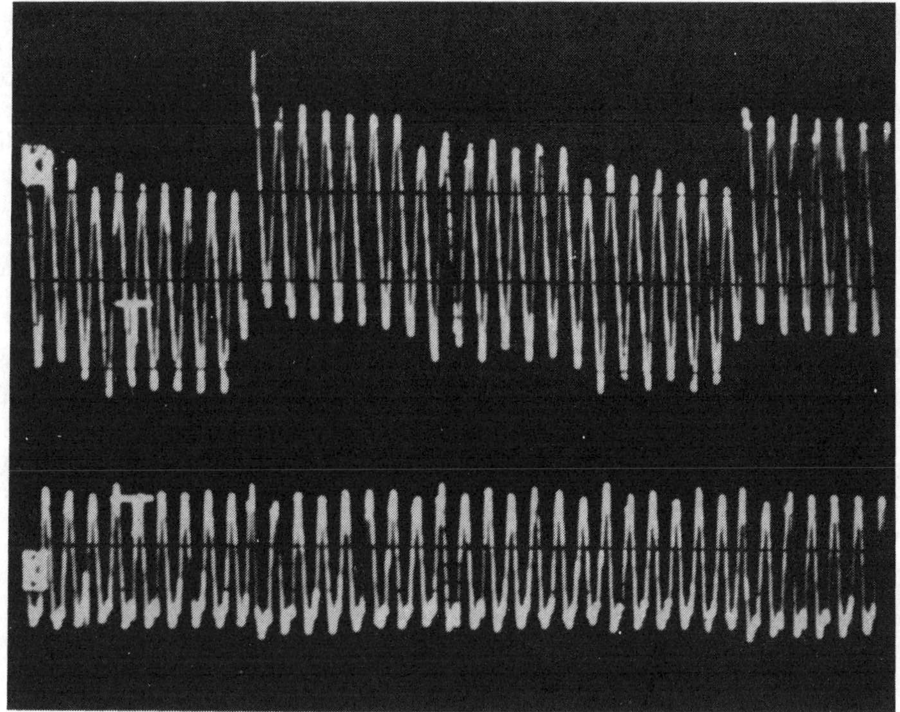

Fig. 13. Plot of inductor current i_L (upper trace) and dc bus voltage (lower trace) under similar IPWM conditions, showing significant instantaneous change in i_L (V_{dc} = 300 V peak, i_L = 50 A peak-to-peak, 18-kHz switching frequency).

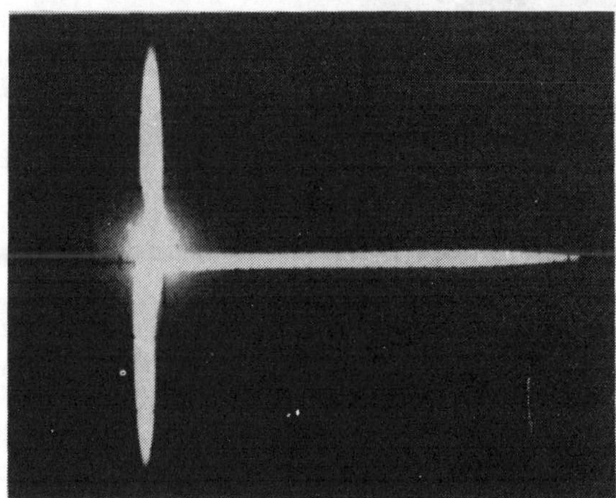

Fig. 14. $V_{CE} - I_C$ switching locus for resonant dc link transistor (switch S) showing absence of switching losses.

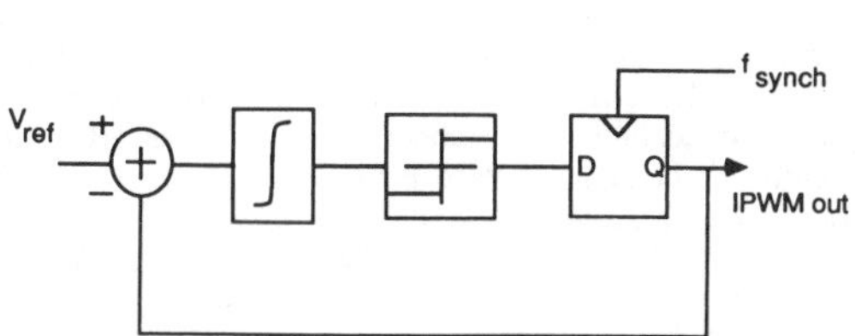

Fig. 15. Block schematic of delta DPM controller. Note absence of any hysteresis in comparator. DC link oscillation frequency and low-frequency ac signal are not synchronized in any manner.

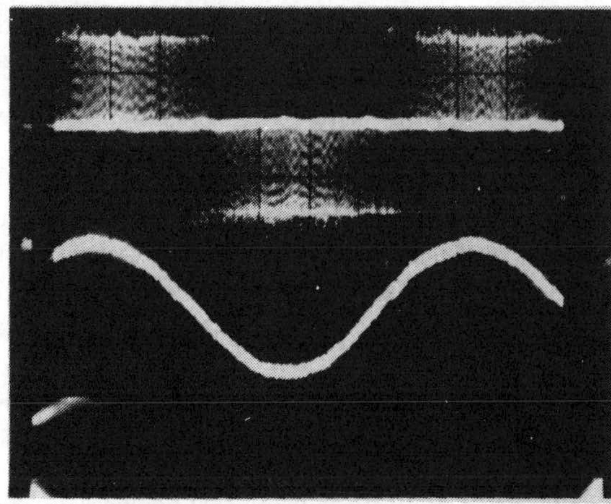

Fig. 16. Line–line voltage and line current waveforms when connected to induction motor load (voltage: 200 V/div; current: 5 A/div; time: 5 ms/div).

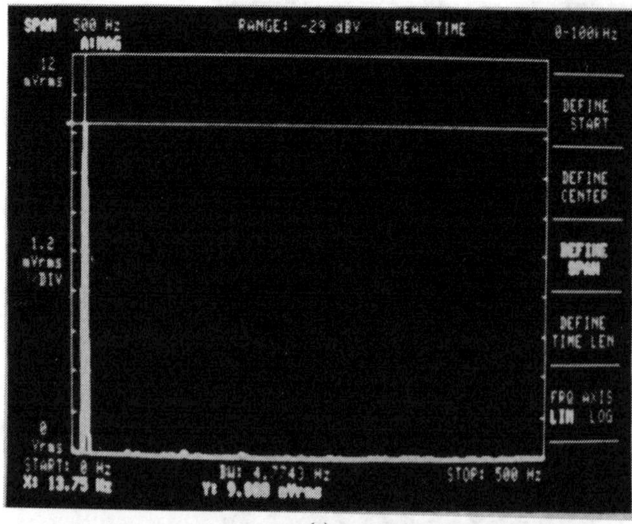

(a)

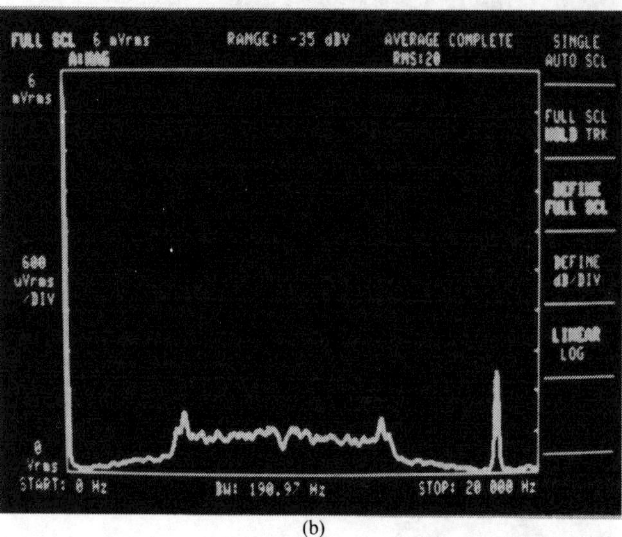

(b)

Fig. 17. (a) Frequency spectrum of line–line voltage showing low harmonic content with fundamental at 13.7–500 Hz bandwidth. (b) Same spectrum as (a), but over 20-kHz bandwidth shows characteristic folded spectrum of sampled data system.

constantly dithering carrier-to-signal-frequency ratios. This has a profound effect on the audible noise generated by the system. Instead of the "wailing banshee" effect typical of PWM systems, the motor–inverter combination is quiet and produces an inoffensive hissing sound. It is also felt that the lower noise levels are due, at least in part, to the moderate dv/dt lelvels experienced by the motor windings.

Conclusion

This paper has presented a new approach to realizing efficient high-performance power converters. The concept of a resonant dc link inverter has been proposed and realized with the addition of only one small inductor and capacitor to a conventional voltage source inverter circuit. The new topology is capable of switching an order of magnitude faster than state-of-the-art VSI's at significantly improved efficiencies using the same family of devices. The topology is especially suitable for high-power applications using GTO devices.

The topology exhibits unique operating characteristics which enhance its usefulness in an industrial environment. The deadbeat response gives excellent control of transient stresses and minimizes the impact of most load or supply side faults on the system. The circuit has a simple power structure, low losses, and no snubbers. System reliability is improved because the devices have no switching losses. The high switching speed makes it possible to design very high bandwidth current regulators with all the concomitant advantages. Acoustic noise associated with variable-speed drives, often a problem in industrial and commercial plants, is also dramatically reduced. The resonant dc link concept can also be simply extended to a multiquadrant three-phase-ac-to-three-phase-ac power converter with low harmonic currents on both the input and the output sides.

Summing up the various features of the resonant dc link inverter, we can see the following advantages:

- minimum number of power devices,
- elimination of switching losses and snubbers,
- high switching frequency,
- low acoustic noise,
- excellent dynamics and transient response,
- multiquadrant operation,
- unity PF and low harmonics on ac line side,
- low sensitivity to parasitic impedance and device recovery effects,
- maximization of power density,
- suitable for high power levels with GTO devices,
- simple control strategy and power structure.

A 4.5-kW inverter has been fabricated and tested extensively in the laboratory, and the superior characteristics of the resonant dc link topology have been amply verified.

Acknowledgment

Fabrication assistance from G. Skiblinski, O. Patterson, and M. Kheraluwala is greatly appreciated.

References

[1] E. T. Calkin and B. H. Hamilton, "Circuit techniques for improving the switching loci of transistor switching regulators," in *IEEE Annu. Conf. Rec.*, 1972, pp. 477–484.

[2] W. McMurray, "Selection of snubbers and clamps to optimize the design of transistor switching converters," *IEEE Trans. Ind. Appl.*, vol. IA-16, no. 4, pp. 513–523, July/Aug. 1980.

[3] —, "Efficient snubbers for voltage source GTO inverters," in *IEEE Power Electronics Specialists Conf. Rec.*, 1985, pp. 20–27.

[4] T. M. Undeland, F. Jenset, and A. Steinbakk, "A snubber configuration for both power transistors and GTO PWM inverters," *IEEE Power Electronics Specialists Conf. Rec.*, 1984, pp. 42–53.

[5] F. C. Zach, K. H. Kaiser, J. W. Kolar, and F. J. Haselsteiner," New lossless turn-on and turn-off (snubber) networks for inverters, including circuits for blocking voltage limitation," *IEEE Trans. Power Electron.*, vol. PE-1, no. 2.

[6] F. C. Schwarz and J. Ben Klaassens, "A controllable 45 kW current source for dc machines," *IEEE Trans. Ind. Appl.*, vol. IA-15, no. 4, pp. 437–444, July/Aug. 1979.

[7] R. L. Steigerwals, "High frequency resonatn transistor dc–dc converters," *IEEE Trans. Ind. Electron.*, vol. IE-31, no. 2, pp. 181–191, May 1984.

[8] R. Oruganti and F. C. Lee, "Resonant power processors: Part 1—State plane analysis," in *IEEE Industry Applications Soc. Annu. Meeting Conf. Rec.*, 1984, pp. 860–867.

[9] P. D. Ziogas, V. T. Ranganathan, and V. R. Stefanovic, "A four-quadrant current regulated converter with a high frequency link,"

IEEE Trans. Ind. Appl., vol. IA-18, no. 5, pp. 499–506, Sept./Oct. 1982.

[10] P. M. Espelage and B. K. Bose, "High frequency link power conversion," in *IEEE Ind. Appl. Soc. Annu. Meeting Conf. Rec.*, 1975, pp. 802–808.

[11] L. Gyugyi and F. Cibulka, "The high-frequency base converter—A new approach to static high-power conversion," *IEEE Trans. Ind. Appl.*, vol. IA-15, no. 4, July/Aug. 1979.

[12] H. Huisman and S. W. H. deHaan, "A dc to 3-phase series-resonant converter with low harmonic distortion," *IEEE Trans. Ind. Electron.*, vol. IE-32, no. 2, pp. 142–149, May 1985.

[13] F. C. Schwarz, "A doublesided cycloconverter," *IEEE Trans. Ind. Electron. Contr. Instrum.*, vol. IECI-28, no. 4, pp. 282–291, Nov. 1981.

[14] B. D. Bedford, "Versatile cycloinverter power converter circuits," U.S. Patent 3 742 336, June 26, 1975.

[15] L. Gyugyi, "Static power conversion arrangement for converting direct current power to alternating current power," U.S. Patent 3 875 494, Apr. 1, 1975.

[16] B. R. Pelly and L. Gyugyi, "Naturally commutated cycloconverter with controlled input displacement power factor," U.S. Patent 4 013 037, Mar. 22, 1977.

[17] P. Sood and T. A. Lipo, "Power conversion distribution system using a resonant high-frequency ac link," *IEEE Ind. Appl. Soc. Annu. Meeting Conf. Rec.*, 1986.

[18] D. M. Divan, "Design considerations for very high frequency resonant mode dc/dc converters," *IEEE Ind. Appl. Soc. Annu. Meeting Conf. Rec.*, 1986.

AN INDUCTION MOTOR DRIVE USING AN IMPROVED HIGH FREQUENCY RESONANT DC LINK INVERTER[1]

Jih-Sheng Lai[2]
Power Electronics Applications Center
Tennessee Center for Research & Development
Knoxville, Tennessee 37932
Telephone: (615) 675-9585

Bimal K. Bose[3]
Department of Electrical Engineering
University of Tennessee, Knoxville
Knoxville, Tennessee 37996-2100
Telephone: (615) 675-9505

Abstract

This paper presents an induction motor drive using an improved high frequency resonant *dc* link inverter. The resonant circuit was systematically analyzed first to establish the criteria for initial current selection, and a new circuit was then proposed to establish the bidirectional initial current. The proposed current initialization scheme solves voltage overshoot and zero crossing failure problems in the ordinary resonant *dc* link inverters. A 3-phase 3kW *IGBT* based 60kHz resonant link inverter has been constructed and successfully tested with an induction motor drive. The speed control system is implemented using two microprocessors – TMS320C25 for computation and INTEL 80386 for monitoring and user interface. Experimental results are presented to show superior operation of the proposed resonant *dc* link inverter drive.

1. Introduction

Resonant link inverters show tremendous promise for next generation adjustable speed *ac* machine drives. The resonant link circuit provides periodic zero voltage or zero current interval to eliminate switching loss, and thus permitting the inverter switching at high frequency [1~8]. The resonant circuit connection can be in series or in parallel, and the link voltage can be *ac* or *dc*. Among several types of resonant link inverters, the zero voltage switching parallel resonant *dc* link inverter is most promising for next generation *ac* motor drives [7].

Zero voltage switching of devices provides a number of advantages over the full voltage switching in a regular *PWM* inverter. The major advantages of zero voltage switching resonant *dc* link inverter are zero switching loss, minimal cooling requirement, high power density, high efficiency, high reliability, no snubber circuit, no acoustic noise, low capacitive coupling current on machine windings because of low inverter output voltage change rate dV/dt, low *EMI*, and smooth generated torque and acceleration.

However, the zero voltage switching resonant *dc* link inverter has some fundamental problems such as voltage overshoot, zero crossing failure, and inverter phase current ripple due to integral cycle switching. With *dc* supply voltage V_s, the peak resonant link voltage swings to $2V_s$ under no-load condition. If the inverter input current changes from maximum positive (motoring mode) to maximum negative (regenerative mode), the overshoot voltage will be higher than $3V_s$. To solve the voltage overshoot problem, numerous approaches had been proposed. A passive clamping technique was proposed [2] to limit the voltage to $2.5V_s$. While an active clamping technique could limit the voltage to $1.3V_s$, its delay of resonance causes performance degradation [2]. The inverter in this paper uses a current initialization scheme [9,10] to solve voltage overshoot and zero voltage crossing problems simultaneously. The current initialization resonant link circuit limits the link voltage to $2V_s$ and assures zero crossing under all conditions of inverter operation. The initial current is bidirectional in nature and is established by an auxiliary circuit which operates at low frequency. The resonant circuit has been analyzed to establish the criteria of the initial current. The inverter-machine system has been simulated using *PC-SIMNON* and performance has been studied at 25kHz and 50kHz resonant frequencies [9,10].

After computer verification, a 3-phase, 3kW, Insulated Gate Bipolar Transistor *(IGBT)* based 60kHz resonant link inverter was fabricated. The induction motor drive system uses vector or field oriented with hysteresis-band current in the inner loop. The three-phase reference currents are generated by a computer control system. The complete microcomputer system consists of a digital signal processor *(DSP)* TMS320C25 with two-channel input and two-channel output data acquisition board and a 80386 *IBM PC-AT* compatible computer.

2. An Improved Resonant DC Link Inverter

Figure 1 shows the proposed resonant *dc* link inverter with bidirectional current initialization. Normally, switch S_A remains closed for regular operation. For positive initial current establishment, simply turn on switch S_r, and the inductor current will increase with slope V_s/L_r. For decreasing the inductor current, S_A is turned off and S_B and S_r are turned on so that the current decrementation is ob-

[1]This project was funded to University of Tennessee, Knoxville by Electric Power Research Institute through Power Electronics Applications Center.

[2]Dr. Lai is also with the University of Tennessee, Knoxville as an Adjunct Assistant Professor.

[3]Dr. Bose is also the Chief Scientist of the Power Electronics Applications Center.

Reprinted from *IEEE Power Electron. Specialists Conf. (PESC) Rec.*, pp. 792–799, 1990.

tained with slope V_B/L_r, where V_B is the auxiliary *dc* voltage established by a half-wave rectifier. In normal motoring condition of the system, switches S_A and S_B operate at a small fraction of the resonant frequency and contribute some additional loss, but the overall efficiency improvement of the resonant inverter is retained.

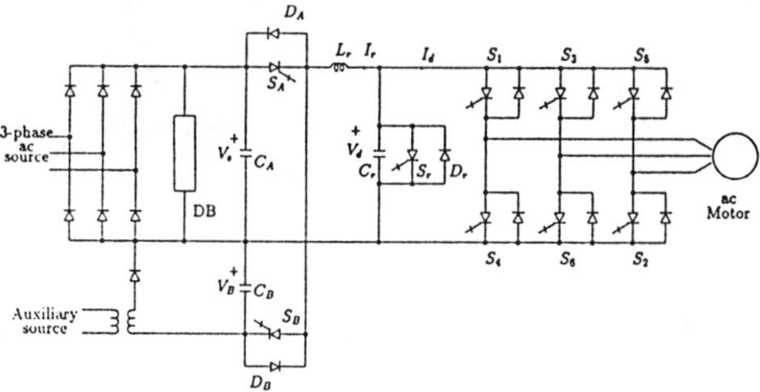

Figure 1: Resonant *dc* link inverter with bidirectional current initialization.

Basic operation of the resonant link circuit is a function of *LC* resonance and switch modulation. The operation can be divided into three different modes as shown in Figure 2 [10].

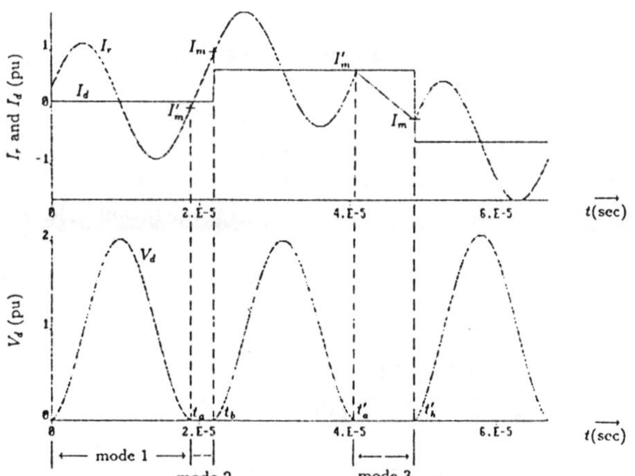

Figure 2: Operation modes of the resonant *dc* link inverter.

- Mode 1: This is the regular resonant cycle when S_A is on, but S_r and S_B are off. The network equations can be written as

$$V_s(t) = I_r(t)R_r + \frac{d\,I_r(t)}{dt}L_r + V_d(t) \qquad (1)$$

$$I_r(t) = I_d(t) + C_r\frac{d\,V_d(t)}{dt} \qquad (2)$$

with initial states $V_d(0) = 0$ and $I_r(0) = I_m$. The inverter input current I_d is assumed to be constant during each resonant cycle if the load inductance is sufficiently high. This assumption is true for most motor loads. The maximum voltage in a resonant cycle can be derived as

$$V_d(t_1) = (V_s - I_dR_r)[1 - \frac{1}{\sqrt{1-\zeta^2}}e^{-\alpha t_1}\sin(\omega t_1 + \theta)] + \frac{(I_m - I_d)Z_r}{\sqrt{1-\zeta^2}}e^{-\alpha t_1}\sin\omega t_1 \qquad (3)$$

where

$$t_1 = [\pi + \tan^{-1}\frac{2\sqrt{1-\zeta^2}(I_d - I_m)Z_r}{2V_s - (I_d + I_m)R_r}]/\omega$$

and

$\omega_r = 1/\sqrt{L_rC_r}$ = resonant frequency
$\alpha = R_r/2L_r$ = decrement factor
$\zeta = R_r/2Z_r$ = damping ratio
$Z_r = \sqrt{L_r/C_r}$ = characteristic impedance
$\omega = \omega_r\sqrt{1-\zeta^2}$ = oscillation frequency
$\theta = \cos^{-1}\zeta = \tan^{-1}\frac{\sqrt{1-\zeta^2}}{\zeta}$

The minimum voltage in a resonant cycle can be given as

$$V_d(t_2) = (V_s - I_dR_r)[1 - \frac{1}{\sqrt{1-\zeta^2}}e^{-\alpha t_2}\sin(\omega t_2 + \theta)] + \frac{(I_m - I_d)Z_r}{\sqrt{1-\zeta^2}}e^{-\alpha t_2}\sin\omega t_2 \qquad (4)$$

where

$$t_2 = [2\pi + \tan^{-1}\frac{2\sqrt{1-\zeta^2}(I_d - I_m)Z_r}{2V_s - (I_d + I_m)R_r}]/\omega$$

The voltage $V_d(t_1)$ is the maximum voltage at time t_1, and $V_d(t_2)$ is the minimum voltage at time t_2. The voltage overshoot occurs when $V_d(t_1) > 2V_s$, and the zero voltage crossing is lost when $V_d(t_2) > 0$. Figure 3 shows the general plot of $V_d(t_1)$ from (3) for different inverter input currents ($I_d = -1.0I_L \sim 1.0I_L$). Figure 4 gives the general plot of $V_d(t_2)$ from (4). It is evident from the curves that the initial current I_m has to be made programmable as a function of the inverter input current I_d in order to satisfy the criteria for voltage overshoot and zero voltage crossing requirement. Typical zone of I_m variation is shown in Figures 3 and 4. The zero skew of 0.3 occurs because of positive initial current requirement. For example, if the inverter is unloaded (i.e., $I_d = 0$), the initial current $I_m = 0.3$ will satisfy the initial current requirement.

- Mode 2: In this mode, the current I_d increases as a result of inverter switching so that I'_m has to be incremented to match with the incoming I_d. Therefore, S_A and S_r remain on, but S_B remains off during the zero crossing interval. The inductor current I'_m at the leading edge increases to I_m at the trailing edge where the current increases with the slope V_s/L_r. With t_a and t_b as the time at the leading edge and the trailing edge, respectively, the operation can be expressed as

$$I_r(t_b) - I_r(t_a) \approx \frac{V_s}{L_r}(t_b - t_a) \tag{5}$$

where $I_r(t_b) = I_m$ and $I_r(t_a) = I'_m$. The control circuit should detect I_r and return to mode 1 when the desired current is reached.

- Mode 3: In this mode, the current I_d transitions to a lower values (which can be positive or negative), i.e., the current I_d is less than I'_m such that I'_m requires decrementation ($I_m < I'_m$). By turning off S_A and turning on S_B and S_r during zero crossing interval, the inductor current will decrease at the slope V_B/L_r. With time t'_a at leading edge and t'_b at the trailing edge, the current decrementation can be given as

$$I_r(t'_b) - I_r(t'_a) = I_m - I'_m \approx \frac{V_B}{L_r}(t'_b - t'_a) \tag{6}$$

where V_B can be assumed as constant.

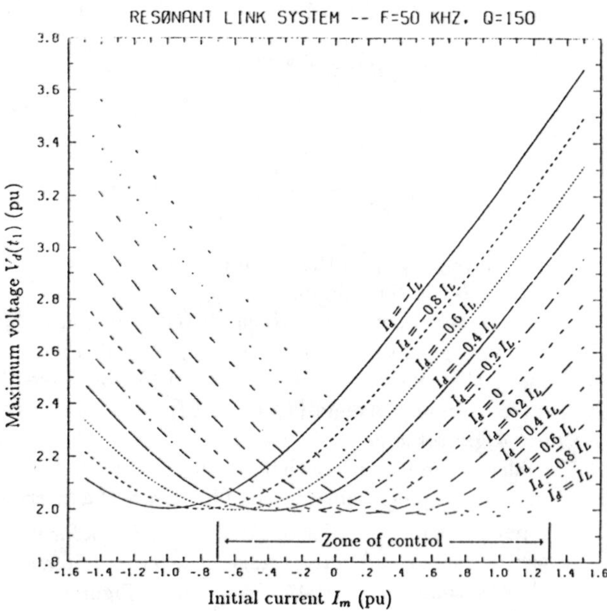

Figure 3: Maximum resonant circuit voltage $[V_d(t_1)]$ as function of I_m for different inverter input currents.

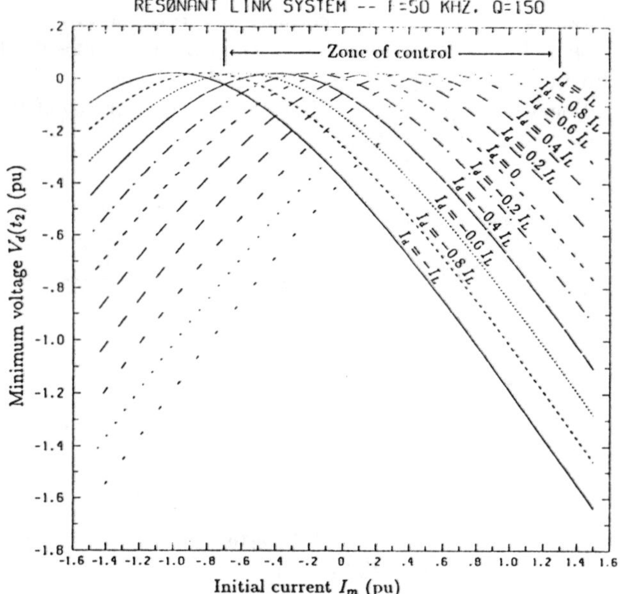

Figure 4: Minimum resonant circuit voltage $[V_d(t_2)]$ as function of I_m for different inverter input currents.

In most industrial drives, the regenerative mode operation occurs much less frequently as compared to the motoring mode. In other words, mode 3 occurs at low frequency, and therefore the additional $-I_m$ initialization switching loss is negligible. In some cases, the inverter requires more regenerative operation and sees more $-I_m$ initialization. However, the overall efficiency in these cases will not be degraded because the motor energy is being pumped back to the input side.

3. The Resonant Link Inverter Induction Motor Drive

The block diagram of the complete inverter induction motor speed control system is shown in Figure 5. The control system uses indirect method of vector control where the speed control loop generates the torque component of current I^*_{qs} whereas the flux component of current I^*_{ds} is set independently [11,12]. Both the currents I^*_{qs} and I^*_{ds} are converted into stationary reference frame and then to three phase reference currents I^*_a, I^*_b, and I^*_c. The reference currents are compared with the actual phase currents I_a, I_b, and I_c to give the required switching pattern. The hysteresis-band current controller generates the switching logic for the inverter and the current prediction circuits. The predicted current $\hat{I}_d$ is then fed into resonant link control circuit to ensure reliable resonant operation. The inverter input current prediction circuit can be simply implemented by an analog multiplexer as shown in Figure 6.

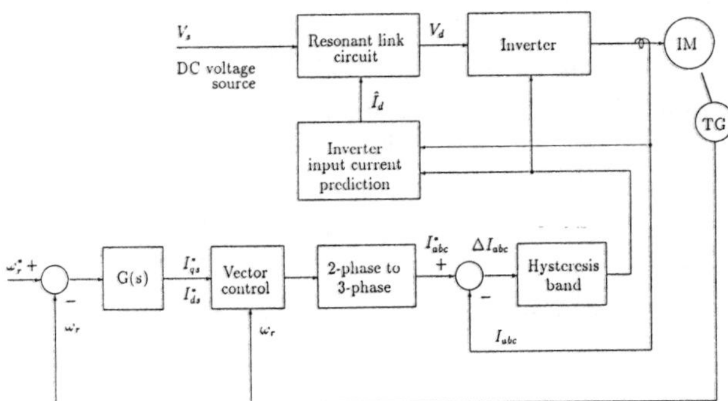

Figure 5: Block diagram of resonant link inverter and induction motor speed control system.

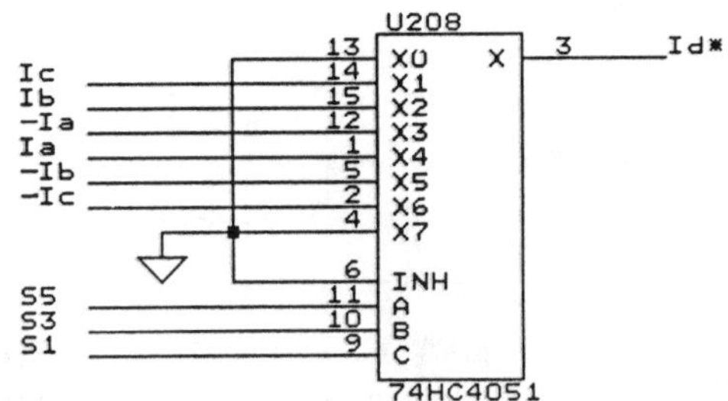

Figure 6: Inverter input current prediction implemented by an analog multiplexer.

Using *PC-SIMNON* [13], the simulated resonant link voltage and current waves are shown in Figure 7. The resonant link voltage remains constant although the inverter input current varies between positive and negative depending on the induction motor currents and inverter switching patterns.

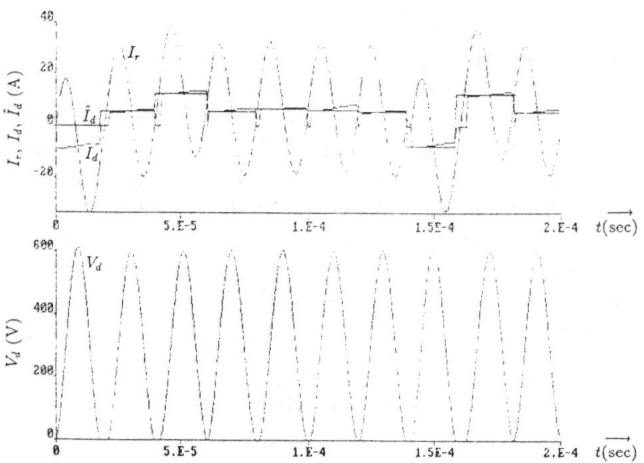

Figure 7: Simulated resonant link voltage and current of the proposed resonant link inverter.

4. Experiment

After computer simulation verification, a 60kHz resonant link inverter was constructed. The high speed *IGBT* [14,15] is selected as the switching device because of its high switching speed and low conduction loss. The value of passive components L_r and C_r can be simply determined by resonant frequency and characteristic impedance, i.e.,

$$f_r = 1/\sqrt{L_r C_r}$$
$$Z_r = \sqrt{L_r/C_r}$$

The experimental resonant link circuit components are listed in Table 1.

Table 1: Resonant link Circuit Components.

Device	Specification
IGBT	600 V, 40 A, IXGH40N60A
Diode	600 V, 30 A, MUR3060PT
Capacitor	0.328 μF, SBE716P600V (.082μF × 4)
Inductor	21.2 μH, Litz wire, air core

4.1 No Load Test

Under no-load condition, the resonant voltage and current waveforms are shown in Figure 8. With supply voltage 150V, the peak resonant voltage is 300V, and the peak current is 20A. It can be seen that under constant initial current control the peak voltage maintains constant as expected.

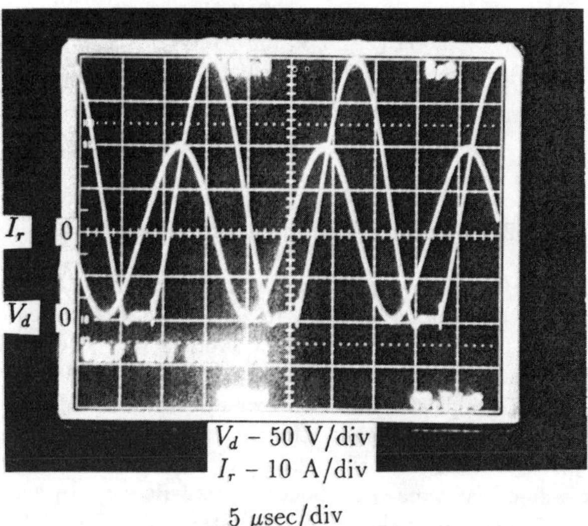

Figure 8: Experimental results of resonant voltage and current under no-load condition.

4.2 Load Test

After successful test under no-load operation, the resonant link circuit was then tested with two 3-phase induction motors rated at 2-HP and 5-HP, respectively which were coupled to a 7.5HP regenerative dynamometer. Typical resonant link current and voltage under loaded condition are shown in Figure 9. Mostly, the inverter input current appears positive but drops to negative occasionally. Although the resonant link current I_r varies with the inverter input current I_d, the peak resonant voltage V_d remains constant. The zero voltage crossing interval also varies with different inverter input current.

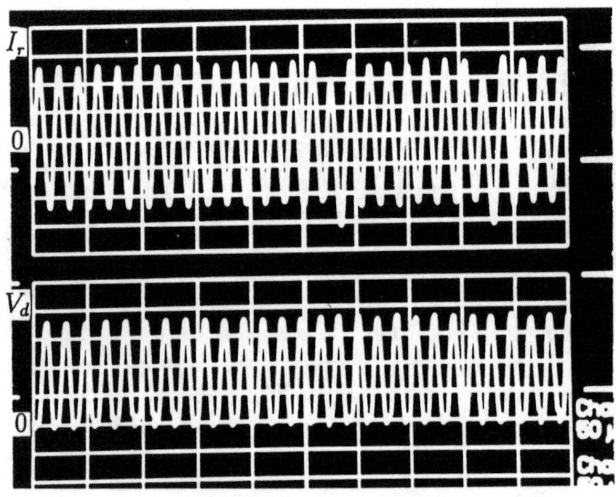

upper trace – I_r (5 A/div)
lower trace – V_d (50 V/div)

Figure 9: Resonant link voltage and current under loaded condition.

4.3 Zero Voltage Switching Characteristics

Figure 10(a) shows *IGBT* zero voltage turn-on behavior. After the link voltage V_d drops to zero, the device current gradually builds up by applying a gate voltage V_{GS}. The gate voltage reaches the threshold voltage $V_{GS(th)}$ within 100*n*sec. Figure 10(b) indicates *IGBT* zero voltage turn-off behavior. The device turns off rapidly after the gate voltage drops to $V_{GS(th)}$. The turn-off delay time $t_{d(off)}$ is about 200*n*sec, and the trun-off fall time t_f is about 100*n*sec. Both $t_{d(off)}$ and t_f are 5 times faster than the specification values [16]. The tail current which typically lasts 300 ~ 500*n*sec [15] in full voltage switching disappears in zero voltage switching.

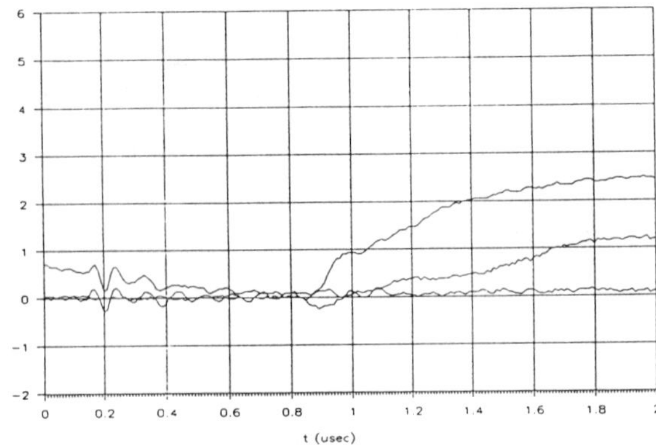

(a) Zero voltage turn-on.

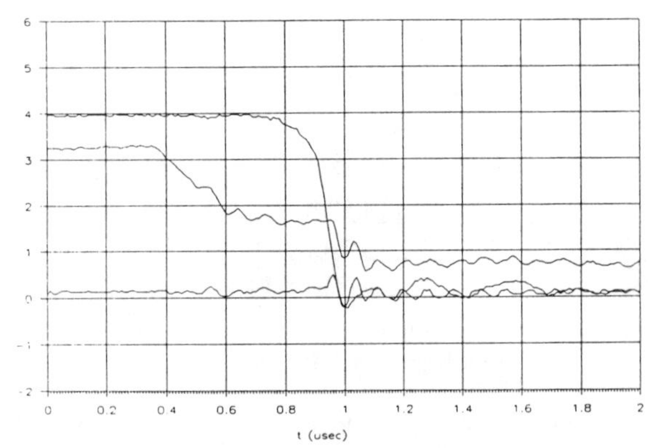

(b) Zero voltage turn-off.

Figure 10: *IGBT* zero voltage switching characteristics.

4.4 Output Characteristics

With *dc* supply voltage 100V and 50Hz fundamental reference input frequency, the resulting output phase current and voltage are shown in Figure 11. The upper trace shows phase A current which is a clean sinusoidal wave. Most harmonic contents are less than −50db. Only few components including 55kHz switching frequency are high at about −40db. The lower trace shows the phase A output voltage which is synthesized by the resonant pulse train. The most significant harmonic content is −20db at 55kHz switching frequency. However most objectionable harmonic contents are at −40db range. It can be seen that the high frequency resonant link inverter requires only small size filter if the output is to serve as a power supply.

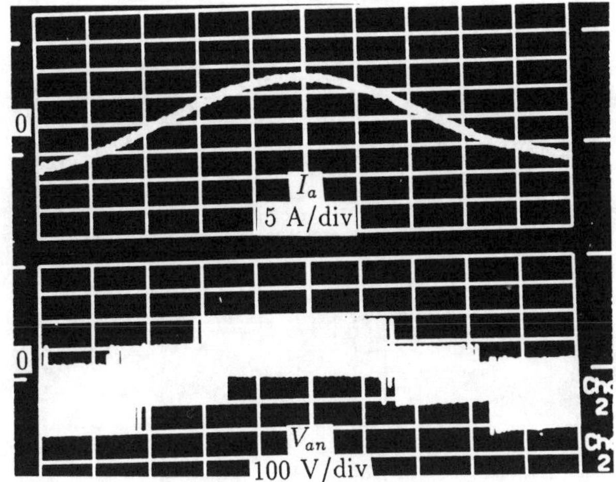

(a) phase current and voltage (2ms/div)

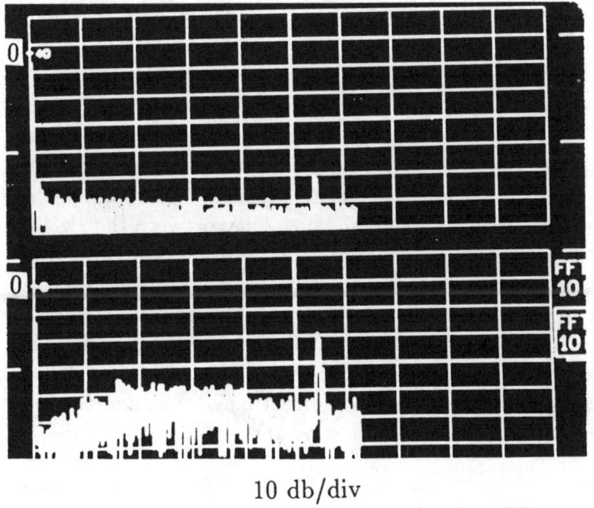

10 db/div

(b) corresponding frequency spectra (10kHz/div)

Figure 11: Experimental results of phase voltage and current for the resonant link inverter.

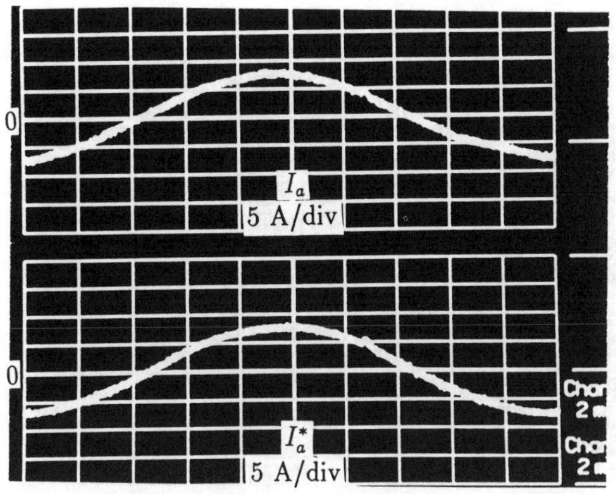

(a) actual and reference currents (5A/div, 2ms/div)

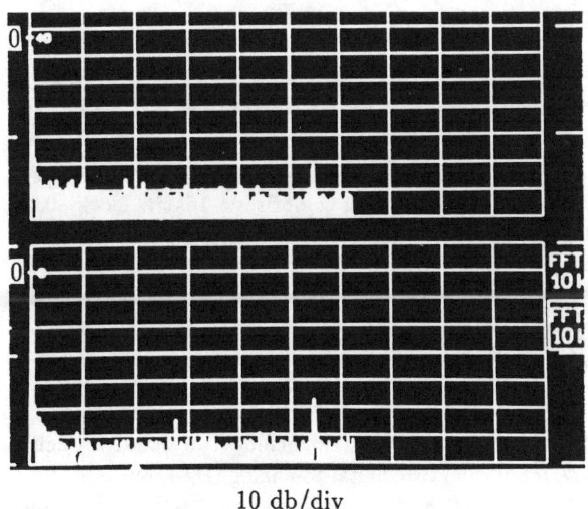

10 db/div

(b) corresponding frequency spectra (10kHz/div)

Figure 12: Comparison of the actual and reference phase currents.

Figure 12 compares the actual and reference phase currents. Although the reference current is somewhat corrupted by circuit noises, the output phase current remains a clean sinusoidal wave. With higher than 50kHz switching, the output current ripple is smoothed out.

Figure 13 compares the predicted and actual inverter currents. The inverter input current is correctly predicted at every resonant cycle. Notice that the assumption made in Section 2 that the inverter input current I_d maintains constant during each resonant cycle appears to be acceptable by looking at the actual measurement.

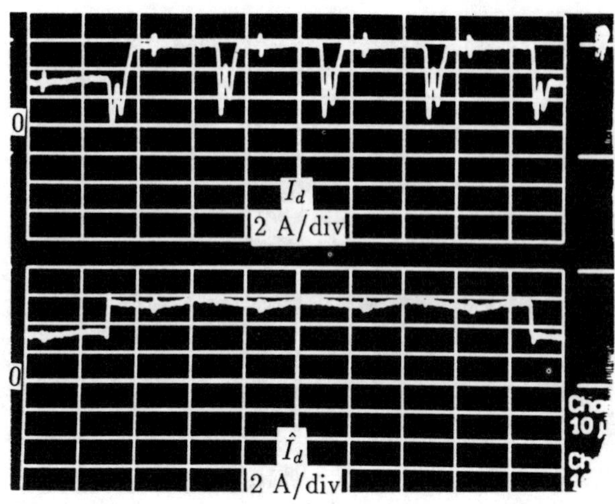

10 μsec/div

Figure 13: Comparison of the actual and predicted inverter input currents.

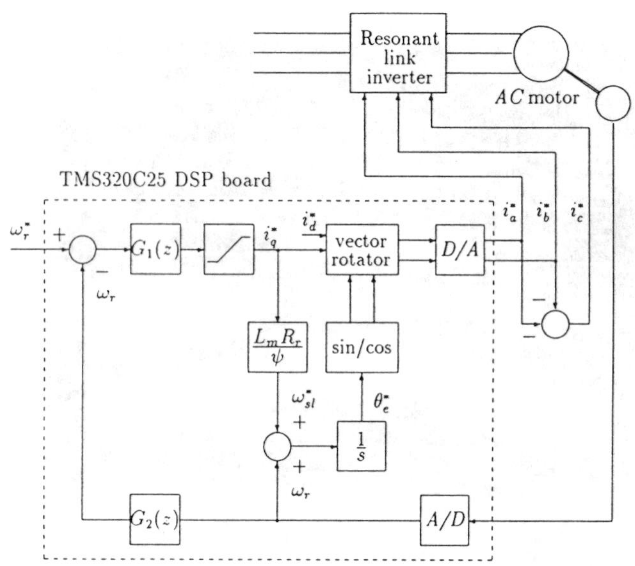

Figure 14: Computer speed control system for resonant link inverter drive.

5. Microcomputer Speed Control System

The induction motor speed is controlled by a microcomputer system. This system comprises a 16MHz clock 80386 *CPU PC-AT* compatible personal computer – *PEP-301* and a 40MHz clock TMS320C25 *CPU* data acquisition system *DSP-16* [17]. The *PEP-301* serves for user interactive interface and program development while the *DSP-16* does most computations and data *I/O.* The complete computer speed control system block diagram for resonant *dc* link inverter drive is shown in Figure 14.

The data acquisition system includes two analog-to-digital *(A/D)* inputs and two digital-to-analog *(D/A)* outputs. Both input and output signals are filtered by 20kHz anti-aliasing low pass filters. Only one input channel is used for speed feedback while two output channels are feeding reference current signals into the resonant link inverter.

There are two portions in the induction motor speed control system. The first portion is a speed error detector and a *PI* controller, and the second portion is a vector controller to generate 3-phase sinusoidal currents for inverter reference. Because the TMS320C25 is not efficient in doing floating point computation, the controller is designed in such a way that all numbers are scaled to be suitable for integer manipulation.

As shown in Figure 14, there are two digital controllers in the control system. The first is a *PI* controller $G_1(z)$, and the second controller is a low pass filter $G_2(z)$ for feedback speed. The design procedure is to obtain the transfer function in s-domain first, and then transform it into z-domain using bilinear transformation to ensure stability.

The real time closed-loop speed control was implemented using assembly language, and the interactive monitor program was written in *C* language. Although the monitor program introduces a communication delay between the *PC* bus and the *DSP* board, the motor acceleration is smooth. Figure 15 shows the acceleration characteristics of the resonant link inverter induction motor drive. The upper trace shows speed responses accelerating from 300rpm to 750rpm. The lower trace shows the induction motor phase current. When running at steady-state, the current magnitude and the fundamental frequency remain constant.

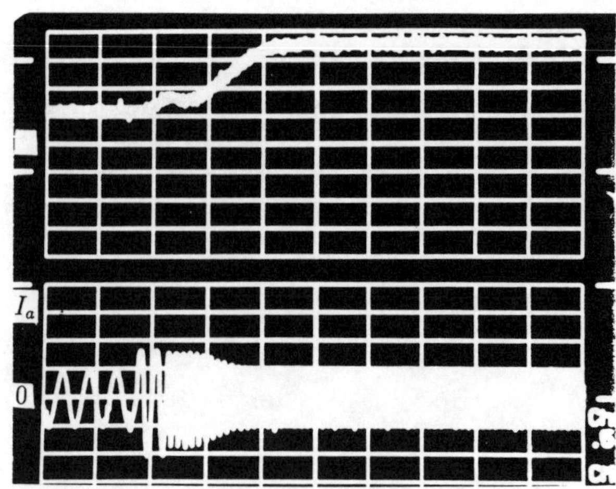

Figure 15: Induction motor acceleration profile.

6. Discussion and Conclusion

In this paper, an improved high frequency resonant *dc* link inverter was proposed and implemented. The resonant frequency has been raised to 60kHz, and the inverter has been tested with a 2HP and a 5HP induction motor. The voltage overshoot and zero crossing failure problems in resonant *dc* link inverters have been solved by the proposed current initialization scheme.

When driving the induction motor, the inverter does not introduce any objectionable harmonics or torque pulsation, and thus the operation condition is extremely quiet and smooth. The resonant link inverter has shown success for high efficiency and high performance *ac* motor drives.

Although the resonant link inverter experiment has been successfully tested at 5-HP level, a potential problem in extending the power range is the limitation of power switching device. The current high frequency high power devices can be comfortably used for 230V *ac* systems. But for 480V systems, higher voltage rated devices are desirable even though voltage clamping methods are employed to reduce the peak voltage. In addition to power device limitation, the high frequency high power passive components are also having availability problem. The resonant inductor must be made of small stranded Litz wire in order to reduce high frequency skin effect. Custom design of such wire is necessary and is costly. The source of resonant capacitor is another problem when extending resonant frequency and power range. In the above experimental setup, four polypropylene capacitors are parallelled together in order to have enough current handling capability because there is no off-the-shelf capacitor at the required current level.

Notice that the inverter heat sink requirement is negligible compared to conventional *dc* link inverters. The snubber circuit is definitely not necessary in this type of inverter. Once the component availability problem is solved, the size and cost of the resonant *dc* link inverter will be further brought down. The proposed generic resonant link converter topology can also be extended and used for other applications like *UPS*, *dc* machine drives, and active power line filters. With promising features and excellent performance, it can be expected that resonant link inverters will become the main stream of the new generation of power conversions.

References

[1] D. M. Divan, "The Resonant DC Link Converter - A New Concept in Static Power Conversion," in *Conf. Rec. IEEE IAS Annual Meeting*, pp. 648-656, 1986.

[2] D. M. Divan and G. Skibinski, "Zero Switching Loss Inverters for High Power Applications," in *Conf. Rec. IEEE IAS Annual Meeting*, pp. 627-634, 1987.

[3] D. M. Divan, G. Venkataramanan, and R. W. De-Doncker, "Design Methodologies for Soft Switched Inverters," in *Conf. Rec. IEEE IAS Annual Meeting*, pp. 758–766, 1988.

[4] T. G. Habetler and D. M. Divan, "Performance Characterization of a New Discrete Pulse Modulated Current Regulator," in *Conf. Rec. IEEE IAS Annual Meeting*, pp. 395–405, 1988.

[5] R. D. Lorenz and D. M. Divan, "Dynamic Analysis & Experimental Evaluation of Delta Modulators for Field Oriented AC Machine Current Regulators," in *Conf. Rec. IEEE IAS Annual Meeting*, pp. 196–201, 1987.

[6] K. S. Rajashekara, H. Le-Huy, R. Mahfoudhi, and L. A. Dessaint, "Resonant DC Link Inverter-Fed AC Machines Control," in *Conf. Rec. Power Electronics Specialists*, pp. 491–496, 1987.

[7] Jih-Sheng Lai, *High Frequency Resonant Link Inverter Induction Motor Drives Using Microcomputer Control,* Ph.D. Dissertation, University of Tennessee, Knoxville, Tennessee, 1989.

[8] F. H. Choo, B. R. Duggal, V. Rajagopalan, and A. Chandrasekaran, *Multi-Resonant DC to AC Converter,* in *Conf. Rec. IEEE IAS Annual Meeting*, pp. 1010–1014, 1989.

[9] B. K. Bose and Jih-Sheng Lai, "A Novel Programmable Current Initialization Scheme in Resonant DC link Converter for AC Motor Drives," *Invention Disclosure Letter*, April 19, 1988.

[10] Jih-Sheng Lai and B. K. Bose, "An Improved Resonant DC Link Inverter For Induction Motor Drives," in *Conf. Rec. IEEE IAS Annual Meeting*, pp. 742–748, 1988.

[11] B. K. Bose, *Power Electronics and AC Drives*, Prentice-Hall, Englewood Cliffs, N. J., 1986.

[12] B. K. Bose (Ed.), *Microcomputer Control of Power Electronics and Drives*, IEEE Press, New York, N. Y., 1987.

[13] H. Elmqvist, K. J. Åström, and T. Schönthal, *SIMNON - User's Guide for MS-DOS Computers*, Version 1.0, 1986.

[14] B. J. Baliga, M. Chang, P. Shafer, and M. W. Smith, "The Insulated Gate Transistor *(IGT)* - A New Power Switching Device," in *Conf. Rec. IEEE IE Annual Meeting*, pp. 794, 1983.

[15] L. Rinehart and A. Plunkett, "The Use of MOSIGTs and MOSFETs," *Proceedings of Motor-Con*, September, 1987.

[16] IXYS Corporation, *MegaMOS IGTs Preliminary Information*, IXYS Corporation, June, 1987.

[17] Ariel, *Operating Manual for the DSP-16 Data Acquisition Processor*, Ariel Corp., August 1987.

Selected Bibliography

[1] O. Sugimoto, T. Koga, S. Sugawara, H. Hayashi, and T. Nozaki, "High frequency carrier PWM inverter by static induction (SI) thyristor," *IEEE PESC Rec.*, pp. 455-46l, 1988.

[2] J. Nishizawa, T. Tamamushi, T. Koga, S. Sugawara, H. Hayashi, and T. Nozaki, "60 kHz, 100 kW static induction (SI) thyristor type voltage-controlled series resonant inverter for induction heating," *IEEE PESC Rec.*, pp. 508-515, 1987.

[3] P. K. Sood, T. A. Lipo, and I. G. Hansen, "A versatile power converter for high frequency link system," *IEEE Trans. Power Electron.*, vol. 3, pp. 383-390, Oct. 1988.

[4] A. K. S. Bhatt and S. B. Dewan, "A novel utility interfaced high frequency link photovoltaic power conditioning system," *IEEE Trans. Ind. Electron.*, vol. 35, pp. 153-160, Feb. 1988.

[5] J. van Wyk and J. A. Ferriera, "Transistor inverter design optimization in the frequency range above 5 kHz up to 50 KVA," *IEEE Trans. Ind. Applicat.*, vol. IA-19, pp. 296-302, Mar./Apr. 1983.

[6] A. Ueda, M. Ibamoto, H. Narita, T. Hori, T. Tsuboi, and Y. Yamada, "GTO inverter for ac traction drives," *IEEE Trans. Ind. Applicat.*, vol. IA-19, pp. 343-348, May/June 1983.

[7] P. K. Sood and T. A. Lipo, "Power conversion distribution system using a high frequency ac link," *IEEE Trans. Ind. Applicat.*, vol. 24, pp. 268-300, Mar./Apr. 1988.

[8] J. B. Klaasens, "DC-ac series resonant converter system with high internal frequency generating multiphase ac waveforms for multikilowatt power levels," *IEEE Trans. Power Electron.*, vol. PE-2, pp. 247-256, July 1987.

[9] W. McMurray, "Efficient snubbers for voltage source GTO inverters," *IEEE PESC Rec.*, pp. 20-27, 1985.

[10] J. S. Lai and B. K. Bose, "High frequency quasi-resonant dc voltage notching inverter for ac motor drives," *IEEE/IAS Ann. Meet. Conf. Rec.*, pp. 1202-1207, 1990.

[11] Y. Murai and T. A. Lipo, "High frequency series resonant dc link power conversion," *IEEE/IAS Ann. Meet. Conf. Rec.*, pp. 772-779, 1988.

[12] F. G. Turnbull and R. E. Tompkins, "Design of a pulsewidth-modulated resonant converter for a high-output voltage power supply," *IEEE Trans. Ind. Applicat.*, vol. IA-23, pp. 1016-1021, Nov./Dec. 1987.

[13] F. G. Turnbull et al., "Transistor inverter for high performance 70 HP drive system," *1988 SATECH Conf.*, Oct. 1988.

[14] G. Fregien, H. G. Langer, and H.-C. Skudelny, "A regenerative snubber for a 200 kVA GTO-inverter," *IEEE PESC Rec.*, pp. 498-505, 1988.

[15] J. Holtz, S. F. Salama, and K.-H. Werner, "A nondissipative snubber circuit for high-power GTO-inverters," *IEEE/IAS Ann. Meet. Conf. Rec.*, pp. 613-618, 1987.

[16] J. S. Lai and B. K. Bose, "A PC-based simulation and DSP-based control of an improved high frequency resonant dc link inverter induction motor drive," *Proc. IECON'90*, pp. 882-888, 1990.

[17] R. L. Steigerwald and R. E. Tompkins, "A comparison of high-frequency link schemes for interfacing a dc source to a utility grid," *IEEE/IAS Ann. Meet. Conf. Rec.*, pp. 759-766, 1982.

[18] D. M. Divan and G. Skibinski, "Zero switching loss inverters for high power applications," *IEEE/IAS Ann. Meet. Conf. Rec.*, pp. 627-634, 1987.

[19] J. H. R. Enslin, J. D. van Wyk, P. van Rhyn, and J. J. Schoeman, "Low-voltage, high-efficiency switch-mode high-power inverters for ac link converter applications," *IEEE Trans. Ind. Electron.*, vol. 37, pp. 167-172, Apr. 1990.

[20] E. P. Wiechmann, P. D. Ziogas, and V. R. Stefanović, "A novel bilateral power conversion scheme for variable frequency static power supplies," *IEEE Trans. Ind. Applicat.*, vol. IA-21, pp. 1226-1233, Sept./Oct. 1985.

[21] C. G. Steyn, "Analysis and optimization of regenerative linear snubbers," *IEEE Trans. Power Electron.*, vol. 4, pp. 362-370, July 1989.

[22] K. Harada, H. Sakamoto, and M. Shoyama, "Phase controlled dc-ac converter with high frequency switching," *IEEE Trans. Power Electron.*, vol. 3, pp. 406-411, Oct. 1988.

[23] J. S. Lai and B. K. Bose, "An improved resonant dc link inverter for induction motor drives," *IEEE/IAS Ann. Meet. Conf. Rec.*, pp. 742-748, 1988.

[24] R. Ester, "Computer aided optimum design of the series resonant inverter," *IEEE PESC Rec.*, pp. 721-730, 1989.

[25] D. M. Divan, "A new topology for single-phase UPS system," *IEEE/IAS Ann. Meet. Conf. Rec.*, pp. 931-936, 1989.

[26] S. Nonaka and K. Shinohara, "GTO current source inverter," *IEEE/IAS Ann. Meet. Conf. Rec.*, pp. 791-796, 1984.

[27] D. M. Divan, G. Venkataramanan, and R. W. De Doncker, "Design methodologies for soft switched inverters," *IEEE/IAS Ann. Meet. Conf. Rec.*, vol. 1, pp. 758-766, 1988.

[28] R. W. De Doncker and J. P. Lyons, "The auxiliary resonant commutated pole converter," *IEEE/IAS Ann. Meet. Conf. Rec.*, vol. 2, pp. 1228-1235, 1990.

[29] M. N. Kheraluwala and D. M. Divan, "Optimal discrete pulse modulation waveforms for resonant link inverters," *IEEE PESC Rec.*, pp. 567-574, 1988.

[30] J. He, N. Mohan, and B. Wold, "Zero-voltage-switching PWM inverter for high-frequency dc-ac power conversion," *IEEE/IAS Ann. Meet. Conf. Rec.*, vol. 2, pp. 1215-1221, 1990.

[31] K. E. Bornhardt, "Novel soft-switched GTO-inverter circuits," *IEEE/IAS Ann. Meet. Conf. Rec.*, vol. 2, pp. 1222-1227, 1990.

[32] A. Nabae, I. Takahashi, and H. Akagi, "A new neutral-point-clamped PWM inverter," *IEEE Trans. Ind. Applicat.*, vol. IA-17, pp. 518-523, Sept./Oct. 1981.

[33] F. H. Choo, B. R. Duggal, V. Rajagopalan, and A. Chandrasekaran, "Multi-resonant dc to ac converter," *IEEE/IAS Ann. Meet. Conf. Rec.*, vol. 1, pp. 1010-1014, 1989.

[34] Y. Murai, S. Mochizuki, P. Caldeira, and T. A. Lipo, "Current pulse control of high frequency series resonant dc link power converter," *IEEE/IAS Ann. Meet. Conf. Rec.*, vol. 1, pp. 1023-1030, 1989.

[35] I. Takahashi and Y. Itoh, "Electrolytic capacitorless PWM inverter," *Int. Power Electron. Conf. Rec.*, Tokyo, pp. 131-138, 1990.

[36] H. Saotome and S. Konishi, "High voltage GTO inverter using reverse conduction GTO thyristor," *Int. Power Electron. Conf. Rec.*, Tokyo, pp. 421-427, 1990.

[37] K. Nakajima et al., "Three phase IGBT inverter with improved voltage waveform," *Int. Power Electron. Conf. Rec.*, Tokyo, pp. 115-120, 1990.

[38] A. Mertens and D. M. Divan, "A high frequency resonant dc link inverter using IGBT's," *Int. Power Electron. Conf. Rec.*, Tokyo, pp. 152-160, 1990.

Part 7
Pulsewidth Modulation

Paper 7.1

A CURRENT-CONTROLLED PWM TRANSISTOR INVERTER DRIVE

A.B. Plunkett
General Electric Company, Schenectady, New York 12305

Abstract - A method of controlling a pulse width modulated transistor inverter to minimize the peak output current will be discussed. The method adaptively modulates the inverter switching times so as to produce the maximum possible torque in the attached motor for the minimum ac peak current. As the method involves a transition for operation of the inverter as a current source to operation as a voltage source, a method of system control must be applied that is suitable for use in either mode of operation. A motor angle controller is used to supply the primary system stabilization. The described method of control generates the appropriate angle command and current amplitude signals by using feedback signals of motor torque and flux.

A hybrid computer simulation of the described method of control has been performed and the results are presented. A transistor pulse width modulated dc link inverter driving an induction motor is modeled. The method of inverter control allows for a relatively simple adaption to the use of either induction or synchronous machines and renders the inverter relatively insensitive to specific machine parameters.

Introduction

In the process of designing a transistor inverter ac induction motor drive system, it has become apparent that the development of an improved method of pulse width modulation (PWM) control is desirable. The control system must achieve several important objectives:

- Minimization of motor loss so that conventional motors can be used without derating
- Minimization of peak transistor current
- Simplification of the control to reduce cost

These objectives can be met by employing an instantaneous current control system with independent current control on each inverter output phase. The resulting system has operating characteristics similar to both current inverters and voltage inverters. However, the use of such a hybrid inverter control system leads to a number of problems. A current inverter system operates very well at low speeds but is limited in performance at high speeds (high output frequencies). A voltage inverter tends to perform poorly at low speeds. The present system eliminates these problems by acting as a hybrid of the two types; it retains the good low speed performance of the current inverter and the good high speed performance of the voltage inverter.

The method of accomplishing this desirable end and the results of a complete simulation on a hybrid analog-digital system are presented below.

Description of the Drive System

The drive system consists of a transistor inverter using power Darlington transistors and an induction motor optimized for maximum efficiency on inverter waveforms. The inverter is a simple three half bridge arrangement with feedback diodes, thus giving a defined voltage on the ac output lines at all times. Figure 1 shows the inverter's circuit diagram. Note that the inverter consists of six half-phase sections. Figure 2 is a photograph of a half-phase module, six of which are required to make a complete inverter. Figure 3 shows the ac induction motor referred to above, along with a General Electric dc motor of equivalent power, voltage and speed range rating. The induction motor designed by Dr. G.B. Kliman of General Electric contains an integral 3:1 gear box to reduce the maximum motor speed of 15,000 rpm to a maximum shaft speed of 5,000 rpm. The motor is a four-pole design and thus has a maximum frequency of 500 Hz.

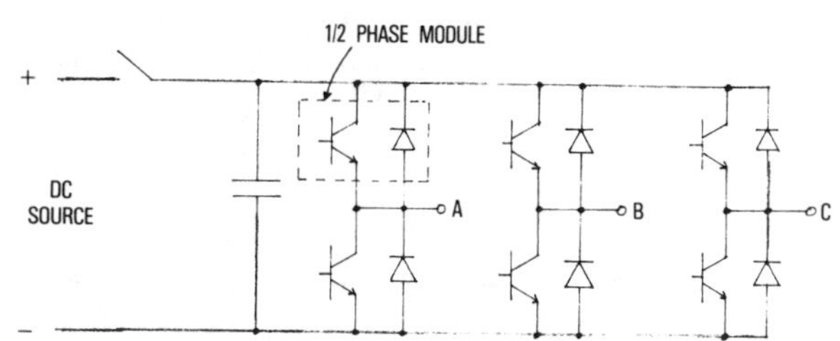

Fig. 1. Transistor Inverter Circuit

Fig. 2. Inverter Half Phase Module

Fig. 3. AC Induction Motor (left) and Equivalent DC Commutator Motor

Reprinted from *IEEE/IAS Ann. Meet. Conf. Rec.*, pp. 785–792, 1979.

The motor is designed to supply constant torque with constant flux up to a speed of 5000 rpm and constant power to maximum speed with constant voltage applied. The leakage inductance is maximized consistent with the constant power requirements.[1] Maximizing the leakage inductance minimizes harmonic current but limits the pull-out torque and thus the maximum speed for constant power output at constant applied voltage. Figure 4 shows the torque, ac voltage, and ac current as a function of speed.

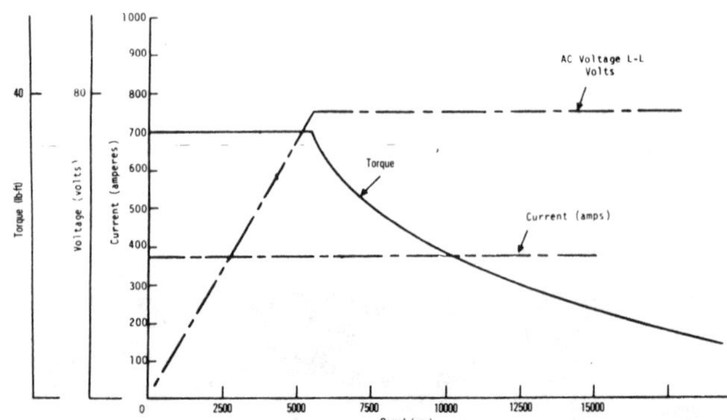

Fig. 4. Induction Motor Torque, Voltage, and Current

The Appendix shows the equivalent circuit and parameters used in the analysis.

Voltage Control

The inverter will operate from a nominally fixed dc source voltage and thus will require some sort of voltage control capability to appropriately vary the ac motor voltage. There are a number of pulse width modulation methods which could be used.[2,3,4,5]

One method presently in wide use dates back to the original paper of Schonung and Stemmler.[2] Figure 5 is an illustration of the method of generating the inverter switching waveforms and the resultant output waveform across the motor line to neutral connection. The resulting output waveform causes motor current ripple which adds to the motor losses and requires extra inverter current handling capability. In addition, because the waveform is a voltage waveform, a small imbalance in the motor voltage, due to the small motor stator resistance, can cause a relatively large current imbalance in the motor current. An imbalance in phase voltages will translate to a motor frequency ripple in the dc link and since the motor frequency varies from 0 to 500 Hz, any resonances in the dc link filter tend to be excited. In addition, it is possible to generate in the motor dc currents which will cause extra heating and torque ripple in the motor output.

All the pulse width modulation methods in References 2,3,4, and 5 have in common two disadvantages. The first, that these methods are voltage control systems; the second, that a special transition mode of operation involving the synchronization of the reference waveform with the desired output waveform is required. The requirements that the waveforms have very little imbalance and a very small dc offset impose a requirement for a high degree of precision on the waveform generation. This means that the control electronics must precisely generate a waveform with a fairly smooth sinusoidal output.

A second problem arises when an inverter output voltage greater than about 80% of maximum is required, as at high speed. For maximum output voltage (V line to neutral = .45 Vdc), the inverter must operate in the square wave mode without notches in the output

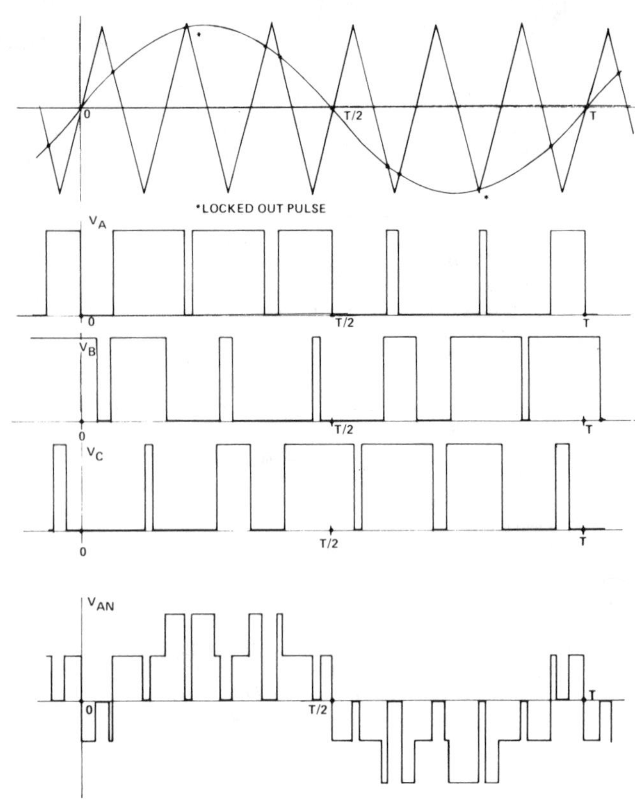

Fig. 5. Sine Wave - Triangle Wave Pulse Width Modulation

waveform. One normally uses a transition mode of pulse width modulation which synchronizes the chopping reference waveform to the output frequency waveform. References 3,4, and 5 examine some of these methods.

Reference 4 describes a method used as a transition mode of PWM. The method is to place the voltage controlling notches in the inverter output waveform near the zero crossings of the ac voltage cycle rather than in the middle of the wave. The effect of eliminating a minimum width pulse at the end of an ac cycle is almost negligible since the contribution to the fundamental frequency output waveform is small. Of course, to prevent phase jumps when a pulse is dropped, the pulses must be dropped symmetrically so that even harmonics are never developed. The transistor inverter is able to switch much faster than an equivalent thyristor inverter so the transition problem should be less significant. Nevertheless, this problem must be considered.

Current-Controlled PWM

A method has been devised to eliminate these two problems. The method involves generating a 3-phase reference sine wave at the desired output frequency and current amplitude and comparing this reference with the actual motor current. If the motor current is more positive than the reference, the inverter will switch in the negative direction and vice versa. The frequency of the inverter chopping can be controlled by introducing a small amount of hysteresis into the comparison so that in effect the amount of current ripple is regulated. Figure 6 is a block diagram of the basic concept while Figure 7 shows the current control circuit, including the hysteresis and a 25 μsec time lockout on the inverter switching frequency.

A problem one must face is the maximum operating frequency of the inverter, which the chopping frequency determines at low speeds. The inverter switching losses are proportionate to frequency and must be controlled; thus the chopping frequency should, on the average, be

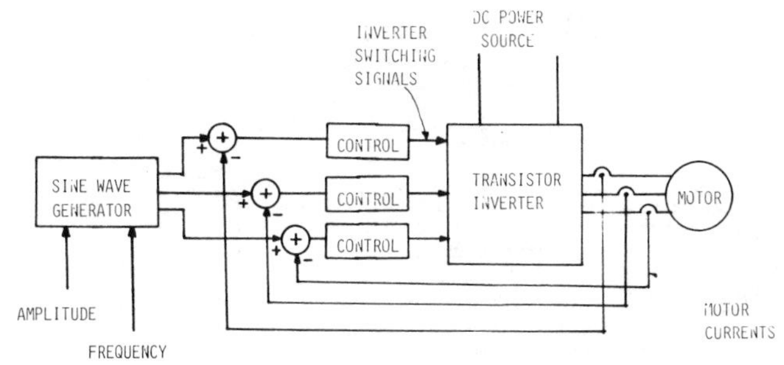

Fig. 6. Current-Controlled PWM Block Diagram

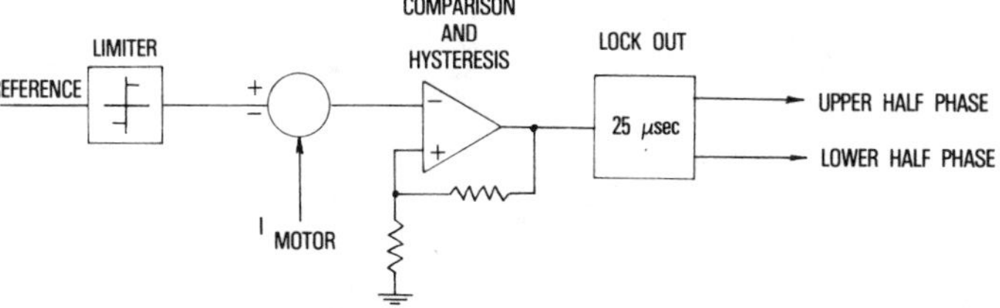

Fig. 7. Current Control Circuit for One Phase

limited. The chopping frequency is automatically controlled by the comparator hysteresis, the motor stator plus rotor leakage inductance, and the dc link voltage by the equation

$$V = -L \frac{di}{dt}$$

which, however, applies only approximately since the motor leakage inductance is a function of frequency and the voltage is actually the dc link voltage minus the motor back emf. However, the net result is that, in the PWM range, the average chopping frequency is relatively constant and not greatly affected by speed.

An additional feature of the current-controlled PWM system is its instantaneous current limit, easily achievable by limiting the maximum value of the current waveform reference generator. Limiting the reference generator's output creates a more square current reference which limits the transistor current but (up to a point) not the motor torque producing capability sinc since the fundamental frequency torque producing component of the current in a square wave is about 11% higher than in a sine wave. Of course, torque ripple at the fifth and seventh harmonics of the fundamental frequency will appear when the current waveform becomes flat-topped.

The method of controlling inverter current in effect causes the transistor inverter to become the same as a current inverter, with all the inherent advantages, stability, and problems of the current inverter at low speeds. However, at high speed the system can operate without pulse width modulation and thus has the control characteristics of a voltage inverter and does not suffer the inherent frequency limits of the current inverter. As the motor speed increases, the output voltage of the inverter will increase as necessary to maintain the motor current. Eventually the maximum output voltage capability of the inverter will be achieved. The result is a relatively smooth transition from PWM to square wave operation of the inverter, as far as amplitude of the current and voltage is concerned. A problem arises because at low speeds before the transition, the reference wave represents motor current which in an induction motor may lag the voltage by about 30° at full load to 90° at no load. After the transition, the reference represents motor voltage. Thus, as pulses are dropped (chops in the ac output waveform eliminated), jumps in the phase of the reference are required to eliminate torque transients. In addition, some sort of stabilizing control is required for low speed current inverter operation which should ideally be compatible with the voltage inverter operation at high speed.

Some known methods of controlling current inverters for motor stability include some form of slip frequency control combined with current regulation when induction motors are used,[6,7] or the well-known shaft position sensing when synchronous motors are used. Both these methods are difficult to use to handle the transition from current-controlled PWM to voltage control. An alternative stabilizing control suitable for both current and voltage control, is described in Reference 8 which shows a method of motor electrical angle control applicable to both synchronous and induction motors. This control method measures and regulates the motor internal angle between the motor air gap flux vector and the stator (inverter) current vector. Figure 8 is an illustration of the variation of angle as a function of load. Figure 9 from Reference 8 shows an example relating the motor electrical angle $\sin \theta_{eq}$ to the motor slip frequency and torque for constant flux operation.

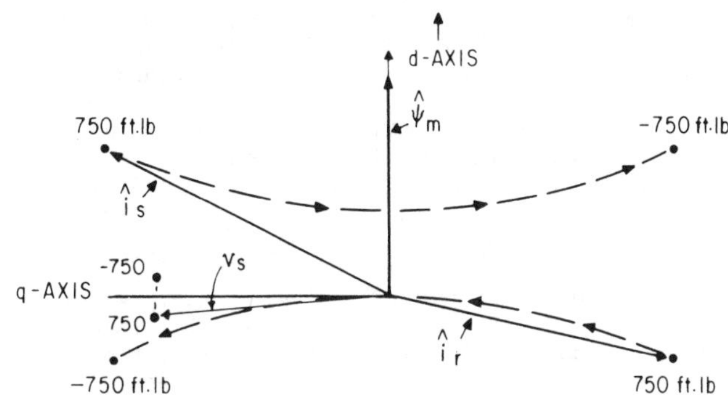

Fig. 8. Vector Diagram Showing Definition of Motor Angle

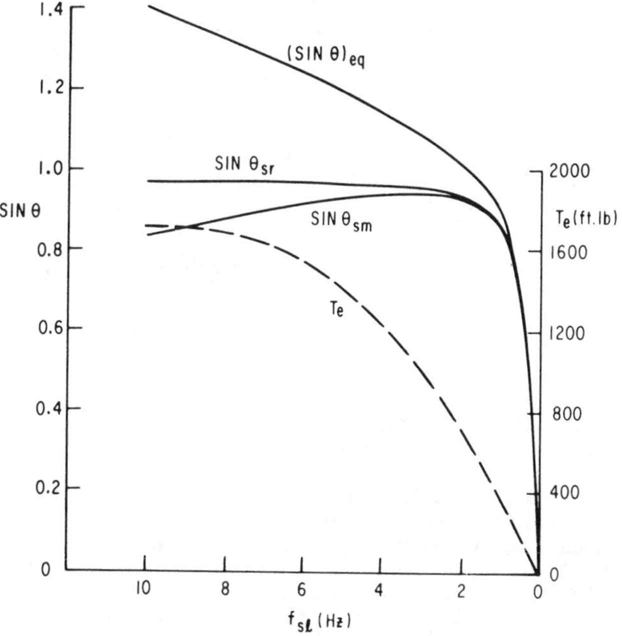

Fig. 9. Induction Motor Angle and Torque as a Function of Slip Frequency

There are two angle signals shown in Figure 9. The actual motor angle $\sin\theta_{sm}$ reaches a maximum of about 60° at about one half the induction motor pull-out torque. A modified angle signal, $\sin\theta_{eq}$, which does not have this distressing (for feedback control) property, is actually used in the control system. For a synchronous motor, either angle signal is satisfactory for control system use. However, use of the $\sin\theta_{e}$ signal will reduce the control gain variation as a function of the steady state angle.

Use of this control method will stabilize the drive system in current inverter operation and allow for a feedback-controlled transition between current control and voltage control. Note that the reference waveform generator phase angle will be varied as pulses are dropped to maintain the motor operation in a satisfactory manner.

The method of measuring the motor's operating angle involves measuring the motor stator current and the motor air gap flux as vectors. The air gap flux can be inferred from the motor terminal voltage but will suffer some inaccuracy for very low speed operation due to the stator resistance voltge drop; or can be measured directly by air gap flux sensing coils wound around a motor stator tooth in a manner similar to that described in Reference 10. The method of making and inserting the sensing coils without disturbing the main motor winding was developed by J. Franz of General Electric (U.S. patent No. 4,011,489). A block diagram of the motor current, flux, torque, and angle circuits is shown in Figure 10 for the situation in which flux sensing coils (the simplest circuits) are used. The inputs to the circuit are V_{ma}, V_{mb}, V_{mc}, the airgap voltages; and i_{as}, i_{bs}, and i_{cs}, the ac line currents. A block diagram of the basic drive system is shown in Figure 11, with the angle control loop indicated. The commanded inputs to the drive system shown in Figure 11 are the magnitude of motor current and the angle between the air gap flux and stator current vectors. These inputs are satisfactory for complete control of the drive system but do not allow for an easily generated operator command signal. For example, to increase torque, both the angle command and the current command must be increased. However, the relative amount of increase of these signals is a non-linear function of the desired motor flux level. The flux level in the motor will affect the speed of response to an increasing torque command as the motor may need to increase flux to be able to produce more torque.

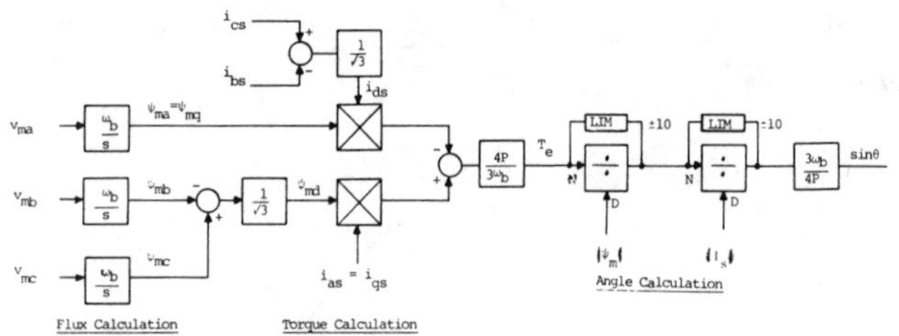

Fig. 10. Motor Flux, Torque, and Angle Sensing Block Diagram

Extra current is required to increase flux level in the induction motor so that a conflict may occur between the increased torque requirement and the necessity of increased flux. This conflict will thus tend to slow the drive system response to an increased torque command if the motor flux level is too low before the commanded torque increase. Also the gain of the control system is affected by motor flux level. Therefore, at least one, and preferably two, outer control loops are desirable to enable the use of simple operator

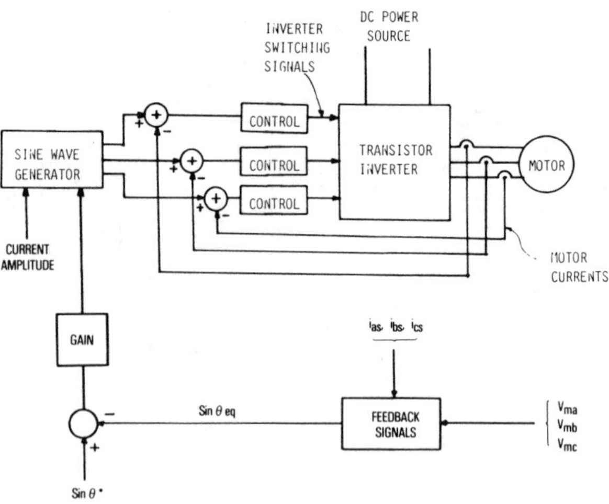

Fig. 11. Block Diagram of Drive System with Angle Loop Control

commands without the use of arbitrary non-linear functions. The outer loops chosen are a torque regulator operating through the inverter frequency input to regulate torque in order to obtain the fastest transient response and to retain torque regulation at high speed when the inverter is in the square wave mode of operation and current control is lost due to control loop saturation. At low speeds in the PWM mode of operation, some form of voltage regulation is desired. Regulation of the air gap flux level in the motor by varying the magnitude of motor current is an ideal way of controlling the effective inverter voltage output. Both of the feedback signals of torque and flux are available as by-products of the motor angle sensing circuits. Use of these signals eliminates the need of precise mechanical tachometers or the shaft position sensors required for many previously used high performance ac motor drives. A block diagram of the complete control system emphasizing the torque and flux control system is shown in Figure 12.

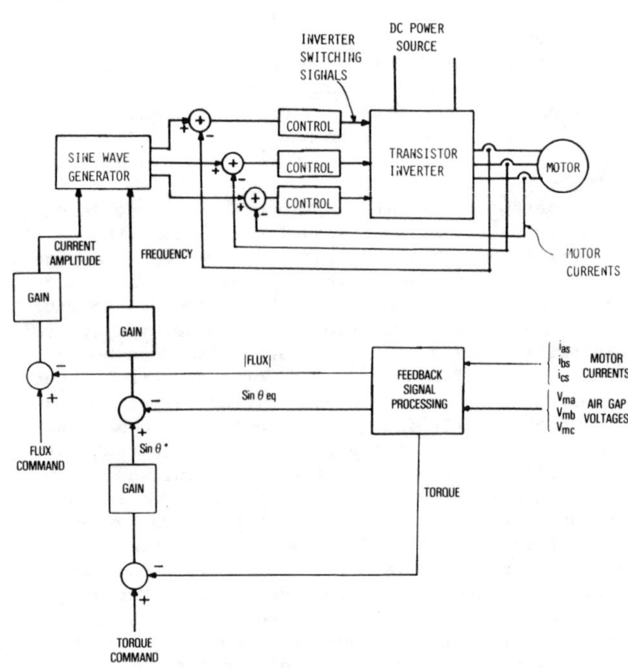

Fig. 12. Overall Drive System Block Diagram

Simulation of Current-Controlled PWM

The drive system described has been simulated on a hybrid digital and analog computer. The control system, including the reference sine wave generator is implemented in essentially the same way that it would be implemented using standard digital and analog integrated circuits. The power transistor inverter and the induction motor are simulated using standard techniques such as those described in Reference 11. The Appendix gives the simulated induction motor equivalent circuit. The inverter is simulated using a set of six ideal switches that simulate the effect of the parallel transistor and diode in the one-half-phase module of Figure 2. The detailed effect of the snubbers in this inverter circuit is not important to the control system operation and is not included in the simulation. However, the effect of the dc link inductance and capacitance is important and is included in the simulation. The results of the operation of the control system are presented below in a series of oscillograph traces as a function of time.

Figure 13 shows a typical example of operation in the current controlled PWM mode of operation. Note that the motor line current is quite sinusoidal and that the current is constrained to be within 50 A of the reference waveform, the hysteresis value chosen in the control system. The pulse width modulator has a built-in 25 μsec lock out to prohibit the generation of conflicting transistor switching signals, but for the case shown, the lock out has no detrimental effect.

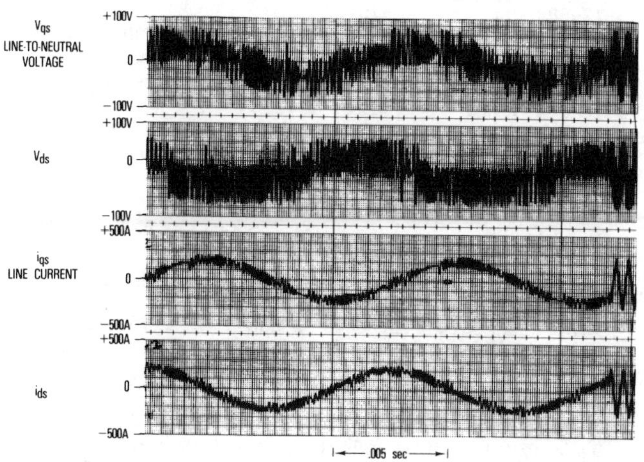

Fig. 13. Steady State Operation in PWM at Rated Motor Torque, Flux, and Current at One-Half Rated Speed

Figure 14 shows steady state operation at the rated operating conditions of the motor. Note that a few pulses still exist even though the design is for full square wave output voltage. The current regulated PWM system adaptively controls the type of waveform generated to cause a smooth transition between full PWM and square wave operation by causing the remaining chops to be near the ac voltage zero crossings. The effect of these extra chops is to minimize the peak motor current while retaining the capability for essentially full ac output voltage. As motor speed and hence frequency increase, the extra chops disappear due to the improved smoothing of the inverter chopped voltage wave by the motor leakage inductance at high ac output frequency. The system operation in steady state shows that the current-controlled PWM method controls the motor current ripple exactly as desired and, in addition, generates an optimum waveform in the operating region between PWM and square wave.

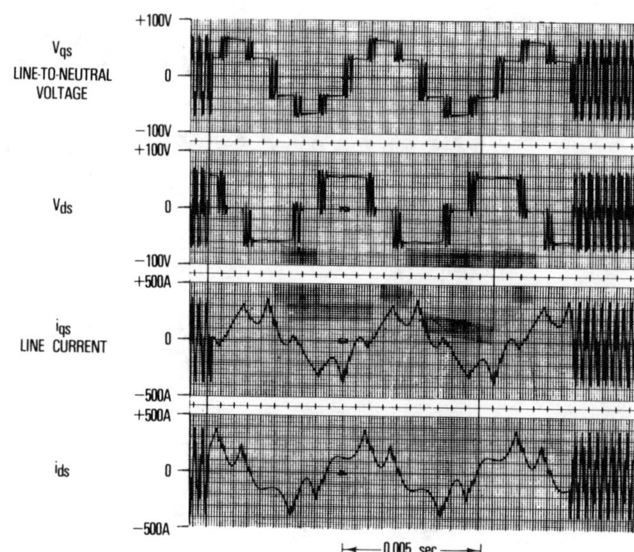

Fig. 14. Steady State Operation in PWM at Rated Motor Torque, Flux, and Current at Rated Motor Speed

Next, the transient performance of the control loops is examined to determine if satisfactory regulation of motor operating conditions such as flux level and torque can be obtained. Figure 15 shows the drive system performance, including the effect of the flux regulation loop which controls motor flux level by varying the magnitude of ac current. Note that the angle control loop controlling motor frequency is also present as is always required in PWM operation to ensure stable operation of the drive system at low speeds in the current-controlled mode of operation. Step changes of the flux command signal cause increases in ac current to change flux level at essentially constant motor angle; then the ac current drops back to a lower level as soon as the desired motor flux is obtained.

An example of sudden step changes in the current command signal upon the inverter waveforms and upon the motor torque is shown in Figure 16. Note that as the current command increases, the angle control detects the change in motor angle and compensates the reference waveform generator phase to minimize disturbances. Note that for a constant angle command, increasing the current command causes an increase in motor torque output. As the inverter waveform changes to square wave operation, no net change in average torque occurs but a six times frequency motor torque ripple appears.

The final drive system configuration includes both torque and flux regulation. The performance of the complete system in the braking mode of operation is shown in Figure 17. Both the torque and flux commands are maintained constant as the speed decreases. Note that the inverter waveform varies between quasi-square wave operation and full PWM operation with virtually no change in motor torque. The motor current waveform maintains the sinusoidal shape all the way to a standstill at which speed the current becomes dc since for safety reasons the waveform generator does not allow speed reversal. The motor torque declines to zero as the flux disappears at standstill.

The simulation results show that the complete current-controlled PWM drive system with the torque and flux regulators has very satisfactory dynamic performance at any speed, handles the transition from current-controlled PWM to square wave operation in a graceful manner, and controls the inverter current to minimize the inverter peak current requirement.

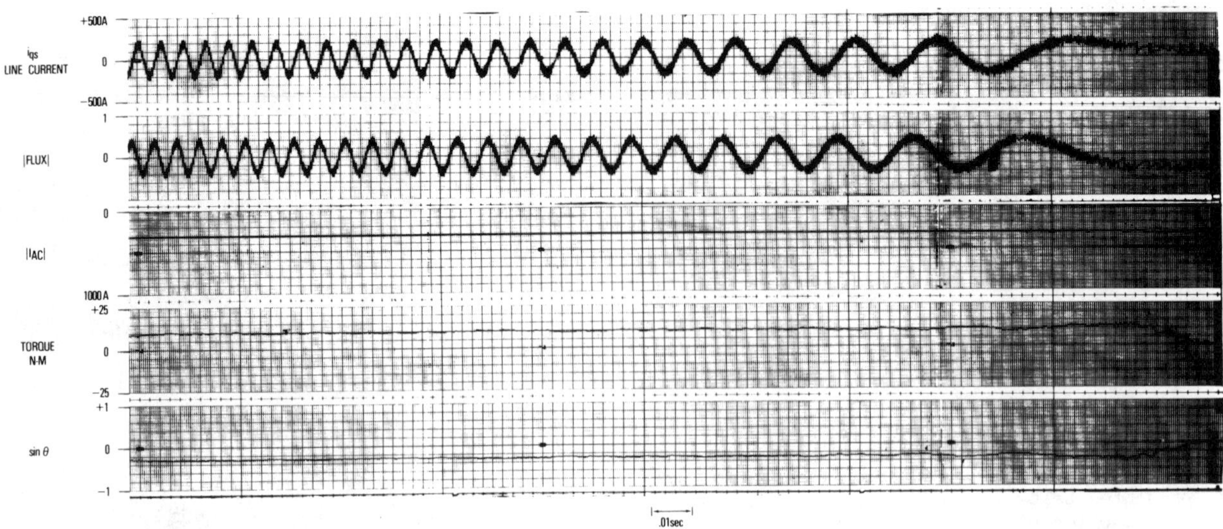

Fig. 15. Performance of the Flux and Angle Regulators for Step Changes in Flux Command and Constant Angle Command

CONCLUSIONS

The described current-controlled PWM system combines the advantages of both current and voltage inverters. The major disadvantages of the two systems are eliminated in the implementation shown here. Very fast dynamic performance with good motor current waveform control is available at any speed of operation. Motor losses are minimized so that it is possible to use conventional induction motors in this drive system with only a small penalty in increased motor heating. The use of current control eliminates the need for as critical a balancing between phases as required in a voltage inverter system and allows relatively easy and non-critical implementation of the control electronics. The current-controlled PWM system also eliminates the need to include a transition mode of PWM normally needed in order to maintain maximum inverter output power capability. If extremely good torque regulation near zero speed is not required, then the motor terminal voltage can be sensed instead of the air gap flux voltage and used in the same manner to develop the stabilizing angle control feedback signal as well as the magnitude of flux and torque signals.

REFERENCES

1. A.B. Plunkett and D.L. Plette, "Inverter-Induction Motor Drive for Transit Cars," IEEE Trans. Ind. Appl., vol. IA-13, No. 1, pp. 26-37 Jan./Feb. 1977.
2. A. Schonung and D. Stemmler, "Static Frequency Changers with Subharmonic Control in Conjunction with Reversible Variable Speed AC Drives," The Brown-Boveri Review, pp. 555-577 Aug./Sept. 1974.
3. A. Abbondanti, J. Zubek and C.J. Nordby, "Pulse Width Modulated Inverter Motor Drives with Improved Modulation," Conf. Proc. 1974 9th IAS Meeting.
4. G.B. Kliman and A.B. Plunkett, "Development of a Modulation Strategy for a PWM Inverter Drive," IEEE Trans. Ind. Appl., vol. IA-15, no. 1, pp. 72-79, Jan./Feb. 1979.
5. Von Konrad Heintze, Hermann Tappeiner and Manfred Weibelzahl, "Pulswechselrichter zur Drehzahlsteuerung von Asynchronmaschinen," Siemens Review, vol. 45, no. 3, p. 154, 1971.
6. K.P. Phillips, "Current Source Converter for AC Motor Drives," IEEE Publication 71-C1-IGA, Conf. Rec. 1971 IGA 6th Annu. Meet., pp. 385-392, Oct. 18-21, 1971.
7. E.P. Cornell and T.A. Lipo, "Modeling and Design of Controlled Current Induction Motor Drive Systems," Conf. Rec. IEEE-IAS 1975 10th Annu. Meet., Sept. 28-Oct. 2, 1975.
8. A.B. Plunkett, J.D. D'Atre and T.A. Lipo, "Synchronous Control of a Static AC Induction Motor Drive," Conf. Rec. 1977 IAS Annu. Meet., p. 609, Oct. 1977.
9. A.B. Plunkett, "Direct Torque and Flux Regulation in a PWM Inverter-Induction Motor Drive," IEEE Trans. Ind. Appl., vol. IA-13, no. 2, pp. 139-146, Mar./Apr. 1977.
10. T.A. Lipo, D.W. Novotny, A.B. Plunkett, and V.R. Stefanovic, "Dynamics and Control of AC Drives," course notes, Univ. of Wisconsin Extension, Nov. 3-5, 1976.
11. R.H. Nelson, T.A. Lipo, and P.C. Krause, "Stability Analysis of a Symmetrical Induction Machine," IEEE Transactions on Power Apparatus & Systems, vol. PAS-88, no. 11, pp. 1710-1717, Nov. 1969.

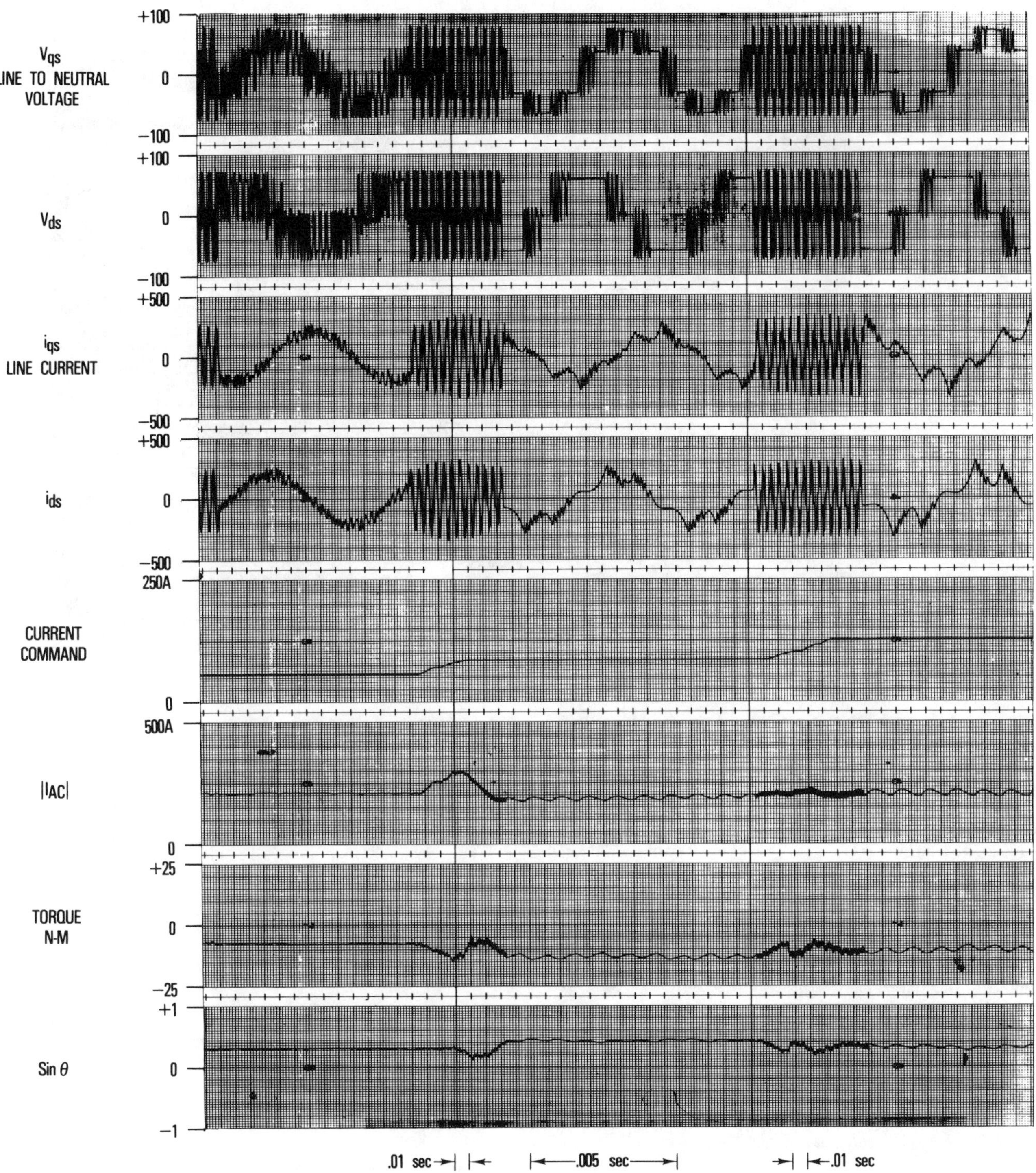

Fig. 16. The Effect of Increasing the Current Command Signal Showing the Automatic Optimum Waveform Control

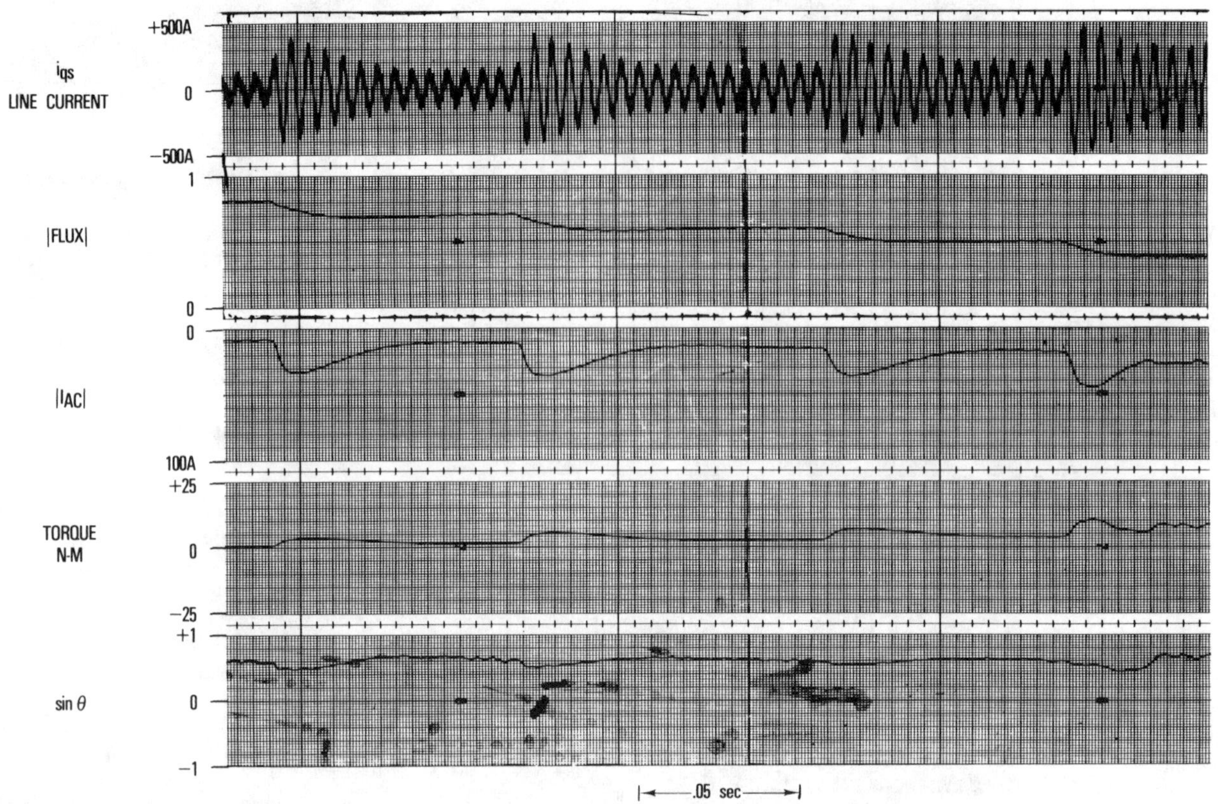

Fig. 17. Performance of the Complete Drive System When Braking to a Standstill

APPENDIX

The induction motor equations and equivalent circuit used in the analysis describe the instantaneous operation of the inverter and induction motor. These are given in the simple to use form used here in Reference 11. The motor equivalent circuit is reproduced below for reference. The factors λ^e_{ds}, λ^e_{dr}, λ^e_{qs}, and λ^e_{qr} are found simply by computing the flux linkages across the inductors as shown in Figure 18. Note that

$$\lambda = \frac{d}{dt}\ (Li).$$

The parameters of the motor analyzed are given below:

r_s = .0039Ω/phase

$L_{\ell s}$ = .0106 mhy

L_m = .320 mhy

$L'_{\ell r}$ = .0101 mhy

r'_r = .0033Ω

w_b = 2π 180 rad/sec

V_{qs}(rated) = 45 v rms/phase

P(number poles) = 4

Rated Power = 17 hp output

I_{rated} = 173.9 amps rms

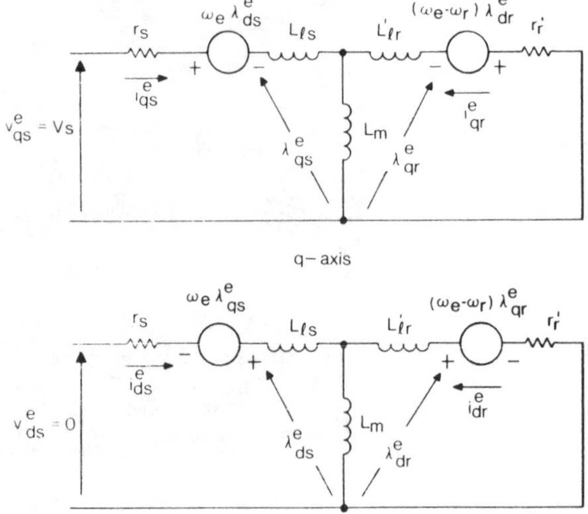

Fig. 18. Induction Motor Equivalent Circuit

Paper 7.2

Current Control of VSI-PWM Inverters

DAVID M. BROD, MEMBER, IEEE, AND DONALD W. NOVOTNY, SENIOR MEMBER, IEEE

Abstract—**The inherent limitations of commanding voltages and currents in a three-phase load with an inverter are examined. An overview of several current controllers described in the literature is presented, and computer simulations are used to compare performance. A switching diagram is developed which reveals some of the operating characteristics of hysteresis controllers. For ramp comparison controllers, a frequency transfer function analysis is used to predict the line currents and provide some insight into the compensation required to reduce the current errors.**

INTRODUCTION

CURRENT-CONTROLLED PWM inverters offer substantial advantages in eliminating stator dynamics in high-performance ac drives and are widely applied in such systems. A basic VSI–PWM system with current control is shown in Fig. 1. Presently, current controllers can be classified as hysteresis, ramp comparison, or predictive controllers. Hysteresis controllers utilize some type of hysteresis in the comparison of the line currents to the current references [1]–[4]. The ramp comparison controller compares the current errors to a triangle waveform to generate the inverter firing signals [5]. Predictive controllers calculate the inverter voltages required to force the currents to follow the current references [4], [6], [7].

This paper presents a general overview of the behavior and inherent limitations of current controllers when commanding currents in a three-phase load. Typical simulation results for several current controllers are presented to illustrate important performance characteristics. The hysteresis controller and the ramp comparison controller are studied in greater depth because of their simplicity and widespread use. A switching diagram for a hysteresis controller is developed and utilized to help explain the controller operation. For the ramp comparison controller, a frequency domain transfer function analysis is presented, and its use in compensator design is illustrated.

GENERAL CURRENT CONTROLLER PROPERTIES

Before analyzing specific controllers, the general properties of current controllers are examined. The concept of the voltage (current) vector is utilized because it is a very convenient representation of a set of three-phase voltages (or currents). The voltage vector is defined by the following expression:

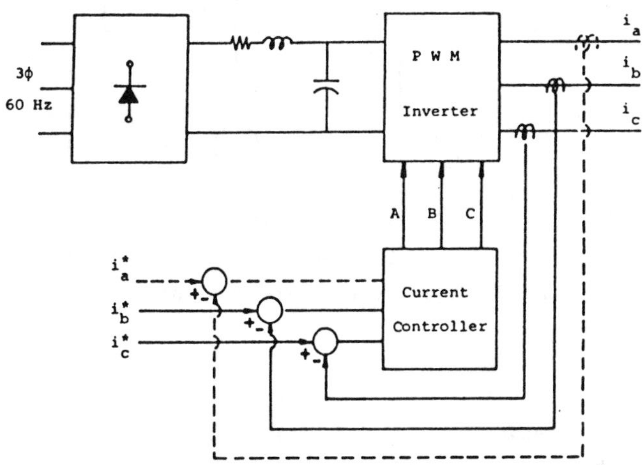

Fig. 1. Basic system diagram of PWM current controller.

$$\bar{v}=\frac{2}{3}\,(v_a+\bar{a}v_b+\bar{a}^2v_c) \tag{1}$$

where

$$\bar{a}=e^{j(2\pi/3)}$$

which defines a two-dimensional vector (or complex number) associated with the three-phase voltages. The actual voltages can be recovered from $\bar{v}$ and the zero sequence component v_0 using the equations

$$v_a=|\bar{v}|\ \cos\ \theta+v_0$$

$$v_b=|\bar{v}|\ \cos\ \left(\theta-\frac{2\pi}{3}\right)+v_0$$

$$v_c=|\bar{v}|\ \cos\ \left(\theta+\frac{2\pi}{3}\right)+v_0 \tag{2}$$

where θ is the angle between the voltage vector and the real axis.

Fig. 2 shows the basic circuit of a three-phase voltage source inverter. Notice that the dc bus midpoint is assumed to be the ground reference. The inverter operates in one of eight conduction modes to produce one of six nonzero voltage vectors or a zero voltage vector as illustrated in Fig. 3. The line-to-ground voltages: v_{ag}, v_{bg}, and v_{cg} are uniquely specified by the inverter with the line-to-neutral voltages equal to the line-to-ground voltages if the neutral is connected to the dc bus midpoint. Otherwise, the line-to-neutral voltages sum to zero, and the inverter cannot apply a zero sequence voltage across the load.

Paper IPCSD 84-31, approved by the Industrial Drives Committee of the IEEE Industry Applications Society for presentation at the 1984 Industrial Applications Society Annual Meeting, Chicago, IL, April 3-6, 1984. Manuscript released for publication August 9, 1984. This work was supported in part by the Wisconsin Alumni Research Foundation and in part by the Wisconsin Electric Machine and Power Electronics Consortium.

D. M. Brod is with the Borg-Warner Corporation, Wolf and Algonquin Roads, Des Plaines, IL 60018.

D. W. Novotny is with the Department of Electrical and Computer Engineering, University of Wisconsin, 1415 Johnson Drive, Madison, WI 53706.

Reprinted from *IEEE Trans. Ind. Applicat.*, vol. IA-21, no. 4, pp. 562–570, May/June 1985.

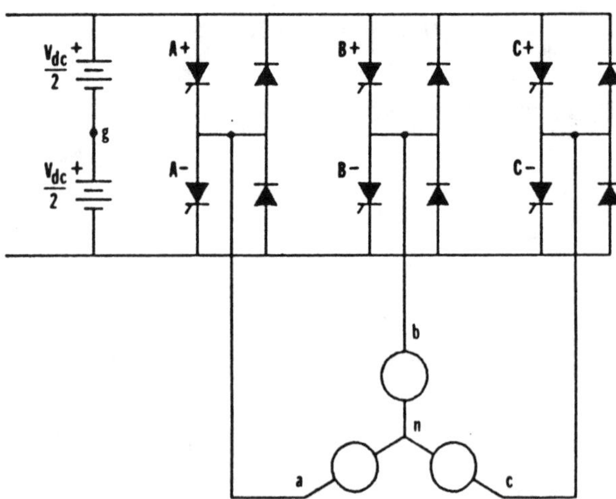

Fig. 2. Power circuit configuration of VSI inverter.

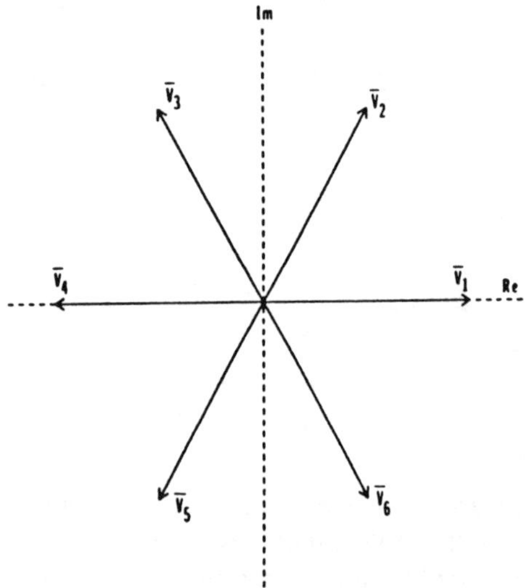

Fig. 3. Six nonzero voltage vectors associated with VSI inverter.

Effect of Unconnected Neutral

A current controller can exhibit an ambiguity when commanding the firing signals to an inverter that supplies a load with an unconnected neutral. When an inverter leg switches state, the resulting voltage vector is dependent on the state of the other two inverter legs. For example, if phase A switches from high to low, the following inverter voltage vectors can result:

$$\bar{v}_1(A+,\ B-,\ C-)\rightarrow\bar{v}_8(A-,\ B-,\ C-)$$
$$\bar{v}_2(A+,\ B+,\ C-)\rightarrow\bar{v}_3(A-,\ B+,\ C-)$$
$$\bar{v}_7(A+,\ B+,\ C+)\rightarrow\bar{v}_4(A-,\ B+,\ C+)$$
$$\bar{v}_6(A+,\ B-,\ C+)\rightarrow\bar{v}_5(A-,\ B-,\ C+).$$

If the neutral is not connected, the individual line-to-neutral voltages are not independent of each other, and the response of each line current will depend not only on the state of the corresponding inverter leg but also on the state of the other two inverter legs. Therefore, a current controller can be expected to experience interaction between the phases if the load has no neutral connection.

Some current controllers may exacerbate this interaction between the phases by adding offsets to the current errors. The added offsets may cause unexpected and even incorrect line-to-neutral voltages to be produced. For example, if the current in phase A is too low and the currents in phases B and C are too high, then the controller probably should apply the voltage vector $\bar{v}_1$, $(A+,\ B-,\ C-)$, to reduce the current errors quickly. If the current controller adds an offset to the phase A current error, the controller might switch phase A low and attempt to drive all three line currents lower by producing the voltage vector $\bar{v}_8$, $(A-,\ B-,\ C-)$. Under this condition the load is effectively allowed to coast, and the controller seems to experience a lack of control during this time.

In this example, the controller attempted to command a zero sequence current change. A current controller should not need to command a zero sequence current change because the current errors sum to zero if the three-phase current reference sums to zero. Adding offsets to the line current errors may be beneficial in reducing the inverter switching frequency. However, if the offsets are added improperly, higher current errors and a poorer dynamic response may result.

Effect of DC Voltage Limit

For a current controller to operate properly, there must be sufficient voltage to force the line currents in the desired direction. For loads with low counter EMF the dc bus voltage is not critical, but as the counter EMF is increased, a point is reached where the current controller is not able to command the desired current. This condition is reached when the line-to-neutral voltages approach a six-step quasi-square wave. In the following sections it is assumed that there is sufficient voltage to command the line currents.

Inverter Switching Frequency

To determine the factors that influence the inverter switching frequency, let one phase of the load be described by the following differential equation:

$$v=Ri+Ldi/dt+e \tag{3}$$

where

- v line-to-neutral load voltage,
- i line current,
- e counter EMF,
- L leakage inductance.

The time Δt in which the line current will increase by Δi can be found from (3) assuming that v and e do not change appreciately over the interval and that the resistance is negligible:

$$\Delta t=L\Delta i/(v-e). \tag{4}$$

Equation (4) shows that the inverter switching frequency is influenced by several factors: inductance and the counter EMF of the load, dc bus voltage, and the current ripple. The fundamental of the line-to-neutral voltage and the counter EMF vary periodically. Therefore, either the inverter switching frequency or/and the current ripple will vary over a fundamental inverter period.

DESCRIPTION OF CURRENT CONTROLLERS

Several of the current controllers described in the literature are briefly reviewed to provide a basis for the subsequent sections.

Hysteresis Controller: Three Independent Controllers

One version of hysteresis control, described in [1], uses three independent controllers, one for each phase. The control for one inverter leg is shown in Fig. 4. When the line current becomes greater (less) than the current reference by the hysteresis band, the inverter leg is switched in the negative (positive) direction, which provides an instantaneous current limit if the neutral is connected to the dc bus midpoint. Therefore, the hysteresis band specifies the maximum current ripple assuming neither controller nor inverter delays. The inverter switching frequency will vary over a fundamental inverter period since the current ripple is specified by the hysteresis band. In a system without a neutral connection, the actual current error can reach double the hysteresis band assuming the three-phase current reference sums to zero. A more complete discussion of this phenomenon is given later.

Hysteresis Controller: Three Dependent Controls

In many applications the inverter switching frequency can be reduced if a zero voltage vector is applied at the appropriate time. Also, the maximum current error can be limited within the hysteresis band, rather than twice the band, with proper control.

A controller has been suggested which incorporates three dependent hysteresis controls and the intelligent application of the zero voltage vector to accomplish these improvements. The controller is described in [4] and requires knowledge of the load counter EMF for the proper application of the zero voltage vector. A new inverter state is commanded when the current error in any line exceeds the hysteresis band providing an instantaneous current limit. First, a zero voltage vector is applied if the counter EMF is in the appropriate direction to reduce the current error in all three lines. If a line current error exceeds the hysteresis band after a time delay, then new inverter firing signals are obtained from comparators without hysteresis. If the line current error is positive (negative), then the corresponding inverter leg is fired in the positive (negative) direction, reducing the current error as quickly as possible.

Ramp Comparison Controller: Asynchronous Sine-Triangle PWM with Current Feedback

A ramp comparison control for one inverter leg is shown in Fig. 5. The controller can be thought of as producing asynchronous sine-triangle PWM with the current error considered to be the modulating function. The current error is compared to a triangle waveform and if the current error is greater (less) than the triangle waveform, then the inverter leg is switched in the positive (negative) direction.

With sine-triangle PWM, the inverter switches at the

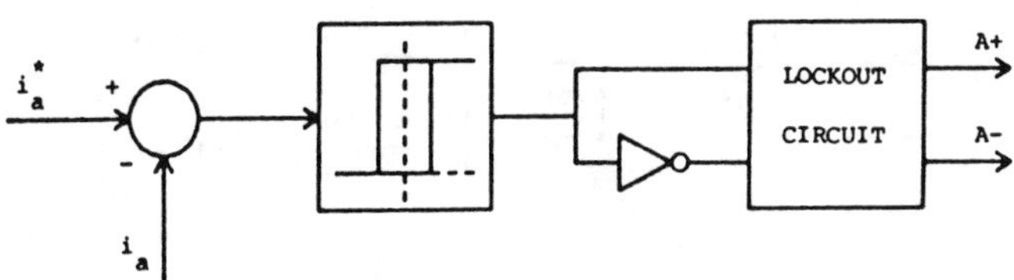

Fig. 4. Hysteresis control for one phase.

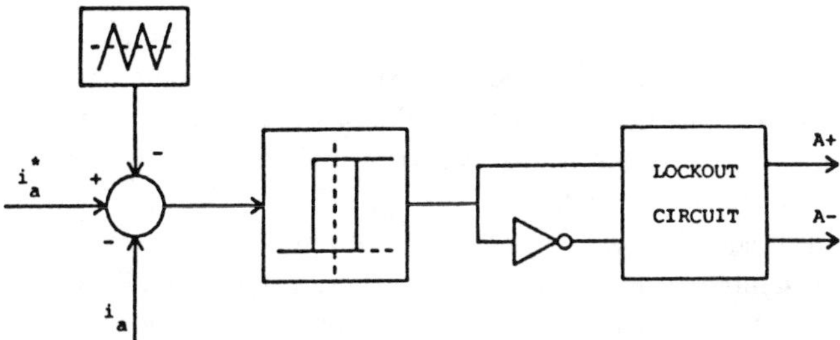

Fig. 5. Ramp comparison controller for one phase.

frequency of the triangle wave and produces well-define harmonics [5]. Multiple crossings of the ramp by the current error may become a problem when the time rate of change of the current error becomes greater than that of the ramp.

It will be shown later that there is an inherent magnitude and phase error in the line currents. The errors can be reduced by increasing the controller gain or adding compensation. The gain of the controller can be adjusted by either adjusting the triangle amplitude or amplifying the current error.

Predictive Controller: Constant Switching Frequency

The constant inverter switching frequency predictive controller calculates an inverter voltage vector, once every sample period, that will force the current to track the current command. The controller is shown in Fig. 6 and is described in [4], [6]. The following is a description of the controller operation. Let the load be represented by the differential equation in (3) which can be converted to a difference equation and solved for $\bar{i}$:

$$\bar{i}(T_{n+1}) = f(\bar{i}(T_n),\ \bar{v}(T_n),\ \bar{e}(T_n)) \tag{5}$$

where the inverter voltage and counter EMF are assumed to be constant over one sample period. A current command $\bar{i}^*(T_{n+1})$ can be substituted for $\bar{i}(T_{n+1})$, and the voltage vector $\bar{v}(T_n)$that changes the current from $\bar{i}(T_n)$ to the commanded value $\bar{i}^*(T_{n+1})$ can be written as follows:

$$\bar{v}(T_n) = g(\bar{i}^*(T_{n+1}),\ \bar{i}(T_n),\ \bar{e}(T_n)). \tag{6}$$

If the load is described by (3), then $\bar{v}(T_n)$ is given by

$$\bar{v}(T_n) = \frac{R[\bar{i}^*(T_{n+1}) - \bar{i}(T_n)e^{-TR/L}]}{1 - e^{-TR/L}} + \bar{e}(T_n) \tag{7}$$

where T is the sample period. The voltage vector $\bar{v}(T_n)$ has to be transformed into a weighted average of three inverter voltage vectors. Each inverter voltage vector is applied for a portion of the sample period with each inverter leg switched

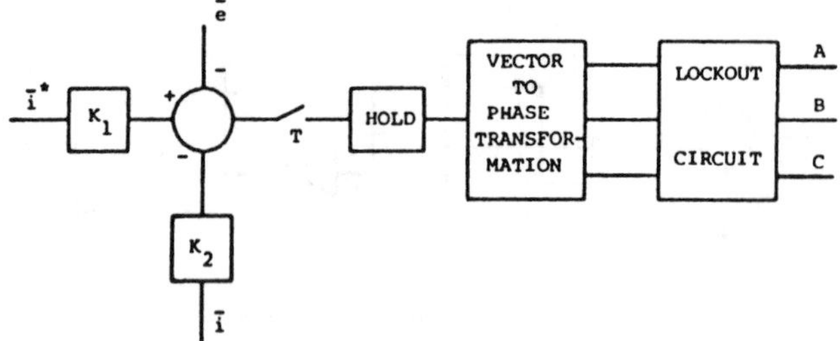

Fig. 6. Predictive controller: constant inverter switching frequency.

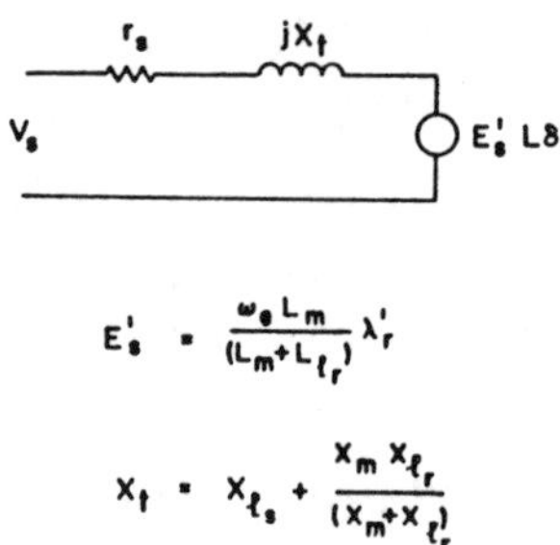

Fig. 7. Transient model for induction motor.

once every sample period, producing a constant inverter switching frequency of $1/(2T)$. For faster dynamic response, the closest inverter voltage vector to $\bar{v}(T_n)$ can be applied for the entire sample period.

The actual current lags the current reference by as much as one sample period. Longer lags probably will be realized due to calculation delays. The current ripple cannot be explicity specified as with a hysteresis controller but the inverter switching frequency is well-defined. The controller does not provide an inherent instantaneous current limit.

Predicitve Controller: Minimum Switching Frequency

The minimum inverter switching frequency controller is similar to the previous predicitve controller in that the proper inverter voltage vector is found with knowledge of the load and operating conditions. When the current error vector magnitude exceeds a specified value, the controller predicts the current trajectory for each possible inverter state and determines the length of time that the current error vector will remain within the specified value. The inverter switching frequency is minimized by selecting the inverter state that maximizes the following expression:

$$t(k)/n_c(k) \tag{8}$$

where

- t predicted time before next inverter switching,
- n_c number of commutations required to reach the new inverter state,
- k new inverter state.

The controller is discussed in detail in [7]. This controller provides an instantaneous current limit, although there will be a calculation delay in determining the next inverter state. The controller response might be slower than any of the hysteresis controllers due to the necessary calculations, but this was not investigated.

SIMULATION OF THE CURRENT CONTROLLERS

Simulations were carried out on a VAX 11/780 using the Advanced Continuous Simulation Language (ACSL). Since the inverter switching period is very short, the constant flux linkage model for the transient behavior of the induction machine is employed in the simulations. The machine is assumed to be in a high-performance field-oriented drive operating at constant speed over the period of the simulation. The magnitude and phase of the counter EMF is calculated assuming that the actual currents track the current references

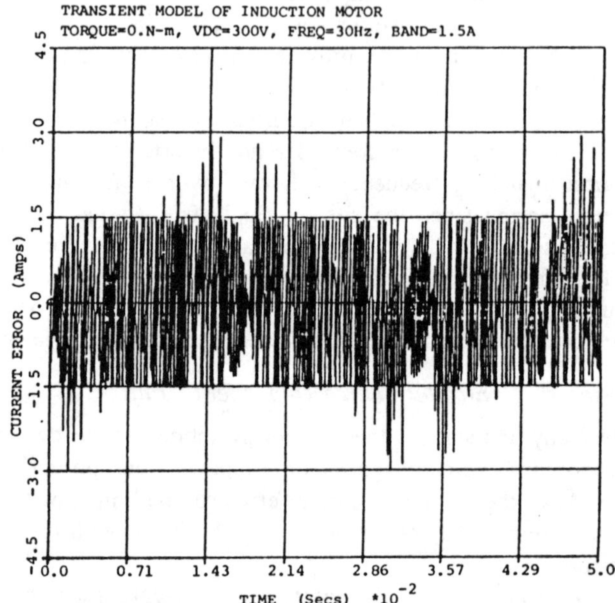

Fig. 8. Simulated current error waveform of typical 10-hp induction motor operating at no-load and one-half rated speed with hysteresis controller incorporating three independent controls.

within a reasonable tolerance. This assumption will create an error for the ramp comparison controller which can produce relatively large current errors if the controller gain is low.

The transient model for the induction motor is shown in Fig. 7 with the parameters for a typical 220-V three-phase 60-Hz four-pole 10-hp induction motor listed in the Appendix. The simulations only investigated the steady-state operation of the current controllers using the transient model with an operating frequency of 30 Hz and were run for one and one-half cycles with the load currents initialized to zero. The simulations did not incorporate controller or inverter delays and did not account for variation of motor parameters, i.e., saturation. More detail on the simulation technique and additional simulation results can be found in [8].

Hysteresis Controller: Three Independent Controls

Simulation results for the hysteresis controller with three independent controls illustrate the properties of the controller. Fig. 8 shows the current error when the induction motor operates at no-load and one-half rated speed with the hysteresis band set at 1.5 A. The average inverter switching frequency

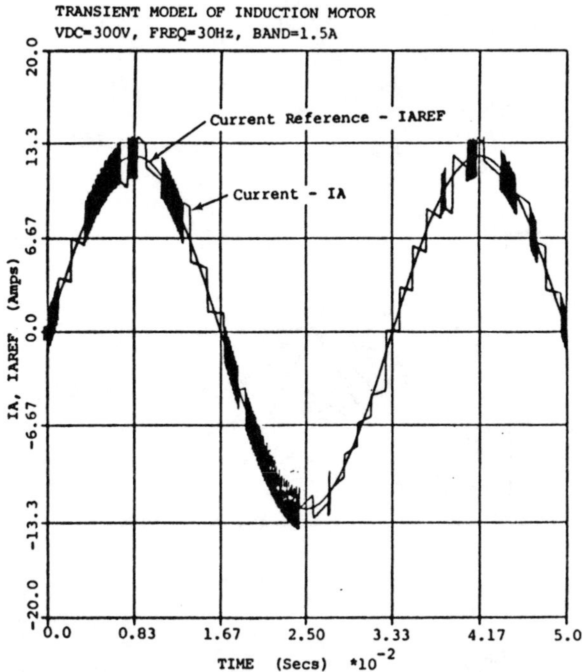

Fig. 9. Simulated waveforms of stalled typical 10-hp induction motor with hysteresis controller incorporating three independent controls.

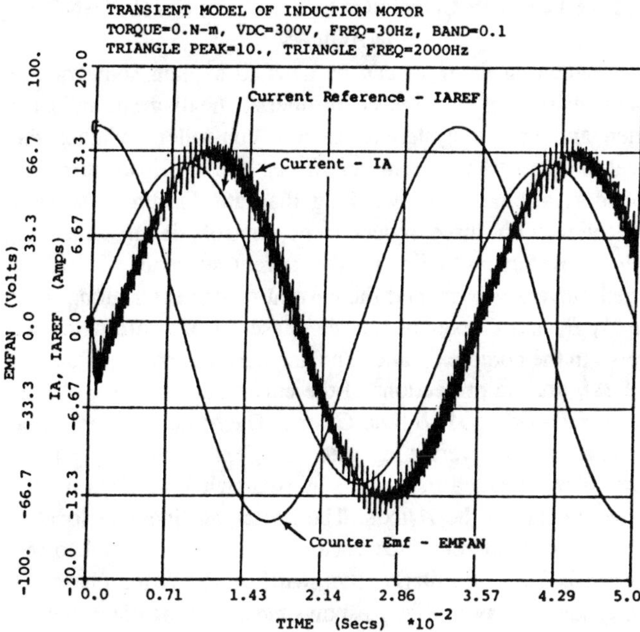

Fig. 10. Simulated waveforms of typical 10-hp induction motor operating at no-load and one-half rated speed with ramp comparison controller.

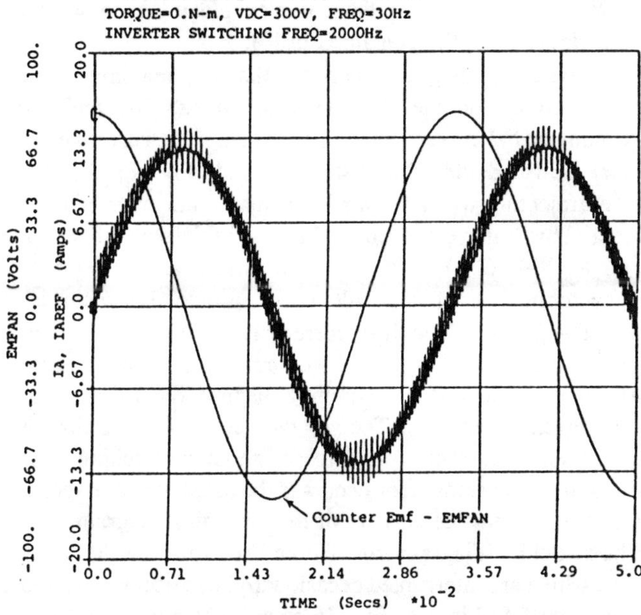

Fig. 11. Simulated waveforms of typical 10-hp induction motor operating at no-load and one-half rated speed with constant inverter switching frequency predictive controller.

is approximately 2600 Hz. The figure shows that the maximum line current error can be double the hysteresis band.

A load consisting of a stalled induction motor was simulated to observe the operating characteristics of the hysteresis controller when the load counter EMF is zero. The line current and current reference are shown in Fig. 9. The inverter has periods of high switching frequency which are interrupted occasionally when the inverter applies a zero voltage vector across the load. The periods of high switching frequency are referred to as limit cycles in this paper. The switching frequency during the limit cycles is approximately 6600 Hz.

Hysteresis Controller: Three Dependent Controls

Simulation results for the hysteresis controller with three dependent controls and the programmed application of the zero voltage vector indicate that the magnitude and phase error in the line currents are small. Also, the current errors remain within the hysteresis band. The average inverter switching frequency is approximately 5350 Hz when the induction motor operates at no-load and one-half rated speed with a hysteresis band of 1.5 A. The switching frequency is much higher than for the previous hysteresis controller. There are two reasons for this: 1) the maximum current error is smaller, and 2) when any one hysteresis band is exceeded, more than one inverter leg may switch.

A load consisting of a stalled induction motor was also simulated. The simulation showed that the limit cycles that occur with the previous controller are eliminated, and the average inverter switching frequency is much lower (approximately 550 Hz) than that of the hysteresis controller with three independent controls.

Ramp Comparison Controller

Fig. 10 shows the line current, current reference, and counter EMF that result with the ramp comparison controller without any additional compensation. Some hysteresis was added to the controller to prevent multiple crossings of the triangle ramp. There is a magnitude and phase error in the line current which results in a sinusoidal current error. The inverter switching frequency is approximately equal to the triangle frequency of 2000 Hz. The current ripple amplitude is reduced when the triangle frequency is increased.

Predictive Controllers

The predictive controllers performed as expected with a typical simulation for the constant inverter switching frequency controller shown in Fig. 11. Additional simulation results are given in [8].

HYSTERESIS CONTROLLERS—THE SWITCHING DIAGRAM

A switching diagram can be used to explain some of the characteristics of hysteresis controllers. The diagram indicates when and how a hysteresis current controller switches the inverter given the current references and the load currents. The derivation of the switching diagram for the hysteresis controller with three independent controls is presented as follows. Referring to Fig. 12, the current reference vector, the actual current vector, and the current error vector along with the A, B, and C axes of a three-phase set of coordinates are drawn in the complex plane. The line current errors Δi_a, Δi_b, and Δi_c are the projections of the current error vector $\Delta \bar{i}$ on the corresponding A, B, and C axes. The hysteresis controller switches the A inverter leg when Δi_a exceeds the hysteresis band as represented in Fig. 13 by two switching lines drawn perpendicular to the A axis. The switching lines are located from the current reference vector by a distance equal to the hysteresis band. Similarly, the switching lines for phases B and C can be drawn. Fig. 14 shows the switching diagram that results when the switching lines for each phase are combined. The switching diagram will move with the current reference vector since the current reference vector locates the center of the switching diagram in the complex plane. A somewhat similar development is contained in [9].

The switching diagram confirms that the maximum line current can be double the hysteresis band, $2h$, and the maximum spatial current error (magnitude of the current error vector) is also double the hysteresis band. Fig. 15 shows a current trajectory which results in the maximum error in a line current. This trajectory occurs when the initial voltage vector $\bar{v}_1$, $(A+, B-, C-)$, forces the line current vector to hit the $-A$ switching line which results in the zero voltage vector $\bar{v}_8$, $(A-, B-, C-)$. The line current error in phase A can increase further because of the load resistance, load counter EMF, or movement of the switching diagram due to variation of the current references. The voltage vector will not change until the actual current vector crosses another switching line. The maximum current error occurs if the actual current vector hits one of the outside corners of the switching diagram.

The switching diagram can also be used to show that limit cycles, which are interrupted occasionally, can occur when the load counter EMF is low. Fig. 16 shows a current trajectory, indicated by the solid line, that may occur during a limit cycle. The initial voltage vector $\bar{v}_1$, $(A+, B-, C-)$, forces the current vector to travel in the same direction as the voltage vector since the counter EMF and resistance are assumed to be zero. The current vector hits the $+C$ switching line, causing inverter leg C to switch and produce the inverter voltage vector $\bar{v}_2$, $(A+, B-, C+)$. Next, the current vector will hit the $-A$ switching line producing the voltage vector $\bar{v}_3$, $(A-, B-, C+)$. Continuing with the same line of reasoning, the six nonzero voltage vectors are applied repeatedly, and a high switching frequency results if there is a low leakage inductance and a small hysteresis band. Notice that the magnitude of the current error vector is not reduced to zero during the limit cycle. The dashed line in Fig. 16 represents a current trajectory when there is a nonzero counter EMF.

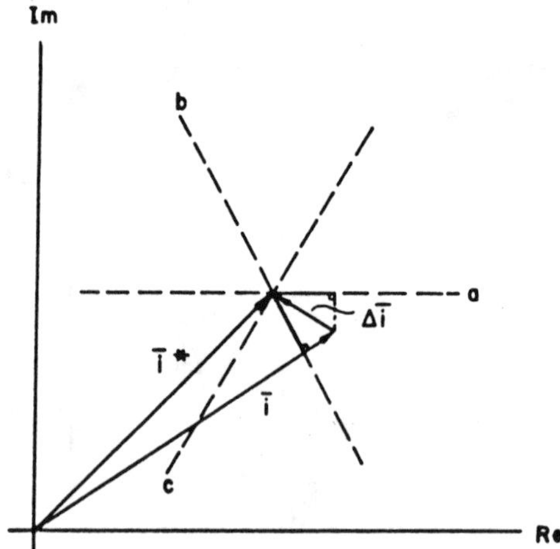

Fig. 12. Current vectors in complex plane.

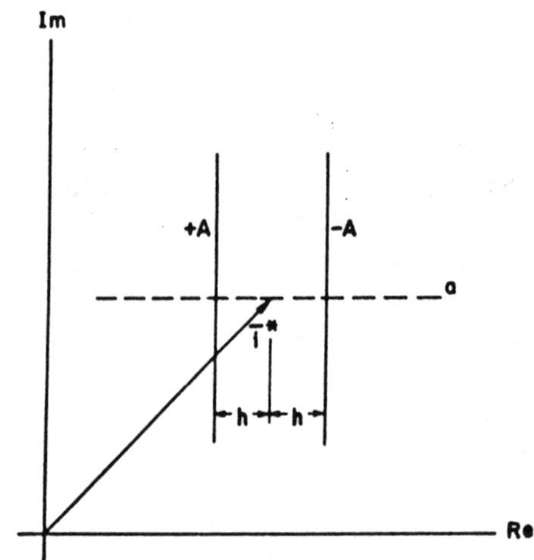

Fig. 13. Switching lines for phase A.

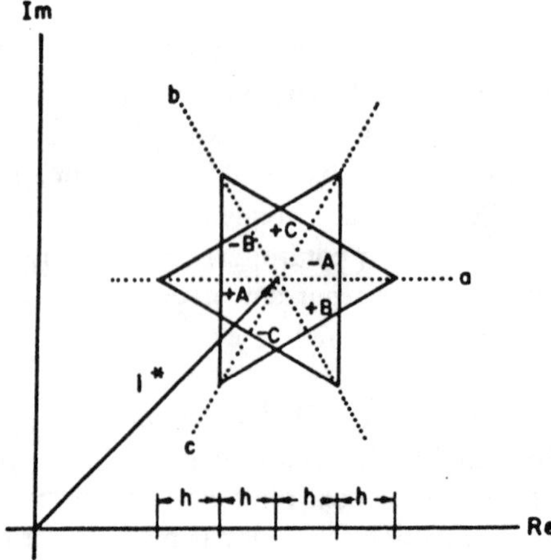

Fig. 14. Switching diagram for hysteresis controller with three independent controls located in complex plane.

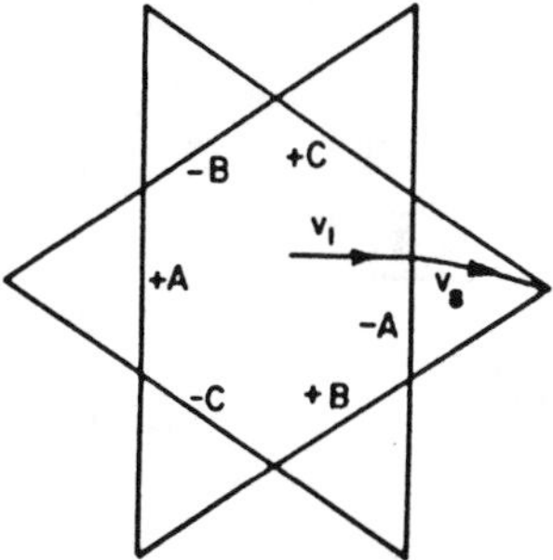

Fig. 15. Current trajectory which results in maximum line current error.

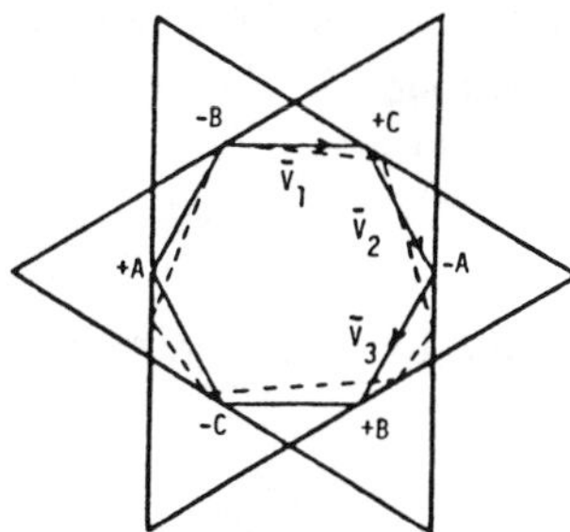

Fig. 16. Current trajectory for two limit cycles. Solid line: zero load counter EMF. Dashed line: nonzero counter EMF.

The frequency of the limit cycle can be found by dividing the velocity of the current trajectory by the distance traveled in one complete inverter switching period. The velocity is given by (for zero counter EMF):

$$\text{vel} = \frac{di}{dt} = \frac{\frac{2}{3} V_{dc}}{L}, \tag{9}$$

and the distance traveled by a limit cycle is approximately

$$d = 6h. \tag{10}$$

Therefore, the inverter switching frequency can be written as

$$f_s = \frac{\text{vel}}{d} = \frac{V_{dc}}{9hL}. \tag{11}$$

Equation (11) can be used to estimate the inverter switching frequency of the limit cycles observed in the simulation in Fig. 9:

$$f_s = \frac{300}{9(1.5)(0.00336)} = 6614 \quad \text{Hz} \tag{12}$$

which is close to the value estimated from the simulation. The highest inverter switching frequency occurs during the limit cycles when the counter EMF is zero (since the counter EMF tends to reduce the switching frequency). Therefore, the inverter has to be designed to handle the switching frequency that occurs with zero counter EMF. This is an important limitation of this type of controller.

The limit cycle may be occasionally interrupted by the intermittent occurrence of a zero voltage vector. For example, consider the limit cycle in the previous example. A zero voltage vector occurs when one of the switching lines in the sequence is skipped due to the load counter EMF, load resistance, or the movement of the switching diagram. If the switching diagram moves, the voltage vector $\bar{v}_1$, $(A+, B-, C-)$, in Fig. 16 may cause the current vector to cross the $-A$ switching line instead of the $+C$ switching line which results in the zero voltage vector $\bar{v}_8$, $(A-, B-, C-)$. The application of a zero voltage vector will significantly reduce the inverter switching frequency when the counter EMF is low since the velocity along a trajectory with a zero voltage vector is much lower (zero if the counter EMF is zero) than with a nonzero voltage vector.

RAMP-COMPARISON CONTROLLERS: FREQUENCY-DOMAIN ANALYSIS

The following analysis assumes that the ramp comparison controller produces asynchronous sine-triangle pulsewidth modulation. Sine-triangle PWM produces fundamental line-to-neutral voltages which are proportional to the ratio of the sine wave peak and triangle peak. The block diagram of the frequency domain model for the ramp comparison controller is shown in Fig. 17. The line current $\hat{I}$ can be found from the following quantities:

- $\hat{I}^*$ current reference,
- $\hat{E}$ load counter EMF,
- $\hat{Z}$ load impedance,
- $\hat{K}$ system gain.

The system gain is given by the following expression [5], [10]:

$$\hat{K} = \hat{K}_s G \tag{13}$$

where

$$K_s = \frac{V_{dc}}{2A_t} \tag{14}$$

- A_t triangle peak,
- G additional gain and/or compensation.

The line-to-neutral voltage phasor $\hat{V}$ is given by

$$\hat{V} = \hat{K}(\hat{I}^* - \hat{I}), \tag{15}$$

and the line-to-neutral voltage and load current are related as follows:

$$\hat{V} = \hat{I}\hat{Z} + \hat{E}. \tag{16}$$

Equations (15) and (16) can be equated and written as

$$\hat{K}(\hat{I}^* - \hat{I}) = \hat{I}\hat{Z} + \hat{E}. \tag{17}$$

Equation (17) can be rearranged to give an expression for the load current

$$\hat{I} = \frac{\hat{K}\hat{I}^* - \hat{E}}{\hat{K} + \hat{Z}} \tag{18}$$

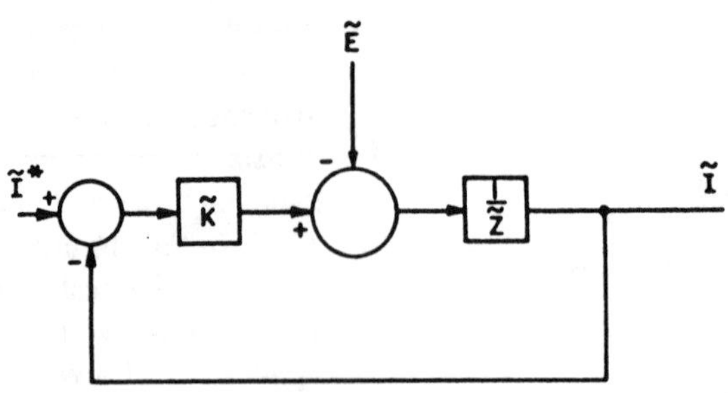

Fig. 17. Frequency domain transfer function model for ramp comparison controller.

which shows that the counter EMF can have a significant effect on the line currents and current error especially at higher motor speeds. The magnitude and phase errors of the line currents are reduced by increasing the controller gain or including some type of compensation.

This frequency-domain analysis is substantiated by the previous simulations. For example, substituting the following information, obtained from Figs. 7 and 10,

$$\hat{K}=15\angle 0^\circ \qquad \hat{I}^*=12.4\angle 0^\circ \quad \text{A}$$

$$\hat{E}=76.6\angle 90^\circ \quad \text{V} \qquad \hat{Z}=0.66\angle 72.9^\circ \quad \Omega$$

into (18) results in a line current of $13.2\angle -24.8^\circ$ A which corresponds to that shown in Fig. 10.

The analysis can be extended to incorporate the steady-state equivalent circuit for the induction motor. This is useful since the counter EMF is not normally known explicity. The equivalent circuit can be reduced to an equivalent impedance $\hat{Z}_{eq}$ which provides the following expression for the line current

$$\hat{I}=\frac{\hat{K}\hat{I}^*}{\hat{K}+\hat{Z}_{eq}}. \tag{19}$$

This expression can be useful in evaluating system response at specific operating points (i.e., evaluating the effect of load or changes in machine parameters).

As an illustration of the use of (18) for compensation design, consider a proportional-integral compensator to improve the low-frequency response. The transfer function of a proportional-integral controller is

$$G=K_c\,\frac{1+j\omega T_c}{j\omega} \tag{20}$$

where T_c is the time constant of the compensation network. Using the transient model of the induction motor and substituting (20) into (18), the following expression for the current results:

$$\hat{I}=\frac{K_sK_c\left[\dfrac{(1+j\omega T_c)}{j\omega}\right]\hat{I}^*-\hat{E}}{r_s\left(1+\dfrac{j\omega L_t}{r_s}\right)+K_sK_c\,\dfrac{(1+j\omega T_c)}{j\omega}}. \tag{21}$$

Using the concept of cancellation compensation, the time constant of the controller T_c can be set equal to the motor stator transient time constant

$$T_c=T_s'=L_t/r_s \tag{22}$$

which results in the following expression:

$$\hat{I}=\frac{1}{1+\dfrac{j\omega r_s}{K_sK_c}}\,\hat{I}^*-\frac{\dfrac{j\omega}{K_sK_c}}{(1+j\omega T_s')\left(1+\dfrac{j\omega r_s}{K_sK_c}\right)}\,\hat{E}. \tag{23}$$

The compensation gain K_c would be set to as large a value as permitted by the parasitic poles (and/or the delays associated with the inverter switching and sampling effects).

For systems in which the closed loop phase error is a major concern (i.e., field orientation), the best choice of a compensator will depend on the speed range of the system. If small phase errors at high speed are required, the compensator should be chosen to minimize the phase error near the cutoff frequency. This design problem was not considered in this project.

SUMMARY

Of the controllers studied, the hysteresis controller with three independent controls is the simplest to implement. The predictive controllers are the most complex and require knowledge of the load and extensive hardware which may limit the dynamic response of the controller. The ramp comparison controller has the advantage of limiting the maximum inverter switching frequency and producing well-defined harmonics, but the controller requires a large gain and compensation to reduce the current error and generally has lower bandwidth than hysteresis controllers.

The hysteresis controller with three independent controls works very well except the inverter switching frequency is higher than required when there is low counter EMF due to limit cycles. The switching frequency can be reduced by introducing zero voltages at the appropriate times (when the counter EMF is low). A combination of a ramp comparison controller for low-speed operation and a simple hysteresis controller for high-speed operation may provide a good overall solution.

APPENDIX

TYPICAL 10-hp INDUCTION MOTOR PARAMETERS 220 V, FOUR POLE, 60 Hz

r_s Stator resistance, 0.195 Ω.

r_r Rotor resistance, 0.195 Ω.

x_{ls} Stator leakage reactance, 0.649 Ω.

x_{lr} Rotor leakage reactance, 0.649 Ω.

x_m Magnetizing reactance, 12.98 Ω.

REFERENCES

[1] A. B. Plunkett, "A current-controlled PWM transistor inverter drive," in *Conf. Rec. 1979 14th Annu. Meet. IEEE Ind. Appl. Soc.*, pp. 785–792.

[2] S. C. Peak and A. B. Plunkett, "Transistorized PWM inverter-induction motor drive system," in *Conf. Rec. 1982 17th Annu. Meet. IEEE Ind. Appl. Soc.*, pp. 892–898.

[3] W. McMurray, "Modulation of the chopping frequency in dc choppers and PWM inverters having current-hysteresis controllers," in *Conf. Rec. 1983 IEEE PESC*, pp. 295–299.

[4] G. Pfaff, A. Weschta, and A. Wick, "Design and experimental results of a brushless ac servo-drive," in *Conf. Rec. 1982 17th Annu. Meet. IEEE Ind. Appl. Soc.*, pp. 692–697.

[5] A. Schonung and H. Stemmler, "Static frequency changers with 'subharmonic' control in conjunction with reversible variable-speed a.c. drives," *Brown Boveri Rev.*, pp. 555–577, Aug./Sept. 1964.

[6] I. Takahashi, "A flywheel energy storage system having harmonic power compensation," Univ. of Wisconsin, Madison, WEMPEC Res. Rep. 82-3, June 1982.

[7] J. Holtz and S. Stadtfeld, "A predictive controller for the stator current vector of ac machines fed from a switched voltage source," in *Conf. Rec. 1983 Annu. Meet. Int. Power Electronics Conf.*, pp. 1665–1675.

[8] D. Brod, "Current control in VSI-PWM inverters," M.S. thesis, Univ. of Wisconsin, Madison, 1984.

[9] G. Pfaff and A. Wick, "Direct current control of ac drives with pulsed frequency converters," *Process Automat.*, vol. 2, pp. 83–88, 1983.

[10] P. Wood, *Switching Power Converters*. New York: Van Nostrand Reinhold, 1981, ch. 4, pp. 152–153.

An Adaptive Hysteresis-Band Current Control Technique of a Voltage-Fed PWM Inverter for Machine Drive System

BIMAL K. BOSE, FELLOW, IEEE

Abstract—**A Hysteresis-band instantaneous current control PWM technique is popularly used because of its simplicity of implementation, fast current control response, and inherent peak current limiting capability. However, a current controller with a fixed hysteresis band has the disadvantage that the modulation frequency varies in a band and, as a result, generates nonoptimum current ripple in the load. This paper describes an adaptive hysteresis-band current control method where the band is modulated with the system parameters to maintain the modulation frequency to be nearly constant. Although the technique is applicable to general ac drives and other types of load, an interior permanent magnet (IPM) synchronous machine load is considered. Systematic analytical expressions of the hysteresis band are derived as functions of system parameters. An IPM machine drive system with a voltage-fed current-controlled PWM inverter has been simulated on computer to study the performance of the proposed method.**

I. Introduction

SINCE the introduction of the general sine-triangle voltage PWM technique by Schonung and Stemmler [9] around two-and-a-half decades ago, the literature in power electronics abounds with various PWM techniques and their implementation. For ac machine drive applications, the PWM voltage control is usually associated with stator current control because the current directly relates to the developed torque of a machine. Besides, the control of current amplitude is particularly important for power semiconductor devices of the inverter. A PWM voltage-controlled inverter may have either scalar or vector current control in outer loops. Scalar current control may be adequate for a simple low-performance drive system. In a high-performance vector or field-oriented drive control system, the vector currents I_{qs} (torque component of current) and I_{ds} (flux component of current) are controlled independently to control the torque and flux, respectively. The different PWM voltage control techniques, such as sine-triangle and notch angle look-up table, are generally difficult to implement. Besides, the current feedback loops may have delay, which will not permit instantaneous-peak current control of a device. Asynchronous sine-triangle PWM voltage control can be used in conjunction with instantaneous current feedback control to solve the above problem. However, in this method, the current loop errors will be nearly sinusoidal in nature, and the response will be somewhat limited by the stability requirement of the feedback loops. Besides, multiple crossings of the triangle ramp by the current error may become a problem when time rate of change in the current error becomes greater than that of the ramp. Predictive voltage control techniques [13] to achieve balance between instantaneous command and feedback currents have been forwarded. Although these techniques tend to give optimum performance in terms of response time and accuracy, these are very complex to implement.

Among the various PWM techniques, the hysteresis-band current control PWM method is popularly used because of its simplicity of implementation. Besides fast-response current loop and inherent-peak current limiting capability, the technique does not need any information about system parameters. However, the current control with a fixed hysteresis band has the disadvantage that the PWM frequency varies within a band because peak-to-peak current ripple is required to be controlled at all points of the fundamental frequency wave. As a result, the load current contains excess harmonics, which cause additional machine heating. Besides, the difficulty of vector conversion of harmonic rich feedback currents and phase lag of the fundamental current with respect to the reference wave make high-performance machine control difficult. Consider a battery-fed inverter drive system where the battery voltage in the worst case may vary by a factor of two (see Table II) from full motoring to full regeneration. Since maximum inverter switching frequency is a limiting factor and switching frequency tends to increase with the increase of battery voltage for a fixed hysteresis band, the band is to be designed on worst-case basis, i.e., for the maximum battery voltage. This means that most of the time, the drive system will operate with nonoptimum stator current ripple. Malesani and Tenti [3] have proposed a programmable hysteresis-band current control method by using a phase-locked loop (PLL) technique to constrain the inverter switching at a fixed predetermined frequency. The PLL loop with large LP filter tends to create stability problem. Besides, during large transients, the PLL tends to lose synchronization.

The paper describes an adaptive hysteresis-band current control PWM technique where the band can be programmed as a function of load and supply parameters to optimize the PWM performance. Although various criteria of optimization are possible, the paper illustrates a case where the modula-

Manuscript received July 17, 1989.
The author is with the Department of Electrical Engineering, University of Tennessee, Knoxville, TN 37996-2100.
IEEE Log Number 9038039.

Reprinted from *IEEE Trans. Ind. Electron.*, vol. 37, no. 5, pp. 402–408, October 1990.

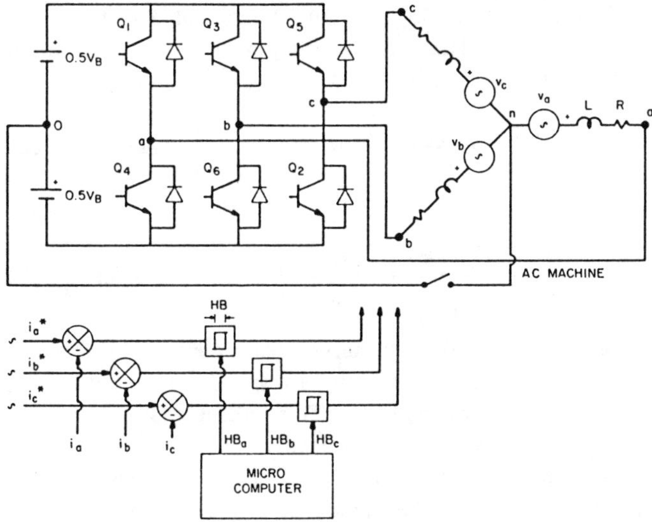

Fig. 1. Three-phase PWM inverter ac machine drive with hysteresis-band current controller.

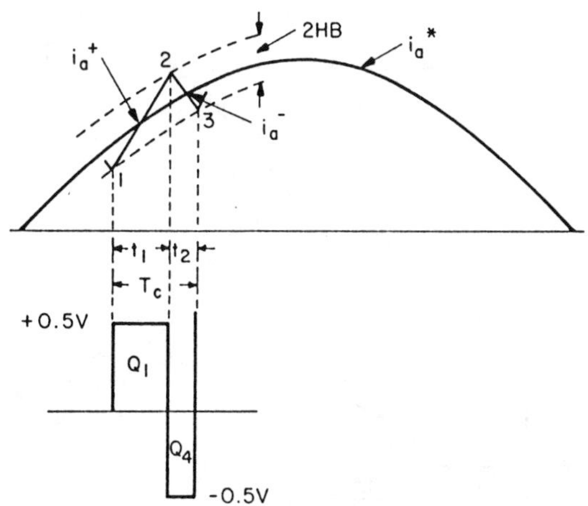

Fig. 2. Current and voltage waves with hysteresis-band current control (machine neutral connected).

tion frequency is held nearly constant. Modern high-performance ac drive systems invariably use microcomputer control where all the system variables are already available in the memory. An algorithm relating the hysteresis-band with the system variables can be easily computed and updated to a dedicated hardware hysteresis-band current control for an interior permanent-magnet synchronous machine drive application. An analytical derivation of the band has been made and then verified by simulation on computer.

II. System Analysis

Fig. 1 shows a three-phase PWM inverter feeding an ac machine load where each machine phase is represented by a counter emf in series with inductance and resistance. Sinusoidal command currents (i_a^*, i_b^*, i_c^*) are compared with the respective machine phase currents (i_a, i_b, i_c), and the resulting errors through hysteresis-band current controllers command the transistor base drives, as is shown. The hysteresis bands that are normally fixed and the same for all phases in a conventional system are shown being updated from a microcomputer in the proposed adaptive band system. The band (HB) can be modulated at different points of the fundamental frequency cycle to control the PWM switching pattern of the inverter. For symmetrical operation of all the three phases, it is expected that the band profiles HB_a, HB_b, and HB_c will be same, but phase will be displaced.

A. Case 1: Neutral Connected with Pure Inductance Load

Consider a simple case where a wye-connected machine neutral is connected to the center tap of the supply battery, and the load is purely inductive, i.e., the counter emf and resistance are neglected. In this case, each phase is independent and is supplied by a half-bridge inverter leg. Fig. 2 shows the PWM current and voltage waves for phase a. The current i_a tends to cross the lower hysteresis band at point 1, where the transistor Q_1 is switched on. The linearly rising current ($i_a +$) then touches the upper band at point 2, where the transistor Q_4 is switched on. The following equations can be written in the respective switching intervals t_1 and t_2:

$$L\frac{di_a^+}{dt} = 0.5V_B \tag{1}$$

$$L\frac{di_a^-}{dt} = -0.5V_B \tag{2}$$

$$\text{i.e.}\quad \frac{di_a^+}{dt} + \frac{di_a^-}{dt} = 0 \tag{3}$$

where L = phase inductance, and $i_a +$ and $i_a -$ are the respective rising and falling current segments.

From the geometry of Fig. 2, we can write

$$\frac{di_a^+}{dt}t_1 - \frac{di_a^*}{dt}t_1 = 2HB \tag{4}$$

$$\frac{di_a^-}{dt}t_2 - \frac{di_a^*}{dt}t_2 = -2HB \tag{5}$$

$$t_1 + t_2 = T_C = \frac{1}{f_c} \tag{6}$$

where t_1 and t_2 are the respective switching intervals, and f_c is the modulation frequency.

Adding (4) and (5) and substituting (6), we can write

$$t_1\frac{di_a^+}{dt} + t_2\frac{di_a^-}{dt} - \frac{1}{f_c}\frac{di_a^*}{dt} = 0. \tag{7}$$

Subtracting (5) from (4), we get

$$4HB = t_1\frac{di_a^+}{dt} - t_2\frac{di_a^-}{dt} - (t_1 - t_2)\frac{di_a^*}{dt}. \tag{8}$$

Substituting (3) in (8), we get

$$\begin{aligned} 4HB &= (t_1 + t_2)\frac{di_a^+}{dt} - (t_1 - t_2)\frac{di_a^*}{dt} \\ &= \frac{1}{f_c}\frac{di_a^+}{dt} - (t_1 - t_2)\frac{di_a^*}{dt}. \end{aligned} \tag{9}$$

Again, substituting (3) in (7) and simplifying

$$t_1 - t_2 = \left(\frac{di_a^*}{dt}\right)/f_c\left(\frac{di_a^+}{dt}\right). \tag{10}$$

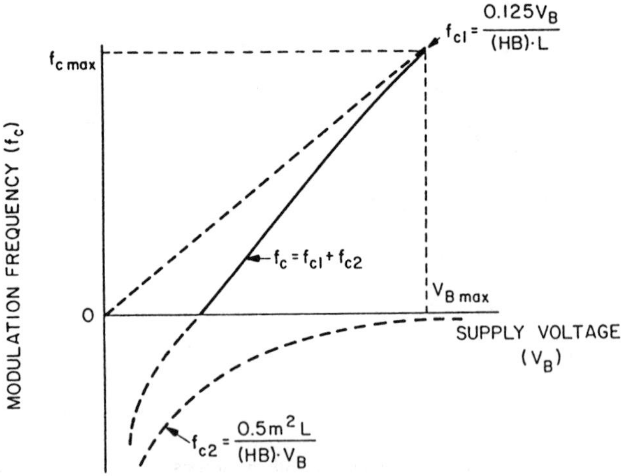

Fig. 3. Sensitivity of modulation frequency with the supply voltage.

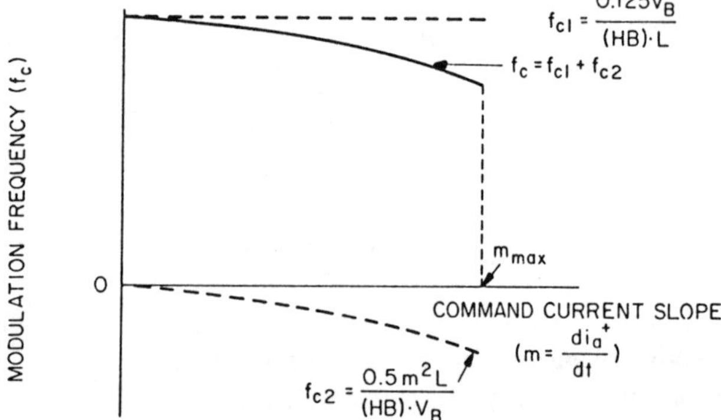

Fig. 4. Sensitivity of modulation frequency with the command current slope.

Substituting (10) in (9) gives

$$4HB = \frac{1}{f_c}\left[\frac{di_a^+}{dt} - \frac{(di_a^*/dt)^2}{\left(\frac{di_a^+}{dt}\right)}\right]. \tag{11}$$

Substituting (1) in (11) and simplifying

$$HB = \frac{0.125V_B}{f_c L}\left[1 - \frac{4m^2L^2}{V_B^2}\right] \tag{12}$$

i.e.

$$f_c = \frac{0.125V_B}{(HB)L}\left[1 - \frac{4m^2L^2}{V_B^2}\right] \tag{13}$$

where $m = di_a^*/dt$ is the slope of command current wave.

Equation (12) shows the band as a function of modulation frequency, supply voltage, and the slope of the i_a^* wave. Equation (13) indicates that for a fixed band, the modulation frequency will vary with V_B and m. Fig. 3 shows the sensitivity of f_c with V_B indicating that the modulation frequency increases with the dc voltage. Fig. 4 shows the sensitivity of f_c with the slope of command current wave. Since

$$m^2 = \left[\frac{d}{dt}(I_m^* \sin \omega t)\right]^2 = 0.5\omega^2 I_m^2 (1 + \cos 2\omega t)$$

the frequency f_c in Fig. 4 will be modulated at twice the signal frequency. The corresponding maximum and minimum values of f_c can be derived as

$$f_{c_{\max}} = \frac{0.125V_B}{(HB)L} \text{ at } \omega t = \frac{\pi}{2}, \frac{3\pi}{2}, \text{etc.} \tag{14}$$

and

$$f_{c_{\min}} = \frac{0.125V_B}{(HB)L}\left[1 - \frac{4\omega^2 I_m^2 L^2}{V_B^2}\right] \text{ at } \omega t = 0, \pi, \text{etc.} \tag{15}$$

Therefore, for constant hysteresis-band control, the band is to be designed for $f_{c_{\max}}$, which corresponds to the highest V_B and $m = 0$ point of the cycle. This indicates large harmonic distortion of current, and especially, the problem becomes severe with large variation of dc voltage. Equation (12) indicates that HB can be modulated as a function of V_B and m so that the modulation frequency f_c remains constant. This will improve the PWM performances substantially.

B. Case 2: Neutral Connected with Counter emf Load

The machine always develops a counter emf at a speed, and therefore, this type of load is more practical. The counter emf wave is sinusoidal and is at a phase angle with respect to the fundamental frequency applied voltage. During a modulation period, the emf magnitude can be considered to be constant. The following equation can be written from Fig. 2:

$$\frac{di_a^+}{dt} = \frac{1}{L}(0.5V_B - v_f) \tag{16}$$

$$\frac{di_a^-}{dt} = -\frac{1}{L}(0.5V_B + v_f) \tag{17}$$

where v_f = counter emf.

Note that the magnitudes of the current slopes are different because the counter emf v_f is subtractive in positive slope but additive in negative slope. The general equations (7) and (8) of *Case 1* will be valid here. Substituting (16) and (17) in (7), we get

$$\frac{t_1}{L}(0.5V_B - v_f) - \frac{t_2}{L}(0.5V_B + v_f) - \frac{1}{f_c}\frac{di_a^*}{dt} = 0$$

$$\text{i.e. } -\frac{0.5V_B}{L}(t_2 - t_1) - \frac{1}{f_c}\left(\frac{v_f}{L} + \frac{di_a^*}{dt}\right) = 0$$

$$\text{or } t_2 - t_1 = -\frac{2L}{V_B f_c}\left(\frac{v_f}{L} + \frac{di_a^*}{dt}\right). \tag{18}$$

Substituting (16), (17), and (18) in (8), we get

$$4HB = \frac{t_1}{L}(0.5V_B - v_f) + \frac{t_2}{L}(0.5V_B + v_f) - \frac{2L}{V_B f_c}\left(\frac{v_f}{L} + \frac{di_a^*}{dt}\right)$$

$$\text{i.e., } HB = \frac{0.125V_B}{f_c L}\left[1 - \frac{4L^2}{V_B^2}\left(\frac{v_f}{L} + m\right)^2\right] \tag{19}$$

where m is substituted for di_a^*/dt.

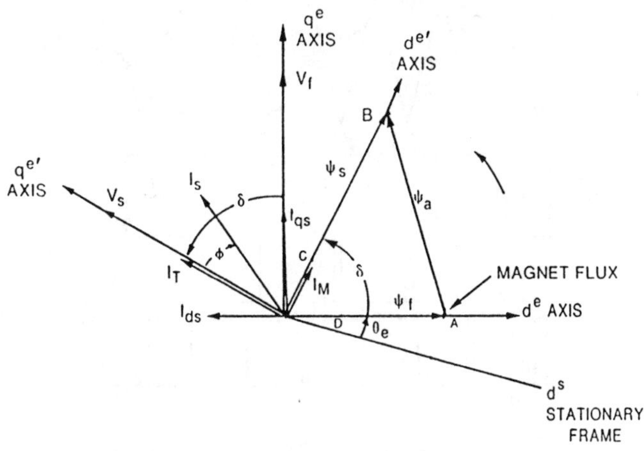

Fig. 5. Phasor diagram of interior permanent magnet synchronous machine.

Equation (19) is similar to (12), except the counter emf parameter is introduced. In this equation, the variables v_f and m depend on the type of load machine and its operating condition.

An interior permanent-magnet synchronous machine load will be considered here, although (19) is valid for any type of ac machine. Fig. 5 shows the phasor diagram [11] of an IPM machine. In forward direction of motion, the phasor diagram can be considered to be rotating counter clockwise at synchronous speed (ω_e) with respect to the stationary reference frame d^s axis, and at any instant, the angle between the magnet axis (d^e) and d^s axis is $\theta_e = \omega_e t$. The armature reaction flux Ψ_a adds with the magnet pole flux Ψ_f to constitute the stator flux Ψ_s, which is aligned at an angle δ (torque angle), as shown. The stator phase voltage V_s and induced emf V_f are at quadrature to the respective flux components Ψ_s and Ψ_f. A new set of $d^{e'} - q^{e'}$ axes that align with Ψ_s and V_s is shown in the figure. The machine phase current I_s is shown at arbitrary lagging power factor angle Φ. This current can be resolved as an I_{ds}-I_{qs} pair on d^e-q^e axes or an I_m-I_T pair on $d^{e'}$-$q^{e'}$ axes. The in-phase current I_T contributes to machine torque, whereas the reactive current I_M controls the stator flux. From the phasor diagram, the following equation can be written:

$$v_f = V_{fm} \sin 0_e \tag{20}$$

$$i_s = I_{sm} \sin(\theta_e + \delta - \Phi) \tag{21}$$

$$I_{qs} = I_{sm} \cos(\delta - \Phi) \tag{22}$$

$$I_{ds} = I_{sm} \sin(\delta - \Phi) \tag{23}$$

where

$$V_{fm} = \sqrt{2} V_f = \sqrt{2} \Psi_f \omega_e \text{ and } I_{sm} = \sqrt{2} I_s.$$

The phase current i_s (i.e., i_a) can be considered to be tracking accurately with respective commanded current (i_a^*) with the hysteresis-band current control. Therefore, differentiating (21)

$$m = \frac{di_s}{dt} = \omega_e[\cos\theta_e I_{sm} \cos(\delta - \Phi) - \sin\theta_e I_{sm} \sin(\delta - \Phi)] \tag{24}$$

and then substituting (22) and (23)

$$m = \omega_e(I_{qs} \cos\theta_e - I_{ds} \sin\theta_e). \tag{25}$$

Substituting (20) and (25) in (19), the complete expression of HB can be derived to be

$$HB = \frac{0.125 V_B}{f_c L}\left[1 - \frac{4L^2\omega_e^2}{V_B^2}\left\{\left(\frac{\sqrt{2}\Psi_f\omega_e}{L} - I_{ds}\right)\sin\theta_e + I_{qs}\cos\theta_e\right\}^2\right]. \tag{26}$$

Equation (26) can be written in the form

$$HB = \frac{0.125 V_B \omega_b}{f_c X_L}\left[1 - \frac{4X_L^2}{V_B^2}\left(\frac{\omega_e}{\omega_b}\right)^2 \cdot \left\{\left(\frac{\sqrt{2}V_{fB}\omega_e}{X_L} - I_{ds}\right)\sin\theta_e + I_{qs}\cos\theta_e\right\}^2\right] \tag{27}$$

where ω_b = base frequency (rad/s), $X_L = \omega_b L = 0.5(X_{qs} + X_{ds})$, and $V_{fB} = \Psi_f \omega_b$. The IPM machine has some saliency but only the average reactance is taken into consideration. Substituting the trigonometrical relation

$$(A\sin\theta_e + B\cos\theta_e)^2 = 0.5(A^2 + B^2)[1 - \cos 2(\theta_e + \alpha)]$$

and simplifying (27) can also be written in the form

$$HB = (A - B) + B\cos 2(\theta_e + \alpha) \tag{28}$$

where

$$A = \frac{0.125 V_B \omega_b}{f_c X_L}$$

$$B = \frac{0.25\omega_b X_L}{f_c V_B}\left(\frac{\omega_e}{\omega_b}\right)^2\left[\left(\frac{\sqrt{2}V_{fB}\omega_e}{X_L} - I_{ds}\right)^2 + I_{qs}^2\right]$$

and

$$a = \tan^{-1}\frac{I_{qs}}{\left(\frac{\sqrt{2}V_{fB}\omega_e}{X_L} - I_{ds}\right)}.$$

Fig. 6 shows the typical plot of (28) for a fixed modulation frequency, where it is given in phase relation with the phase current and induced voltage. Evidently, modulation of HB occurs at twice the stator frequency with the average value A-B.

C. Case 3: Isolated Neutral with Counter emf Load

Since machines normally operate with isolated neutral, this is the most practical case. Unfortunately, with isolated neutral, the machine phase voltages interact and can no longer be $0.5V_B$ as with a connected neutral. The derivation of the exact expression of HB is somewhat difficult in this case. In Fig. 1, the phase voltages with floating neutral can be given

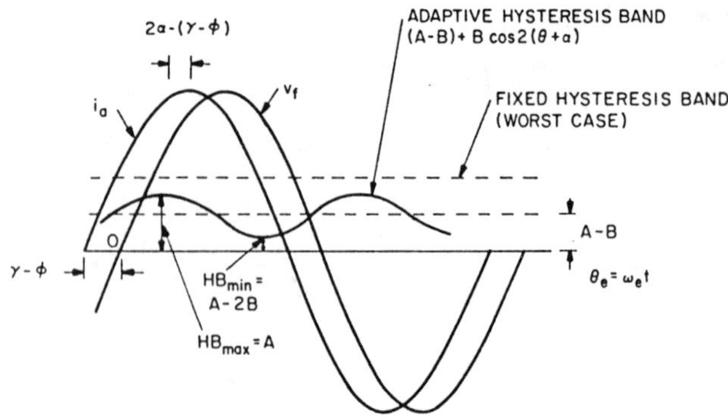

Fig. 6. Adaptive hysteresis-band profile for constant modulation showing relation phase current and induced voltage waves.

TABLE I
SWITCHING MODES OF THE INVERTER AND PHASE a IMPRESSED VOLTAGES

MODE	ON-DEVICE	PHASE a VOLTAGE
1	Q_1 Q_6 Q_5	+1/3V_B
2	Q_1 Q_6 Q_2	+1/3V_B
3	Q_1 Q_3 Q_5	0
4	Q_1 Q_6 Q_2	+2/3V_B
5	Q_4 Q_6 Q_2	0
6	Q_4 Q_3 Q_5	-2/3V_B
7	Q_4 Q_3 Q_2	-1/3V_B
8	Q_4 Q_6 Q_5	-1/3V_B

as [1]

$$v_{an} = \frac{2}{3}v_{ao} - \frac{1}{3}(v_{bo} + v_{co}) \tag{29}$$

$$v_{bn} = \frac{2}{3}v_{bo} - \frac{1}{3}(v_{ao} + v_{co}) \tag{30}$$

$$v_{cn} = \frac{2}{3}v_{co} - \frac{1}{3}(v_{ao} + v_{bo}) \tag{31}$$

Table I gives all the switching modes of the inverter, and Fig. 7 shows [2] typical PWM voltage waves in the isolated neutral case. When Q_1 is on, the possible phase-a voltage may be 0, 1/3, or $2/3V_B$, and when Q_4 is on, the corresponding voltage may be 0, $-1/3$, or $-2/3$VB. Typical PWM phase voltage and current waves during a modulation cycle are shown in Fig. 8. With the assumed polarity of counter emf when Q_1 is on, the phase current in a time segment will rise or fall, respectively, depending on the dominating phase voltage or counter emf, but the current will always fall during the Q_4-on period. The general expression of incremental current rise ΔHB during Q_1-on period is given by

$$\Delta HB = \frac{t_{1n}}{L}(aV_B - v_f) - t_{1n}m \tag{32}$$

where

$$a = 0, \frac{1}{3} \text{ or } \frac{2}{3} \text{ and } m = \frac{di_a^*}{dt}.$$

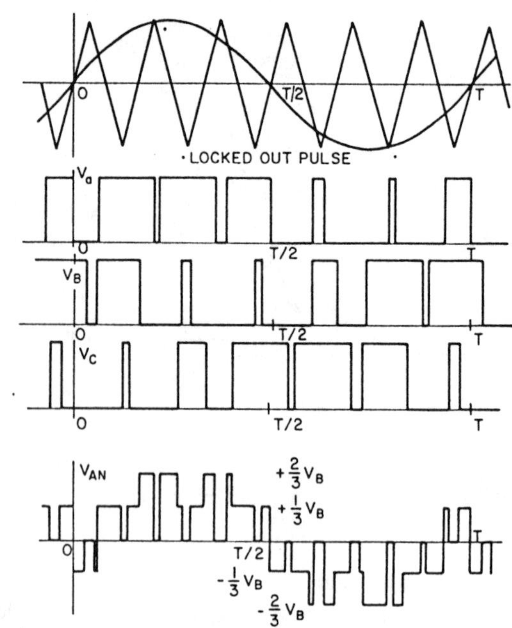

Fig. 7. Typical PWM voltage waves when the machine neutral is isolated.

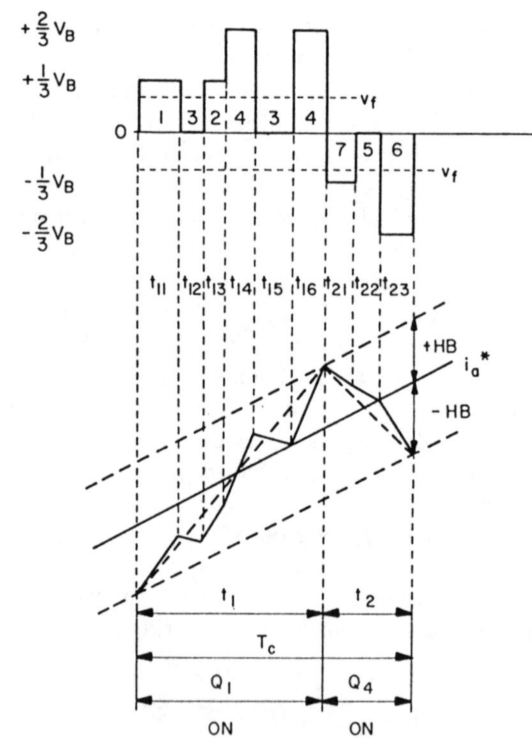

Fig. 8. Typical PWM phase voltage and current waves in a modulation cycle in isolated neutral case.

Therefore, summing up the total current

$$2HB = \Sigma\Delta HB = \Sigma\left[-t_{1n}\left(m + \frac{v_f}{L}\right) + \frac{1}{L}t_{1n}aV_B\right]$$

$$= -t_1\left(m + \frac{v_f}{L}\right) + \frac{1}{L}\Sigma t_{1n}aV_B. \tag{33}$$

The general expression of incremental current fall during the Q_4-on period is given by

$$-\Delta HB = \frac{t_{2n}}{L}(aV_B + v_f) - t_{2n}m. \tag{34}$$

Therefore, the total fall is

$$-2HB = \Sigma - \Delta HB = \Sigma\left[-t_{2n}\left(m + \frac{v_f}{L}\right) - \frac{1}{L}t_{2n}aV_B\right]$$
$$= -t_2\left(m + \frac{v_f}{L}\right) - \frac{1}{L}\Sigma t_{2n}aV_B. \quad (35)$$

The average current rise and fall during the periods t_1 and t_2, respectively, are shown by the dotted lines in Fig. 8. The slope of these lines will be determined by the weighted average supply voltage. In (33) and (35), the second term can be expressed as

$$\Sigma t_{1n}aV_B = t_1 a' V_B \quad (36)$$
$$\Sigma t_{2n}aV_B = t_2 a'' V_B \quad (37)$$

or

$$a' = \frac{\Sigma t_{1n}a}{t_1} \quad (38)$$
$$a'' = \frac{\Sigma t_{2n}a}{t_2} \quad (39)$$

where a' and a'' are the respective applied voltage coefficients. Although the average applied voltages in the two intervals may have some asymmetry, we will assume these same (i.e., $a' = a''$) as in *Case 1* and *Case 2* for computational simplicity. The computation of HB on this assumption will give a small amount of inaccuracy. The parameters a, a', and a'' will typically vary between 1/3 and 2/3, and the later is the worst case. Combining (33), (35), (38), and (39), we get

$$HB = \frac{0.25a' V_B}{f_c L}\left[1 - \frac{L^2}{a'^2 V_B^2}\left(\frac{v_f}{L} + m\right)^2\right]. \quad (40)$$

Equation (40) is same as (19) except 0.5 V_B has been replaced here by $a' V_B$. Therefore, the complete expression of HB for the isolated case of IPM machine is

$$HB = \frac{0.25a' V_B \omega_b}{f_c X_L}\left[1 - \frac{X_L^2}{a' V_B^2}\left(\frac{\omega_e}{\omega_b}\right)^2 \cdot \left\{\left(\frac{\sqrt{2}V_{fB}\omega_e}{X_L} - I_{ds}\right)\sin\theta_e + I_{qs}\cos\theta_e\right\}^2\right]$$
$$= (A' - B') + B'\cos 2(\theta_e + a) \quad (41)$$

where

$$A' = 2a'A$$
$$B' = \frac{B}{a'}.$$

The A, B, and a parameters have been defined in (28).

III. Control Implementation and Simulation

The hysteresis-band HB in (41) can easily be implemented by microcomputer in a high-performance drive system where all the essential parameters may exist in the memory. In this equation, the parameters a', ω_b, f_c, X_L, and V_{fB} can be treated as constants, whereas the terms V_B, ω_e, I_{ds}, I_{qs}, and θ_e are variables at any steady-state operating condition.

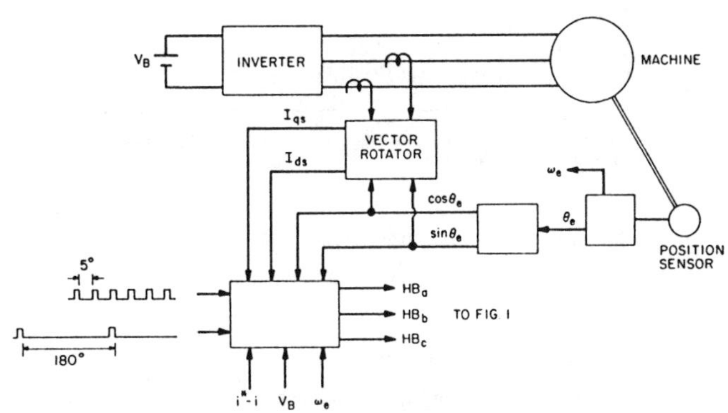

Fig. 9. Block diagram for implementation of adaptive hysteresis-band current control.

Fig. 9 shows the block diagram for the implementation of (41). The absolute position of the machine rotor is sensed by an analog resolver and then converted to speed (ω_e) and position (θ_e) outputs by a resolver-to-digital converter. The θ_e signal is then converted to $\cos\theta_e$ and $\sin\theta_e$ signals by look-up tables. The stator phase currents are converted to synchronously rotating frame signals I_{ds} and I_{qs} using the $\cos\theta e$ and $\sin\theta e$ unit vectors. Note that the HB signals (HB_a, HB_b, HB_c) for all the phases are symmetrical but phase shifted by 60°. A digital signal-processor-type TMS 320C25 by Texas Instruments is ideally suited for the control implementation. Because of the symmetry, a segment of HB for the interval 0° to 180° can be computed and stored in the form of a look-up table, which can then be retrieved sequentially for each phase. The table is to be refreshed every sampling interval in steady-state condition. The algorithm for implementation is as follows:

- Sample the variables V_B, ω_e, I_{ds}, and I_{qs} every 2 ms.
- With the known parameters a', ω_b, f_c, X_L, and V_{fB}, compute HB every 5° interval for 0 to 180° (36 samples) and load the table every 2 ms.
- Using the 5° interval pulse train, retrieve the HB look-up table (with the help of phase location pointers) and load HB_a, HB_b, and HB_c.

The 180° pulse train as shown is used for synchronization purposes. Since the algorithm is not valid for transient operation, which is indicated by the current loop error exceeding the band, the automatically worst-case HB (Fig. 6) is commanded.

The adaptive hysteresis-band current control for the isolated neutral case of the IPM machine drive system has been implemented in digital simulation using the SIMNON (Lund Institute of Technology, Sweden) language. The details of the drive system are described in [11] and [12]. Table II shows the parameters of the drive system. Fig. 10 shows the simulation result of phase current waves and HB profile for f_c = 4 KHz, V_B = 204 V and $a' = 2/3$ (worst case).

The inaccuracy of the a' parameter will cause some spread of modulation frequency, and a conservative a' value in practical implementation will result in the maximum modulation frequency below that of the optimum value. The re-

TABLE II
PARAMETERS OF THE IPM MACHINE DRIVE SYSTEM

70 hp, 4-Pole, Wye-Connected Neodymium-Iron-Boron (Crumax 30A) Machine

*Base Speed (ω_b) = 710.48 rad/s (elec.) (3394 RPM)

Magnet flux ($\omega_b\psi_f$) = 40.2 Volts (at 75°C)

Rated Stator Flux ($\omega_b\psi_{sr}$) = 58.5 Volts

Battery Voltage (V_B) = 204 Volts (nominal)

(135 - 264 Volts variation)

Rated Stator Current (I_{sr}) = 315 Amps

Stator Resistance (R_s) = 0.00443 Ohms

Stator Leakage Reactance ($\omega_b L_{qs}$) = 0.0189 Ohms

De-Axis Magnetizing Reactance ($\omega_b L_{dm}$) = 0.0785 Ohms

Qe-Axis Magnetizing Reactance ($\omega_b L_{qm}$) = 0.1747 Ohms

*At Battery Voltage of 135 Volts

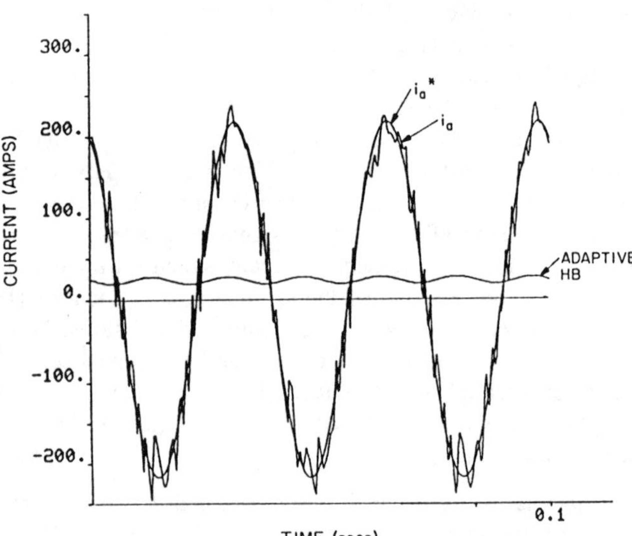

Fig. 10. Simulation phase current wave with adaptive hysteresis-band current control.

finement of the above method by real time search of the a' parameter is at present under investigation and is indicated in Fig. 11. In the beginning, HB is computed on the basis of conservative value $a' = 2/3$. The a' parameter is then iterated on the basis of actual average modulation frequency $f_{c(av)}$ until $f_{c(av)} = f_{c(opt)}$. The $f_{c(av)}$ can be determined by counting the transistor base drive logic transition of a phase leg of the inverter over a full cycle.

IV. CONCLUSION

A novel adaptive hysteresis-band current control PWM technique has been described in the paper. A hysteresis-band current control PWM method is popularly used because it is simple to implement by dedicated hardware, has fast response, and device peak current is automatically limited. The conventional fixed hysteresis-band current control generates excessive current ripple because modulation frequency varies within a band. In an adaptive hysteresis-band method, the band is modulated as a function of system parameters to maintain the modulation frequency to be nearly constant. Systematic mathematical analysis has been presented, and band expressions have been derived as a function of the load machine and supply parameters for connected and isolated neutral cases. An IPM machine drive system with the proposed adaptive band has been studied by digital simulation.

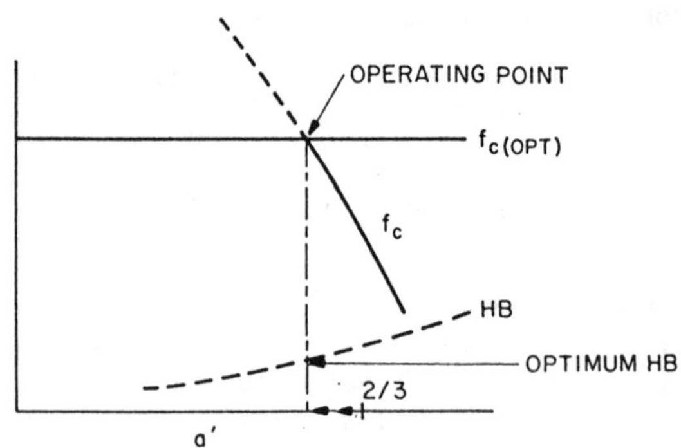

Fig. 11. Real-time search of parameter a' for optimum hysteresis band.

REFERENCES

[1] B. K. Bose, *Power Electronics and AC Drives*. Englewood Cliffs, NJ: Prentice-Hall, 1986.

[2] A. B. Plunkett, "A current controlled PWM transistor inverter drive," in *Proc. Conf. Rec. IEEE/IAS 1979 Ann. Mtg.*, 1979, pp. 785-792.

[3] L. Malesani and P. Tenti, "A novel hysteresis control method for current-controlled VSI PWM inverters with constant modulation frequency," in *Proc. Conf. Rec. IEEE/IAS Ann. Mtg.*, 1987, pp. 851-855.

[4] H. Le-Huy and L. A. Dessaint, "An adaptive current controller for PWM inverters," in *Proc. Conf. Rec. IEEE/PESC Conf.*, 1986, pp. 610-616.

[5] A. Kawamura and R. G. Hoft, "Instantaneous feedback controlled PWM inverters with adaptive hysteresis," *IEEE Trans. Industry Appl.*, vol. IA-20, pp. 769-775, 1984.

[6] D. M. Brod and D. W. Novotny, "Current control of VSI-PWM inverters," *IEEE Trans. Industry Appl.*, vol. IA-21, pp. 562-570, 1985.

[7] G. Pffaf, A. Weschta, and A. Wick, "Design and experimental results of a brushless ac servo drive," in *Proc. Conf. Rec. IEEE/IAS Ann. Mtg.*, 1982, pp. 692-697.

[8] A. Nabae, S. Ogasawara, and H. Akagi, "A novel control scheme of current-controlled PWM inverters," in *Proc. Conf. Rec. IEEE/IAS Ann. Mtg.*, 1985, pp. 473-478.

[9] A. Schonung and H. Stemmler, "Static frequency changers with subharmonic control in conjunction with reversible variable speed ac drives," *Brown Boveri Rev.*, pp. 555-577, 1964.

[10] B. K. Bose and H. Sutherland, "A high-performance pulsewidth modulator for an inverter-fed drive system using a microcomputer," *IEEE Trans. Industry Appl.*, vol. IA-19, pp. 235-243, 1983.

[11] B. K. Bose, "A high performance inverter-fed drive system of an interior permanent magnet synchronous machine," in *Proc. Conf. Rec. IEEE/IAS Ann. Mtg.*, 1987, pp. 269-276.

[12] B. K. Bose and P. M. Szczesny, "A microcomputer-based control and simulation of an advanced IPM synchronous machine drive system for electric vehicle propulsion," in *Proc. IECON '87*, 1987, pp. 454-463.

[13] J. Holtz and S. Stadtfeld, "A predictive controller for the stator current vector of ac machine-fed from a switched voltage source," in *Proc. Int. Power Electron. Conf. Rec.* (Tokyo), 1983, pp. 1665-1675.

[14] B. K. Bose, "Power electronics—an emerging technology," *IEEE Trans. Ind. Electron.*, vol. 36, pp. 403-412, Aug. 1989.

An Adaptive Current Control Scheme for PWM Synchronous Motor Drives: Analysis and Simulation

HOANG LE-HUY, SENIOR MEMBER, IEEE, AND LOUIS A. DESSAINT

Abstract—**A study is presented on an adaptive current control scheme for synchronous motor drives using PWM inverters. An analysis of the control scheme in two operation modes is given and the characteristics are studied by simulation. The implementation of the proposed control scheme using a microprocessor-based system is considered.**

I. Introduction

AC servo motor drives using permanent magnet synchronous machines are being used more and more in high performance servo and robotics applications because of their desirable features. These drives are characterized mainly by high power-to-weight ratio, high torque-to-current ratio, high dynamics, low maintenance, and ability to operate in explosive or corrosive environment.

In its basic configuration, a servo synchronous motor drive consists of a permanent-magnet synchronous machine fed by a self-controlled inverter. The inverter drive signals are synchronized to the rotor position signals provided by a position sensor mounted on the motor shaft so that synchronism is ensured for any speed. The drive characteristics depend greatly on the motor feeding scheme. In high-performance drives, pulsewidth modulated (PWM) inverters are used to provide effective current control. Fig. 1 shows a simplified diagram of such a drive that is considered in this paper. The permanent-magnet synchronous motor is fed by a current-controlled PWM inverter using bipolar or MOSFET transistors as power switches. The current in each motor phase is forced to follow a reference waveform derived from the position signals. By selecting appropriate feed current waveforms, unwanted torque harmonics can be cancelled out to provide smooth torque [6].

In such systems, the current controller has direct influence on the drive performance and its design requires particular considerations. The basic requirements for the controller are: low harmonics to reduce losses and noise in the motor, and fast response to provide high dynamics.

Manuscript received September 3, 1986; revised August 18, 1989. This paper was presented at the 1986 IEEE Power Electronics Specialists Conference, Vancouver, BC, Canada, June 23-27.

H. LeHuy is with the Department of Electrical Engineering, Laval University, Quebec, PQ, Canada G1K 7P4.

L. A. Dessaint is with the Department d'Electricite Ecole de Technologie Superieure, Montreal, PQ, Canada H2T 1RO.

IEEE Log Number 8931451.

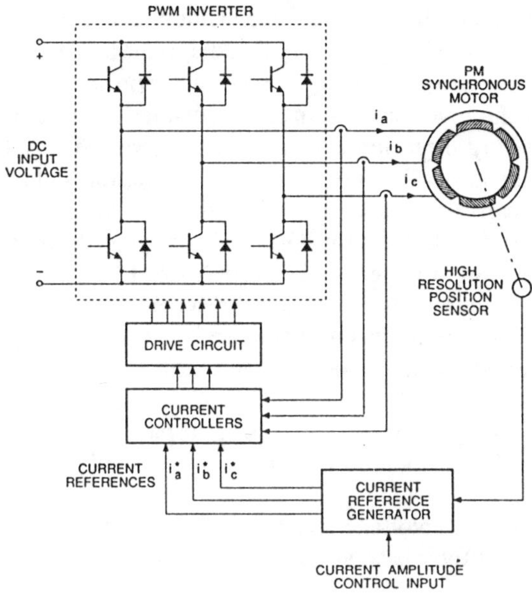

Fig. 1. Current-controlled PWM synchronous motor drive.

Various techniques of current control of PWM inverters have been studied and reported in the literature [1]-[5]. They can be classified into two large classes: on-off control and predictive control. In on-off control schemes, the currents are compared to their references using hysteresis comparators or comparators to determine the switching instants for the inverter power switches. On-off control is characterized by a fast response but the current ripple is usually large. Also, the switching frequency depends on the motor parameters and the operating conditions. On the other hand, in predictive control scheme the switching instants of the power switches are determined by calculating the required voltage to force the motor currents to follow the references. This control scheme provides constant switching frequency and lower current ripple. However, the response time is longer and the machine parameters and the operating conditions have to be known with sufficient accuracy.

In this paper, an adaptive current control scheme for PWM inverters in servo synchronous motor drives is studied. In this scheme, the control mode is changed according to the operating conditions in order to optimize the static and dynamic performances of the system.

Reprinted from *IEEE Trans. Power Electron.*, vol. 4, no. 4, pp. 486-495, October 1989.

First, a comparative study on two current control schemes: hysteresis control and predictive control is presented. The proposed adaptive control scheme which is based on the two previous schemes is described and studied. The characteristics and performance are studied by simulation using actual parameters of a 1-kW servo synchronous motor drive. The implementation of the proposed control scheme using a microprocessor-based system is considered.

II. Current Control of VSI-PWM Inverters

The operation of the current-controlled PWM inverter of Fig. 1 can be studied by considering the equivalent circuit shown in Fig. 2(a). In this diagram, the single pole double throw switches, QA, QB, QC represent the three legs of the inverter. The inverter conduction state is represented by three logic variables, SA, SB, SC. A logic "1" means that the upper switch is conducting and a logic "0" means that the lower switch is conducting.

The switching of QA, QB, QC results in 8 operating states for the inverter as shown in Table I.

The synchronous motor is represented by a simplified equivalent circuit that is composed of a resistor, an inductor, and a voltage source representing the emf for each phase.

The concept of voltage and current space vectors is used to simplify the notation in representing a set of three-phase voltages and currents.

The inverter voltage space vector is defined as a combination of the phase voltages v_a, v_b, v_c:

$$\boldsymbol{v} = \tfrac{2}{3}[v_a + av_b + a^2v_c] \tag{1}$$

where $a = e^{j2\pi/3}$.

The inverter current space vector is defined in the same manner as

$$\boldsymbol{i} = \tfrac{2}{3}[i_a + ai_b + a^2i_c]. \tag{2}$$

The 8 voltage space vectors that correspond to 8 switching states of the inverter are shown in Fig. 2(b). The voltage vectors corresponding to the 6 active states are of length 2 $V_{dc}/3$ and form a hexagon. The voltage vectors $V0$ and $V7$ corresponding to the free-wheeling states are zero voltage vectors.

The function of the current controllers is to force the motor current vector $\boldsymbol{i}$ to follow as closely as possible the reference current vector $\boldsymbol{i}^*$. This can be accomplished by comparing the actual motor currents and the references. The inverter power switches are then activated in such a manner that reduces the current error vector $\Delta \boldsymbol{i} = (\boldsymbol{i}^* - \boldsymbol{i})$ to a minimum.

Among various control schemes reported, two schemes merit consideration: hysteresis control, because of its simplicity, and predictive control because of its steady-state performance.

Hysteresis Control Scheme

A simplified diagram of a typical three-phase hysteresis current controller is depicted in Fig. 3. The motor currents are detected and compared to the references using three independent hysteresis comparators having a hysteresis band h. The comparators output signals are used to produce the drive signals for the inverter power switches. The state of the switches depend on the comparison results. The motor phase is connected to the (+) terminal of the dc source if the current in this phase is lower than $i_{ref} - h/2$. It is connected to the (−) terminal of the dc source if the current is higher than $i_{ref} + h/2$.

This control scheme is characterized by the simplicity and good dynamic performance. Also, an inherent instan-

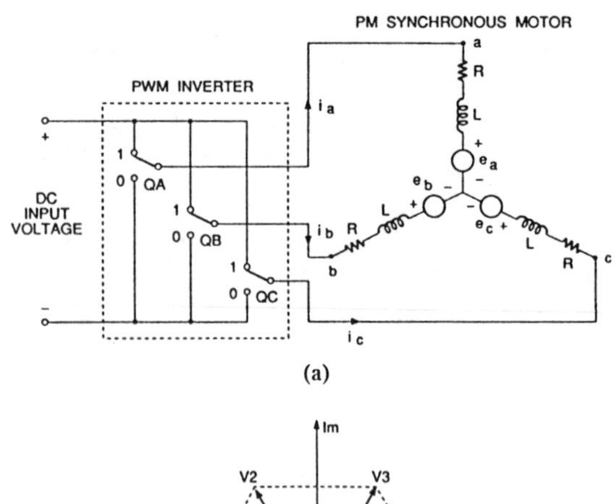

(a)

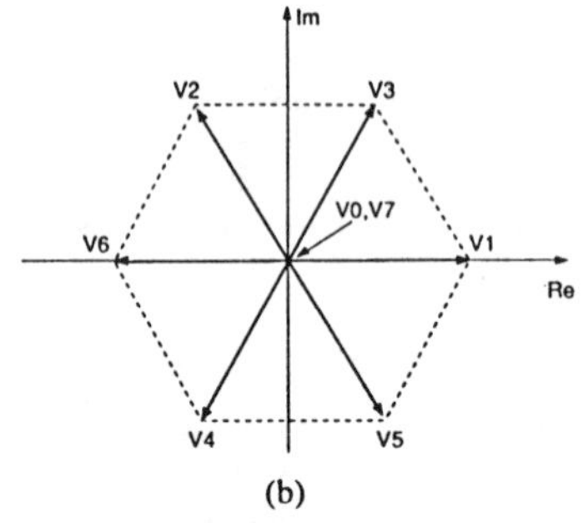

(b)

Fig. 2. (a) Equivalent circuit of drive. (b) Inverter voltage space vectors.

TABLE I

State	SC	SB	SA	Operation Mode	Voltage Vector
0	0	0	0	free-wheeling	$V0$
1	0	0	1	active	$V1$
2	0	1	0	active	$V2$
3	0	1	1	active	$V3$
4	1	0	0	active	$V4$
5	1	0	1	active	$V5$
6	1	1	0	active	$V6$
7	1	1	1	free-wheeling	$V7$

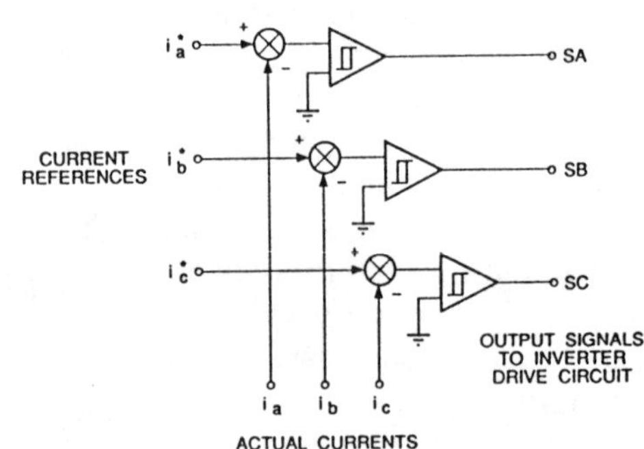

Fig. 3. Hysteresis current control scheme using independent comparators.

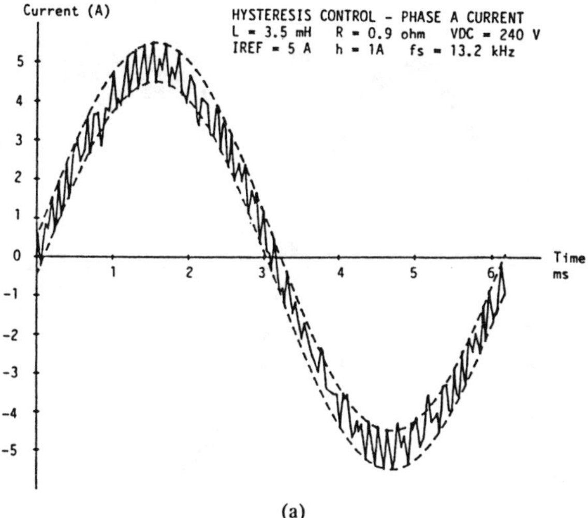

(a)

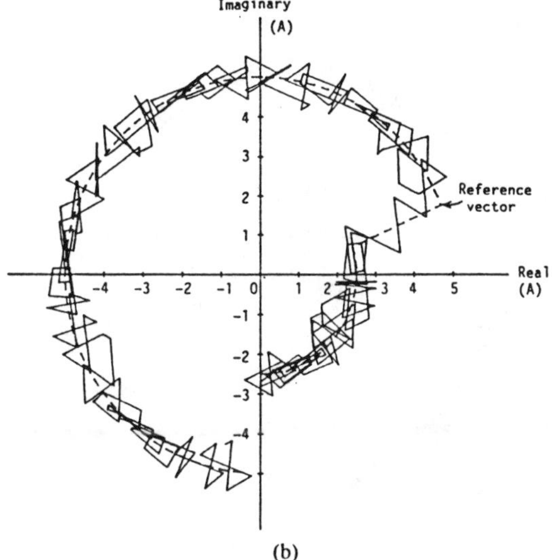

(b)

Fig. 4. Performance of hysteresis current control scheme (Simulation). (a) Current waveform in one phase. (b) Response to step change of reference current vector.

taneous current limiting exists. Fig. 4 shows current waveforms obtained by simulation, illustrating the static and dynamic performance of the hysteresis control scheme. Fig. 4(a) shows the current in one phase along with the upper and lower limits. It is noted that the current varies around the reference with a certain ripple that is function of the comparator hysteresis band. It has been shown in [8] that the ripple can reach twice the hysteresis band due to the interaction between the inverter legs. The current ripple can be reduced by using free-wheeling states ($V0$ or $V7$) and by taking into account the interaction between the three phases [2], [8].

Fig. 4(b) shows the response of the controller to a step change of the amplitude of the reference current vector.

The major drawback of the hysteresis control scheme is the dependence of the switching frequency on the motor parameters, on the operating conditions, and on the hysteresis band, resulting in the variable switching frequency. In certain applications where the drive operates in a wide speed range, variable switching frequency may be unacceptable.

Predictive Current Control Scheme

In this scheme, the motor current vector is controlled by an unique controller instead of three independent controllers as in hysteresis control scheme.

The currents are sampled at a constant rate. The current vector is calculated and compared to the reference current vector. An appropriate voltage vector that would reduce the current error vector $\boldsymbol{\Delta i}$ to zero is calculated. This calculation can be based on the simplified motor equivalent circuit shown in Fig. 2(a).

The required voltage vector at the $\boldsymbol{k}$-th sampling instant is given by

$$V(k) = e(k) + L\frac{d}{dt}[i(k)] + Ri(k) \tag{3}$$

where $\boldsymbol{V}$ is the inverter voltage space vector, $\boldsymbol{e}$ is the emf space vector, $\boldsymbol{i}$ is the motor current space vector, L is the stator inductance (per phase), R is the stator resistance (per phase).

In permanent-magnet synchronous motors, the armature reaction is usually negligible so that the emf space vector necessary for the solution of (3) can be determined with acceptable accuracy from the speed and position information.

If the emf is sinusoidal, it can be calculated as

$$e_a = E_m \sin(n\theta) \tag{4}$$

where E_m is the emf amplitude, n is the number of pole pairs, and θ is the rotor position.

The emf ampitude is a function of the motor speed. It can be approximated as

$$E_m = E_m(\text{nom})\,[\omega/\omega_{\text{nom}}] \tag{5}$$

where $E_m(\text{nom})$ is the emf nominal amplitude, ω is the motor speed, and ω_{nom} is the nominal speed.

The position θ is obtained from the position sensor that can be an absolute or incremental optical encoder or a resolver.

In the case where the emf is of arbitrary form, it can be calculated as

$$e_a = E_m \cdot f(\theta) \tag{6}$$

where E_m is the emf amplitude given by (5) and $f(\theta)$ is the form function stored in a look-up table.

To be solved by computer, (3) should be written as a difference equation:

$$V(k) = e(k) + (L/T)\,[i^*(k+1) - i(k)] + Ri(k) \tag{7}$$

where $\boldsymbol{V}(k)$ is the inverter voltage vector, $\boldsymbol{e}(k)$ is the emf vector, $\boldsymbol{i}(k)$ is the actual current vector at k-th sampling instant, $\boldsymbol{i}^*(k+1)$ is the reference current vector at $(k+1)$-th sampling instant, T is the sampling period.

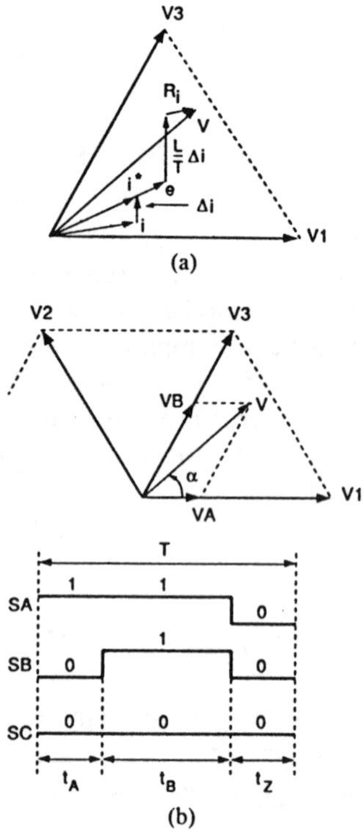

Fig. 5. Predictive current control scheme. (a) Vector diagram. (b) A computation example.

The predictive current control principle is illustrated by the vector diagram shown in Fig. 5(a). The required voltage vector to force the current vector to follow the current reference vector is obtained by additioning three vectors $\boldsymbol{E}(k)$, $(L/T)\,\boldsymbol{\Delta i}(k)$, and $\boldsymbol{Ri}(k)$.

Since the inverter can take only one of the 8 conduction states, pulsewidth modulation can be used to provide the voltage vector $\boldsymbol{V}$. In the example shown in Fig. 5(b), the inverter is switched from $\boldsymbol{V1}$ to $\boldsymbol{V3}$ with the duty cycle determined by the value of V_A and V_B. By referring to Fig. 5(b), the voltages V_A and V_B can be determined as

$$V_B = \frac{2}{\sqrt{3}} \left| V \right| \sin \alpha \tag{8}$$

$$V_A = \left| V \right| \cos \alpha - 0.5 V_B. \tag{9}$$

The time durations of the states 1 and 3 and the zero voltage state are given by

$$t_A = 1.5(V_A/V_{dc})T \tag{10}$$

$$t_B = 1.5(V_B/V_{dc})T \tag{11}$$

$$t_Z = T - t_A - t_B \tag{12}$$

where T is the sampling period and V_{dc} is the dc input voltage.

With the condition $t_A + t_B + t_Z = T$ it can be shown that the obtainable voltage vector resides inside the hexagon formed by the six active voltage vectors corresponding to six active states of the inverter [hexagon shown in dotted line in Fig. 2(b)].

Fig. 6 shows the static and dynamic performance of a predictive current controller obtained by simulation using

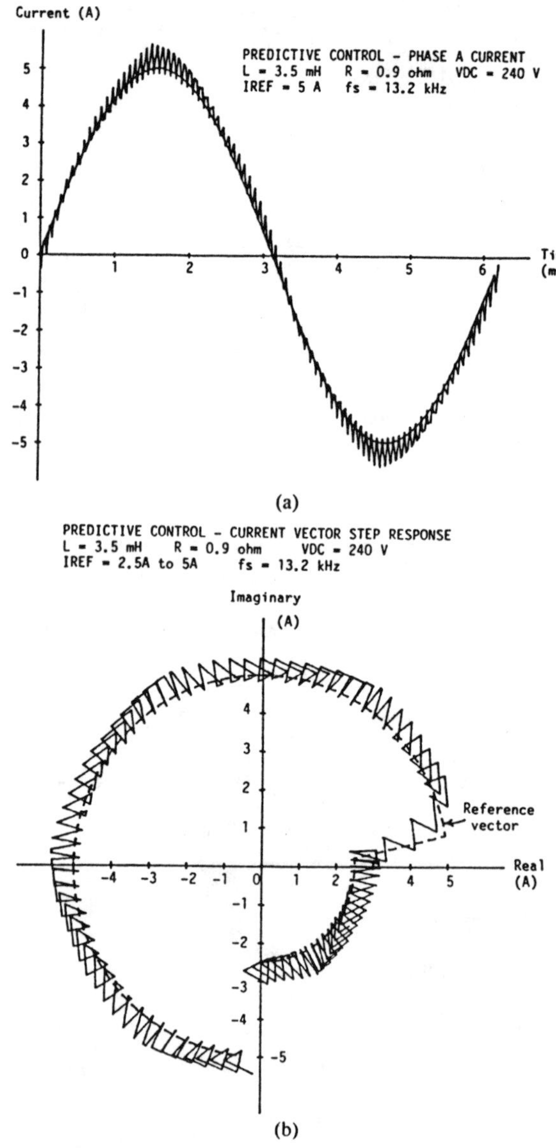

Fig. 6. Performance of predictive current control scheme (simulation). (a) Current waveform in one phase. (b) Response to step change of reference current vector.

the same parameters as in the hysteresis scheme. Fig. 6(a) shows the current in one phase along with its reference. It can be noted that the current ripple is greatly reduced under approximately the same operating conditions. Fig. 6(b) shows the response to a step change of the amplitude of the current reference vector. The response is smooth and rapid because in the simulation the same model is used for the real system and for the predictive calculations. In the reality, there is always an error in the model used for the predictive calculations so the actual response would be less smooth and less rapid than the ideal situation results.

The predictive control scheme provides constant switching frequency and low current ripple. The performance at low-level current is better than that obtained with hysteresis control scheme with comparable switching frequency. However, its implementation is complex because of the numerous calculations required. The predictive control scheme will provide good results only if the motor parameters are known with sufficient accuracy.

At high-level currents and high speeds, the response is slow due to the reduction of the available voltage that can force the current to flow in the motor. Also, some delay (phase shift) of the actual currents versus the references is present due to the anticipation. This delay is a function of the sampling period and may be appreciable at high speeds.

III. An Adaptive Current Control Scheme for PWM Synchronous Motor Dives

As can be noted in the preceding section, each current control scheme has its own advantages and drawbacks that make them optimum for some specific conditions and less suitable for other conditions. The hysteresis control scheme can provide fast transient response but in steady-state, the current ripple may be high and the switching frequency is variable. On the other hand, the predictive control scheme can produce smooth current in steady-state (with comparable switching frequency) but the transient response time is long. By combining the two control schemes in an adaptive manner, that is predictive control for steady-state operation and hysteresis control for transient operation, it is possible to obtain optimum performance. Each control scheme is then used in its favorable domain.

The operation principle of the proposed adaptive control scheme is illustrated by the block diagram shown in Fig. 7.

The controller has two operation modes: predictive mode and hysteresis mode. The mode selection is based on the magnitude of the current error vector $|\Delta \boldsymbol{i}| = |\boldsymbol{i}^* - \boldsymbol{i}|$ where $\boldsymbol{i}^*$ is the reference current vector and $\boldsymbol{i}$ is the actual current vector.

The predictive control mode is selected when $|\Delta \boldsymbol{i}|$ is less than the mode switching level. When $|\Delta \boldsymbol{i}|$ goes beyond this limit, the controller is switched to hysteresis mode in order to reduce as fast as possible the current error vector. In this manner, the current controller will operate in predictive mode in steady-state and during small current transients. During large current transients such as starting or load variations it will operate in hysteresis mode.

Mode Selection

The current error vector can be calculated from the measured values i_a, i_b, i_c and the references i_a^*, i_b^*, and i_c^*:

$$\Delta \boldsymbol{i} = \tfrac{2}{3}(i_a^* + a i_b^* + a^2 i_c^*) - (i_a + a i_b + a^2 i_c) \quad (13)$$

where $a = e^{j2\pi/3}$.

The error magnitude is given by

$$|\Delta \boldsymbol{i}|^2 = \frac{4}{9}\left[\Delta i_a - \frac{\Delta i_b}{2} - \frac{\Delta i_c}{2}\right]^2 + \frac{1}{3}[\Delta i_b - \Delta i_c]^2 \quad (14)$$

where $\Delta i_a = i_a^* - i_a$, $\Delta i_b = i_b^* - i_b$, $\Delta i_c = i_c^* - i_c$.

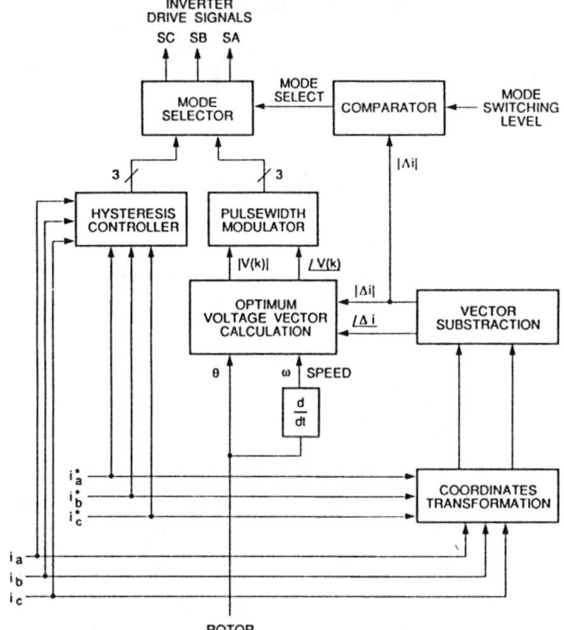

Fig. 7. Proposed adaptive current control scheme.

With the assumption that the neutral is not connected (that is $i_a + i_b + i_c = 0$), $|\Delta \boldsymbol{i}|$ is given by

$$|\Delta \boldsymbol{i}| = \sqrt{\Delta i_a^2 + \tfrac{1}{3}(\Delta i_b - \Delta i_c)^2} \quad (15)$$

Equation (15) can also be written as

$$|\Delta \boldsymbol{i}| = \sqrt{\Delta i_a^2 + \tfrac{1}{3}(\Delta i_a + 2\Delta i_b)^2}. \quad (16)$$

As a result, the controller can handle two current variables instead of three. The number of current sensors can be thus reduced.

The mode selection signal is obtained by comparing the current error magnitude $|\Delta \boldsymbol{i}|$ with the mode switching level. To avoid jitter (switching back and forth between the modes), a small amount of hysteresis can be used in this comparison. Note that the comparison is done at every sampling instant.

The value of the mode switching level has a certain influence on the controller behavior. This level can be chosen to be equal to the maximum current ripple in predictive mode but less than the hysteresis band. This can ensure an equilibrium between the two operation modes.

Optimum Voltage Vector Calculation

The optimum voltage vector can be considered as the voltage vector that would reduce the current error to zero at the next sampling instant. Its calculation is based essentially on the difference between the actual current vector and the reference current vector desired for the next sampling instant.

In referring to Fig. 8, the optimum voltage vector can be written as

$$\boldsymbol{V}(k) = \boldsymbol{e}(k) + (L/T)\left[\boldsymbol{i}^*(k+1) - \boldsymbol{i}(k)\right] + R\boldsymbol{i}(k) \quad (17)$$

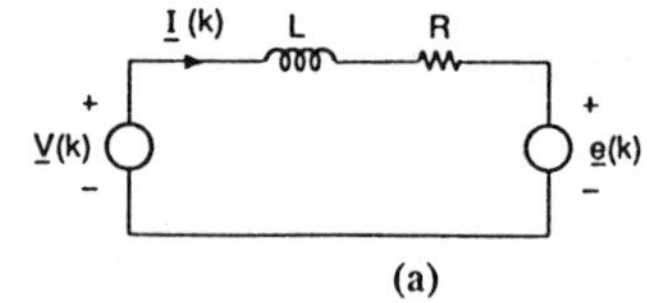

(a)

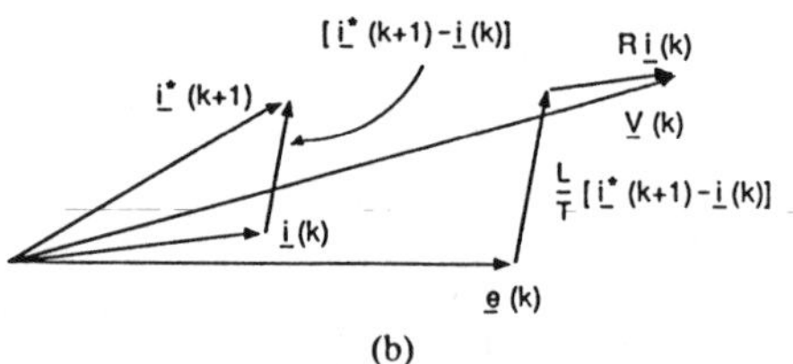

(b)

Fig. 8. Optimum voltage vector calculation. (a) Model for calculation. (b) Vector diagram.

where $e(k)$ is the emf vector, $i(k)$ is the actual current vector at k-th sampling instant, $i^*(k+1)$ is the reference current vector at $(k+1)$-th sampling instant, L and R are the motor parameters, and T is the sampling period.

In permanent-magnet synchronous motors, the emf vector $e(k)$ can be determined with acceptable accuracy from the rotor position $\theta(k)$ and speed $\omega(k)$:

$$|e(k)| = E_m(\text{nom})\,[\omega(k)/\omega_{\text{nom}}]\,f[\theta(k)] \quad (18a)$$

$$\underline{/e(k)} = \theta(k). \quad (18b)$$

where $E_m(\text{nom})$ is the nominal emf amplitude and $f[\theta(k)]$ is the form function of the emf.

The form function $f[\theta(k)]$ takes into account the actual form of the emf of the specific permanent-magnet synchronous motor used.

Vector (17) can be expressed as real and imaginary parts written in terms of the components following a, b, c:

$$Re[V(k)] = e_a(k) + \frac{L}{T}[i_a^*(k+1) - i_a(k)] + Ri_a(k) \quad (19a)$$

$$\begin{aligned} Im[V(k)] = {} & \frac{1}{\sqrt{3}}[e_a(k) + 2e_b(k)] + \frac{1}{\sqrt{3}}\frac{L}{T}[i_a^*(k+1) \\ & + 2i_b^*(k+1) - i_a(k) - 2i_b(k)] \\ & + \frac{1}{\sqrt{3}}R[i_a(k) + 2i_b(k)] \end{aligned} \quad (19b)$$

The amplitude and the angle of $V(k)$ can be calculated as

$$|V(k)| = \sqrt{(Re[V(k)])^2 + (Im[V(k)])^2} \quad (20a)$$

$$\underline{/V(k)} = \text{arctg}\left[\frac{Im[V(k)]}{Re[V(k)]}\right]. \quad (20b)$$

These values will be used in the modulation as explained below.

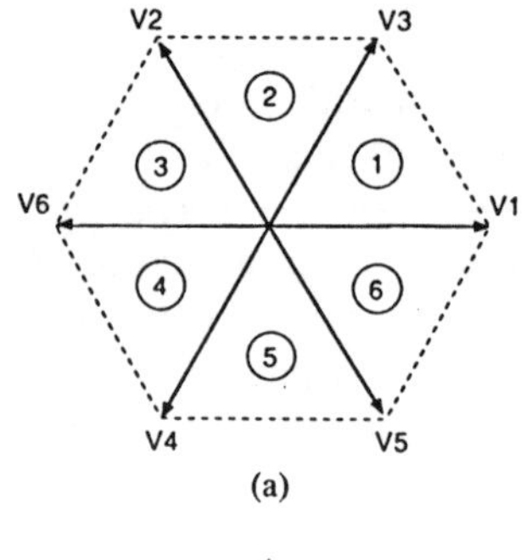

(a)

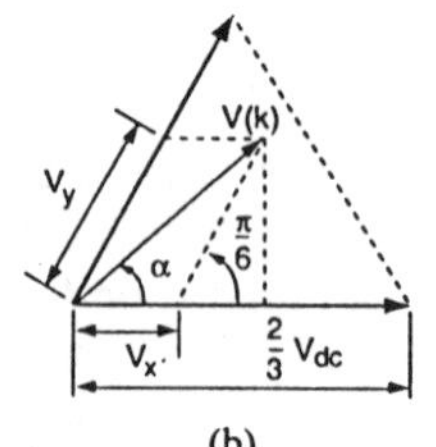

(b)

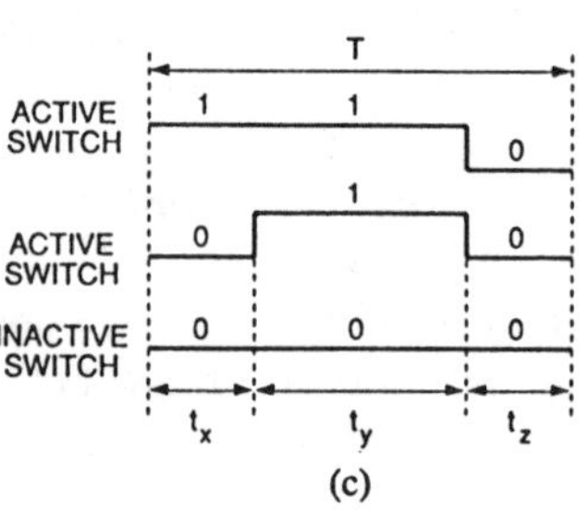

(c)

Fig. 9. Pulsewidth modulation scheme. (a) Sectors in complex plane. (b) Voltage components. (c) Conduction time definition.

Pulsewidth Modulation

The inverter can produce only six fixed voltage vectors ($V1$ to $V6$) and two zero voltage vectors ($V0$ and $V7$). To obtain the required vector $V(k)$, the conduction time of the inverter switches are modulated according to the amplitude and the angle of $V(k)$.

The angle of $V(k)$ permits us to determine the sector of the complex plane where the vector $V(k)$ lies:

$$\underline{/V(k)} = (n-1)(\pi/6) + \alpha \quad (21)$$

where n is the sector number as identified in Fig. 9(a) and α is the modulation angle.

The active voltages and switches for modulation are determined from Table II.

The modulation is achieved by using two adjacent voltage vectors with appropriate duty cycle for the power switches. The conduction times of the active switches are determined by the amplitude $|V(k)|$ and the modulation angle α.

The values of t_x, t_y, and t_z as defined in Fig. 9(c) are calculated as

$$t_x = 1.5(V_x/V_{dc})T \quad (22a)$$

$$t_y = 1.5(V_x/V_{dc})T \quad (22b)$$

$$t_z = T - t_x - t_y \quad (22c)$$

TABLE II

Sector	Active Voltages	QC	QB	QA
1	$V1$, $V3$	0	active	active
2	$V3$, $V2$	0	active	active
3	$V2$, $V6$	active	active	0
4	$V6$, $V4$	active	active	0
5	$V4$, $V5$	active	0	active
6	$V5$, $V1$	active	0	active

where

$$V_y = \frac{2}{\sqrt{3}} \left| V(k) \right| \sin \alpha \tag{22d}$$

$$V_x = \left| V(k) \right| \cos \alpha - 0.5 V_y. \tag{22e}$$

Hysteresis Controller

In the proposed control scheme, since the hysteresis operation is effective only during transient periods, the simple form of hysteresis controller that consists of three independent comparators can be used. Various techniques have been proposed to improve particularly the steady-state response of the hysteresis controller [2], [8], [9], but they are not really useful in the proposed adaptive scheme.

IV. Simulation Results

The performance of the proposed current control scheme has been studied by simulation using actual parameters of a 1-kW brushless ac motor drive. The permanent magnet synchronous motor considered in this study has disk rotor with Samarium-Cobalt magnets.

The following assumptions are made:

Motor is not saturated.

Speed is constant.

Emfs are sinusoidal.

Motor parameters are constant.

Current references are sinusoidal and in phase with the corresponding emfs.

Armature reaction is negligible.

The motor parameters are: 1 kW, 8 poles, $R = 0.9\ \Omega$, $L = 3.5$ mH, $E_m(\text{nom}) = 120$ V.

The dc voltage source is ideal and equal to 240 V.

In the simulation, the inverter switches are ideal switches with zero conduction voltage drop and zero commutation time.

The simulated pulsewidth modulator has a resolution of 1 μs (this means that the conduction time and the off-time of the switches are calculated with 1 μs accuracy). This resolution is used in order to take into account the finite commutation time of the power switches.

The hysteresis controller is composed of three independent comparators. The comparison is executed every 1 μs.

Steady-State Performance

In steady-state, if the current ripple is less than the mode switching level, the controller is in predictive mode and its behavior is similar to that of a predictive controller.

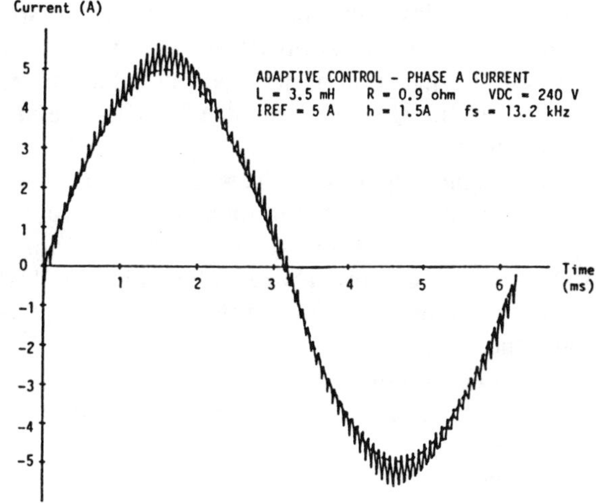

Fig. 10. Steady-state simulation current waveform (Adaptive control scheme).

The current waveform in one motor phase is shown in Fig. 10.

The current ripple depends largely on the sampling frequency, on the motor estimated parameters, and also on the resolution of the pulsewidth modulator. It is practically independent of the reference level.

The sampling frequency has direct influence on the current ripple. A higher sampling frequency will produce lower current ripple at the expense of increased dissipation in the power switches. The sampling frequency is limited by the computation speed of the controller.

The controller will remain in predictive mode as long as the current ripple is less than the mode switching level.

There exists a delay between the reference and the actual currents. This is due to the fact that the correction made by the controller is always a sampling period behind. This delay depends on the sampling period and on the operating conditions of the motor. At low speeds, the current frequency is low and the delay correspond to a small phase shift. However, at high speeds this delay corresponds to a significant phase shift in the current.

Dynamic Performance

The dynamic performance of the proposed current controller has been studied by applying a step change in the reference current vector. This step change simulates the operating conditions during large transients such as starting or load variations.

If the current error vector amplitude exceeds the mode switching level, the controller will switch from predictive mode to hysteresis mode in order to reduce the error as fast as possible. When the error vector amplitude falls below the switching level, the controller will return to predictive mode.

The passage from one mode to another depends mainly on the chosen mode switching level. A high level will make the controller to remain in predictive mode most of the time except for very large transients. On the other hand, a too small level will force the controller to spend most of the time in hysteresis mode. So a compromise has to be done in the selection of the mode switching level to obtain optimum transient performance for the specific operating conditions.

The simulation response of the adaptive current controller to a step change in the reference current vector is shown in Fig. 11(a). The corresponding time-domain current waveform in one motor phase is shown in Fig. 11(b).

One can note large variations in the motor current vector during the transient period. This is a characteristic of the hysteresis control mode which is then active. The passage from one control mode to another is executed without overshoot.

During transient periods, the controller operates in hysteresis mode. The dynamic behavior of the system is then determined essentially by the electrical dynamics of the motor because the speed is supposed to be nearly constant during this period. Therefore, the variation rate of the motor currents will depend mainly on the difference between the inverter voltage vectors and the motor emf vector, and the motor inductance. At low speeds, the motor emf is low so that the current variation is high and the transient response is fast. At high speeds and high current-level, because the motor emf is increased the motor current variation rate is reduced. As a result, the transient response is slower.

Influence of the Motor Model Parameters

The inaccuracy of the motor model parameters influences particularly the steady-state response since the controller is then in predictive mode. This influence can be studied by comparing the predicted current and the actual current.

The motor model is characterized by three parameters: the emf, the stator inductance L, and the stator resistor R.

The effects of these parameters on the system response can be studied in considering each individually while supposing the others are accurate.

In supposing that the parameters L and R are accurate, the inverter voltage vector is calculated by the adaptive controller as

$$V(k) = e_{est}(k) + (L/T)\,[i^*(k+1) - i(k)] + Ri(k) \tag{23}$$

where $e_{est}(k)$ is the estimated emf vector, $i(k)$ is the actual current vector.

This voltage vector $V(k)$ is actually applied to the motor to produce a current vector $i(k+1)$ at the $(k+1)$-th sampling instant which is given by the following difference equation:

$$V(k) = e(k) + (L/T)\,[i(k+1) - i(k)] + Ri(k) \tag{24}$$

By substracting (23) and (24), we obtain

$$i(k+1) - i^*(k+1) = (T/L)\,[e_{est}(k) - e(k)]. \tag{25}$$

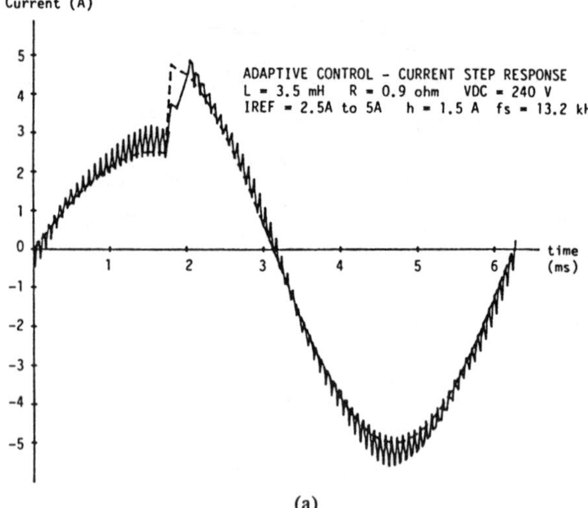

(a)

ADAPTIVE CONTROL - CURRENT VECTOR STEP RESPONSE
L = 3.5 mH R = 0.9 ohm VDC = 240 V
IREF = 2.5A to 5A h = 1.5A fs = 13.2 kHz

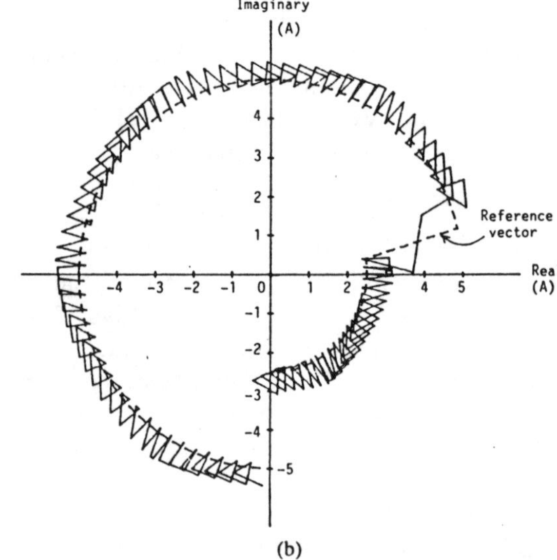

(b)

Fig. 11. Simulation dynamic performance. Response to a step change of reference current vector. (a) Response in complex plane. (b) Time-domain waveform.

This relation points out that the steady-state current error is directly proportional to the error in the estimated emf and the ratio (T/L). It can be thus reduced by reducing the error in the estimated emf, and by increasing the sampling frequency.

The effects of errors in L and R of the model can be studied in supposing that the emf is accurate. The voltage vector calculated by the controller is

$$V(k) = e(k) + [L + \Delta L]\,[i^*(k+1) - i(k)]/T + [R + \Delta R]\,i(k) \tag{26}$$

where ΔL and ΔR are errors in L and R respectively.

This voltage vector being applied to the motor will produce a current vector $i(k+1)$ which is given by the following equation:

$$V(k) = e(k) + L[i(k+1) - i(k)]/T + Ri(k) \tag{27}$$

By substracting (26) and (27) we obtain

$$i(k+1) - i^*(k+1) = (\Delta L/L)\left[i^*(k+1) - i(k)\right] + \Delta R(T/L)\, i(k). \tag{28}$$

This relation points out that the steady-state current error is less sensitive to the error in R than that in L because the factor $\Delta R(T/L)$ is usually very small.

Fig. 12 illustrates the effects of the errors in the motor model parameters on the controller performance. In Fig. 12(a) the step response obtained with 20 percent of error in the emf amplitude is shown. In Fig. 12(b) the step response obtained with 20 percent error in R and L is shown.

We can note that the influence of the error in the emf on the steady-state response is much significant than the influence of the errors in L and R. Therefore, it is important to fine adjust the model emf in order to minimize the steady-state current error.

On the other hand, the transient response is not affected by the inaccuracy of the motor model since hysteresis mode is active during transient periods. However, it is affected by the chosen hysteresis band. A large hysteresis band will produce fast transient response at the expense of large current variations.

V. Implementation of the Adaptive Control Scheme

The implementation of the adaptive current control scheme described above requires numerous control and computation tasks.

The control trasks include current acquisition, level comparison, mode selection, · · · . The computation tasks include current error calculation, vector substraction, coordinates transformation, optimum voltage vector calculation, speed calculation, · · · . A microprocessor-based control system appears to be imperative.

These tasks are to be executed every sampling period. Due to the complexity of the required operations and the constraints imposed by the switching frequency, a compromise has to be done in selecting hardware or software implementation.

Recent progress in large-scale integration technique has made available high-performance 16-bit microcontrollers specially designed for control applications. These microcontrollers provide the most desired features in digital control that are fast input/output operations and fast arithmetic operations. An example of such microcontrollers is the 8097 of the MCS-96 family (Intel Corporation). This microcontroller can do a 16-bit addition in 1 μs and a 16-bit by 16-bit multiplication or 32-bit division in 6.5 μs. Also provided on the same chip are high-speed I/O lines, timers, a 10-bit A/D converter, a serial port, a watchdog timer, and a pulsewidth-modulated output [7]. By using high performance 16-bit microcontrollers, the implementation can by simplified and the required hardware can be greatly reduced.

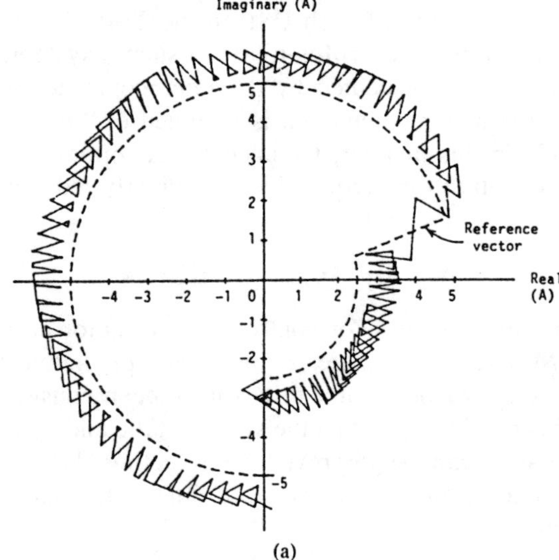

(a)

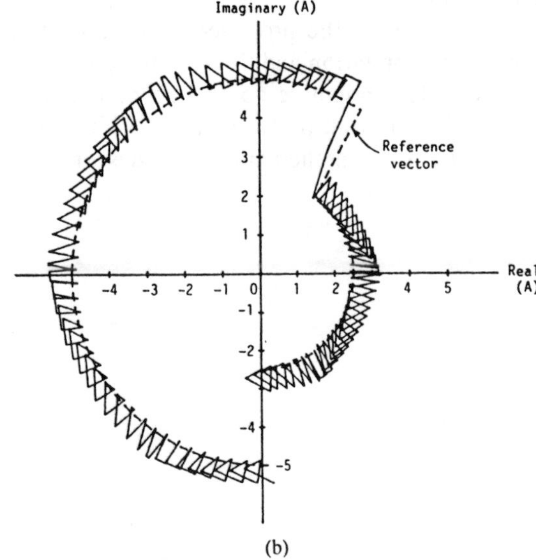

(b)

Fig. 12. Influence of errors in motor model parameters on controller performance. Response to a step change in reference current vector. (a) 20 percent of error in emf amplitude. (b) 20 percent of error in R and L.

The execution time for the control and computation tasks of the proposed adaptive current control scheme is estimated to be about 150–200 μs using the MCS-96 microcontroller. The corresponding sampling frequency is 5 kHz that is acceptable for machines having a large electric time constant. For machines with a small electric time constant, a higher sampling frequency is required and the computation time has to be reduced. This can be accomplished by using additional hardwired logic circuits to execute the time-consuming tasks (such as coordinates transformation). This would increase the hardware and the system cost.

Another approach consists to use in conjunction with the microcontroller a digital signal processor (DSP) which is designed to execute computation algorithms at very high speed. An example of such DSP in the TMS320 (Texas Instruments) or 56000 (Motorola). In such a system, the control tasks are executed by the microcontroller while the algorithm implementation is assumed exclusively by the DSP. In this manner, the execution is optimized and the computation time required can be greatly reduced.

VI. Conclusion

Two main schemes for controlling the motor currents in PWM inverters, hysteresis control and predictive control, in synchronous motor drives have been considered. It has been pointed out that the system static and dynamic performance can be improved by selecting the control mode, in an adaptive manner, according to the operating conditions.

In steady-state, the predictive mode is selected to reduce current ripple and to obtain stable switching frequency. During large transients, such as during starting or load variations, the hysteresis mode is selected to provide fast response.

The performance of the proposed control scheme has been studied by simulation and the results agree well with the prediction. This adaptive control scheme can be implemented using a high-performance 16-bit microcontroller supported by a mathematic co-processor.

References

[1] A. B. Plunkett, "A current-controlled PWM transistor inverter drive," in *IEEE/IAS 1979 Annual Meeting Conf. Rec.*, Oct. 1979, pp. 785-792.

[2] G. Pfaff, A. Weschta and A. Wick, "Design and experimental results of a brushless ac servo drive," in *IEEE/IAS 1982 Annual Meeting Conf. Rec.*, pp. 692-697, Oct. 1982.

[3] J. Holtz and S. Stadtfeld, "A predictive controller for the stator current vector of ac machines fed from a switched voltage source," in *IPEC International Power Electronics Conf. Rec.*, Tokyo 1983, pp. 1665-1675.

[4] D. M. Brod and D. W. Novotny, "Current control of VSI-PWM inverters," in *IEEE/IAS 1984 Annual Meeting Conf. Rec.*, pp. 418-425, Oct. 1984.

[5] A. Nabae, S. Ogasawara, and H. Akagi, "A novel control scheme of current-controlled PWM inverters," *IEEE/IAS 1985 Annual Meeting Conf. Rec.*, Toronto, Oct. 1985, pp. 473-478.

[6] H. Le-Huy, R. Perret, and R. Feuillet, "Minimization of torque ripple in brushless dc motor drives," *IEEE/IAS 1985 Annual Meeting Conf. Rec.*, Toronto, ON, Canada, Oct. 1985, pp. 790-797.

[7] Ira Horden, "Using the 8096," AP-248 Application Note, Intel Corp., Feb. 1985.

[8] M. Lajoie-Mazenc, *et al.*, "Study and implementation of hysteresis controlled inverter on a permanent magnet synchronous machine," in *IEEE/IAS 1984 Annual Meeting Conf. Rec.*, Oct. 1984, pp. 426-431.

[9] T. Kato and K. Miyao, "Modified hysteresis control with minor loops for single-phase full-bridge inverters," in *IEEE/IAS 1985 Annual Meeting Conf. Rec.*, Pittsburgh, PA, Oct. 1988, pp. 689-693.

[10] R. J. Kerkman and T. M. Rowan, "Voltage controlled current regulated PWM inverters," *IEEE/IAS 1988 Annual Meeting Conf. Rec.*, Pittsburgh, PA, Oct. 1988, pp. 381-387.

[11] L. Malesani *et al.*, "Improved current control technique of VSI PWM inverters with constant modulation frequency and extended voltage range," *IEEE/IAS 1988 Annual Meeting Conf. Rec.*, Pittsburgh, PA, Oct. 1988, pp. 722-727.

[12] V. Gosbell and P. Dalton, "Current control of induction motors at low speeds," *IEEE/IAS 1988 Annual Meeting Conf. Rec.*, Pittsburgh, PA, Oct. 1988, pp. 431-436.

A High-Performance Pulsewidth Modulator for an Inverter-Fed Drive System Using a Microcomputer

BIMAL K. BOSE, SENIOR MEMBER, IEEE, AND HUNT A. SUTHERLAND, MEMBER, IEEE

Abstract—**An Intel 8086 microcomputer-based pulsewidth modulator (PWM) is described which receives digital voltage and frequency commands independently at the input, generates precision three-phase PWM waves at the output, and can be used to drive a transistor or thyristor inverter for ac drive systems. A computation intensive uniform sampling technique is used in the low-frequency region, whereas the higher frequency region is based on word recognition and pattern retrieval method. A laboratory breadboard of the modulator has been built and tested for the frequency range 0–250 Hz with resolution of 0.0077 Hz and smooth voltage variation up to square wave within a one-percent step in the whole range. The modulator has been extensively tested with a transistor inverter and hybrid computer simulated induction motor drive system and shows performance improvement over the currently available techniques.**

INTRODUCTION

INTEREST has been growing in microcomputer-based pulsewidth modulator (PWM) schemes for ac drive systems in recent years. Among the several methods, such as dedicated analog/digital, dedicated digital, and microcomputer methods of implementation, the last offers several advantages. A microcomputer-based modulator, if judiciously designed, can provide considerable simplification of hardware with significant improvement in performance. The hardware simplification also adds to the reliability improvement. Modern PWM ac drive systems are continually seeking improvement of performance and reliability with reduction of control and power conversion cost. If the drive control system is implemented with a microcomputer, then the modulator which constitutes a compatible link between the controller and the inverter can be integrated into the hardware and software of the same microcomputer. If the modulator is used in the discrete form as a block box, a possibility exists that a universal hardware module can be designed which can be adapted to transistor or thyristor drives of different specifications simply by modifying the software.

The performance improvement of a microcomputer-based modulator can be briefly reviewed here. In a conventional hardwared modulator, the PWM waveforms are generated by comparing the sine reference wave with the triangular carrier wave by the "natural sampling" process. As the linear PWM region is exceeded into the transition region, the harmonic quality of the waves deteriorates seriously with the introduction of the lower order harmonics. In addition, the dropping of pulses near the middle of the wave causes a current surge problem. In a microcomputer-based modulator, the wave can be fabricated precisely in the transition region controlling the harmonics and voltage jump, and the nonlinearity problem can be easily overcome. However, precision PWM wave generation in real time, as required by the drive system operation, remains a challenge because of the time critical performance requirement of the microcomputer.

The microcomputer-based modulators have been developed principally on the basis of the look-up table method, which hardly meets the needs of practical drive systems. The number of notch angles for a wave pattern tends to increase at lower fundamental frequency, demanding large look-up table memory; thus the lower frequency and the number of wave patterns stored tend to be limited. Even if the memory size is considered to be no constraint the hardware and software designs of the present modulators are such that they often do not provide good angle resolution, and the output waves do not respond adequately in real time with change in voltage and frequency commands. The DMA and FIFO methods, as discussed in the literature [8], [9], have deficiencies as mentioned. An attempt has been made to implement the low-frequency region by the computation intensive natural sampling method, but this has met with limited success.

This paper describes a high-performance PWM which was developed in a GE laboratory several years ago. The modulator satisfies all the practical needs of a superior performance ac drive system which may require wide frequency range with high resolution in voltage and frequency. The modulator synthesizes precision three-phase PWM waves by hybriding the computation intensive and look-up table methods. A modulator breadboard has been tested in the laboratory and shows excellent performance.

DESCRIPTION OF THE MODULATOR

A block diagram of the modulator which drives an induction motor through a transistor inverter is shown in Fig. 1. The modulator receives fundamental frequency voltage and frequency commands V_S and F_S, respectively, in digital form and generates directly the three-phase PWM waves, which can be coupled to the transistors of the inverter through amplification and isolation circuits. Independent voltage and frequency control meets the requirement of the modern high-performance drive systems, where any arbitrary combination of these parameters may be demanded by the outer

Paper IPCSD 82-30, approved by the Static Power Converter Committee of the IEEE Industry Applications Society for presentation at the 1982 Industry Applications Society Annual Meeting, San Francisco, CA, October 4–8. Manuscript released for publication September 15, 1982.

The authors are with the General Electric Company, Corporate Research and Development, P. O. Box 43, Schenectady, NY 12301.

Reprinted from *IEEE Trans. Ind. Applicat.*, vol. IA-19, no. 2, pp. 235–243, March/April 1983.

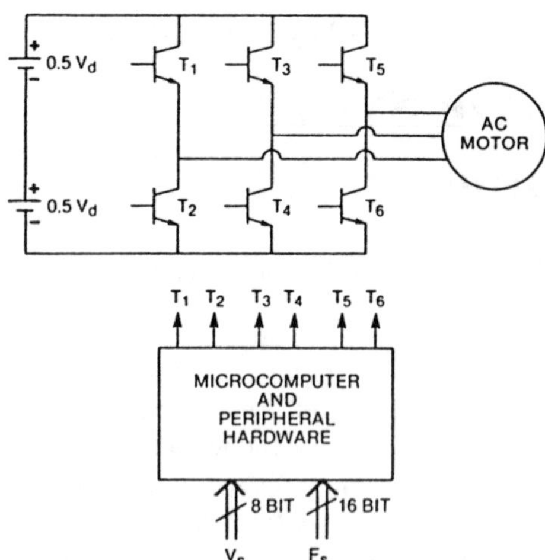

Fig. 1. Block diagram of PWM modulator with inverter and machine.

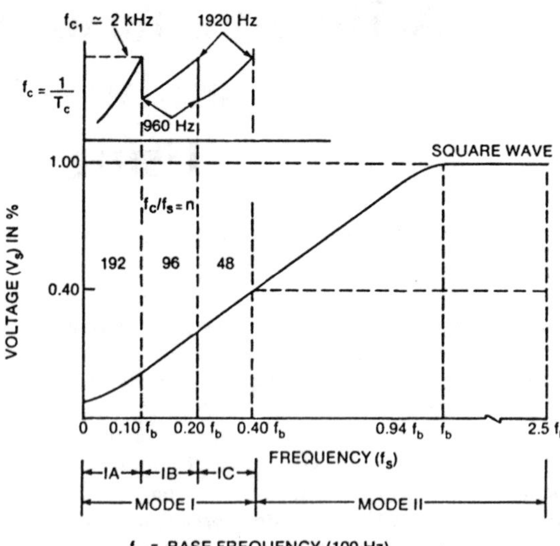

Fig. 2. Typical voltage-frequency diagram showing different modes of modulator.

control loops. The 8-bit V_S signal permits 0.39 percent voltage resolution from zero to full square wave range, whereas the 16-bit F_S signal can generate frequency in the range 0-250 Hz with a resolution of 0.0077 Hz. Very low frequency operation including the zero frequency (dc) chopping mode may be required for the servo motor drive. The signals may be available as compatible software parameters if the modulation and control functions are integrated into a single microcomputer. Fig. 2 shows the typical voltage-frequency relation of an induction motor which also illustrates the different modes of operation of the modulator. The parameter values shown in the diagram correspond to the breadboard which was tested in the laboratory. The modulator essentially operates in two different modes which can be defined as follows:

Mode I uniform sampling equilateral triangulation method,

Mode II word recognition and pattern retrieval method.

Mode I is valid in the low-frequency region which typically extends up to 0.40 f_b, where f_b is the base frequency, and Mode II holds in the upper frequency region as shown in the figure. Several submodes exist in Mode I which will be explained later.

The principle of uniform sampling as compared to the normally used natural sampling method is explained in Fig. 3. In natural sampling, the carrier is compared directly with the modulating wave to determine the switching instants, i.e., it is a process of intrinsic natural selection of the sampling points. In the uniform sampling method which is based on the sample-and-hold principle, the sampling frequency is equal to the carrier frequency. In addition, a natural sampling pulse is normally asymmetrical about the trough of the carrier with the sinusoidal modulating wave, whereas the uniform sampling pulse is always symmetrical, as shown in the figure. The two sampling methods have been extensively evaluated in the literature [2], and the latter shows significant improvement in low-frequency harmonics and elimination of the subharmonic problem at noninteger frequency ratios. It is also more easily adaptable to microcomputer implementation.

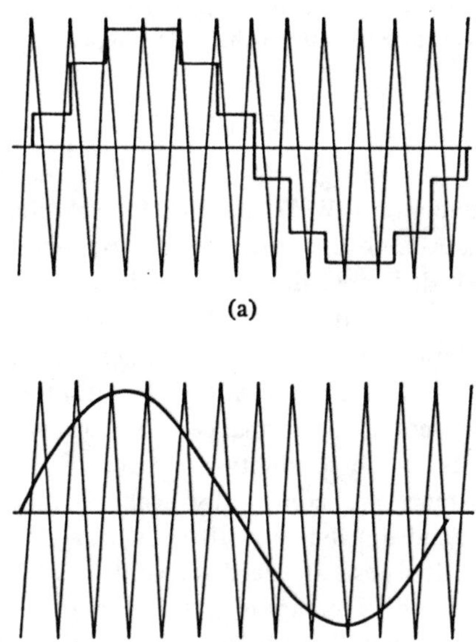

Fig. 3. Comparison between sampling methods. (a) Uniform sampling. (b) Natural sampling.

The uniform sampling method implementation in the present modulator is explained in Fig. 4. The microcomputer memorizes n number of amplitudes of 1-pu quarter-cycle sine reference wave at equal angular intervals as shown. Because of the 120° phase shift between the phases and the quarter-cycle symmetry of a sine reference wave, the amplitude information for three-phase PWM outputs can be obtained by appropriately locating the address pointers. The 1-pu samples of the reference wave are shown to correspond with the troughs of an equilateral triangular wave of period T_C, as characteristic to uniform sampling principle. In actual operation, the microcomputer periodically samples the voltage command V_S, multiplies with the 1-pu sample amplitude at that instant, and then generates a symmetrical pulsewidth as shown in the figure. A more expanded view showing the details of the synthesis of three-phase pulsewidths is given in Fig. 5. The sam-

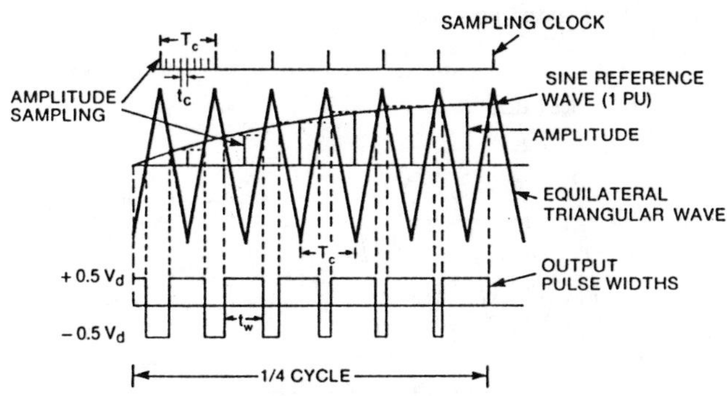

Fig. 4. Uniform sampling modulation principle in Mode I.

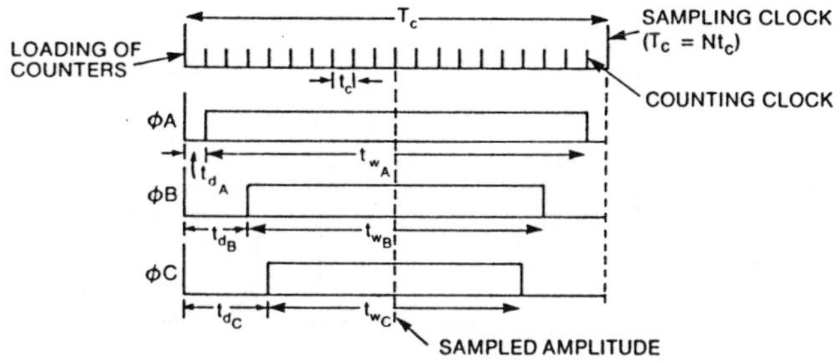

Fig. 5. Synthesis of pulsewidths in Mode I for three phases.

pling clock T_C can be generated from the frequency command F_S by the following relations:

$$W_{T_C} = \left(\frac{F_{S_{max}}}{f_{S_{max}}}\right) \cdot \frac{f_1}{nF_S} \tag{1}$$

$$T_C = \frac{W_{T_C}}{f_1} \times 10^6 \qquad \mu S \tag{2}$$

where

W_{T_C} digital word for T_C interval,
$F_{S_{max}}$ maximum value of F_S (FFFF hexadecimal),
$f_{S_{max}}$ maximum fundamental frequency in Hz (250 Hz),
n number of samples for cycle of 1-pu reference sine wave,
f_1 clock frequency in MHz (20 MHz).

The word W_{T_C} is computed, and then the corresponding interval T_C is generated by a 20-bit programmable down counter which is clocked by the frequency f_1. The digital words for the pulsewidths and delay times shown in Fig. 5 are given by the following expressions:

$$W_{t_{W_A}} = 0.5\,N\left(\frac{V_S}{V_{SM}} \cdot \phi_A + 1\right) \tag{3}$$

$$W_{t_{W_B}} = 0.5N\left(\frac{V_S}{V_{SM}} \cdot \phi_B + 1\right) \tag{4}$$

$$W_{t_{W_C}} = 0.5N\left(\frac{V_S}{V_{SM}} \cdot \phi_C + 1\right) \tag{5}$$

$$W_{t_{d_A}} = 0.5(N - W_{t_{W_A}}) \tag{6}$$

$$W_{t_{d_B}} = 0.5(N - W_{t_{W_B}}) \tag{7}$$

$$W_{t_{dc}} = 0.5(N - W_{t_{W_C}}), \tag{8}$$

where

N constant (256),
V_{SM} maximum value of V_S which corresponds to square wave output (FF hexadecimal),
$\phi_A, \phi_B,$
ϕ_C 1-pu amplitude of Phase A, B, and C, respectively.

The pulsewidth and the delay times of each phase are generated by the respective pulsewidth counter clocked by the pulse train of period t_c. The counting clock t_c is a submultiple of the sampling period T_C ($T_C = N\,t_c$) and can be generated by a 16-b down counter from the following relations:

$$W_{t_c} = \frac{W_{T_C}}{N} \cdot \frac{f_2}{f_1} \tag{9}$$

$$t_c = \frac{W_{t_c}}{f_2} \cdot 10^6\ \mu s \tag{10}$$

where f_2 is the clock frequency in MHz (40 MHz).

High accuracy of the sampling and counting clocks is mandatory for precision synthesis of the PWM waves. For this reason, the T_C and t_c counters are operated in parallel and are clocked independently by a precision high-frequency oscillator.

At the leading edge of the interval T_C, an INTERRUPT pulse loads the delay times (W_{t_d}) to the respective pulsewidth counters simultaneously. When a pulsewidth counter clears, its INTERRUPT output automatically loads the pulsewidth (W_{t_w}) and so on. At the end of the second delay time interval, the pulsewidth counter INTERRUPTs are superseded by the T_C INTERRUPT to maintain synchronization. Obviously, the quiescent time intervals for $V_S = 0$ are given by

$$T_{W_A} = T_{W_B} = T_{W_C} = 0.5T_C \tag{11}$$

$$t_{d_A} = T_{d_B} = t_{d_c} = 0.25T_C. \tag{12}$$

The 1-pu reference wave, in fact, is sampled one T_C period ahead of time (see Fig. 4), and the words for the delay and pulse times for the three phases are computed and loaded into the respective phase buffers. These are then loaded into the respective pulsewidth counters in correct instants of time. This mode of operation will result in a response delay of T_C μs which can be neglected in the overall response time of the drive system.

The Mode I operation is subdivided into several submodes, as shown in Fig. 2. The submode IA corresponds to the free running mode with a nominal carrier frequency f_{c_1} = 2 kHz, whereas the submodes IB and IC are inherently synchronous, as explained before. The number of reference wave samples

$n = fc/fs$ per cycle of fundamental frequency and the distribution of sampling frequency fc are also shown in Fig. 2. In submode IA, all the 192 samples of the reference wave are used, whereas in submodes IB and IC every alternate and one in every four, respectively, are used. The operation of submode IA needs some further explanation. The exploded view of part of a cycle in IA is shown in Fig. 6, which is somewhat self-explanatory. The free running carrier frequency deviates from the sampling frequency ($f_{c_1} > fc$) because of the limited number of samples available. Here, the reference wave is sampled every T_C period and stored into a memory buffer. The fixed carrier frequency clock $T_{C_1} = 1/f_{c_1} = 512$ μs fetches the sample, multiplies by the V_S amplitude, and converts into equivalent pulsewidth by the mechanism explained before. The counting clock t_{c_1} is a submultiple of T_{C_1} by the relation $T_{C_1} = N\, t_{c_1}$, where $N = 256$. The maximum carrier frequency which determines the number of commutations/s (4000 in this case) is limited by the switching and commutation losses of the power semiconductor devices. The minimum fundamental frequency is limited by the size of the T_C counter, and in the present design it is 0.1 Hz, which corresponds to F_S = 0019 Hexadecimal. If the F_S command falls below this limit, the ideal chopper operation of the inverter begins with the frozen reference wave amplitudes for all three phases.

Mode II operation is restricted in the higher frequency region, where, because of the timing constraint, a look-up table oriented word recognition and pattern retrieval method is used. Fig. 7 shows a typical voltage wave of a half-bridge inverter in Mode II which is characterized by three basic notch angles: α_1, α_2, and α_3. The angles are precomputed for a harmonically optimum wave and stored in the memory. Again, because of the symmetry and absence of notches in the middle of the wave, only the pattern for the 0-60° segment need be stored, and three-phase full wave PWM outputs can be generated by appropriately locating the address pointers. Two different methods of a notch angle look-up table have been used here. These are 1) the harmonic elimination (HE) method and 2) the minimum rms ripple (MRR) current method. The HE method [1] is briefly reviewed as follows. The wave in Fig. 7 can be described by the general Fourier series:

$$f(\omega t) = \sum_{n=1}^{\infty} [a_n \sin n\omega t + b_n \cos n\omega t] \tag{13}$$

where

$$a_n = \frac{1}{\pi} \int_0^{2\pi} f(\omega t) \sin n\omega t \, d\omega t \tag{14}$$

$$b_n = \frac{1}{\pi} \int_0^{2\pi} f(\omega t) \cos n\omega t \, d\omega t. \tag{15}$$

For quarter-cycle cosine symmetry,

$$a_n = \frac{4}{n\pi} \left[1 + 2 \sum_{k=1}^{M} (-1)^k \cos n\alpha_k \right] \tag{16}$$

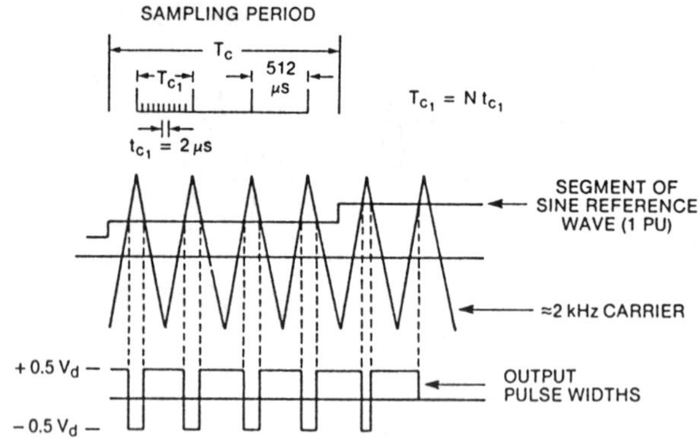

Fig. 6. PWM wave generation in submode IA.

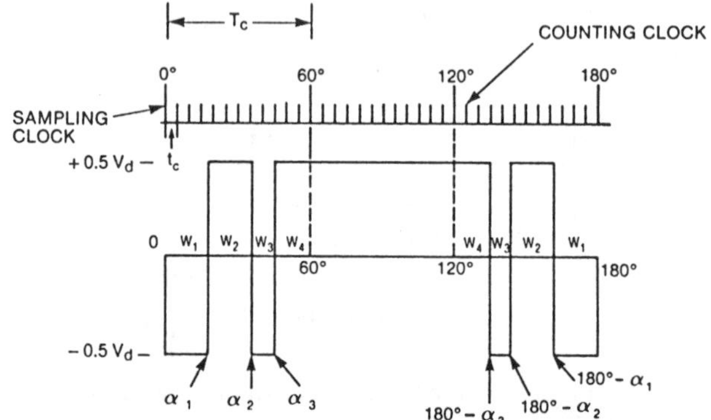

Fig. 7. Voltage wave of half-bridge inverter in Mode II.

$$b_n = 0. \tag{17}$$

If voltage control and elimination of fifth and seventh harmonics are desired, then

$$a_1 = \frac{4}{\pi} [1 - 2 \cos \alpha_1 + 2 \cos \alpha_2 - 2 \cos \alpha_3] \tag{18}$$

$$a_5 = \frac{4}{5\pi} [1 - 2 \cos 5\alpha_1 + 2 \cos 5\alpha_2 - 2 \cos 5\alpha_2] = 0 \tag{19}$$

$$a_7 = \frac{4}{7\pi} [1 - 2 \cos 7\alpha_1 + 2 \cos 7\alpha_2 - 2 \cos 7\alpha_3] = 0. \tag{20}$$

Equations (18)-(20) are solved to generate the look-up table shown in Fig. 8. The maximum available magnitude of the fundamental is only about 93 percent for complete elimination of the fifth and seventh harmonics. As a result of the elimination of lower order harmonics, the higher order significant harmonics such as the eleventh and thirteenth become prominent, as shown in the figure. An improved harmonic performance can be obtained by solving harmonic heating loss for different harmonics as a function of the notch angles and then iterating the angles so that the loss (i.e., the rms ripple current) is minimum [3]. The effective resistance, though, varies as a function of temperature, and skin effect is assumed to be constant.

Mode II operation typically extends from 40 to 100 percent of the fundamental voltage, and the wave patterns characterized by the α angles are stored in 1 percent increments,

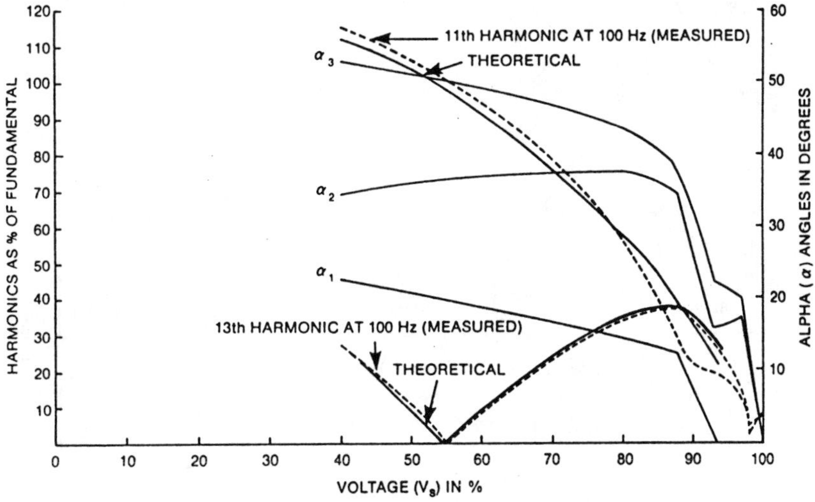

Fig. 8. Notch angle curves for harmonic elimination (fifth and seventh).

which may be adequate for most of the drive system requirements. The lower step size is limited by the resolution of α angle implementation. At about 93 percent of fundamental voltage, α_1 approaches zero in both the methods, and from this point, the voltage is increased by a one-percent step by symmetrically shifting the notches towards the edges of half-cycle and simultaneously reducing their widths. This segment of the look-up table is given in Table I. Obviously, the harmonic quality of the waveform is sacrificed to limit the voltage jump within the one percent.

The wave patterns, each characterized by the string of words W_1, W_2, W_3, and W_4 in the 0-60° interval, are stored in the memory. The sampling and counting clocks T_C and t_c, respectively, are generated by the same mechanism as explained before. The voltage command V_S is interrogated every 60° interval by the T_C INTERRUPT; the corresponding wave pattern is identified and retrieved from the memory. The string of words is then converted to alternate notch and pulsewidths in sequence by the pulsewidth counters. In fact, the words for each phase are stored in the I/O buffer 60° ahead of time so that these can be loaded to the respective pulsewidth counters at appropriate instants of time. The accuracy of α angle generation at the output is of paramount importance for harmonic content and step size control within limit. In the present design, the angle resolution is 0.24°, which can be improved to 0.12° if the parameters N and f_2 are increased to 512 and 80 MHz, respectively.

TABLE I
LOOK-UP TABLE FOR V_S FROM 93 TO 100 PERCENT

	Counts				Degrees		
V_S	W_1	W_2	W_3	W_4	α_1	α_2	α_3
93	0	68	26	162	0	15.94	22.03
94	0	69	23	165	0	16.17	21.56
95	0	70	19	167	0	16.41	20.86
96	0	72	15	168	0	16.88	20.39
97	0	74	11	170	0	17.34	19.92
98	0	47	11	198	0	11.02	13.59
99	0	20	11	224	0	4.69	7.27
100	0	0	0	256	0	0	0

HARDWARE AND SOFTWARE DESIGN

A simplified hardware block diagram of the modulator is shown in Fig. 9. The microcomputer is based on the Intel 8086 CPU, and a single board computer SDK-86 with appropriate peripheral hardware was used in the laboratory breadboard. The 5-MHz CPU clock was increased somewhat to enhance the execution speed. The Assembly language program, including the look-up tables, is contained in 2.5 kbytes of EPROM memory, and it is supported by 128 bytes of random access memory (RAM). The 8253 chips are used as three-phase pulsewidth and T_{C_1} counters which generate the INTERRUPT signals for the 8259 chips. All the PWM output signals with phase polarity are interfaced through the synchronizing flip-flops to prevent any timing error. The high-speed T_C and t_c (also t_{c_1}) timing counters use Schottky TTL chips and are triggered by a 40-MHz oscillator as shown.

The software implementation of the modulator has been qualitatively explained in the previous section. It is based on Assembly language and consists of the following sets of routines:

- sampling and calculation,
- phase sign output generation ,
- PWM output generation.

Fig. 10 shows the general flowchart of main software which includes sampling, calculation, and phase sign output routines. It is executed every T_c interval as indicated. Fig. 11 shows the general flowchart of PWM output software which is executed during the pulsewidth counting interval. Fig. 12 gives the mode transition diagram which shows the permissible transition between various modes and submodes at different conditions of frequency. A hysteresis band of 1 Hz is provided between the adjacent states to ensure smooth transition.

MODULATOR PERFORMANCE

A breadboard modulator was built in the laboratory for operation in the frequency range 0-250 Hz and was subjected to extensive performance evaluation in the whole region of operation. A wattless half-bridge inverter was built using phototransistors and was interfaced with the modulator to study the voltage harmonics in detail with the help of a spectrum ana-

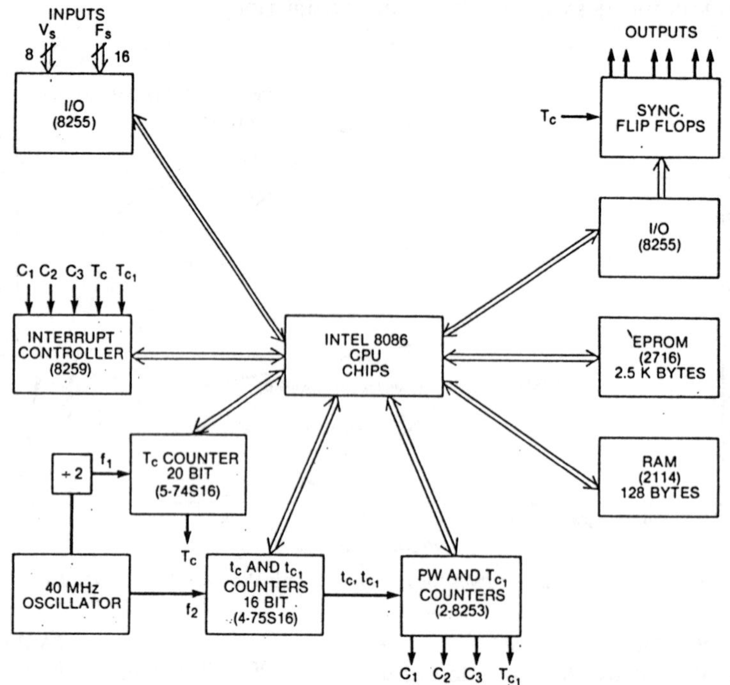

Fig. 9. Simplified hardware.

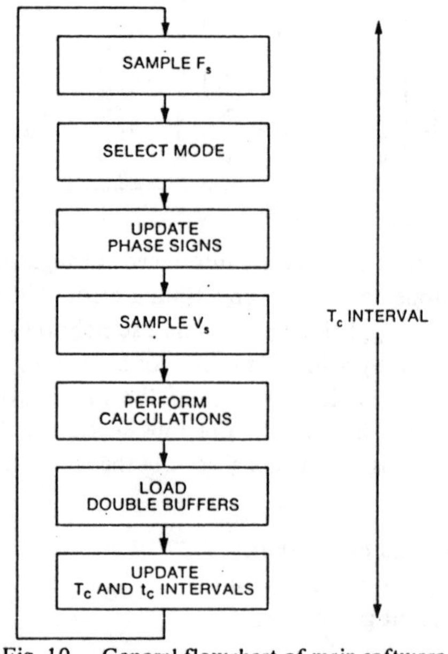

Fig. 10. General flowchart of main software.

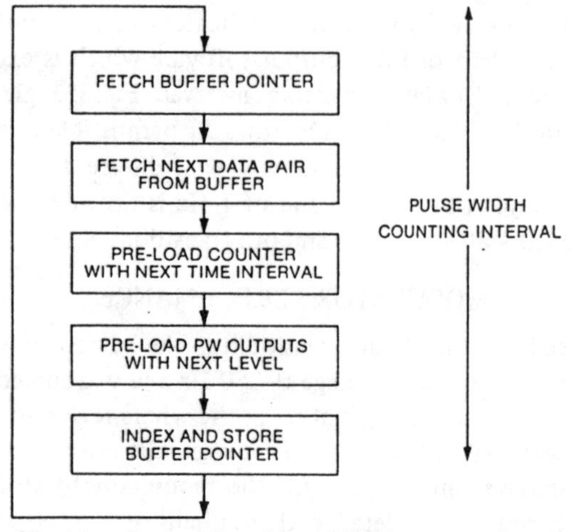

Fig. 11. General flowchart of PWM output software.

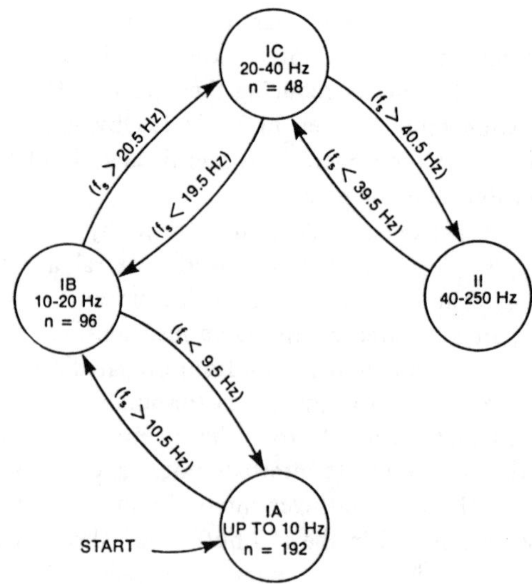

Fig. 12. Mode transition diagram.

lyzer (HP type 3580 A). Fig. 13 shows the spectrum in submode IC for V_s = 50 percent and f_s = 36 Hz. The fundamental component and the carrier frequency related harmonics (f_c $\pm 2f_s$, $f_c + 4f_s$, f_c $\pm 6f_s$, etc.), as accurately predicted by theory, appear at the output. Fig. 14 shows the spectrum in Mode II for V_s = 50 percent and f_s = 100 Hz in the harmonic elimination method. The fifth and seventh harmonics are practically nonexistent, as predicted by the theory. The triplen harmonics, though considerably dominant in amplitude, are of no significance when the machine is star connected with the isolated neutral. Fig. 15 shows the spectrum in minimum rms ripple method for the same conditions as in Fig. 14. Since the collective contribution of the harmonics is optimized, individual harmonic magnitude is of no concern here. The amplitudes of eleventh and thirteenth harmonics were measured in the harmonic elimination method and were plotted in Fig. 8 with the predicted amplitudes. Similar measurements were

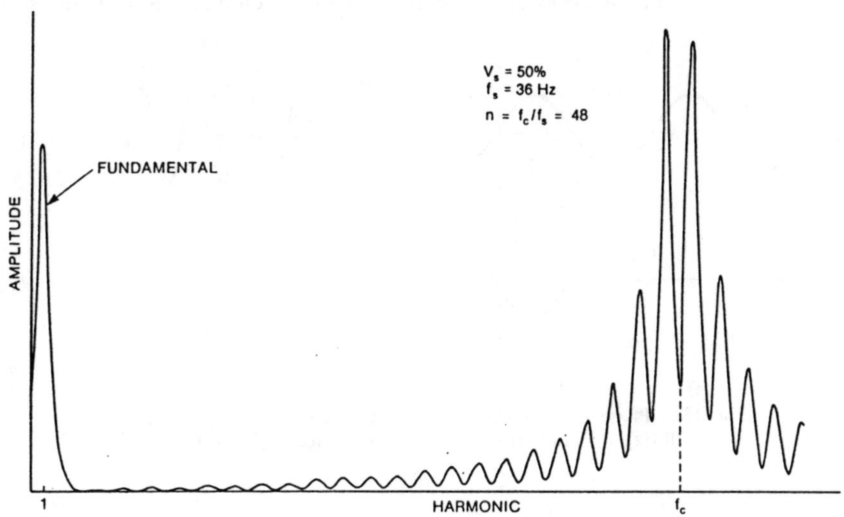

Fig. 13. Spectrum of half-bridge inverter output in Mode IC.

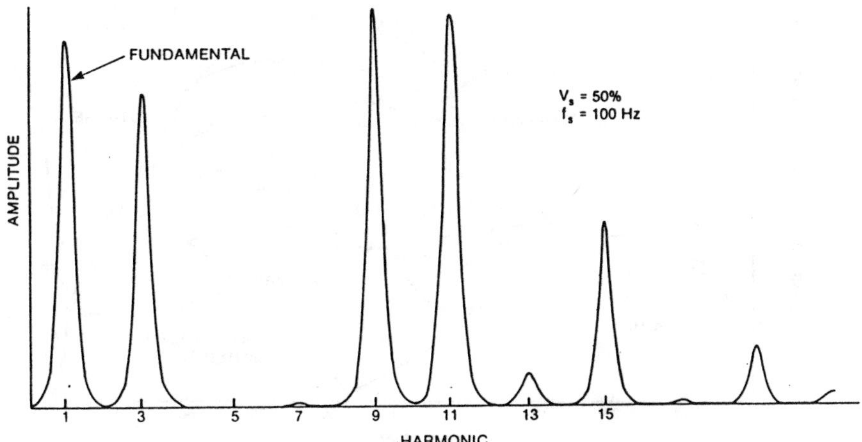

Fig. 14. Spectrum of half-bridge inverter output in Mode II (HE method).

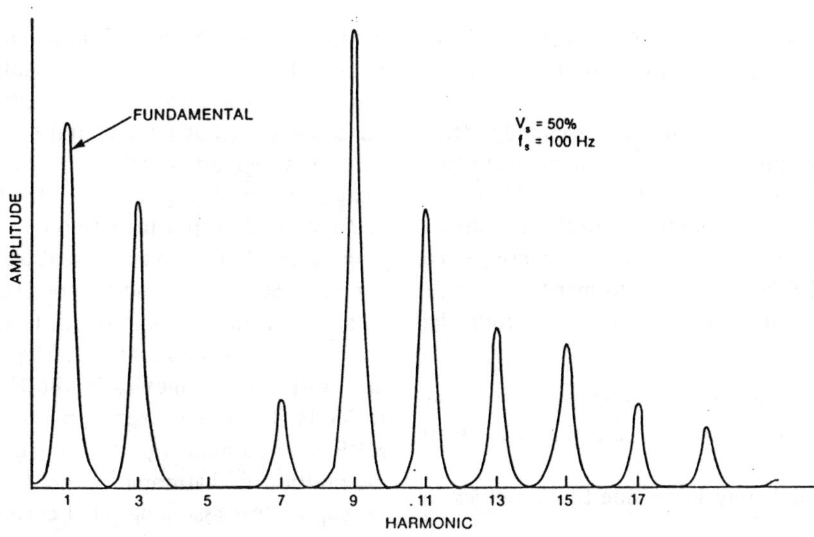

Fig. 15. Spectrum of half-bridge inverter output in Mode II (MRR method).

made for the MRR method and in Mode 1 to verify the precision performance of the modulator.

Though the spectrum analyzer study adequately verifies the performance of the modulator, it was decided to interface it with a simulated ac drive system to test the dynamic performance of the modulator and ripple currents in the machine. The drive system consisting of the three-phase inverter and induction motor was simulated on a hybrid computer (EA1681) by using simple open loop V/Hz control, and the modulator breadboard with actual software was directly interfaced with the simulation. A typical industrial motor of 25 hp, 230 V, 60 Hz was simulated using the direct-quadrature axis stationary reference frame model with a time scale factor of 100. The motor parameters are shown in Fig. 17. The three-phase out-

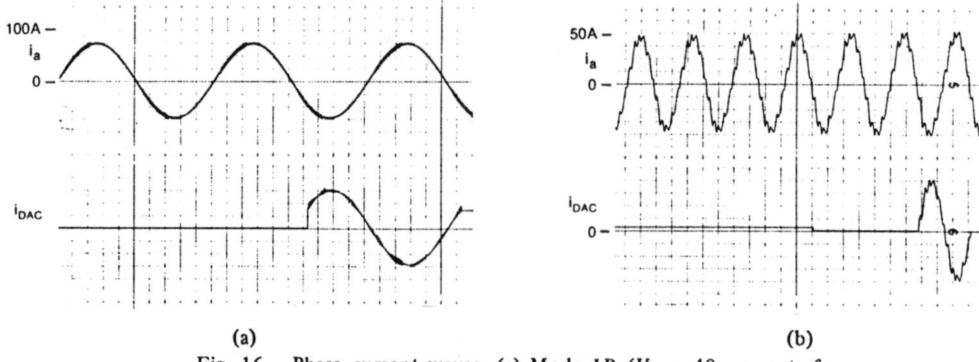

(a) (b)

Fig. 16. Phase current waves. (a) Mode IB (V_S = 40 percent, f_S = 20 Hz). (b) Mode II (MRR) (V_S = 60 percent, f_S = 60 Hz).

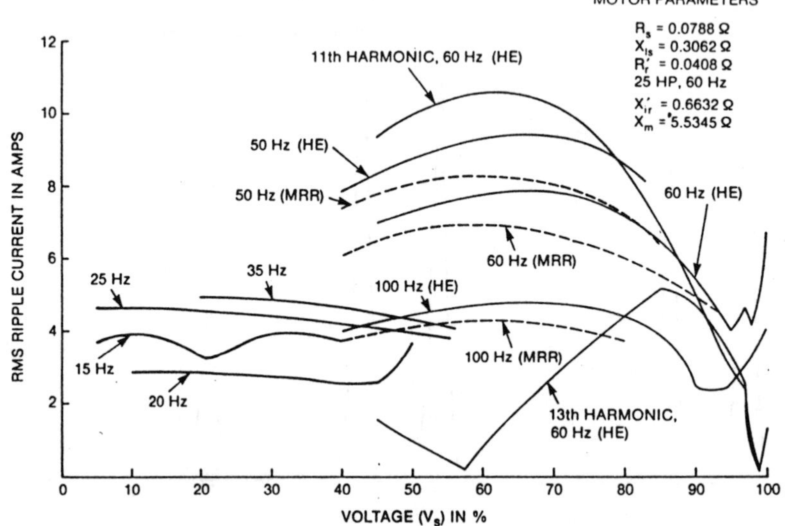

Fig. 17. RMS ripple currents in machine.

put waves of the inverter were checked to be symmetrical with precision phase balance, and no dc offset was observed at any condition.

Recall that the harmonic currents are essentially determined by the passive per phase equivalent circuit parameters and the respective amplitude of harmonic voltages. Therefore, the steady-state operating condition relating to the magnitudes of speed and stator fundamental current is of no consequence. Of course, the simulated drive system performance will differ principally from the actual drive system in the following aspects.

- The machine parameters are assumed to be constant (i.e., the temperature, saturation, and skin effects are neglected).
- The machine iron and stray losses due to harmonics are neglected.
- No lock-out time is provided between the adjacent transistors of the inverter leg. Therefore, the lock-out time effect and other switching delays and imperfections due to power semiconductor switches are neglected.

The modulator was operated at steady state and under transient conditions in a wide operating region and was found to give excellent performance. At steady state, the machine stator current was analyzed by the Fourier series to determine the harmonic contents. A digital Fourier analysis program (NAFOUR) with 200 samples/cycle was available in the hybrid computer. The current wave was sampled digitally through analog-to-digital converter (ADC) for digital processing and was read back through a digital-to-analog converter (DAC) to check the sampling inaccuracy. Fig. 16 shows the typical phase current wave and the DAC output in submode IB for $V_s = 40$ percent and $f_s = 20$ Hz. Similar waves are also shown in the MRR method for $V_s = 60$ percent and $f_s = 60$ Hz. Fig. 17 shows the plot of total rms ripple current for different voltage and frequency conditions in Modes I and II. The ripple currents at eleventh and thirteenth harmonics in the HE method are also shown. In Mode II, the improved ripple performance is evident in the MRR method compared to the HE method. Fig. 18 shows the distribution of harmonic copper loss compared to fundamental copper loss assuming rated current (46•82 A) in both constant torque and constant power regions. The overall loss improvement in MRR scheme is also indicated in the same figure.

CONCLUSION

A high-performance Intel 8086 microcomputer-based pulse-width modulator has been described in this paper. The modulator is designed to operate with a transistor inverter but can be easily adapted to thyristor inverter with some change in the

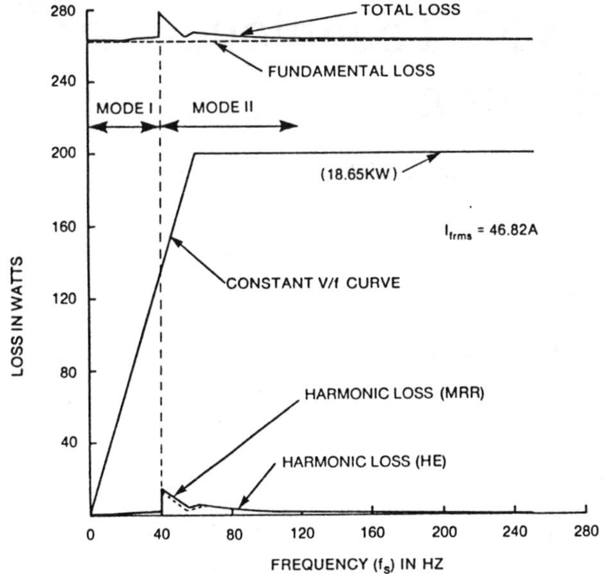

Fig. 18. Copper loss distribution at different frequencies.

software. The modulator operates on the computation intensive uniform sampling method in the low-frequency region, whereas the higher frequency region is based on a look-up table. Between the harmonic elimination and minimum rms ripple current methods, the latter shows considerable improvement in harmonics.

A breadboard modulator was built in the laboratory and tested extensively with a simulated induction motor drive system showing excellent performance. The modulator was tested in the frequency range 0-250 Hz with resolution of 0.0077 Hz and smooth voltage variation up to square wave within one percent voltage step.

ACKNOWLEDGMENT

The authors are thankful to Prof. F. Zach of Vienna University who worked as a consultant to General Electric for generating the minimum rms ripple look-up table. Thanks are also due to P. Szczesny for the help in hardware and software development.

REFERENCES

[1] B. K. Bose, *Adjustable Speed AC Drive Systems*. New York: IEEE Press, 1981, pp. 1–21, 110–125.

[2] S. R. Bowes, "New sinusoidal pulse width modulated inverter," *Proc. Inst. Elec. Eng.*, vol. 122, p. 1279–1285, Nov. 1975.

[3] G. S. Buja and G. B. Indri, "Optical pulse width modulation for feeding ac motors," *IEEE Trans. Ind. Appl.*, vol. IA-13, pp. 38–44, Jan./Feb. 1977.

[4] J. B. Casteel and R. G. Hoft, "Optimum PWM waveforms of a microprocessor controlled inverter," in *Conf. Rec. Power Elec. Spec. Conf.*, 1978, pp. 243–250.

[5] J. M. D. Murphy, R. G. Hoft, and L. S. Howard, "Controlled slip operation of an induction motor with optimum waveforms," in *IEEE Int. Conf. Rec. on Electrical Variable Speed Drives*, 1979, pp. 157–160.

[6] P. D. Zoigas, "Optimum voltage and harmonic control PWM techniques for three-phase static UPS system," in *Conf. Rec. IEEE/IAS 1979 Annual Meeting*, 1979, pp. 370–374.

[7] K. Mauch and M. R. Ito, "A multimicroprocessor ac drive controller," in *Conf. Rec. IEEE/IAS 1980 Annual Meeting*, 1980, pp. 634–640.

[8] K. S. Rajashekara and J. Vithayathil, "Microprocessor based sinusoidal PWM inverter by DMA transfer," *IEEE Trans. Ind. Electron.*, vol. IE—29, pp. 46–51, Feb. 1982.

[9] W. J. Tuten, "Microprocessor controller for integrated power module inverter," in *1977 IEEE/IAS Intl. Semi. Power Conv. Conf.*, 1977, pp. 470–475.

[10] B. K. Bose, "Adjustable speed ac drives—A technology status review," *Proc. IEEE*, vol. 70, pp. 116–135, Feb. 1982.

State-of-the-Art Carrier PWM Techniques: A Critical Evaluation

MICHAEL A. BOOST, STUDENT MEMBER, IEEE, AND PHOIVOS D. ZIOGAS, MEMBER, IEEE

Abstract—**With the introduction and wide acceptance of gate turn-off power devices (e.g., bipolars, power FET's, GTO's, etc.), the switching behavior of converters has reached the point where further improvements in firing and switching networks bring only marginal benefits. Consequently, the research interests in the area of static converters have been shifting toward improving the process of power conversion through a combination of new circuit topologies and improved voltage and harmonic control PWM techniques. As a result, several such techniques have been proposed lately. Although these techniques are clearly superior to the original sine PWM technique, little or conflicting data is available about their merits relative to each other. Consequently, selection of the best PWM technique for most applications is accompanied by uncertainty, which can lead to less than optimum results. A critical evaluation of the aforementioned PWM techniques on the basis of application is provided, thereby giving the framework and guidelines for the selection of the best technique for each area of application.**

I. Introduction

A. General

IN power electronics, pulsewidth modulation (PWM) is an operation performed on "raw" voltage and current waveforms to shape their spectra in a way beneficial to the application under consideration. Spectra shaping typically means the creation of a "dead band" between wanted and unwanted spectral components. For a given switching frequency it is desirable that the dead band be as wide as possible. To illustrate this point, Figs. 1(a), 1(b), 1(d), and 1(e) show a typical inverter line-to-line output voltage waveform and its respective spectra before and after it has been pulsewidth modulated (PWMed). Figs. 1(c) and 1(f) show the resulting line current waveforms obtained with a load PF = 0.8 lagging. In particular, Fig. 1(f) shows that PWM allows static inverters to generate close to ideal output waveforms while providing variable-voltage and variable-frequency operation.

Further investigation of the results shown in Fig. 1 also reveals that PWM has several disadvantages, which include

i) attenuation of the wanted fundamental component of the PWMed waveform, in this case from 1.1–0.866 pu;
ii) drastically increased switching frequencies (in this case from 1 pu to 21 pu)—this means greater stresses on associated switching devices and therefore derating of those devices;

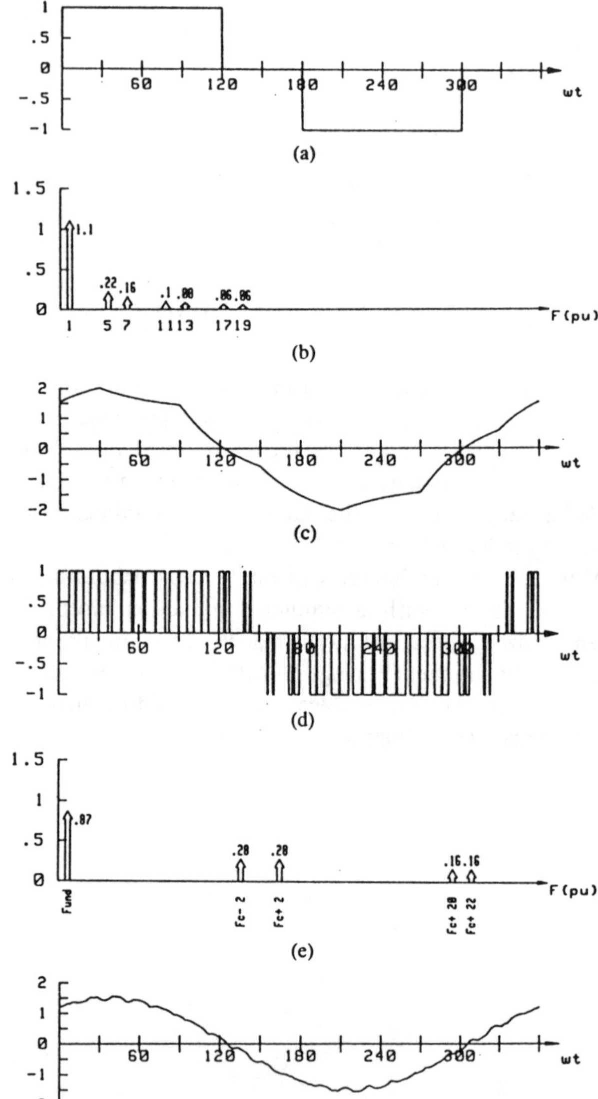

Fig. 1. Inverter voltage and current waveforms with six-step and sinusoidal PWM (SPWM) operation. (a) Square-wave output line-to-line voltage. (b) Line-to-line voltage spectrum (square wave). (c) Output line current (square wave). (d) SPWM output line-to-line voltage. (e) Line-to-line spectrum (SPWM). (f) Output line current (SPWM).

iii) generation of high-frequency harmonic components previously not present.

However, in addition to the importance of spectral shaping, the main advantage of pulsewidth modulation is that it allows linear amplitude control of the output voltages/currents from

Paper IPCSD 87-29, approved by the Static Power Converter Committee of the IEEE Industry Applications Society for presentation at the 1986 Power Electronics Specialists Conference, Vancouver, BC, Canada, June 23–27. Manuscript released for publication June 10, 1987.

The authors are with Concordia University, 1455 de Maisonnueve Boulevard West, Montreal, PQ, Canada H35 1M8.

IEEE Log Number 8717547.

Reprinted from *IEEE Trans. Ind. Applicat.*, vol. 24, no. 2, pp. 271–280, March/April 1988.

within the converter. Consequently, inverters can be supplied from diode (instead of thyristor) rectifiers, resulting in a simpler and cheaper power conversion system.

B. Specifics of PWM Techniques Treated in this Paper

Since the advantages of PWM clearly outweigh the respective disadvantages, a considerable research effort has gone into minimizing the PWM disadvantages mentioned earlier. As a result, several specific PWM techniques that focus on improving source utilization and generated input/output harmonic content have been proposed lately [2]–[4]. It is noted that the advantages of all these improved PWM techniques over the original sine PWM technique are obtained at the "cost" of generating third line-to-neutral voltage harmonics. However, under balanced and open neutral operating conditions, third-harmonic currents cannot flow and thus the third-order voltage harmonics are neutralized.

Previous work related to these improved techniques has been focused on converter output spectra, neglecting other important criteria such as input spectra, input/output distortion factor, switching frequencies and hardware implementation considerations. Furthermore, another focus of previous work has been inverter applications neglecting in the process some other equally important areas such as dc drives, rectifier power supplies, and rectifier–inverter type frequency changers. Consequently, selection of the best PWM technique for most applications is accompanied with uncertainty, which can lead to less-than-optimum results.

For these reasons this paper provides a critical evaluation of all the aforementioned PWM techniques on the basis of application, thereby providing the framework and guidelines for the selection of the best technique for each area of application. The applications considered include

1) voltage and current source inverters for
   a) variable-speed ac motor drives,
   b) UPS power supplies;
2) rectifiers for
   a) dc motor drives,
   b) power supplies;
3) high-performance rectifier–inverter type frequency changers.

C. Other Improved PWM Techniques

Another class of improved PWM techniques that are not included in this paper are the so-called programmed PWM techniques [7]–[9]. These techniques offer even better voltage utilization and lower switching frequencies when employed with inverters supplied from independently regulated voltage or current sources. However, when these techniques are employed with variable-frequency/variable-voltage inverters and an unregulated dc bus, they have a number of disadvantages, which include the following.

i) Quite sophisticated control hardware is required to store and access the required large number of switching patterns.
ii) For ac motor drives, and at low operating frequencies, the number of switching points becomes too large to evaluate analytically, even with mainframe computers.
iii) When a large number of harmonics needs to be eliminated, the respective switching pattern cannot be reproduced accurately by the inverter due to delays associated with the inverter switches and their respective base drives.
iv) Associated hardware becomes practical and cost effective only through VLSI implementation. The expertise required to design such hardware is not available to most small to mid-size companies. Also the number of units produced must be large enough to justify initial development costs.
v) Reliability of VLSI technology in high-current switching environments is still questionable.

Consequently, it appears that even with projected technological advances the programmed PWM techniques could only partially replace the carrier PWM techniques discussed in this paper.

II. Characterization of Improved PWM Techniques

A. Preliminary

The main features of the improved PWM techniques treated in this paper are brought out in this section. These features include the derivation of switching points, the resulting ac and dc term gains, the resulting frequency spectra, the harmonic distortion at the converter input and output terminals, and finally, the degree of difficulty of hardware implementation for each technique. Since there are four PWM techniques and three types of converters involved in this evaluation, care must be taken to present relevant results with clarity. For this purpose, a generalized bridge converter (Fig. 2) comprised of six ideal four-quadrant switches has been employed.

The main advantage of this converter is that because of the nature of its switches it can function either as an inverter (voltage or current source) or as a rectifier by simply applying the proper gating signals. The generalized converter thus permits the ac terminal waveforms (ac term) to represent [6] either

a) the line-to-line voltage of a voltage source inverter (VSI);
b) the output line current of a current source inverter (CSI); or
c) the input line current of a controlled rectifier (CR);

and the dc terminal (dc term) waveforms to represent

a) the input current of a VSI;
b) the input voltage of a CSI; or
c) the output voltage of a CR.

Also, in the evaluation that follows, the switching frequency of the bridge is kept constant to provide a common ground for comparison of each technique under rectifier and inverter operation.

B. The Original Sine PWM Technique

This technique [2] has been included for the purpose of using it as a "benchmark" to evaluate respective improved

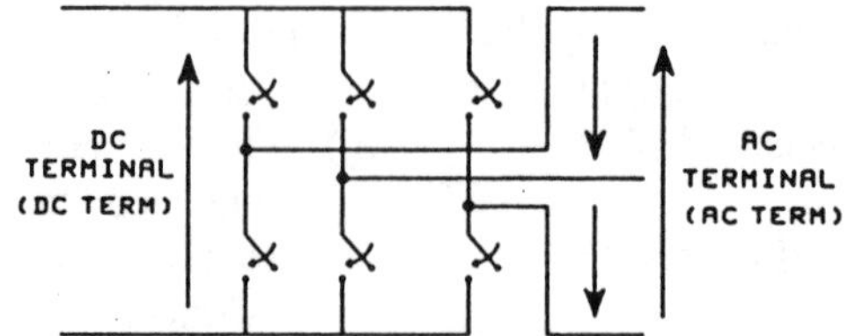

Fig. 2. Generalized bridge configuration.

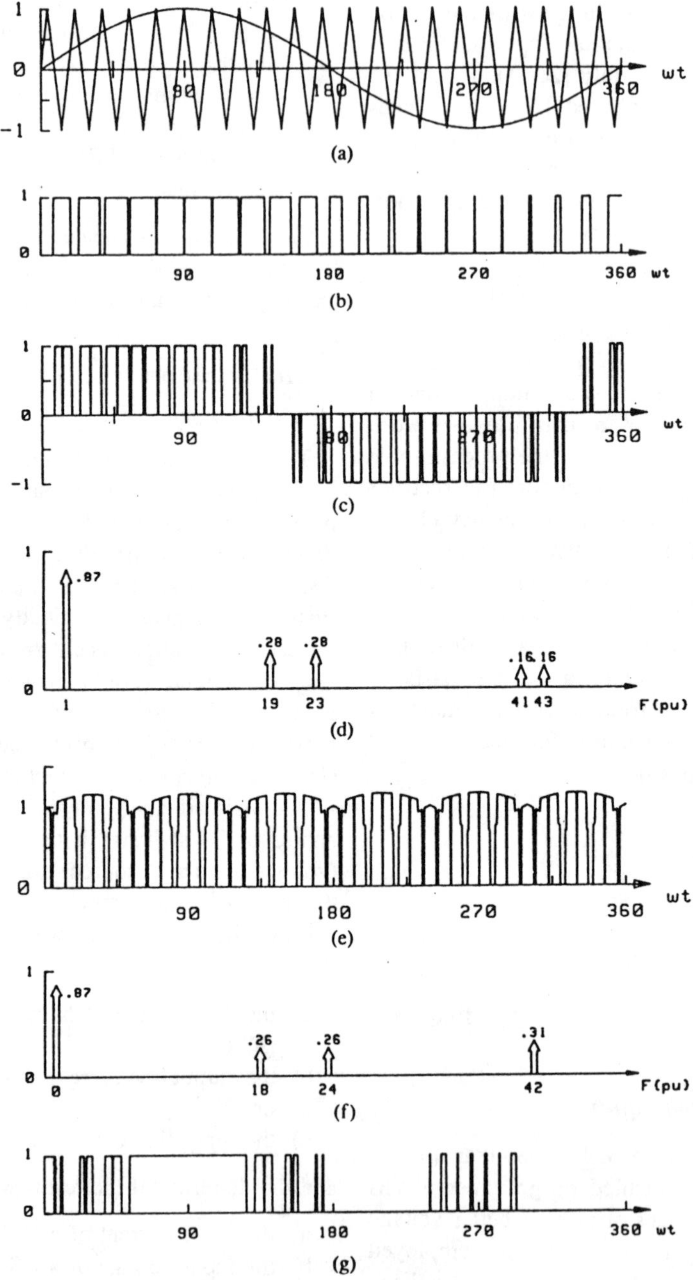

Fig. 3. Sinusoidal PWM (SPWM). (a) SPWM scheme. (b) VSI switch #1 gating signal (SW1). (c) AC term. (d) AC term spectrum. (e) DC term. (f) DC term spectrum. (g) CSI/CR switch #1 gating signal.

techniques. Its main intrinsic features are shown in Fig. 3. The main disadvantage with this technique is that the maximum possible ac term and dc term gain values are only $G\text{ac} = 0.866$ and $G\text{dc} = 0.75$, respectively, where

i) ac term gain is the ratio of maximum value (peak) of the fundamental component of the ac term to the amplitude of the unfiltered pulses comprising the same term; and
ii) dc term gain is the ratio of the maximum value of the dc component of the term to the maximum amplitude of the unfiltered pulses comprising the same term.

For many applications this low $G\text{ac}$ value means the use of a voltage-matching transformer. The main advantage of this technique is that it generates line-to-neutral ac spectra with no low-order third harmonics. This allows the use of neutral-to-neutral connections (if required) and decoupled (individual) control of each one of the three inverter phases.

C. The Modified Sine PWM Technique

This is the first of the improved PWM techniques [3] treated in this paper. Its main intrinsic features are shown in Fig. 4. For this technique spectra are shown for VSI and CSI/CR operation, respectively, in order to maintain the same switching frequency. The particulars follow.

a) This technique defines the ac term (Fig. 4(c)) on a line-to-line basis for VSIs and on a line basis for CSIs and CRs.
b) As shown in Figs. 4(a) and 4(b), only the first and last 60° intervals (per half-cycle) of the ac term waveform are directly defined through intersections of respective sine reference) and triangular (carrier) waveforms. The 60° to 120° intervals are obtained by "folding" the first and last 60° intervals around the 60° and 120° points, respectively.
c) As shown in Fig. 4(d), this technique provides a substantially higher ac term gain as compared with the original sine PWM technique (Fig. 3). However, from the aforementioned b) it follows that hardware implementation for this technique is rather complex. Also, this technique generates a substantial (21-percent) ac term third-harmonic component on a line-to-neutral basis.

D. The Third-Harmonic Injection PWM Technique

This improved technique [2], [4] (Fig. 5) has been derived from the original sine PWM technique (Fig. 3) through the addition of the 17-percent third-harmonic component to the original sine reference waveform. The resulting flat-topped waveform (Fig. 5(a)) allows overmodulation (with respect to the original sine PWM technique) while maintaining excellent ac term and dc term spectra. The particulars follow.

a) The analytical expression for the reference waveform is $y = 1.15 \sin(wt) + 0.19 \sin(3\,wt)$.
b) The ac term gain (Fig. 5(d)) is equal to the respective gain obtained with the modified sine PWM (Fig. 4(d)) and substantially higher than the one obtained with the original PWM technique (Fig. 3(d)).

Furthermore, as shown in Fig. 5(a), the hardware implementation of this technique is quite simple. However, this technique also generates a substantial ac term third-harmonic component (17 percent) on line-to-neutral basis.

E. The Harmonic Injection PWM Technique

This technique (Fig. 6) is a variation of the previously discussed third-harmonic injection technique. The variation is obtained by injecting additional harmonics in the respective reference waveform. The resulting flat-topped waveform (Fig. 6(a)) again allows overmodulation while improving even further the resulting frequency spectra of the ac term and dc term waveforms. The particulars follow.

a) The analytical expression for the reference waveform is now $y = 1.15 \sin(wt) + 0.27 \sin(3\,wt) - 0.029 \sin(9\,wt)$.
b) The ac term again (Fig. 6(d)) is equal to the one obtained with the previous two improved PWM techniques while the harmonic spectra of ac and dc terms are clearly better.

Again, as shown in Fig. 6(a), the hardware implementation of this technique is as simple as with the original sine and the third-harmonic injection techniques.

F. Waveform Quality Under Variable Modulation Index Conditions

Although the waveforms shown in Figs. 3, 4, 5, and 6 provide an accurate characterization of the evaluated PWM techniques, they also have the disadvantage of showing respective harmonic spectra at only one modulation index value (i.e., $M = 1$). However, in most applications, output converter power is controlled by varying the respective modulation index value. Therefore it is also necessary to investigate the quality of the various converter (voltage and current) waveforms obtained with each technique for all modulation index (M index) values. In particular, these waveforms are the ac and dc terminal waveforms (Figs. 3(c), 3(e); 4(c), 4(e); 5(c), 5(e); and 6(c), 6(e)) obtained with the generalized converter shown in Fig. 2. They include the line-to-line voltages of VSIs output line currents of CSIs, and input line currents of CRs (all three represented by the ac terminal waveform); and the input (dc link) current of VSIs, the input voltage of CSIs and the output voltage of CRs (all three represented by the dc terminal waveform).

Furthermore, the three quality indexes used to evaluate these waveforms are defined as follows:

$$DF_1 = \frac{100}{H(1)} \sqrt{\sum_{n=3}^{\infty} \left(\frac{H(n)^2}{n^2} \right)}$$

$$DF_2 = \frac{100}{H(1)} \sqrt{\sum_{n=3}^{\infty} \left(\frac{H(n)^2}{n} \right)}$$

$$DF_3 = \frac{100}{H(0)} \sqrt{\sum_{n=6}^{\infty} \left(\frac{H(n)^2}{n} \right)}$$

where

- DF_1 ac terminal distortion factor for second-order ac-side filtering;
- DF_2 ac terminal distortion factor for first-order ac-side filtering;
- DF_3 dc terminal distortion factor for first-order dc-side filtering;
- $H(n)$ amplitude of the nth harmonic;
- $H(1)$ maximum ac gain Gac;
- $H(0)$ maximum dc gain Gdc.

The variations of these three quality indices as a function of the M index are shown in Figs. 7, 8, and 9, respectively.

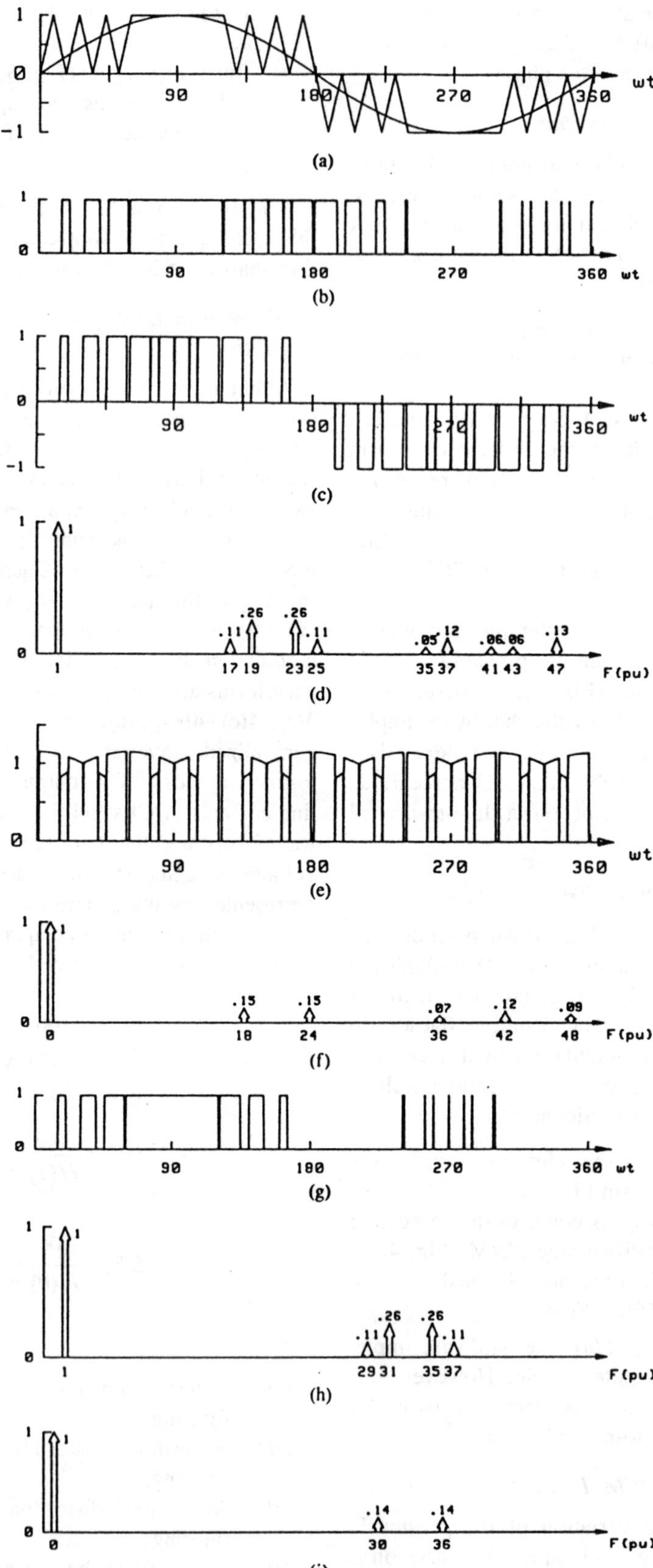

Fig. 4. Modified sinusoidal PWM (MSPWM). (a) MSPWM scheme. (b) VSI switch #1 gating signal (SW1). (c) VSI output voltage. (d) VSI output voltage spectrum. (e) VSI input current. (f) VSI input current spectrum. (g) CSI/CR switch #1 gating signal. (h) CSI/CR line current spectrum. (i) CSI/CR voltage spectrum.

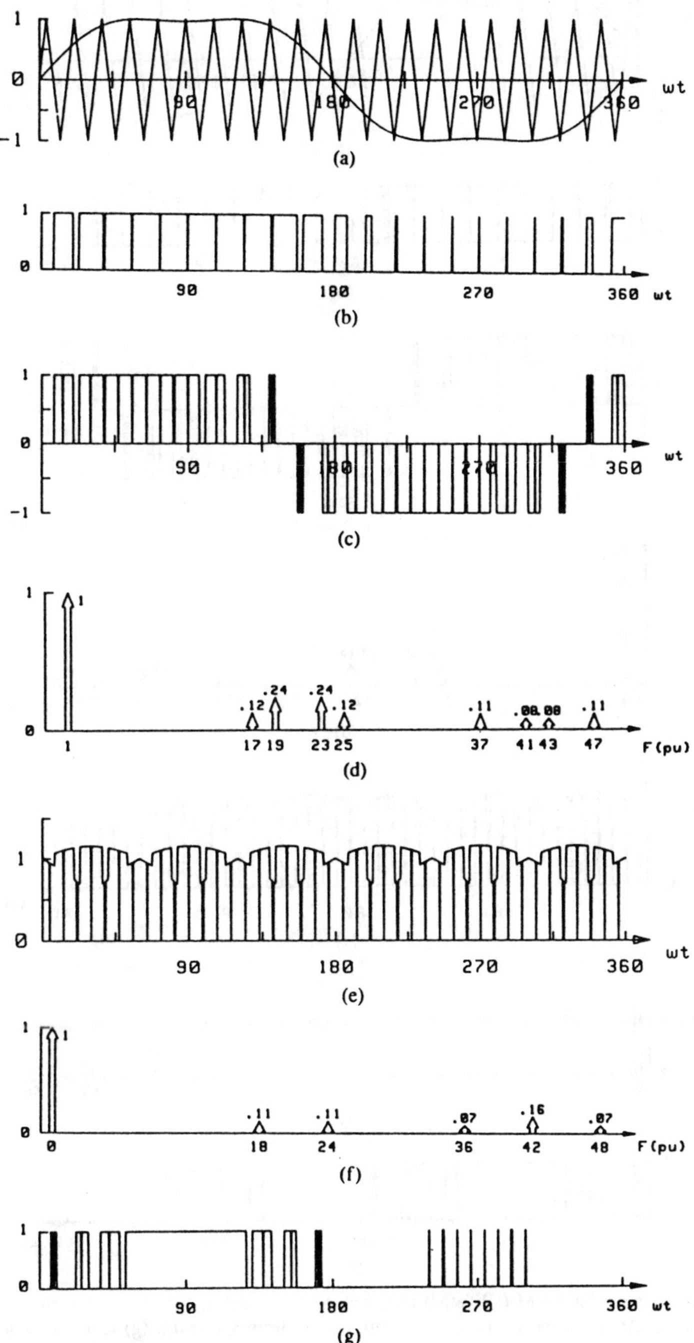

Fig. 5. Harmonic injection sinusoidal PWM (HIPWM) (1st and 3rd). (a) HIPWM scheme. (b) VSI switch #1 gating signal (SW1). (c) AC term. (d) AC term spectrum. (e) DC term. (f) DC term spectrum. (g) CSI/CR switch #1 gating signal.

It is noted that DF_1, DF_2, and DF_3 have been defined in ways that reflect actual levels of harmonic distortion experienced in practical applications. For example, practical static uninterruptible power supplies (UPS) employ a second-order LC filter between respective inverters and loads. Such filters provide harmonic attenuation, which is approximately inversely proportional to the square of the order (n) of the harmonic. Therefore the DF_1 data shown in Fig. 7 are relevant to UPS (i.e., load voltage) and any other static power supply that employs a second-order filter. Similarly, ac and dc motors supplied from PWM static converters utilize their respective leakage and armature inductances to produce quasi-sinusoidal and quasi-dc input current waveforms. These inductances provide first-order attenuation to voltage harmonics, which is equivalent to dividing the amplitude of each harmonic by its respective order. Therefore the DF_2 and DF_3 data shown in Figs. 8 and 9 are applicable to ac and dc motor drives and any other application that uses an actual or equivalent first-order filter. Moreover, to stress emphasis on the input spectral content of each technique, a quality index is defined for the rms ripple value that the input filter must tolerate or support. The rms current rating I_{ci} of the dc link capacitor for VSI operation and the rms voltage rating V_{li} of the dc link inductor for CSI operation is shown in Fig. 10 as a function of

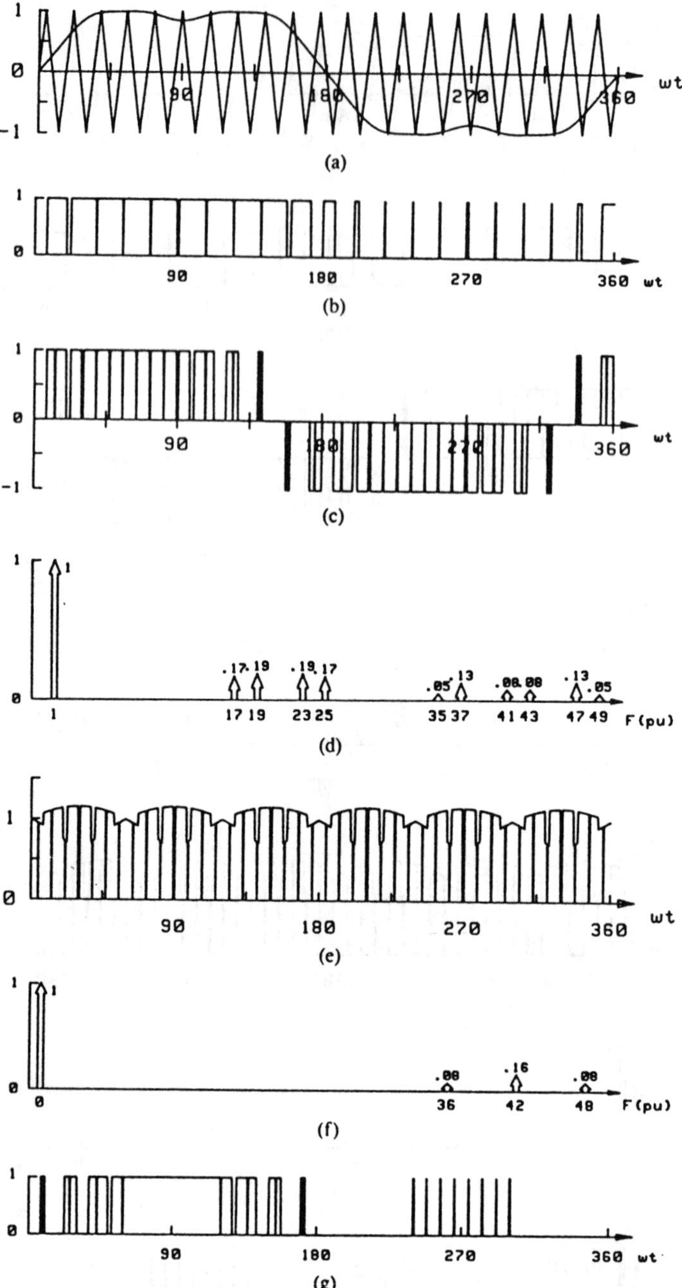

Fig. 6. Harmonic injection sinusoidal PWM (HIPWM) (1st, 3rd, and 9th). (a) HIPWM scheme. (b) VSI switch #1 gating signal (SW1). (c) AC term. (d) AC term spectrum. (e) DC term. (f) DC term spectrum. (g) CSI/CR switch #1 gating signal.

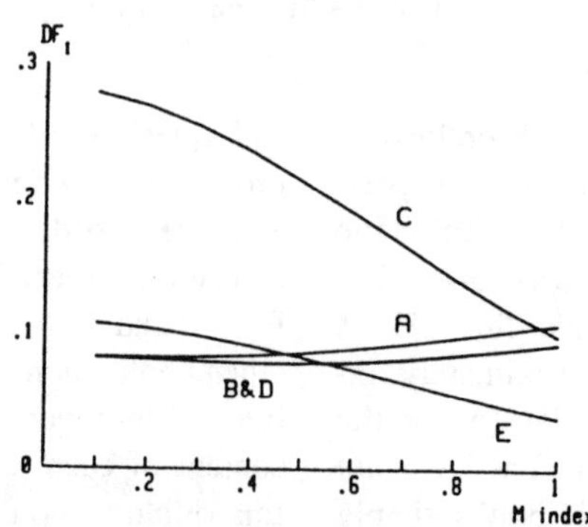

Fig. 7. Second-order filter distortion factor (ac term). (a) SPWM. (b) HIPWM (1st and 3rd). (c) MSPWM VSI operation. (d) HIPWM (1st, 3rd, and 9th). (e) MSPWM CSI/CR operation.

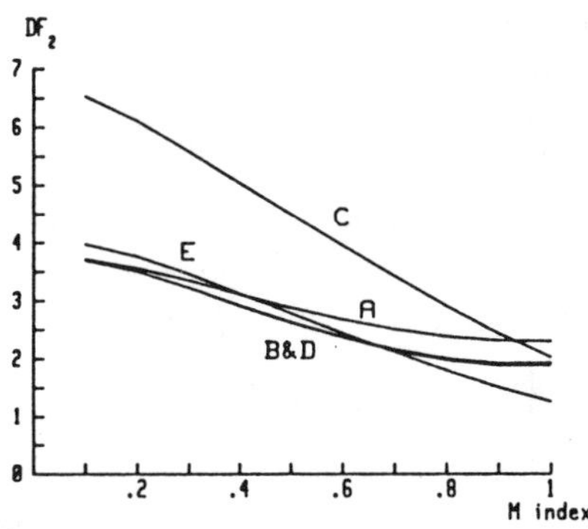

Fig. 8. First-order filter distortion factor (ac term). (a) SPWM. (b) HIPWM (1st and 3rd). (c) MSPWM VSI operation. (d) HIPWM (1st, 3rd, and 9th). (e) MSPWM CSI/CR operation.

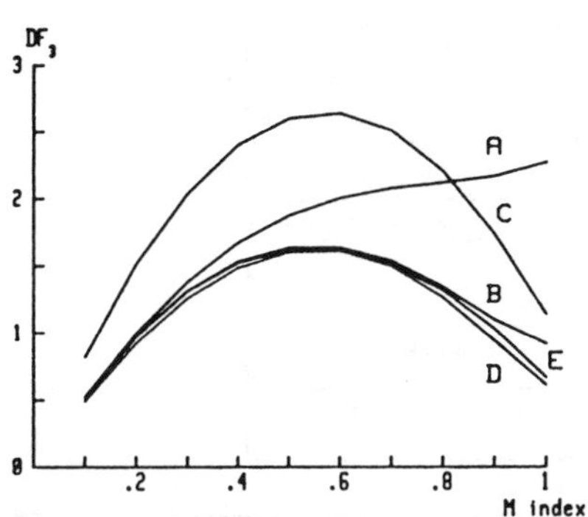

Fig. 9. First-order filter distortion factor (dc term). (a) SPWM. (b) HIPWM (1st and 3rd). (c) MSPWM VSI operation. (d) HIPWM (1st, 3rd, and 9th). (e) MSPWM CSI/CR operation.

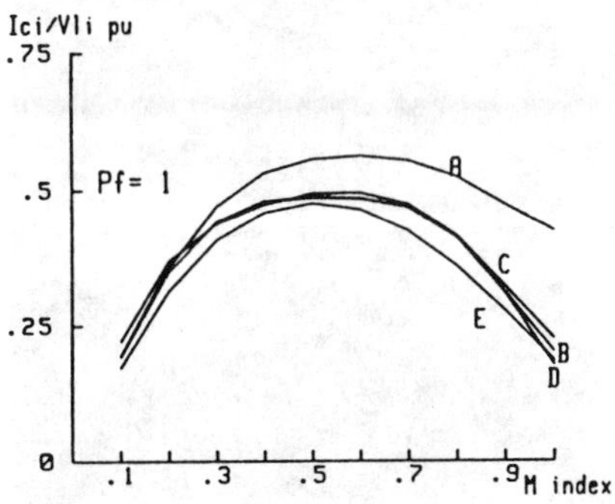

Fig. 10. Inverter dc terminal rms ripple. VSI operation—capacitor ripple current (I_{ci}); CSI operation—inductor ripple voltage (V_{li}). (a) SPWM. (b) HIPWM (1st and 3rd). (c) MSPWM VSI operation. (d) HIPWM (1st, 3rd, and 9th). (e) MSPWM CSI operation.

modulation index. The rms current of the input capacitor I_{cr} for controlled expressions for I_{ci}, V_{li}, and I_{cr} are

$$I_{ci} = \sqrt{\sum_{n=6}^{\infty} Iin(n)^2}$$

$$V_{li} = \sqrt{\sum_{n=6}^{\infty} Vin(n)^2}$$

$$I_{cr} = \sqrt{\sum_{n=3}^{\infty} Iin(n)^2}$$

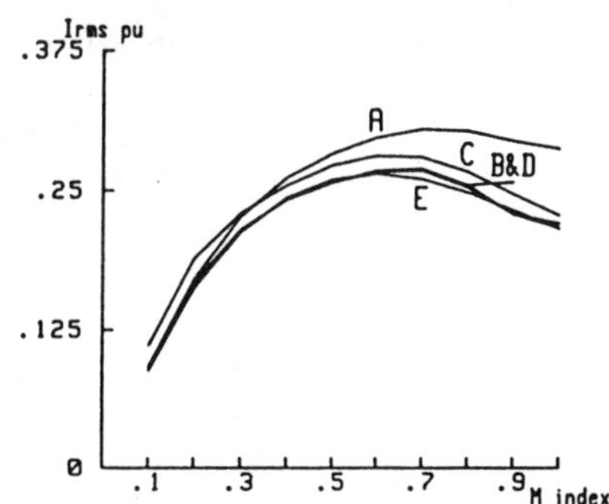

Fig. 11. Rectifier input capacitor rms ripple current. (a) SPWM. (b) HIPWM (1st and 3rd). (c) MSPWM VSI operation. (d) HIPWM (1st, 3rd, and 9th). (e) MSPWM.

where

I_{ci}	VSI rms input ripple current,
V_{li}	CSI rms input ripple voltage,
I_{cr}	CR rms input ripple current,
$Vin(n)/Iin(n)$	rms magnitude of nth harmonic.

The variation of these performance indices as a function of modulation (M index) and rated load current conditions is shown in Figs. 10 and 11 (for all four PWM techniques treated in this paper).

It is finally noted that although the exact DF_1, DF_2, DF_3, and I_{ci}, V_{li}, I_{cr} values shown in Figs. 7–11 are valid for only one particular common-carrier frequency (shown in Figs. 3(a), 4(a), 5(a), and 6(a)), their shapes and their relative position are independent of carrier frequency. Consequently, these data can be used for the general evaluation of the subject PWM techniques.

III. Evaluation of Improved PWM Techniques

In this section the previously discussed and analyzed techniques are evaluated by using relevant data obtained in previous sections. For the meaningful interpretation of evaluation data, the switching frequency variable has been eliminated by using the same switching frequency for all PWM techniques. However, careful investigation of the modified sine PWM technique shows [3] that for the same ac term and dc term waveforms, CSIs, and CRs require lower switching frequencies than VSIs. Because of this asymmetry, this technique has been represented twice in Figs. 7–10.

A. AC and DC Term Gains

Respective ac term and dc term gains for all four PWM techniques are shown in Figs. 3(d), 3(f), 4(d), 4(f), 4(h), 4(i), 5(d), 5(f), 6(d), and 6(f) and are summarized in Table I. It is noted that these gain values are independent of switching frequency and are directly proportional to the respective modulation index values (M index).

From this table it is obvious that regarding ac/dc gains, all improved PWM techniques are

a) better than the original sine technique;
b) equivalent among themselves.

B. Quality Factors DF_1, DF_2, DF_3 and I_{ci}, I_{li}, I_{cr}

The variations of DF_1, DF_2, and DF_3 as a function of M index are presented in Figs. 7–9. These figures show that

TABLE I
MAXIMUM AC AND DC GAIN VALUES Gac AND Gdc ($m = 1$)

TECHNIQUE	Gac	Gdc
ORIGINAL SINE PWM (fig.3)	0.866	0.750
MODIFIED SINE PWM (fig.4)	1	0.866
THIRD HARMONIC INJECTION (fig.5)	1	0.866
HARMONIC INJECTION (fig.6)	1	0.866

TABLE II
OPTIMUM PWM TECHNIQUES ACCORDING TO APPLICATION

APPLICATION	OPTIMUM PWM TECHNIQUE	REFERENCES
VSI BASED AC MOTOR DRIVES	LOW SPEEDS: HARMONIC INJECTION TECHNIQUE	FIGS. 6 8,9,10
	HIGH SPEEDS: PROGRAMMED HARMONIC ELIMINATION TECHNIQUES (PHETs)	SEE REFS. [7] [8] [9]
CSI BASED AC MOTOR DRIVES	HIGH PERFORMANCE: MODIIFIED SINE PWM TECHNIQUE	FIGS. 4,8,9,10
	TYPICAL: PHETs	SEE REFS. [7] [8] [9]
PWM RECTIFIERS FOR CSI INVERTER AND DC MOTOR DRIVES	HARMONIC INJECTION TECHNIQUE	FIGS.6 8,9,11
UPS (WITH UNREGULATED DC BUS)	HARMONIC INJECTION TECHNIQUE	FIGS. 6,7 9,10
UPS (WITH REGULATED DC BUS)	PHETs	SEE REFS. [7] [8] [9]

i) for voltage source inverter (VSI) applications the harmonic injection technique offers the overall best quality ac term waveforms;
ii) for current source inverter (CSI) applications the harmonic injection technique is best for $M < 0.65$ (approximately) while the modified sine technique becomes increasingly better for $M > 0.065$ (approximately).

Next, the variation of I_{ci}, V_{li}, and I_{cr} as a function of the M index is shown in Figs. 10 and 11. It is noted that the maxima of the I_{ci} and V_{li} curves occur around the $M = 0.6$ point instead of the $M = 1$ point. This fact should not be overlooked when considering the ratings of respective filter components. From the figures it can be seen that

i) for VSI operation, the harmonic injection PWM (HIPWM) technique demands the lowest ripple current from the input filter capacitor;
ii) for CSI operation, modified sinusoidal PWM (MSPWM) produces the lowest ripple voltage across the link reactor;
iii) for CR operation, HIPWM and MSPWM offer the best results.

IV. Selection of Optimum PWM Technique According to Application

As stated earlier, quality factors DF_1, DF_2, and DF_3 reflect actual levels of harmonic distortion experienced in practical applications. Therefore it is possible to use respective analytical data from Figs. 7–11 to select the optimum technique(s) for each of these applications. For example, from the DF_1 definition given earlier and the results presented in Fig. 7 it is justifiable to say that for UPS VSI applications (without a dc voltage control stage) the harmonic injection technique is the best choice. By following the same approach, similar conclusions can be drawn for CSI-based UPS, VSI, and CSI-based motor drives, etc. Because of the apparent importance of this subject, detailed information is given in Table II.

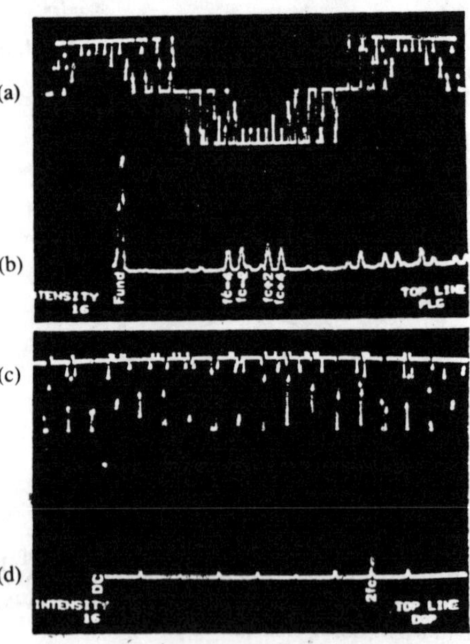

Fig. 12. Experimental waveforms for VSI using HIPWM (1st, 3rd, and 9th). (a) Output line-to-line voltage. (b) Output line-to-line voltage spectrum. (c) Input current. (d) Input current spectrum.

V. Experimental Results

The validity of selected results predicted in previous sections has been verified experimentally on a 1-kVA laboratory prototype system. Samples of these results are shown in

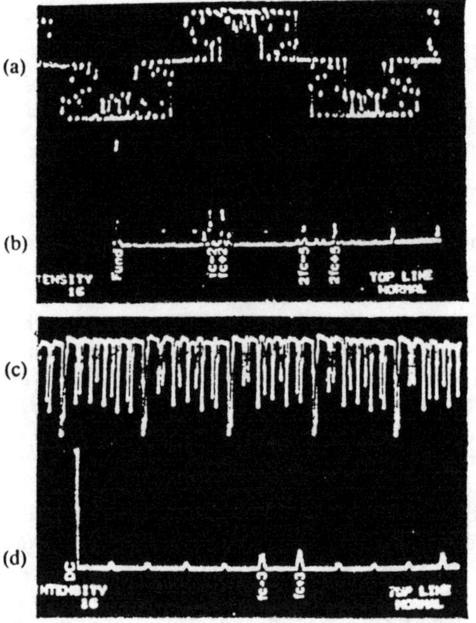

Fig. 13. Experimental waveforms for CSI using MSPWM. (a) Output line current. (b) Output line current spectrum. (c) Input voltage. (d) Input voltage spectrum.

Figs. 12 and 13. In particular, Fig. 12 shows the experimental terminal waveforms and the associated spectra of a VSI operating with HIPWM (1st, 3rd, and 9th) at modulation index = 1 and a carrier frequency of 21 pu. The theoretical results for the same operation are shown in Fig. 6. Fig. 13 shows the experimental terminal waveforms and the associated spectra of a CSI operating with MSPWM at modulation index = 1 and a carrier frequency of 33 pu (results in 22-pu switching frequency). The theoretical results for the same operating conditions are shown in Fig. 4.

The close agreement between the analytical and experimental results prove the validity of the theoretical evaluations made.

VI. Conclusion

In this paper a critical evaluation of state-of-the-art carrier PWM techniques has been presented. Through the use of relevant theoretical and experimental results it has been shown that for each major area of application there is a specific optimum PWM technique. Detailed information has been presented in Tables I and II.

References

[1] V. R. Stefanovic, "Present trends in variable speed ac drives," presented at IPEC 1983, Tokyo, Japan.

[2] R. Bonnert and R. S. Wu, "Improved three phase pulse width modulation for overmodulation," in *Conf. Rec. 1984 IEEE-IAS Annual Meeting,* Chicago, IL.

[3] T. Onishi and H. Okitsu, "A novel PWM technique for three phase inverter/converter," in *Conf. Rec. 1983 IPEC,* Tokyo, Japan.

[4] J. A. Houldsworth and D. A. Grant, "The use of harmonic distortion to increase the output voltage of a three-phase PWM inverter," *IEEE Trans. Ind. Appl.,* vol. IA-20, no. 5, Sept./Oct. 1984.

[5] A. Schonung and H. Stemmler, "Static frequency changers with subharmonic control in conjunction with reversible variable speed ac drives," *Brown Boveri Rev.,* Aug./Sept. 1964.

[6] E. P. Wiechmann, P. D. Ziogas, and V. R. Stephanovic, "Time domain functional model for three phase PWM inverter/rectifier converters," in *IEEE-IAS 1985 Conf. Record,* Toronto, ON, Canada.

[7] H. S. Patel and R. G. Hoft, "Generalized techniques of harmonic elimination and voltage control in thyristor inverters: Part I, harmonic elimination," *IEEE Trans. Ind. Appl.,* vol. IA-9, no. 3, May/June 1973.

[8] H. S. Patel and R. G. Hoft, "Generalized techniques of harmonic elimination and voltage control in thyristor inverters: Part II, voltage control techniques," *IEEE Trans. Ind. Appl.,* vol. IA-10, vol. 5, Sept./Oct. 1974.

[9] W. Lienau, A. Muller-Hellmann, and H. C. Skudelny, "Power converters for feeding asynchronous traction motors of single phase ac vehicles," *IEEE Trans. Ind. Appl.,* vol. IA-16, no. 1, Jan./Feb. 1980.

Selected Bibliography

[1] A. Schonung and D. Stemmler, "Static frequency changer with subharmonic control in conjunction with reversible variable drives," *Brown Boveri Rev.*, Aug./Sept. 1964.

[2] S. R. Bowes, "New sinusoidal pulsewidth-modulated inverter," *IEE Proc.*, vol. 122, pp. 1279–1285, Nov. 1975.

[3] G. Buja and P. P. Nardi, "Application of a signal processor in PWM inverter control," *IEEE Trans. Ind. Electron.*, vol. IE-32, pp. 50–55, Feb. 1985.

[4] M. Hashi, "New approach to a high power GTO PWM inverter for ac motor drives," *IEEE Trans. Ind. Applicat.*, vol. IA-23, pp. 263–269, Mar./Apr. 1987.

[5] J. Holtz, P. Lammert, and W. Lotzkat, "High-speed drive system with ultrasonic MOSFET PWM inverter and single-chip microprocessor control," *IEEE Trans. Ind. Applicat.*, vol. IA-23, pp. 1010–1015, Nov./Dec. 1987.

[6] C. Namduri and P. C. Sen, "Optimal pulsewidth modulation for current source inverters," *IEEE Trans. Ind. Applicat.*, vol. IA-22, pp. 1052–1072, Nov./Dec. 1986.

[7] P. D. Ziogas, Y.-G. Kang, and V. R. Stefanović, "PWM control techniques for rectifier filter minimization," *IEEE Trans. Ind. Applicat.*, vol. IA-21, pp. 1206–1214, Sept./Oct. 1985.

[8] J. B. Casteel and R. G. Hoft, "Optimum PWM waveforms of a microprocessor controlled inverter," *IEEE PESC Rec.*, pp. 243–250, 1978.

[9] K. S. Rajashekara and J. Vithayathil, "Microprocessor based sinusoidal PWM inverter by DMA transfer," *IEEE Trans. Ind. Electron.*, vol. IE-29, pp. 46–51, Feb. 1982.

[10] A. Kawamura and R. G. Hoft, "Instantaneous feedback controlled PWM inverter with adapting hysteresis," *IEEE Trans. Ind. Applicat.*, vol. IA-20, pp. 769–775, July/Aug. 1984.

[11] H. Le-Huy, "A microprocessor-controlled pulsewidth modulated inverter," *IEEE IECI Proc.*, pp. 223–226, 1978.

[12] G. S. Buja and P. Florini, "A microprocessor-based quasi-continuous output controller for PWM inverters," *IEEE IECI Proc.*, pp. 107–111, 1980.

[13] J. M. D. Murphy, L. S. Howard, and R. G. Hoft, "Microprocessor control of a PWM inverter induction motor drive," *IEEE PESC Rec.*, pp. 344–348, 1979.

[14] S. R. Bowes and M. J. Mount, "Microprocessor control of PWM inverters," *IEE Proc.*, vol. 128, Pt. B, pp. 293–305, 1981.

[15] F. G. Turnbull, "Selected harmonic reduction in static dc–ac inverters," *IEEE Trans. Commun. & Electron.*, vol. 83, pp. 374–378, July 1964.

[16] V. V. Deshpande and S. R. Doradla, "Microprocessor (8085A) based multimode pulsewidth modulator," *IEEE/IAS Ann. Meet. Conf. Rec.*, vol. 1, pp. 3–11, 1986.

[17] A. Pollmann, "A digital pulse width modulator employing advanced modulation techniques," *IEEE/IAS Int. Semicond. Power Conv. Conf. Rec.*, pp. 116–121, 1982.

[18] D. A. Grant, M. Stevens, and J. A. Houldsworth, "The effect of word length on the harmonic content of microprocessor-based PWM waveform generators," *IEEE Trans. Ind. Applicat.*, vol. IA-21, pp. 218–225, Jan./Feb. 1985.

[19] J. Zubek, A. Abbondanti, and C. J. Nordby, "Pulsewidth modulated inverter motor drives with improved modulation," *IEEE Trans. Ind. Applicat.*, vol. IA-11, pp. 695–703, Nov./Dec. 1975.

[20] H. S. Patel and R. G. Hoft, "Generalized techniques of harmonic elimination and voltage control in thyristor inverters. Part I—Harmonic elimination," *IEEE Trans. Ind. Applicat.*, vol. IA-9, pp. 310–317, May/June 1973.

[21] H. S. Patel and R. G. Hoft, "Generalized techniques of harmonic elimination and voltage control in thyristor inverters. Part II—Voltage control techniques," *IEEE Trans. Ind. Applicat.*, vol. IA-10, pp. 666–673, Sept./Oct. 1974.

[22] G. B. Kliman, "Harmonic effects in pulsewidth-modulated inverter induction motor drives," *IEEE/IAS Ann. Meet. Conf. Rec.*, pp. 783–790, 1972.

[23] G. S. Buja and G. B. Indri, "Optimal pulsewidth modulation for feeding ac motors," *IEEE Trans. Ind. Applicat.*, vol. IA-13, pp. 38–44, Jan./Feb. 1977.

[24] G. B. Kliman and A. B. Plunkett, "Development of a modulation strategy for a PWM inverter drive," *IEEE Trans. Ind. Applicat.*, vol. IA-15, pp. 72–79, Jan./Feb. 1979.

[25] L. Malesani and P. Tenti, "A novel hysteresis control method for current-controlled VSI PWM inverters with constant modulation frequency," *IEEE/IAS Ann. Meet. Conf. Rec.*, pp. 851–855, 1987.

[26] H. Le-Huy and L. A. Dessaint, "An adaptive current controller for PWM inverters," *IEEE PESC Rec.*, pp. 610–616, 1986.

[27] A. Nabae, S. Ogasawara, and H. Akagi, "A novel control scheme of current controlled PWM inverters," *IEEE/IAS Ann. Meet. Conf. Rec.*, pp. 473–478, 1985.

[28] J. M. D. Murphy and M. G. Egan, "A comparison of PWM strategies for inverter-fed induction motors," *IEEE Trans. Ind. Applicat.*, vol. IA-19, pp. 363–369, May/June 1983.

[29] H. Jonokuchi and K. Nagatake, "A carrier frequency modulation method for sinusoidal PWM inverters," *Proc. IECON'88*, pp. 678–683, 1988.

[30] F. C. Zach and F. A. Thiel, "Pulsewidth-modulated (PWM) inverters for efficiency optimal control of ac drives: Switching angles and efficiency/loss profiles," *Proc. IFAC Symp. Contr. Power Electron. Elec. Drives*, 1983.

[31] F. C. Zach, R. J. Berthold, and K. H. Kaiser, "General purpose microprocessor modulator for a wide range of PWM techniques for ac motor control," *IEEE/IAS Ann. Meet. Conf. Rec.*, pp. 446–451, 1982.

[32] F. C. Zach and H. Ertl, "Efficiency optimal control for ac drives with PWM inverters," *IEEE/IAS Ann. Meet. Conf. Rec.*, pp. 651–658, 1983.

[33] H. W. van der Broeck, H.-C. Skudelny, and G. V. Stanke, "Analysis and realization of a pulsewidth modulator based on voltage space vectors," *IEEE Trans. Ind. Applicat.*, vol. 24, pp. 142–150, Jan/Feb. 1988.

[34] G. Pfaff, A. Weschta, and A. Wick, "Design and experimental results of a brushless ac servo-drive," *IEEE/IAS Ann. Meet. Conf. Rec.*, pp. 692–697, 1982.

[35] P. D. Ziogas, "The delta modulation technique in static PWM inverters," *IEEE Trans. Ind. Applicat.*, vol. IA-17, pp. 199–204, Mar./Apr. 1981.

[36] J. Holtz and S. Stadtfeld, "A predictive controller for the stator current vector of ac machines fed from a switched voltage source," *Int. Power Electron. Conf. Rec.*, Tokyo, pp. 1665–1675, 1983.

[37] Y. Iwaji and S. Fukuda, "PWM pulse pattern optimization for sinusoidal inverters," *Int. Power Electron. Conf. Rec.*, Tokyo, pp. 825–832, 1990.

Part 8
Power Electronics Applications

Paper 8.1

Transistorized PWM Inverter-Induction Motor Drive System

STEVEN C. PEAK, MEMBER, IEEE, AND ALLAN B. PLUNKETT, MEMBER, IEEE

Abstract—**The development of a transistorized pulsewidth modulated (PWM) inverter-induction motor traction drive system is described. A vehicle performance analysis was performed to establish the vehicle tractive effort-speed requirements. These requirements were then converted into a set of inverter and motor specifications. The inverter was a transistorized three-phase bridge using General Electric power Darlington transistors. The description of the design and development of this inverter is the principal object. The high-speed induction motor is a design which is optimized for use with an inverter power source. The primary feedback control is a torque angle control with voltage and torque outer loop controls. A current-controlled PWM technique is used to control the motor voltage. The drive has a constant torque output with PWM operation to base motor speed and a constant horsepower output with square wave operation to maximum speed. The drive system was dynamometer tested, and the results are presented.**

INTRODUCTION

PRESENTLY, the dc motor and dc controller combination is the dominant electric vehicle drive system configuration, with only a few vehicles using an ac system. However, recent studies comparing various electric vehicle propulsion system approaches have concluded that the most promising drive system for near-term electric vehicle use is the ac induction motor with a pulsewidth modulated (PWM) transistor inverter based controller [1]. The impetus behind the ac drive system is the cost, maintenance, size, reliability, and efficiency advantages of the ac induction motor. The size, cost, and complexity of the controller for this motor represent the technical challenge to the potential and desirable advantages of the ac induction motor. Much of the complexity of the controller exists in the signal level controls, where advances in microelectronics technology will play a significant role in reducing cost and parts count. The evolution and downward price trend in high-power transistors will allow the inverter to be economically feasible and reliable.

The purpose of this development project was to design, fabricate, test, evaluate, and cost analyze an engineering model ac motor controller for a variable speed traction ac polyphase induction motor. The feasibility and the performance of a transistorized ac inverter based drive system were demonstrated.

Paper IPCSD 82-83, approved by the Static Power Converter Committee of the IEEE Industry Applications Society for presentation at the 1982 Industry Applications Society Annual Meeting, San Francisco, CA, October 4–8. Manuscript released for publication September 28, 1982. This work was supported in part by the US Department of Energy under Contract DEN3-59 with the NASA Lewis Research Center.

The authors are with General Electric Company, Corporate Research and Development, Schenectady, NY 12345.

As a general requirement, the drive system is designed for use in urban electric vehicles according to the SAE J227a-Schedule D driving cycle. This determines the drive system thermal rating. In addition, a practical electric vehicle must satisfy performance requirements in excess of the J227a-D duty cycle in order to merge with traffic, start on a steep grade, pull out of a pothole, climb hills, and pass. The additional specifications define the maximum (peak) desired vehicle performance. All of these specifications are primarily vehicle performance requirements and must be analyzed to establish the vehicle tractive effort-speed requirements. These requirements were then converted into a set of motor and inverter specifications.

The overall system configuration, consisting of the inverter, induction motor, and control electronics, is shown in Fig. 1. The control electronics include an improved method of PWM control [2]. This method adaptively modulates the inverter switching times to produce the maximum possible torque in the load motor for the minimum ac peak current. There is an instantaneous feedback current control with independent current control on each inverter output phase. The improvements in this current-controlled PWM method are to minimize both peak transistor current and motor loss with better sinusoidal waveforms.

The system control method involves a transition of operation of the inverter from a current source to a voltage source, as the control transits from the PWM mode to the square wave mode of operation. The system control must therefore be suitable for use in either mode of operation. A motor torque angle control is used to supply the primary system stabilization [2]. The system control generates the appropriate frequency and current amplitude signals by using the feedback signals of motor current and flux and the driver commands [3]. The resulting system has operating characteristics similar to both voltage inverters and current inverters. As a hybrid of these two types, the system has the good low-speed performance of a current inverter and the good high-speed performance of a voltage inverter.

In dc machines, the sensing of armature and field currents will yield a fairly accurate measure of the flux level in the machine and hence the developed torque. However, the flux and torque of an induction motor are not as easily measured, particularly when the voltage supplied to the terminals of the machine is not sinusoidal. The method used involves the sensing of the motor air gap flux and stator current. The air gap flux can be inferred from the motor terminal voltage but will suffer some inaccuracy for very low-speed operation due to the stator resistance voltage drop, or can be measured directly

Reprinted from *IEEE Trans. Ind. Applicat.*, vol. IA-19, no. 3, pp. 379–387, May/June 1983.

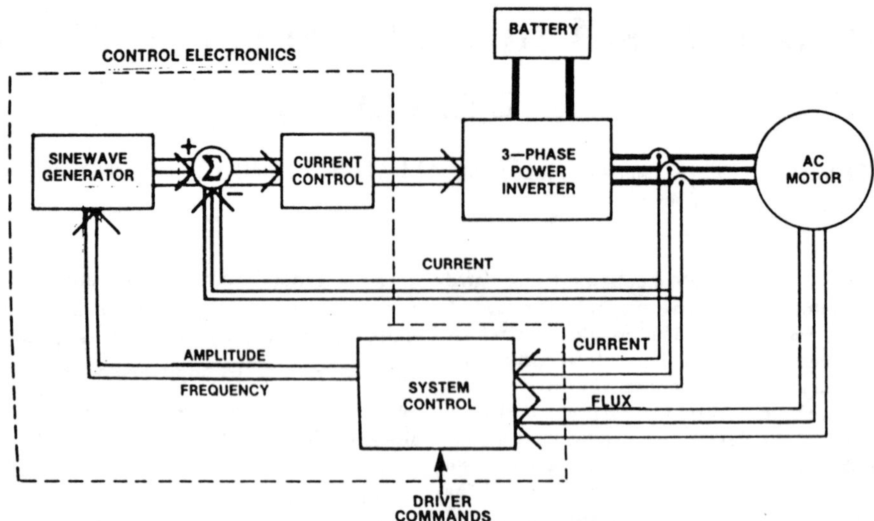

Fig. 1. Simplified system block diagram.

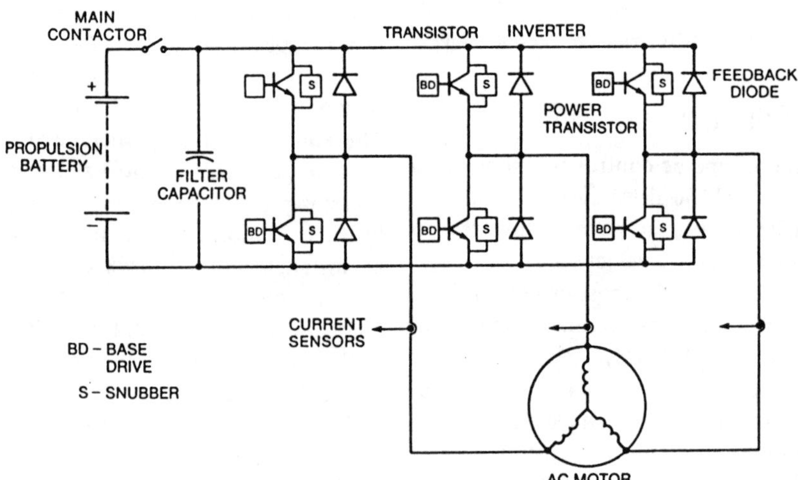

Fig. 2. Inverter power circuit.

by air gap flux sensing coils wound around a motor stator tooth [4].

Fig. 2 shows the three-phase inverter power circuit, which is a three-phase bridge connection with feedback diodes and uses six power modules. Each power module contains a combination of power Darlington transistors and antiparallel fast recovery diodes capable of switching 600 A at up to 300 V peak. There are four power Darlington transistors in parallel, each rated at 200 A and 450 V. There are two diodes in parallel, each rated at 250 A and 600 V. Fig. 3 shows a photograph of the completed inverter, which is an engineering model for development tests.

A dc filter capacitor bank is connected across the dc input to the inverter and serves to filter the dc input voltage and to provide a low-impedance path for the high-frequency currents generated by the inverter during PWM switching. Each power module is driven by a separate base drive circuit with its own isolated power supply. A snubber is placed across each power module to maintain the instantaneous current and voltage switching locus within the ratings of the power Darlington transistors. The inverter is modularized into six identical half-phase modules built up on heatsink material, which is forced air cooled (Fig. 4).

The PWM approach for motor voltage control is chosen because of the fixed dc battery bus, small dc filter, inherent regeneration capability, and dual use of the power switches for inversion and voltage control. The choice of transistors over thyristors was made because transistors obviate the need for commutation circuits and have the switching speed required by the current-controlled PWM method. The design of the inverter and motor must take into account the presence of the extra time harmonics in the inverter output voltage which tend to cause increased motor heating and peak transistor current [5], [6].

HARMONIC CURRENT ANALYSIS

The control system used in this drive system combines the ability to control both ac frequency and ac voltage by PWM control of the inverter transistors. The PWM is accomplished by switching the transistors at a high frequency and then varying the switching duty cycle at the desired motor frequency.

The system used (Fig. 1) is to feed back the motor current,

Fig. 3. Engineering model inverter.

Fig. 4. Half-phase module.

compared with a sine wave (or other) reference wave, and switch the inverter to contain the error within a fixed band set by the current comparator hysteresis (current control). This method causes the inverter switching to be adaptive to load variations such as motor back electromotive force (EMF) and inductance. In addition, the inverter switching losses are proportional to frequency and must be controlled; thus the chopping frequency should, on the average, be limited. The rate of change of current and thus the chopping frequency are automatically controlled by the comparator hysteresis, the motor stator plus rotor leakage inductance, and the dc link voltage by the equation

$$\frac{di}{dt} \approx \frac{E_{dc} - E_m \sin \omega t}{L_{eq}}$$

where

E_{dc} dc link voltage,

L_{eq} equivalent motor leakage inductance,

$E_m \sin \omega t$ motor back EMF voltage.

This, however, applies only approximately since the motor leakage inductance is a function of frequency, and the voltage is actually the dc link voltage minus the motor back EMF.

With the three-phase inverter shown in Fig. 2 and the three-wire wye motor, there is no neutral connection. Thus the operation of the inverter is constrained because the sum of the three line currents must be zero at all instants

$$i_a + i_b + i_c \equiv 0.$$

The current in any one phase is completely determined by controlling the currents in the other two phases, rendering one phase of a current controller redundant. The switches of one phase should not, however, be removed and the circuit simplified because the conventional three-phase configuration is more efficient under square wave operation at high speed.

The effect of the high-frequency inverter chopping is to cause extra ripple in the motor ac current. This ripple current causes extra motor losses and increases the required inverter transistor current rating. A method of calculating these extra losses and peak currents has been developed for the more commonly used sine wave-triangle intersection voltage-controlled PWM and is described in [5], [6]. For a large number of chops per motor frequency cycle, the extra motor losses due to current-controlled PWM operation should be similar to that of sine-triangle voltage PWM, so that the method described in the two papers has been used to predict the increased motor losses and inverter peak current.

The motor used with this drive is a specially designed high-efficiency induction motor. The motor parameters are shown in Table I. The required peak load is a torque of 42.7 lbf•ft. Applying this load to the inverter at the maximum speed, for which full PWM with no lost chops is possible, results in the operating conditions of Table II. The inverter design is based on the peak and average currents of Table II. The required chopping frequency is 1740 Hz; however, the motor always sees two phases chopping simultaneously which results in a motor torque ripple at 3480 Hz. Fig. 5 shows the transistor current required for the peak load condition of Table II. Tran-

TABLE I
MOTOR PARAMETERS

Parameter	
$R_1 = 0.00298\ \Omega$	STATOR
$L_1 = 12.69 \times 10^{-6}$ hy	STATOR
$R_2 = 0.00145\ \Omega$	ROTOR
$L_2 = 10.15 \times 10^{-6}$ hy	ROTOR
$L_3 = 240 \times 10^{-6}$ hy	
$F_{BASE} = 180$ Hz	
$V_{BASE} = 45$ volts rms/phase	

TABLE II
PEAK LOAD OPERATING CONDITION (SINE–TRIANGLE PWM USED IN CALCULATION)

DC Voltage	108 volts
AC Voltage	35.96 volts rms L-N
AC Current	321 amps rms
AC Frequency	145 Hz
Slip	1.7 Hz
Torque	42.7 lb-ft
Speed	4299 rpm
Peak Current	593 amps
Average Transistor Current	116 amps
Average Diode Current	30 amps
Average dc Link Current	262 amps
Chopping Frequency	1740 Hz/phase
Chopping Frequency	3480 Hz (Motor Effect)

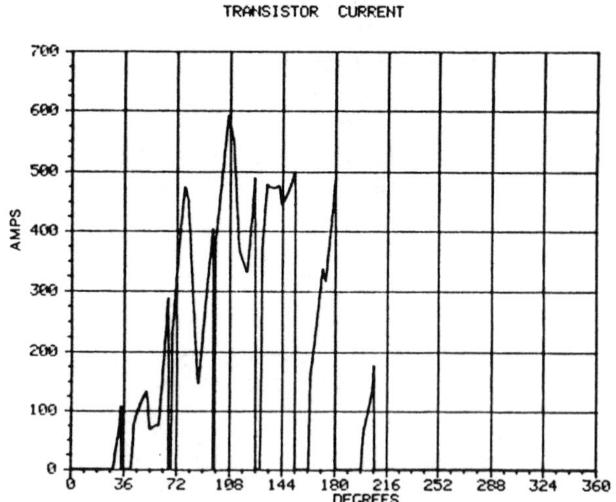

Fig. 5. Calculated transistor current waveform for peak load condition.

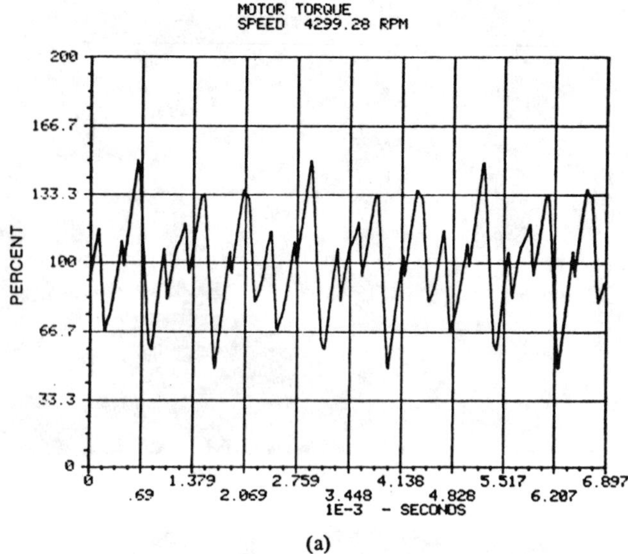

(a)

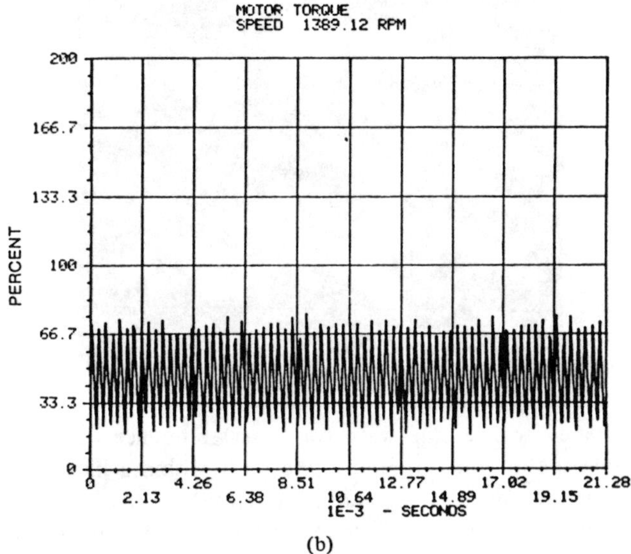

(b)

Fig. 6. Calculated motor torque waveform. (a) Peak load condition. (b) Test condition.

sistor conduction is limited to 180° with the opposite transistor in the same phase conducting during the second 180° period. The notches in the transistor current represent the opposite diode conduction periods.

Fig. 6 shows the motor torque ripple for two cases. Fig. 6(a) shows the motor torque ripple at the peak load condition of Table II. For the sine-triangle voltage PWM method, the torque ripple shows a considerable nonsmooth ripple effect. However, at a lower speed of 47 Hz, the torque ripple as illustrated in Fig. 6(b) shows a more uniform ripple character with the ripple frequency being twice the per phase chopping frequency.

A series of tests was performed on the completed drive system in order to test the predictions of the computer analysis. Fig. 7 shows the calculated motor current for the selected test condition at a speed of 47 Hz. Fig. 8 shows the actual measured motor current for the same operating condition. The current-controlled PWM system causes equal ripple current over the ac motor frequency cycle, while the sine-triangle voltage PWM causes a cyclic variation in motor current ripple. The operating conditions were matched by adjusting the calculated PWM frequency so that the measured and calculated fundamental currents match. Another interesting effect of current-controlled PWM can be observed by comparing the frequency spectra of motor current illustrated in Figs. 9 and 10. Note that the chopping frequency in Fig. 10 shows a broadened principal chopping frequency spectral line due to the expected cyclic variation in chopping frequency resulting from the motor back EMF. Fig. 9 shows spectral lines of 3.4 kHz for the sine-triangle voltage PWM chopping.

A comparison of the measured and calculated drive system performances at the test condition is shown in Table III. Very good correlation is observed except for a difference in predicted and measured chopping frequency, which is probably due to the approximation of using sine-triangle voltage PWM to predict current-controlled PWM performance.

The predicted currents of Table II are used for the inverter design with the expectation that the worst case sine-triangle voltage PWM with a few chops per cycle (145 Hz) will require

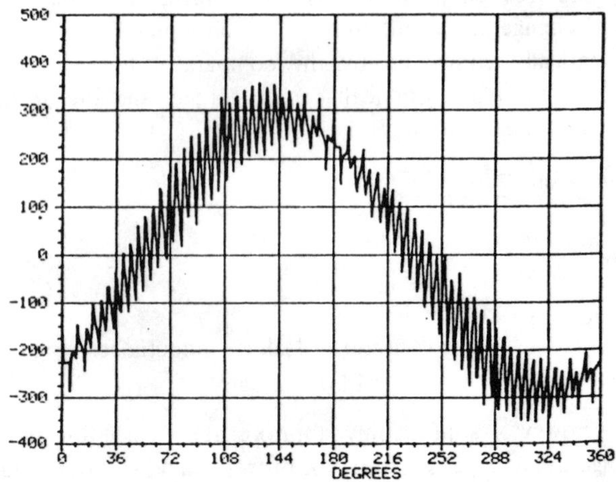

Fig. 7. Calculated motor ac current waveform for test condition.

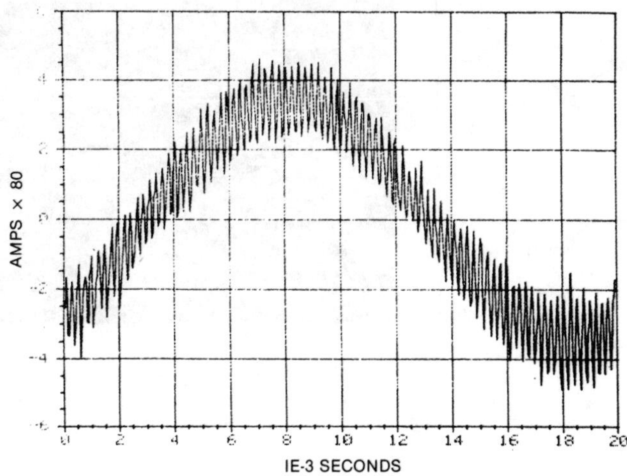

Fig. 8. Measured motor ac current waveform for test condition.

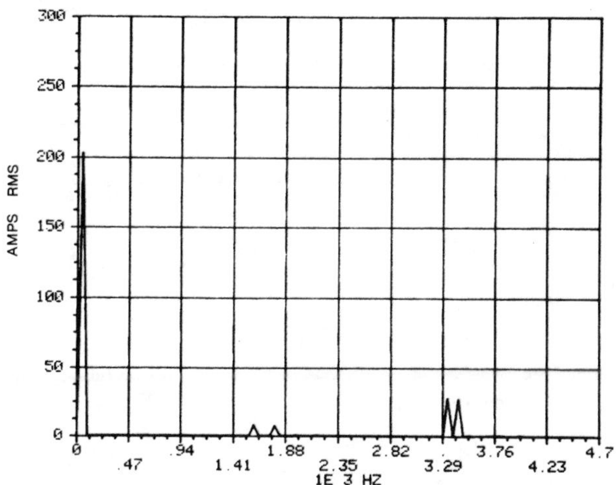

Fig. 9. Frequency spectrum of calculated motor ac current waveform for test condition.

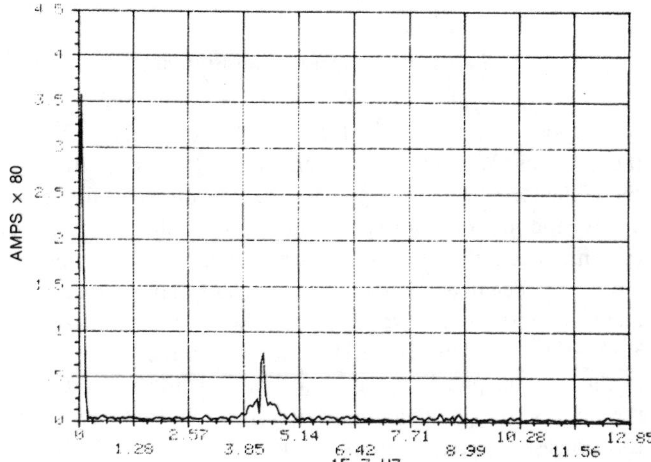

Fig. 10. Frequency spectrum of measured motor ac current waveform for test condition.

TABLE III
COMPARISON OF MEASURED AND CALCULATED RESULTS FOR TEST CONDITION

	Calculated	Measured
DC Voltage	108 volts	107.5 volts
AC Voltage	12.31 volts rms L-N	–
AC Current	203 amps rms	202 amps rms
AC Frequency	47.24 Hz	47.24 Hz
Slip	0.7 Hz	–
Torque	20.25 lb-ft	20.32 lb-ft
Speed	1389 rpm	1438 rpm
Peak Current	356 amps	366 amps
Chopping Ripple Frequency	3.4 kHz	4.3 kHz (avg)
Chopping Ratio	36	–
Current Band	150 amps	160 amps
Motor Harmonic Loss	68 watts	–
Motor Total I^2R Loss	495 watts	–
PWM Method	sine-triangle	current control

somewhat more peak current than the actual current-controlled PWM.

INVERTER DESIGN

Base Drive Design

Both bases, B1 and B2, of the power Darlington transistor are driven. B1 is the base of the n-p-n driver transistor, and B2 is the base of the n-p-n output transistor. Fig. 11 shows the collector to emitter voltage and the base 1 current of a single Darlington transistor switching off about 100 A with a 10-A reverse base 1 drive and without any reverse base 2 drive. Note the initial slow rise of collector voltage as the device turns off and the relatively long storage time (from the base 1 current reversal to the steep rise of collector voltage). Fig. 12 shows the result of applying a reverse base 2 current of about 1.5 A to the same device, base 1 drive and switching conditions. The reverse base 2 drive is achieved by adding an external diode and resistor between base 2 and base 1. The base drive current in Fig. 12 shows the sum of the two base currents. Note the initial slow rise of collector voltage is shortened and the storage time is reduced, thus reducing the transistor switching loss.

The power module base drive circuit (Fig. 13) supplies a total forward (positive) base current into the power module of 4-A peak and a total reverse (negative) current of 5-A peak. This is based on the gain characteristic of the Darlington transistor, the base drive power supply requirements and the desired turn-off switching time. The diode and resistor between B1 and B2 are shown in Fig. 13. There are four Darlington transistors in parallel in each power module. A 0.5-Ω resistor is in series with base 1 for each Darlington transistor in the power module to assist in the sharing of the base current. A blocking diode is in series with each base 2, which allows a reverse base 2 drive but isolates base 2 during a Darlington transistor fault and prevents the consequential failure of the other transistors. Each power module base drive circuit has its own isolated base drive power supply.

Snubber Design

The snubbering for the power Darlington transistors (Fig. 14) is composed of two circuits: a resistor-capacitor snubber circuit in parallel with the power module and a parasitic, but intentionally placed, snubber inductance in series with the

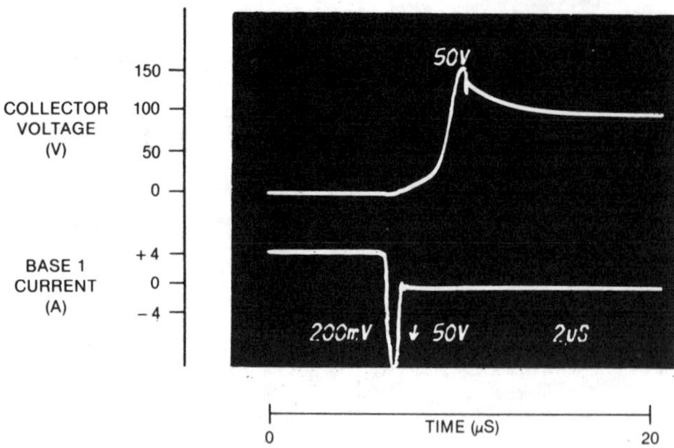

Fig. 11. Power Darlington turn-off without reverse base 2 drive.

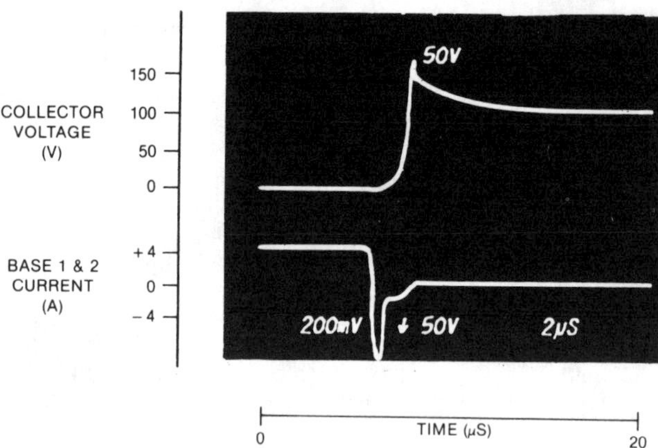

Fig. 12. Power Darlington turn-off with reverse base 2 drive.

power module. The snubber circuit is effective during the turn-off of the Darlington transistors, and the snubber inductance is effective during the turn-on of the Darlington transistors, as described in the following. The two snubbers actually operate on the parallel combination of the four power Darlington transistors, i.e., the power module. The four Darlington transistors are matched so that each one is operated safely when the set is protected by the snubbers. The dc filter capacitor bank provides a low impedance path (much lower than the power cables and battery) for the high-frequency currents generated during switching.

The small parasitic inductances (approximately 0.25 μH) in series with the power modules (Fig. 14) are obtained by the routing of the bus bars between the input capacitor bank and the half-phase modules and between the upper and lower half-phase modules in each phase (Fig. 3). These inductances are required during turn-on to limit the power module transistor current to a safe value. Several currents flow through the transistors during turn-on, with an inductive load: the load current, the snubber capacitor discharge current, the opposite snubber capacitor charging current, and the recovery current of the opposite feedback diode. With an inductive load (such as a motor), the turn-on switching of the transistor transfers the load current from the opposite feedback diode in the same phase of the inverter to the oncoming transistor. The inductance limits the rate-of-change of current (di/dt) during this transfer which prevents an excessively large recovery current in the opposite feedback diode. The inductance also interacts with the capacitance of the opposite snubber to limit the peak magnitude of its charging current. Lastly, the inductance reduces the transistor turn-on switching loss, because as soon as the transistor starts to conduct current the dc bus voltage appears across the inductances, allowing the voltage across the transistor to fall from the dc bus voltage to its low on-state voltage. This loss is, however, only moved from the transistor to the snubber, not eliminated completely.

The snubber circuit is required because transistors have safe operating area (SOA) limitations during turn-off to avoid catastrophic second breakdown failure. The SOA (Fig. 15) is a locus of points of maximum permissible simultaneous occurrences of collector current and collector-emitter voltage. With an inductive load (such as a motor), the turn-off switching of the transistor transfers the load current from the transistor to the opposite oncoming feedback diode in the same phase of the inverter. Without a snubber, as the transistor turns off, the collector-emitter voltage rises from its low on-state voltage up to the dc bus voltage, while still conducting the load current. Then the transistor current falls, and the opposite diode can begin to conduct load current. This simultaneous locus of current and voltage must be within the transistor SOA (Fig. 15). Unfortunately, the two snubber inductances in the inverter phase now generate an overshoot voltage above the dc bus voltage, which appears across the transistor during the transistor current fall time ($V_{pk} = 2L di/dt$). This overshoot can be as high as 150 V above the maximum 140-V dc bus (Fig. 15).

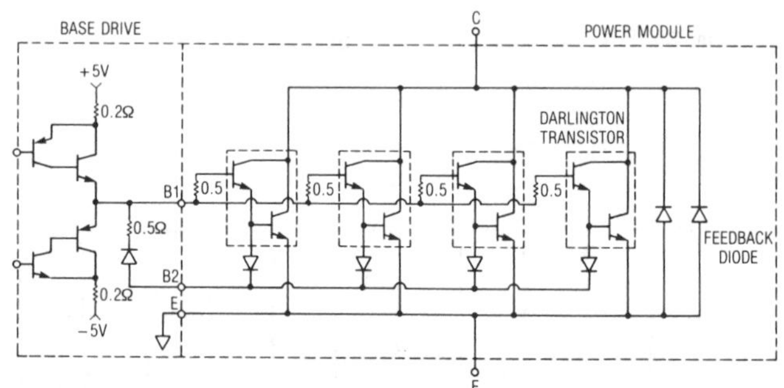

Fig. 13. Power module base drive circuit.

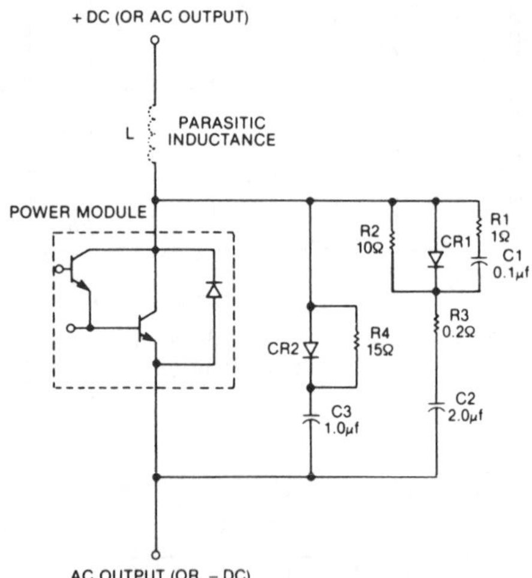

Fig. 14. Power Darlington transistor snubber.

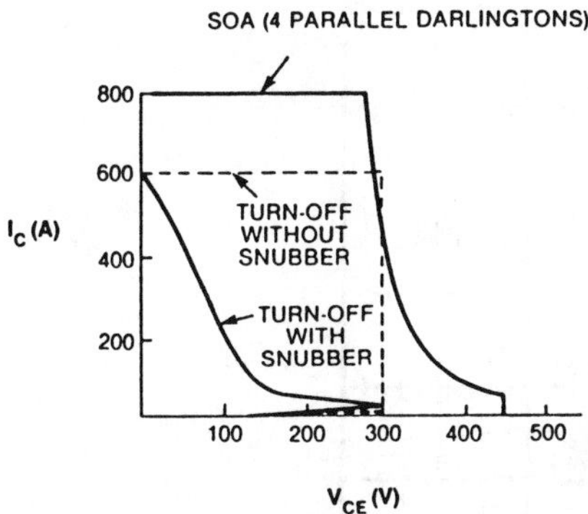

Fig. 15. Power Darlington transistor turn-off safe operating area (SOA) and switching locus.

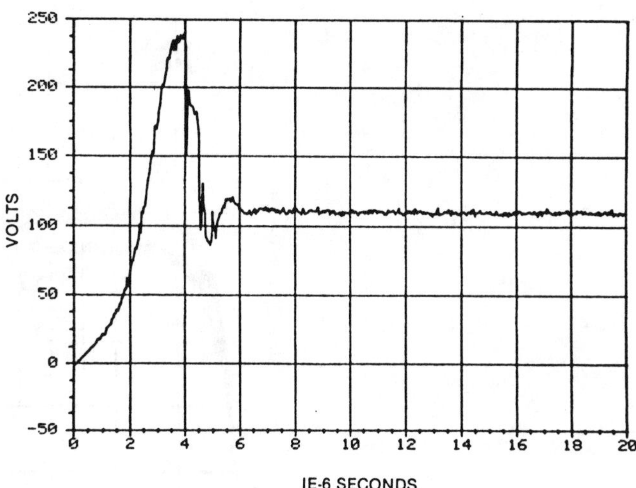

Fig. 16. Power module collector-emitter voltage at turn-off of peak load condition.

The action of the snubber circuit is to alter this locus of current and voltage to a safe condition with the SOA (Fig. 15) and provide margin for paralleling. With a snubber, as the transistor turns off and the collector-emitter voltage begins to rise, the snubber capacitance begins to charge. The charging current is a current diverted from the transistor, and eventually all the load current is in the snubber, charging the snubber capacitance to the dc bus voltage. At this point the oncoming opposite feedback diode can begin conduction, and the current transfers from the snubber to the diode based on the interaction of the snubber inductances and the snubber capacitors. The choice of snubber capacitance limits the peak overshoot voltage [7]. Therefore, the snubber displaces the transistor current and voltage so they are within the SOA (Fig. 15). The snubber circuit also reduces the transistor turn-off switching loss, because as the collector-emitter voltage rises the collector current is falling instead of remaining constant. The loss is, however, only moved from the transistor to the snubber, not eliminated completely.

The snubbers, as can be seen from the foregoing discussion, depend a great deal on the parasitic inductance of the layout of the inverter power circuit and of the snubber circuit itself. The final snubber design and component values were selected after experimentation, using the actual inverter package layout. A two-stage snubber is used (Fig. 14). The first stage is the C3 capacitor, and the second is the R3-C2 resistor-capacitor. The stages are polarized with a diode (CR1, CR2) so that large resistors (R2, R4) are in series with the capacitors to reduce the peak currents when they discharge during turn-on. The second stage diode is also snubbered (R1, C1).

Fig. 16 is the collector-emitter voltage across a power module at the peak load condition (switching 600 A). The first-stage snubber is tightly coupled to the power module and, in the first few microseconds, controls the reapplied voltage. This initial control of the rate of reapplied voltage (dv/dt) prevents the high gain Darlington transistors from turning on again. The second stage, less tightly coupled due to the component physical sizes, then comes into action to continue control of the reapplied dv/dt and peak voltage. The transient at 4 μs (Fig. 16) is the CR2 diode recovery, and the transient at 5 μs is the CR1 diode recovery. The CR1 diode is itself snubbered, so that its snap-off recovery does not turn on the high gain Darlington transistor.

Darlington Transistor Paralleling

The reverse breakdown of the Darlington transistors chosen for power module fabrication was at least 450 V at 0.5 mA. The transistors were matched using the collector-emitter voltage V_{CE} for a base current of 2 A and an emitter current of 140 A, with the transistor mounted on a hot plate held at 125°C. This higher temperature, rather than room temperature, was used for matching because of the gain falloff with temperature and the desire to match at the more critical junction temperature. Values of V_{CE} at 140 A varied from 0.88 V to 1.20 V, but transistors could be chosen to match within 0.04 V. In addition, values of h_{FE} and $V_{BE(SAT)}$ (base 2 to emitter) were matched in order to obtain similar speeds for the four transistors in parallel.

The maximum current through one power module of the three-phase inverter circuit is 600 A. While individually mounted transistors could be operated at well over 200 A and three transistors could, in principle, supply 600 A, it was desirable to parallel four transistors to provide some safety margin for current sharing among the transistors. Furthermore, with four transistors there was better thermal dissipation to limit the junction temperature under the most demanding conditions of power delivery.

Fig. 17 shows the turn-off of four matched transistors each carrying between 150 and 200 A. The steady-state current sharing among them is within 30 A. However, during turn-off, three of the transistors turn off ahead of the fourth, causing the fourth to carry a transiently higher current. This illustrates the need for careful matching of transistors to maintain each transistor within its own SOA.

INVERTER LOSSES

The inverter losses versus speed and current are shown in Fig. 18. The speed is the drive system output speed after the 2.923 to 1 reduction of the motor speed by an integral gear box. Depending on the current and speed, the inverter may be operating in the PWM or square wave mode. Below base speed (1833 r/min, 180 Hz), the inverter operates in PWM regardless

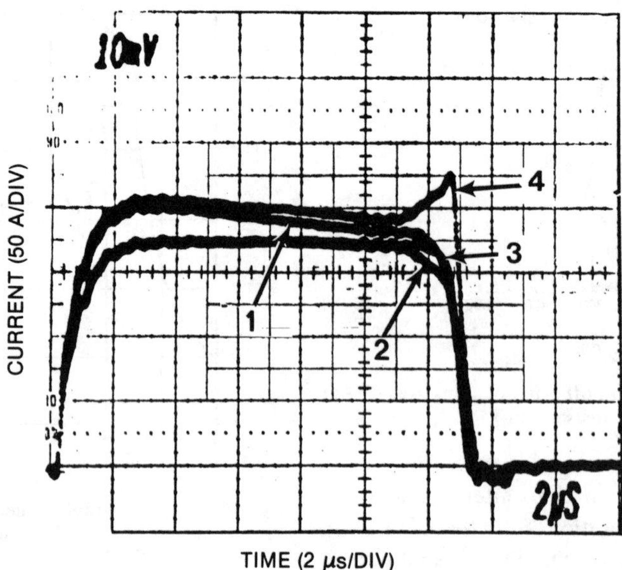

Fig. 17. Turn-off of four matched Darlington transistors.

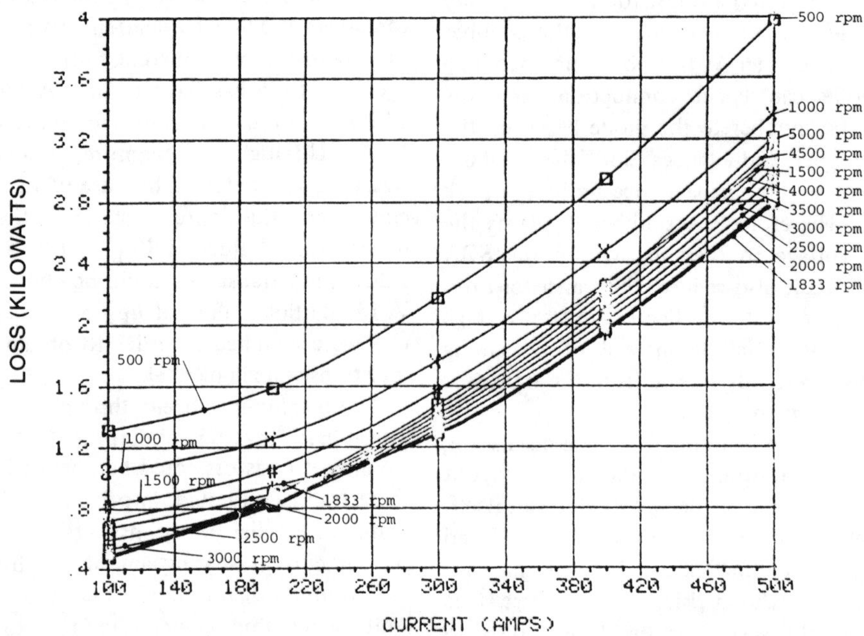

Fig. 18. Inverter losses as function of speed and current. Note: Current is average of three-phase full wave rectified motor current.

of the current, but as the speed increases, the inverter transits to square wave. Because the flux level in the motor is varied as a function of torque, this transition does not occur at the same speed. At low currents, the inverter operates in PWM up to relatively high speeds, but at high currents, it transits to square wave at base speed.

As the inverter drops the number of chops in the current-controlled PWM operation, the inverter loss in PWM decreases with speed (for a constant current) while the loss in square wave increases with speed as the frequency increases. The inverter loss increases with current (for any constant speed). The inverter loss has several components: constant loss (blowers), loss proportional to current (conduction), loss proportional to squared current (conduction, parasitic resistance), loss proportional to current and frequency (switching), and loss proportional to squared current and frequency (snubber).

CONCLUSION

The feasibility of a three-phase ac transistorized inverter for an electric vehicle ac induction motor propulsion system application was demonstrated. This type of system has potential cost and maintenance advantages over a dc chopper-based system. The ac motor has a simple yet rugged construction without commutators and brushes, requires no routine maintenance, is amenable to mass production, is capable of high speeds which reduces its size, and can be totally enclosed allowing advanced packaging and cooling techniques. The engineering model drive system weight was 100 lb for the motor and 130 lb for the inverter. The inverter utilizes the advances in high-power Darlington transistors to obviate the need for costly power level commutation circuits that would be needed for a thyristor approach. The inverter is consequently allowed to operate at higher switching frequencies, to improve the current waveform delivered to the motor, and thereby to increase the motor efficiency. Four power Darlington transistors were successfully paralleled in the power module. Good agreement between the calculated sine-triangle voltage PWM parameters and the measured current-controlled PWM parameters was observed. The measured inverter losses were mapped over the full current and frequency range.

ACKNOWLEDGMENT

The authors with to acknowledge the contributions of Dr. G. B. Kliman for the high-speed high-efficiency motor, A. J. Yerman for the power module, and A. J. Yerman and J. C. Driscoll for the power Darlington paralleling.

REFERENCES

[1] A. B. Plunkett and G. B. Kliman, "Electric vehicle ac drive development," SAE Paper 800061.

[2] A. B. Plunkett, "A current-controlled PWM transistor inverter drive," in *Conf. Rec. 1979 IEEE Ind. Applications Society Annu. Meeting*, Oct. 1979.

[3] ——, "Direct flux and torque regulation in a PWM inverter-induction motor drive," *IEEE Trans. Ind. Appl.*, vol. IA-13, Mar./Apr. 1977.

[4] T. A. Lipo, D. W. Novotny, A. B. Plunkett, and V. R. Stefanovic, "Dynamics and control of ac drives," Course notes, University of Wisconsin Extension, Nov. 3–5, 1976.

[5] G. B. Kliman and A. B. Plunkett, "Development of a modulation strategy for a PWM inverter drive," *IEEE Trans. Ind. Appl.*, vol. IA-15, Jan./Feb. 1979.

[6] G. A. Kaufman and A. B. Plunkett, "Steady-state performance of a voltage source inverter synchronous machine drive system," in *Conf. Rec. 1981 IEEE Industry Applications Society Annu. Meeting.*, Oct. 1981.

[7] W. McMurray, "Optimum snubbers for power semiconductors," in *Conf. Rec. 1971 IEEE Industry Applications Society Annu. Meeting*, Oct. 1971.

Paper 8.2

CONTROL OF A DOUBLE VOLTAGE INVERTER SYSTEM

COUPLING A THREE PHASE MAINS WITH AN AC-DRIVE

H. Kohlmeier, D. Schröder

Technische Universität München, Arcisstr. 21, D-8000 München 2

Lehrstuhl für Elektrische Antriebstechnik

ABSTRACT

An ac-drive is coupled via two voltage source inverters to the three phase mains in order to improve the power factor and the waveforms of the line currents. The mains, dc-voltage link and the ac-drive are controlled via an extensive control system. Two current vector controllers for the line- and machine current control employ a fast on-line algorithm for generation of the inverter states at steady state and transient operations. All actual currents on both sides are enforced inside a given margin around the current references. These references are determined by superimposed dc-voltage, speed-, and flux-controllers. This paper shows the theoretical base of the complete converter system and presents the practical realization with results.

KEYWORDS

GTO-Inverter, Optimal Power Factor, Current Vector Controller, On-line Pulse Pattern, AC-Drive

INTRODUCTION

Voltage source inverters are widely used for controlled ac-drives. Up to now the dc-link circuit is fed either by uncontrolled rectifiers or line-commutated static power converters. Such converter concepts have the inherent properties of harmonic distortion and a fundamental reactive power. These characteristics can be avoided by using forced commutated inverters on the line side. Fig. 1 shows the structure of the drive system. The ac-drive is fed by a two-state voltage source inverter. An identical two-state inverter is connected to the three phase mains by an external first order three phase L-filter. The new control system will be described in this paper.

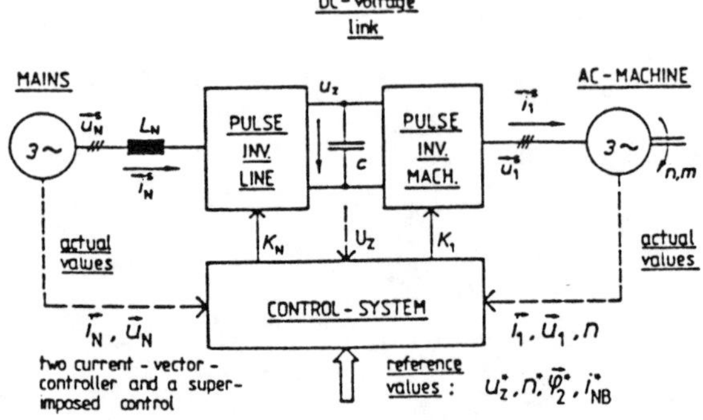

Fig. 1 Structure of the drive system

SUMMARY OF THE CONTROL SYSTEM

The total control system can be subdivided into a superimposed control concept, which is different referring to the line-side and machine-side objectives and similiar for the subordinated current controllers. The machine- and line-side are coupled by the dc-voltage controller in the superimposed control of the line-side, shown in Fig. 2.

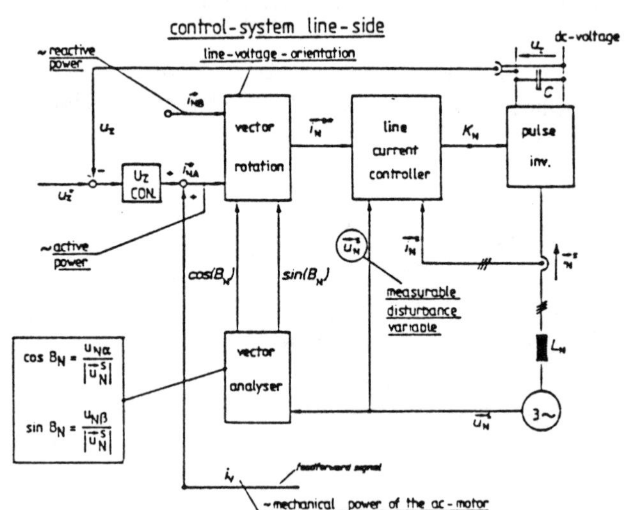

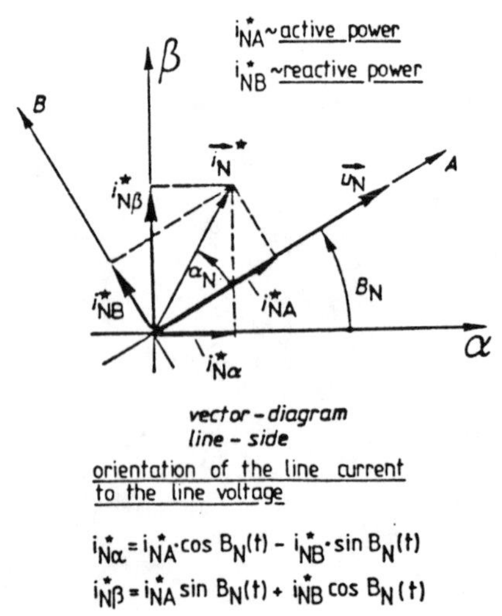

$$i^*_{N\alpha} = i^*_{NA} \cdot \cos B_N(t) - i^*_{NB} \cdot \sin B_N(t)$$
$$i^*_{N\beta} = i^*_{NA} \sin B_N(t) + i^*_{NB} \cos B_N(t)$$

Fig. 2 Control system line-side

The dc-voltage controller output represents the active power in the mains, which is converted from the mains to the dc-link or reverse. Additionally the line side inverter can be used as a reactive power compensator.

Reprinted from *IEEE/IAS Ann. Meet. Conf. Rec.*, pp. 593–599, 1987.

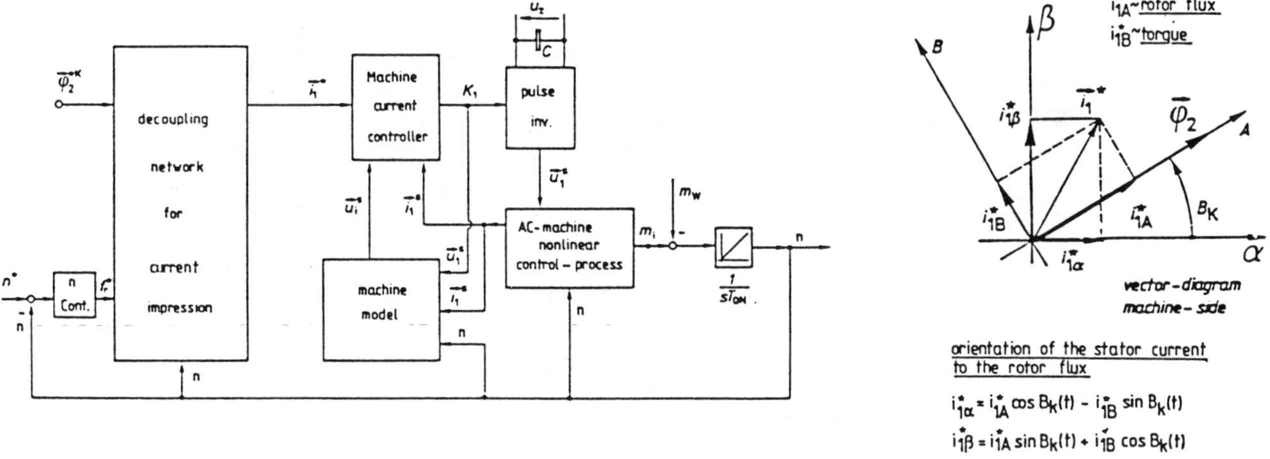

Fig. 3 Control system machine-side

In order to realize an orientation of the line currents to the line voltages the current references have to be synchronous to the line voltages. The phasor of the line voltage $\vec{u}_N$ is linked with the axis A of the rotating reference frame with the axes A and B. This coordinate system rotates with the line frequency. The current reference i^*_{NA} (~active power) and i^*_{NB} (~reactive power) are dc-signals in a steadystate operation. Normally a in-phase or a phase-opposition operation of the line current in respect to the line voltage takes place. According to the line current orientation in the mains, on the machine-side the ac-drive control has to realize an orientation of the stator current to the flux of the ac-drive. Fig. 3 illustrates the control system and the vector diagram of the machine-side.

The stator current reference $\vec{i}^*_1$ is oriented in relation to a flux-oriented reference system with the axes A and B. This decomposition yields to the reference signals i^*_{1A} (~rotor flux) and i^*_{1B} (~torque). The major differences between both sides is first the variable frequency on the machine side and second the phase shift of the stator current in respect to the inner voltage of the ac-drive. The stator current reference signals are calculated either by a decoupling method, shown in Fig. 3, or a field oriented control. First the subordinated current control strategies for both sides will be explained.

CURRENT CONTROL STRATEGY

Both controlled systems on the line side and machine side consist of the same two-state voltage inverter, a three phase filter (external inductance L_N respectively stator leakage inductance $L_{\sigma 1}$ and a three phase voltage system (line voltage respectively inner machine voltage). In contrast to the line side, the inner machine voltage has a variable magnitude and frequency. The similarity of both controlled systems yields to a common current control concept. The control strategy is based on an on-line modulation technique in order to control stationary and in particular transient operations. All three actual line- respectively stator-currents should be kept inside a given margin around predetermined current references. Hence the inverter switching sequence must be controlled directly by a current controller. The output voltages of one two-state inverter across two terminals can be set by the switching state between three possible values ($+U_z, 0, -U_z$). But the voltages across the three inductances cannot be set independently, for the inverter has an inherent cross coupling of all three phases. In the case of the line side, the current gradients in the mains are determined by the voltages across the external inductances L_N and the value of L_N itself. The voltage across the inductance, given by the inverter state and the actual value of the line voltage determines the switching times from one boundary intersection to the next. Therefore the line voltage (respectively the inner machine voltage) should be taken into consideration in order to minimize the average inverter switching frequency. A block diagram of the current control strategy is shown in Fig. 4, examplary for the line side.

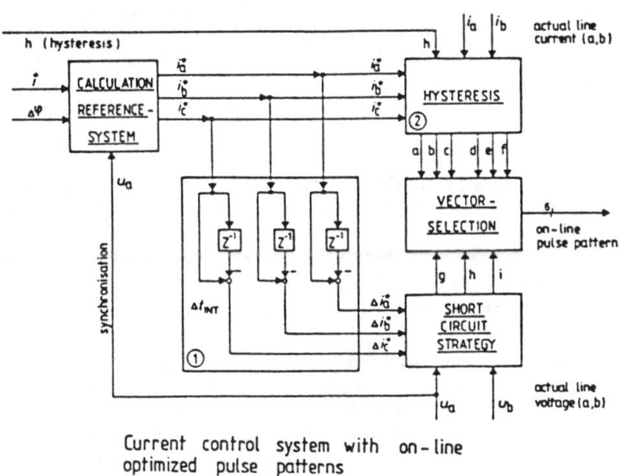

Fig. 4 Current control strategy

A three phase sinusoidal reference system is calculated by a coordinate transformation from a line voltage fixed reference system into a static reference system. Major parts of the control strategy are the detection of a boundary intersection, short circuit strategy and the vector-selection. A comparison of all three references with the actual currents yields to a six bit-information about inside or outside the margin and the signs of the control deviations. A special inverter state is the short circuit of all three output terminals, realized either by switching all terminals to the positive dc-bus or to the negative dc-bus. If the control strategy considers only the signs of the current control deviations, the short circuit of the inverter state cannot be switched. Therefore it must be calculated by the current controller, whether the short circuit results in a stable behaviour of all three phase currents. A simple decision criterion, whether the currents are kept inside the margin by the short circuit, can be derived with a comparison between the actual reference derivative and the possible derivative of the actual current. If the short circuit is selected, the

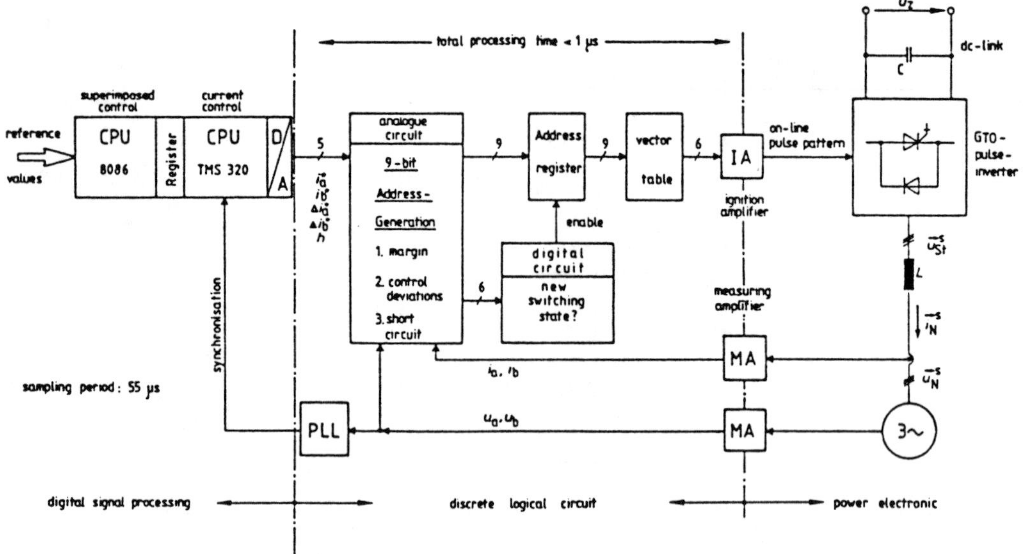

Fig. 5 Hybrid current controller

actual phase currents are mainly changed by the line voltages respectively inner machine voltage. These voltages must be converted into a current variation with the inductances $\Delta t_{INT}/L$. where Δt_{INT} is the sampling period of the reference calculation (55 µsec) and L the inductance of the load. The comparison of the derivatives in all three phases yields to a three-bit-information about the short circuit is able to force the actual current back into the margin. The inverter state is determined by addressing a switching state table with the 9-bit-information (a+i). In order to avoid an overshoot of the actual current above the margin, the processing time of the inverter state determination has to be minimized. The practical realization of the control strategy is shown in Fig. 5.

The signal processor TMS 320 performs a vector orientation of the current components in the line voltage system into a fixed reference frame. A time counter in the signal processor is controlled by a phase-lock-loop circuit, indicating the zero crossing of the line voltage phase a. The current components i^*_{NA} and i^*_{NB} have to be multiplied with a sine- and cosine function for generating a three phase sinusoidal reference system. The trigonometric function is stored in the program memory of the TMS 320. The instantaneous phase angle of the current reference in phase a is obtained with the frequency of the last period and the actual value of the time counter. The references are d/a-converted into a discrete logic circuit. The comparison between the references and the actual values results in a 9-bit-address, which is stored into an address register, if a boundary intersection has been detected.

EXPERIMENTAL RESULTS OF THE LINE CURRENT CONTROL

The signal processor control system was put into operation with 30 KVA GTO-inverter on the line side. Fig. 6 shows a reversion of power flow.
In the first period the line voltages are in phase with their respective actual currents, whereas in the second period the line voltage system is in phase opposition to the reference system. A change of the sign of the reference component i^*_{NA} initiates a step variation of all references. The actual values are outside the margin during the transient operation. Hence the control strategy selects a switching state such that the error is reduced in minimum time. The delay is determined by the voltage difference across the line inductance L_N, L_N itself and the value of the step variation.

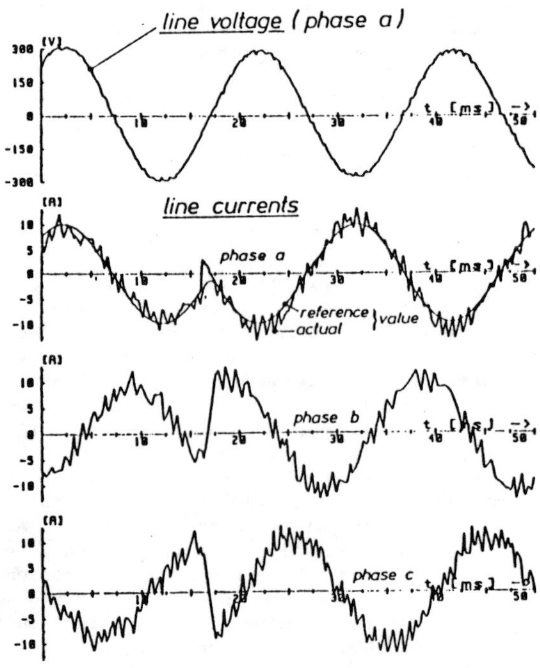

Fig. 6 Experimental results line-side

If the actual currents are controlled inside a small margin, the harmonic distortion can be reduced, but the average switching frequency will be increased. The optimal operation of the mains and the inverter is a compromise between the contrary demands of a maximal total power factor on one hand and a minimal average switching frequency on the other hand.

AC-DRIVE CONTROL

On the machine side the same current control strategy, illustrated in Fig. 5, was used for ac-drive control. Therefore impressed stator currents can be assumed for the superimposed control either a field-oriented control or a decoupling network. For the first practical investigations a decoupling strategy for an independent flux- and speed control was chosen, shown in Fig. 3. The first detailed description of ac-drive control via decoupling methods were published in /3/. In the case of a voltage source inverter a decoupling network for voltage impression was developed, respectively a network for current impression applying a current source inverter. The advantages of both concepts are combined by employing a subordinated current control and a network for current impression to control flux and speed. Assuming constant flux, torque can be controlled via rotor frequency. With constant stator flux the dynamic behaviour between rotor frequency and torque in the range up to about one half of pullout frequency is approximately linear and a first order lag. Rotor frequency is defined as difference between the rotational frequency of stator flux vector $f_{\varphi 1}$ and speed n.

$$/\vec{\varphi}_1/ = \text{const.}: \frac{\Delta m}{\Delta f_2} = V_{m1} * \frac{1}{1 + sT_2}$$

$$\text{with} \quad f_2 = f_{\varphi 1} - n$$

With constant rotor flux the dynamic behaviour proves to be exactly linear without any delay and rotor frequency is defined as difference between the rotational frequency of rotor flux $f_{\varphi 2}$ and speed n in this case.

$$/\vec{\varphi}_2/ = \text{const.}: \frac{m}{f_2} = V_{m2}$$

$$\text{with} \quad f_2 = f_{\varphi 2} - n$$

Thus employing rotor frequency as correcting variable for torque a very simple structured speed control loop, shown in Fig. 7, is obtained and optimization can be performed with conventional linear control theory.

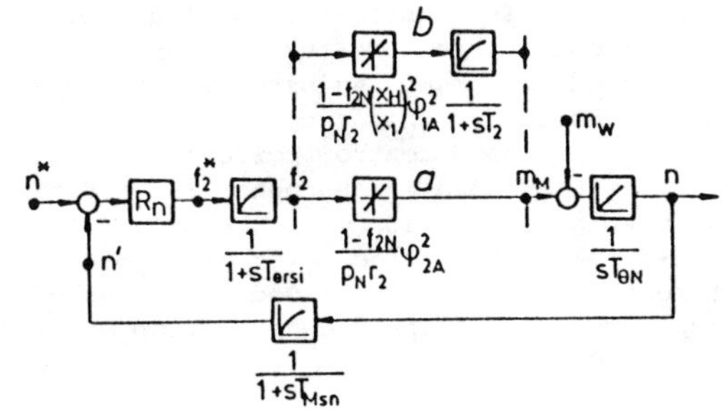

Fig. 7 Speed control loop
a) constant rotor flux
b) constant stator flux

The practical realization of decoupling networks with current impression is shown in Fig. 8 (constant rotor flux) and Fig. 9 (constant stator flux).

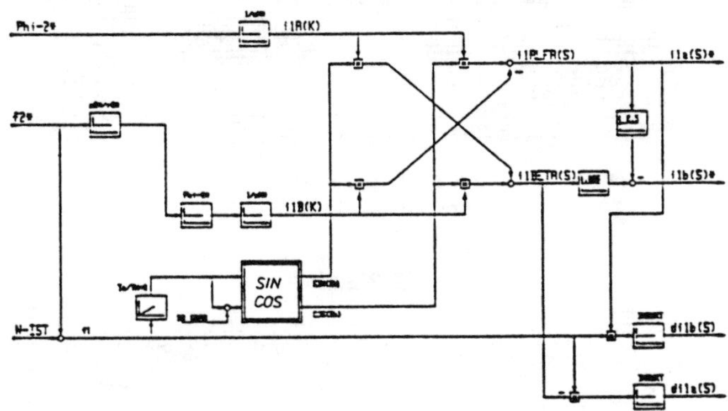

Fig. 8 Decoupling at constant rotor flux

First the current references i_{1A}^* and i_{1B}^* are determined with the references of the rotor frequency and the corresponding flux. Then a coordinate transformation of these current references from the flux-fixed reference frame into a static reference system takes place with the frequency of the flux vector, given by the speed n and the rotor frequency f_2^*. The main difference between realization of decoupling at constant stator flux or constant rotor flux are two coupled first order lags in the case of $/\vec{\varphi}_1/$= const. At the practical realization the speed control loop, the decoupling networks and the

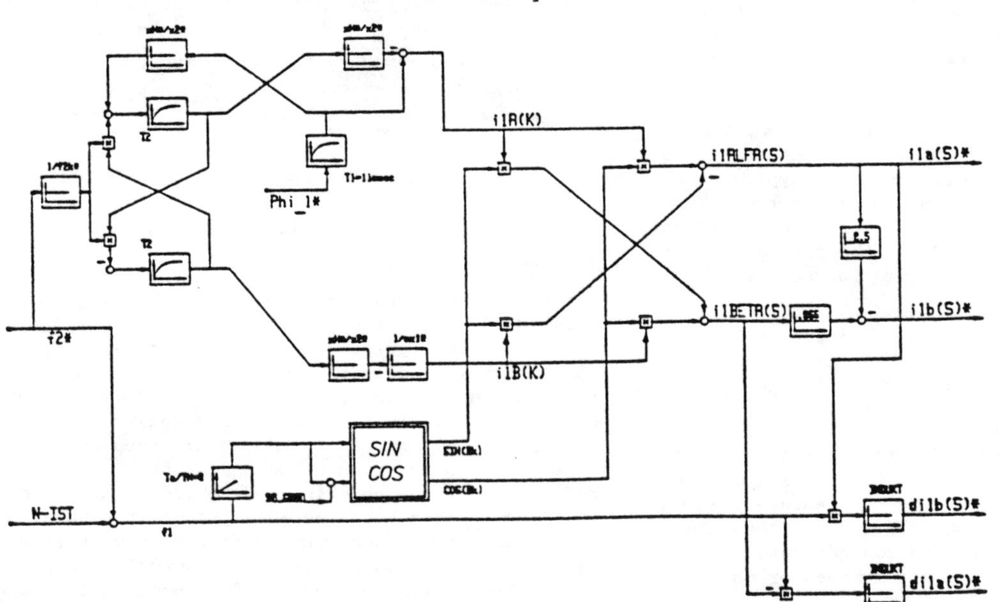

Fig. 9 Decoupling at constant stator flux

calculation of the stator current references in a fixed reference frame are realized with two microprocessors (8086, TMS 320). PI- (constant rotor flux) or PID-speed controller (constant stator flux) are applied with a sampling period of 5 msec, adjusted to the Symmetrical Optimum. The choice of this sampling period is a compromise between a good control performance and a high resolution of the speed measurement. The signal processing was put into operation with the same GTO-inverter and an ac-drive with a rated power of 5 kW and a short circuit reactance of 0.16 p.u. Some examples of transient responses of the speed control loop are reproduced in Fig. 10 and Fig. 11.

Fig. 10 Speed step response (constant rotor flux)

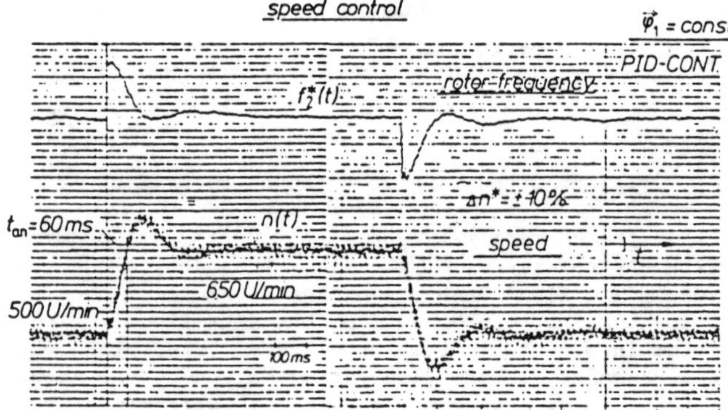

Fig. 11 Speed step response (constant stator flux)

In both figures the upper channel represents the speed controller output f_2^* (corresponding to the rotor frequency reference) and the lower channel the measured speed n. The obtained response times of the speed control are in the range of 40 msec till 60 msec as well as with stator flux- or rotor flux orientation. The step responses were measured without a first order lag in the speed reference channel. Hence the typical overshoot of the Symmetrical Optimum can be observed. The transient behaviour of the actual and reference currents (upper two signals, phase a and b), the flux and the rotor frequency reference at a speed increase are shown in Fig. 12.

The inverter was operated with an average switching frequency of 2÷3 kHz, caused by the small short circuit reactance. The speed reference step results in a higher current magnitude and a phase shift in respect to the flux for a torque generation, realized by a decoupling network. The only difference of this control principle in respect to the known field oriented control is the application of the rotor frequency reference - for controlling the stator current phasor in respect to the flux - whereas the field oriented control has to determine an actual rotor frequency via a model or observer.

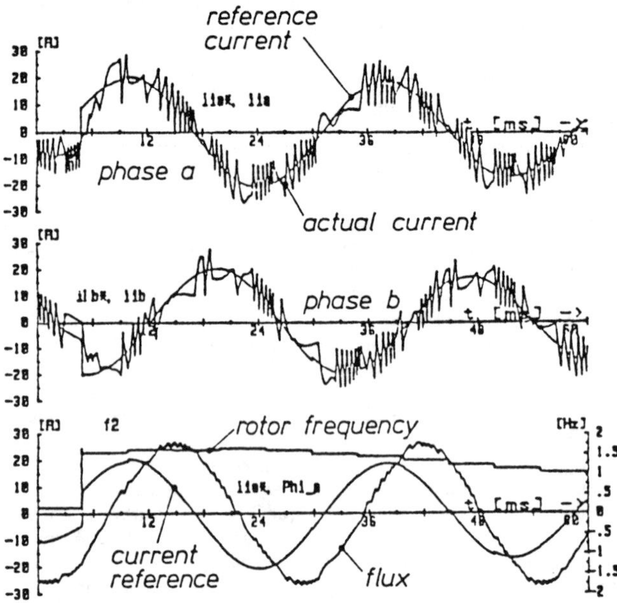

Fig. 12 Transient operation (speed increase)

In the case of a correct adjustment of the decoupling network both control principles obtain the same results.

THE COMPLETE CONVERTER SYSTEM

The superimposed control was extended by the dc-voltage control loop in order to put the complete converter system in operation. A block diagram of the signal processing is given by Fig. 13.

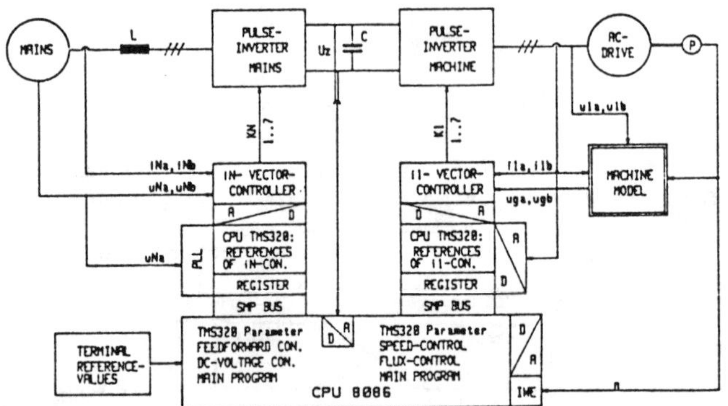

Fig. 13 Complete signal processing

The mains, the dc-link-circuit and the ac-drive are controlled by three microprocessors. Two signal processors TMS 320 for line current and stator current control and a 8086 processor for dc-voltage-, speed- and flux control. One current control unit can be divided into the TMS 320 board, with its own 4K-word memory and the discrete logic circuit for generation of the online pulse pattern. Both TMS 320 are coupled with register-files to the 8086 processor in order to get the references of the superimposed control. The dc-voltage is a/d-converted into the 8086 processor with a sampling period of 1 msec. The current control strategy need not an a/d-conversion of the actual currents, but if the field oriented control for the ac-drive is used, an a/d-conversion of the stator currents is necessary. An extensive main program in the 8086 manages the initialization and operation of the complete converter system.

EXPERIMENTAL RESULTS OF THE COMPLETE CONVERTER SYSTEM

A PI-algorithm was programmed for the dc-voltage control, generating the current reference i^*_{1A} (~active power). A similiar controlled system like the speed control loop yields also to a Symmetrical Optimization of the dc-voltage controller. The transient behaviour in the mains and ac-drive, initiated by a higher speed reference, is shown in Fig. 14.

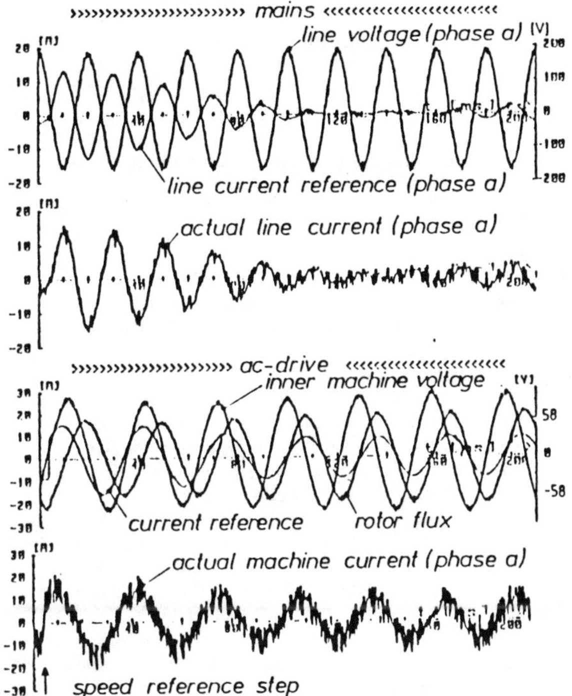

Fig. 14 Transient operation (10% speed reference step) complete converter system subordinated current control

First the ac-drive control requires a higher stator current (signals machine side). Hence the dc-voltage will decrease, informing the dc-voltage controller to increase the line current magnitude (signals line side). The higher active power (fundamental reactive power is zero) in the mains is converted by the line side inverter into the dc-link in order to recharge the dc-link capacitor. The phase shift of 180 degrees between line voltage and line current at a power conversion from the mains into the dc-link is only a consequence of the defined current sign. In order to improve the disturbance behaviour of the dc-voltage control, a feedforward control signal for the line current controller was implemented. This feedforward signal is proportional to the ac-drive power and is calculated with speed and rotor frequency of the ac-drive. The experimental results in Fig. 14, 15 were obtained with feedforward control. The speed control is represented by the actual speed n and rotor frequency reference f^*_2, upper two channels in Fig. 15. If the feedforward signal is correctly adjusted to the ac-drive power, no control error in the dc-voltage (Fig. 15) can be observed. Hence the feedforward signal is directly the current reference i^*_{NA}, which is proportional to the active power in the mains.

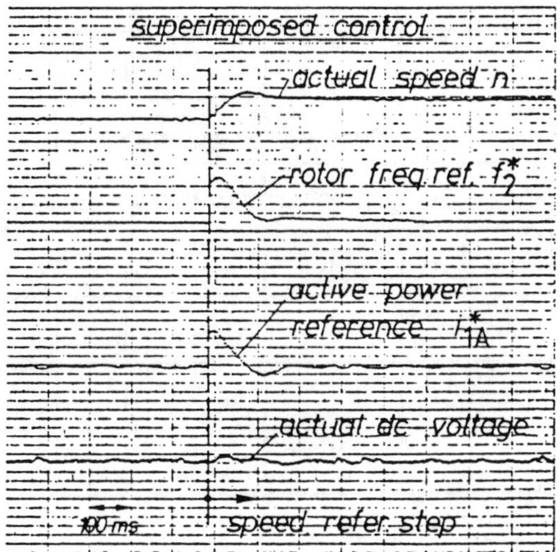

Fig. 15 Transient operation (10% speed reference step) complete converter system superimposed control

The rated phase voltage of the ac-drive is 127 V_{eff}, therefore a dc-link voltage of 350 V is sufficient for the ac-drive control. For controlling the line current the line phase voltage was reduced to 127 V_{eff} and an external inductance of L=5 mH between the mains and the line side inverter was used. A non-reversible capacitor of only $C_= = 4,3$ mF and an ac-capacitor of $C_\sim = 75$ µF were installed in the dc-link. If no feedforward control is implemented, the line current is out of control, for the recharging of the dc-capacitor takes place too slow (Fig. 16). An essential improvement of the transient behaviour in the dc-link can be realized with feedforward control, shown in Fig. 17.

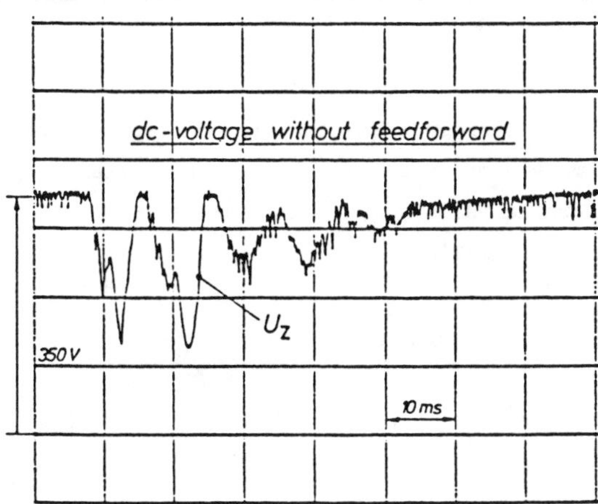

Fig. 16 dc-voltage without feedforward control

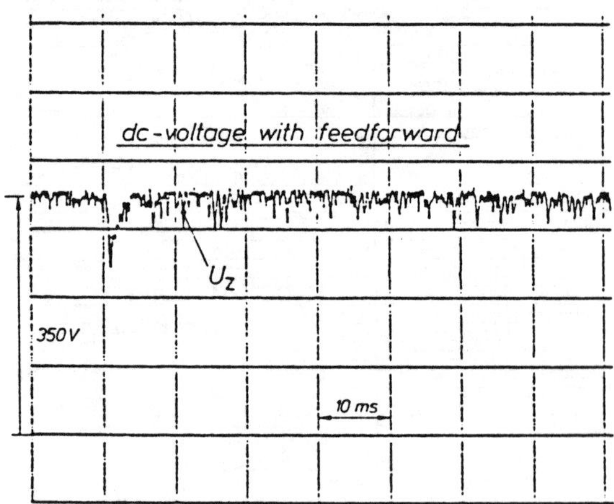

Fig. 17 dc-voltage with feedforward control

CONCLUSION

A multiloop control of a double voltage inverter system, coupling a three phase mains with an ac-drive, was successfully put into operation. A bidirectional ac-dc-conversion between the mains and a dc-voltage link can be performed at unity power factor using GTO-pulse inverters. The current vector controllers, based on an on-line optimiziation technique for the inverter control, impress sinusoidal line- and stator currents in stationary and particular transient operations. Load changes or variations of the speed reference on the machine side are overcome by a superimposed control.

APPENDIX

SUBSCRIPTS

s: space vector in a (stator)-fixed reference frame

K: space vector in a rotating reference frame

*: reference value

1: stator variable

2: rotor variable

N: line variable

Δ: deviation from operating point

COMPONENTS OF THE REFERENCE FRAMES

α: real axis of a (stator)-fixed reference frame

β: imaginary axis of a (stator)-fixed reference frame

A: real axis of a rotating reference frame

B: imaginary axis of a rotating reference frame

MACHINE PARAMETERS

$T_2 = \sigma x_2/r_2$ transient rotor time constant

$f_{2K} = r_2/\sigma x_2$ rotor pullout frequency

ACKNOWLEDGEMENT

Thanks to Mr. O. Niermeyer for inverter design

REFERENCES

/1/ H. Kohlmeier, O. Niermeyer, D. Schröder: High dynamic four-quadrant ac-motor drive with improved power factor and on-line optimized pulse patterns. Power Electronics and Applications, 1. EPE, Brüssel 1985, page 3.173

/2/ H. Kohlmeier, D. Schröder: GTO-pulse inverters with on-line optimized pulse patterns for current control. International conference on electrical machines ICEM, München 1986, page 668

/3/ W. Flügel, R. Weninger: Control of inverter-fed asynchronous motors via decoupling networks. IFAC-Control in Power Electronics and Electrical Drives. Lausanne 1983, page 305

/4/ W. Flügel: Drehzahlregelung umrichtergespeister Asynchronmaschinen bei Steuerung des Flusses durch Entkopplungsnetzwerke. Dissertation TU München 1981

/5/ R. Weninger: Drehzahlregelung von Asynchronmaschinen bei Speisung durch einen Zwischenkreisumrichter mit eingeprägtem Strom. Dissertation, TU München 1982

Paper 8.3

10-MW GTO Converter for Battery Peaking Service

LOREN H. WALKER, FELLOW, IEEE

***Abstract*—A bidirectional 18-pulse voltage source converter utilizing gate turn-off thyristors (GTO's) is described. The converter, which is rated 10 MVA, was placed in service in early 1988 to connect an energy storage battery to a utility grid. The converter is rated and controlled to operate in all four quadrants (discharge, charge, leading vars, or lagging vars) at the full 10-MVA rating. It is capable of independent rapid control of real and reactive power with a transient response of 16 ms to changes in commanded value of real or reactive power. Thus it is usable as a reactive power controller (static var control), voltage control, frequency control, power system stabilizer, or as a real power peaking station. For use as a reactive power controller only, no battery would be needed. The design, construction, control, and application of the converter are described, and performance data taken at factory power test and at the installation are given.**

Introduction

A 10-MW GTO voltage source converter was placed in service at the Chino Battery Energy Storage Facility in California in early 1988. The facility is to be used as a load leveling and energy management system on the Southern California Edison electric grid. The project was constructed by Edison and cofunded by the International Lead Zinc Research Organization and the Electric Power Research Institute (EPRI) to encourage the commercialization of battery energy storage for utility application. The power conditioning system was procured by EPRI and was designed and manufactured by General Electric Drive Systems, Salem, VA.

The dynamic regulation capability of the converter was intentionally made much better than would be required for the battery energy storage application. This was in response to recent interest in power system stabilization utilizing solid-state converters [1], [2]. These and other references have cited a need for a static power converter which could make rapid changes in real power without undesired simultaneous changes of reactive power. The use of self-commutating gate turn-off thyristors (GTO's) rather than line-commutated thyristors to make up the converter gave the power circuit the desired capability. The control circuit was designed to preserve the performance of which the power circuit is capable.

Paper IPCSD 89-18, approved by the Static Power Converter Committee of the IEEE Industry Applications Society for presentation at the 1988 Industry Applications Society Annual Meeting, Pittsburgh, PA, October 2-7; also partially presented the Intersociety Energy Conversion Engineering Conference, Philadelphia, PA, August 1987. Manuscript released for publication April 17, 1989.

The author is with Drive Development Engineering, Drive Systems Department, General Electric Company, 1501 Roanoke Boulevard, Room 500, Salem, VA 24153.

IEEE Log Number 8931456.

This paper will describe the design of the converter and show some performance results of the installed system. The application and performance of the converter is summarized as follows:

battery voltage	1750–2860 V dc,
utility voltage	12 kV ac ±5 percent,
utility voltage unbalance	±2 percent from average,
rating	10 MVA lag, lead, charge, discharge,
cooling	forced air, two speed fans,
reliability	redundant GTO's, redundant fans,
ambient temperature	0–47°C,
efficiency	97 percent at 10 MW, 95 percent at 2 MW,
voltage harmonics	<1.5 percent individual, two percent total,
transient response	16 ms time constant to step in command for real or reactive power.

The operating modes include backstart—the energizing of the utility lines from the converter, starting with only battery power and UPS control power available.

Diagnostics consist of automatic self-test of power and control components at startup and continuous diagnosis when on-line. Diagnostic information is output to a self-contained printer, and via a digital data link to the higher level control.

A distributed microcontroller (DMC) provided with the converter (but not discussed in this paper) provides for automatic startup, control of battery charging profiles, logging of ampere-hours, megawatthours, etc.

Overview of the Installation

Fig. 1 is a one-line diagram of the installation. The battery is arranged as two buildings, each containing four strings. Strings are labeled 1 EAST through 4 WEST. Each string consists of 1032 cells in series. Each battery string is connected to the bus by a contactor, a manual disconnect and fuses at both ends of the feeder. The entire battery installation is rated 10 MW for 4 h.

Each bank of four batteries is connected to the converter bus by a high-speed circuit breaker rated 3000 A, 3000 V. The converter consists of three identical power units feeding nine single-phase transformers (represented as three transformers on Fig. 1).

The ac capacitor is connected to the utility terminals of the

Reprinted from *IEEE Trans. Ind. Applicat.*, vol. 26, no. 1, pp. 63–72, January/February 1990.

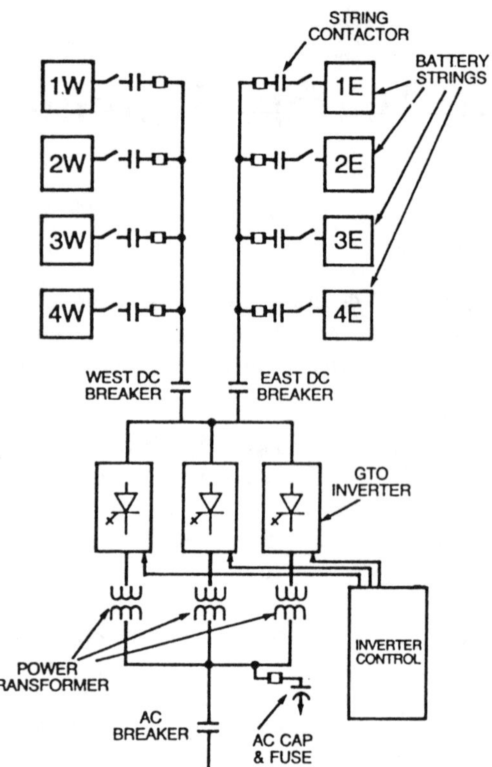

Fig. 1. One-line diagram of converter installation.

converter to absorb converter harmonics. The converter controls cause the converter to supply the leading current to this capacitor so that its vars are not on the grid unless commanded. The converter transformers are connected to the 12-kV bus by a vacuum breaker with the usual protective relaying.

Converter Design

A simplified circuit diagram of the converter is shown in Fig. 2. The converter is an 18-pulse stepped-wave bidirectional voltage source GTO converter. At each position on Fig. 2 where a GTO is indicated (for example, GAP) there are two GTO's in series, each rated 2500 A, 4500 V. In parallel with each GTO is a reverse diode to give the converter the capability of handling power flow in both directions. The two GTO's in series at each position provide full redundancy against a GTO failure: the converter can continue to run with one GTO failed in a series string.

The converter is constructed as three identical six-pulse inverter cabinets. The cabinets are called power conversion modules (PCM's). Each cabinet contains two three-phase bridges of GTO's. The PCM's are labeled "0°," "20°," and "40°" to indicate the phase displacements of the gating times of the sets of GTO's with respect to the reference phase position. Within each PCM there is a leading three-phase bridge and a lagging three-phase bridge. Each GTO is gated with a 60-Hz square wave, 180° conduction. Within the three phase bridges the GTO gating is displaced 120° in the conventional manner. Within the array of three leading bridges one GTO is gated on every 20°. Within the retarded array, the same is true. The transformer primaries are connected between corresponding points on the two three-phase bridges. The two converter legs that are connected to a single transformer primary could be viewed as a single-phase H bridge of four GTO's as described Fig. 4.

The partitioning of the converter into three PCM's is implemented so that each cabinet could be used as a six-pulse voltage source inverter with controllable output voltage rated 3.3 MVA. The controls are designed to accept a fourth cabinet to form 24-pulse converter of rating higher than 10 MVA. Each of the three PCM's is housed in a cabinet 26 ft long, 4 ft deep, and 8 ft high. These dimensions include the inverters and their controls. Fig. 10 shows a photograph of one of the 3.3-WM PCM's with its doors open.

Transformer Array

The secondaries of the nine single-phase transformers are connected in a zig-zag connection to form an 18-pulse stepped wave whose lowest harmonic is the seventeenth. The angular position of the transformer primaries in Fig. 2 represents the relative phase position of the voltage on that winding. The turns ratios of the transformers are selected to eliminate all harmonics lower than the seventeenth from the line-to-line voltage. This results in only two transformer types among the nine transformers. T11, T12, and T13 are identical, with one secondary each. The other six transformers are identical, having two secondaries each. The ratios are selected by the rules described by Corey [3]: "Voltage of each step should be proportional to the cosine of the angle between the step position and the voltage zero."

Step positions are 20° apart with no step at 0°, so transformer secondary windings are in the ratios:

T21 (sum of two secondaries) $= K * \cos 10°$
T11 (only one secondary) $= K * \cos 30°$
T21 (higher voltage secondary) $= K * \cos 50°$
T21 (lower voltage secondary) $= K * \cos 70°$

where K is selected to get the proper output voltage.

The leakage reactance of the transformer array is 0.19 pu. This value of reactance is selected to optimize the converter rating. Converter rating is increased if a low-reactance transformer is used because

- higher unbalance currents flow in the converter due to the specified two percent unbalance in utility voltage, and
- larger capacitance CF is needed to keep voltage harmonics within specifications when disconnected from the grid.

The transformers are of cast coil design, located outdoors.

AC Filter Capacitors

The ac filter capacitors (CF) act with the leakage reactance of the transformers to form a low-pass filter to reduce the harmonic voltages to specified limits. These capacitors draw a current of about 0.15 pu leading from the converter. The LC filter thus formed has its pole just below the sixth harmonic. Fig. 3 shows the ideal 18-pulse voltage waveform V_i before filtering. Fig. 12 shows the actual 12-kV output waveform,

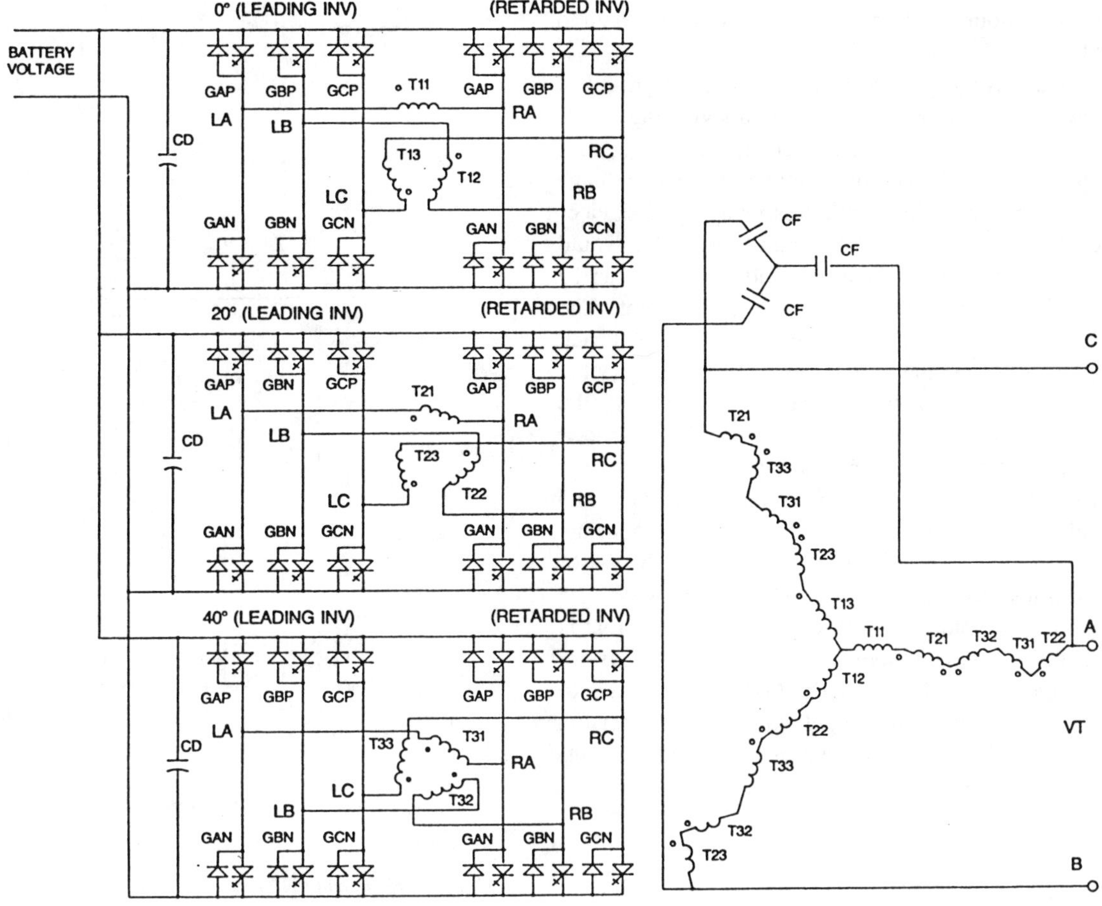

Fig. 2. Simplified circuit diagram of converter.

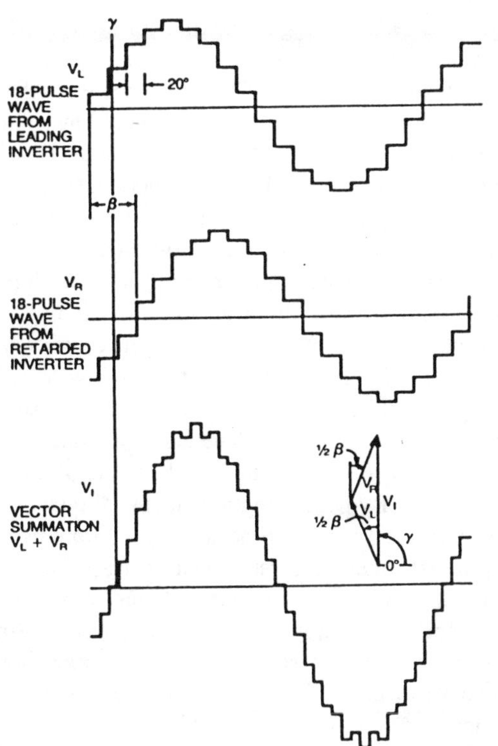

Fig. 3. Vector sum of two stepped waves to form a wave of controlled magnitude.

both unfiltered and filtered by the connection of the ac capacitors CF.

DC Capacitors

The dc capacitance (CD) is necessary to absorb ac currents reflected by the converter stages onto the dc bus. This capacitance is physically distributed throughout the converter cabinets to absorb rapid steps in current with minimum overshoot on the dc bus. Oil paper capacitors are used for ripple current absorption. Aluminum electrolytic capacitors and metal oxide varistors are used for voltage transient supression across the dc bus.

Choice of Stepped-Wave Versus Pulsewidth Modulated Operation

In many converters designed for this type of application, the GTO's are gated to switch several times per fundamental half-cycle to introduce notches in the voltage waveform. This mode of operation may be called pulsewidth modulation (PWM). It can provide reduction of harmonics at the ac terminals and control of ac voltage amplitude on the individual phases.

This PWM mode of operation was considered for this converter but not used. The multiple switchings of the GTO's increase losses in the GTO devices and in their snubber circuits. These extra losses reduce the efficiency of the converter and may introduce problems in cooling the GTO devices. If a way can be found to get harmonic reduction and voltage control without the increase in losses, it would seem to be preferable.

In the stepped-wave approach chosen for this design, all of the GTO's switch at a 60-Hz rate. No extra switching losses occur, and efficiency is maximized. Obtaining the control flexibility necessary for harmonic reduction and voltage control without extra switchings requires many GTO devices and requires that they be gated at different times. This would at first appear to be a penalty, but in a rating as large as 10 MVA, many GTO's are required to carry the current. The design as shown has six GTO's equivalently in parallel at each position. By using the number of devices required to carry the load and gating them in the stepped-wave pattern, the harmonics can be kept low, and the control flexibility provided without extra switching. The stepped-wave configuration inherently provides for current sharing among the GTO's, and it is inherently free of voltage unbalance and dc component.

Operation in the PWM mode would have allowed the use of a lower rated transformer array and would have provided the control flexibility to voltage match to a utility voltage that is unbalanced. It would have required features to assure current balance between effectively paralleled GTO devices and to eliminate dc component in the output voltage. The decision was made to use the inherently symmetrical and current-shared stepped-wave approach.

Converter Control

Voltage Magnitude Control

The power converter control is most easily understood if the converter is regarded not as three inverters, each with leading and lagging bridges, but rather if the converter is regarded as two complete 18-pulse stepped wave inverters; a leading 18-pulse inverter (the left half of the circuit in Fig. 2), and a retarded 18-pulse inverter (the right half of Fig. 2). Each inverter would then produce a stepped wave of no harmonics lower than the seventeenth, with the amplitude of the wave proportional to battery voltage. Such a wave is shown as V_L at the top in Fig. 3. If two such waves are generated, with the phase position of one wave leading a reference position by a small amount, and the phase position of the other retarded by a similar amount (V_R in Fig. 3), then the two waves could be added in series to obtain a new wave (as shown at the bottom V_i in Fig. 3). The phase position of V_i would be at the reference position (halfway between the phase position of the two component waves). The amplitude of V_i would be determined by the vector summation of the two component waves. In Fig. 3 the reference phase position is labeled "γ" and the displacmeent of each of the component waves from the reference is labeled 1/2 β. Thus the magnitude of V_i is given by

$$|V_i| = 2 * |V_L| \cos 1/2\, \beta. \qquad (1)$$

The voltage magnitude control mechanism in the 18-pulse converter is by controlling the angle β. The control characteristic is given by (1).

The physical generation of waveforms as shown in Fig. 3 would take two sets of nine transformers. By controlling the gating as represented by Fig. 3, but connecting the transformers as shown in Fig. 2, only one set of nine transformers is needed, and the net kVA rating of the transformers is reduced. The resultant waveforms at one transformer primary are as shown in Fig. 4. In this figure the GTO's connected to the ends of the transformer winding have been represented by switches. The switches are in the topology referred to as an H bridge. The switches are operated in 180° conduction so that they produce a 60-Hz square-wave voltage at each end of the transformer winding. At full output, the two square waves are 180° out of phase with each other ($\beta = 0$) so that there is a square wave VTA across the transformer winding. Any difference in phase position of the two square waves (β) will produce a period of zero dwell in the square wave across VTA. This type of wave is often called a "quasi-square" wave. The magnitude of the fundamental component of the quasi-square wave will be controlled by the value of the angle β as noted in Fig. 4. By generating nine identical quasi-square waves displaced 20° apart in time and by combining these waves using transformer ratios such that an 18-pulse wave is formed, an 18-pulse wave of controllable amplitude is generated. The effect is that the vector addition of the 18-pulse waves has been done at the square-wave level, and then the stepped wave is formed of the quasi-square waves whose amplitudes have already been controlled.

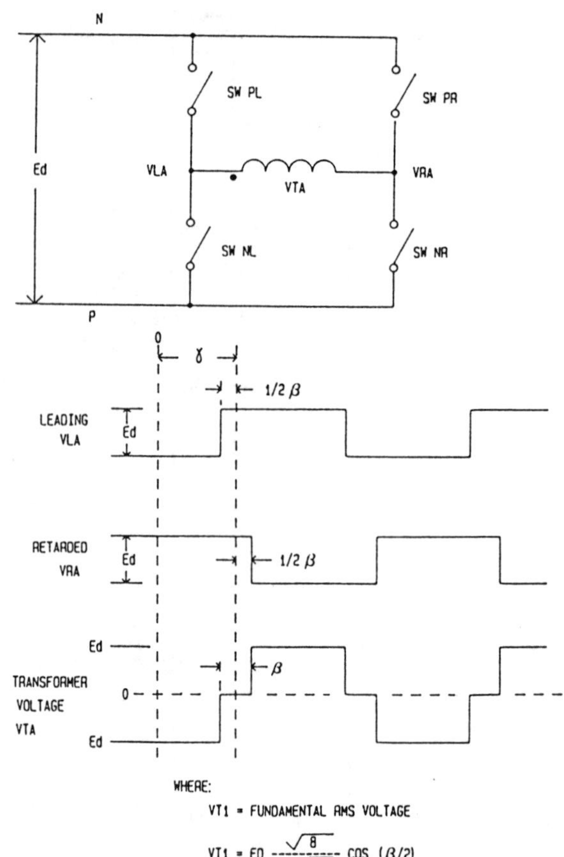

Fig. 4. Operation of H bridge-vector addition at square-wave level.

The Reference Angle γ

The reference angle γ is the "power angle," the angle by which the converter internal voltage is displaced from the

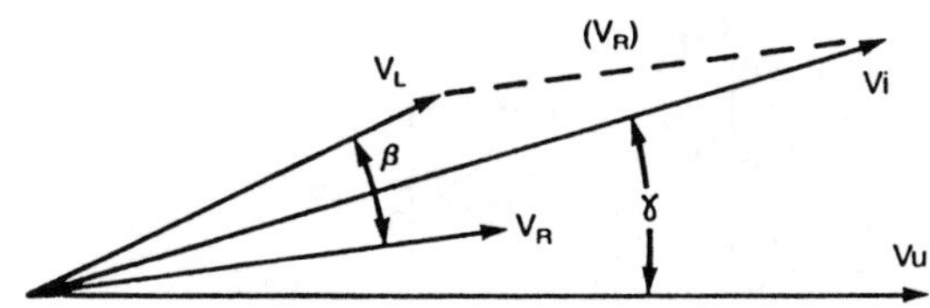

Fig. 5. Relationship of angles β and γ. V_L is voltage of leading inverter at $\gamma + (\beta/2)$. V_R is voltage or retarded inverter at $\gamma - (\beta/2)$. V_i is converter internal voltage at γ. V_u is utility voltage (reference angle).

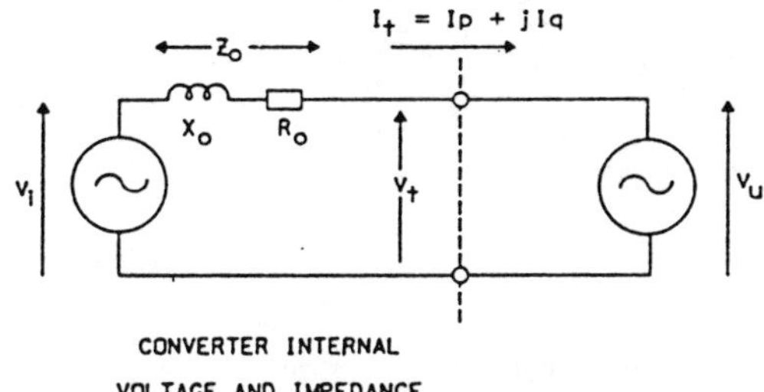

Fig. 6. Model of converter connected to utility.

utility line. The relationship between β and γ is shown in Figs. 3 and 5. Variations in β adjust the amplitude of the converter voltage without disturbing its phase position. Likewise, variations in the angle γ change the phase position of the output voltage without disturbing the amplitude. The decoupling of these angular variables is important to the independent control of real and reactive power.

Control of Real and Reactive Power

Fig. 6 shows the model used for the output impedance of the converter. It is shown as having an internal voltage V_i as in Fig. 3 and an output impedance Z_o consisting primarily of the reactance of the output transformers X_o but having a small resistive part R_o also. The utility voltage is represented as the infinite bus voltage V_u. If the utility has nonzero impendance, the utility impedance can be combined into Z_o for the purposes of analysis and control. The instantaneous difference between the utility voltage V_u and the converter internal voltage V_i is imposed across the impedance Z_o. By controlling the magnitude and phase of this difference voltage, the magnitude and phase of converter current can be controlled.

Controls Implementation

Control Hardware: Fig. 7 shows the implementation of the control in the 80286 microprocessor. At the left the commands for real and reactive power are input. Similarly, the feedback signals for watts and vars are input. The difference between the desired watts and vars and the commands are calculated in the microprocessor. The microprocessor then calculates the magnitude and angle of the voltage drop across Z_o to get the desired power and vars. It then calculates the values of magnitude and angle of internal voltage to produce the desired voltage difference between V_i and V_u. It further calculates the values of γ and $\beta/2$ to cause the desired voltage magnitude and angle. These values of γ and β are output as binary numbers to the digital gate timing logic as shown in Fig. 7.

The digital gate timing in Fig. 7 is similar to that in [4]. It has a phase-locked loop (PLL) consisting of the synchronizing PLL 123-kHz variable-frequency oscillator (VFO), and the countdown. The output of the countdown is a 12-bit number representing the instantaneous phase position of the utility voltage V_u. There are three summing junctions which combine the values of γ, $\beta/2$, and the utility reference phase to make up the values of (utility phase $+ \gamma + (\beta/2)$) and (utility phase $+ \gamma - (\beta/2)$) as needed to gate the GTO's. These instantaneous phase signals are converted into GTO gating times in the manner of [4].

Diagnostic Hardware: Although all the control of the converter is in a single microprocessor located in the PCM40 control, there is a microprocessor in each of the other converters that serves only to accumulate diagnostic information and return it to the central processor via a digital data link connecting the three converter cabinets.

Factors Limiting Speed of Response: The factors that could limit the speed of response of such a system are many. Effort has been expended to minimize each of them to obtain the transient response.

Power converter basic transport delay: The 18-pulse nature of the power converter implies that a new pair of GTO's will be gated in each the leading and lagging inverters 18 times per cycle, or a little more often than every 1 ms. The frequent gatings reduce the transport delay of the power converter so that it is not a major factor in the transient response of the regulators.

Phase-locked loop: Most phase-locked loops that are locked to utility busses have a low crossover frequency in the phase-locked loop itself. This is to keep the output of the countdown free of 120-Hz modulation and to avoid response to noise pulses. The same is true of this PLL. In many prior converter load controls [5], the phase offset between the utility voltage and the converter input voltage γ was introduced as a bias to the phase-locked loop. When introduced in this manner, the ability of the entire converter to make rapid changes in γ was limited by the transient response of the phase-locked loop. In this converter. The value of γ is added after the phase-locked loop so that no change is required in the relatively slow phase-locked loop when a fast change of γ is needed.

Microprocessor calculation delay: By using a powerful 16-bit microprocessor, the 80286, and by carefully partitioning the code, it was possible to cause the microprocessor to update the values of γ and $\beta/2$ at a rate equal to the GTO gating frequency, slightly faster than once per millisecond. Not all loops could be updated that often, only the loops critical to transient response.

Ripple filter on watt and var feedback: These feedback signals are generated by analog multipliers, operating on instantaneous signals of terminal voltage and current, implementing the traditional expressions for three-phase watts and vars. As such, they will produce ripple-free signals if the currents are balanced. Since there is little ripple in these signals, little filtering is needed, and the transient response of the converter was not limited by the filters.

Because of these features of the design, the watt and var regulators could be adjusted with well damped responses with crossover frequency as fast as 50 rad/s. Thus they would

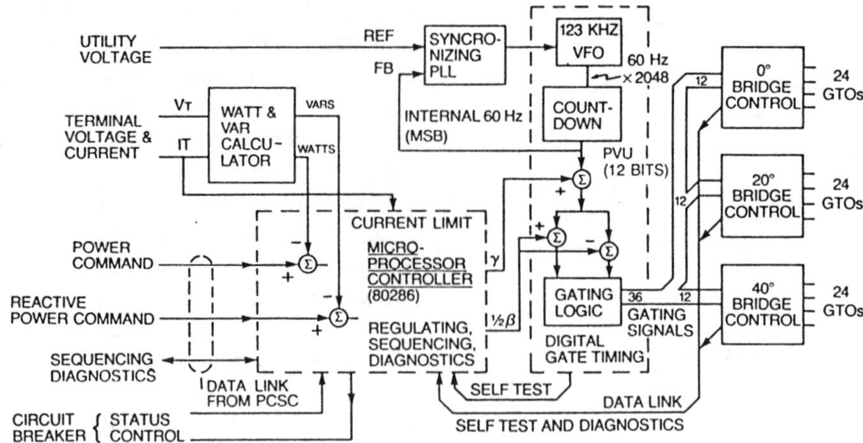

Fig. 7. Controls implementation.

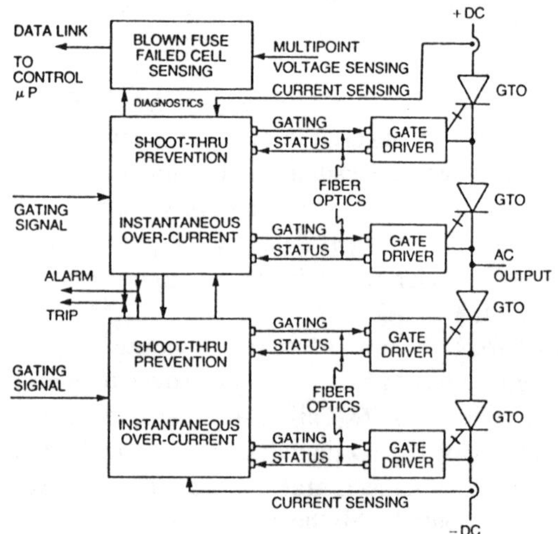

Fig. 8. Bridge control and protective control of each inverter leg.

follow accurately commands at frequencies of 5 Hz or more. This is amply fast for power system stabilizer requirements mentioned in the literature.

Protection

The primary overcurrent protection in case of overload or power component failure in the converter is by fast-acting electronic protection at the gates of the GTO's. The protective logic switches off any GTO carrying a current approaching its peak turn-off rating. This is practical in the case of ac faults, since the reactance of the output transformers limits rate of change of current to levels which allow time for gate turn-off.

If there is a power component failure which prevents a GTO from turning off in normally loaded operation, the gate protection prevents the turn-on of the diametric GTO, and thus prevents fuse blowing in most cases. If the fault cannot be isolated by gate control there are fast-acting fuses to terminate the buildup of dc fault current and thus prevent further damage.

Fig. 8 shows the implementation of the GTO gate protection. The figure shows the signal path from the digital gate timing of Fig. 7 to the GTO's. The gating signals are brought to this card which controls the four GTO's making up a leg. The logic blocks marked "shoot-thru protection" and "instantaneous overcurrent protection" are implemented in a single-chip logic cell array (LCA) which serves all four GTO's. This implements the protective features designed to prevent the blowing of leg fuses on all but the most severe failures. This card also contains the sensors necessary to the self-diagnosis of the power components.

The outputs of the LCA are transmitted to the gate drivers by fiber optics. Each gate driver returns a signal by fiber optic which tells if the GTO is on, off, or failed. The fiber optics provide the ohmic isolation of the control logic at ground potential and the gate drivers at GTO cathode potential. The gate drivers themselves contain logic to prevent damaging a GTO if false drive signals appear, and to generate the diagnostic information fed back to the control logic.

Converter Construction

Fig. 9 shows the layout of one of the inverter cabinets (PCM's). Starting at the left end is a control cabinet which serves the GTO's in this PCM. In the case of PCM40 this control cabinet also houses the control of the entire converter. Following the control is a repeated pattern of H bridges arranged with a leading leg, a capacitor panel, and a retarded leg. The H bridges are labeled in phases A, B, and C, and the individual legs are denoted L for leading or R for retarded. The entire content of each GTO leg cabinet is mounted on a single rack that can be rolled out for easy access or for replacement as a module. The capacitor panels contain dc capacitors and fuses associated with each H bridge. By locating 1/9 of the capacitance at each H bridge, inductance between each leg and the nearest dc capacitor is minimized. The PCM is designed to interface to the dc bus at the right-hand end.

Cooling: The converter is cooled by fans on top of the cabinets, with air entering from the room on the front of the cabinets and exhausting through ducts to the outdoors from the top. In Fig. 9 the rectangles shown in the doors of the enclosure are air inlets strategically located at heat sinks, fuses, and di/dt reactors. There is one fan per converter leg (two per H bridge) labeled BA1–BA6 in Fig. 9. Fans are variable speed. In case of the failure of one fan redundancy is provided by increasing the speed of the two fans adjacent to it.

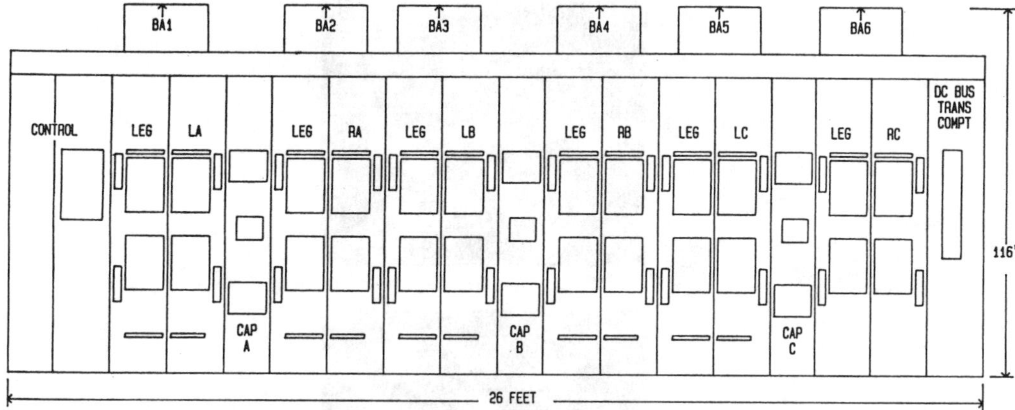

Fig. 9. Layout of one 3.3-MW PCM inverter cabinet.

Fig. 10. One 3.3-MW power conversion module with doors open.

Fig. 11. Closeup of two GTO leg assemblies and one capacitor cabinet.

Fan speed will also increase when the ambient temperature is high.

Fig. 10 is a photograph of the PCM with the doors opened. Fig. 11 shows a closeup of a leg assembly showing how the GTO's and diodes are arranged in a plane, with each heat sink receiving fresh air from the front. The features shown in each leg assembly of Fig. 11 are, at the top and bottom, four gate drivers; and at the center, eight heatsinks for the four GTO's and four diodes of the leg. The thermal impedance, sink to ambient of the sinks, is 0.033°C/W at maximum fan speed. Thus at 47°C maximum ambient, if GTO losses are 1000 W/device, heat sink temperature is only 80°C. Heat sinks are also provided for the fuses.

For a converter of this rating, water cooling is available. Water cooling would have made the equipment smaller and obtained more rating from the same devices.

Converter Performance Evaluation

The converter has been evaluated by a power test at the factory and by test data at the final installation.

Harmonics

Fig. 12 shows the voltage waveforms of the 12-kV ac output. Fig. 12(a) shows is the stepped wave with the converter isolated from the utility and the ac capacitors disconnected. It is the ideal stepped wave with the ringing of

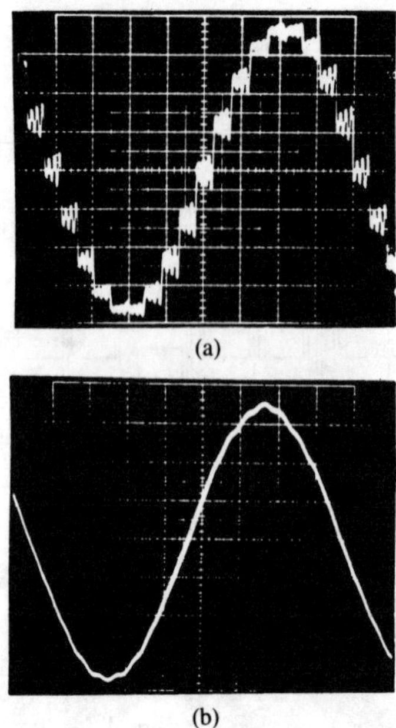

(a)

(b)

Fig. 12. AC terminal voltage waveforms, disconnected from utility. (a) With ac filter capacitors disconnected. (b) With capacitors connected.

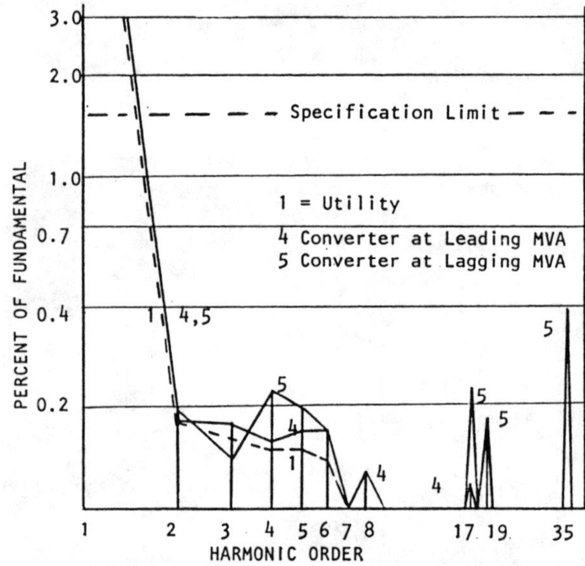

Fig. 13. Voltage harmonics, utility alone and with converter connected at full MVA.

the transformers at each step due to the unterminated secondaries. Fig. 12(b) shows the output voltage with the capacitors connected but still disconnected from the utility. This waveform has a maximum individual harmonic of 1.1 percent of the seventeenth harmonic, compared to 1.5 percent specification limit.

The voltage harmonics of the utility with and without the converter connected are shown in Fig. 13. The broken line marked "1" shows the harmonics of the utility alone. Lines 4 and 5 show the harmonics of the utility with the converter at full rating: line 4 for 10 MVA leading and line 5 for 10 MVA lagging. Line 1 shows that the utility alone has a broad spectrum of low-order harmonics out to the sixth with amplitudes less than 0.2 percent. The connnection of the converter and its capacitance changes those low-order harmonics very little. The converter would be expected to add harmonic components at the seventeenth, nineteenth, thirty-fifth, and thirty-seventh. The values measured at the seventeenth and nineteenth are as expected. The component at the thirty-fifth is larger than expected but still 4:1 below the specification limit. This is indicative of a resonance between the converter capacitance and the grid impedance at the point of connection. The resonance had been predicted from the harmonic analysis which was performed in advance for the Chino substation. As predicted, the harmonic voltages resulting from the resonance were at acceptable levels.

Efficiency

The converter efficiency was evaluated by combining the measurements of battery currents under load and the calcu-

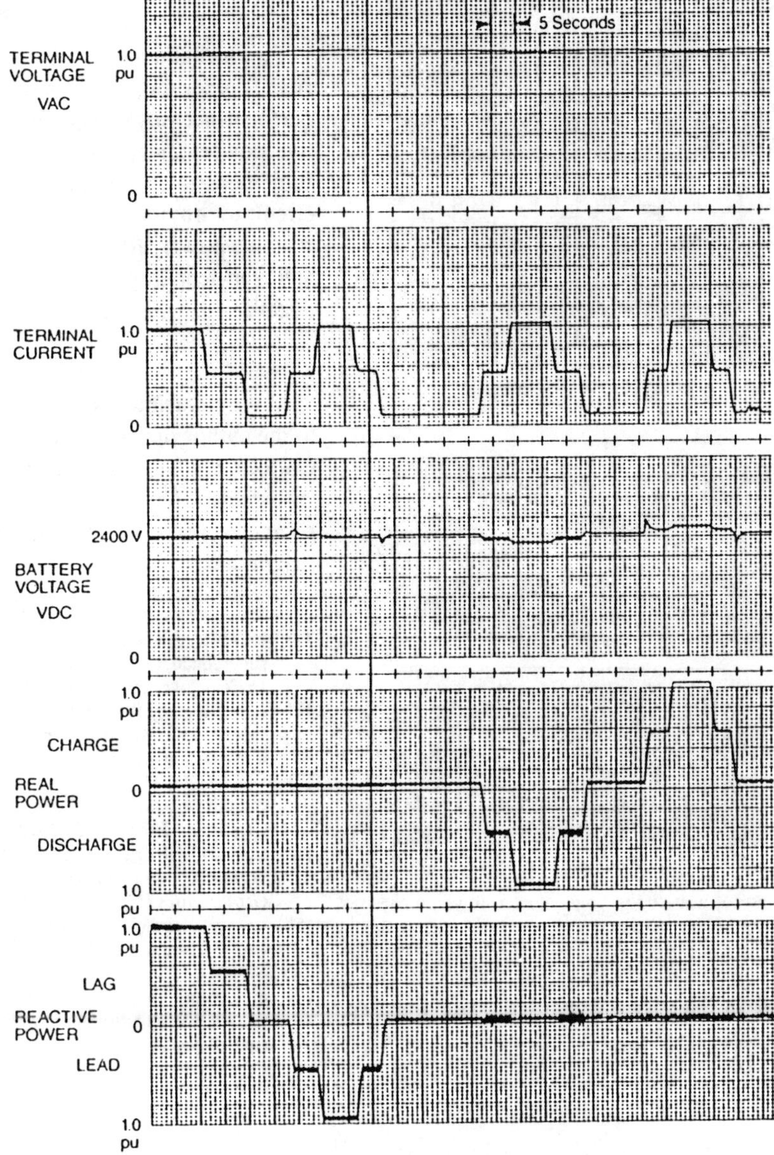

Fig. 14. Transient response of watt and var regulators with rate limited reference steps.

lated or measured losses for blowers, control power, etc. The result was 97.4 percent compared to a goal of 97.0 percent at 10 MW. This efficiency was not a strong function of battery voltage. (As battery voltage goes up, current-related losses go down, but switching and snubber losses increase.)

At 2 MW, the efficiency was measured at 95.4 percent at minimum battery voltage, compared to a goal of 95 percent. This efficiency degraded by approximately one percent as battery voltage increased.

Transient Response

Figs. 14 and 15 show oscillograms of converter transient response performance. In Fig. 14, the commands are rate limited to 0.5 pu/s. Rate limits for load leveling applications would be at this rate or slower. In the traces shown, the converter is at rated MVA lagging when the trace begins (see the bottom trace). It is commanded in steps of 0.5 pu from rated MVA lagging to rated MVA leading. The reactive power command is then returned to zero and the real power command is stepped through a similar pattern, first discharge, then charge at full rating. When the reactive power changes are being made, the real power is not disturbed. The battery voltage is only slightly disturbed, since no real power flows, and the utility voltage is raised slightly by the large leading load. When the real power changes are being made, the reactive power is not disturbed. The battery voltage is substantially affected, and the utility voltage at the terminals is slightly affected.

Fig. 15 shows oscillograms under the same conditions as Fig. 14, but at 200:1 faster recording speed and 2:1 expanded vertical scale. The command steps are no longer rate limited. The step command amplitude is 0.1 pu. Fig. 15(a) shows the changes in real and reactive power with a step applied to the reactive power command. Note that the response of the reactive power trace reaches 0.63 of the command step in 16 ms, as specified. The real power is undisturbed by even such a rapid change of reactive power. Fig. 15(b) shows a 0.1-pu step applied to the real power command. The real power changes

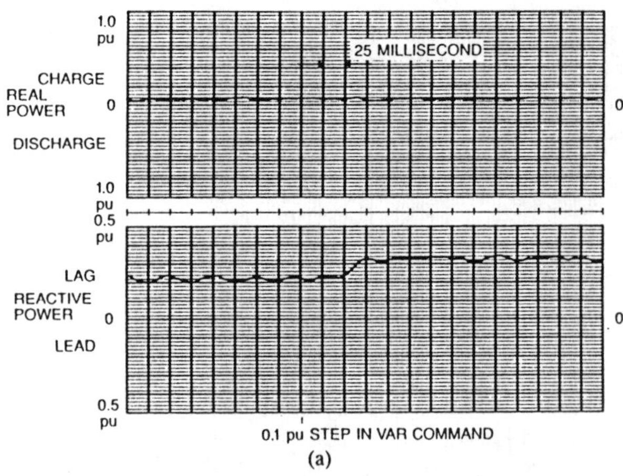

(a)

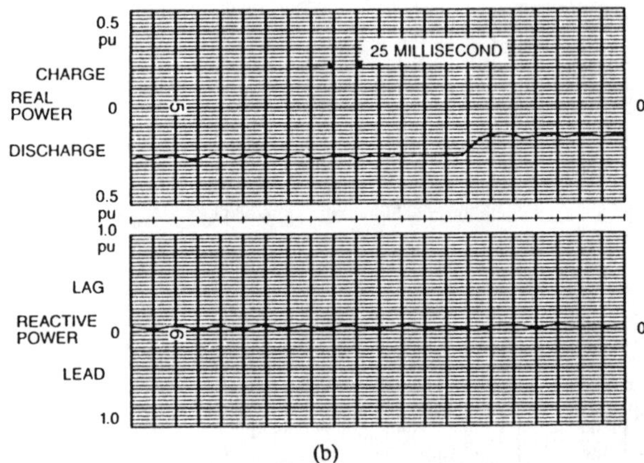

(b)

Fig. 15. Transient response of watt and var regulators with commands not rate-limited (a) 0.1-pu step in reactive power command. (b) 0.1-pu step in real power command.

0.63 of the command in 16 ms as specified. The reactive power is essentially unchanged.

Conclusion

This installation is commissioned and working satisfactorily. It is serving as a demonstration of the practicality of high performance power conversion for energy management, reactive power control, and power system stabilizer applications. It demonstrates the capability of the GTO thyristor power circuit to provide independent fast-response control of real and reactive power. It is a benchmark for the size, cost, efficiency, and transient response which typifies this type of conversion installation.

Acknowledgment

Major contributors to the design of this converter in addition to the author include T. F. Beason (mechanical design), R. A. Carter (regulator software), and R. G. Shiflett (controls and software). The author is grateful to these and many other people whose contribution was essential to a project of this magnitude.

References

[1] J. F. Hauer and H. J. Boenig, "Control aspects of the Tacoma superconducting magnetic energy storage project," in *Conf. Rec. IEEE Power Engineering Society Meeting,* July 20-25, 1986.

[2] J. D. Rogers, R. I. Schermer, B. J. Miller, and J. F. Hauer, "30 MJ superconducting magnetic energy storage system for electric utility transmission stabilization," *Proc. IEEE,* pp. 1099-1107, Sept. 1983.

[3] P. D. Corey, "Methods for optimizing the waveform of stepped-wave static inverters," *Conf. Proc., Aerospace Electrical Conf.,* Denver, CO, June 17-22, 1962, AIEE Paper CP62-1147.

[4] L. H. Walker, "Inverter for UPS with subcycle fault clearing capability," in *Conf. Rec. IEEE/Industry and General Applications Group,* vol. 71, C1-IGA, Oct. 18-21, 1971, pp. 361-370.

[5] ——, "Parallel redundant operation of static power converters," in *Conf. Rec., IEEE/IAS Annual Meeting,* vol. 73, CHO 763-31A, pp. 603-614.

[6] S. Hirose *et al.,* "Multi-microcomputer-based controller for 12MW GTO Power conditioning systems," in *PESC '88 Rec.,* 88CH2523.9, Apr. 1988, pp. 611-618.

Microcomputer Control of a Residential Photovoltaic Power Conditioning System

BIMAL K. BOSE, SENIOR MEMBER, IEEE, PAUL M. SZCZESNY, AND ROBERT L. STEIGERWALD

***Abstract*—Microcomputer-based control of a residential photovoltaic power conditioning system is described. The microcomputer is responsible for array current feedback control, maximum power tracking control, array safe zone steering control, phase-locked reference wave synthesis, sequencing control, and some diagnostics. The control functions are implemented using Intel 8751 single-chip microcomputer-based hardware and software. The controller has been tested in the laboratory with the prototype power conditioner and shows excellent performance.**

INTRODUCTION

As THE WORLD'S conventional sources of energy are dwindling fast, with corresponding rise in cost, solar photovoltaic energy offers a promising alternative source. It is free, abundant, pollution-free, and distributed throughout the earth; the only drawback is that the initial installation cost is considerably high. Photovoltaic energy sources have been well established for space applications where cost is not a consideration, but their terrestrial applications are very limited at present. With the present trend of research, the cost of photovoltaic cells is expected to go down substantially in the future, making them attractive for widespread terrestrial applications.

Photovoltaic power can be generated in houses, intermediate-size commercial installations, or large central power stations. In a residential photovoltaic system (typically a few kilowatts in size), the array is mounted on the roof. The available dc power, which varies with solar insolation and temperature, is converted to single-phase 60-Hz ac and fed to the utility line. The consumer's load is connected at the ac line terminal. In daytime, the solar power supplies to the consumer and the surplus is fed to the utility line; in cloudy weather or after dusk, the utility line feeds the load.

The paper describes microcomputer-based control of a residential photovoltaic power conditioning system, where the microcomputer is responsible for control of the output ac power in accordance with the generated array dc power, maintaining a unity power-factor condition at the ac line terminal. The microcomputer also has the functions of maximum power tracking, steering converter operation within the safe voltage and current zone, mode sequencing, and diagnostics. The power conditioning system with the prototype controller has been designed and thoroughly tested in the laboratory.

Paper IPCSD 85-5, approved by the Static Power Converter Conference of the IEEE Industry Applications Society for presentation at the 1984 Industry Applications Society Annual Meeting, Chicago, IL, April 3–6, 1984. Manuscript released for publication January 21, 1985. This work was supported by the U.S. Department of Energy under Sandia Contract 68-4806.

The authors are with the General Electric Corporate Research and Development Center, 1 River Road, Schenectady, NY 12345.

DESCRIPTION OF POWER CONDITIONING SYSTEM

The power conversion scheme used in the present system is shown in Fig. 1. Basically, the dc array power is converted to 60-Hz ac line power through an isolated high-frequency transformer link. The dc voltage of the photovoltaic array is first converted to high-frequency ac by an inverter, which is then transformer-coupled and converted to 60-Hz ac line current through a dc link ac–ac converter. The ac–ac converter consists of a high-frequency rectifier, filter, and a polarity-reversing inverter as shown. The principal waveforms at different stages of conversion, which will be explained later, are indicated in the figure. Compared to the conventional 60-Hz line commutation scheme with transformer isolation, the high-frequency link scheme used here permits considerable weight reduction of the power converter and smooth fabrication of the sinusoidal output current wave in phase with the *line voltage*. Of course, the multistage power conversion is somewhat more expensive and adversely affects the efficiency of the converter. The electrical isolation in the high-frequency link is essential because it permits easy array grounding, flexibility in selecting array voltage range, array isolation from the utility in case of fault, and safety of personnel.

The power circuit details with the controller block diagram are shown in Fig. 2, and Table I gives the power conditioner specifications. The variable dc array voltage is inverted to high-frequency ac by a full-bridge transistor inverter which operates in the frequency range 10–16 kHz.

The ac voltage in high-frequency link has a PWM waveshape which is sinusoidally modulated by a 60-Hz wave, as shown in Fig. 1. The high-frequency PWM wave is rectified by a diode-bridge rectifier, which, after filtering the carrier components, has the waveshape of full-wave rectified sine wave. The resulting sinusoidal dc link current is alternately flipped by the polarity-reversing transistor inverter and is fed to the ac line so that it is in phase with the ac voltage. The high-frequency transistor inverter with the rectifier and filter inductance L can be considered a high-frequency link dc–dc buck chopper where the transistors are being controlled to synthesize a full-wave rectified sine current wave in the dc link. The chopper is operating with a full-wave rectified sine voltage counter-EMF wave impressed by the polarity-reversing inverter. Since the fundamental frequency power at converter output must balance the array output, the dc array current fluctuates with a large second harmonic, as shown in

Reprinted from *IEEE Trans. Ind. Applicat.*, vol. IA-21, no. 5, pp. 1182–1191, September/October 1985.

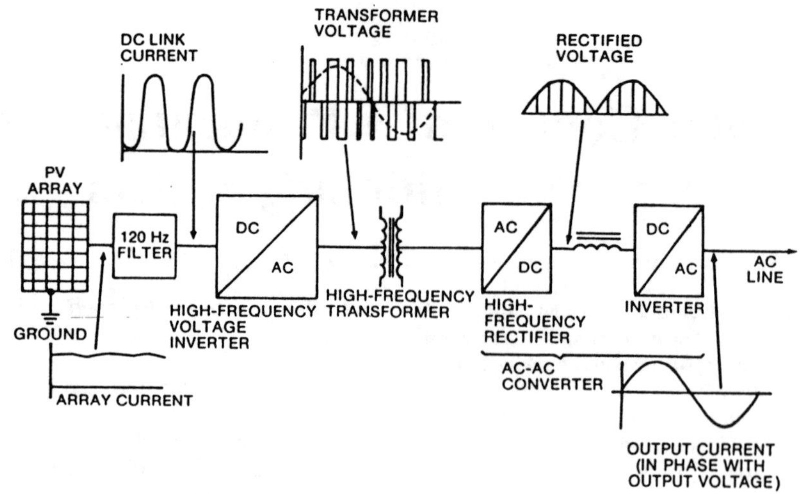

Fig. 1. High-frequency link power conversion scheme.

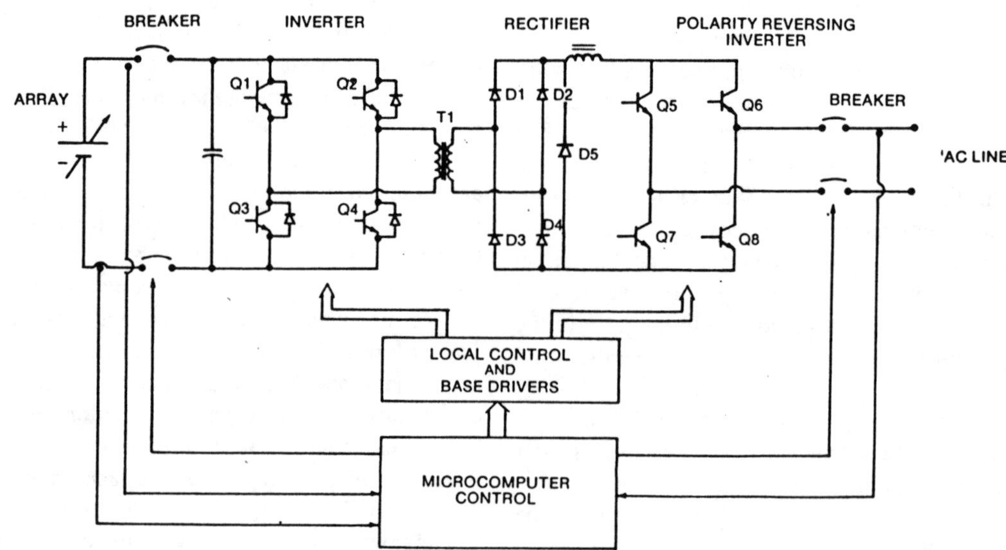

Fig. 2. Power circuit with controller.

TABLE I
POWER CONDITIONER SPECIFICATIONS

DC Input	nominal voltage = 200 V (dc) voltage range = 160 to 240 V (dc) Survival range = 0 to 350 V (dc)
AC Output	nominal voltage = 230 V (ac) voltage range = 86.7–105.8% of nominal nominal output = 4 kW power factor = unity line frequency = 58–62 Hz total harmonic distortion (current) ≤5 percent (no single harmonic > 3 percent) total harmonic distortion (voltage) ≤2 percent (no single harmonic > 1 percent) dc injection to line < 0.5 percent of rated dc input current nominal efficiency = 90 percent switching frequency = 10–16 kHz

Fig. 1. A large capacitor filter is provided to smoothen the array current.

SOLAR ARRAY CHARACTERISTICS

The solar array characteristics profoundly influence the converter and control system, and therefore these will be briefly reviewed here. Fig. 3 shows the typical array volt-ampere curves at different light intensity λ but at constant temperature. More generally, the array cell static characteristics, as a function of light intensity and temperature, are given by the equation

$$I = I_{LG} - I_0 \left\{ \exp\left[\frac{q}{AKT}(V + I_A R_S)\right] - 1 \right\} \tag{1}$$

where

$$I_0 = I_{or}\left[\frac{T}{T_r}\right]^3 \exp\left[\frac{qE_{G0}}{BK}\left\{\frac{1}{T_r} - \frac{1}{T}\right\}\right] \tag{2}$$

$$I_{LG} = [I_{SCR} + K_1(T_C - 28)]\lambda/100. \tag{3}$$

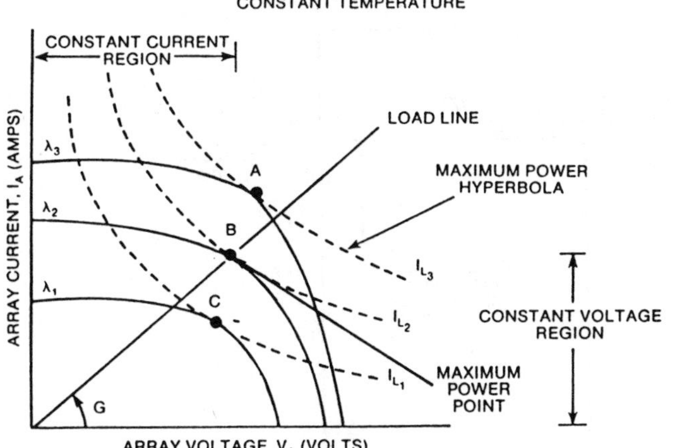

Fig. 3. Array volt-ampere curves showing maximum power and load line hyperbolas.

All the symbols in (1)–(3) can be defined as

- I cell output current,
- V cell output voltage,
- I_0 cell saturation current,
- T cell temperature in K,
- K/q Boltzmann's constant divided by electronic charge 8.62×10^{-5} eV/K,
- T_c cell temperature in °C,
- K_I short circuit current temperature coefficient at I_{SCR} 0.0017 A/°C,
- λ cell illumination (mW/cm^2),
- I_{SCR} cell sort circuit current at 28°C and 100 mW/cm^2 2.52 A,
- I_{LG} light-generated current,
- E_{GO} band gap for silicon = 1.11 eV,
- B = A, ideality factors = 1.92,
- T_r reference temperature = 301.18 K,
- I_{or} saturation current at T_r = 19.9693×10^{-6},
- R_S series resistance = 0.001.

The converter which is connected at the array terminal can be represented by an equivalent resistive load at static condition. The intersection of the load line with conductance slope G and the array $V_A - I_A$ curve defines the operating point and the corresponding dc power absorbed by the converter. A constant power locus is a hyperbola, and the maximum power hyperbolas touch the respective $V_A - I_A$ curves as shown. If the converter is assumed lossless and the utility line voltage remains constant, then, from the power balance equation,

$$P_L = V_L I_L = V_A I_A = P_A$$

$$\text{or } I_L = \frac{V_A I_A}{V_L} = \kappa P_A \tag{4}$$

where the line voltages and currents are given in rms values.

Equation (4) indicates that each maximum power hyperbola corresponds to a definite magnitude of line current I_L. The region of the $V_A - I_A$ curve above the maximum power point is defined as the constant current region, whereas the region below is defined as the constant voltage region. The array output power can be controlled by controlling the load line slope G. For a certain $V_A - I_A$ curve, as the value G is increased from zero, the array power first increases until it reaches the maximum value and then decreases. In steady-state operation, it is desirable to adjust G so that maximum array power becomes available.

DESCRIPTION OF CONTROL SYSTEM

The power conditioner has a microcomputer-based control system, and the control functions can be described as follows.

Feedback Array Current Control

The function of the feedback control is to maintain a balance between array power and the power fed to the utility line, assuring stability under all operating conditions. A block diagram of the control system is shown in Fig. 4, where the portion under microcomputer control is indicated within the dotted line. The feedback control system is designed in such a way that the power conditioner appears as a resistive load at the array terminal in steady-state condition with load line slope G. It is essentially a feedback array current control system where the command array current I_A^* is generated from the actual array voltage V_A by multiplying with the desired load line slope G. The feedback array current I_A is compared with I_A^*, and the resulting error generates the line current command $I_L^{*\prime}$ through a PI compensator. The current $I_L^{*\prime}$ is multiplied by a unit peak amplitude sine reference wave i_u to generate the line current reference wave I_L^*. The current i_u is generated by the phase-locked loop (PLL) principle to be cophasal with the utility voltage. Therefore, the current I_L^*, if flipped alternately by the polarity-reversing inverter, will be cophasal with the line voltage wave. The actual ac link current is forced to track the command I_L^* by the hysteresis band bang-bang control principle of the high-frequency transistor inverter. If G is increased in the constant voltage region, the voltage V_A remains relatively constant, but I_A^* increases which correspondingly increases I_L^* until I_A balances I_A^*. If G is increased in constant current region, I_L^* tends to increase, but reduction of V_A reduces I_L^* while maintaining approximately constant I_A, so that the power balance is restored. For the constant G, if the array light intensity, the λ, or temperature T changes, similar power balance is maintained by the feedback loop. In practical operation, hardly any large transient is impressed on the system because of gradual change of the λ and T parameters. In the worst case, if a shadow is cast by a plane flying over the array or by a cloud, the feedback loop response will be fast enough so as to appear as a steady-state condition during the transition. The command G is available from safe-zone steering control, maximum power tracking control, or from a manually operated potentiometer for test purposes. The manual G command is normally ramped in software to induce slow transient though there is provision for step input.

Discretization of Compensator: The proportional–integral (PI) compensator in the feedback loop is being implemented by microcomputer, and, therefore, it requires time domain

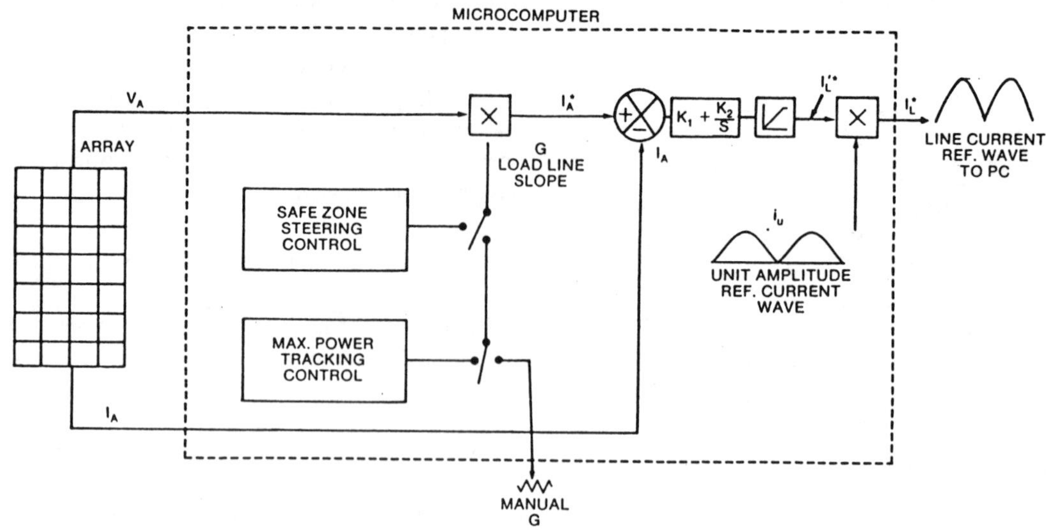

Fig. 4. Block diagram of control system.

discretization. The compensator transfer function is given as

$$\frac{Y(S)}{X(S)}=K_1+\frac{K_2}{S} \tag{5}$$

where K_1 is the proportional gain and K_2 is the integral gain. Equation (5) can be written in the form

$$SY(S)=K_2X(S)+K_1SX(S). \tag{6}$$

Equation (6) can be represented in finite-difference form as follows, assuming that the feedback loop computation sampling time T_S (2.3 ms) is relatively small:

$$\frac{Y(n+1)-Y(n)}{T_S}=K_2X(n)+K_1\left[\frac{X(n+1)-X(n)}{T_S}\right] \tag{7}$$

where n, $n+1$, etc., are the sampling instants. Equation (7) can be simplified as

$$Y(n+1)-Y(n)=K_2T_SX(n)+K_1X(n+1)-K_1X(n) \tag{8}$$

or

$$Y(n+1)=Y(n)+K_1X(n+1) + [K_2T_S-K_1]X(n). \tag{9}$$

Equation (9) can be expressed in standard state variable form as

$$Z(n+1)=AZ(n)+BX(n) \tag{10}$$

$$Y(n)=CZ(n)+DX(n) \tag{11}$$

where $Z(n)$ is the state variable, $A = 1$, $B = K_2T_S$, $C = 1$, and $D = K_1$. The block diagram for digital implementation of the compensator is shown in Fig. 5.

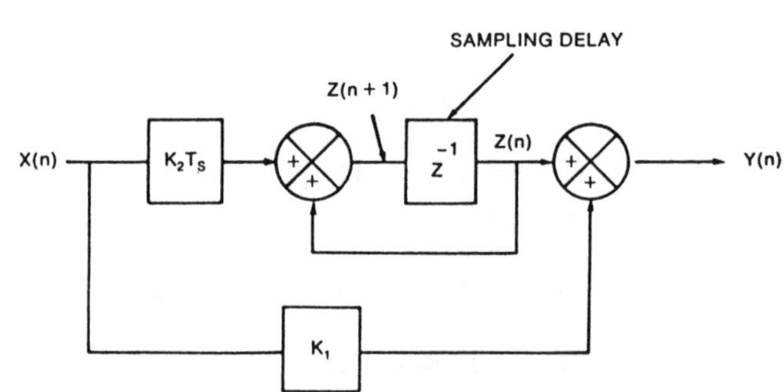

Fig. 5. Digital implementation of PI compensator.

Phase-Locked Line Current Reference Wave Synthesis: As explained earlier, the power conditioner is controlled in such a way that it operates as a sinusoidal current source synchronized in-phase with the utility line voltage. The phase position of the current wave I_L* is dictated by the unit amplitude reference current wave i_u which is generated in the microcomputer by the PLL technique. Fig. 6 shows the waveforms for this reference wave synthesis. The utility line voltage v_L, which normally contains ripple, is filtered (v_L'), and correspondingly an in-phase square wave is generated by a zero crossing detector. The v_L' wave lags the v_L wave by $\theta°$ as shown. The i_u wave is to be in phase with the v_L wave irrespective of line frequency variation (typically 58–62 Hz). The phase locking is achieved by a set of three timers: a frequency timer (T_C), a synchronous timer (T_S), and a 2° timer (T_L). The i_u reference wave is synthesized with a 2° sampling period and an 8-b amplitude resolution, i.e., 90 samples in the half-cycle period. The T_C timer counts a clock of 1 MHz in the half-cycle period to determine the line frequency. If the frequency deviates from 60 Hz, the deviation Δf or the corresponding count deviation ΔW_C is determined by linear extrapolation. The 2° timer, which is autoreload type, generates interrupts at 2° intervals, and a lookup table is retrieved to generate the i_u wave. The i_u wave is terminated at $\alpha_1 = 176°$ to assure that the dc link current reduces to zero at 180°. The pointer for the sine wave lookup table is synchronized at 0° of the v_L wave by the sync. timer (T_S) interrupt. The T_S and T_L timers are initially loaded with counts corresponding to 60-Hz but are corrected periodically for frequency deviation by the following relations

$$\Delta W_C=W_C-W_{60} \tag{12}$$

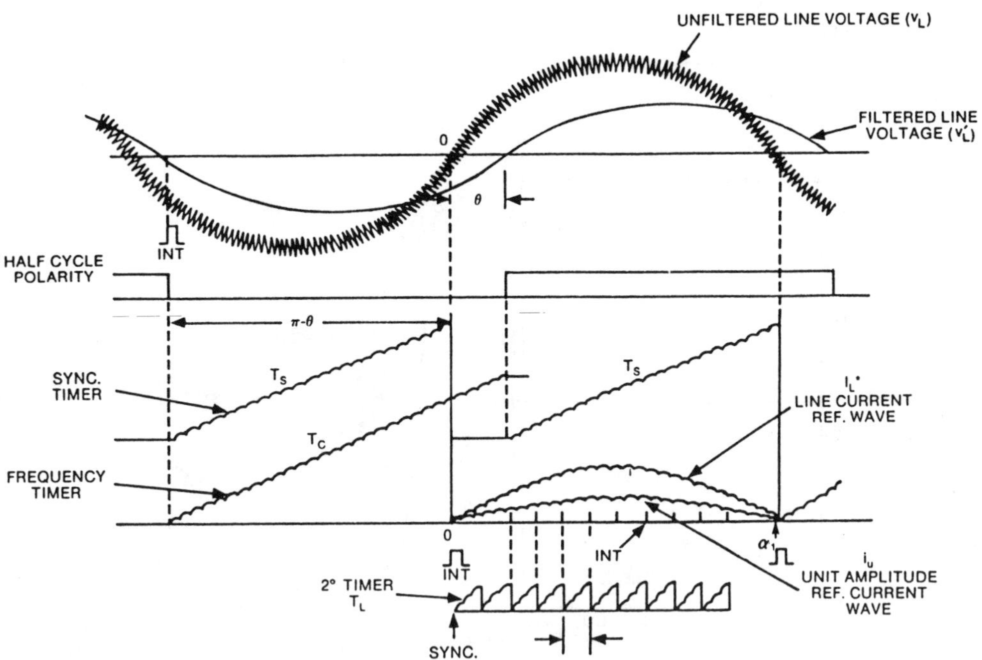

Fig. 6. Waveforms for phase-locked line current reference wave synthesis.

$$\Delta W_S = \frac{\pi - \theta}{\pi} \Delta W_C \tag{13}$$

$$\Delta W_L = \frac{2}{\pi} \Delta W_C \tag{14}$$

$$W_S = W_{S0} + \Delta W_S \tag{15}$$

$$W_L = W_{L0} + \Delta W_L \tag{16}$$

where

W_{60}, W_{S0}, W_{L0}	count at 60 Hz of T_C, T_S, and T_L counters, respectively,
ΔW_S, ΔW_L	count correction of T_S and T_L, respectively,
W_S, W_L	corrected count of T_S and T_L, respectively.

The i_u wave is loaded to a multiplying DA converter where it is multiplied by the analog form of the I_L*' signal to generate the I_L* wave. This method maintains 8-b amplitude resolution at any magnitude of I_L*'.

Safe Zone Steering Control

The function of the safe zone steering control is to limit the array voltage and current within the specified range so as to assure safe operation of the power conditioner. This type of control becomes especially important if the power conditioner is required to operate on arbitrary array size. Fig. 7 shows the safe zone operation on the array volt-ampere curves. The power conditioner cannot operate below the minimum array voltage of 160 V because excessive counter-EMF due to utility voltage will cause discontinuous conduction, and, as a result, the harmonics in the array and ac line become excessive. The higher array voltage is limited to 240 V as dictated by the voltage rating of the high-frequency inverter. The lowest array current, which is typically 1 A, is limited by the power conditioner losses. The upper array current is limited by the kilowatt size of the power conditioner. Note that the power conditioner current capability is clamped for I_L = 17.4 A, irrespective of ac line voltage. This means that if line voltage increases above 230 V nominal, the corresponding array power will go up, causing a shift of the upper boundary hyperbola of the safe zone, and vice versa.

The safe zone steering control is achieved by manipulating the load line slope G. Fig. 4 shows that the safe zone steering has an overriding control on G, over the maximum power tracking and manual G controls. The dotted lines within the safe zone indicate margin beyond which the safe zone steering control is to be exercised. If, for example, the array voltage tends to fall below the lower limit, G is decremented, whereas if the voltage tends to exceed the upper limit, G is incremented. The system then settles down within the dotted line boundaries with the response delay of the feedback control system. If the operating point tends to move outside the upper boundary hyperbola, the clamping of I_L*' (in Fig. 4) is detected, which immediately restores G to the value I_A/V_A so that the feedback loop always remains active. An active feedback loop is essential for safe zone steering control to be effective. Anytime the safe zone steering routine becomes active, the maximum power tracking control is halted for 1 min which will be discussed later. The power conditioner is shut down in case the array voltge falls beyond the safe zone limits.

Maximum Power Tracking

The maximum power tracking control permits extraction of maximum available power from the solar array in steady-state operation. This is done by an on-line search technique by manipulation of G, as explained in Fig. 8. Assume that

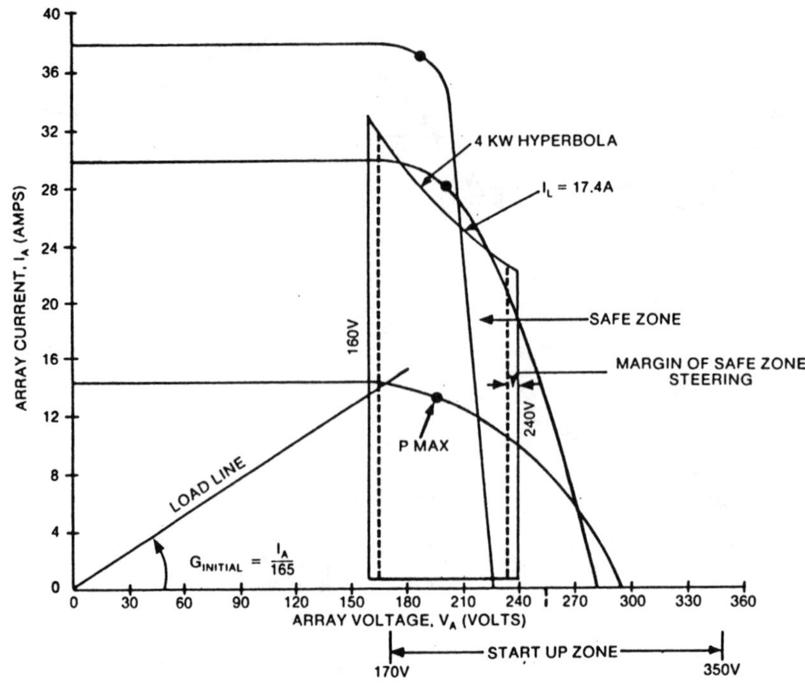

Fig. 7. Array volt-ampere curves showing safe zone operation of power conditioner.

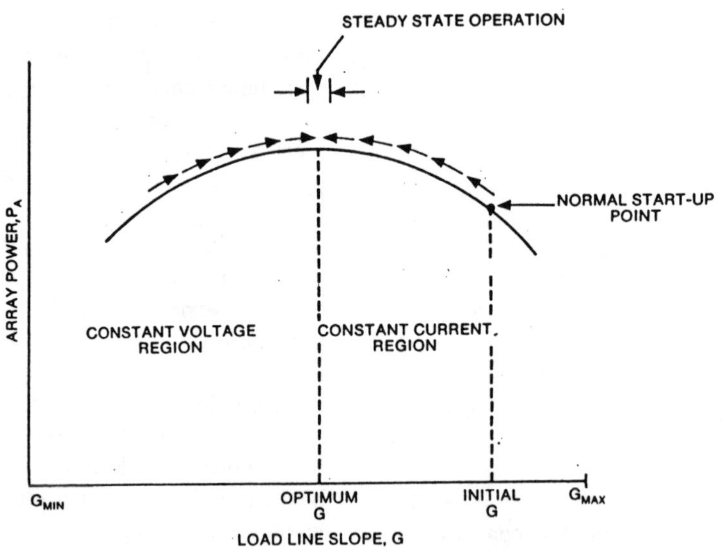

Fig. 8. Maximum power tracking control principle.

initially the feedback loop becomes active in the constant current region with initial G as shown. The microcomputer decrements G and compares the new power with the old power. If ΔP_A is positive, the decrementing is continued in the same direction until optimum G corresponding to maximum P_A is reached. If initially G is incremented, indicating negative ΔP_A, the search will be abandoned in that direction. If initial operation starts in the constant current region, G is incremented to reach the optimum point. In steady state, operate oscillates at the margin of constant voltage and constant current regions. Fig. 9 shows the flowchart for the maximum power tracking algorithm. Note that for P_A computation, four consecutive samples are taken and averaged to prevent ambiguity due to the jitter effect. The routine is executed at a shorter sampling time (185.1 ms) initially but settles down to longer time (185.1 × 3 ms) at steady-state condition. The splitting of sampling time minimizes acquisition time to the PMAX point after the startup condition but reduces the subharmonic ripple of I_L at steady operating condition.

At the boundary of the safe zone, it is possible that safe zone and maximum power tracking controls exercise conflicting commands of G inducing sustained oscillation of current $I_L{}^{*\prime}$. This will occur if the PMAX point falls outside the safe zone boundary. This condition is avoided by halting the PMAX search for 1 min when safe zone control is activated.

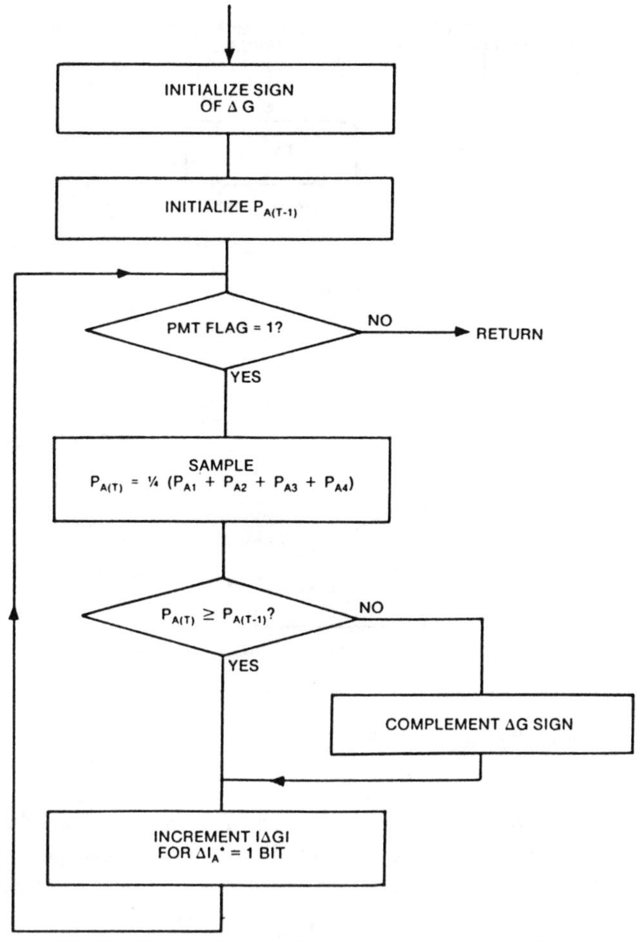

Fig. 9. Flowchart for maximum power tracking algorithm.

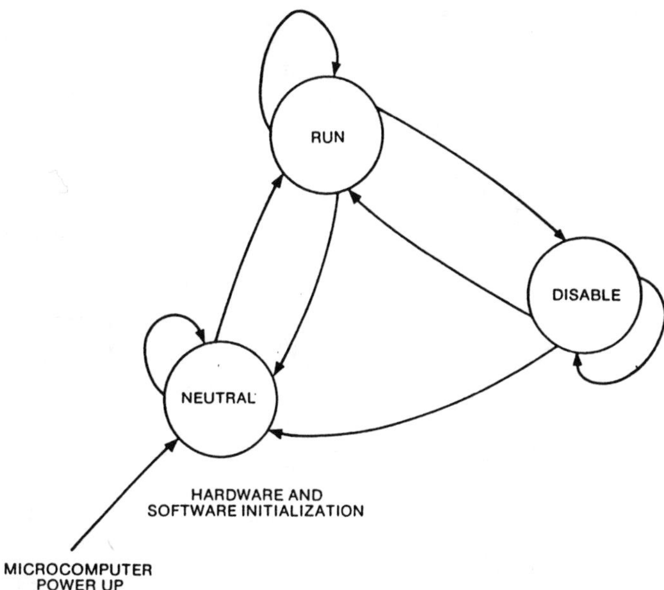

Fig. 10. Simplified system sequencing diagram.

Mode Sequencing

The system has several modes of operation which can be explained by the simplified sequence diagram shown in Fig. 10. As indicated, there are essentially three modes of operation, and the permissible transition paths between the modes are shown by arrows. A mode transition is initiated if a Boolean function corresponding to a set of conditionals is satisfied; the transition is completed by executing a set of action routines. When operating within a mode, the microcomputer tests the Boolean functions repeatedly (92.6 ms) and falls back to the present mode if transition is unsuccessful.

With the power supply activated, the microcomputer attains NEUTRAL mode after hardware and software initialization. The transition to RUN mode is initiated if the following conditions are satisfied:

- 58 Hz < line frequency < 62 Hz for 5 s
- 87 percent < line voltage < 105 percent for 5 s
- 170 *V* < array voltage < 350 V for 5 s.

Then the array and line breakers are closed, and the input filter capacitor starts charging at a nearly constant current rate. When the safe zone is entered, the feedback control is activated with initial *G* value. Then, as the system stabilizes, the maximum power tracking control shifts the operation to the PMAX point. The system goes to the DISABLE mode if line frequency falls beyond the range of 58–62 Hz but restores to the RUN mode when the range is revived and open-loop array voltage is within the permissible limit. At any operating condition, the system will transition to the NEUTRAL mode for the following conditions:

- 58 Hz > line frequency > 62 Hz for 2 s
- 110 percent < line voltage < 80 percent for 2 s
- 240 V < array voltage < 160 V.

At dawn or dusk, there is the possibility that the system will chatter between the RUN and NEUTRAL modes when the operating point is near the lower left-hand corner of the safe zone. This condition is prevented by providing a 2-min time delay at shutdown.

HARDWARE AND SOFTWARE DESIGN

The controller hardware is based on the Intel 8751 8-b single-chip microcomputer, which is supported by analog and digital I/O hardware. The microcomputer contains 4 kbytes of EPROM, 128 bytes of RAM, 32 I/O lines, and two 16-b timer/counters, as well as two external interrupts. With a 10-MHz crystal, the typical instruction cycle time is 1.2 μs, and unsigned 8-b multiply and divide instructions take 4.8 μs. The microcomputer has, in addition, powerful Boolean processing capability, which makes the sequencing software very efficient.

The controller software is implemented in Assembly language, and a structure chart of the software is shown in Fig. 11. The six tasks and functions under each task are summarized in the figure. Tasks 1, 5, and 6 are interrupt-driven and have highest priority, whereas tasks 2, 3, and 4 are time-scheduled and are controlled by the real time scheduler (RTS). The interrupt-driven tasks all have equal priority which is greater than the RTS-activated tasks. Task 1 is executed nominally at a 92.5-μs (2°) interval and the task 2, 3, and 4 intervals are generated by software timers where each time interval has integral ratio with the corresponding lower level

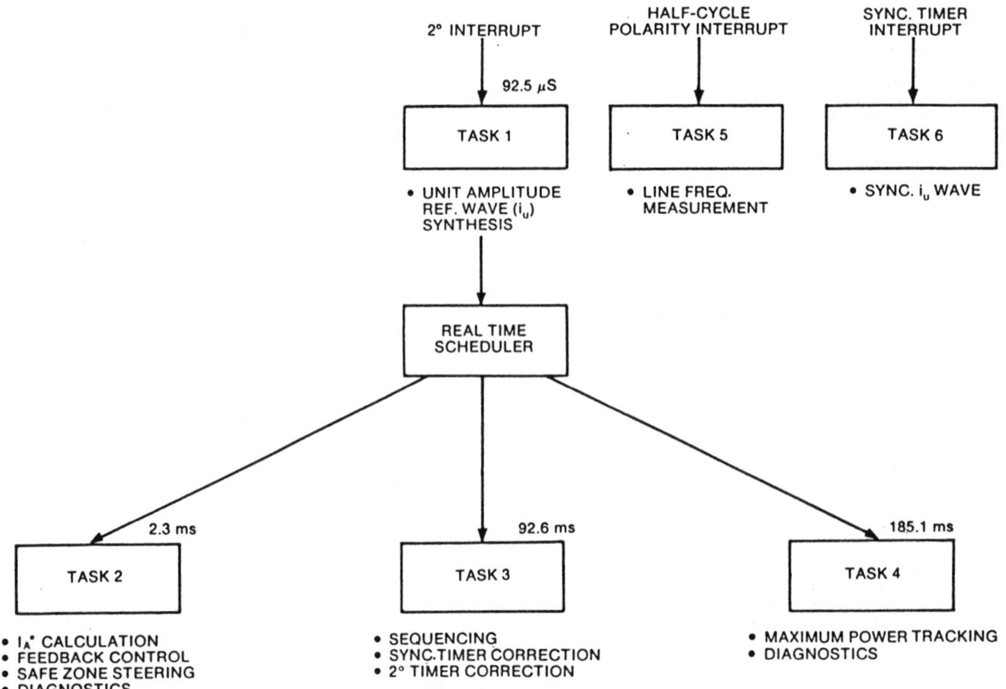

Fig. 11. Structure chart of controller software.

interval. The RTS executes the tasks in order of their priority levels, and a lower scheduling interval is given higher priority level. The RTS is designed to allow a task to temporarily overrun its time allotment without causing any malfunction in the system. This feature has been especially useful in NEUTRAL → RUN sequencing (task 3) when task 4 is temporarily suspended. A software idle time counter indicates loading of the microcomputer. A watchdog timer with red and green lights is provided; it is essentially a retriggerable one-shot that is triggered every 2.3 ms. The red lights indicate any maloperation of the microcomputer; the green light indicates healthy conditions.

A plug-in type diagnostic panel is designed to debug and test the controller software. The instrument is extremely useful, especially in developmental stage debugging. The panel has two DA converters, hex LED displays, and thumbwheel switches by which the specified memory locations can be read or written. For example, the selected software variables in the feedback loop can be updated to DAC's at a 2.3-ms rate, which can then be displayed on a scope or chart recorder to indicate transient performance. The adjustable constants, such as compensator gains, can be fine-tuned with the diagnostic panel during the operating condition of the system.

LABORATORY TESTS

A prototype power conditioner and microcomuter controller were built and thoroughly tested in the laboratory, and performances were found to be excellent. A Sorenson power supply, type DCR 300-35A with adjustable voltage and current limit control was available to simulate the solar array. It should be mentioned that the power supply does not exactly simulate the array. For example, in the crossover between the constant voltage and constant current modes, there is a hysteresis which depends on the rate of transition. Since the power supply has a large output filter capacitor, the power conditioner input capacitor had to be precharged during startup operation.

All the software functions, including the sequencing software, were tested. The proportional and integral gains for the compensator were found to be different in constant voltage and constant current regions to achieve optimal responses. However, for simplicity, a compromise was made so as to ensure stability in both regions with common gain values. Fig. 12 shows step response of the feedback loop in the constant voltage region with a manual G step initiated from the diagnostic panel. Fig. 13 shows the corresponding response in the constant current region. At the onset of the transient, I_A*, I_A, and I_L*' increase temporarily, extracting the stored energy from the input filter capacitor, but the fall of array voltage V_A gradually restores operation to the steady state when I_L*' is reduced. It is important to note that this type of disturbance is unlikely in a practical system and is intended to assure adequate stability conditions. Again, it is expected that with the actual array the responses will be much better.

Fig. 14 shows the maximum power tracking control when it is activated with minimum G in the constant operation when it is activated with minimum G in the constant voltage region. It takes 17 s to attain the PMAX point (2 kW), as shown in the figure. The overshoot in the I_L*' curve is due to the characteristics of the power supply, as mentioned above. There will be a small amount of overshoot in the actual array, but it is expected to be much smaller than in Fig. 14.

The actual waveform of I_L was found to have some distortion due to the lagging effect of the dc link inducatance L. This was corrected experimentally by squeezing 2° intervals as a function of array voltage during 90° and 180° intervals.

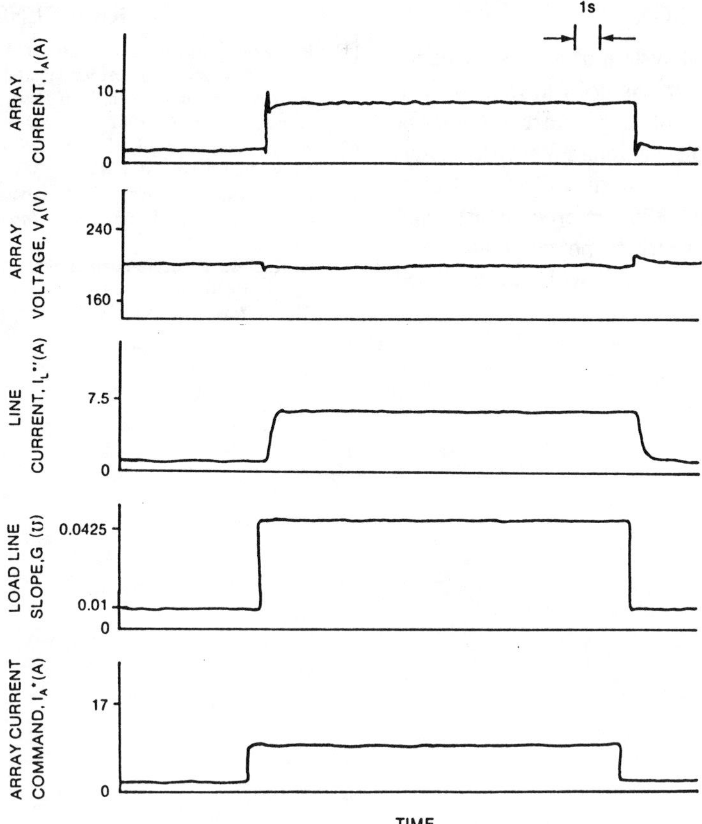

Fig. 12. Step response in constant-voltage region.

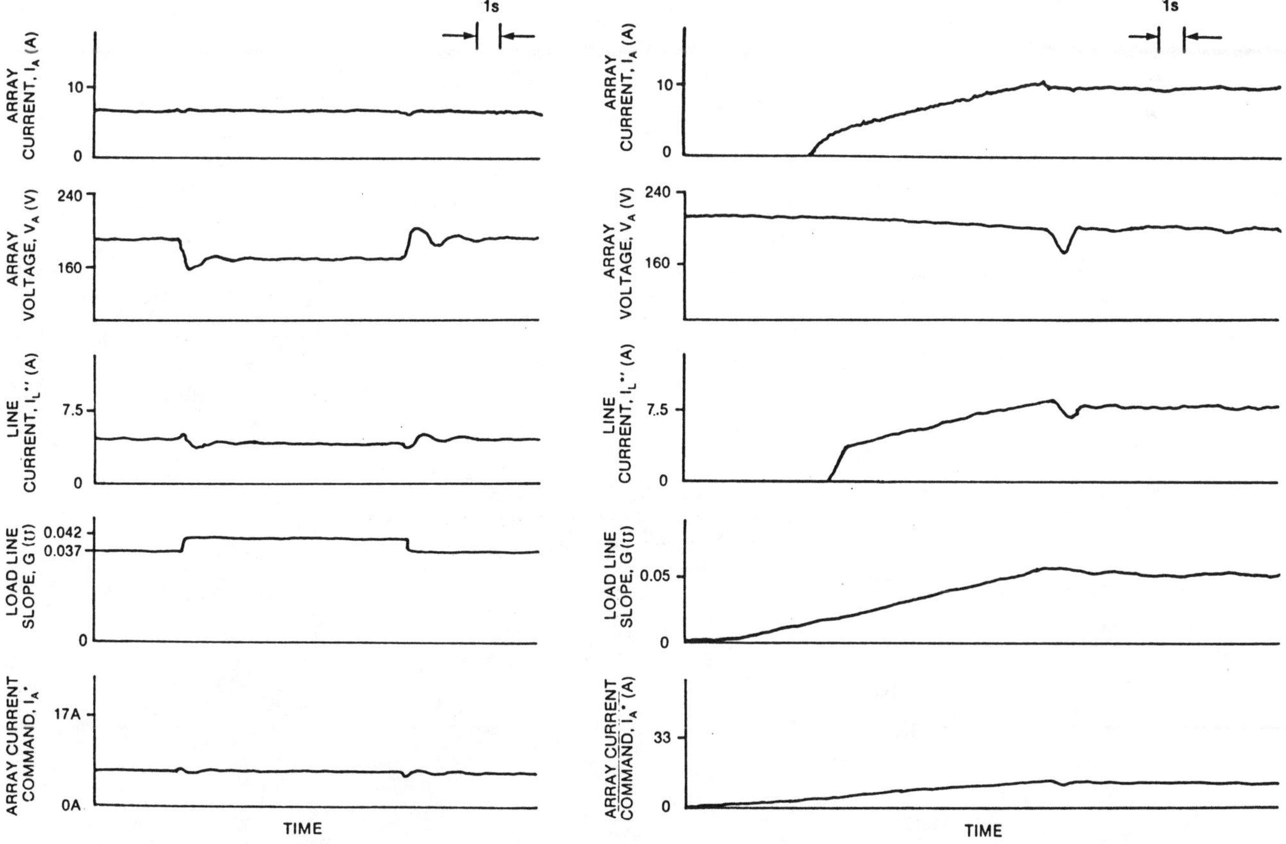

Fig. 13. Step response in constant-current region.

Fig. 14. Maximum power tracking control operation.

CONCLUSION

A microcomputer-based control system of a 4-kW residential photovoltaic power conditioner has been described. The microcomputer has the functions of array current feedback control, safe zone steering control, maximum power tracking, sequencing, and some amount of diagnostics. The controller has been designed with an Intel 8751 microcomputer and tested in the laboratory with the prototype power conditioner, and test results were found to agree well with the predicted performance.

REFERENCES

[1] R. L. Steigerwald, A. Ferraro, and F. G. Turnbull, "Application of power transistors to residential and intermediate rating photovoltaic array power conditioners," in *Proc. IEEE/Intl. Static Power Conv. Conf.*, pp. 84–96, 1982.

[2] H. S. Rauschenback, *Solar Cell Array Design Handbook* New York: Van Nostrand, 1980.

[3] B. K. Bose, "A microprocessor-based control system for a near-term electric vehicle," *IEEE Trans. Ind. Appl.*, vol. IA-17, pp. 626–631, Nov./Dec. 1981.

[4] B. K. Bose, C. B. Somuah, and H. A. Sutherland, "A microcomputer-based propulsion control system of a hybrid electric vehicle," *IEEE Trans. Ind. Electron.*, vol. IE-31, pp. 61–68, Feb. 1984.

Paper 8.5

Control Strategy of Active Power Filters Using Multiple Voltage-Source PWM Converters

HIROFUMI AKAGI, AKIRA NABAE, MEMBER, IEEE, AND SATOSHI ATOH

Abstract—**The control strategy of active power filters using switching devices is proposed on the basis of the instantaneous reactive power theory. This aims at excellent compensation characteristics in transient states as well as steady states. The active power filter is developed, of which the power circuit consists of quadruple voltage-source PWM converters. As the result, interesting compensation characteristics were verified experimentally which could not be obtained by the active power filter based on the conventional reactive power theory.**

Introduction

IN RECENT YEARS, active power filters have been researched and developed to suppress harmonics generated by static power converters and large capacity power apparatus [1]–[5]. Notably, attention has been paid to the active power filter using switching devices such as power transistors, gate-turn-off (GTO) thyristors, and static induction (SI) thyristors, which have made remarkable progress in capacity and switching performance. Various power circuit configurations of the active power filter have been proposed, and the compensation characteristics in steady states have been shown experimentally by Gyugyi and others [6]–[8]. To put the active power filter into practical use, however, it is important to discuss the following:

1) the control strategy, taking into account transient states as well as steady states,
2) the high-efficiency large-capacity converter used as the power circuit,
3) the current control scheme of the converter.

In this paper, the control strategy of the active power filter is proposed on the basis of the instantaneous reactive power theory developed in [9]. This is quite different in principle from the conventional control strategy, thus giving better compensation characteristics in transient states. An experimental active power filter was constructed, of rating 7 kVA (200 V, 20 A). The power circuit consisted of quadruple voltage-source PWM converters using 24 power transistors as the switching devices. The main purpose of the multiple converters was to suppress the harmonics caused by the switching operation without increasing the switching frequency.

The validity of the active power filter was confirmed experimentally. A three-phase thyristor bridge converter of rating 20 kVA was used as an example of harmonic current generators. It was verified that the harmonic current[1] can be fully eliminated not only in steady states, but also in transient states, applying the control strategy proposed in this paper. Through the experiments, the average switching frequency of the power transistors was set to a practical value, i.e., 1.5 ~ 2 kHz, and the total efficiency of the active power filter was 90 ~ 92 percent, including the loss of the multiple transformers.

Paper IPCSD 85-46, approved by the Industrial Drives Committee of the IEEE Industry Applications Society for presentation at the 1985 Industry Applications Society Annual Meeting, Toronto, ON, Canada, October 6–11.

H. Akagi and A. Nabae are with the Technological University of Nagaoka, Nagaoka 949-54, Japan.

S. Atoh is with the Toyo Electric Manufacturing Company, Ltd., Yamato 242, Japan.

IEEE Log Number 8607513.

Active Power Filter System

Basic Compensation Principle

Fig. 1 shows a basic compensation principle of active power filters. The compensation objectives of active power filters are the harmonics present in the input currents i_{Lu}, i_{Lv}, and i_{Lw} of the load. Since the compensating currents i_{Cu}, i_{Cv}, and i_{Cw} are controlled so as to eliminate the harmonic currents of the load, the source currents i_{Su}, i_{Sv}, and i_{Sw} become sinusoidal.

Power Circuit Configuration

Fig. 2 shows the active power filter system developed in this paper. The quadruple voltage-source PWM converters are adopted as the power circuit. Note that the primary windings of the four three-phase transformers are connected to each other in series. So, the primary voltage of each transformer is 50 V and the secondary is 100 V. The primary windings of the four transformers can be connected to each other in parallel if the transformers of primary voltage (200 V) and secondary voltage (100 V) are applied. The multiple converters in parallel, however, are less efficient than those in series because of the increase of harmonic currents in each secondary winding and converter.

The converter is a conventional three-phase bridge converter consisting of six power transistors and six power diodes connected back-to-back, as shown in Fig. 3. The turn-off time of the power transistors was about 15 μs and nearly equal to that of large capacity GTO thyristors.

Control Strategy Based on Instantaneous Reactive Power Theory

Instantaneous Reactive Power Theory

Transformation of the phase voltages e_u, e_v, and e_w and the load currents i_{Lu}, i_{Lv}, and i_{Lw} into the $\alpha - \beta$ orthogonal

[1]The term "harmonic" is used in a broad sense to apply to all the distortion components, regardless of their frequency relationship to the fundamental line frequency. Likewise, the term "subharmonic" frequency is taken to mean any frequency below the line frequency, and the term "superharmonic" frequency is taken to mean any frequency above the line frequency [10].

Reprinted from *IEEE Trans. Ind. Applicat.*, vol. IA-22, no. 3, pp. 460–465, May/June 1986.

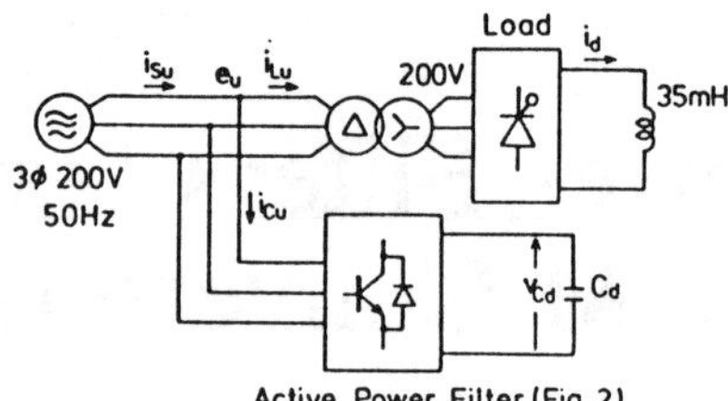

Fig. 1. Basic compensation principle.

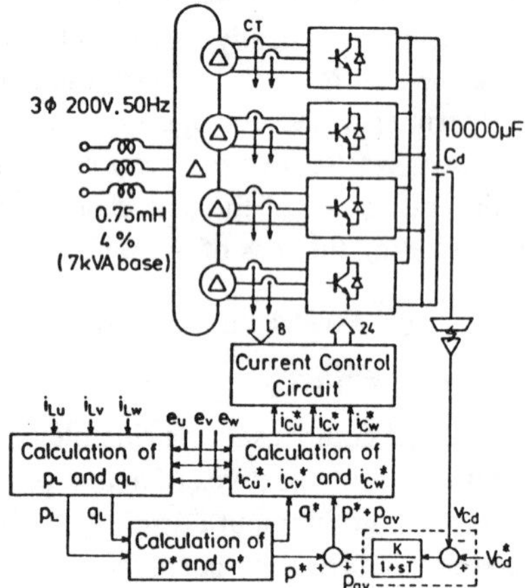

Fig. 2. Active power filter system.

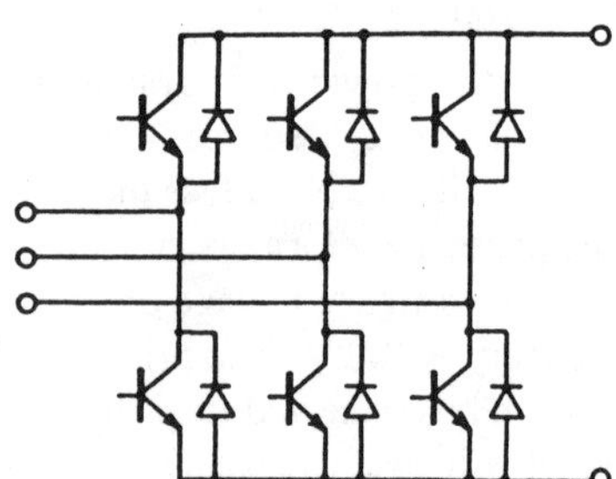

Fig. 3. Three-phase bridge converter.

coordinates gives the following expressions:

$$\begin{bmatrix} e_\alpha \\ e_\beta \end{bmatrix} = \sqrt{\frac{2}{3}} \begin{bmatrix} 1 & -1/2 & -1/2 \\ 0 & \sqrt{3}/2 & -\sqrt{3}/2 \end{bmatrix} \begin{bmatrix} e_u \\ e_v \\ e_w \end{bmatrix} \tag{1}$$

$$\begin{bmatrix} i_{L\alpha} \\ i_{L\beta} \end{bmatrix} = \sqrt{\frac{2}{3}} \begin{bmatrix} 1 & -1/2 & -1/2 \\ 0 & \sqrt{3}/2 & -\sqrt{3}/2 \end{bmatrix} \begin{bmatrix} i_{Lu} \\ i_{Lv} \\ i_{Lw} \end{bmatrix}. \tag{2}$$

According to [9], the instantaneous real power p_L and the instantaneous imaginary power q_L on the load side can be defined as

$$\begin{bmatrix} p_L \\ q_L \end{bmatrix} = \begin{bmatrix} e_\alpha & e_\beta \\ -e_\beta & e_\alpha \end{bmatrix} \begin{bmatrix} i_{L\alpha} \\ i_{L\beta} \end{bmatrix}. \tag{3}$$

Note that the dimension of q_L is not watt, volt·ampere, or var because $e_\alpha \cdot i_\beta$ and $e_\beta \cdot i_\alpha$ are defined by the product of the instantaneous voltage in one phase and the instantaneous current in the other phase. The authors, therefore, introduce to q_L a new dimension IVA, i.e., imaginary volt·ampere.

Equation (3) is changed into

$$\begin{bmatrix} i_{L\alpha} \\ i_{L\beta} \end{bmatrix} = \begin{bmatrix} e_\alpha & e_\beta \\ -e_\beta & e_\alpha \end{bmatrix}^{-1} \begin{bmatrix} p_L \\ q_L \end{bmatrix}. \tag{4}$$

The determinant with respect to e_α and e_β in (4) is not zero.

Let $\bar{p}_L$ and $\tilde{p}_L$ be the dc and ac components of p_L. Likewise, let $\bar{q}_L$ and $\tilde{q}_L$ be the dc and ac components of q_L, respectively. The following relations exist:

$$p_L = \bar{p}_L + \tilde{p}_L \qquad q_L = \bar{q}_L + \tilde{q}_L. \tag{5}$$

From (3)–(5), the α-phase load current $i_{L\alpha}$ is divided into the following components:

$$i_{L\alpha} = \frac{e_\alpha}{e_\alpha^2 + e_\beta^2}\bar{p}_L + \frac{-e_\beta}{e_\alpha^2 + e_\beta^2}\bar{q}_L + \frac{e_\alpha}{e_\alpha^2 + e_\beta^2}\tilde{p}_L + \frac{-e_\beta}{e_\alpha^2 + e_\beta^2}\tilde{q}_L. \tag{6}$$

The physical meaning and the reason for the naming of the instantaneous active and reactive currents are clarified in [9]. Table I shows the relation between the conventional terms concerning "harmonic" currents and frequency components of p_L and q_L. Here, f_i is the line frequency.

Calculation Circuits

In the calculation circuit of p_L and q_L, the calculations of (1)–(3) are performed. In the calculation circuit of the compensating reference currents, the following expression results

$$\begin{bmatrix} i^*_{Cu} \\ i^*_{Cv} \\ i^*_{Cw} \end{bmatrix} = \sqrt{\frac{2}{3}} \begin{bmatrix} 1 & 0 \\ -1/2 & \sqrt{3}/2 \\ -1/2 & -\sqrt{3}/2 \end{bmatrix} \cdot \begin{bmatrix} e_\alpha & e_\beta \\ -e_\beta & e_\alpha \end{bmatrix}^{-1} \begin{bmatrix} p^* + p_{av} \\ q^* \end{bmatrix} \tag{7}$$

where p_{av} is the instantaneous real power corresponding to the loss of the active power filter, and p^* and q^* are given by

$$p^* = -\tilde{p}_L \qquad q^* = -\tilde{q}_L. \tag{8}$$

Fig. 4 shows the calculation circuit of p^* and q^*. This basically consists of a high-pass filter configuration using a Butterworth low-pass filter. So, this circuit outputs $\tilde{p}_L$ from p_L and $\tilde{q}_L$ from q_L, respectively. The design of the low-pass filter is the most important in the control circuit, because various compensation characteristics are obtained in accordance with the cutoff frequency and order of the low-pass filter, as shown in the experimental results. All the calculation circuits consist of analog multipliers, dividers, and operational amplifiers.

Control Circuit of DC Capacitor Voltage

The control circuit of the dc capacitor voltage is shown in Fig. 2, within the dashed line. The dc capacitor voltage can be controlled by trimming the instantaneous real power p_{av},

TABLE I
RELATION BETWEEN CONVENTIONAL TECHNICAL TERMS AND FREQUENCY COMPONENTS OF p_L AND q_L

Frequency Components of p_L and q_L	Conventional Terms
Equal to 0 (dc)	Active current Reactive current
Lower than $2f_i$	Subharmonic current Superharmonic current
Equal to $2f_i$	Negative-sequence current Superharmonic current (third-order)
Higher than $2f_i$	Superharmonic current

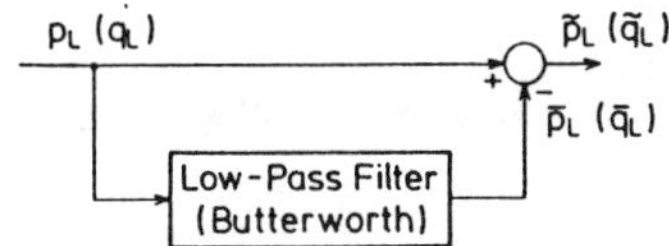

Fig. 4. Calculation circuit of p^* and q^*.

which corresponds to the loss of the active power filter, while the instantaneous imaginary power q^* does not have any effect on the dc capacitor voltage. The control circuit has the negative feedback loop to trim p_{av} automatically, where the time constant T and the gain K determine the response of the control circuit. Note that the active power filter is considered as a harmonic generator rather than a harmonic suppressor when p_{av} is fluctuating. In Fig. 2, the average voltage across the dc capacitor is controlled so as to coincide with the reference voltage V_{Cd}^*, because T is set to 1.5 s and K to 30.

Capacity of the DC Capacitor

To eliminate the harmonics fully, it is necessary to compensate for $\tilde{p}_L$ and $\tilde{q}_L$, as shown in Table I. Elimination of $\tilde{p}_L$, however, causes voltage flucuation of the dc capacitor because $\tilde{p}_L$ is absorbed into the dc capacitor.

Now, let the voltage regulation ϵ be defined by

$$\epsilon = (v_{Cd\,\max} - v_{Cd\,\min})/2\,V_{Cd} \tag{9}$$

where V_{Cd} is the average voltage of v_{Cd}, and nearly equal to V_{Cd}^*. Considering that $\tilde{p}_L$ is sinusoidal, i.e.,

$$\tilde{p}_L = P_m \cdot \sin \omega t,$$

the voltage regulation is derived as follows:

$$\epsilon = P_m/\omega \cdot C_d \cdot V_{Cd}^2. \tag{10}$$

From (10) it is evident that the lower the frequency of $\tilde{p}_L$, the larger the capacity of the dc capacitor to suppress the voltage fluctuation.

CURRENT CONTROL SCHEME OF MULTIPLE VOLTAGE-SOURCE PWM CONVERTERS

The current control scheme of the multiple voltage-source PWM converters must provide the following:

1) quick current controllability,
2) suppression of the harmonics caused by the switching operation, and
3) equalization of the average switching frequency of each PWM converter.

Basic Current Control Schemes

Generally, there are two basic schemes for PWM current control. The first, as shown in Fig. 5(a), determines the PWM switching sequence by means of comparing the current error signal amplified by the gain K_p with a triangular carrier signal. Thus the switching frequency of the power transistors is equal to the frequency of the triangular carrier signal. When the scheme is applied to the multiple PWM converters, the phase of each carrier signal is shifted as usual. For example, the phase is shifted by $\pi/2$ in the case of quadruple converters. The harmonic currents, therefore, are reduced as if the switching frequency were increased. However, the error between the reference current and the actual current is produced because of the finite gain.

The second scheme, shown in Fig. 5(b), consists of imposing a deadband or hysteresis around the reference current. Whenever the actual current tries to leave the band, the appropriate device is switched on (off), forcing the current to return to the band. This enables quick current controllability, but it is difficult in requirements 2) and 3) to apply the scheme to the multiple converters.

Proposed Current Control Scheme

Turning attention to quick current controllability of the second scheme, a current control scheme satisfying the foregoing requirements is proposed. Fig. 6 shows the basic principle of this scheme. The reference current is directly compared with the actual current. Then, the output signal of the comparator is sampled and held at a regular interval T_s synchronized with the clock of frequency equal to $1/T_s$. In the following experiments, T_s was set to 30 μs. Note that the 12 external clocks applied to each converter and to each phase in one converter do not overlap. Therefore, the harmonic currents are reduced considerably as if the switching frequency were increased.

EXPERIMENTAL RESULTS

Waveforms of p_L and q_L

The experimental compensation system is shown in Fig. 1. The load is a three-phase thyristor bridge converter of rating 20 kVA. Fig. 7 shows the experimental active power filter of rating 7 kVA. To discuss the compensation characteristics in the transient states, the firing angle of the thyristor bridge converter is controlled so as to generate the following dc output current:

$$i_d = I_d + I_{d0} \cdot \sin 2\pi f_0 \cdot t. \tag{11}$$

Then the harmonic frequencies f_h present in the input current are given by

$$f_h = f_i \pm n f_0 \qquad (6m \pm 1) f_i \pm n f_0 \tag{12}$$

where f_i is the line (input) frequency, $m = 1, 2, 3, \cdots$, and $n = 0, 1, 2, \cdots$. Fig. 8 shows the experimental frequency

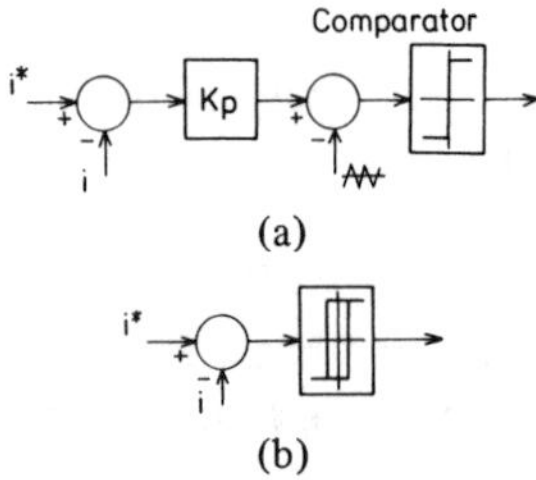

(a)

(b)

Fig. 5. Basic current control schemes. (a) Carrier signal. (b) Hysteresis comparator.

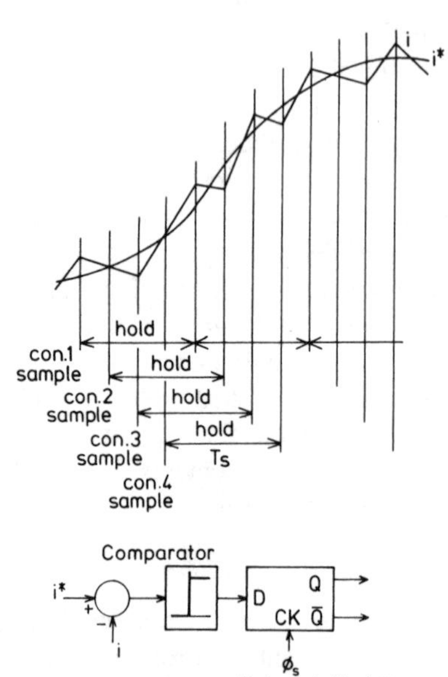

Fig. 6. Proposed current control scheme.

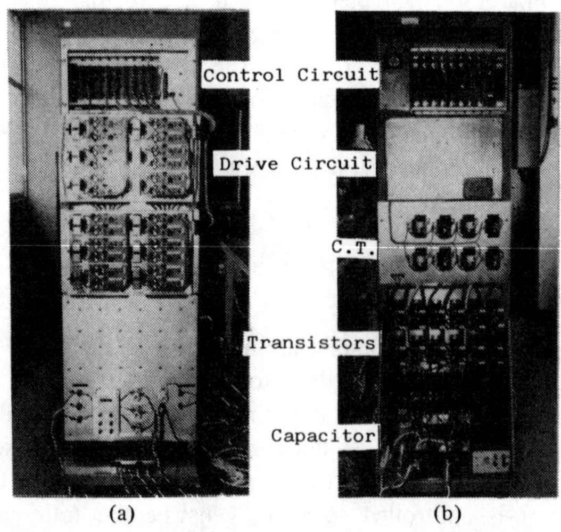

(a) (b)

Fig. 7. Photograph of experimental active power filter. (a) Front. (b) Back.

spectrum around the line frequency under the following condition: line voltage (rms) = 200 V, f_i = 50 Hz, f_0 = 10 Hz, I_d = 50 A, I_{d0} = 30 A. The reason why f_0 was chosen as 10 Hz is that the frequency of the "flicker" caused by arc furnaces is about 10 Hz.

The experimental waveforms shown in Fig. 9 are the u-phase voltage e_u, the dc output current i_d, the u-phase input

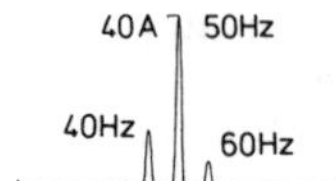

Fig. 8. Frequency spectrum of i_{Lu}.

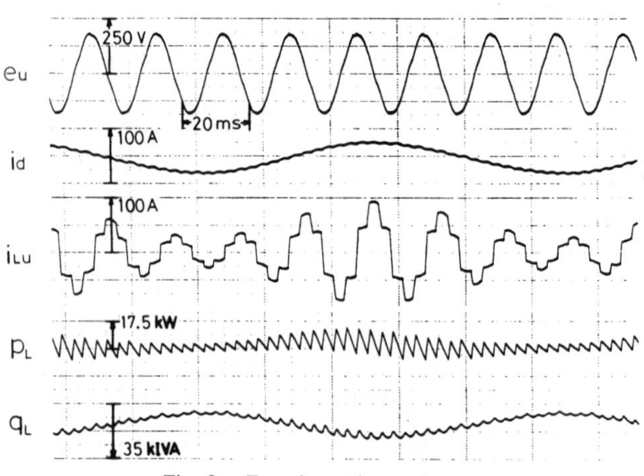

Fig. 9. Experimental waveforms.

current of the thyristor bridge converter, i.e., the u-phase load current i_{Lu}, and the instantaneous real and imaginary powers p_L and q_L under the same condition. The subharmonic current of 40 Hz and the superharmonic current of 60 Hz are caused by the component of 10 Hz present in $\tilde{p}_L$ and $\tilde{q}_L$. The amplitude of the sub- and superharmonic currents depends on the amplitude and phase of the component of 10 Hz in $\tilde{p}_L$ and $\tilde{q}_L$.

Compensation Characteristics

As shown in the previous section, the design of the low-pass filter in the calculation circuit of p^* and q^* has a significant effect on the compensation characteristics. In accordance with the compensation objectives, the Butterworth low-pass filter was designed as follows:

- *compensating condition a)*, i.e., when eliminating the harmonic currents of $5f_i \pm nf_0$, $7f_i \pm nf_0$, $\cdots$

  cutoff frequency = 150 Hz (fifth-order) for p^*,
  cutoff frequency = 150 Hz (fifth-order) for q^*;

- *compensating condition b)*, i.e., when eliminating the sub- and superharmonic currents related to $\tilde{q}_L$ around the fundamental and the harmonic currents of $5f_i \pm nf_0$, $7f_i \pm nf_0$, $\cdots$

  cutoff frequency = 150 Hz (fifth-order) for p^*,
  cutoff frequency = 0.9 Hz (second-order) for q^*;

- *compensating condition c)*, i.e., when eliminating all the harmonic currents of $f_i \pm nf_0$, $5f_i \pm nf_o$, $7f_i \pm nf_0$, $\cdots$

  cutoff frequency = 0.9 Hz (second-order) for p^*,
  cutoff frequency = 0.9 Hz (second-order) for q^*.

Fig. 10(a), (b), and (c) show the experimental compensation characteristics, corresponding to compensating conditions a),

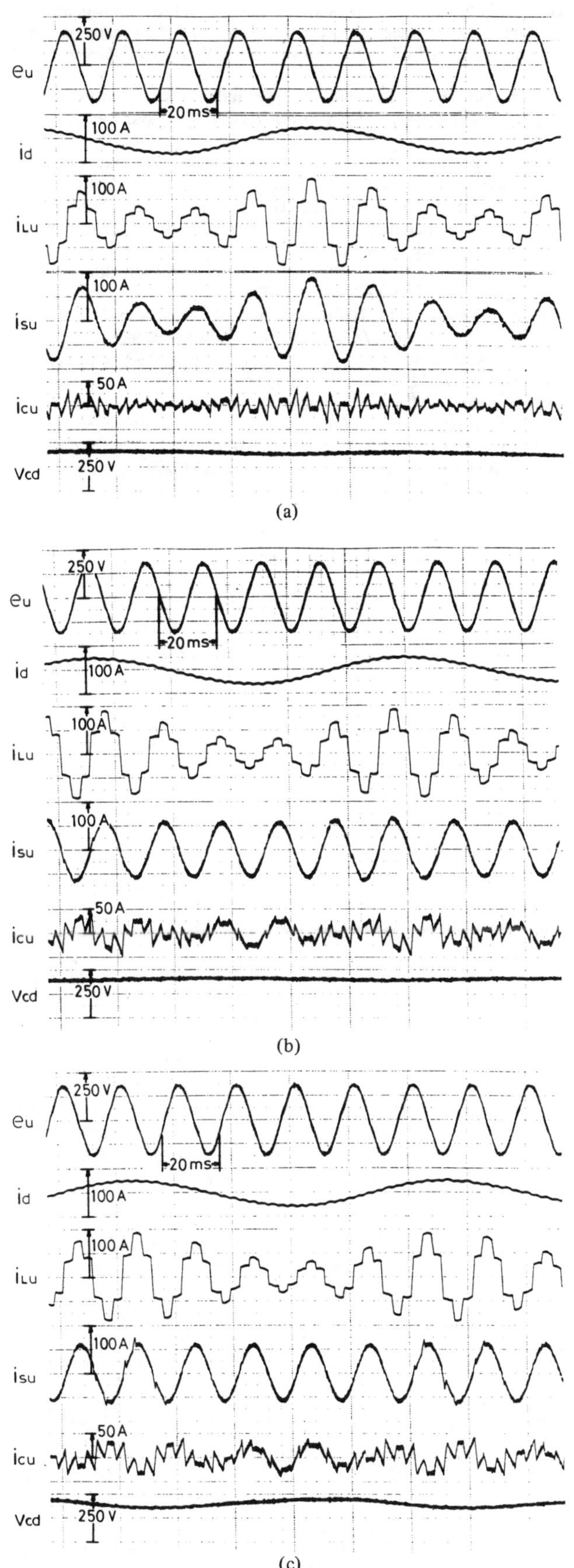

Fig. 10. Experimental compensation characteristics. (a) Condition a). (b) Condition b). (c) Condition c).

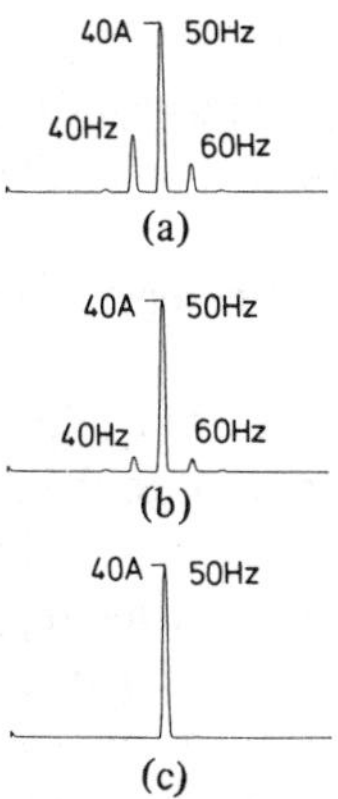

Fig. 11. Frequency spectrum of i_{Su}.

b), and c), respectively. Likewise, Fig. 11(a), (b), and (c) show the experimental frequency spectrum of i_{Su} around the fundamental frequency.

In compensating condition a), the harmonic currents having the frequencies of $5f_i \pm nf_0$, $7f_i \pm nf_0$, $\cdots$ are fully eliminated as shown in Fig. 10(a). On the other hand, the sub- and superharmonic currents around the fundamental are not eliminated at all, as shown in Fig. 11(a). However, this means that the experimental and theoretical compensation characteristics coincide under compensation condition a).

In Fig. 10(b) and (c), it is difficult to distinguish the compensation characteristics in compensating condition b) from those in compensating condition c) with respect to the waveform of i_{Su}. The sub- and superharmonic currents related to the component of 10 Hz present in $\tilde{p}_L$ exist in Fig. 11(b), while they are fully eliminated in Fig. 11(c). In Fig. 10(c), i_{Su} is sinusoidal and the amplitude is constant except for the intervals when the voltage across the dc capacitor drops below the reference voltage V^*_{Cd} (= 205 V). Note that the rms value of the subharmonic current of 40 Hz is equal to that of the superharmonic current of 60 Hz in compensating condition b).

The experimental results shown in Figs. 10 and 11 lead to the following essentials. To eliminate the sub- and superharmonic currents related to the component of 10 Hz present in $\tilde{p}_L$, the dc capacitor of the active power filter has to absorb the variation of the energy stored in the dc reactor of the thyristor bridge converter. This causes the variation of the dc capacitor voltage. Note that the dc capacitor voltage is constant in Fig. 10(b), while it varies at 10 Hz in Fig. 10(c). Accordingly, the active power filter which eliminates fully the sub- and superharmonic currents around the fundamental should be considered as the energy storage system, the purpose of which is to smooth the energy variation. Compensating condition b), therefore, is suitable for the active power filter using multiple voltage-source PWM converters, which is not realized by means of the conventional control strategy.

Conclusion

In this paper, the control strategy of the active power filter using multiple voltage-source PWM converters was proposed on the basis of the instantaneous reactive power theory. This was quite different from the conventional control strategy, thus succeeding in better compensation characteristics. The cutoff frequency and order of the low-pass filter in the calculation circuit of p^* and q^* effected on the compensation characteristics in transient states. Thus various types of low-pass filters were designed, according to the compensation objectives. The better compensation characteristics were verified by experiments.

From the viewpoint of the initial and running cost, the active power filter is inferior to the passive power filter, i.e., the *LC* power filter at present. It is, however, most suitable to apply the active power filter to the suppression of the harmonic components present in the input current of large-capacity cycloconverters, because it is difficult for the passive power filter to eliminate their harmonic components having various frequencies.

References

[1] B. M. Bird *et al.*, "Harmonic reduction in multiplex converters by triple frequency current injection," *Proc. Inst. Elec. Eng.*, vol. 116, p. 1730, 1969.

[2] H. Sasaki and T. Machida, "A new method to eliminate ac harmonic currents by magnetic flux compensation—Consideration on basic design," *IEEE Trans. Power App. Syst.*, vol. PAS-90, p. 2009, 1771.

[3] A. Ametani, "Harmonic reduction in thyristor converters by harmonic current injection," *IEEE Trans. Power App. Syst.*, vol. PAS-95, no. 2, 1976.

[4] N. Mohan *et al.*, "Active filters for ac harmonic suppression," presented at the IEEE/PES Winter Meeting, 1977, A77 026-8.

[5] I. Takahashi and A. Nabae, "Universal power distortion compensator of line commutated thyristor converters," in *Proc. IEEE/IAS Annual Meeting*, 1980, p. 858.

[6] L. Gyugyi and E. C. Strycula, "Active ac power filters," in *Proc. IEEE/IAS Annual Meeting*, 1976, p. 529.

[7] H. Kawahira, T. Nakamura, and S. Nakazawa, "Active power filters," in *Proc. JIEE IPEC-Tokyo*, 1983, p. 981.

[8] K. Hayafune *et al.*, "Microcomputer controlled active power filters," in *Proc. IEEE/IES IECON*, 1984, p. 1221.

[9] H. Akagi, Y. Kanazawa, and A. Nabae, "Instantaneous reactive power compensators comprising switching devices without energy storage components," *IEEE Trans. Ind. Appl.*, vol. IA-20, p. 625, 1984.

[10] B. R. Pelly, *Thyristor Phase-Controlled Converters and Cycloconverters.* New York: Wiley, 1971.

Paper 8.6

A PRACTICAL APPROACH TO HARMONIC COMPENSATION IN POWER SYSTEMS — SERIES CONNECTION OF PASSIVE AND ACTIVE FILTERS —

Hideaki Fujita and Hirofumi Akagi
Nagaoka University of Technology
Nagaoka, 940-21, Japan

Abstract — This paper presents a combined system of a passive filter and a small-rated active filter which are both connected in series with each other. The passive filter removes load produced harmonics, just like a conventional one does. On the other hand, the active filter plays a role in improving the filtering characteristics of the passive filter. This results in a great reduction of the required rating of the active filter and in eliminating all the limitations faced by using only the passive filter, leading to a practical and economical system. Experimental results obtained from a prototype model are shown to verify the theory developed in this paper.

Introduction

"Harmonic interferences" in power systems, which are caused by harmonic-producing loads such as diode or thyristor converters and cycloconverters, have been serious problems to solve. Passive filters consisting of a bank of tuned LC filters and/or a high pass filter have been broadly used to suppress harmonics because of a low initial cost and high efficiency. However, they have the following disadvantages;

1. Source impedance strongly affects filtering characteristics.
2. Parallel resonance between a source and a passive filter causes amplification of harmonic currents on the source side at specific frequencies.
3. A passive filter may fall into series resonance with a source, so that voltage distortion produces excessive harmonic currents flowing into the passive filter.

With remarkable progress in the speed and capacity of semiconductor switching devices such as GTO thyristors and IGBT's, active filters consisting of voltage- or current-source PWM inverters have been studied and put into practical use [1] ~[6], because they have the ability to overcome the above-mentioned disadvantages inherent in passive filters. However, they have the following problems:

1. It is difficult to construct a large-rated current source with a rapid current response.
2. Initial costs and running costs are high.

A few approaches to rating reduction in active filters have been proposed on the basis of a combination of active filters and passive elements such as capacitors and reactors [7]~[10]. Fig.1 shows a combination of a series active filter and a shunt passive filter [9],[10]. The shunt passive filter connected in parallel with a load suppresses the harmonic currents produced by the load, while the active filter connected in series to a source acts as a "harmonic isolator" between the source and the load.

This paper presents a combined system of a passive filter and a small-rated active filter, which are connected in series with each other. The passive filter suppresses harmonic currents produced by the load, while the active filter improves the filtering characteristics of the passive filter. As a result, the proposed system can solve the problems inherent in using only the passive filter. In addition, the active filter is much smaller in rating than a conventional active filter.

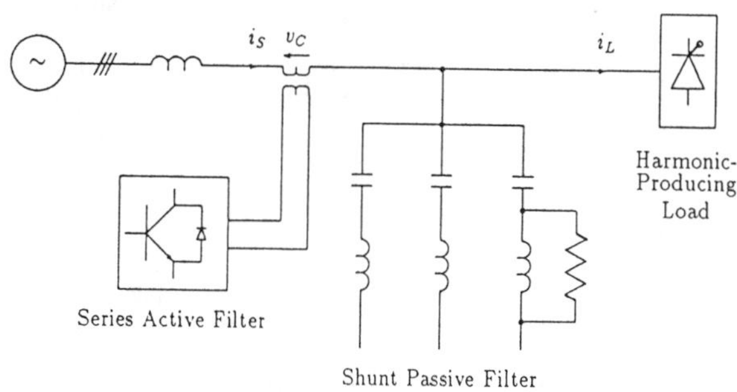

Fig.1. Combination of a series active and shunt passive filter.

System Configuration

Fig.2 shows a proposed system consisting of an active filter and a passive filter which are connected in series with each other. It is installed in parallel with a harmonic-producing load, that is, a three-phase thyristor bridge converter of rating 20kVA as shown in Fig.2. The passive filter of rating 10kVA consists of a 5th- and 7th-tuned LC filter and a high pass filter. The main circuit of the active filter with a rating 0.5 kVA is a three-phase voltage-source PWM inverter using six MOSFET's. The PWM inverter has a dc capacitor of 1200μF. The purpose of a small-rated LC filter (L_R,C_R) is to suppress switching ripples generated by the active filter. Table 1 shows the constants of the passive filter and the small-rated LC filter used in the following experiment. Three current transformers of turn ratio 1:10 are connected to match the voltage-current rating of the active filter with that of the passive filter.

Control Circuit

A control circuit is also shown in Fig.2. Three-phase source currents, i_{Su}, i_{Sv} and i_{Sw} are detected and a source harmonic current in each phase, i_{Sh} is calculated by applying the p-q theory [11]. Terminal voltages and the source currents are transformed from three- to two-phase quantities as follows.

Reprinted from *IEEE/IAS Ann. Meet. Conf. Rec.*, pp. 1107–1112, 1990.

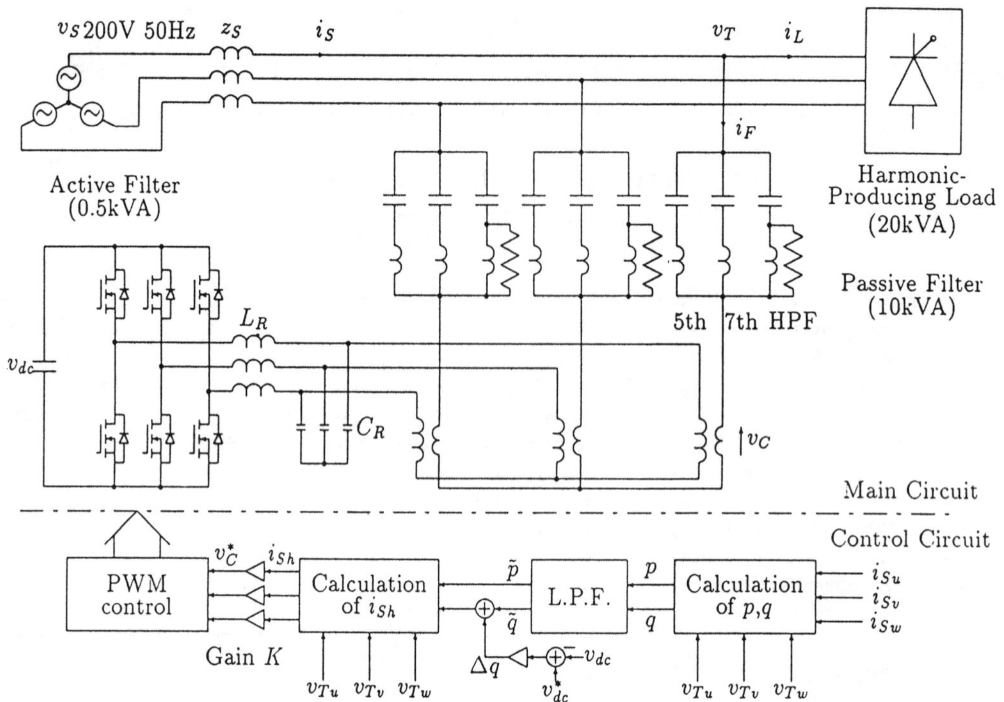

Fig.2. Proposed system configuration.

Table 1. Circuit constants.

Passive Filter			
5th	L=1.2mH	C=340μF	Q=14
7th	L=1.2mH	C=170μF	Q=14
HPF	L=0.26mH	C=300μF	R=3Ω
Small-Rated LC Filter			
L_R=10.0mH	C_R=0.1μF		

$$\begin{bmatrix} e_\alpha \\ e_\beta \end{bmatrix} = \sqrt{\frac{2}{3}} \begin{bmatrix} 1 & -\frac{1}{2} & -\frac{1}{2} \\ 0 & \frac{\sqrt{3}}{2} & -\frac{\sqrt{3}}{2} \end{bmatrix} \begin{bmatrix} e_u \\ e_v \\ e_w \end{bmatrix} \quad (1)$$

$$\begin{bmatrix} i_{S\alpha} \\ i_{S\beta} \end{bmatrix} = \sqrt{\frac{2}{3}} \begin{bmatrix} 1 & -\frac{1}{2} & -\frac{1}{2} \\ 0 & \frac{\sqrt{3}}{2} & -\frac{\sqrt{3}}{2} \end{bmatrix} \begin{bmatrix} i_{Su} \\ i_{Sv} \\ i_{Sw} \end{bmatrix} \quad (2)$$

Here, e_u, e_v and e_w are the fundamentals of the terminal voltages, v_{Tu}, v_{Tv} and v_{Tw}, respectively. Hence, the instantaneous real power p and the instantaneous imaginary power q [11] are given by

$$\begin{bmatrix} p \\ q \end{bmatrix} = \begin{bmatrix} e_\alpha & e_\beta \\ -e_\beta & e_\alpha \end{bmatrix} \begin{bmatrix} i_{S\alpha} \\ i_{S\beta} \end{bmatrix}. \quad (3)$$

In Eq.(3), the fundamental of i_S is transformed to dc components $\bar{p}$ and $\bar{q}$, and the harmonics to ac components $\tilde{p}$ and $\tilde{q}$. The ac components are extracted by two high-pass-filters, and the harmonics of the three-phase source currents, i_{Shu}, i_{Shv} and i_{Shw} are obtained by the following calculation.

$$\begin{bmatrix} i_{Shu} \\ i_{Shv} \\ i_{Shw} \end{bmatrix} = \sqrt{\frac{2}{3}} \begin{bmatrix} 1 & 0 \\ -\frac{1}{2} & \frac{\sqrt{3}}{2} \\ -\frac{1}{2} & -\frac{\sqrt{3}}{2} \end{bmatrix} \cdot \begin{bmatrix} e_\alpha & e_\beta \\ -e_\beta & e_\alpha \end{bmatrix}^{-1} \begin{bmatrix} \tilde{p} \\ \tilde{q} \end{bmatrix} \quad (4)$$

The calculated harmonic current in each phase i_{Sh} is amplified by the gain K and input to a PWM controller as a voltage reference

$$v_C^* = K \cdot i_{Sh}. \quad (5)$$

To produce PWM switching patterns, the PWM controller compares v_C^* with a triangle-wave carrier whose frequency is 20kHz.

In addition, the active filter can build up and regulate the dc capacitor voltage without any external power supply. If the active filter outputs a fundamental voltage which is in phase with the fundamental leading current of the passive filter, the active power formed by the leading current and the fundamental voltage is supplied to the dc capacitor. Therefore, the electrical quantity to be controlled in a dc voltage feedback loop is not Δp but Δq.

Compensation Principle

Fig.3 shows single-phase equivalent circuits of the proposed system. Assuming that the active filter is an ideal controllable voltage source $\mathbf{V}_C$ and that the load is a current source $\mathbf{I}_L$, Fig.2 can be re-drawn as Fig.3(a), where $\mathbf{Z}_S$ is a source impedance and $\mathbf{Z}_F$ is the total impedance of the passive filter.

When no active filter is connected ($\mathbf{K}$ = 0), a load harmonic current $\mathbf{I}_{Lh}$ is compensated by the passive filter, filtering characteristics of which depend on the ratio of $\mathbf{Z}_S$ and $\mathbf{Z}_F$. From Fig.3, the source harmonic current $\mathbf{I}_{Sh}$ is given by

$$\mathbf{I}_{Sh} = \frac{\mathbf{Z}_F}{\mathbf{Z}_S + \mathbf{Z}_F} \mathbf{I}_{Lh}. \quad (6)$$

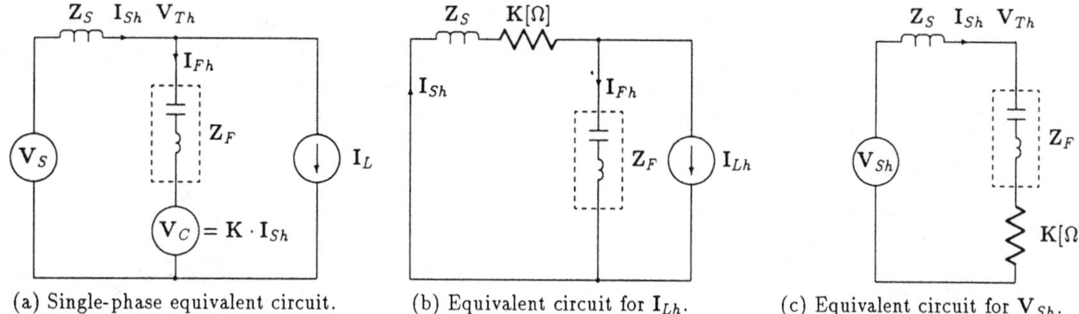

(a) Single-phase equivalent circuit. (b) Equivalent circuit for $\mathbf{I}_{Lh}$. (c) Equivalent circuit for $\mathbf{V}_{Sh}$.

Fig.3. Equivalent circuits of proposed filter system.

If the source impedance is so small ($|\mathbf{Z}_S| \approx 0$), or unless the passive filter is tuned to harmonic frequencies generated by the load ($|\mathbf{Z}_F| \gg |\mathbf{Z}_S|$), desirable filtering characteristics would not be obtained. Moreover, parallel resonance between $\mathbf{Z}_S$ and $\mathbf{Z}_F$ occurs at specific frequencies ($|\mathbf{Z}_S+\mathbf{Z}_F| \approx 0$), causing a harmonic-amplifying phenomena. A much larger amount of harmonic current flows in the source than in the load.

When the active filter is connected, and is controlled as a voltage source

$$\mathbf{V}_C = \mathrm{K} \cdot \mathbf{I}_{Sh}, \tag{7}$$

the active filter forces all the harmonics contained in the load current to flow into the passive filter, so that no harmonic current flows in the source. The function of the active filter is to solve the problems inherent in using the passive filter alone. In addition, no fundamental voltage is applied to the active filter. This results in a great reduction of the voltage rating of the active filter.

Filtering Characteristics

Let's consider filtering characteristics for the load harmonic current $\mathbf{I}_{Lh}$. Let us assume that a source voltage $\mathbf{V}_S$ is sinusoidal. The source harmonic current $\mathbf{I}_{Sh}$, the terminal harmonic voltage $\mathbf{V}_{Th}$ and the output voltage of the active filter $\mathbf{V}_C$ are given by the following three equations.

$$\mathbf{I}_{Sh} = \frac{\mathbf{Z}_F}{\mathrm{K}+\mathbf{Z}_S+\mathbf{Z}_F}\mathbf{I}_{Lh} \tag{8}$$

$$\mathbf{V}_{Th} = \mathbf{V}_{Sh} - \mathbf{Z}_S\mathbf{I}_{Sh} = -\frac{\mathbf{Z}_F\mathbf{Z}_S}{\mathrm{K}+\mathbf{Z}_S+\mathbf{Z}_F}\mathbf{I}_{Lh} \tag{9}$$

$$\mathbf{V}_C = \mathrm{K}\mathbf{I}_{Sh} = \frac{\mathrm{K}\mathbf{Z}_F}{\mathrm{K}+\mathbf{Z}_S+\mathbf{Z}_F}\mathbf{I}_{Lh} \tag{10}$$

Eq.(8) tells us that Fig.3(a) is equivalent in $\mathbf{I}_{Sh}$ to Fig.3(b). This means that a pure resistance K[Ω] is connected in series with $\mathbf{Z}_S$ as shown in Fig.3(b). If $\mathrm{K} \gg |\mathbf{Z}_F|$, all the harmonic currents produced by the load would sink into the passive filter. If $\mathrm{K} \gg |\mathbf{Z}_S|$, K would dominate the filtering characteristics. In addition, K acts as a resistor to dump parallel resonance between $\mathbf{Z}_S$ and $\mathbf{Z}_F$.

Fig.4 shows filtering characteristics in the case of $\mathbf{Z}_S$ =0.02pu, the vertical axis of which indicates the ratio of the source harmonic current to the load current. In the case of the passive filter used alone (K = 0), parallel resonance occurs near the 4th-harmonic frequency. In the case of the proposed system (K = 2Ω), the filtering characteristics are improved for all over the harmonic frequencies, and no parallel resonance occurs.

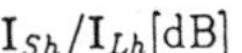

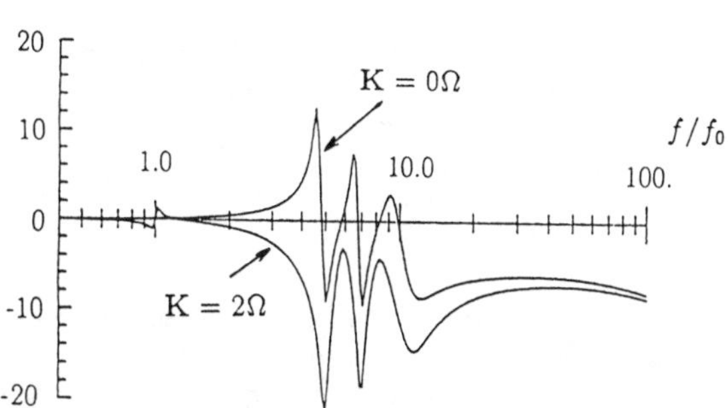

Fig.4. Filtering characteristics for load harmonic current.

Now, let's discuss the harmonics present in the source voltage, assuming no load ($\mathbf{I}_{Lh}$ =0) in Fig.3(a). The active filter behaves just like a pure resistor K[Ω] as shown in Fig.3(c). From Fig.3(c), the following equations are obtained.

$$\mathbf{I}_{Sh} = \frac{\mathbf{V}_{Sh}}{\mathrm{K}+\mathbf{Z}_S+\mathbf{Z}_F} \tag{11}$$

$$\mathbf{V}_{Th} = \frac{\mathrm{K}+\mathbf{Z}_F}{\mathrm{K}+\mathbf{Z}_S+\mathbf{Z}_F}\mathbf{V}_{Sh} \tag{12}$$

$$\mathbf{V}_C = \frac{\mathrm{K}}{\mathrm{K}+\mathbf{Z}_S+\mathbf{Z}_F}\mathbf{V}_{Sh} \tag{13}$$

If $\mathrm{K} \gg |\mathbf{Z}_S+\mathbf{Z}_F|$, $\mathbf{V}_{Sh}$ would be applied to the active filter. This prevents harmonic currents caused by $\mathbf{V}_{Sh}$ from flowing into the passive filter. However, $\mathbf{V}_{Sh}$ appears in the terminal voltage $\mathbf{V}_T$.

Fig.5 shows compensation characteristics of the source harmonic current caused by the source harmonic voltage. In the case of K = 0, series resonance exists at the 4th-harmonic frequency. If the harmonic voltage included in the source is 1%, the 4th-harmonic current flowing into the passive filter would be about 20%. However, it would be only 1% in the case of K = 2[Ω], because the series resonance is dumped by the active filter.

The following ideal filtering characteristics are obtained by assuming that K is infinite.

$$\mathbf{I}_{Sh} = 0 \tag{14}$$

$$\mathbf{V}_{Th} = \mathbf{V}_{Sh} \tag{15}$$

$$\mathbf{V}_C = \mathbf{Z}_F\mathbf{I}_{Lh} + \mathbf{V}_{Sh} \tag{16}$$

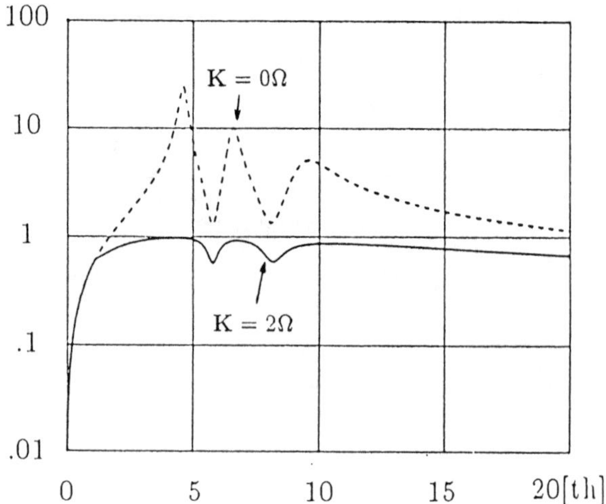

Fig.5. Compensation characteristics for source voltage distortion.

The fundamental leading current from the source, and the harmonic current from the load, both flow into the active filter, so that the required rating of the active filter is given by

$$|\mathbf{Z}_F \mathbf{I}_{Lh} + \mathbf{V}_{Sh}| \cdot |\mathbf{I}_{F0} - \mathbf{I}_{Lh}| .$$

Experimental Results

The following experimental results are obtained by a laboratory model. In the experiments, two 1st-order high-pass-filters with cutoff frequency $f_c = 10$[Hz] were used for the extraction of $\tilde{p}$ and $\tilde{q}$, **K** was 2[Ω](=1pu), and a diode bridge rectifier was connected to the dc capacitor to supply the switching and conducting losses of the active filter.

Fig.6 shows experimental waveforms, where $\mathbf{Z}_S$ is 0.02pu. Before the active filter was started, a large amount of the 5th-harmonic current was included in the source current, but the source current became sinusoidal after starting. The simulation result shown in Fig.7 agrees with the experimental result shown in Fig.6. Since the output voltage of the active filter was about 2.5V, the required rating of the active filter was only 1.5% of the harmonic-producing load, that is, the thyristor converter of rating 20kVA. Frequency spectra of the source currents i_S and the terminal voltage v_T in Figs.8 and 9 were measured before and after the active filter was started. Although the 5th- and 7th-harmonics are contained in i_S before starting, they were eliminated after it was started.

Fig.10 shows experimental waveforms under the same condition as Fig.5 except that $\mathbf{Z}_S$ is 0.06pu. Here, the passive filter fell in parallel resonance at the 4th-harmonic frequency with source impedance before the active filter was started. Not only the source current but also the terminal voltage was distorted. After starting, the parallel resonance disappeared, and both the source current and the terminal voltage became sinusoidal.

Fig.11 shows an experimental result of build-up of the dc capacitor voltage under no harmonic-producing load. Here no external diode rectifier was connected to the dc capacitor of the active filter. Before the active filter was started, the dc capacitor voltage was zero, and the source current was distorted by the source harmonic voltage. The dc capacitor voltage started to rise as soon as the active filter was started. After build-up, the dc capacitor voltage was regulated at a constant level, and the source current became sinusoidal because the active filter prevented harmonic currents from entering into the passive filter from the source.

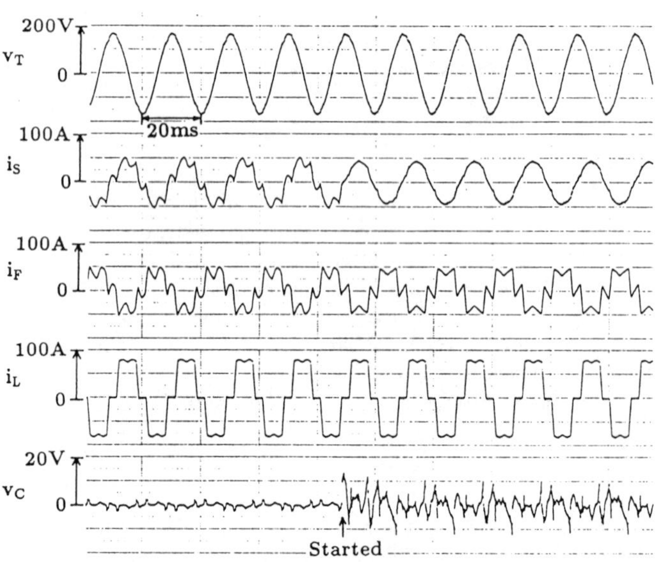

Fig.6. Experimental waveforms in case of $\mathbf{Z}_S$=0.02pu.

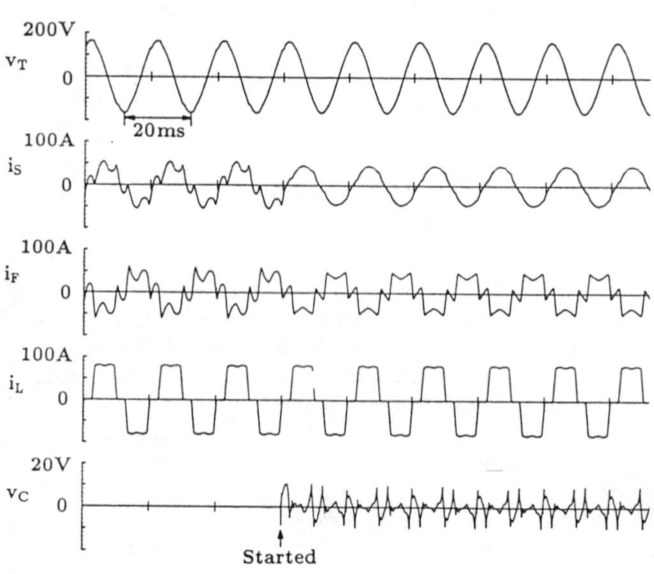

Fig.7. Simulation waveforms in case of $\mathbf{Z}_S$=0.02pu.

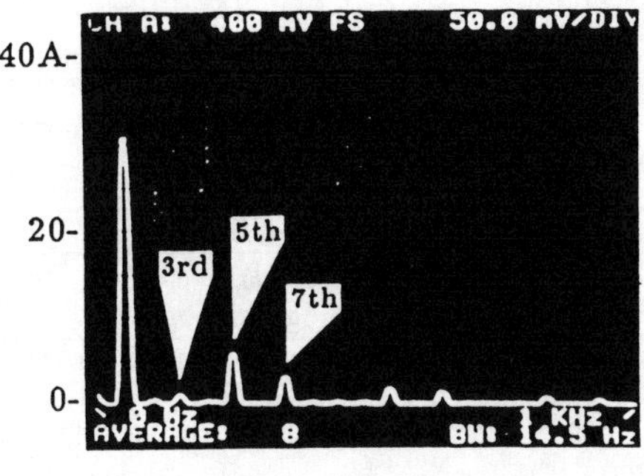

(a) Before started.

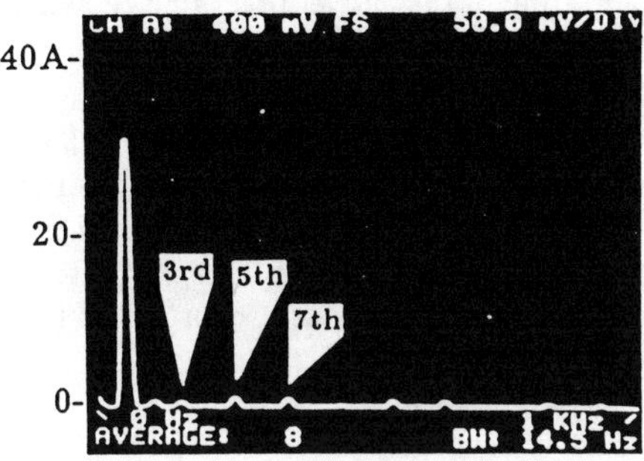

(b) After started.

Fig.8. Frequency spectra of i_S

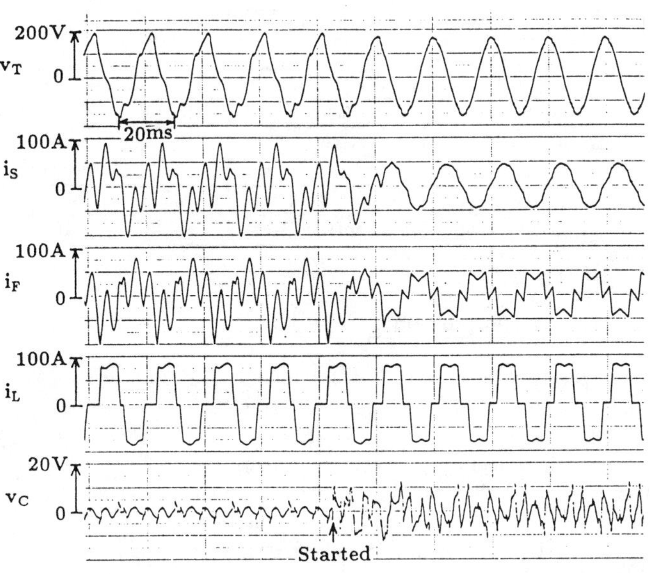

Fig.10. Experimental waveforms in case of Z_S=0.06pu.

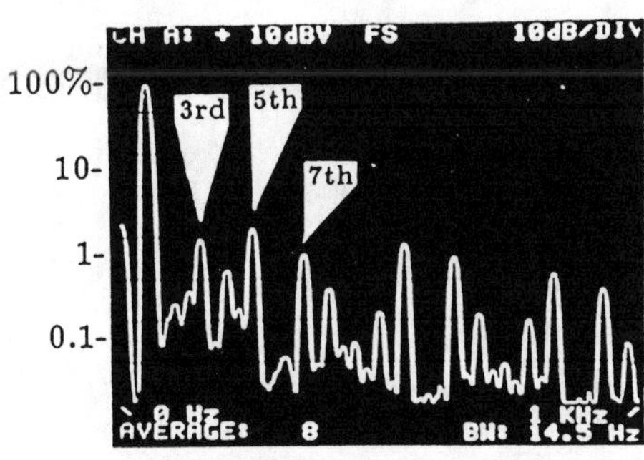

(a) Before started.

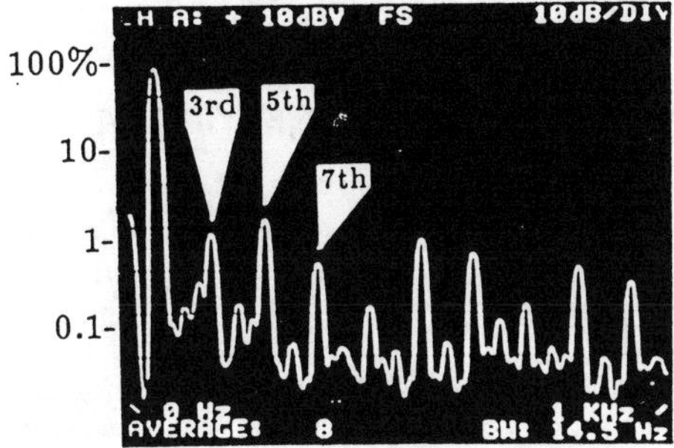

(b) After started.

Fig.9. Frequency spectra of v_T

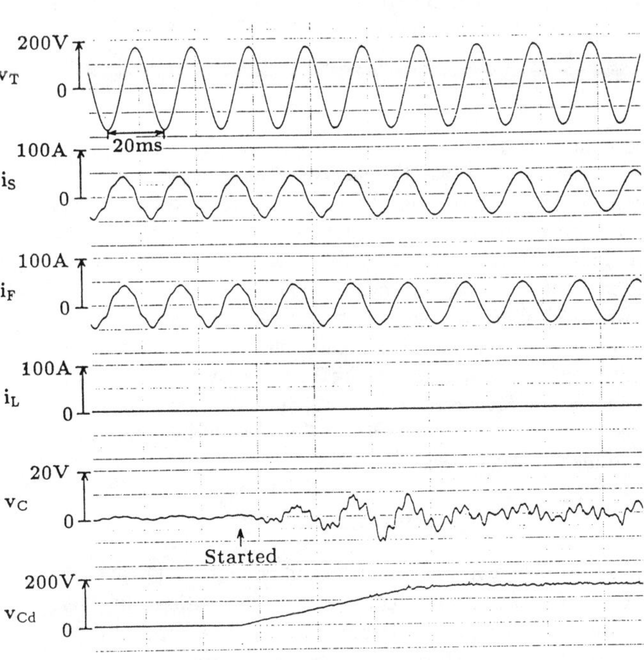

Fig.11. Experimental result of built-up of the dc capacitor voltage.

Table 2. Comparison of Figs.1 and 2.

	combination of series active and shunt passive filters	series-connection of active and passive filters
current to be detected	source current	source current
control scheme of active filters	$v_C^* = Ki_{Sh}$	$v_C^* = Ki_{Sh}$
source harmonic current $\mathbf{I}_{Sh}$	0	0
terminal harmonic voltage $\mathbf{V}_{Th}$	$-\mathbf{Z}_F\mathbf{I}_{Lh}$	$\mathbf{V}_{Sh}$
output voltage of active filters $\mathbf{V}_C$	$\mathbf{Z}_F\mathbf{I}_{Lh} + \mathbf{V}_{Sh}$	$\mathbf{Z}_F\mathbf{I}_{Lh} + \mathbf{V}_{Sh}$
current flowing through active filters	$\mathbf{I}_{F0} + \mathbf{I}_{Lf}$ only fundamental	$\mathbf{I}_{F0} - \mathbf{I}_{Lh}$ containing harmonic
required rating of active filters	small in case of low power factor load	small in case of high power factor load
isolation and protection of active filters	difficult	easy

Comparison of Figs.1 and 2

Table 2 presents a comparison of the combination of a series active and shunt passive filter shown in Fig.1[9],[10] and the series-connection of a passive and active filter shown in Fig.2. The same harmonic detection and control scheme are applicable to both systems, and they obtain the same compensation characteristics except for the terminal voltage. The terminal harmonic voltage in Fig.1 corresponds to a voltage drop across the passive filter $-\mathbf{Z}_F\mathbf{I}_{Lh}$, while that in Fig.2 is equal to the source harmonic voltage $\mathbf{V}_{Sh}$.

The current flowing through the active filter in Fig.1 is the sum of the leading current of the passive filter and the fundamental of the load current, which does not contain any harmonics. But in Fig.2, the harmonic current produced by the load and the leading current of the passive filter flow through the active filter. The harmonic current causes a harmonic voltage drop across the matching transformer. On the other hand, it is easy to supply electric power corresponding to the switching and conducting loss of the active filter to the dc capacitor in Fig.2. Fig.1 requires an external power supply, because the fundamental current flowing through the active filter is varied by the operating conditions of the load.

The required rating of the active filter depends on the power factor of the load, because the passive filter is usually designed according to the reactive power of the load to be canceled. Therefore, in the case of a low power factor, Fig.1 is smaller in the required rating of the active filter than Fig.2, while in the case of a high power factor, Fig.2 is smaller than Fig.1.

In Fig.1, it is difficult to isolate the active filter from the source and to protect it against a short-circuit fault because of the series-connection with the source. In Fig.2, it is easy to protect and isolate the active filter connected to the neutral point of the wye-connected passive filter. Accordingly Fig.2 would be more applicable to high-voltage power systems.

Conclusion

The authors have proposed a combined system of a passive and an active filter, which are connected in series with each other. The theory developed in this paper was verified analytically and experimentally. The features of the proposed system are summarized as follows.

1. Filtering characteristics are independent of the source impedance.
2. Parallel and series resonance between the source and the passive filter can be dumped by the active filter.
3. The required rating of the active filter is much smaller than that of a conventional active filter used alone.

In the laboratory experiment, the required rating of the active filter is only 1.5% of a harmonic-producing load, which is a three-phase thyristor converter of 20kVA. Since a passive filter having a higher quality factor ($Q = 50 \sim 100$) may be used in a practical system, the required rating of the active filter connected in series would be reduced according to inverse proportion of the quality factor of the passive filter.

Reference

[1] L. Gyugyi and E. Strycula. "Active ac power filter" IEEE Trans., Ind. Appl., pp.529-535, 1976.

[2] H. Akagi, A. Nabae and S. Atoh. "Control strategy of active power filters using voltage-source PWM converters" IEEE Trans. Ind. Appl., IA-22, Vol.3, pp.460, 1986.

[3] K. Komatsugi, et al. "Harmonic current compensator composed of static power converter" IEEE/PESC, pp.283, 1986.

[4] S. Moran. "A line voltage regulator/conditioner for harmonic-sensitive load isolation" IEEE/IAS Annual Meeting, pp.947-951, 1989.

[5] S. Deb, B. W. Sherman and R. G. Hoft. "Resonant converter power line conditioner: Design and Evaluation" IEEE/IAS Annual Meeting, pp.952-958, 1989.

[6] B. S. Acharya, R. W. Gascoigne and D. M. Divan. "Active power filter using resonant pole inverters" IEEE/IAS Annual Meeting, pp.967-973, 1989.

[7] A. Nakagima, J. Nishidai and T. Shiraishi. "Development of active filter with series resonant circuit" IEEE/PESC, pp.1168, 1988.

[8] M. Takeda, K. Ikeda, Y. Tominaga and K. Oku. "Harmonic current compensation with active filter" IEEE/IAS Annual Meeting, pp.808, 1987.

[9] F. Z. Peng, H. Akagi and A. Nabae. "A new approach to harmonic compensation in power system" IEEE/IAS Annual Meeting, pp.874-880, 1988.

[10] F. Z. Peng, H. Akagi and A. Nabae. "Compensation characteristics of combined system of shunt passive and series active filters" IEEE/IAS Annual Meeting, pp.959-966, 1989.

[11] H. Akagi et al. "Instantaneous reactive power compensators comprising switching device without energy storage components" IEEE Trans. on IA, IA-20, No.3, 1984

Paper 8.7

LARGE CAPACITY PARALLEL REDUNDANT TRANSISTOR UPS

Takao KAWABATA, Shiroo DOI, Tetsuroo MORIKAWA
Tooru NAKAMURA, Masahiro SHIGENOBU
Mitsubishi Electric Corporation, Power & Industrial Systems Center
Wadasaki-cho, Hyogo-ku, Kobe 652, Japan

Abstract

A large capacity parallel redundant UPS (Uninterruptible Power System) using power transistor modules instead of thyristors has been developed recently. Utilizing the high frequency switching capability of the transistor, harmonics neutralization method with multiple pulse width modulation has been adopted successfully, and output of the inverter is modulated at 420Hz pulses or 300Hz pulses and 6, 12 or 18 phase configuration is selected, depending upon the rating of inverters. As the parallel control method of the system, fully independent control system has been developed and high reliability and maintenability have been realized.

1. INTRODUCTION

According to the growth of information handling products such as the large on-line computer system, the communication system and the complicated plant control system, the demand of UPS is growing steadily year by year, and its application is also spreading throughout various fields. Since the first production of UPS around 1965, typical UPSs have been the thyristor type using single pulse width modulation method, for long years. But within the last 2 or 3 years, the progress of the large transistor and the GTO has brought the possibility of the development of large capacity inverters without commutation circuits. Also the investigation of various methods of multiple pulse width modulation techniques for the past several years and the progress of the digital control circuit using ROMs have enabled to design the ideal modulation system to eliminate the harmonics. Considering the switching devices to be employed, there were two possibility of selection between the GTO and the transistor. And the transistor was finally selected, because the UPS is essentially a low voltage equipment having the typical DC link voltage around 100 ∿ 400V. As the typical voltage ratings of the available transistors are around 500 and 1000V, this is enough for the design of UPS, and the high voltage rating of the GTOs is too excess for UPS. In addition, the transistor has better switching characteristics such as high switching speed and small switching loss which brings more advantageous design conditions.
That is, realization of ideal modulation pattern, high speed protection against short circuit and operation without bulky snubbers.

Combining above mentioned new devices and techniques together, the development of new generation UPS which can replace the conventional thyristor UPS became possible.
This paper will especially elaborate upon details of large parallel redundant transistor UPS of 2 x 200 kVA rating.

Reprinted with permission from *Int. Power Electron. Conf. (IPEC) Rec.*, vol. 1, pp. 660–671, March 1983.

2. FEATURES OF TRANSISTOR UPS

Features of transistor UPS are as follows.

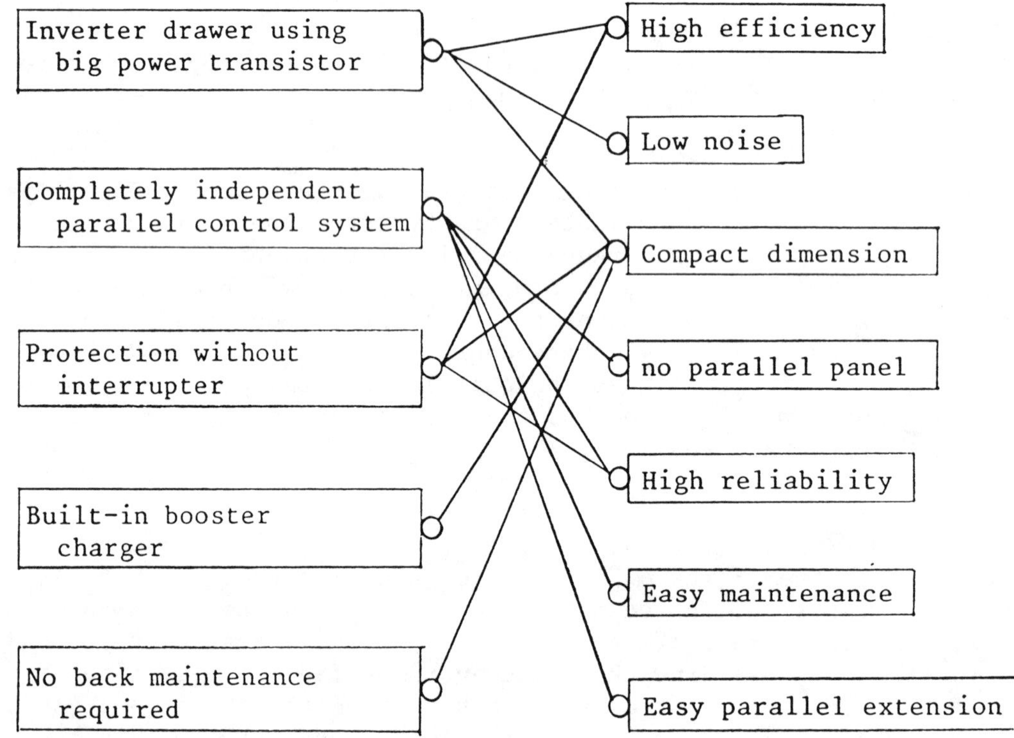

2-1 Inverter using transistor

In this inverter, big transistor modules are employed as main switching devices to eliminate commutating circuit. Consequently, compact design, high efficiency and low audible noise have been realized. And also, transistors can operate at high switching frequency, without serious switching loss as thyristors with commutation circuit, then harmonics neutralization method by multipule pulse width modulation can be adopted easily, so the numbers of inverter transformers and the capacity of the out put filter can be decreased.

2-2 Completely independent parallel control system

In case of the conventional parallel control system, common parts such as master oscillator and parallel interlocking circuit and etc are necessary as shown in Fig. 1(b), so a parallel control panel is required. But in the case of completely independent parallel control system, each UPS has own oscillator and voltage control circuit as shown in Fig. 1(a), and controls its own load sharing by adjusting own frequency, phase and voltage according to the voltage and load informations taken from the output bus. Consequently, no common parallel panel is necessary. And also, in this system the possibility of system down caused by the failure of the common part can be avoided, so high system reliability can be expected. As the result of no common parallel panel, easy maintenance and inspection of total system without stopping the load can be realized and also future extension of parallel number of UPS becomes very easy.

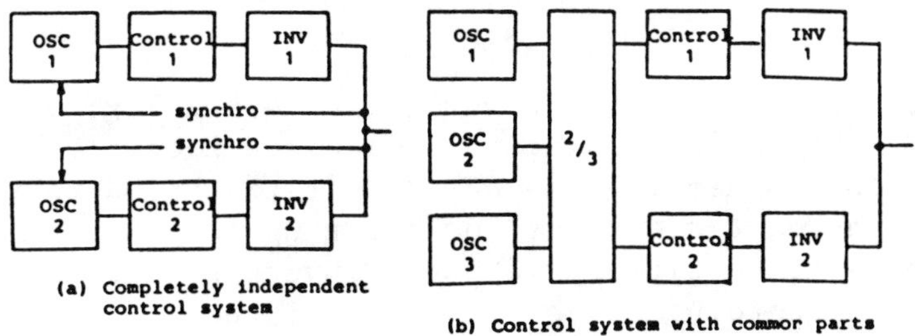

Fig.1 Comparison of parallel control system

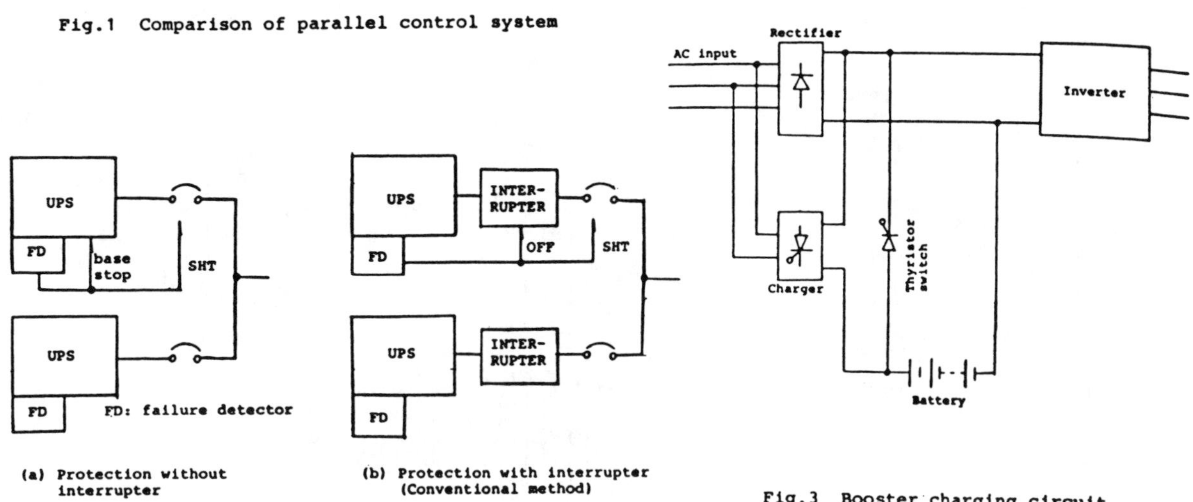

Fig.2 Comparison of protection system

Fig.3 Booster charging circuit

2-3 Protection without interrupter

In case of the conventional parallel redundant system, the interrupter is used to cut off the faulty UPS as shown in Fig. 2(b). But if the interrupter itself has a failure, before the failure of the UPS, this interrupter will not protect the redundant system. In case of transister UPS the inverter itself is used as the interrupter as shown in Fig. 2(a). The inverter itself acts as an impedance to power flow by interrupting the base signal of the transister. In this configuration,operation is confirmed every cycle, then there is no possibility of the former failure of the interrupting function. Consequently, much higher reliability will be realized by the interrupterless protection method. In addition, the efficiency can be improved by elliminating the loss of the interrupter, and also the compact dimension can be realized.

2-4 Built-in booster charger

In stead of the separate charger system, the built-in booster charger system has been adopted as shown in Fig.3. Consequently, compact design and low input harmonics have been realized.

2-5 No back maintenance construction

Remarkable saving of the installation space has been realized.

3. MAIN CIRCUIT

The circuit diagram of the transistor UPS is shown in Fig. 4,and Fig. 5 is the photograph of 200 kVA UPS. UPS mainly consists of a diode rectifier for AC/DC conversion, a DC switch for connecting the DC circuit to the battery in case of AC input power failure, a booster charger for charging the batteries in cooperation with the diode rectifier, 12 phase inverter, two transformers and an output filter. According to the capacity of the UPS, the configurations of the inverter will be selected as shown in Fig. 6.

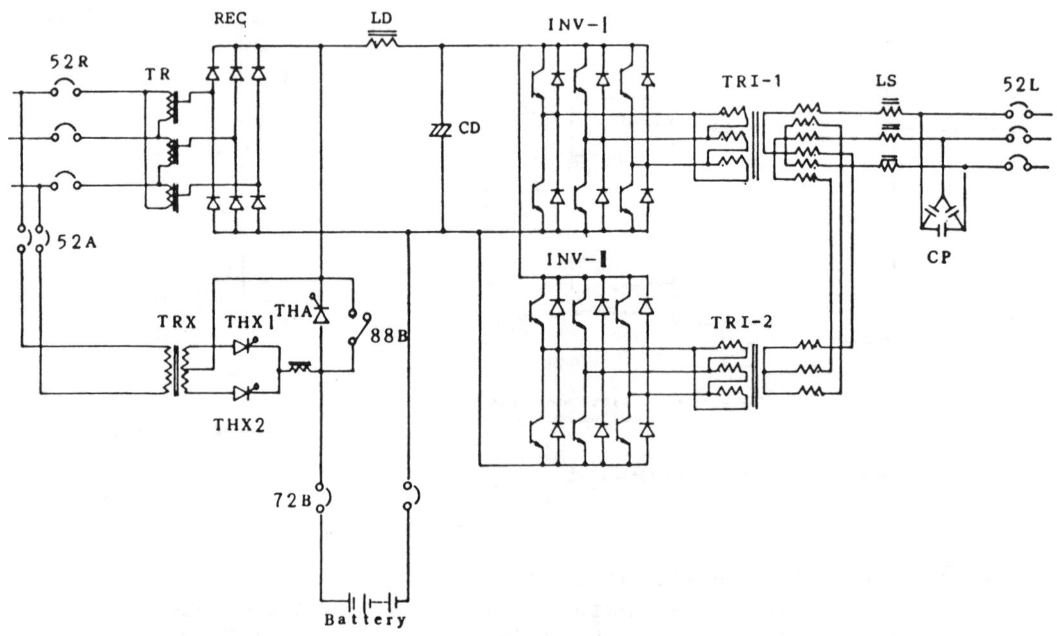

Fig. 4 Main circuit of transistor UPS

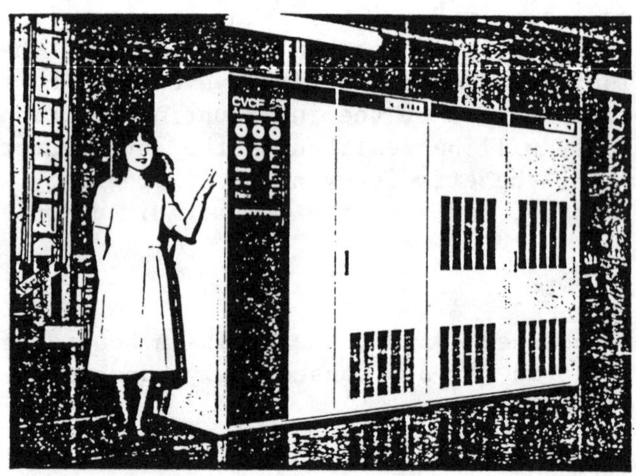

Fig.5 Outlocking of 200kVA UPS.

3-1 Harmonics neutralization method

Harmonics are neutralized by the combination of the multiple pulse width modulation and the connection of the transformers as shown in Fig.6 and 7. The pattern of the switching point to eliminate specific harmonics as shown in Fig. 8 is memorized in ROM, and the inverter poles operate according to this pattern. In case of 6 phase inverter, 5th and 7th harmonics are completely neutralized by modulation, and 3rd harmonics is neutralized by transformer and, remainning higher harmonics are eliminated by the output filter.

In case of 12 phase inverter, 3rd, 5th and 7th harmonics are neutralized by the transformers, and to minimize the 11th and 13th harmonics, special modulation patter shown in Fig. 8 is adopted. Using this pattern, the 11th and 13th become less than 5% and remaining harmonics can be easily eliminated by the output filter. In Fig. 9, the output voltage wave forms of the inverter transformer before filtering are shown for various conditions of the control signal Vc (or X). A typical examples of the wave forms of the transformer primary voltage and current are as shown in Fig. 10(a), and the voltage and the current of the filter are shown in Fig. 10(b), and the typical output voltage becomes as Fig. 10(c).

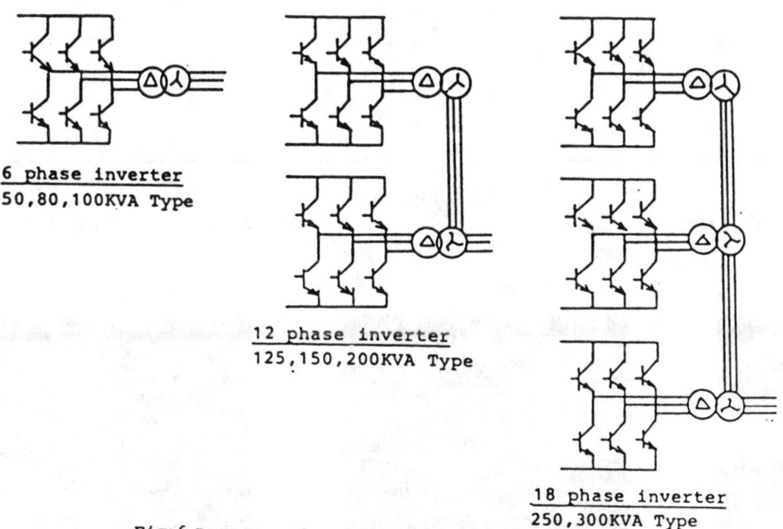

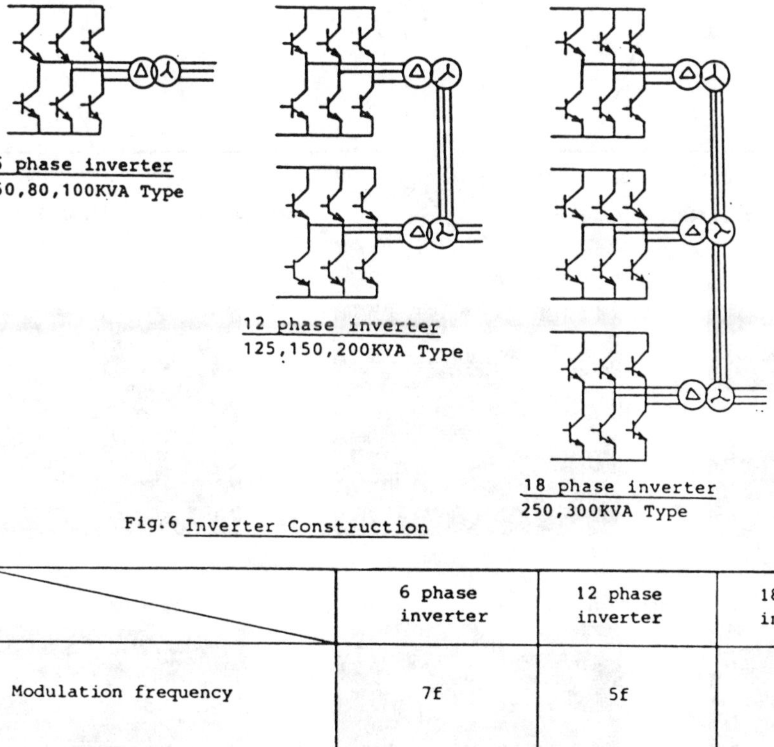

Fig. 6 Inverter Construction

	6 phase inverter	12 phase inverter	18 phase inverter
Modulation frequency	7f	5f	5f
Neutralized harmonics by modulation	5, 7th = 0	11, 13th < 5%	11, 13th < 5%
Neutralized harmonics by transformer	3rd = 0	3, 5, 7th = 0	3, 5, 7 11, 13th = 0

Fig. 7 Harmonics neutralization method

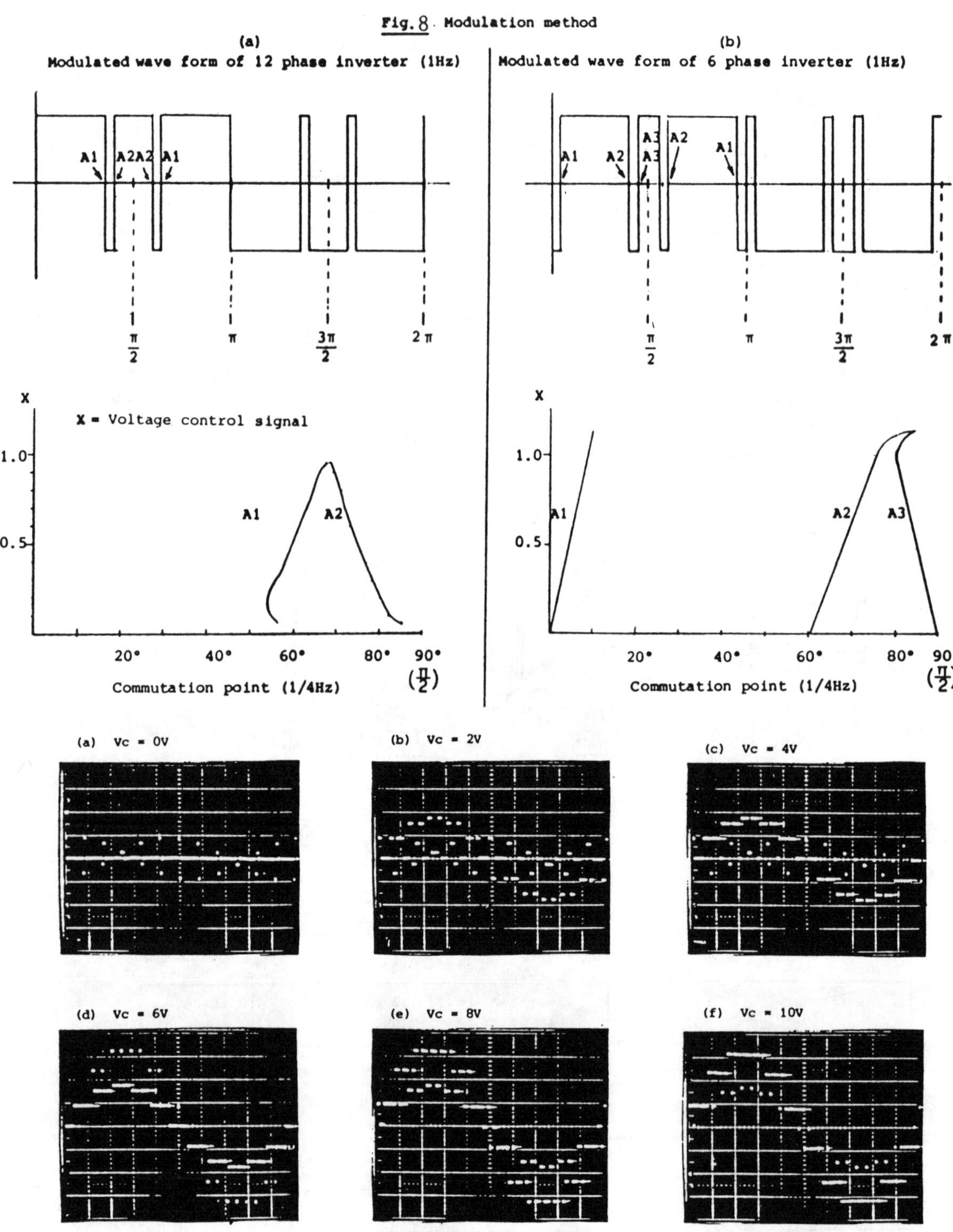

Fig. 8 Modulation method

Fig. 9 Multistage HF. PWM inverter voltage waveform before AC filter controled by Vc
(100V/div, 2m sec/div)

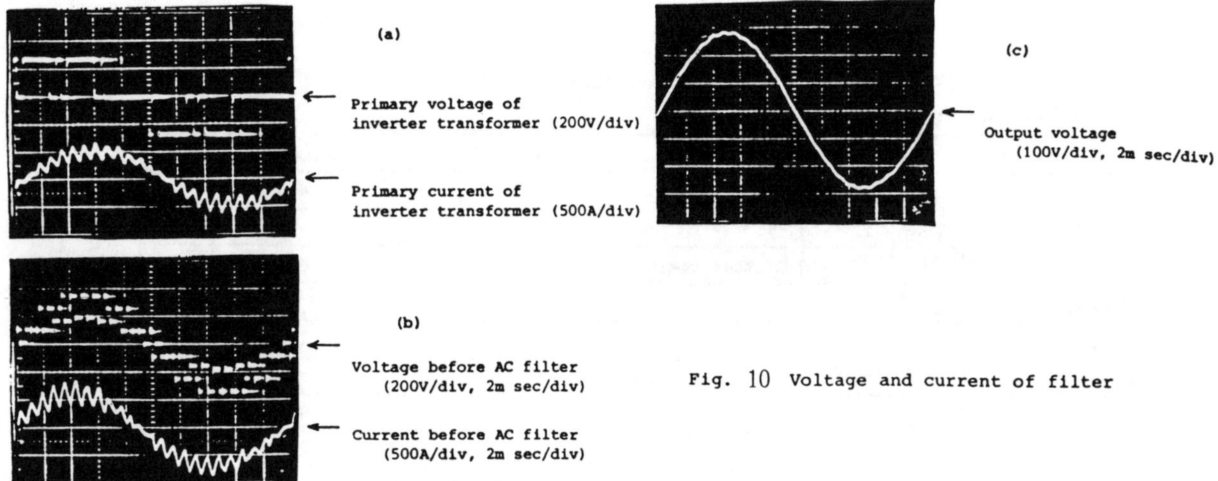

Fig. 10 Voltage and current of filter

3-2 Transistor inverter unit

Large power transistor as listed in Fig. 11 and shown in Fig. 12 are employed to the inverter units for high frequency pulse width modulation method. This transistor module consists of two arm of 100A, 450V darlington transistors and feedback diodes. These elements are insulated from the case, so very simple construction of the inverter unit is possible. To construct large capacity inverter unit, parallel connection of the transistor modules is necessary. Fortunately, transistors have the self balancing characteristics, so several numbers of transistors can be easily paralleled by selecting the hfe within certain limits. In this case, six transistor modules are paralleled as shown in Fig. 14.

Fig. 13 shows the photograph of transistor inverter unit. Advantages of the inverter unit employing transistor modules are as follows.

(a) Small dimension and light weight. No commutating capacitor, reactor and auxiliary thyristor are necessary for transistor inverter. This results in simple construction, small dimensions and light weight.

(b) High efficiency.
Owing to the elimination of the commutation loss and the resistance loss of the commutation reactor, high efficiency can be realized.

(c) High switching frequency operation.
Because of small switching loss of the transistor, high switching frequency operation, between several hundred Hz and two or three kHz, can be easily realized, consequently multiple pulse width modulation method can be adopted without deteriorating the efficiency.

(d) Reduction of operating sound.
The operating sound caused by high di/dt current of commutation reactor is inevitable in case of thyristor inverter, however transistors are free from such problems, so considerable reduction of audible noise can be easily realized.

(e) Constant switching capacity regardless of DC link voltage.
In case of thyristor inverters, the commutation capacility depends on the DC link voltage. This fact is an undesirable design condition of thyristor inverters. However, switching capability of transistor does not change by the DC link voltage, therefore stable operation under the considerable change of DC link voltage is ensured.

Fig. 11 Large power transistors

MAXIMUM RATINGS (T_j=25°C)

Symbol	Item	Conditions	QM100DY-H	Unit
$V_{CEX(SUS)}$	Collector-emitter voltage	I_C=1A, V_{BE}=-2V	450	V
V_{CEX}	Collector-emitter voltage	V_{BE}=-2V	600	V
V_{CBO}	Collector-base voltage	Emitter open	600	V
V_{EBO}	Emitter-base voltage		7	V
I_C	Collector current	DC.	100	A
$-I_C$	Reverse collector current	DC (forward diode current)	100	A
P_C	Collector dissipation		700	W
I_B	Base current		6	A
$-I_{CRSM}$	Reverse surge collector current	Peak value of one cycle of 60Hz (half wave) (forward diode surge current)	1000	A
T_j	Junction temperature		-40 ∿ +150	°C
Tstg	Storage temperature		-40 ∿ +125	°C
Visol	Insulation withstand voltage	AC for 1 minute between the case and current carrying points	2000	V
-	Mounting torque	Main terminals M6 screw and M6 mounting screw carrying points	15 ∿ 20	kg-cm
-	Weight	Typical value	420	g

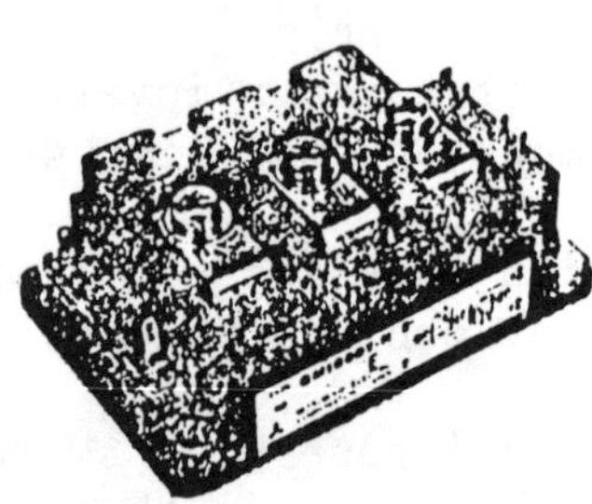

Fig. 12 Large power transistor

Fig. 13 Transistor inverter unit

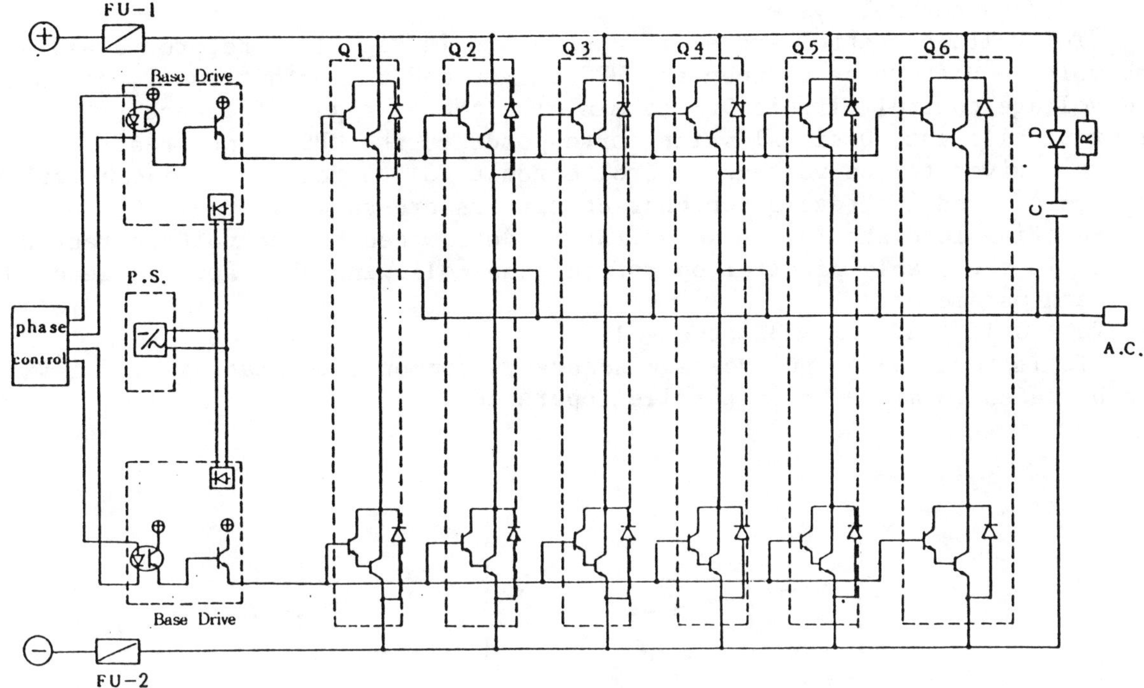

Fig. 14 Circuit diagram of inverter unit

4. CONTROL OF PARALLEL OPERATION

The control system of the completely independent parallel operation consists of (1) Synchronization control system and (2) Voltage control system.

4-1 Synchronization control system

The synchronization control system is shown in Fig. 17. Before paralleling, the phase difference $\Delta\varphi$ between the UPS output and the output bus is detected and this $\Delta\varphi$ signal controls the phase of UPS through V/F converter. After paralleling by closing the output mechanical power switch MPS1, the control switch SW2 is opened and SW1 is closed. And then P signal which corresponds to the UPS output active power is given to V/F converter to reduce the output frequency Fo to Fo - ΔF, and its characteristics are shown in Fig. 15.

And then, UPSs operate in parallel at the coincident point of each UPS frequency regulation. To achieve stable parallel operation, the following accuracy are necessary for each parameter:

Fo : $1 \sim 3 \times 10^{-6}$ ΔF : $1 \sim 5 \times 10^{-4}$ at P = 1

If it is necessary to improve the output frequency accuracy, common compensating signal Fx can be added to all UPSs in parallel.

4.2 Voltage control system

The voltage control system is also shown in Fig. 17. Before paralleling the voltage difference between the UPS output and the output bus is given to the voltage control circuit VC2 to minimize the voltage difference.
After paralleling, Q signal which corresponds to the UPS output reactive power is given to the voltage control circuit VC1 to reduce the output voltage Vr to Vr - ΔV, and its regulation characteristics are shown in Fig. 16.
The reactive load sharing between UPSs is determined by the voltage regulation. To get stable parallel operation, the following accuracy are necessary for each parameter.
Vr, Vc : 0.1%   ΔV : 2 ∿ 3% at Q = 1

To improve the output voltage accuracy, common compensating signal Vx can be added to all UPSs in parallel operation.

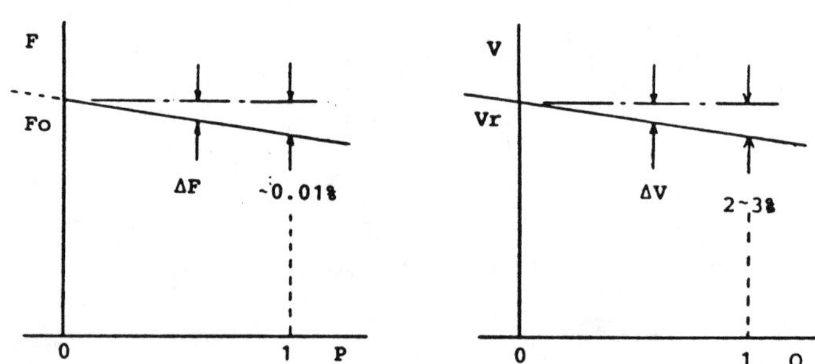

Fig.15 Frequency regulation.   Fig.16 Voltage regulation.

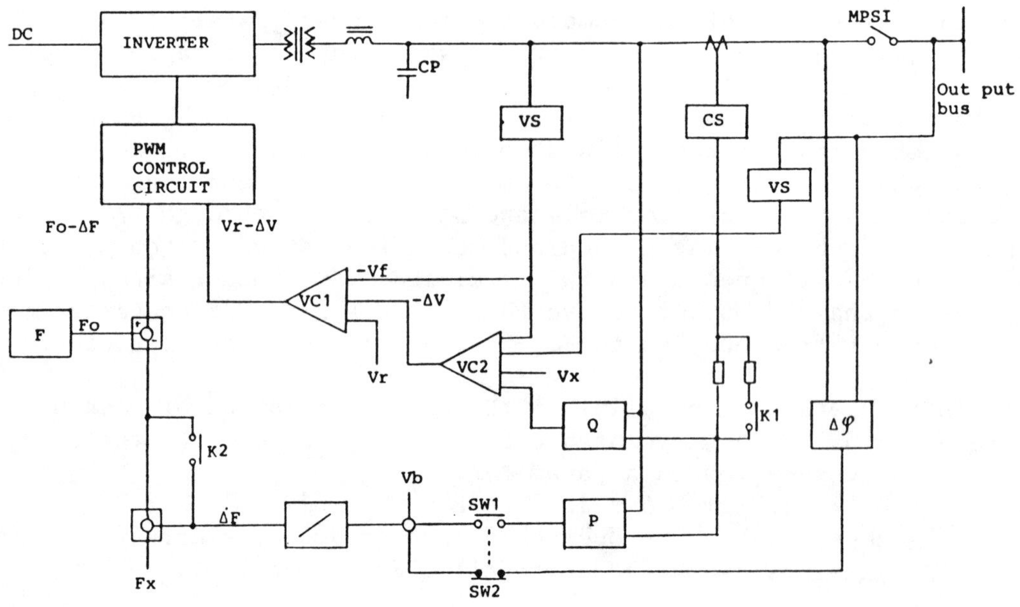

Fig. 17 Synchronization and voltage control system.

4-3 Features of control system

This control system has following merits compared to the conventional system with common parts.

(a) No possibility of system down due to the failure of the common parts.
(b) Maintenance and inspection of the total system can be performed without stopping the load.
(c) Almost no connection of delicate small control signal is necessary between UPSs, so the earthing of the control circuit of each UPS can be separated. This means the possibility of remote installation.
(d) Parallel operation will be possible even with different DC voltage. This characteristics will be utilized to change over the multiple UPSs from the battery to the generator at different timing to avoid the stoppage of the engine.
(e) To avoid the transient voltage change caused by connection or disconnection of a UPS to the output bus, smooth transfer control of the load can be realized.

5. TEST RESULTS

Test results of 2 x 200 kVA parallel redundant system are shown from Fig.18 to 25.These results indicate good performance of the transistor UPS as follows.

(a) High efficiency ----- 3 ∿ 4% better than conventional thyristor UPS.
(b) Good transient performance ----- almost same or better than that of multi stage single PWM UPS having many inverter stages. (e.g. more than 9 stages)
(c) Smooth load sharing control and protection function of interrupter-less protection system.

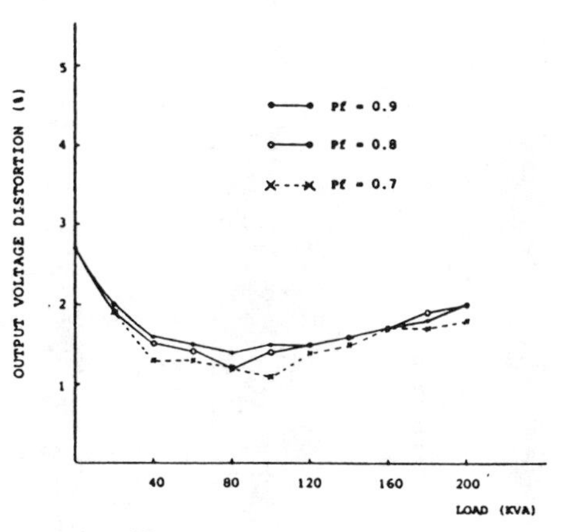

Fig. 19 VOLTAGE DISTORTION

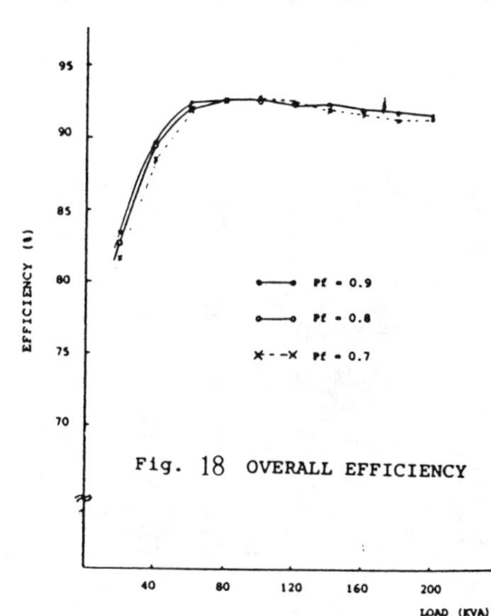

Fig. 18 OVERALL EFFICIENCY

6. ACKNOWLEDGEMENTS

The development of this transistor UPS described has been carried out as a project with many members, and the authors wish to acknowledge the contributions to the program from many participated members.

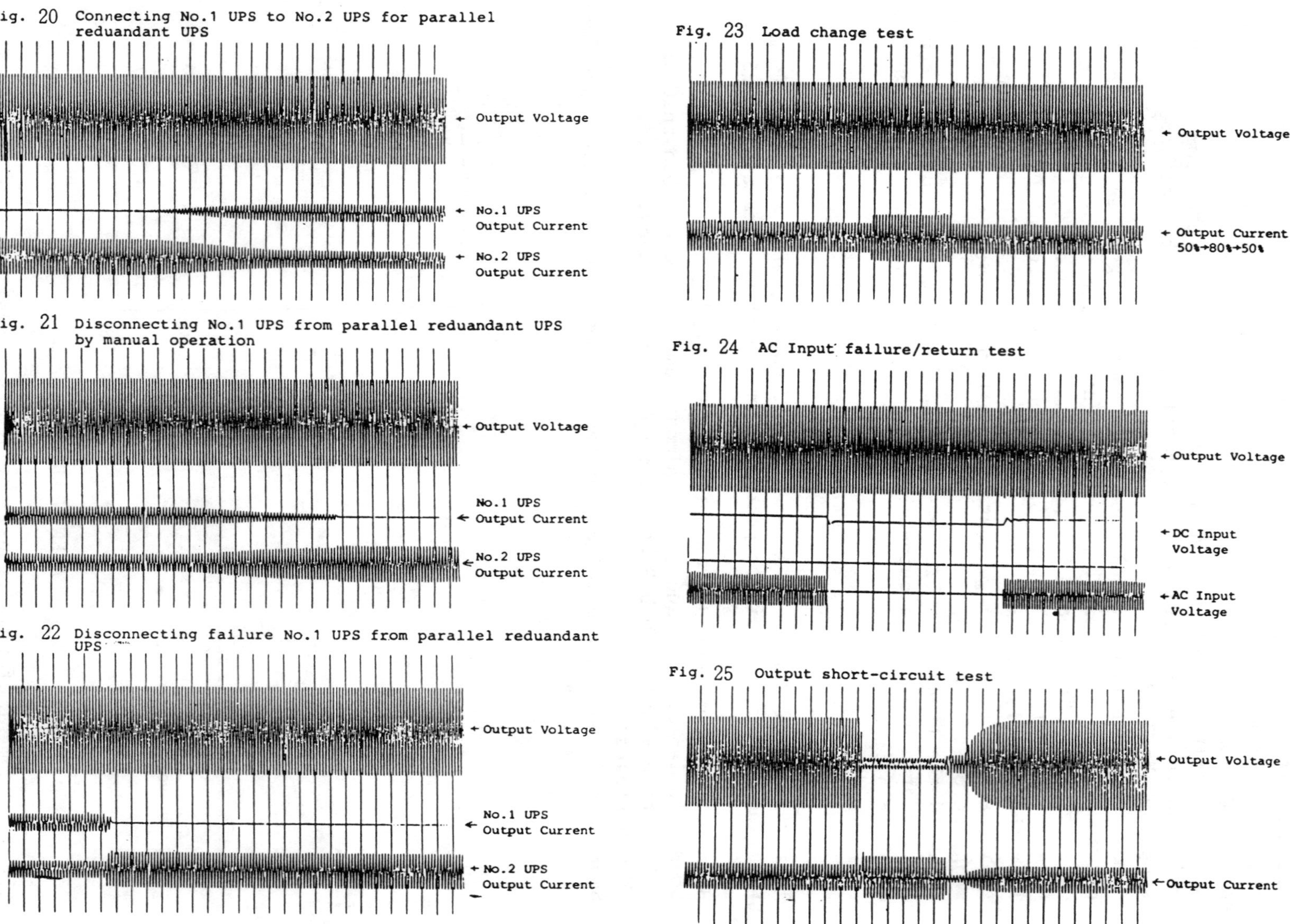

Fig. 20 Connecting No.1 UPS to No.2 UPS for parallel reduandant UPS

Fig. 21 Disconnecting No.1 UPS from parallel reduandant UPS by manual operation

Fig. 22 Disconnecting failure No.1 UPS from parallel reduandant UPS

Fig. 23 Load change test

Fig. 24 AC Input failure/return test

Fig. 25 Output short-circuit test

Paper 8.8

PARALLEL PROCESSING INVERTER SYSTEM

T. KAWABATA (Member IEEE), N. SASHIDA (Member IEEE),
Y. YAMAMOTO, K. OGASAWARA, Y. YAMASAKI

Mitsubishi Electric Corp.
Power Electronics Dept.
Wadasaki 1-1-2, Hyogo, Kobe, 652 JAPAN

ABSTRACT

This paper proposes a novel method of "Instantaneous Voltage and Power Balance Control of Parallel Processing Inverter System" which consists of high speed switching PWM inverter with instantaneous current minor loop controller, voltage major loop controller and power balance controller.

This system realizes following functions with only one inverter: (1) Constant AC output voltage control with reactive power control, (2) Active filtering to absorb load harmonic current, (3) DC voltage and current control as AC to DC converter, (4) No break power supply for stand-alone operation.

This system has a wide application area including UPS, new energy system and active filter with voltage control function.

1. Introduction

Inverter application systems can be classified as shown in Fig. 1 and TABLE 1, according to the connection types of their output to the other AC power source and the load. Typical examples of other AC power sources are utility power source or other inverters.

In this table, [A], [B], [C] and [D] are suitable types of inverters as shown in TABLE 2. Being seen from the output terminal, the types of inverter can be categorized to the VOLTAGE SOURCE and the CURRENT SOURCE. And this is mainly determined by the control system regardless of the types of the main circuit, as shown in TABLE 2. This principle had been presented for example in the references[1] and [2].

The most popular inverter application system is the stand-alone system and the parallel connection systems have been widely adopted, too.

Although the series connection system had also been proposed for the active filter system by L. Gyugyi in 1976 [3], this system has not been adopted popularly for a long time. But, recently an excellent active filter system using this connection topology had been proposed by A. Nabae, H. Akagi, et al., so this system is also expected to be widely used. [4]

In the existing parallel connection system, there is no large coupling inductance between the output of the inverter and the other AC source. But in case of the parallel processing UPS, the active filter system or the utility interface of new energy system with a long distribution line, they usually have 0.1 or larger p.u. value of the coupling inductance.

These systems have basically following three problems. The first one is that with such inductances of low resistance, the system become very oscillatory as explained in following sections.

TABLE 1 Connection types of inverter output to other AC power source and load

Connection type	Example	Feasible inverter type
Stand-alone	Usual single UPS V-F motor drive	Voltage source [A]
	Vector control motor drive	Current source [C], [D]
Series connection	New type of active filter	Voltage source [A], [B]
Parallel connection	Parallel processing UPS Parallel redundant UPS	Voltage source [A], [B]
	Static VAR generator	
	Active filter	Current source [C], [D]

TABLE 2 Types of inverter as seen from output

Main \ Control	Voltage control	Current control
Voltage type PWM (or PAM) inverter	TYPE [A] Voltage source	TYPE [C] Current source
Current type PWM or PAM inverter	TYPE [B] Voltage source	TYPE [D] Current source

Reprinted with permission from *Int. Power Electron. Conf. (IPEC) Rec.*, vol. 1, pp. 107–114, April 1990. © 1990 IEE of Japan.

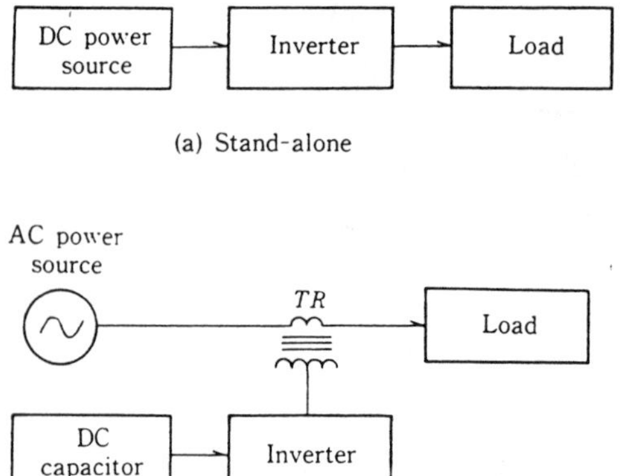

(a) Stand-alone

(b) Series connection

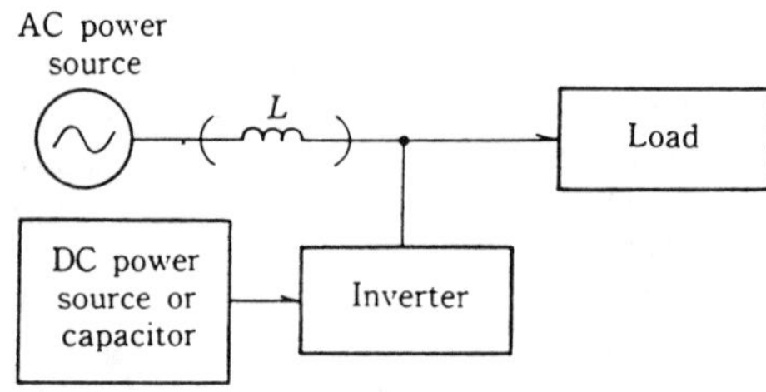

(c) Parallel connection

Fig. 1 Inverter application systems

The second problem is the use of PLL to power balance control of the system. If PLL is adopted to control the phase angle between the inverter and the other AC power source, it is difficult to obtain fast response of power balance control, because of inherently slow response of PLL.

The third problem is inverter protection from overcurrent against disturbances of the other AC power source and inrush or short circuit load current.

In the following sections, system design of the parallel processing inverter system, its control system to solve above problems and some applications are proposed.

2. System design

2.1 Main circuit configuration

Fig. 2 shows the basic configuration of the proposed parallel processing inverter system. This system consists of a three phase PWM inverter which is connected in parallel to utility power source through a coupling reactance (L_B), an electronic switch and DC power source such as batteries. The parallel processing inverter system has two operation modes, (A) Parallel processing mode and (B) Stand-alone mode.

In the parallel processing mode, the electronic switch is on and the effective power is supplied from the utility to the load. The inverter acts the following three functions:

1. Constant output voltage control with reactive power control

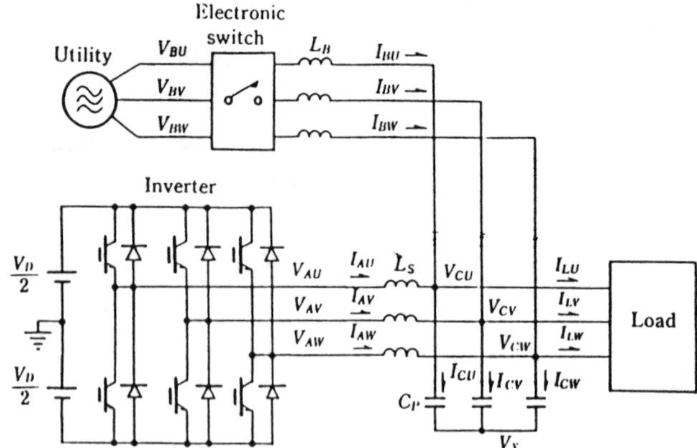

Fig. 2 Main circuit configuration of parallel processing inverter system

2. Absorption of the load harmonics current
3. Charging of the battery

When a power failure happens, the parallel processing inverter system changes to the stand-alone mode. The electronic switch is turned off and the inverter converts the DC power to AC and supplies the load.

One important point of this mode transfer is there is no interruption of power supply unlike the OFF-LINE UPS. The reasons are that the load is always connected to the inverter which output voltage is controlled constantly and that the input voltage disturbances are isolated by the coupling reactance.

The parallel processing inverter system can have the following four functions:

1. Constant voltage power source in both parallel processing and stand-alone modes
2. Uninterruptible power supply in stand-alone mode
3. Harmonics absorbing active filter in parallel processing mode
4. DC to AC power link with variety of DC power sources including batteries, solar cells, fuel cells and so on

The advanced points of the parallel processing inverter are summarized as the following three items:

1. Inherently high efficiency with the least number of power conversion
2. Compact and economical
3. Realization of new power conditioning system with a lot of functions

2.2 Output voltage control with the inverter current

In the parallel processing mode, the output voltage V_C is controlled by the inverter current (I_A) as follows:

$$I_A = I_L + I_C - I_B \qquad \text{--- (1)}$$

$$\therefore \quad I_B = I_L + I_C - I_A \qquad \text{--- (2)}$$

where I_L : load current
I_C : filter capacitor (C_P) current
I_B : input current

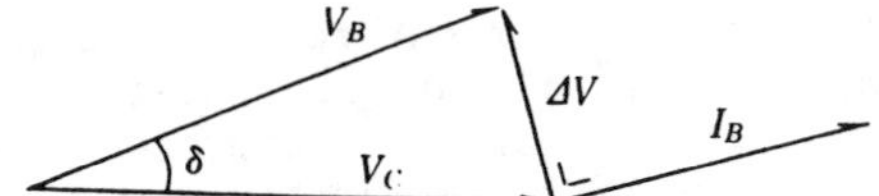

Fig. 3 Relations among V_B, V_C and I_B

and

$$V_C = V_B - \Delta V \quad \text{--- (3)}$$
$$= V_B - I_B \cdot X_B \quad \text{--- (4)}$$

where V_B : input voltage
ΔV : voltage across the coupling reactance X_B ($j\omega L_B$)

from (2) and (4)

$$V_C = V_B - (I_L + I_C - I_A) \cdot X_B \quad \text{--- (5)}$$

In the steady state, the capacitor current I_C can be considered as constant and the coupling reactance X_B is also constant, the output voltage V_C is controllable with the inverter current I_A against the variation of the input voltage V_B or load current (I_L) change (Fig. 3). δ is the angle between V_B and V_C.

Fig. 4 shows the vector diagram of the inverter. Required reactive power of the inverter which maintains the output voltage constant, is examined against the input voltage variations ΔV_B of $\pm 10\%$. Other conditions are:

1. The parallel capacitor C_P is 40% of inverter rated capacity
2. The load is from no-load to full load with the power factor of 0.8 lagging.

The segment $OX = V_C$ indicates the unity output voltage. The segment XQ indicates the voltage requisite to apply the coupling reactance X_B for the input current $OA = I_1 = I_C + I_L$ to flow and the segment OQ indicates the assumed input voltage V_B to obtain unity output voltage V_C, without inverter control ($I_A = 0$). But, for example, when $V_B = 110\%$, actual input voltage V_B is on locus CL-1, then the inverter should supply reactive current of $AA_1 = I_{A1}$.

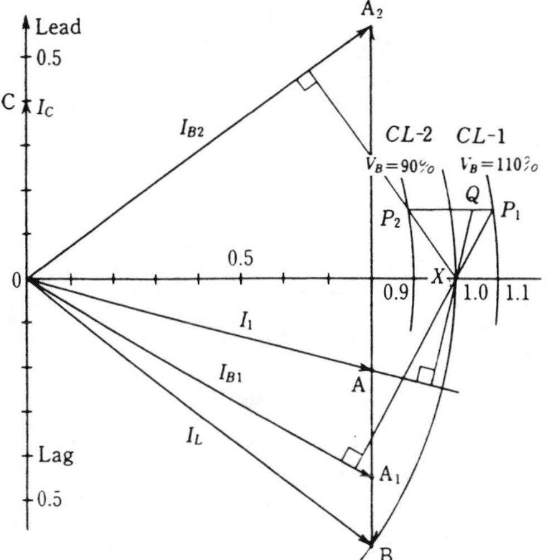

Fig. 4 Vector diagram

$$I_{A1} = \frac{QP_1}{X_B} = \frac{0.052}{0.2} = 0.26 \text{ (P.U.)} \quad (6)$$

When the input voltage drops by 10% and the locus of V_B is CL-2, the inverter should absorb reactive current of $AA_2 = I_{A2}$.

$$I_{A2} = \frac{QP_2}{X_B} = \frac{0.15}{0.2} = 0.75 \text{ (P.U.)} \quad (7)$$

Thus the point Q moves to P_1 or P_2 and the output voltage is maintained constantly.

Fig. 5 shows the requisite reactive power output of the inverter, which is obtained as mentioned above, for no load and full load conditions in cases of $L_B = 20\%$ and 30%. This figure shows two important points in the system design.

First, the reactive power capacity of the inverter is within 1 p.u. of the system capacity. Point (A) shows the maximum lead current of 0.75 p.u. flows at full load and -10% input voltage variation for $L_B = 20\%$. Point (B) shows the maximum lag current of 0.9 p.u. flows at no load and +10% input voltage variation. This means that the same inverter of 1 p.u. can be used in both parallel processing and stand-alone modes.

Second, the inverter current is nearly zero at normal operating condition. Point (C) shows inverter current is zero at about 70% load and no input voltage variation. This means that the efficiency becomes highest at normal operating conditions.

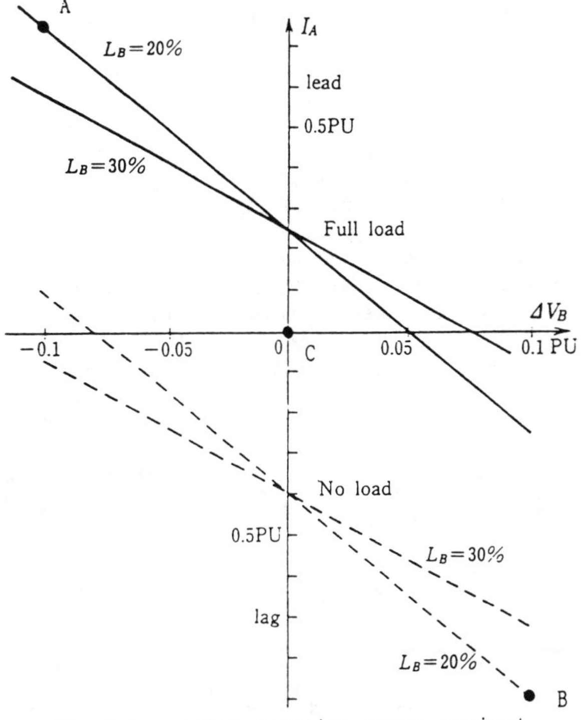

Fig. 5 Requisite reactive power against input voltage variation

3. Control system

The proposing control system of the parallel processing inverter system consists of:

(A) Output bus voltage control system and

(B) Power balance and DC voltage control system.

3.1 Output voltage control system

Output voltage V_C is controlled by the inverter current I_A against the variation of the input voltage V_B and the load current I_L, as explained above. So the high frequency PWM inverter is controlled as a current source having current control minor loop. As the major control loop, it has voltage controller which controls the output voltage as harmonicsless sinusoidal waveforms [2]. The reference signal V_C^* of this voltage controller is given by another higher level control system, "Power balance controller" which is explained later.

Fig. 6 shows the block diagram of the output voltage control system. To obtain high performance of control, the controller is constructed on the d-q coordinates.

As the PWM method, the triangle carrier comparison method is adopted, and the carrier is synchronized with the output frequency.

As the current controller, IP-control with the decoupling of the d-q component and the compensation of the filter capacitor (C_P) voltage, is adopted. The output of this current controller is transformed from the d-q coordinates to the u-v-w coordinates, and given to the PWM circuit.

As the reference of the current minor loop, sum of the following two signals is given through a limiter as shown in Fig. 6.

First, the difference (I_L - I_B) of the load current I_L and the utility source input current I_B is given as the feed-forward signal. As explained in section 2, the input current I_B contains necessary effective power of the system. Then the signal (I_L - I_B) corresponds to the load harmonics current and the load current transient. The current minor loop follows this feed-forward signal quickly, therefore this system can respond to distortions and disturbances of the load current.

Second, the current reference signal from the voltage major loop controller is given. This voltage controller is a proportional controller on the d-q coordinates with the decoupling control of d-q components. The voltage reference signal is given from the "Power balance controller" which is explained in the following subsection. The controller gives command of necessary inverter current to correct the instantaneous output voltage deviation, assures the constant voltage characteristics and stabilizes the system. The voltage controller also gives reference signal of charging current of the filter capacitor as the result of the decoupling control.

Thus this inverter system forms a low impedance sinusoidal voltage source from a current source. Providing a limiter for the sum of above signals before giving it to the current minor loop, this system can get an inherent protection against overcurrent.

One of very good points of this output voltage control system is that no control mode change happens at the operation mode change.

In the parallel processing mode, the difference between the load current I_L and the input current I_B is fed forward to the current controller. When the system changes into the stand-alone mode and the electronic switch is turned off, the input current I_B automatically becomes zero and the feed forward signal automatically becomes I_L. The output voltage is thus continuously controlled as constant magnitude sinusoidal waveforms.

3.2 Power balance and DC voltage control system

Another higher level control system is the power balance and DC voltage control system. The parallel processing system is simplified as two voltage sources (utility V_B and inverter V_C) and the coupling reactance L_B (Fig. 7). The effective power P_{IN} which flows through the reactance L_B is decided by equation

$$P_{IN} = V_B \cdot V_C \cdot \sin\delta \;/\; \omega \cdot L_B \qquad \text{--- (8)}$$

From this equation we can see that by controlling the phase difference angle δ the power P_{IN} can be controlled.

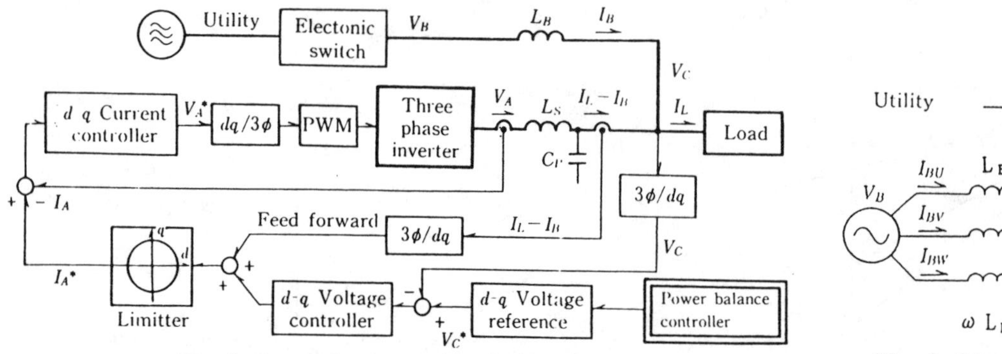

Fig. 6 Control system block diagram

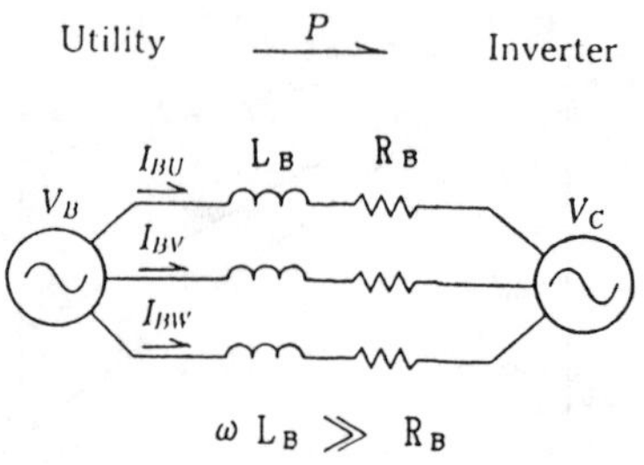

Utility — P → Inverter

$\omega L_B \gg R_B$

Fig. 7 Simplified model

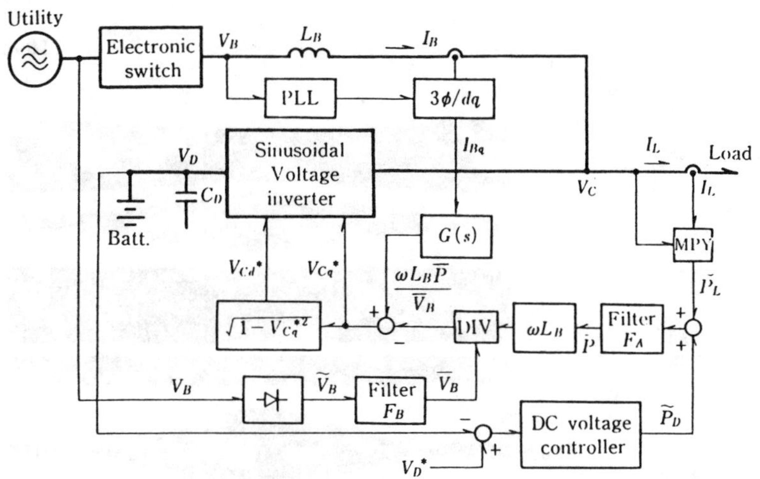

Fig. 8 Power balance and DC voltage control system

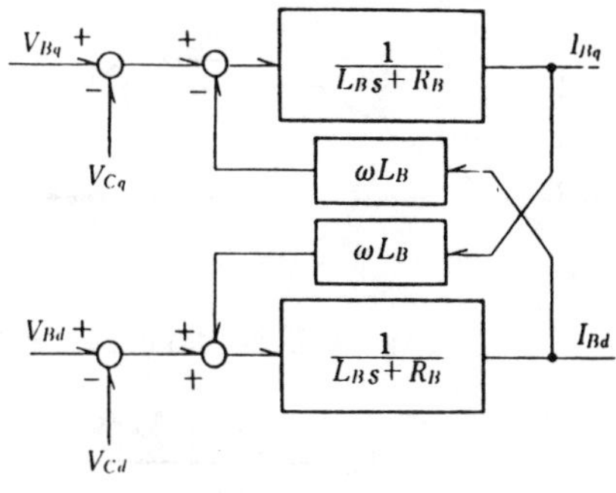

Fig. 9 Block diagram of voltage and current of L_B

Fig. 8 shows the control system for phase lag angle δ and the DC voltage (V_D). δ is so controlled to balance the input power from the utility with the required power of the system (sum of load power, DC input/output power and loss of the system). Input voltage or load may change suddenly and cause transient power unbalance. As this unbalance can be absorbed by battery or capacitor in the inverter DC circuit, the control of δ can be performed slowly to regulate the charging DC voltage. To reduce unnecessary DC power fluctuation, load power and source voltage are given to the controller as feed forward signals. The control of δ must be slow response to restrain the phase change of the output voltage within several degrees per cycle, because too quick response of the control of δ may cause sudden phase change of the output voltage.

If the DC capacitor is large enough or the control speed of δ is fast enough to limit the DC voltage fluctuation within an acceptable level, a new type of active filter without batteries can be realized. In this case, the parallel processing inverter works only as an active filter with voltage regulating function.[5]

One thing we must be very careful is that this system is oscillatory by nature having only coupling inductance and no resistance. The block diagram of voltage and current of L_B is shown in Fig. 9. For a reactor L_B of 0.2 P.U., typical value of its resistance R_B is about 0.002 P.U. Consequently this block diagram is a resonant circuit which has resonance frequency of ω.

Using voltage applied across the inductance L_B ($V_{BC} = V_B - V_C$), transfer function from V_{BCq} to I_B is expressed as follows:

$$\frac{I_{Bq}}{V_{BCq}} = \frac{\frac{1}{L_B}\left(s + \frac{R_B}{L_B}\right)}{s^2 + 2\frac{R_B}{L_B}s + \left(\frac{R_B^2}{L_B^2} + \omega^2\right)} \quad \cdots\cdots(9)$$

$$\frac{I_{Bd}}{V_{BCq}} = \frac{\omega / L_B}{s^2 + 2\frac{R_B}{L_B}s + \left(\frac{R_B^2}{L_B^2} + \omega^2\right)} \quad \cdots\cdot(10)$$

Natural frequency (ω_n) and damping coefficient (ζ) are given by the following equations:

$$\omega_n = \left(\frac{R_B^2}{L_B^2} + \omega^2\right)^{1/2} \quad \cdots\cdots\cdots\cdots(11)$$

$$\zeta = \frac{R_B}{L_B\ \omega_n} \quad \cdots\cdots\cdots\cdots(12)$$

From equations (11) and (12), conditions to get $\zeta = 0.7$ for $\omega L_B = 0.2$ are $\omega_n = 1.4$ and $R_B = 0.194$. Namely, to get $\zeta = 0.7$, about 0.2 P.U. of resistance must be connected in series to the coupling inductance L_B. However, as loss generating damping resistance in the main circuit is not acceptable, a damping controller is added in the control system to give damping with the input current signal I_B.

As shown in Fig. 8, to get the power supplied from the utility ($\bar{P}$), the sum of the effective powers consumed at load ($\tilde{P}_L$) and at DC side of the inverter ($\tilde{P}_D$) is given as the reference signal through a filter (F_A). Response of δ control is decided by this filter. The q-component of the output voltage reference (V_{Cq}^*) is given by the following equation:

$$V_{Cq}^* = V_C^* \cdot \sin\delta = -\omega L_B \cdot P / V_B \quad \text{-- } (13)$$

where V_B is the average value of the utility voltage.

V_{Cq}^* in equation (13) is steady state value, therefore, voltage drop of the resistance by the damping control method to V_{BCq} must be given in transient period to restrain the I_B oscillation. So the transfer function G(s) which has resistance characteristics around the natural frequency (60Hz) of I_B is adopted. G(s) is expressed as follows:

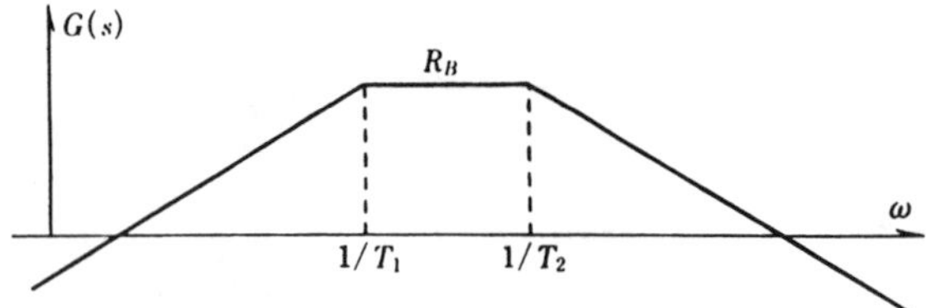

Fig. 10 Bode diagram of G(s)

$$G(s) = R_B \frac{T1 \cdot s}{(1 + T1 \cdot s)(1 + T2 \cdot s)} \quad \text{-- (14)}$$

where $T1 = 1/2\pi 50$ and $T2 = 1/2\pi 70$ (Fig. 10)

Therefore $V_{Cq}{}^{*}$ is given by the following equation:

$$V_{Cq}{}^{*} = -\omega L_B \cdot P/V_B + G(s) \cdot I_{Bq} \quad \text{--- (15)}$$

To keep the amplitude of the output bus voltage reference constant, the d-component of $V_C{}^{*}$ ($V_{Cd}{}^{*}$) is given by the following equation:

$$V_{Cd}{}^{*} = \sqrt{1 - V_{Cq}{}^{*2}} \quad \text{--- (16)}$$

When batteries or large capacitors are connected in the DC side of the inverter, transient power unbalances can be absorbed by them. So the effective power balance controller can have rather slower response. The output signal $V_C{}^{*}$ is given to the inverter as the voltage reference signal.

4. Experiment with a 10 kVA model set

4.1 Experimental conditions

A three phase 10 kVA experimental set is made and tested. Experimental conditions are as follows:

Inverter capacity : 10 kVA
Output voltage : 3 ph 200 V 60 Hz
DC voltage : 273 V
Battery : 240 V 24 Ah
L_S = 220 μH (8%)
L_B = 2.2 mH (21%)
C_P = 315 μF (36%)
Inverter switching frequency : 8.1 kHz

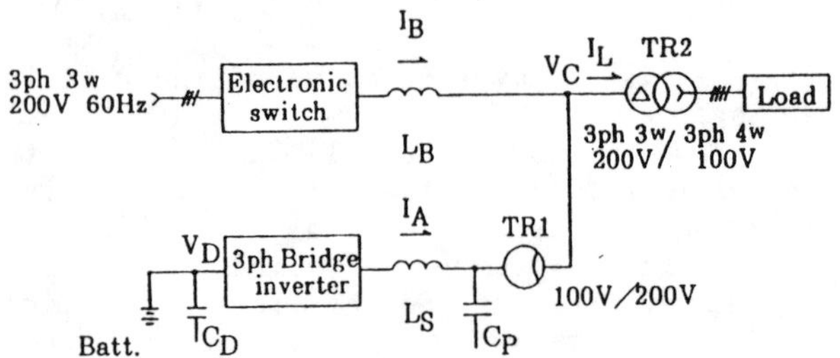

Fig. 11 Configuration of experimental set

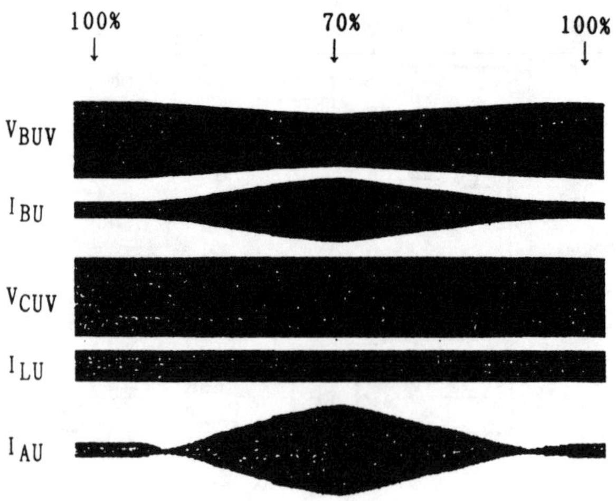

Fig. 12 Operation against input voltage change

4.2 Experimental results

(1) Steady state

Fig. 12 shows the constant output voltage characteristics against 0 ~ -30% input voltage change at 40% resistive load. At the rated input voltage of 200V, the inverter supplies lag current to compensate the lead current of Cp so as to controls the output voltage unity. The output voltage is maintained constantly against 0 ~ -30% input voltage change. At -30% input voltage, the inverter supplies 119% of lead current.

Fig. 13 shows an operation at a single phase rectifier load. Harmonics and unbalance of the load current (I_{LU}, I_{LV} and I_{LW}) are compensated by the inverter and the input current (I_{BU}, I_{BV} and I_{BW}) becomes harmonicsless balanced current.

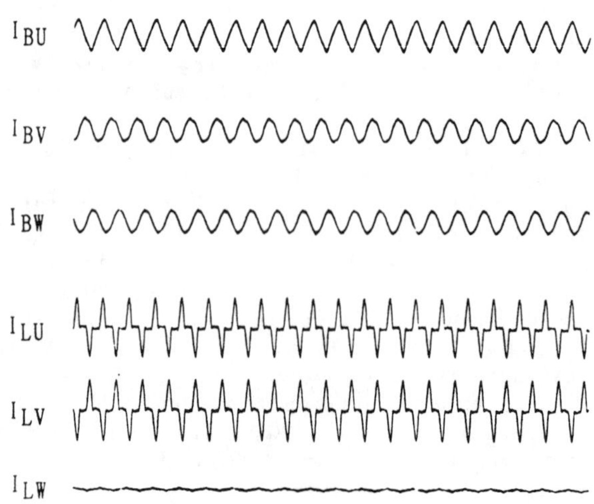

Fig. 13 Single phase rectifier load
(Harmonics absorption and load balancing)

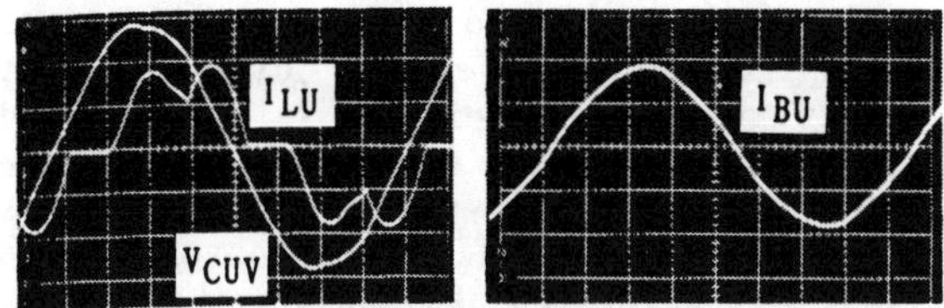

Fig. 14 Output voltage (V_{CUV}) and Load current (I_{LU}) Fig. 15 Input current (I_{BU})

Fig. 14 shows the output voltage (V_{CUV}) and load current (I_{LU}) waveforms. Fig. 15 shows the input current (I_{BU}). The distortion factors of V_{CUV} and I_{BU} are 3.2% and 3.5% respectively.

The total efficiency of the experimental set is higher than 89% at rated input voltage and rated load (10 kVA / 8kW).

(2) Transient state

Fig. 16 shows an operation at a sudden load change. A 100% resistive load is switched on and off as the load current (I_{LU}) indicates. The output voltage (V_{CUV}) is maintained constantly. The DC voltage (V_D) changes at the load change and slowly controlled by the Power balance controller.

Fig. 17 shows an operation at a sudden input voltage change. The input voltage (V_B) is changed from 100% to 90% and then to 100%. The input current (I_B) increases to supply the same effective power for -10% voltage drop. The output voltage (V_{CUV}) and the load current (I_{LU}) are kept constantly.

Fig. 18 shows an operation at input power failure. The inverter supplies the load current (I_{LU}) immediately after the power failure and the DC voltage (V_D) drops from float charging voltage to discharging voltage. After the power failure is over, the inverter current decreases gradually to give a shockless load transfer to the utility input.

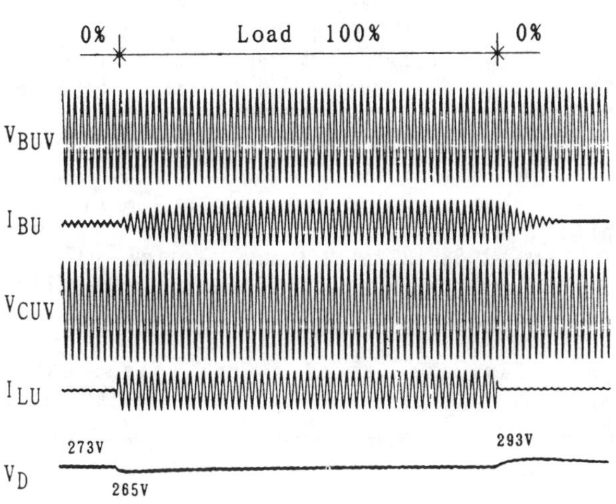

Fig. 16 Sudden load change

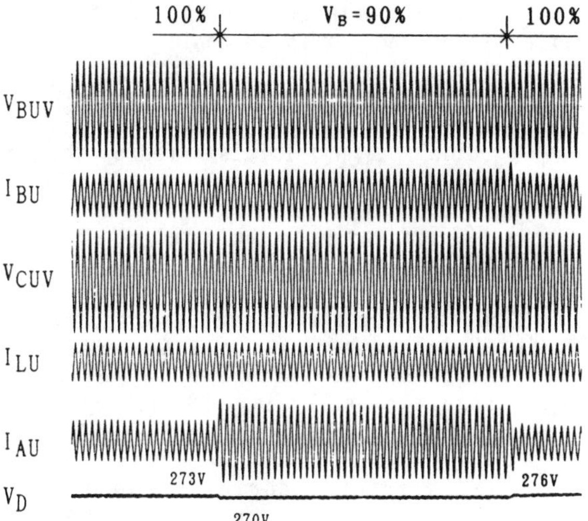

Fig. 17 Sudden input voltage change

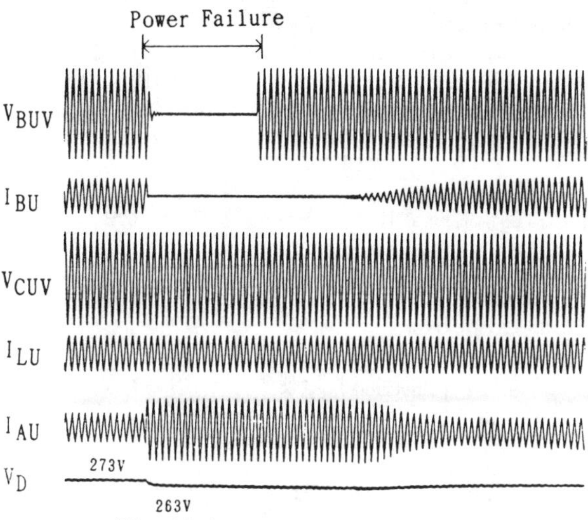

Fig. 18 Input power failure

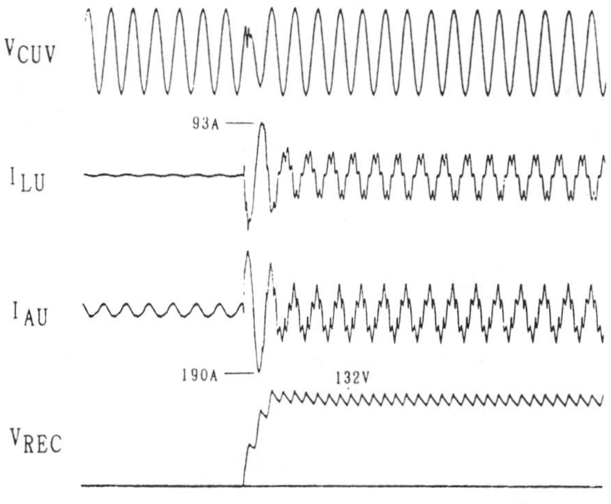

V_{REC}: Capacitor voltage of a rectifier load

Fig. 19 Switching on of a rectifier load

Fig. 19 shows a switching on of a rectifier load. The inrush current of the load is supplied by the inverter current (I_{AU}). At the initial peak, the inverter current is constrained by the current minor loop and the output voltage (V_{CUV}) is distorted at this moment.

5. New UPS systems with the parallel processing inverter system

The parallel processing inverter can replace the conventional thyristor converter of UPS systems and realizes a wide variety of power conditioning systems. [6] Fig. 20 shows a typical example of such system, dual frequency output UPS.

The inverter-1 converts the input AC power to DC and at the same time controls the supply voltage of the load-A and absorbs the harmonics current of the load-A. The inverter-2 converts the DC power to 400Hz AC which is supplied to the load-B.

When the input power fails, SW_1 is turned off and the inverter-1 immediately changes to stand-alone operation to support the load-A.

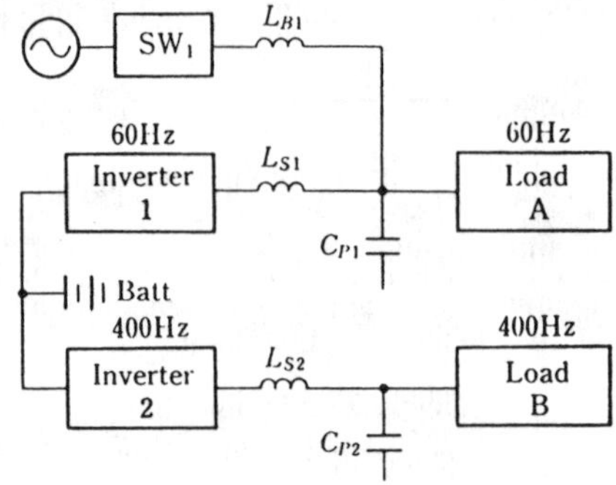

Fig. 20 Dual output frequency UPS system

Fig. 21 shows a redundant dual frequency output UPS system. The inverter-1 can operate at either 60Hz or 400Hz. SW_{2S} is inserted between the inverter-1 and the load-A and usually turned on. SW_{1L} connects the inverter-1 and the load-B and is usually turned off. SW_{2L} is inserted between the inverter-2 and the load-B and usually turned on.

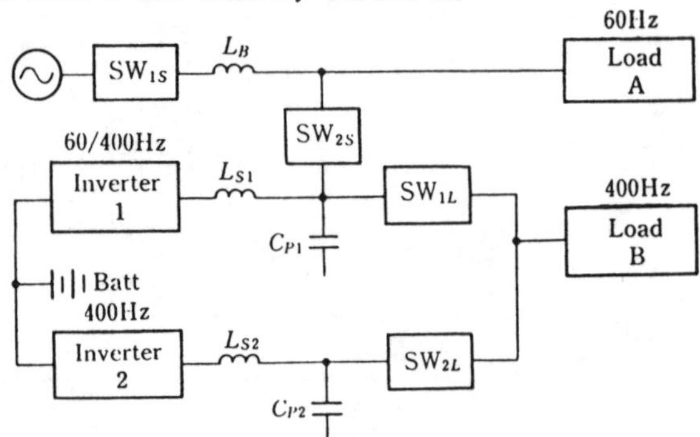

Fig. 21 Redundant dual frequency output UPS system

In a usual state and during a power failure, this system operates just like that of Fig. 20. When the inverter-2 fails, SW_{2S} and SW_{2L} are turned off and SW_{1L} is turned on immediately and the inverter-1 changes its operating mode from 60Hz AC/DC conversion to DC/400Hz AC conversion and support the load-B. An operator get a time to shut down the load-B safely before the battery expires. The load-A is continuously supported directly from the power source.

These systems can realize dual frequency output UPS systems with minimum hardware.

6. Conclusions and acknowledgments

A new type of Parallel Processing Inverter System has been proposed. The exclusively advanced points of the proposed system are summarized as follows:

(1) The instantaneous inverter output current and voltage are controlled, so sudden load change, load harmonic current and unbalance are compensated by active filter function, and balanced sinusoidal input current is obtained.

(2) The DC link voltage and current can be controlled stably for any type of DC circuit conditions. Namely, depending on the application system, batteries, only capacitors or new energy sources such as fuel cells can be used as DC power source. [5]

(3) This system has also the function of a harmonics-less AC to DC converter, so efficient economical system can be realized without dedicated rectifier.

(4) A new method of high speed power balance control has been successfully adopted, thus, this system can stably control the power flow of low resistance networks.

The authors deeply appreciate the support of the Institute of Applied Energy for the work reported in this paper.

REFERENCES

[1] P. D. Ziogas, S. Manias et al. :"Application of Current Source Inverter in UPS Systems ", IEEE Trans. on IAS, IA20, No. 4, JULY/AUGUST 1984

[2] T. kawabata, et al. :"Dead Beat Control of Three Phase PWM Inverter", IEEE Trans. on Power Electronics, Jan. /Feb. 1990

[3] L. Gyugyi, et al. :"Active AC Power Filters", 1976 IEEE IAS Annual Meeting, p529

[4] H. Akagi, A. Nabae & F. Z. Peng :"A New Approach to Harmonic Compensation in Power Systems", 1988 IEEE IAS Annual Meeting, p874

[5] T. Kawabata, et al. :"Three phase parallel processing UPS using multi-functional inverters", 1989 IEEE IAS Annual Meeting, p982

[6] T. Kawabata, et al. :"UPS systems using multi-functional inverters" IEEE INTELEC 1987, Session 12-6

Paper 8.9

Consideration on Large Capacity PWM Inverter for LSM Drives

Susumu TADAKUMA* Shigeru TANAKA* Haruhisa INOGUCHI*
Yoshirou TANOUE* Haruo IKEDA** Shigeo KAGA**

* Toshiba Corp., 1, Toshiba-cho, Fuchu-shi, Tokyo 183, Japan
** Railway Technical Research Institute, 2-8-38 Hikari-cho, Kokubunji-shi, Tokyo 185, Japan

Abstract

High speed magnetically levitated transportation system requires large capacity power converters which supply three phase sinusoidal currents to the armature coils of the linear synchronous motor (LSM). A pulse width modulated (PWM) inverter by GTO devices is one of the high quality power converters for LSM drives.

This paper discusses a procedure for reducing the output voltage harmonics of the PWM inverter and a control method to prevent the magnetic saturation of output transformer which is met in large capacity inverters.

1. Introduction

Study of a high speed transportation system proceeds toward construction of a new test track at Yamanashi.

The new transportation system by magnetic levitation requires large capacity power converters which supply the sinusoidal currents to the armature winding of linear synchronous motor.[1],[2]

Until today, the circulating current type cycloconverters[3] of rated capacity 16MVA have been applied to the linear motor drives at Miyazaki test track. This power conversion system contributed to high speed running of about 400km/h by a prototype vehicle MLU002 with 44 passenger seats.

On the other hand, the progress of power switching devices, such as gate turn off thyristors (GTOs), has accelerated development of pulse width modulated (PWM) inverters for large capacity ac motor drives.

Authors consider on a PWM inverter for LSM drives instead of the cycloconverter system.

The PWM inverter composed of GTOs can supply three phase sinusoidal currents of 0 to 56.6Hz to linear synchronous motor with the superconductive magnetic field of a short pole pitch.

In this system, the output transformers are used for increasing the inverter output voltage and for decreasing the load current ripple by multi-PWM control. When the inverter is operated at low output frequency, the alternating flux of each transformer is apt to deviate from the state of equilibrium toward saturation by dc bias voltage, based on the switching characteristics irregularities of GTOs.

A half-bridge inverter directly connected to the LSM without the output transformer generates the voltage unrelated to the output frequency. The output voltage harmonics from the half-bridge inverter which does not participate in the multi-PWM control causes the fluctuation of load currents.

This paper proposes a procedure for reducing the output voltage harmonics of the PWM inverter and a control method to prevent the magnetic saturation of output transformers. The effects of those procedure are clarified by digital simulation.

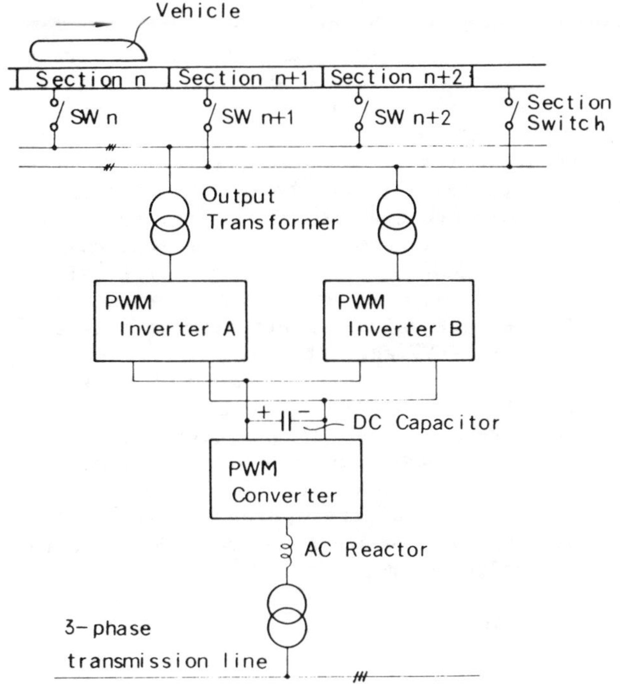

Fig.1 LSM drive system

Reprinted with permission from *Int. Power Electron. Conf. (IPEC) Rec.*, vol. 1, pp. 413–420, April 1990. © 1990 IEE of Japan.

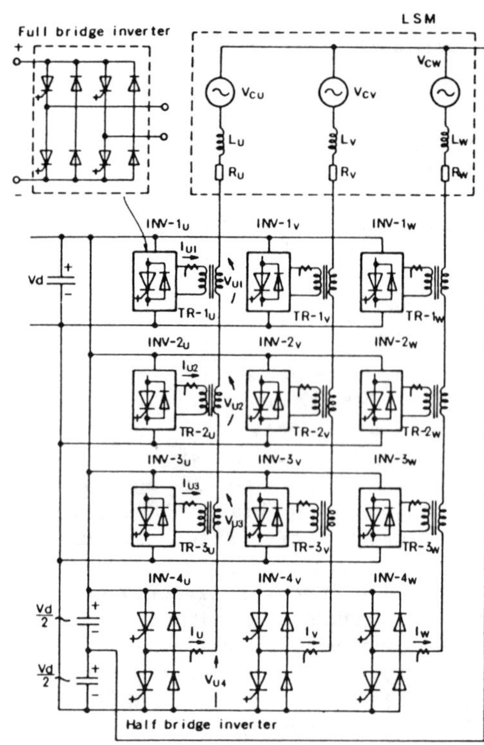

Fig.2 Main circuit of PWM inverter for LSM drive

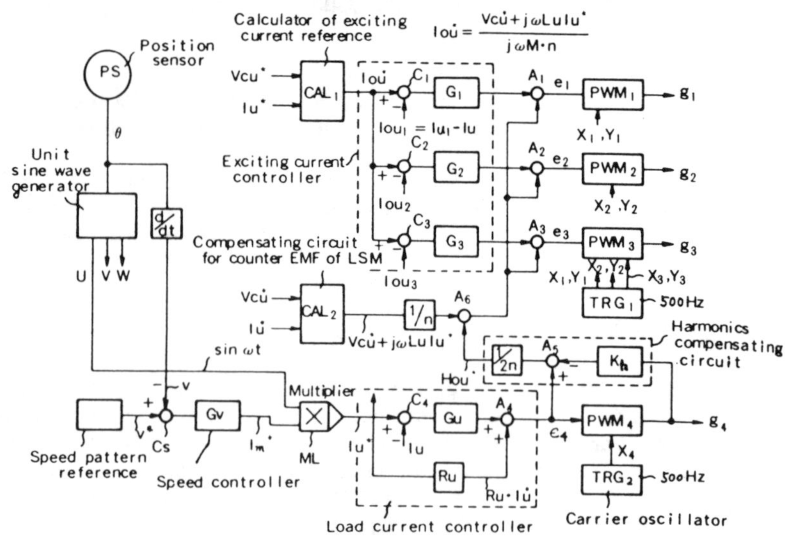

Fig.3 Block diagram for PWM inverter control system

2. System Configuration

2.1 LSM Drive system

The power conversion system to drive the linear motor car is shown in Fig.1.

The superconductive magnets are on the vehicle as the fields of LSM. Three phase armature coils of LSM are arranged along the course of railways on the ground. The armature coils are divided into plural sections. Each section is about 400 meters length.

This power conversion system consists of a PWM controlled ac/dc converter and two PWM inverters which convert from dc constant voltage to VVVF ac voltages.

The PWM converter is available to reduce the harmonics of input currents and to improve the input power factor[4].

Three phase currents are alternately supplied from inverters A and B to the armature coils of the appropriate sections, according to the movement of vehicle with superconductive magnets.

2.2 GTO Inverter

Fig.2 shows the main circuit construction of the PWM inverter for LSM drive[5].

The phase-U PWM inverter is composed of three full-bridge (FB) inverters and a half-bridge (HB) inverter. The output terminals of each full-bridge inverter which consists of four GTOs and four free wheeling diodes are connected in series to the ac load via the output transformer. The half-bridge inverter which consists of two GTOs and two diodes is directly connected to the load without transformer.

The sum of output voltages from the full-bridge inverters and the half-bridge inverter is supplied to one phase of the armature windings of LSM.

When the output frequency is zero, the transformers connected to FB inverters can not induce the output voltages at the secondary windings. Therefore the resistive drop voltage which is independent of the output frequency is supplied by HB inverter without transformer.

2.3 Speed Control

Fig.3 shows a control block diagram for phase U circiut of GTO inverter.

The vehicle speed is controlled by regulating the armature currents according to the speed pattern which is given from central vehicle control center.

The reference of phase U current $I_u{}^*$ is obtained by multiplying the the crest vale $I_m{}^*$ which is the output of the speed controller and the phase U sinusoidal signal which is given from the position sensor of magnetic poles of the LSM.

$$I_u{}^* = I_m{}^* \cdot \sin(\omega t) \qquad (1)$$

where ω is the output angular frequency.

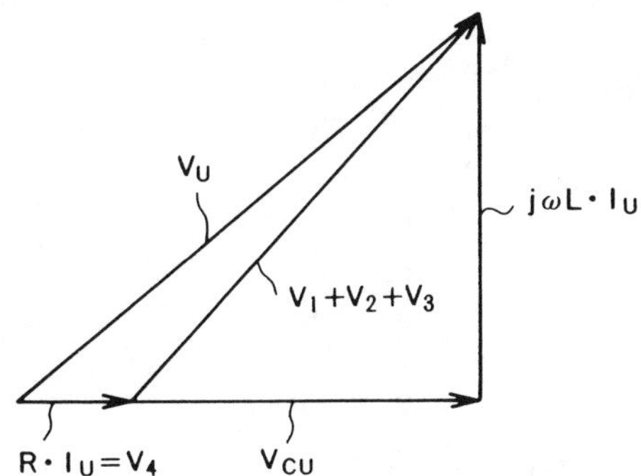

Fig.4 Vector diagram of inverter output voltages

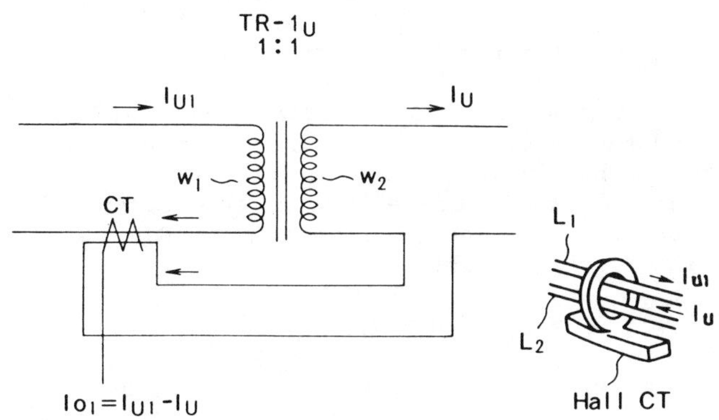

Fig.5 Exciting current detector

2.4 Load Current control

Fig.4 shows a vector diagram of the inverter output voltages (phase U).

In the figure, V_{cu}, $R\cdot I_u$, $j\cdot\omega\cdot L\cdot I_u$, and V_u indicate the counter emf of the LSM, the resistive drop voltage, the inductive drop voltage and the output voltage from inverter INV-U, respectively.

The phase-U load current I_u is controlled at the sinusoidal waveform in phase with the counter electromotive force (emf) V_{cu} by the HB inverter. The HB inverter generates the resistive voltage $R\cdot I_u$ at the same time.

The output voltages of FB inverters are controlled such as constant V/f. The FB inverters generate the total amount of the counter emf and the inductive voltages of the load. The voltage reference of FB inverter INV-1u is given as follows.

$$e_1^*=(V_{cu}^*+j\cdot\omega\cdot L_u\cdot I_u^*)/n \qquad (2)$$

where
- V_{cu}^* : Reference voltage of emf
- ω : Output angular frequency
- L_u : Inductance of load
- I_u^* : Reference signal of load current
- n : Number of F/B inverters

2.5 Exciting current Control

The magnetic flux of output transformer easily meets saturation toward either positive or negative direction by dc bias voltage caused by switching characteristics irregularities of GTOs.

In order to prevent the magnetic saturation of output transformers, each FB inverter controls the exciting currents of the transformers at the state of equilibrium.

The exciting current reference I_{ou}^* of phase U is given as equation (3). Where M is the mutual inductance of the transformer.

$$I_{ou}^*=(V_{cu}^*+j\cdot\omega\cdot L_u\cdot I_u^*)/(j\cdot\omega\cdot M\cdot n) \qquad (3)$$

The exciting currents of three transformers, I_{ou1}, I_{ou2} and I_{ou3}, are controlled according to the same reference I_{ou}^*.

The exciting current I_{ou1} is obtained from the difference between primary current I_{u1} and secondary load current I_u.

Fig.5 shows a method for detecting the exciting current. When the transformer has unity turns ratio, the primary wire and the secondary wire oppositely penetrate through the center of the ring core of a hall CT.

2.6 Harmonics Compensating circuit

The harmonics of the total output voltages from FB inverters decrease by using multi-PWM control. But the harmonics of output voltage from HB inverter usually remains in large quantity.

The compensating circuit for cancelling the harmonic voltages from HB inverter is shown in Fig.3. The compensating signal H_{ou}^* given by equation (4) is transfered to PWM controllers of FB inverters.

$$H_{ou}^*=-(K_h\cdot g_4'-e_4)/(2\cdot n) \qquad (4)$$

where
- K_h : Proportional constant
- e_4 : Input signal of PWM control circuit
- $g_4'=1$ when $g_4=1$
- $g_4'=-1$ when $g_4=0$
  - g_4 : gate signal of inverter INV-4u

The signal e_4 is proportional to the fundamental voltage from HB inverter. The signal H_{ou}^* is proportional to only the harmonic components of HB inverter output voltage. Therefore, the FB inverters generate the compensating voltage corresponding to the signal H_{ou}^*. The harmonic voltage at the output of HB inverter is cancelled by the compensating voltage from FB inverters.

3. Operation of PWM Control

3.1 PWM control of HB inverter

Fig.6 shows HB inverter circuit INV-4u and the waveforms of PWM control operation.

The input signal e_4 of PWM control circuit is compared with a triangular carrier X_4. The gate signals of GTOs S_{41} and S_{42} are decided as follows.

If $e_4 \geq X_4$ then g_4=1, S_{41}:on, S_{42}:off

If $e_4 < X_4$ then g_4=0, S_{41}:off, S_{42}:on

The output voltage V_4 from inverter INV-4u becomes as follows.

$V_4=+V_d/2$ when S_{41}:on (S_{42}:off)

$V_4=-V_d/2$ when S_{42}:on (S_{41}:off)

As the result, the output voltage V_4 becomes the rectangular waveform shown at the bottom in Fig.6. The average value of the output voltage $\bar{V}_4$ shown in broken line is proportional to the input signal e_4.

The ripple current $\Delta i_{L(pp)}$ which is caused by the output voltage V_4 of HB inverter becomes as follows.

$$\Delta i_{L(pp)}=V_d/(L_L \cdot 4 \cdot f_{ch}) \qquad (5)$$

where
- V_d : DC supply voltage
- L_L : Inductance of load
- f_{ch} : Carrier frequency of HB inverter

3.2 PWM control of FB inverter

Fig.7 shows the main circuit of FB inverter INV-1u and the PWM control operation principle.

The input signal e_1 of PWM control circuit is compared with triangular carriers X_1 and Y_1. The phase angle of the carrier signal Y_1 is shifted by 180 degrees from that of the signal X_1. The gate signals of GTOs S_{11}, S_{12}, S_{13} and S_{14} are decided as follows.

If $e_1 \geq X_1$ then g_1=1, S_{11}:on, S_{12}:off

If $e_1 < X_1$ then g_1=0, S_{11}:off, S_{12}:on

If $e_1 \geq Y_1$ then g_1'=1, S_{13}:off, S_{14}:on

If $e_1 < Y_1$ then g_1'=0, S_{13}:on, S_{14}:off

The output voltage V_1 from inverter INV-1u becomes as follows.

$V_1=+V_d$ when S_{11}:on and S_{14}:on

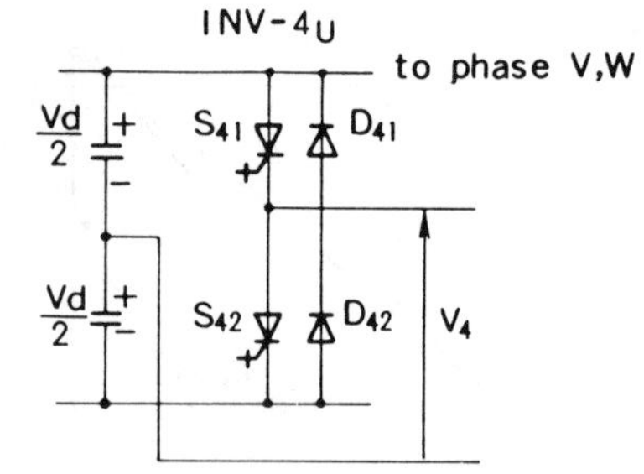

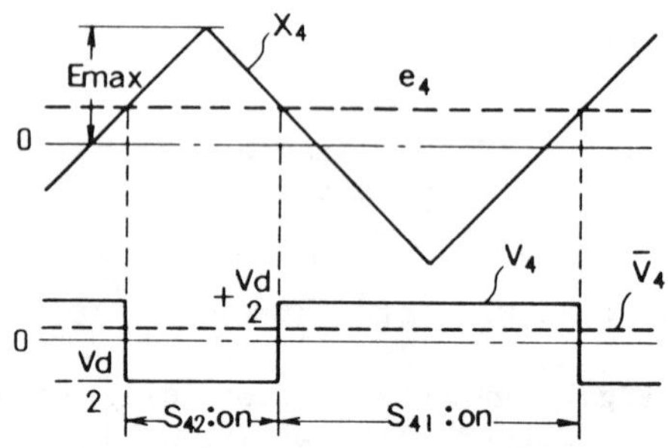

Fig.6 HB inverter and its PWM control operation

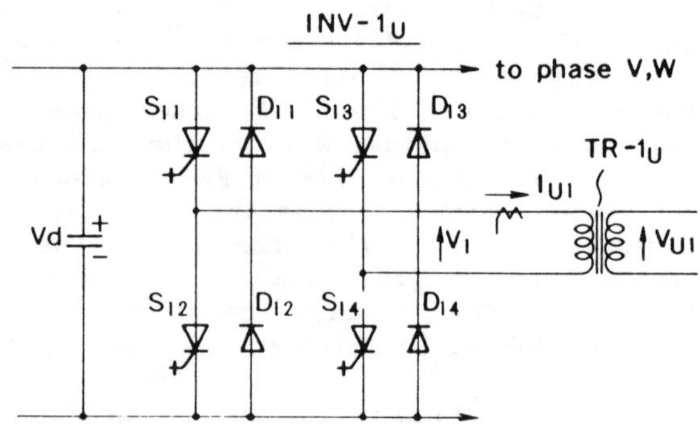

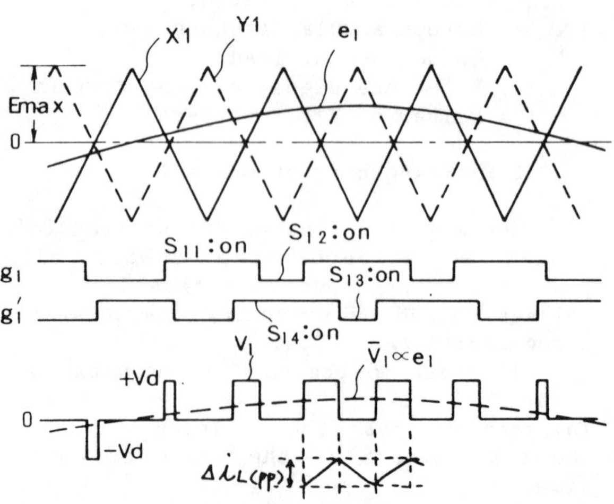

Fig.7 FB inverter and its PWM control operation

$V_1 = -V_d$ when S_{12}:on and S_{13}:on

$V_1 = 0$ when other modes

As the result, the output voltage V_1 becomes the rectangular waveform shown at the bottom in Fig.7. The modulated frequency of output voltage V_1 becomes two times of the carrier frequency for PWM control. The average value of the output voltage $\overline{V}_1$ shown in broken line is proportional to the input signal e_1.

The carrier signals X_2, Y_2 of inverter INV-2u are given by lagging phase angle of 60 degrees against the mentioned carrier signals X_1, Y_1. The carrier signals X_3, Y_3 of inverter INV-3u are given by leading phase angle of 60 degrees against the signals X_1, Y_1.

The total output voltage $V_1+V_2+V_3$ of three FB inverters is controlled by the six times of the original carrier frequency f_{cf}. The ripple current $\Delta i_{L(pp)}$ fluctuated by the total voltage $V_1+V_2+V_3$ is as follows.

$$\Delta i_{L(pp)} = V_d / (L_L \cdot 8 \cdot n \cdot f_{cf}) \qquad (6)$$

Consequently, the ripple current of the load can be reduced by applying the multi-PWM control to three FB inverters. However, the harmonics of output voltage from the HB inverter remain in large quantity, because the HB inverter does not participate in the previous multi-PWM control.

3.3 Harmonics Compensation

Fig.8 is the time chart of PWM control operation for compensating the voltage harmonics of HB inverter.

The carriers X_1, X_2, X_3, Y_1, Y_2 and Y_3 of FB inverters for the multi-PWM control are compared with the compensative reference $H_{ou}*$ given by equation (4).

The gate signals g_1, g_1' of inverter INV-1u are obtained by comparing the carrier signals X_1, Y_1 with the input signal $H_{ou}*$.

The inverter INV-1u generates the voltage V_1 as shown in Fig.8. As the same manner, other FB inverters generate the voltages V_2 and V_3. The total output voltage generated from three FB inverters results to be the lowest waveform.

The average value of total output voltage is proportional to the compensative reference $H_{ou}*$.

As mentioned above, the harmonics from HB inverter are cancelled by compensating voltage from three FB inverters.

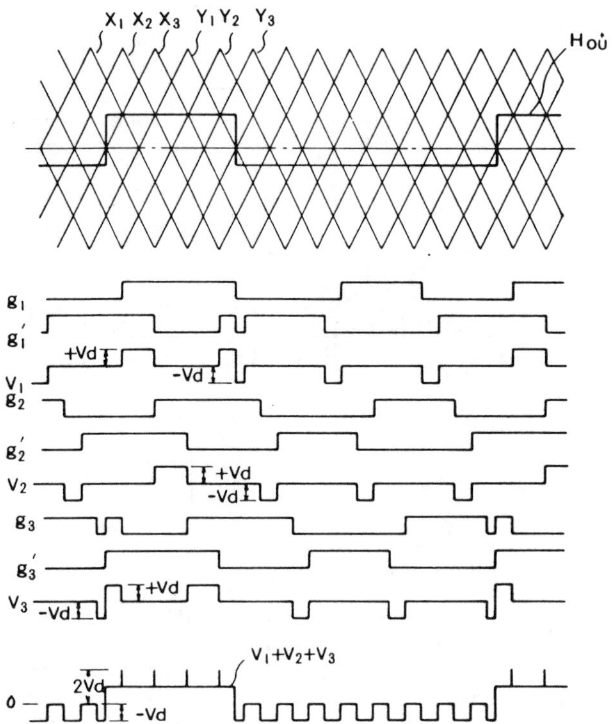

Fig.8 PWM operation of hermonics voltage compensation

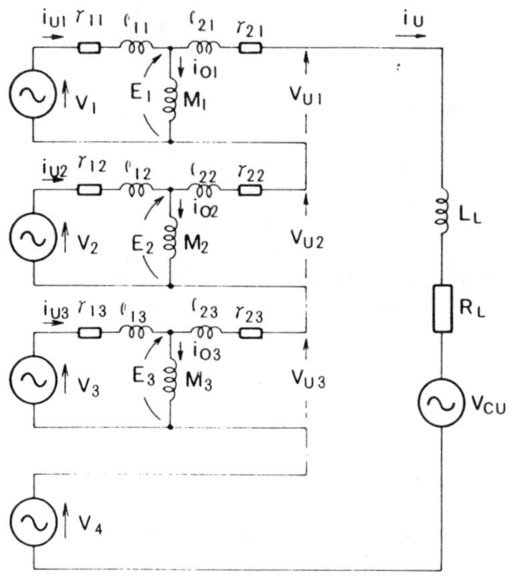

Fig.9 Equivalent circuit

4. Control System

4.1 Voltage Equation

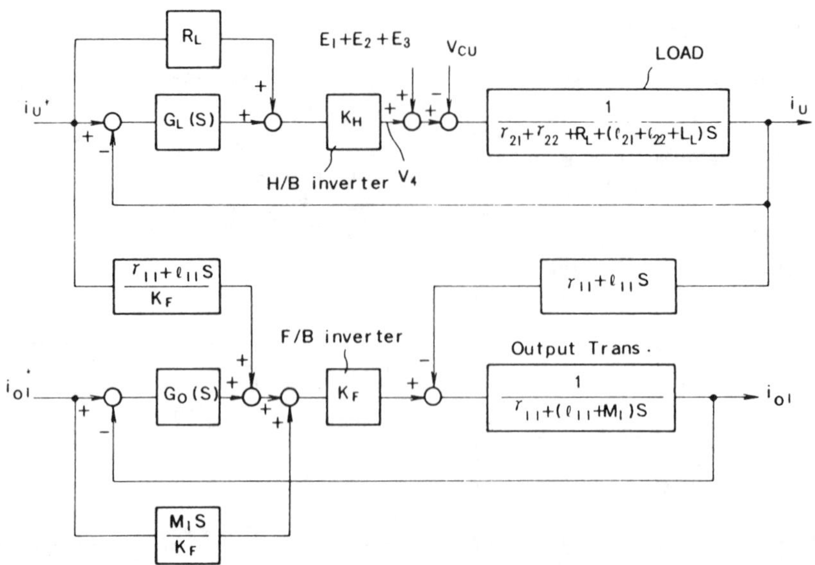

Fig.10 Block diagram of control system

Fig.9 shows the equivalent circuit of the LSM drive GTO inverter (phase U).

Voltage equations are derived from the equivalent circuit. The inverter output voltages V_1, V_2 and V_3 are satisfied the following equations.

$$V_1=E_1+(r_{11}+l_{11}\cdot S)\cdot i_1 \quad (7)$$

$$V_2=E_2+(r_{12}+l_{12}\cdot S)\cdot i_2 \quad (8)$$

$$V_3=E_3+(r_{13}+l_{13}\cdot S)\cdot i_3 \quad (9)$$

Where the induced voltages E_1 to E_3 are decided by exciting currents i_{o1} to i_{o3}, respectively.

$$E_1=M_1\cdot S\cdot i_{o1} \quad (10)$$

$$E_2=M_2\cdot S\cdot i_{o2} \quad (11)$$

$$E_3=M_3\cdot S\cdot i_{o3} \quad (12)$$

The load current i_u is controlled by the next equations.

$$E_1+E_2+E_3+V_4=V_{cu}+(R+L\cdot S)\cdot i_u \quad (13)$$

$$R=r_{21}+r_{22}+r_{23}+R_L \quad (14)$$

$$L=l_{21}+l_{22}+l_{23}+L_L \quad (15)$$

where V_4 is output voltage of HB inverter, r_{21}, r_{22}, r_{23} and l_{21}, l_{22}, l_{23} are secondary resistances and leakage inductances of the output transformers, respectively.

The exciting currents of transformers i_{o1}, i_{o2} and i_{o3} are calculated with the primary currents i_1 to i_3 and the secondary current i_u.

$$i_{o1}=i_1-i_u \quad (16)$$

$$i_{o2}=i_2-i_u \quad (17)$$

$$i_{o3}=i_3-i_u \quad (18)$$

Each exciting current is controlled by the individual output voltage of a suitable FB inverter.

The load current i_u is controlled by regulating the output voltage V_4 of the HB inverter.

Fig.10 shows the block diagram for load current control and exciting current control system.

The load current is controlled by the HB inverter. The disturbance based on the counter emf V_{cu} enters into the load current control system. But the disturbance is cancelled by the output voltages from full bridge inverters.

The exciting current of output transformer is controlled with the reference value I_{ou}* to prevent the transformer from saturation.

Table 1

DC voltage	V_d=9,000V
Load current	I_L=1,000A(rms)
Output frequency	f_o=50Hz
Carrier frequency of FB inv.	f_{cf}=500Hz
Carrier frequency of HB inv.	f_{ch}=500Hz
Counter emf	V_c=5841V(rms)
Inductance of load	L_L=20.25mH
Resistance of load	R_L=0.7104
Mutual inductance of output trans.	M=0.5H

5. Simulated Results

Table 1 is the specification of a simulation model.

5.1 Effect of harmonics compensation

Fig.11 (a) shows the output voltages and the output currents of GTO inverter without harmonics compensation. The load currents I_u, I_v, I_w are fluctuated at carrier frequency 500Hz by the harmonic voltages of the HB inverter. The load ripple current $\Delta i_{L(pp)}$ is about 168A. This nearly equals to the calculated value 222A(pp) obtained by equation (5).

Fig.11 (b) shows those of GTO inverter with the harmonics compensation. The harmonic voltages of the HB inverter are cancelled by compensating voltage from FB inverters. Consequently, the load currents are controlled with sinusoidal waveform without ripple. The load ripple current $\Delta i_{L(pp)}$ which is approximated by equation (6) is reduced to one sixth of that without compensation.

Figs.12(a) and 12(b) show the frequency spectrum of load current I_u without compensation and with compensation, respectively. In this figure, the fundamental current of 50Hz is about 1,390A(peak).

The 10th harmonic current based on harmonic voltages from HB inverter is reduced from 74.4A (5.36%) to 1.3A (0.096%) by using the harmonics compensation.

Fig.13 shows the frequency spectrum in the null load current control with harmonics compensation.

The harmonic frequency of output voltage from the n sets of FB inverters without HB inverter is as follows.

$$f_h = 2 \cdot n \cdot f_{cf} \qquad (19)$$

When the FB inverters compensate the harmonics from HB inverter, the harmonic components are expressed as eq.(20) at the output of FB inverters.

$$f_h' = 2 \cdot n \cdot f_{cf} \pm f_{ch} \qquad (20)$$

In Fig.13, the total output voltage from the inverter includes the harmonic components of 2.5kHz and 3.5kHz, when the carrier frequencies f_{cf} and f_{ch} are 500Hz.

5.2 Exciting current control

Fig.14 shows the waveforms of exciting current of a transformer, output voltages and output currents, where dc bias voltage $V_{dc} = 0.1 \cdot V_{d1}$ is applied to the output transformer TR-1u.

In the case of simulation without exci-

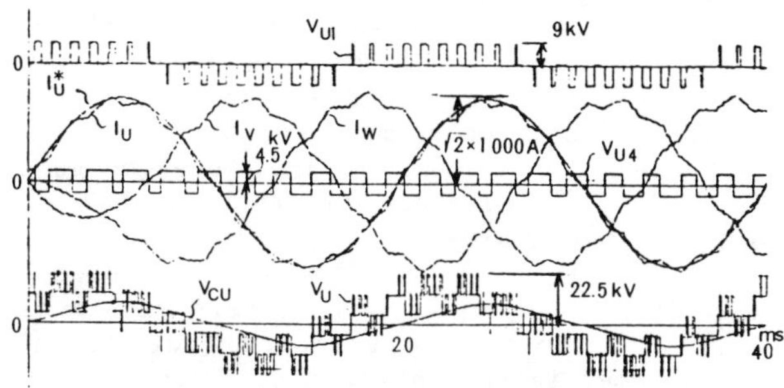

(a) without compensation

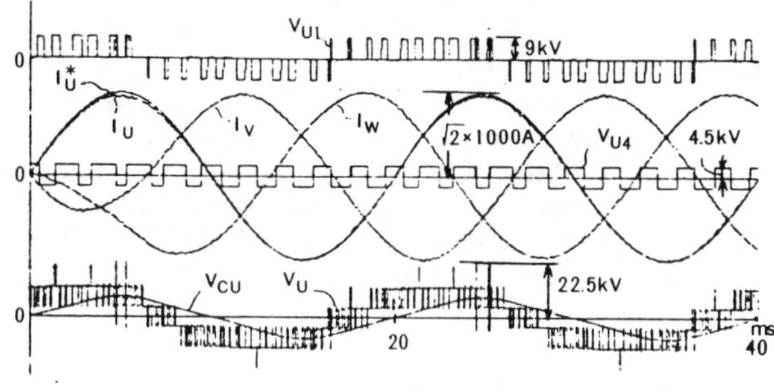

(b) with compensation

Fig.11 Waveforms of PWM inverter (fo=50Hz)

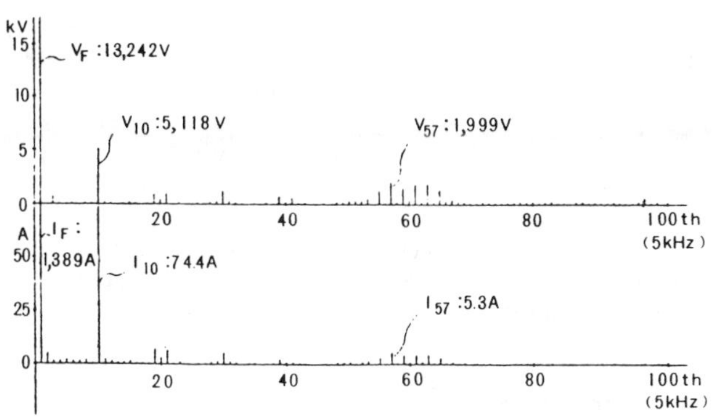

(a) without compensation

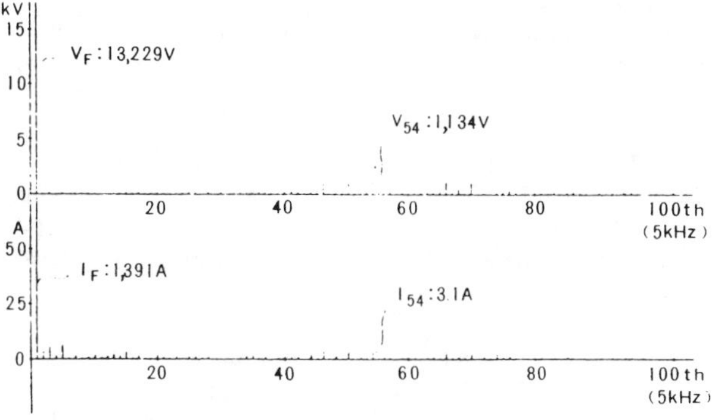

(b) with compensation

Fig.12 Frequencies spectrum (fo=50Hz)

ting current control, the exciting current I_{ou1} gradually increases to the positive direction as shown in Fig.14(a). The exciting current is rapidly increased by the saturation of transformer. If this condition continues for a long period, over-current flows in the inverter and maybe results to break down the GTOs.

In Fig.14(b), the exciting current I_{ou1} is controlled with the reference signal $I_{ou}*$. Therefore, the saturation of output transformer is prevented.

Assuming that the switching characteristics irregularities of GTOs are about 10 micro-second per every PWM control period 1 milli-second, the dc bias voltage become about 1% of dc supply voltage V_d. When the output frequency f_o=0.1Hz and dc voltage V_d=9kV, the product of voltage and time amounts to about 450Vsec in every half cycle of output frequency. Consequently, the exciting current control is indispensable especially at the low frequency operation.

6. Conclusion

Authors considered on the large capacity GTO inverter which was constructed by three full bridge inverters with the output transformers and a half-bridge inverter without transformer for the linear motor drives. It was clarified by digital simulation that the voltage harmonics from HB inverter was perfectly cancelled by the compensative voltage from FB inverters. Furthermore the exciting current control effectively get off saturation of the output transformer.

At the following stage, we would like to apply the proposed method to the practical GTO inverter.

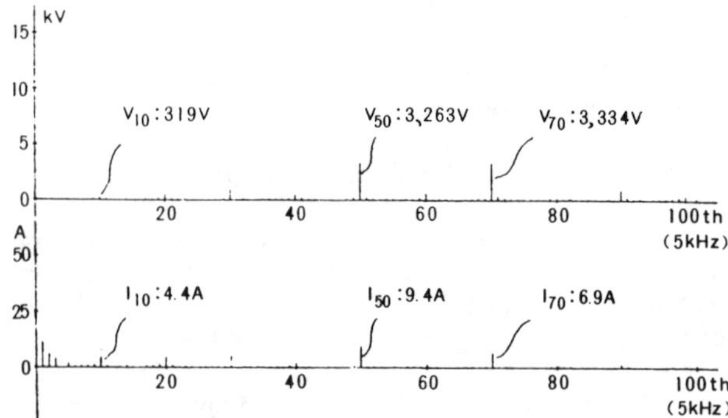

Fig.13 Frequencies spectrum at null load current control (IL=0)

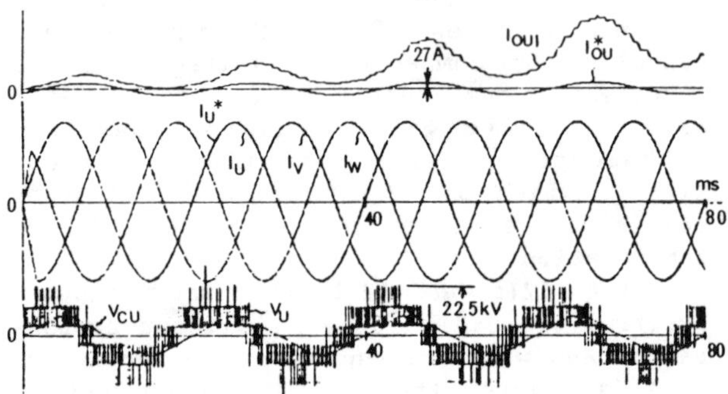

(a) without exciting current control

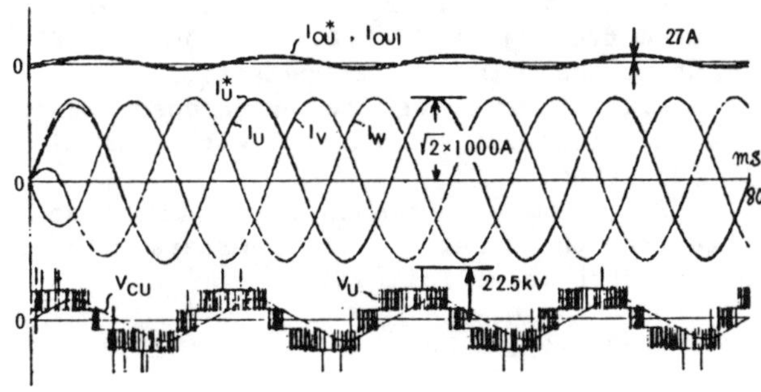

(b) with exciting current control

Fig.14 Similated results of PWM inverter

References

[1] T. Saijo, S. Koike and S. Tadakuma, "Characteristics of Linear Synchronous Motor Drive Cycloconverter for Maglev Vehicle ML-500 at Miyazaki Test Track", IEEE Trans. on IA, Vol. IA-17, No.5, Sep./Oct. 1981.

[2] H. Ikeda, I. Kawaguchi, T. Outake, S. Tanaka and J. Wada, "Power Conversion System for Maglev Vehicle MLU002", Tenth International Conference on Maglev Systems, June 9-10, 1988, p327 to 336.

[3] Y. Tamura, S. Tanaka and S. Tadakuma, "Control Method and Upper Limit of Output Frequency in Circulating Current Type Cycloconverter", IEEE IAS ISPCC p313 to 323, 1982.

[4] S. Ishikawa, S. Tanaka, S. Tadakuma, E. Takahara, " Consideration on High Quality AC Traction Vehicle System using PWM Converter", Trans. IEE of Japan, Vol. 107-D, No.3, Mar., 1987.

[5] T. Saijo, S. Kaga, T. Suzuki, Y. Hosokawa and K. Katuki, " Multi-PWM Inverter for LSM Drives", 1979 National Convention Record IEE of Japan, No.727 to 729.

Paper 8.10

A 500 Hz Power System
– Power Converter and Transmission Lines –

I. Takahashi G.J. Su
Nagaoka University of Technology
Kamitomioka 1603-1, Nagaoka, 940-21 Japan

Abstract

A 500 Hz power system is proposed in this paper for industrial zones, intelligent buildings and commercial areas. The system has not only many applications but also high efficiency, fast system control response and high reliability.

An experimental system composed of two 10KVA power converters, a power transmission line simulator and voltage compensators shows high speed and good system voltage regulation by combining the reactive power control of the voltage compensators and dc link voltage control of the power converters. Reactive power control is also able to compensate for asymmetrically voltage due to unbalanced loading or voltage drop of the transmission line. A naturally commutated thyristor inverter suitable for high applications and a forced commutated transistor inverter suitable for medium power applications are examined. The control circuit is full digitalized and simplified by using 8 bit one-chip microprocessors.

Some typical faults on the transmission line are discussed and the experimental results obtained by the simulator are also presented.

1 Introduction

With the advent of power semiconductors many different frequency power supplies, namely static frequency changers, have increasingly being employed in most industry, and recently in offices and homes. Especially high frequency power can be found widespread applications in such as motor drives, induction heating, fluorescent lighting. Most of them are employing forced commutation inverters such as using GTO's or transistors. This, however, is not economical, and becomes difficult and impractical when so large capacity as above 100MW is required because of their technical problems and lack of reliability. It is apparent that a centralized high frequency power contribution system based on a naturally commutated power converter supplying for particular areas such as chemical and iron plants can provide economical advantages and result in decrease of cost and saving space by replacing those numerous inverters used in dispersed manners.

On the other hand, the need for intertying of dc transmission power systems, cogeneration systems, wind and solar energy generation systems has been increasing.[1] The dispersed small high frequency power system might be one of the most interesting approaches.

By operating the power system at high frequency, the system can be made compact because of the large reduction in the size and weight of the transformers, reactors, capacitors and circuit breakers. Use of high frequency also speeds up system response and offers high quality power. Moreover newly developed materials such as amorphous metal and low dielectric loss materials can be used much effectively than in the conventional 50/60 Hz power system.

It is important to select a proper frequency, which must take into account not only the requirements for much higher frequency from utilities but also the limits of power elements. This is discussed in detail in another paper which will be presented at the conference. The conclusion drawn is that frequencies ranging from 400 Hz to 1 KHz can be found most interesting applications both today and in the near future. In other words, the frequency should vary for different loads, and is selected so as to satisfy mostly load's requirements. Among those a typical one is 500 Hz which is about 10 times the conventional 50/60 Hz and is suitable for todays' applications.

This paper presents a 500 Hz power system to supply for small areas. Because of the effect of the higher frequency on the line impedance the length of the power transmission lines is limited, and therefore it is desirable to locate the 500 Hz power source close to the loads. In addition, the proposed system should be utilized together with the conventional commercial power system.

The research aims to explore the problems and develop essential techniques in the higher frequency power system. The power converter, high frequency power transmission lines, system voltage regulator and voltage unbalance compensator are discussed in this paper.

2 Proposed System

Fig.1 shows the proposed 500 Hz power system in block schematic form. A power converter or frequency changer, which basically composed of a converter and inveter, is utilized to interface the 500 Hz power system to other power sources. Amorphous metal core transformers, which has higher efficiency and reduced size and weight than silicon steel ones, can be effectively employed.

It is important to note that dc power system and natural energy sources can be used easily for the energy source of the system, besides the 50/60 Hz commercial power system. In particular, 500 Hz power can be obtained directly from cogeneration systems which have been increasingly employed. Moreover the frequency changer can easily combine the uninterruptable ability by connecting some energy storage units to the power converter, and therefore the power

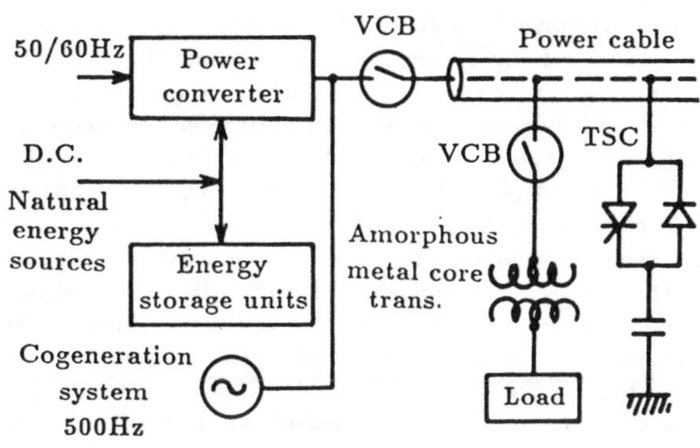

Fig.1 A 500 Hz power system.

Reprinted from *IEEE/IAS Ann. Meet. Conf. Rec.*, Part 1, pp. 988–995, 1989.

system becomes highly reliable.

In the design of the higher frequency power system, it is necessary to consider for the power converter, the power transmission line and the system voltage regulation as follows:

2.1 Inverter

The kind of switching devices used in the inverter is different according to the capacity needed. High speed thyristors are suitable for the capacity ranging from 5MW to 200MW in current source inverters. GTO's suit to the voltage source inverters with capacity ranging from 1MW to 20MW. Another popular switching device, i.e. power transistors, are generally employed in voltage source inverters with the capacity below 2MW. The switching frequencies of those switching devices are also different; ranging from hundreds Hz to thousands Hz.[2]

In the case very large capacity is needed for the power system with it is better to use natural commutation techniques which have been employed very successfully in dc power transmission systems. In the other hand, for the medium and smaller systems supplying to intelligent buildings and commercial areas, forced commutation inverters such as GTO inverters may be also utilized.

To improve the output voltage waveform of the inverter cascade connected inverters must be employed owing to the limitation of the switching frequency.[2]

2.2 Converter

Thyristor converters are usually employed with current source inverters. By cascade and multiphase connection of the converters the input line current waveform can be fairly improved, and by using asymmetrical phase control techniques the power factor can be also corrected. If necessary to further improve the power factor, power converters can be parallel connected and by using asymmetrical phase control strategy. This also reduces the harmonic contents in the line current and therefore makes the passive filters used in the input side much smaller. On the other hand, diode rectifiers are successfully employed in the voltage source inverters, and by using multiply phase rectifiers the input line current waveforms can be compensated.[2]

2.3 Power Transmission Line

One of the most pronounced differences between the 50/60 Hz and the 500 Hz power system is in transmission lines. At the higher frequency, line impedance increase due to the higher inductive inductance and ac-effective resistance. Therefore power cables should be used for the transmission line because they have lower inductance than over head lines. The ac-effective resistance of the cables are increased due to the additional losses resulted from skin effect, proximity effect, and the circulating and eddy currents in the shield or conduit. The increase of the line impedance reduces the capabilities of the cable.

There are two kinds of cables for choice shown in Fig.2, one is the three phase coaxial power cables with six conductors which has less inductance but lack of economy, the another is the normal three phase cables with three conductors which has about twice inductance but advantages of economy. If necessary, the inductance of the cable can be further reduced by using parallel circuit conductors where the individual conductors of the same phase are separated as much as possible. It is clear that the power transmission line is one of the most significant factors to restrict the frequency.

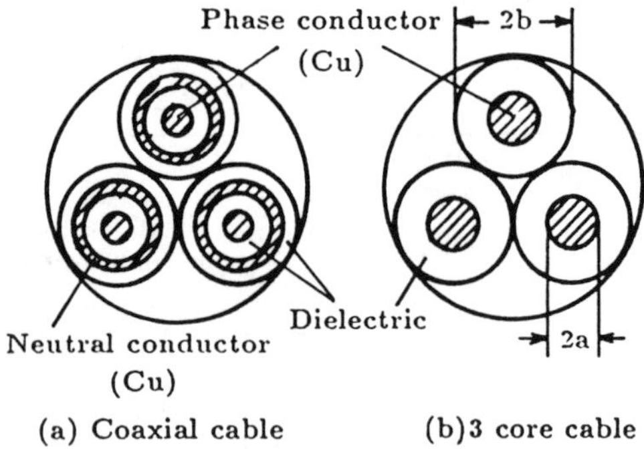

Fig.2 Power cables.

Circuit breakers used in the higher frequency system must have high speed interrupting characteristic to prevent its reignition. VCB(Vacuum Circuit Breaker) seems to be the most proper choice at present.

2.4 TSC - System Voltage Compensator

With the significant voltage drops of the transmission line at 500 Hz, some line voltage drop compensation techniques are necessary to improve the system voltage regulation. It can be accomplished by controlling the system reactive power just like that employed in the commercial power systems. TCR(shortened for thyristor controlled reactor) was the initial choice for the system voltage compensator. However because it creates acoustic noise and has lower efficiency, TSC(Thyristor Switched Capacitors) is utilizing and provides good performance which is discussed later. Forced commutation of the switching thyristors is not required. TSC can be also used to compensate for unbalance voltage due to unbalanced loading.

3 Experimental System

3.1 System Configuration

An experimental system has been built in laboratory to verify the feasibility of the proposed system and to develop the essential techniques for the higher frequency power system. It is composed of two 10KVA power converters, two TSC's, a three phase high frequency power transmission line simulator for a 20Km power cable and loads. As mentioned above, in the case that capacity of the system is larger than 20MVA, forced-commutation based inverters can not be used for the power converter due to their difficulties in control techniques and to lack of reliability. For this reason a naturally commutated thyristor inverter for high power applications and a forced commutated transistor inverter for medium power application are examined in the experiment.

Fig.3 shows the overall system configuration using naturally commutated thyristor inverter. The power converter is constructed by a Graetz bridge thyristor rectifier and a thyristor bridge current source inverter employing load commutation techniques. The inverter simply operates as a three phase rectangle current source with 120 electrical degree conducting duration on each half cycle. A overcurrent protection logic circuit is implemented to prevent the thyristors in the power converter from damaging when faults occur. Passive filters of 5th, 7th and 13th are used to improve the output voltage waveforms. The filters are particularly effective to the harmonics attenuation in the current source inverter. TSC1 located near the inverter is used to adjust the output voltage of the inverter by changing the reactive current, and TSC2 connected to the transmission line simulator at

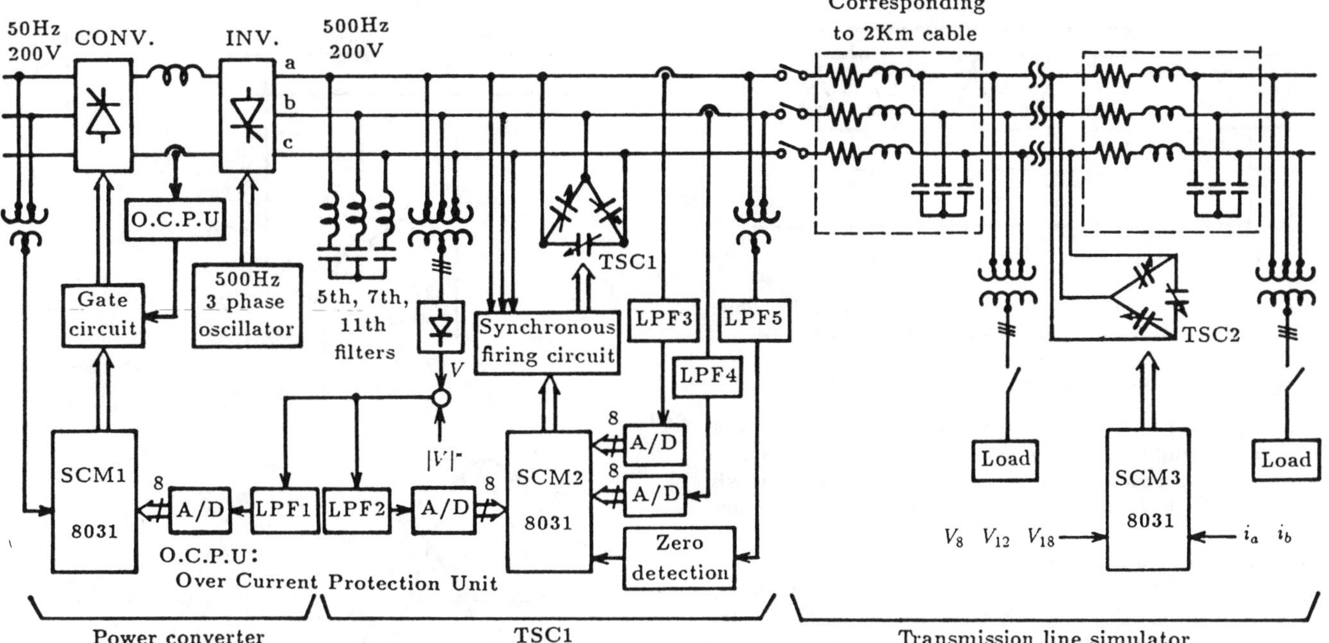

Fig.3 The experimental system I using naturally commutated inverter.

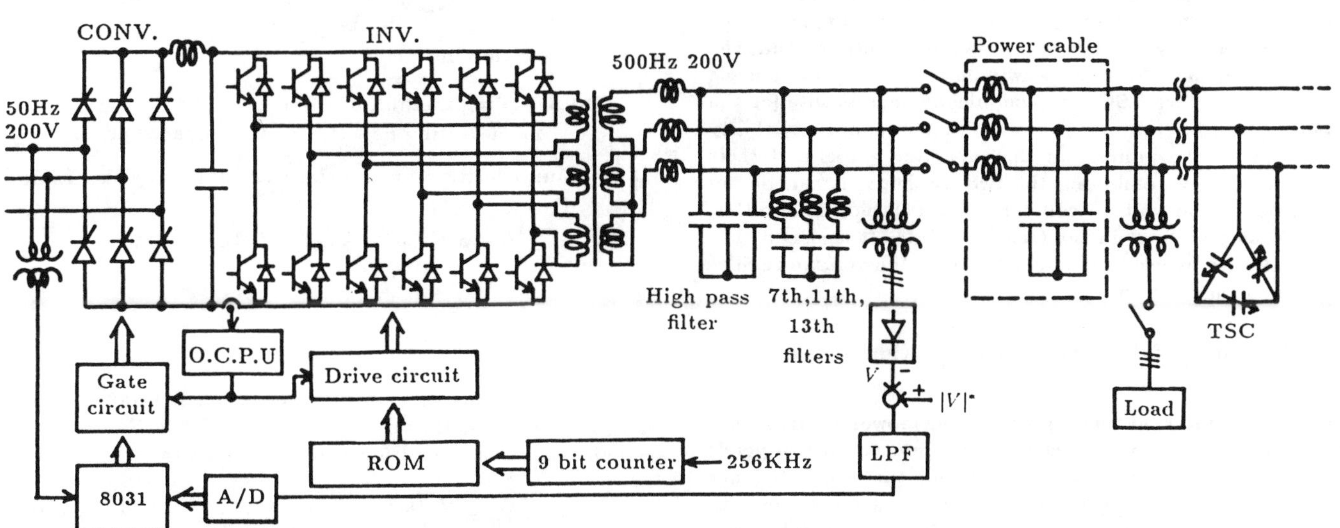

Fig.4 The experimental system II using forced commutated inverter.

the point which is equivalent to 12Km at the cable from the power source is used to compensate for the voltage drop of the transmission line. Both of them are also used to compensate for unbalance voltage due to asymmetrical current components of the loads.[3]

Fig.4 shows another experimental system which consists of a thyristor rectifier and a transistor inverter. The inverter composed of three full bridge inverters is controlled so as to eliminate the 5th harmonics in the output voltage.[4] This is achieved by using a 8bit ROM which is programmed so as to generate a $\pi/5$-shifted three phase square wave. The higher order harmonics are reduced by the 7th, 11th, 13th tuned L-C filters and a high pass filter installed at the secondary windings of the transform. PWM techniques are not employed in the inverter due to the low efficiency and the use of GTO's. Therefor the switching frequency of the transistors is kept at 500 Hz.[5]

Fig.5 shows each phase configuration of the TSC. For ease to implementation of microprocessor based control for the TSC's, capacitors are arranged to be 5 bit binary switched capacitor array. The switches are designed to be controlled in one direction and each switch consists of a thyristor in parallel with a diode. The effect of the diodes is to keep the capacitors charged to the negative peek value of the line voltages. The capacitors should be switched on at the negative peek point of the associated line voltage in order to prevent creating large current surges in the TSC. Therefore the thyristors act essentially as diodes. The switching function of the TSC is defined as

$$S_w = [s_0 \; s_1 \; s_2 \; s_3 \; s_4]^T \qquad (1)$$

where $s_0 \cdots s_4$ equals to 1, when the associated switch is on, or to 0, when the switch is off. Thus the admittance of the TSC is represented as

$$Y = \omega c \cdot (s_0 \cdot 2^0 + s_1 \cdot 2^1 + \cdots + s_4 \cdot 2^4) \qquad (2)$$

where ωc is the admittance of the least significant bit of the TSC. The term in the parentheses represents a binary number. If the admittance is given, the switching function S_w can

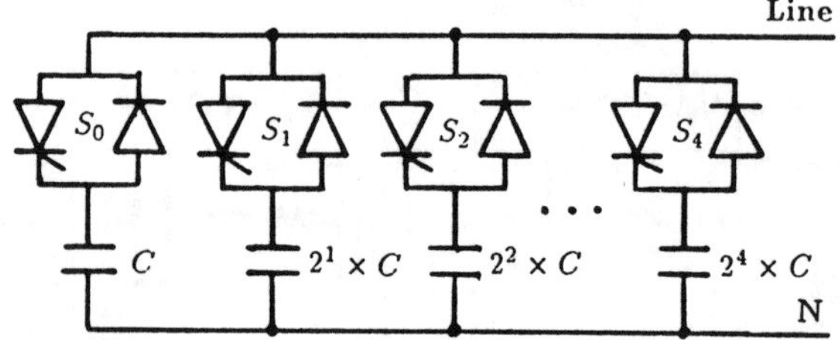

Fig.5 Each phase configuration of the TSC.

be determined by dividing Y by ωc and decoding it, which can be easily performed by using microprocessor.

3.2 System voltage regulation

When employing the forced commutated inverter, the system voltage regulation can be accomplished simply by control the reactive power of the thyristor rectifier,[5] and will not be further discussed. The following discussions are concentrated on the first experimental system and the results are also obtained on the same system unless stated.

The system voltage regulation is achieved by controlling the reactive power of the TSC's and directly adjusting the dc link current of the power converter by means of phase control for the thyristor rectifier. Since the dc link current can not be changed so quickly because of the dc link reactor, the phase control method by rectifiers suits to suppress large voltage variation with slow response. In the other hand, the capacitors in the TSC can be switched on or off in one cycle at least. Therefore TSC can dynamically compensate for the rapid voltage fluctuation. However its compensation ability is limited by the number of the capacitor banks and their capacitance. By combining the two methods, it can be accomplished good voltage compensation characteristic either in the steady state or in the transient state. It is shown that five banks are at least necessary to make the voltage regulation under one percent.

3.3 Principle of Unbalance Voltage Compensation by TSC

The most significant week point of the power system used a current source invreter is that the line voltage depends on the load connected on the line and thereby unbalance loading results in serious unbalance in the system voltages. It is necessary to compensate for unbalance voltage because many single phase loads may exit in the power system. This is achieved by asymmetrically controlling the TSC's so as to absorb the negative phase sequence current created by the unbalanced load.[6]

The TSC acts an continuously variable capacitor, and its equivalent circuit is given in Fig.6(a), where jY_{ab}, jY_{bc} and jY_{ca} represent the three phase admittances of the TSC, respectively.

Designate the positive and negative phase sequence currents as $\dot{I}_{l1}$ and $\dot{I}_{l2}$ flowing to the load, $\dot{I}_{k1}$ and $\dot{I}_{k2}$ flowing to the TSC, respectively, then the positive and negative currents flowing from the inverter, $\dot{I}_1$ and $\dot{I}_2$, are given by

$$\dot{I}_1 = \dot{I}_{k1} + \dot{I}_{l1} \qquad (3)$$

$$\dot{I}_2 = \dot{I}_{k2} + \dot{I}_{l2} \qquad (4)$$

when $\dot{I}_2 = 0$, the system voltage will become balanced. By applying the method of symmetrical components in Fig.6(a) yields

$$\dot{I}_{k1} = j\frac{1}{3}(1-a)\{Y_{ab}(\dot{V}_a - \dot{V}_b) + a \cdot Y_{bc}(\dot{V}_b - \dot{V}_c) + a^2 \cdot Y_{ca}(\dot{V}_c - \dot{V}_a)\} \qquad (5)$$

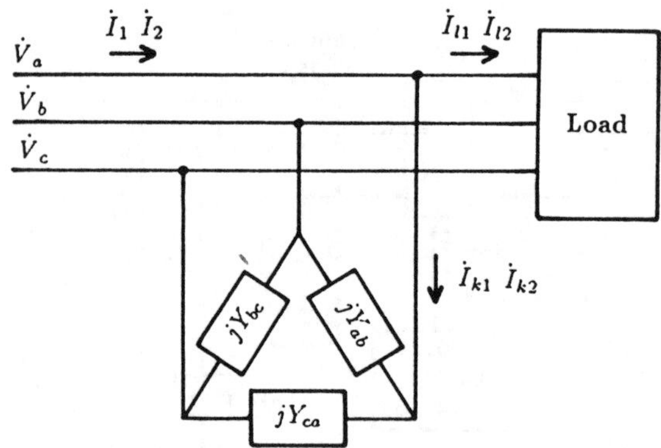

(a) Equivalent circuit of TSC.

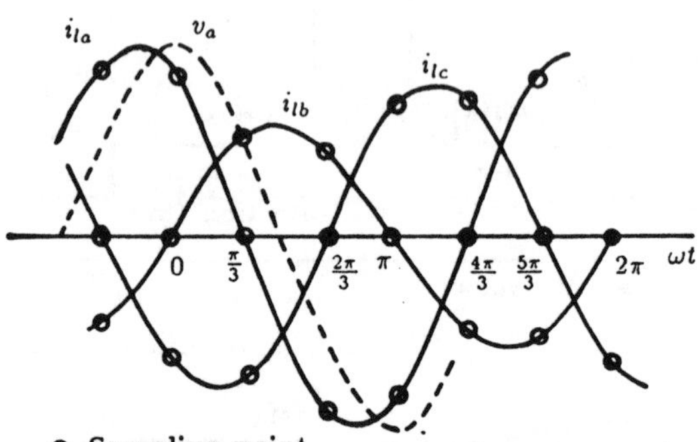

(b) Sampling method of currents for detecting negative phase sequence current

Fig.6 Compensation for unbalanced voltages by the TSC.

$$\dot{I}_{k2} = j\frac{1}{3}(1-a^2)\{Y_{ab}(\dot{V}_a - \dot{V}_b) + a^2 \cdot Y_{bc}(\dot{V}_b - \dot{V}_c) + a \cdot Y_{ca}(\dot{V}_c - \dot{V}_a)\} \qquad (6)$$

where $a = -\frac{1}{2} + j\frac{\sqrt{3}}{2}$.

Assuming the rms value of the line voltage is V, and taking phase voltage $\dot{V}_a$ as the reference phasor. When the voltages are balanced, Eqs. 5 and 6 can be simplified as

$$Y_{ab} + Y_{bc} + Y_{ca} = \frac{\sqrt{3}\dot{I}_{k1}}{jV} \equiv A \qquad (7)$$

and

$$Y_{ab} + a \cdot Y_{bc} + a^2 \cdot Y_{ca} = -\frac{\sqrt{3}\dot{I}_{k2}e^{j\pi/6}}{V} \equiv B + jC \qquad (8)$$

From Equations 7 and 8, Y_{ab}, Y_{bc} and Y_{ca} can be obtained as follows:

$$Y_{ab} = \frac{A}{3} + \frac{2B}{3} \qquad (9)$$

$$Y_{bc} = \frac{A}{3} - \frac{B}{3} + \frac{C}{\sqrt{3}} \qquad (10)$$

$$Y_{ca} = \frac{A}{3} - \frac{B}{3} - \frac{C}{\sqrt{3}} \qquad (11)$$

Equations 9, 10 and 11 show clearly that A/3 represents the mean value of three phase admittances Y_{ab}, Y_{bc} and Y_{ca} which can adjust the positive phase sequence component of the system voltage, and the remained terms are needed to compensate for the negative phase sequence voltage.

In order to determine the admittance of the TSC, it is necessary to detect the negative phase sequence current flowing to the load. A novel technique developed is as follows;

Assuming the three phase load currents, denoted by i_{la}, i_{lb} and i_{lc}, are sinusoidal, the instantaneous current vector i_l is defined as

$$\begin{aligned} i_l(\omega t) &= \frac{2}{3}\{i_{la}(\omega t) + a \cdot i_{lb}(\omega t) + a^2 \cdot i_{lc}(\omega t)\} \\ &= \sqrt{2}\{\dot{I}_{l1}e^{j\omega t} + \dot{I}_{l2}^{*}e^{-j\omega t}\} \end{aligned} \quad (12)$$

where $\dot{I}_{l2}^{*}$ is the conjugate of $\dot{I}_{l2}$. By sampling the three phase currents at every $\pi/3$ in the waveforms, for example, at $\omega t = 0$ and $\pi/3$ as shown in Fig.6(b), yields

$$\begin{aligned} i_l(0) &= \frac{2}{3}\{i_{la}(0) + a \cdot i_{lb}(0) + a^2 \cdot i_{lc}(0)\} \\ &= \sqrt{2}\{\dot{I}_{l1} + \dot{I}_{l2}^{*}\} \end{aligned} \quad (13)$$

and

$$\begin{aligned} i_l(\frac{\pi}{3}) &= \frac{2}{3}\{i_{la}(\frac{\pi}{3}) + a \cdot i_{lb}(\frac{\pi}{3}) + a^2 \cdot i_{lc}(\frac{\pi}{3})\} \\ &= \sqrt{2}\{\dot{I}_{l1}e^{j\frac{\pi}{3}} + \dot{I}_{l2}^{*}e^{-j\frac{\pi}{3}}\} \end{aligned} \quad (14)$$

Eliminating $\dot{I}_{l1}$ from Eqs. 13 and 14, and using the equation of $i_{la}+i_{lb}+i_{lc} = 0$, the negative phase sequence current is given

$$\begin{aligned} \dot{I}_{l2} &= \frac{\sqrt{2}}{3}\{2i_{la}(0) + i_{lb}(0) - i_{la}(\frac{\pi}{3}) - 2i_{lb}(\frac{\pi}{3})\} \\ &\quad + j\frac{\sqrt{6}}{3}\{2i_{la}(0) - i_{lb}(0) - 3i_{la}(\frac{\pi}{3})\} \end{aligned} \quad (15)$$

Keeping in mind $\dot{I}_{l2} = -\dot{I}_{k2}$, from equation 8 B and C are obtained as

$$B = \frac{\sqrt{3}}{V}Re(\dot{I}_{l2}e^{j\frac{\pi}{6}}) \quad (16)$$

$$C = \sqrt{3}Im(\dot{I}_{l2}e^{j\frac{\pi}{6}}) \quad (17)$$

where Re and Im represent the real part and the imaginary part of $\dot{I}_{l2}e^{j\frac{\pi}{6}}$, respectively.

3.4 Microprocessor Based Control circuit

The control circuit is implemented by using two single chip microprocessors (8031); one is for phase control of the rectifier, the other is for the TSC1, as shown in Fig.3. Consequently it makes the hardware very simple and compact. As stated previously, the thyristor converter with phase control suits to compensate for the slow variation voltage, and TSC can suppress the very fast fluctuating voltage. For this reason the time constant of the low pass filter LPF1 needed for filtering the voltage error signal for microprocessor SCM1 is set much larger than that of low pass filter LPF2 for microprocessor SCM2. The low pass filter LPF3, LPF4 and LPF5 used to detect the line current must have good filtering performance, and the identical characteristic owing to the calculation of the equations 9 ~ 11.

The microprocessor SCM1 used for phase control of the rectifier performs PI control strategy. The microprocessor-based phase control method for a thyristor converter is given in detail in [7] and will not be discussed further in this paper. One of the two on-chip timers in the SCM1 is set to generate an interrupt signal to CPU at the period of about 104usec. Whenever interrupt occurs the processor inputs the voltage error signal $|V^*| - V$ and calculates the phase angle α by PI control routine. Therefore by calculating and decoding $\alpha - \omega t$, can the on instant of the switching pattern be determined. The switching patterns are pre-stored in the off-chip ROM. The calculation time of SCM1 is about $85\mu sec$.[8]

The calculation of Y_{ab}, Y_{bc} and Y_{ca} is carried out in microprocessor SCM2 according to equations 9, 10 and 11. To speed up the calculation some table techniques are utilized. The calculation time of the processor SCM2 is obtained about $100\mu sec$, which is much shorter than the sampling period for detecting the currents; 1/6 period of the power source, i.e. $333\mu sec$.[3][6]

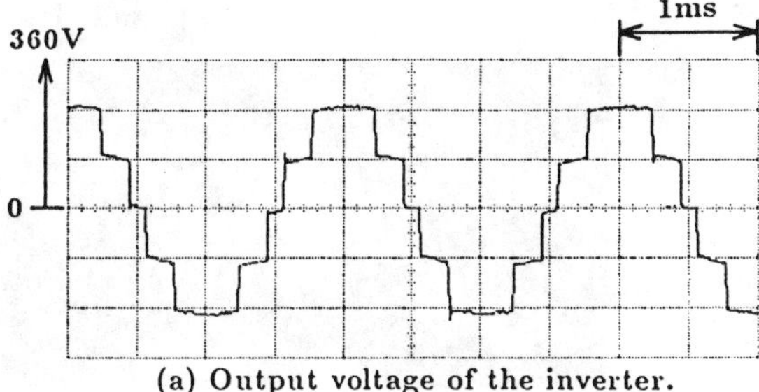

(a) Output voltage of the inverter.

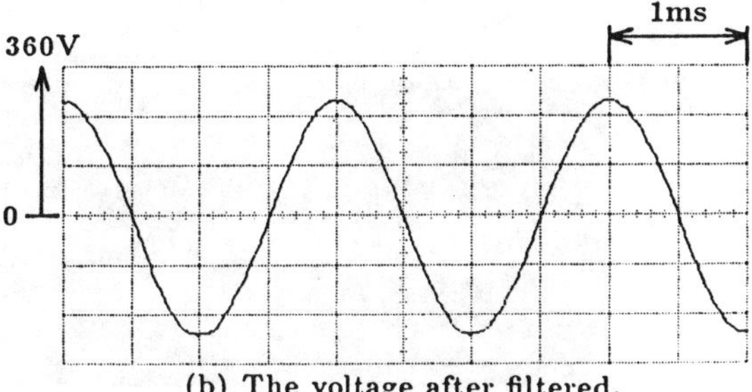

(b) The voltage after filtered.

Fig.7 Output voltage waveforms in the experimental system II.

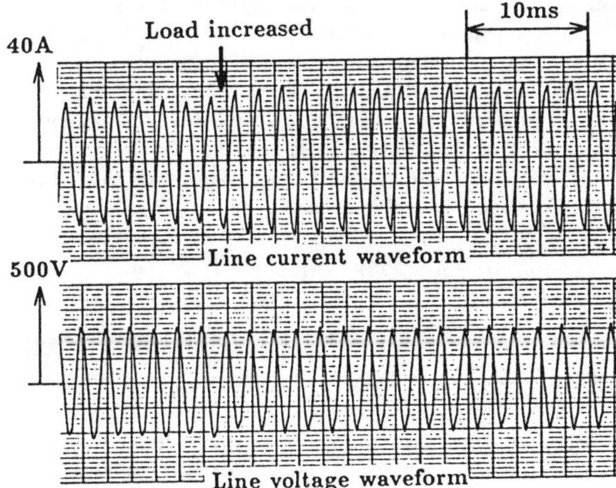

Fig.8 Response of the line voltage to increase of load.

3.5 Experimental Results

The system line voltage regulation in the steady state obtained is under one percent.

Fig.7 shows the output voltage waveforms in the experimental system II. The 5th harmonics in Fig.7(a) is reduced to about 0.5 percent, and after filtered the harmonic content in Fig.7(b) is significantly decreased as less than 0.2 percent.

Fig.8 illustrates system line voltage response when load is suddenly increased. It can be seen that the line voltage reaches the stable state by about 4msec after the load increased.

Fig.9 shows typical line voltage waveforms demonstrated the unbalance voltage compensation by TSC. It is apparent that voltage unbalance is improved very well by TSC.

4 Power Transmission Line Simulator

4.1 Design of the Transmission Line Simulator

As stated earlier, to reduce the line inductance power cables should be utilized for the transmission line. A three-phase

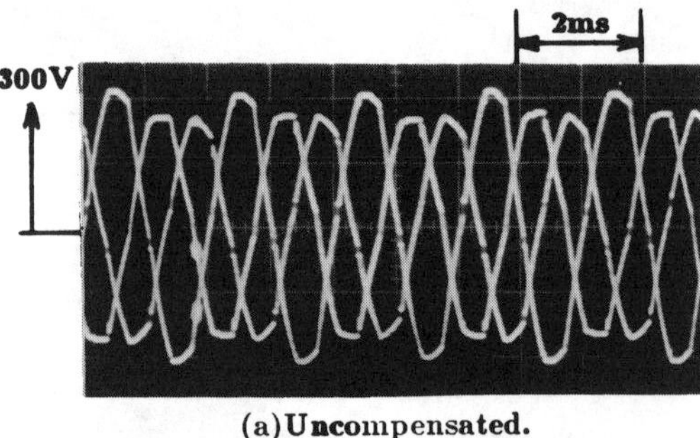

(a)Uncompensated.

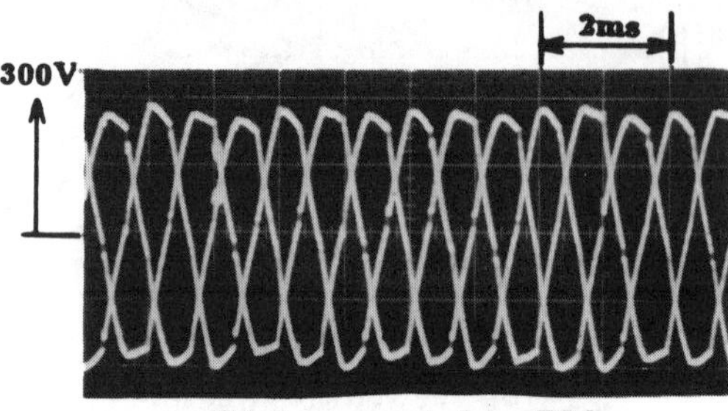

(b)Compensated by TSC.

Fig.9 Line voltage waveforms at unbalanced load.

three-core cable with each conductor separately screened is employed because of economy, as shown in Fig.2. A transmission line simulator is built to simulate the cable circuit with the length of 20Km and electrical ratings of 40KV and 1.5KA. In order to design the simulator, it is necessary to determine the parameters of the cable.

The line inductance L_0 and the capacitance C_0 of the every 1Km cable are generally given by

$$L_0 = 0.2\{ln(\frac{2b}{a}) + 0.25\} \ (mH/Km) \tag{18}$$

and

$$C_0 = \frac{0.0556\varepsilon_r}{ln(b/a)} \ (\mu F/Km) \tag{19}$$

where a and b are the inner and outer radii of the dielectric, and ε_r is the relative permittivity of the dielectric, 2.3 for polyethylene. The dc resistance of the cable is given by

$$R_0 = \frac{1+y}{KCS_0} \ (\Omega/m) \tag{20}$$

where: C; conductance,
S_0;normal cross-sectional area (mm^2),
y;lay ratio coefficient of conductors,
K;conductivity of $1mm^2 \times 1m$.

Let the current density is $2.0A/mm^2$, and the potential gradient in polyethylene is designed to be 1.0KV/mm. Therefore the cross-sectional area of the conductor can be obtained as $787.5mm^2$ and the radius of the conductor is $a = 15.8(mm)$.

Since the maximum potential gradient occurs on the surface of the conductor, and is given by

$$E_m = \frac{V}{aln(b/a)} \tag{21}$$

hence, the outer radius of the dielectric is obtained as $b = 68.1(mm)$.

Substituting a, b in the equations 18, 19 and 20, the parameters of the cable are given as follows:

the dc resistance : $R_0 = 0.02(\Omega/Km)$
the inductance : $L_0 = 0.48(mH/Km)$
the capacitance : $C_0 = 0.09(\mu F/Km)$

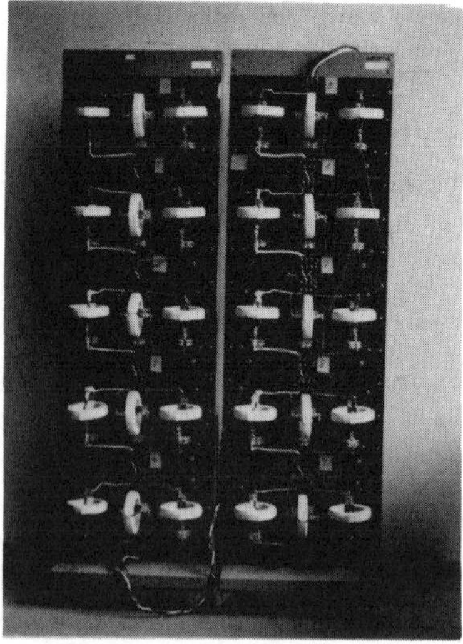

$2Km \times 10$ stages Simulator

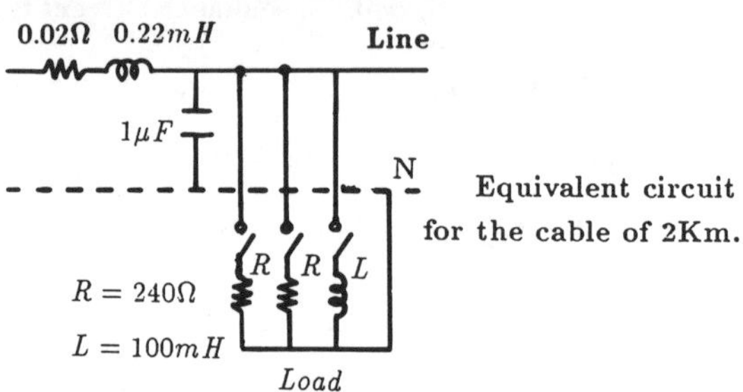

Fig.10 Transmission line simulator.

The ac-effective resistance of the cable is the dc resistance modified by the following factors: the skin effect of the conductor; the eddy currents induced by adjacent conductors (the proximity effect); the equivalent resistance to account for I^2R losses in the sheath. The ac-effective inductance is also influenced by the skin and proximity effects. The determination of these effects is complicated and omitted here. In this case the total factor is about 1.91 for the resistance, and 0.90 for the reactance. Therefore the ac-effective resistance and inductance of the transmission line become

$$R' = 1.91 \times R_0 = 0.04 \ (\Omega/Km)$$
$$L' = 0.90 \times L_0 = 0.43 \ (mH/Km).$$

The transmission line simulator with the rating of 200V and 30A is employed as shown in Fig.10. It consists of 10 stages of lumped L-C circuits, each stage corresponds to 2Km cable; the percent impedance of the simulator is set as same as that of the cable. In addition, in each stage inductive loads are connected to the line through switches needed to vary loads.

4.2 Voltage Drop of the Transmission Line

With increase of frequency, the voltage drop on the inductance increases and thereby results in reduction of the receiving-end voltage. In other hand the charging current to line capacitors also increases and the receiving-terminal voltage may increase on light loads known as Ferranti phenomena. In addition it also results in the increase of the line copper loss due to the skin effect. Therefore the voltage drop of the transmission line is one of the principal reasons that the frequency can not be raised too high. Fig.11 shows the typical voltage distribution along the transmission line without compensation obtained by theoretical analysis and experiment. Notice that the terminal voltage of the cable will rise by 15 per cent at no load, and will reduce by 20 per cent at full load with lagging power factor.

4.3 Voltage Drop Compensation by TSC

Since line voltage distribution along the transmission line is affected by the loading conditions, it is necessary to compensate the voltage drop of the cable at inductive loads. This is achieved by injecting leading reactive power to the line by the TSC2. Selection of the point to install the TSC's is very important in compensation performance for whole voltage distribution. In the experiment the TSC is installed at 12Km away from the power source, where the capacitance is least to obtain the same compensation characteristics.[9]

Fig.12 shows the configuration of the TSC and associated control circuits. The effect of the reactor L in parallel with the TSC is to limit the voltage not rise to excessive levels at no load. The same single chip microprocessor 8031 and control theories are employed for the controller. By detecting the voltages at three points, i.e. 6Km, 12Km and 18Km from the power source. By controlling the mean value of the voltages at the three points can obtain good voltage distribution. Unbalance voltage compensation function is also combined together in the control strategy.

Fig.13 illustrates the line voltage variations area along the line obtained in Fig.12 by randomly switching on/off the loads. The voltage regulation can be decreased by about 2 per cent. A typical voltage distribution along the cable is also shown by dashed line in the same figure.

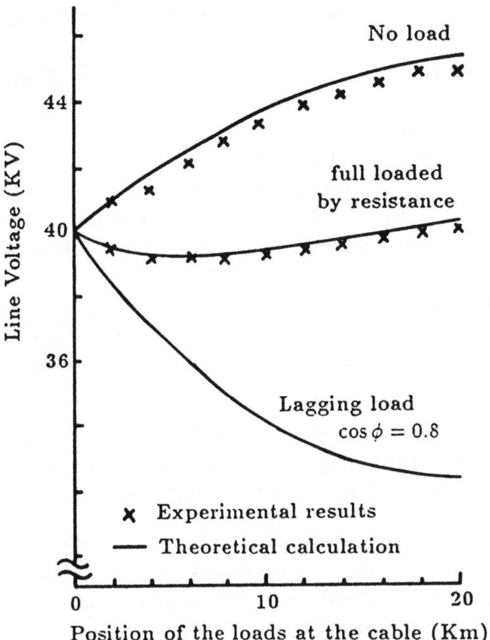

Fig.11 Typical voltage distribution along the cable without voltage drop compensation.

5 Some Typical Faults of the Transmission Line

The analysis of the faults is a essential part of the design of a power system. They are examined by using the simulator for some typical cases. Fig.14 illustrates typical line voltage and current waveforms of the power converter when faults occur at the line 4Km from the power source.

Fig.14(a) shows the waveforms when two lines short circuit fault occurs. The rush current due to the fault is not so large as about 2 times of normal one. The power converter, of course, was shutdown by the overcurrent protection logic unit after fault occurred.

Fig.14(b) demonstrates the transient waveforms at line to ground short-circuited fault. It shows that the line voltage did not changed but the current increased due to the charging current of the cable.

Fig.14(c) shows the line voltage and current waveforms of the power converter when one line is opened. The line voltage reaches the stable state by 3*msec* after the occurrence of the fault.

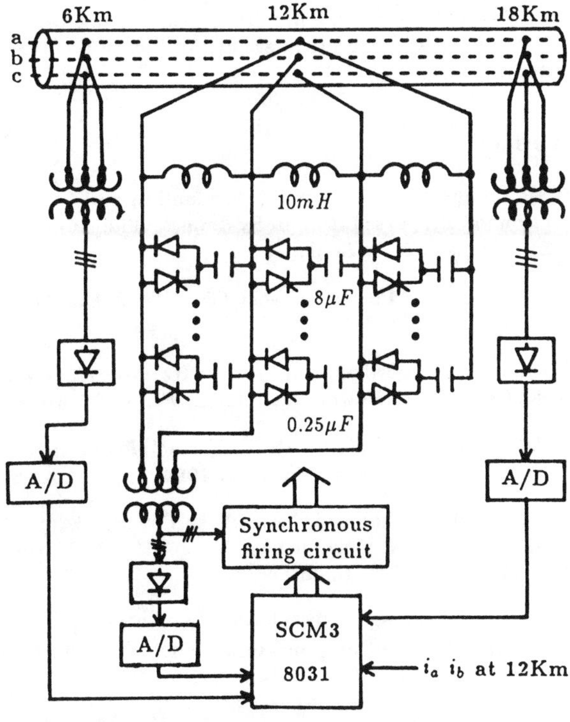

Fig.12 Line voltage drop compensation circuit.

6 Conclusion

This paper has presented a high frequency power system for supply to particular areas such as industrial zones, commercial areas, intelligent buildings and etc. in which high efficiency, low weight and space saving are required. The reasonable frequency would be to range from 400 Hz to 1 KHz.

In this paper, a 500 Hz power system which is suitable for $20 \times 20 Km^2$ industrial zones or 1Km by 1Km commercial areas is investigated by an experimental model system, and the following conclusions are reached:

(1) Power electrical equipment such as transformers, reactors and etc. can be reduced in size from 1/3 to 1/4.

(2) Capacitors can be reduced in size to about 1/8.

(3) Passive filters can be made further smaller due to the increase of the harmonics frequency.

(4) Dramatic reduction in the size and weight of circuit breakers having extinction chamber such as vacuum circuit breaker is also possible.

(5) Thyristors can be in more widespread use at the higher frequency.

(6) The power distortion in the commercial power system

resulted from the 500 Hz system can been reduced because of the filtering effect of the 500 Hz power converter.

(7) It is easily to connect some energy storage units to the power converter, therefore the proposed system has high reliability.

(8) A conventional type of three phase cables can be employed for the transmission of 500 Hz power in about 20 Km at voltage level of 40 to 50KV. However the length of the cable varies with several factors such as the voltage levels and frequency.

(9) Good system voltage regulation can be achieved by controlling the reactive power of the TSC's.

(10) Unbalanced voltage can be also compensated by TSC.

In addition, the proposed high frequency power can find many applications both in industrial and commercial utilizations such as ultra-speed motors, induction heating and fluorescent lighting, which will be discussed in detail in another paper.

In summary, the considerations in design of the higher frequency power system are discussed. Techniques such as voltage regulation and unbalanced voltage compensation are developed. The commercial viability of the proposed higher frequency power system is shown.

Acknowledgment

The authors would like to express their appreciation to Mr. Ikeshita, Mr. Tukahata, and Mr. Sedoguti. Thanks are due to Ms. Nakamura and the members of the Power Electronics Laboratory.

References

[1] S. Sigeta and O. Tukamoto, "Introduction and Interconnection of Dispersed Power Systems", The Journal of JIEE, Vol.107, No.9 Sept., 1987.

[2] "Semiconductor Power Convert Circuit", JIEE, March, 1987.

[3] Tukahata and I. Takahashi, "A 500 Hz Power System", Tech. Commit. of Power Eng., JIEE, PE-84-97, 1984.

[4] B. D. Bedford and R. G. Hoft, "Principles of Inverter Circuits", Jon Wiley & Sons, Inc. 1964.

[5] G.J. Su and I. Takahashi, "A 500 Hz Power System - A 500Hz voltage source frequency changer", 1989 National Conv. Record I.E.E. Japan, No.5.

[6] Setoguti, Nakano and I. Takahashi, "A 500Hz Power System - Line Voltage Compensation by TSC", Tech. Commit. of Power Eng., JIEE, PE-87-51, 1987.

[7] I. Takahashi and M. Yamane, "Multiparallel Asymmetrical Cycloconverter Having Improved Power Factor and Waveforms", IEEE Trans. Ind. Appl. Vol.IA-22. Nov./Dec. 1986.

[8] T. Nakamura, G.J. Su and I. Takahashi, "A 500 Hz Power System - Microprocessor Control of the Power Converter", Record of the 1988 KANSAI-section Joint Conv. of I.E.E., Japan, Nov. 1988..

[9] Ikeshita and I. Takahashi, "A 500 Hz Power System - Transmission Line Simulators", Tech. Commit. of Power Eng., JIEE, PE-86-73, 1986.

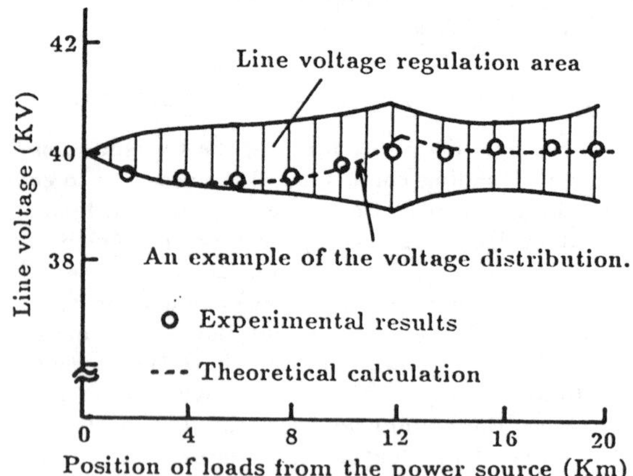

Fig.13 Line voltage distribution with voltage drop compensation

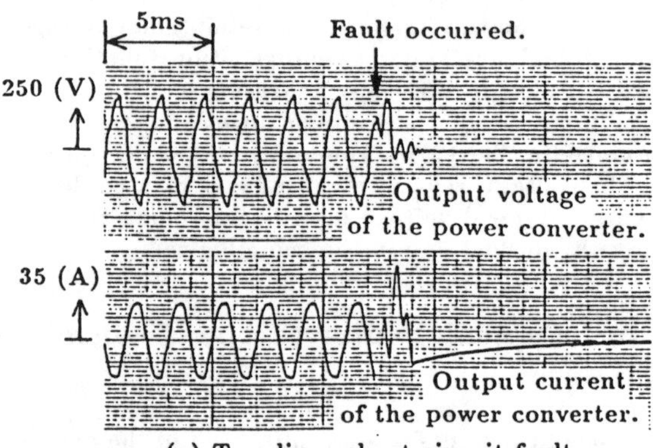

(a) Two lines short circuit fault.

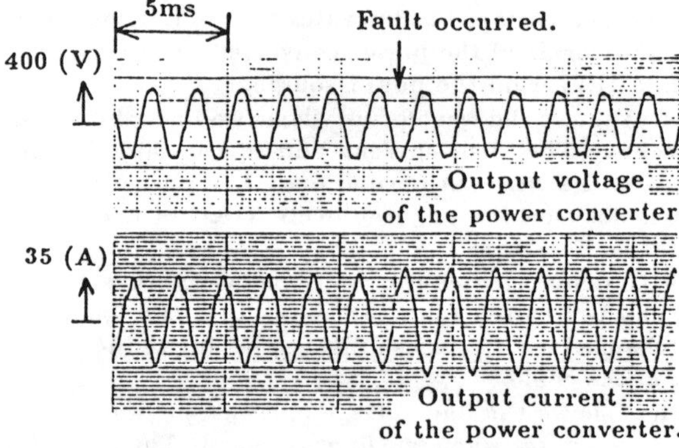

(b) Line to ground fault.

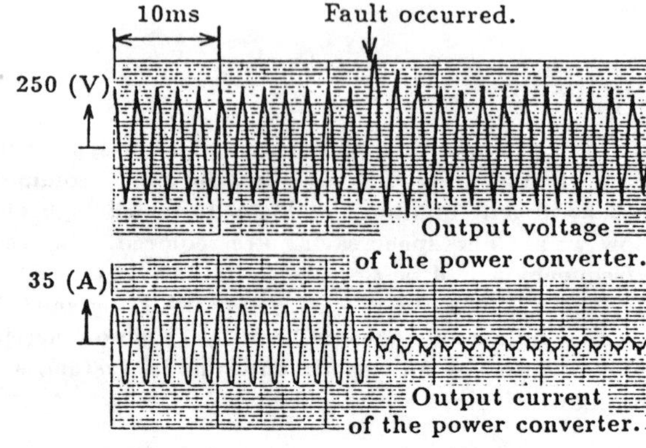

(c) One line opened fault.

Fig.14 Transient waveforms at typical faults.

Paper 8.11

A 500 Hz Power System – Applications –

I. Takahashi G.J. Su
Nagaoka University of Technology
1603-1 Kamitomioka Nagaoka, Japan 940-21

Abstract

Applications and needs of high frequency power supplies in industrial zones, chemical and steel plants, commercial areas has been investigated. It shows that a 500Hz power system can be mostly employed in present and may be found more and more applications in the fields of high speed electric machines, induction heating, and fluorescent lighting providing many advantages such as energy saving and resulting in large reduction in size and weight of electric apparatus. This paper focuses attention on the applications of the higher frequency, and the selection of the frequency are discussed in detail. The conclusion drawn is that the suitable frequency seems range from 400 Hz to 1 KHZ. Energy and space saving, high performance by the use of the higher frequency to fluorescent lighting, amorphous metal core transformers, dc power supplies, and naturally commutated cycloconverters are experimentally demonstrated. In addition, it is shown that the conventional thyristor ac voltage controller can be used for a soft starter of very high speed induction motors.

1 Introduction

In the military and aircraft industries power sources have being used the frequency of 400 Hz because of the size and weight of the electric components. The need for high frequency power in the other industries and commercial utilities is also increasing. Recently centralized high frequency power systems are receiving increasing attention as an alternative to the conventional 50/60 Hz in particular areas such as chemical and iron plants.

As a result of the continual improvement in the rating and characteristics of power semiconductor switching devices such as thyristors, GTO's and power transistors, high frequency power supplies based on solid-state power conversion have being in widespread use to save energy and material, and to provide high quality power in both industry and commercial utilities. Naturally commutated power converter has dominated the high power applications due to the high efficiency and reliability.

This paper presents a 500Hz power system based on a static frequency changer for supply to industrial zones, commercial areas, offices and intelligent buildings, and is related to the applications of the proposed higher frequency power source, and the power converter, the transmission line and the system voltage regulation are discussed in another paper which will be presented at the conference. The higher frequency system should be employing together with the commercial power system.

500 Hz power is to able provide many advantages to the utilization equipment over the conventional 50/60 Hz power as follows:

(1) Large reduction in the size and weight of the transformers, reactors and electric machines, consequently resulting in improved efficiency and reduced cost of those electric apparatus.

(2) Iron losses can be significantly decreased due to large reduction of materials if used amorphous metal cores to reactors and transformers.

(3) Saving dielectric materials of capacitors, which make the capacitors compact and lower cost. Therefore loads with lower power factors can be economically used.

(4) The power system can offer uninterrupted power by connecting some energy storage units to the power converter.

(5) Because the frequency is as 10 times as the 50 Hz, quick response power amplifier or dc power supply, naturally commutated cycloconverters and flickerless TSC(Thyristor Switched Capacitors) used for var compensation become practical.

(6) In addition to the commercial 50/60 Hz power system the following small dispersed systems can be employed for the energy source of the 500 Hz system.

- Small scale dc power system in electric railways and factories.
- Natural energy generation systems; DC power can be directly obtained therefore economical.
- Cogeneration system; 500 Hz power can be directly obtained from turbine generators in factories.

(7) Giving impact on the society and economy.

- Development of applications: Loads suitable for the higher frequency may become popular. For instance, naturally commutated cycloconverters can be found widespread use by replacing PWM inverters.
- Energy and material saving; Electric equipment can be made much smaller as about 1/4 to 1/8.
- Effective use of new materials: Development of new material can be promoted.

2 Applications of 500 Hz Power

An investigation on the needs and applications of the higher frequency power in industrial zones, commercial areas and intelligent buildings at present and in the near future has been made. It shows that 500 Hz can be used in the field of high speed motors, induction heating, fluorescent lighting and etc. as shown in Fig.1.

High Speed Motors

Fig.2 shows the applications of high speed motors which can be applied 500 Hz power.[1] In large power range conventional machines have been driven by steam turbines or gas turbines to obtain high speed, which recently have being replaced by inverter drive systems. It can be seen that motors with capacity of several thousands to 30MW and speed of 5000rpm have been widely employed in the applications to turbine compressors used for condensation of LNG, ammonia, ethylene gas and methanol, and blowers for gas pipeline, in which high speed is often required.

Reprinted from *IEEE/IAS Ann. Meet. Conf. Rec.*, Part 1, pp. 996–1002, 1989.

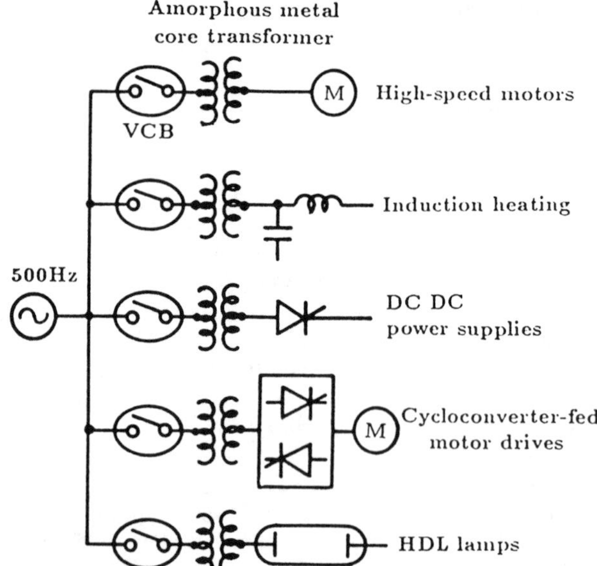

Fig.1 Applications of the 500 Hz power system.

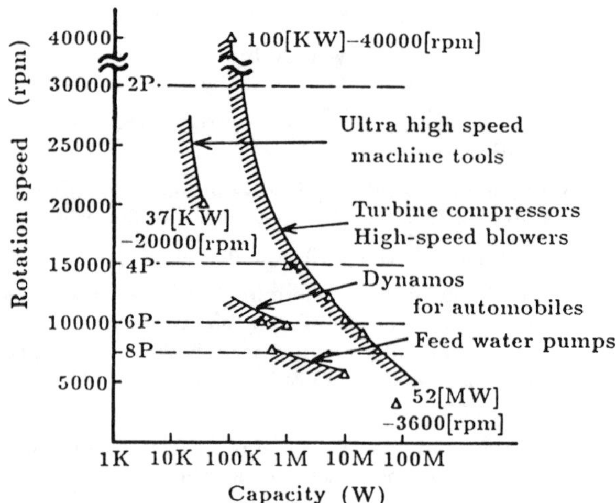

Δ : designates that machine of the capacity and speed shown in the figure have been produced.
nP : Number of poles

Fig.2 Applications of high speed motors.

In medium power range from tens to thousands KW, motors are finding wider applications in high pressure compressors and blowers as shown in the same figure. They will be increasingly employed due to the advantages of its compact and maintenance free.

At 500 Hz high speed motors will be almost using induction motors because of their low cost, brush less and robust construction, and can satisfy most of the applications mentioned above.

Induction Heating

In iron and steel industry, 400 Hz - 1 KHz power has been widely used for melting of cast steel and alloy in induction furnace, heating of steal bar, and heat treatment of seamless steel pipe by offering advantages of high efficiency, cleanness, compact of equipment and ease to control of processes, which are necessary to produce high quality materials.

In the conventional frequency power system, capacitors with several times capacity of the induction furnace are usually employed to improve the power factor because it is as low as 15 - 20 percent. Therefore use of the higher frequency power is an economical solution for those problems.

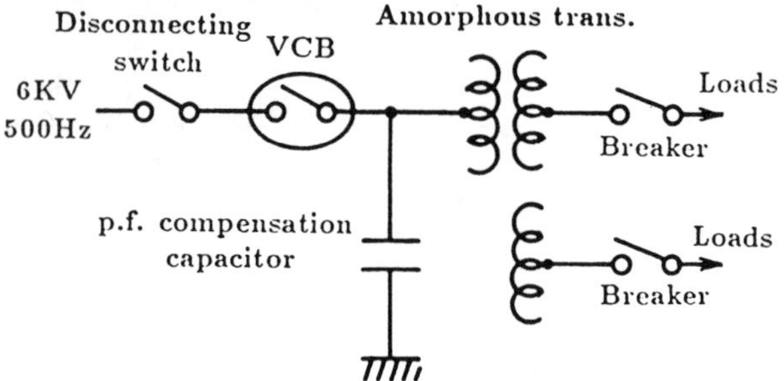

Fig.3 Small 500 Hz power-receiving apparatus.

Commercial Areas

Most of the loads in commercial areas are lighting apparatus and air conditioners. It is necessary to develop fluorescent lighting equipment and turbine pumps for condensation of air operating at 500 Hz. The efficiency can improved by 10 - 20 percent by use of the higher frequency. In addition, it is important large reduction in the size of electric equipment, since space saving in commercial areas is one of the most important objects.

Fig.3 illustrates the circuit of the power receiving apparatus of which most are vacuum circuit breaker and amorphous transformer. It can be made compact by a factor of 1/3 to 1/4.

Intelligent Buildings

The same benefits as above is available in the lighting apparatus and air conditioners. Moreover the power supply components of the computer can be made much smaller for the same capacity and rectified 500 Hz power requires significantly less filter capacitance, which is same for inverters. Additionally the electrical noise from the power source can be reduced by the use of cables for lines.

Lighting Apparatus

The use of 500 Hz power to fluorescent and mercury lamps(HDL) in highways or sports centers will result in dramatic reduction in the size and weight of the lighting apparatus and improve significantly the stability and efficiency. Moreover dimming of the lighting system becomes easily and economically. In this application frequency higher than 500 Hz may be also possible. However difficulty arises from the power transmission, and the further increase of the frequency can not be expected.

Quick Response DC Power Supply

It is clear that high power and quick response dc power supply using thyristor converter is available by use of 500 Hz power. Particularly quick response current control of the dc power supply becomes more easily by applying modern control theory such as deadbeat control.

3 Considerations on Selection of the Frequency

To select proper frequency, many considerations for needs are necessary. As mentioned earlier, the use of 500 Hz can realize many applications and satisfy their requirements today and in the near future. The following factors must be also considered to decide frequency.

Substituting the Use of Cycloconverters for PWM Inverters

A naturally commutated cycloconverter has high efficiency and reliability because it performs direct AC-AC conversion and natural commutation, which has been successfully used in high power applications. Since it consists of only switching devices and no passive components required, it is possible that the cycloconverter will be integrated by using hybrid IC techniques in the future. Consequently, this will make it compact and lower cost. However in general the output frequency of the cycloconverter is limited less than one-fourth of the input frequency. For this reason, at the commercial frequency the application of the cycloconverter has significantly restricted for low frequency use. In 500 Hz power source the output frequency can be up to 120 Hz which satisfies most of industrial drive applications. Therefore if 500 Hz power sources are available, the naturally commutated cycloconverters will be found wide applications by replacing PWM inverters which are very popularly employed for medium power applications.

Limitations of the Switching Devices

Generally in the case of supply to industrial zones, large capacity is required for the 500 Hz power system. Thus the switching device of the 500 Hz power converter must use thyristor or GTO. Thyristors with rating 2.5KV, 1.5KA and reverse bias time of $100\mu sec$ can operate under 800Hz. In other hand, GTO's with rating of 4.5KV, 1KA may be suit to switch under several hundreds Hz even if using proper snubber circuit.

Limitations of the Circuit Breakers

VCB(Vacuum circuit breaker) has dominated the application in medium voltage levels from 3 to 60 KV, and is expanding to ultra-high voltage applications with the continual improvement in voltage, current and dv/dt ratings. Particularly it has excellent high frequency interrupting characteristics.[2] Thus VCB is the best choice for the higher frequency system.

Generally VCB become reigniting as the frequency rises, but it will occur when frequency is higher than 1 KHz. However the lifetime of the breaker may be expanded because the arc time is shorten than that in commercial power system. Therefore the circuit breakers having extinguish chamber can be made compact and have longer lifetime.

Limitations of the Power Transmission Lines

At the higher frequency overhead lines can not be employed due to the larger inductance, and thereby power cables which have much lower inductance must be used to reduce the voltage drop of the transmission line. At the higher voltage levels of 40 - 50 KV, the conventional three phase cable can satisfy the power transmission within a 20Km by 20Km industrial zone, and at 6KV systems, it can be applied within a 1Km by 1Km commercial zone or intelligent building. The problem arises from the cable because the stability of power system may be reduced as frequency rises. For this reason it is desirable to select the frequency less than 800 Hz. However in the shorter distance transmission the much higher frequency may be possible.

Limitations Due to Iron Losses of the Core

At 500 Hz transformers and reactors using amorphous metal core can be made much lighter by a factor of 1/4 to 1/5. Too much reduction in size may not be possible even the frequency is arisen higher than 500 Hz, which reversely resulting in the increase of the voltage drop mentioned above.

In summary the suitable frequency range of several elements are shown in Fig.4. It is apparent that 500 Hz to 600 Hz may be the best choice for supply 20Km by 20Km industrial zones or 1Km by 1Km commercial areas. Frequency, however, should vary with the different loads' requirements. For instance, in small scale system 1 KHz may be the best choice rather than 500 Hz. In general the reasonable frequency seems to range 400 Hz to 1 KHz.

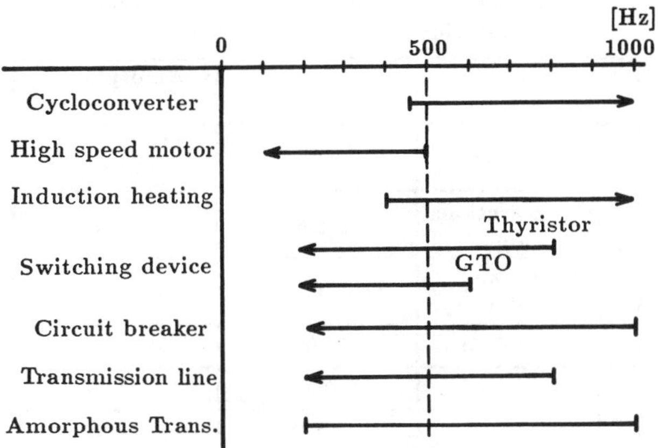

Fig.4 Frequency range for different elements.

Capacity : 15KVA

Primary voltage : 200V Secondary voltage : 200V

Iron loss : 0.9W/Kg % impedance : 4%

Fig.5 Three phase amorphous metal core transformer.

4 Development of an Amorphous Metal Core Transformer

Amorphous metal has been receiving increasing attention due to the low loss characteristics. As stated earlier, it has good characteristic even at high frequency, and can be realized much more effective use at the higher frequency than at 50/60 Hz. A 15 KVA amorphous metal core transformer for 500 Hz has been developed in this experiment as shown in Fig.5.

A comparison with one made of silicon steel as same specifications is shown in Tab.1. The use of amorphous metal core results in large reduction in the total weight and losses to 35 percent and to 67 percent, respectively. A conventional 15 KVA transformer at 50 Hz has weight of 120 Kg. Moreover the weight of the core can be made lighter than that used in the commercial 50 Hz by 20 to 25 percent. This concludes that the use of the higher frequency for amorphous cores causes high efficiency and saving materials.

Test results on the developed transformer at 500 Hz are as follows; the iron losses is reduced as much as 27.5W, and the magnetizing current is little only 86mA which is 0.29

Tab.1 Comparison of the amorphous metal and silicon steel transformers.

		Silicon steel	Amorphous metal
Core	Material	G6H	METGLAS 2605S2
	Cross-sectional area	$114 cm^2$	$39 cm^2$
	Max. flux density	1880 Gauss	4510 Gauss
Number of turns		42T/42T	51T/51T
Loss	Iron loss	88 W	27 W
	Copper loss	121 W	114 W
	Total loss	209 W	141 W
Total weight		106 Kg	37.6 Kg
Dimension		565, 310, 490, 110, 185	465, 280, 395, 75, 150

percent of the rated current. In addition, the efficiency of 98.6 percent at full load and the maximum of 98.9 percent are obtained.

5 Quick Response Thyristor Power Amplifiers

Use of Deadbeat Control

In order to obtain fast current response of the naturally commutated thyristor converter, deadbeat control strategy which is simple but has the fastest response can be applied.[3] The output voltage waveform e_c of the converter is shown in Fig.6, and the mean voltage $\overline{e_c}$ over a sampling interval T_s can be expressed approximately by the stepwise sample-hold wave shown as a dashed line in Fig.6. T_s is given by

$$T_s = 2\pi/\omega_s P_s \tag{1}$$

where ω_s is the angular frequency of the power source and P_s is the phase number of the converter. Considering a R-L series circuit as the load, of which the transfer function is given as

$$G(s) = 1/(1+s\tau) \qquad (\tau = L/R) \tag{2}$$

Fig.7 shows the block diagram of the converter for the minimum time control, in which if setting the gain constant K as

$$K = \frac{e^{-T_s/\tau}}{1-e^{-T_s/\tau}} \tag{3}$$

the deadbeat control can be performed, therefore the minimum time following characteristic without overshoot for the output current can be obtained.

Simulation Results

Fig.8(a) demonstrates the quick response of the output current obtained on a 6 pulse thyristor converter. Fig.8(b) shows

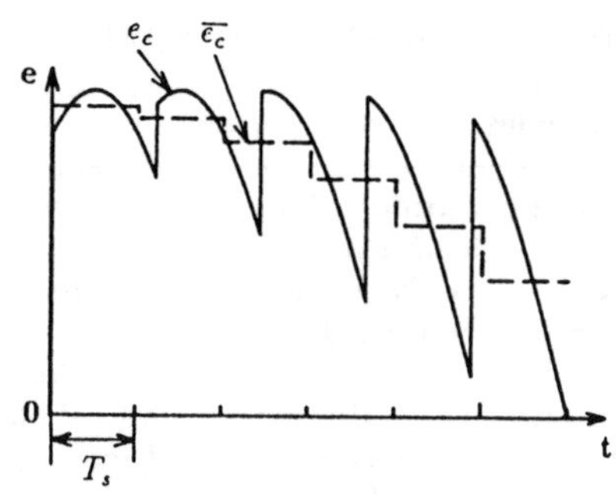

Fig.6 Sample-hold voltage waveform of thyristor converters.

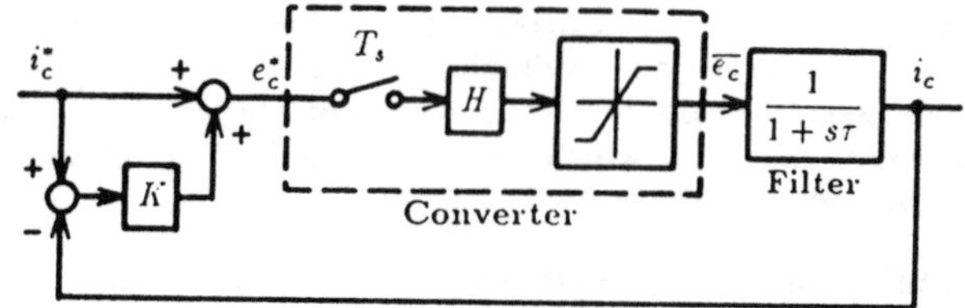

Fig.7 Block diagram of minimum time control.

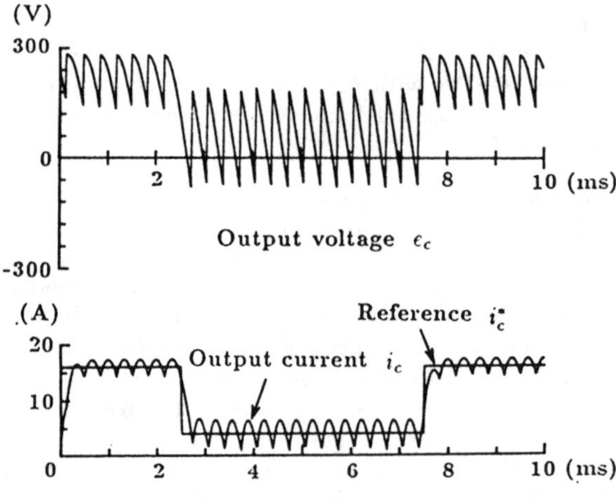

(a) Current response of the thyristor Converter

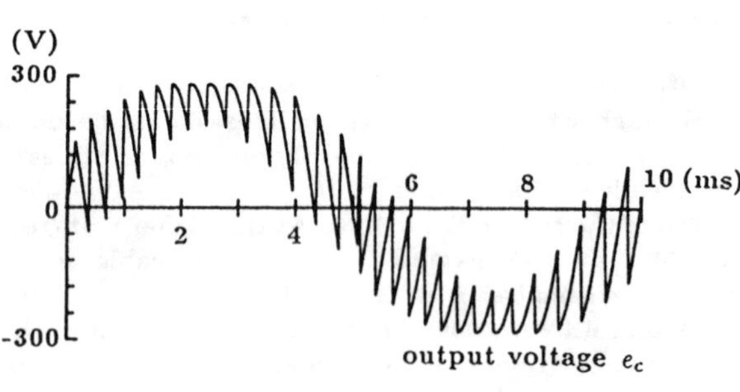

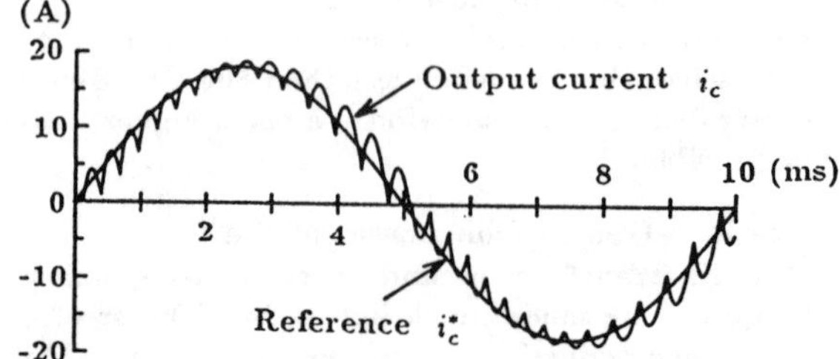

(b) Current response of the cycloconverter

Fig.8 Current response of thyristor converters using deadbeat control.

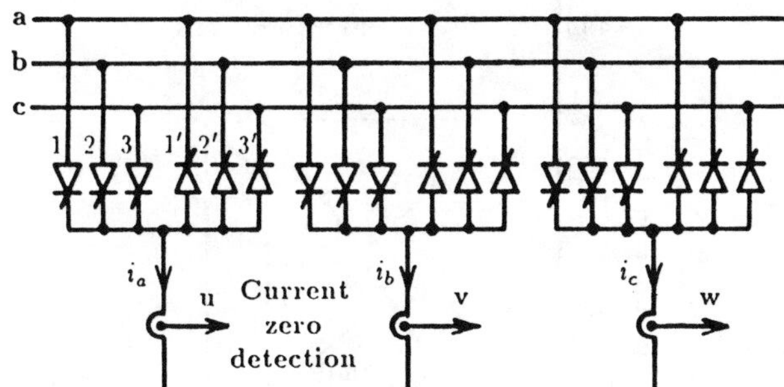

Fig.9 Main circuit of the cycloconverter.

the current following characteristic of a 6 pulse naturally commutated cycloconverter.

Microprocessor Direct Control for the Naturally commutated cycloconverter

Under medium capacity the transistor PWM inverters have dominated the applications at present. However the use of capacitors in the dc link of PWM inverters has caused troubles such as resulting harmonics in the line, shortening the lifetime and having bulky size. In other hand, as stated earlier, the naturally commutated cycloconverter has high efficiency and reliability. But in the commercial power system, the application is limited owing to its slow response. At 500 Hz system, it can replace the PWM inverter in many applications such as variable speed drives.

The gate control circuit for the cycloconverter is usually complicated. The use of microprocessors, however, can make it simple and compact. Higher speed for the microprocessor is required due to the higher frequency. This paper presents a 16 bit microprocessor (MC68000) direct gate control circuit.

Fig.9 illustrates the main circuit of the three phase cycloconverter with non-circulating current. It is necessary to detect the load current polarities for selection of the conduction between the positive and negative converters.

By applying the cosine wave phase control principle, to obtain a sinusoidal output voltage the firing angle is given by

$$\alpha = \pm \cos^{-1}(a \cdot \cos \omega_0 t) \qquad (4)$$

where a and ω_0 are the amplitude and frequency references, respectively. The sign $\pm$ depends on the polarity of the load current; $-$ for positive and $+$ for negative half cycle of the load current. The calculation of α can be rapidly carried out through the microprocessor by using table search techniques. Fig.10 shows the proposed microprocessor base gate control circuit for the three phase cycloconverter.

There are three modes of thyristor conducting in one period of the line voltage for positive and negative converters, and each mode is determined uniquely by $\alpha - \omega t$ as shown in Fig.11.[4] Consequently substituting ωt from α and transferring to the ROM address in which the corresponding switching pattern signal is stored, the firing pulse can be generated only by reading out from addressed ROM.[5]

To calculate ωt in the processor, it is digitized by dividing one cycle, i.e. 2π, by 96. Therefore ωt can be determined by counting the 96×500 Hz or 48 KHz pulse signal which is synchronized to the line frequency. This is accomplished by applying a 48 KHz interrupt signal to the CPU via interrupt level 1 to increment the software counter. To synchronize to the line voltage a zero-voltage detection circuit generates a pulse at $\alpha = 0$, applying the pulse to the CPU via interrupt level 2 resets the counter, i.e. ωt to zero. The software will not be further discussed here, however the calculation time of the microprocessor is $19.4\mu sec$ which is slightly less than one-96th of one period of line voltage i.e. $20.8\mu sec$.

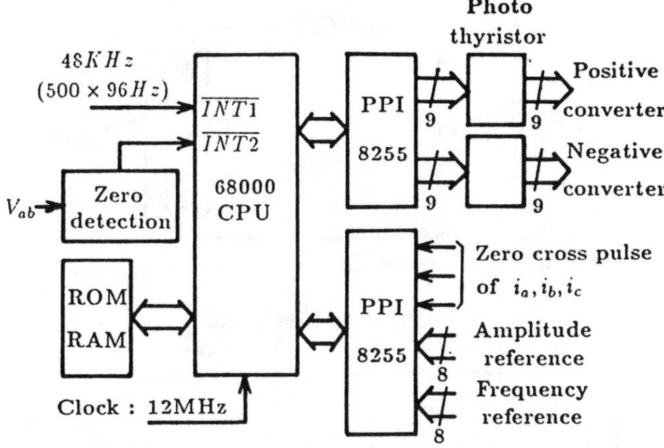

Fig.10 Microprocessor direct digital gate control circuit.

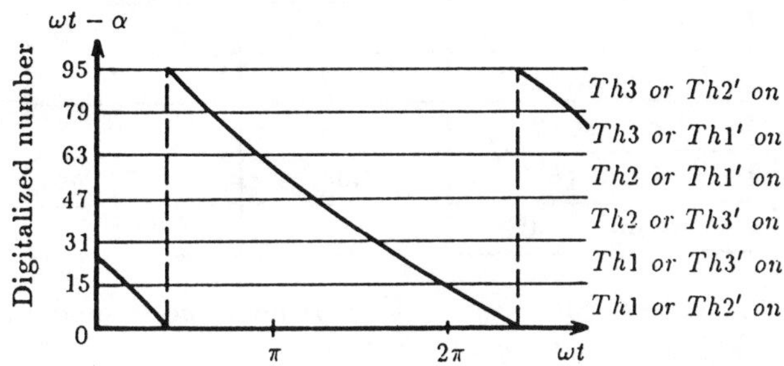

Fig.11 Method to generate firing pulse by $\omega t - \alpha$.

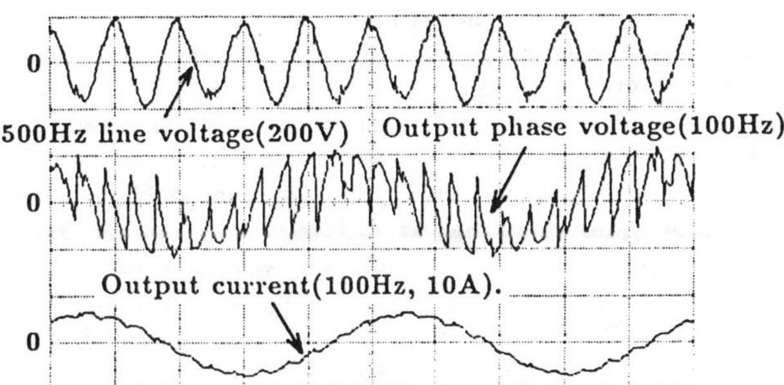

Fig.12 Output waveforms of the cycloconverter.

Typical output phase voltage and current waveforms obtained on a inductive load with $\cos\phi = 0.8$ are shown in Fig.12.

6 500 Hz Fluorescent Lighting Apparatus

Fig.13 shows the 500 Hz fluorescent lighting circuit in which a conventional 36W fluorescent tube and an amorphous metal core ballast are employed. The inductance of the ballast needed is reduced to about 1/10 of that in the commercial frequency because the frequency is increased by about 10 times. Therefore this results in dramatic reduction in the size and weight of the ballast. The use of amorphous metal core provides high efficiency and further reduce the size. A comparison of the ballasts between 50 Hz and 500 Hz is given in Tab.2. It can be seen that the losses of the ballast are much reduced by 70 percent for copper loss and by 80 percent for iron loss. In addition the size and weight of the ballast are decreased to 30 percent and 25 percent of the commercial ballast, respectively.

In general, luminous efficiency of a fluorescent tube can be improved as the frequency rises. This effect, however, did not appear at 500 Hz. Nevertheless the losses in the ballast can be decreased and thereby the total efficiency can

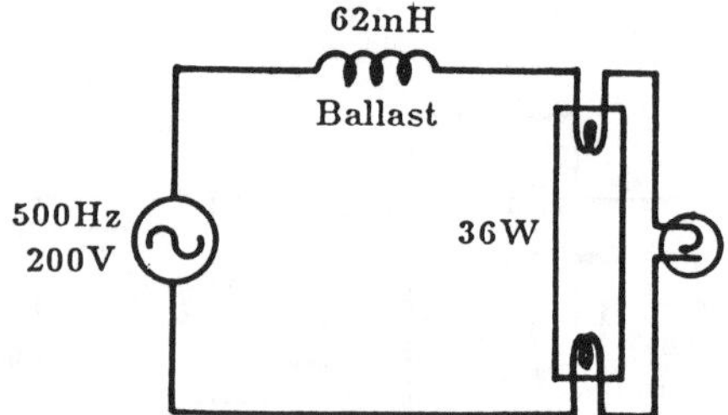

Fig.13 Experimental circuit for fluorescent lighting.

Tab.2 Comparison of 50Hz and 500Hz ballasts in fluorescent lighting.

Frequency	50 Hz	500 Hz
Rated current (A)	0.45	0.45
Number of turns (T)	1950	700
Inductance (mH)	610.0	62.0
Copper loss (W)	4.84	1.47
Iron loss (W)	20.4	4.4
Weight (Kg)	1.03	0.24
Volume (cm^3)	169.2	47.1

be improved. Moreover flicker is reduced and the stability of the tube is improved even at lower source voltage, which means dimming is possible by adjusting the applied voltage.

Fig.14 shows the intensity of illumination measured at the point 1m away from the tube vs. the input power in 50Hz and 500 Hz. It is clear that the total efficiency included the ballast at 500 Hz is higher that at 50 Hz, and is improved by 16 percent. In addition the minimum voltage at which the tube does not work is 127V which is much lower than 140V of 50 Hz. This shows that the dimming area of the tube at 500 Hz is wider than that at 50 Hz.

Finally the influence of the voltage waveform on the acoustic nose of the ballast is examined by applying square and sinusoidal voltages. In the former case, the acoustic nose is larger as $40.5dB$ because of many harmonics, in the later case, however, it is much less as about $34.5dB$ which is slight larger than the background noise of $33.2dB$. Therefore there is no problem in practical use of the 500 Hz fluorescent lighting at sinusoidal power sources.[6]

7 Soft Start of High Speed Induction Motors

The use of the 500 Hz power to induction motors can obtain very high speed. However the start of the motors at the higher frequency becomes difficult. Therefore it is necessary for starting of the motor to reduce the frequency applied to the motor by means of frequency changers. This can be accomplished by using the conventional thyristor ac voltage controller, as shown in Fig.15, which has been widely employed for saving energy throughout industry.

Fig.16 demonstrates the principle of frequency change by the voltage controller. Supposing the line voltage is expressed as

$$V_{uv} = V_m \sin \omega t \tag{5}$$

then the 'cosine crossing waves' are given by

$$V_{uv+} = V_m(\cos \omega t + 1)/2, \quad V_{uv+} = V_m(\cos \omega t - 1)/2 \tag{6}$$

where $\omega = 2\pi \times 500$ $[rad]$. The reference voltage is given by

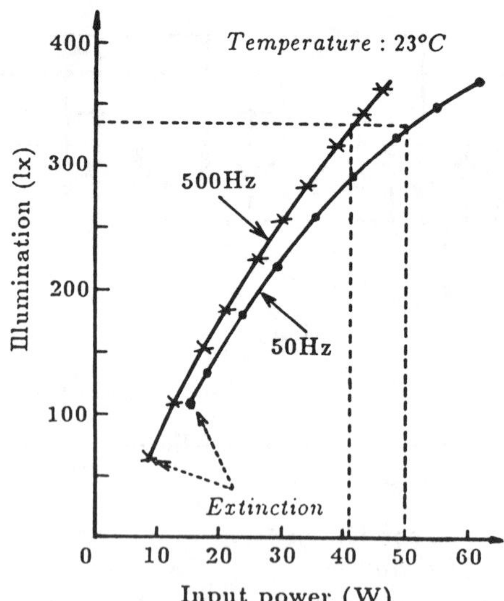

Fig.14 Illumination of the tube vs. the input power.

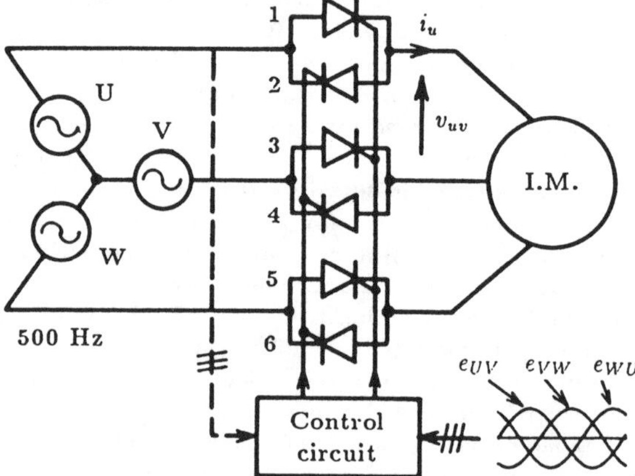

Fig.15 Soft-starter for high speed induction motors.

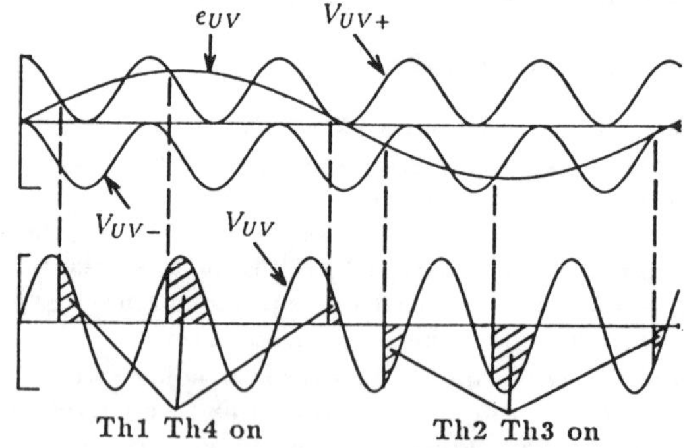

Fig.16 Principle of frequency change for the soft-starter.

$$e_{uv} = E_m \sin(\omega t/k) \tag{7}$$

Over the positive half cycle of the reference e_{uv}, comparing e_{uv} with V_{uv+} at the instant which $e_{uv} > V_{uv+}$ thyristor 1 and 4 are trigged, as the same way, over the negative half cycle of e_{uv}, thyristor 2 and 3 are trigged at instant which $V_{uv-} > e_{uv}$. Therefor the voltage and frequency applied to the motor can be simultaneously controlled so as to meet the V/f control strategy at starting of the motor. For instance, firstly set the frequency reference to $\omega/13$ and start the motor, after the speed of the motor reached the synchronous one, change the reference to $\omega/9$, then to $\omega/5$ and finally to ω. To make the current waveform inner-phase half-wave symmetry. k must be a odd integer. In addition, energy saving can be obtained

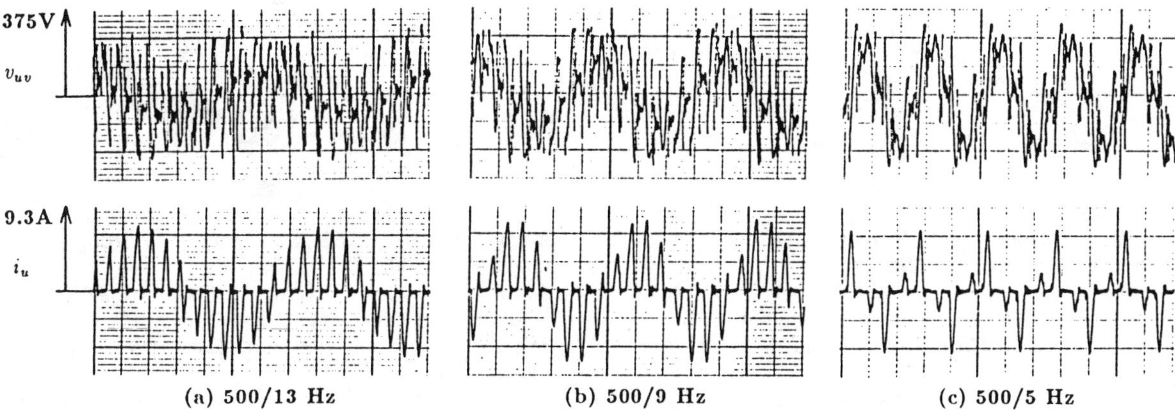

Fig.17 Typical stator voltage and current waveforms of the I.M..

by properly adjusting the amplitude of the applied stator voltage by means of the phase control at light load.[7] which frequently occurs for blowers and compressors in petroleum and chemical plants.[6]

Fig.17 shows typical stator voltage and current waveforms of the motor at the steady state. It can be seen the voltage and frequency are controlled.

8 Conclusion

This paper has presented a high frequency power system for supply to particular areas such as industrial zones, commercial areas, intelligent buildings and offices in which high efficiency, space saving and low weight are required. It is shown that the reasonable frequency seems to rangy from 400 Hz to 1 KHz.

A 500Hz power system suitable for a 20Km by 20Km industrial zone or 1Km by 1Km commercial areas is proposed and its applications are investigated. The advantages such as large reduction in the size and weight and high efficiency by use of the higher power to amorphous metal core transformers, naturally commutated cycloconverters and 500 Hz fluorescent lighting, and soft start of the high speed induction motor are experimentally demonstrated. The following conclusions have been drawn;

(1) Needs for the use of the higher frequency power exist in chemical plants, in which high speed induction motors can used for compressors, and in iron plants for induction heating.

(2) The proposed higher power system can be also effectively employed in commercial areas and intelligent buildings for fluorescent lighting apparatus and OA equipment.

(3) Vacuum circuit breaker, thyristors and amorphous material can be used more effectively than in the commercial power system.

(4) Distributed natural energy generation and cogeneration systems can be directly used for the energy source of the 500 Hz power system.

(5) At 500 Hz, very high speed by use of induction motor is available, therefore they can be used for to turbine compressors and high pressure pumps with dramatic reduction in the size and weight.

(6) Capacitors can be made much smaller as about 1/8 and low cost. Thus it can be economically used to improve the power factor of the loads which have lower power factor such as electric furnace.

(7) Large reduction with a factor of 1/3 to 1/4 in the size of the transformers and reactors is also possible.

(8) Stability and efficiency of the fluorescent lamps and mercury lamps can be improved and be made compact.

(9) Naturally commutated cycloconverters will replace PWM inverters in many applications offering high efficiency and reliability.

Finally the need for high quality power is increasing, and interfacing dispersed different frequency power systems such natural energy generation, cogeneration and energy storage systems to utilization equipment will become necessary. The proposed high frequency power system may be one of the most interesting approaches satisfying those requirements.

Acknowledgment

The authors wish to express their appreciation to Ms. Ikeshita, Ms. Tukahata and Ms. Sedoguti. Thanks are due to Ms. Nakamura and the Power Electronics members of Nagaoka University of Technology.

References

[1] Tanaka and Suzuki, "Ultra-high Speed Motor Drive System", The Journal of JIEE, Vol.105, No.1, Feb.,1985.

[2] Watanabe et al., "Resent trend of development and application of vacuum circuit breakers.", The Journal of JIEE, Vol.102, No.6, Jun., 1982.

[3] I. Takahashi et al., "High Speed Thyristor Power Amplifier Control for JT-60", Fusion Technology, Vol.1 1980, Commission of the European Communities.

[4] I. Takahashi and M. Yamane, "Multiparallel Asymmetrical Cycloconverter Having Improved Power Factor and Waveforms", IEEE Trans. Int. Appl. Vol.A-22.

[5] G.J. Su and I. Takahashi, "A 500 Hz Power System – Microprocessor Direct Gate Control of Naturally commutated Cycloconverter", 1989 National Convention Record I.E.E Japan, NO.5.

[6] I. Takahashi and G.J. Su, " A 500 Hz Power System", Tech. Commit. of Power Eng., JIEE, PE-88-82,1988. Nov./Dec. 1986.

[7] T. M. Rowan and T. A. Lipo, "A Quantitative Analysis of induction Motor Performance Improvement by SCR Voltage Control", IEEE Tran. Ind. Appl., Vol.IA-19,NO.4, Jul./Aug. 1983.

Selected Bibliography

[1] P. D. Ziogas, S. Manias, and E. P. Wiechmann, "Application of current source inverters in UPS systems," *IEEE Trans. Ind. Applicat.*, vol. IA-20, pp. 742-752, July/Aug. 1984.

[2] L. Gyugyi, "Power electronics in electric utilities: Static var compensators," *Proc. IEEE*, vol. 76, pp. 483-494, Apr. 1988.

[3] F. Nozari and H. S. Patel, "Power electronics in electric utilities: HVDC power transmission systems," *Proc. IEEE*, vol. 76, pp. 495-506, Apr. 1988.

[4] N. G. Hingorani, "Power electronics in electric utilities: Role of power electronics in future power systems," *Proc. IEEE*, vol. 76, pp. 481-482, Apr. 1988.

[5] L. Abraham, "Power electronics in German railway propulsion," *Proc. IEEE*, vol. 76, pp. 472-480, Apr. 1988.

[6] M. Hashii, K. Kousaka, and M. Kaimoto, "New approach to a high power GTO PWM inverter for ac motor drives," *IEEE/IAS Ann. Meet. Conf. Rec.*, pp. 467-472, 1985.

[7] L. Gyugyi and E. C. Strycula, "Active ac power filter," *IEEE/IAS Ann. Meet. Conf. Rec.*, pp. 529-535, 1976.

[8] E. Masada et al., "A study on the power supply for a superspeed maglev transport," *Int. Power Electron. Conf. Rec.*, Tokyo, 1990.

[9] W. Schumacher and W. Leonhard, "Transistor-fed ac servo-drive with microprocessor control," *Int. Power Electron. Conf. Rec.*, Tokyo, pp. 1465-1476, 1983.

[10] Y. Konishi et al., "Transistorized power supply for rolling stock," *Int. Power Electron. Conf. Rec.*, Tokyo, pp. 1321-1332, 1983.

[11] E. Sakoguchi et al., "A new inverter and control methods for induction cooking appliance," *Int. Power Electron. Conf. Rec.*, Tokyo, pp. 894-903, 1983.

[12] Y. Jifuku et al., "GTO inverter for adjustable speed ac motor drive system," *Int. Power Electron. Conf. Rec.*, Tokyo, pp. 418-425, 1983.

[13] R. Chauprade and A. Abbondanti, "Variable speed drives: Modern concepts and approaches," *IEEE/IAS Int. Semicond. Power Conv. Conf. Rec.*, pp. 20-37, 1982.

[14] S. Krauthamer, M. Gangal, and R. Das, "State-of-the-art of dc components for secondary power distribution on space station freedom," *IEEE Appl. Power Electron. Conf. Rec.*, pp. 18-32, 1990.

[15] A. M. Campos, R. Vivero, A. Quintero, and V. Serrano, "UPS system employing high frequency PWM techniques," *IEEE Appl. Power Electron. Conf. Rec.*, pp. 414-421, 1990.

[16] H. Le-Huy, P. Viarouge, and K. Slimani, "A current-controlled quasi-resonant converter for switched reluctance motor," *Proc. IECON'90*, pp. 1022-1028, 1990.

[17] M. Yatsu, K. Kuroki, M. Katoh, and M. Fujikura, "Three-phase 200 KVA UPS with IGBT consisting of high power factor converter and instantaneous waveform controlled HF PWM inverter," *Proc. IECON'90*, pp. 1057-1062, 1990.

[18] S. Vukosavic and V. R. Stefanović, "SRM inverter topologies: A comparative evaluation," *IEEE/IAS Ann. Meet. Conf. Rec.*, vol. 2, pp. 946-958, 1990.

[19] I. Takahashi, K. Amei, and Y. Itoh, "High performance and long life uninterruptible power source using a flywheel energy storage unit," *IEEE/IAS Ann. Meet. Conf. Rec.*, vol. 2., pp. 1049-1055, 1990.

[20] P. M. Espelage, J. M. Nowack, and L. H. Walker, "Symmetrical GTO current source inverter for wide speed range control of 2300 to 4160 volt, 350 to 7000 HP induction motors," *IEEE/IAS Ann. Meet. Conf. Rec.*, pp. 302-307, 1988.

[21] F. Z. Peng, H. Akagi, and A. Nabae, "A new approach to harmonic compensation in power systems," *IEEE/IAS Ann. Meet. Conf. Rec.*, pp. 874-880, 1988.

[22] R. L. Steigerwald, A. Ferraro, and F. C. Turnbull, "Application of power transistors to residential and intermediate rating photovoltaic array power conditioners," *IEEE/IAS Int. Semicond. Power Conv. Conf. Rec.*, pp. 84-96, 1982.

[23] Y. Yokoo et al., "High frequency inverter for induction heating equipment by using static induction transistor," *Proc. Powerconv. & Intelligent Motion*, pp. 101-108, 1988.

[24] T. Saijo, S. Koike, and S. Tadakuma, "Characteristics of linear synchronous motor drive cycloconverter for maglev vehicle ML-500 at Miyazaki test track," *IEEE Trans. Ind. Applicat.*, vol. IA-17, pp. 533-543, Sept/Oct. 1981.

Author Index

Subject Index

A

B

C

D

E

F

G

H

I

L

M

N

O

P

Q

R

S

T

U

V

W

Z

Editor's Biography

Bimal K. Bose (S'59–M'60–SM'78–F'89) received the B.E. degree from Calcutta University, Calcutta, India, in 1956, the M.S. degree from the University of Wisconsin, Madison, in 1960, and the Ph.D. degree from Calcutta University in 1966.

He was a member of the faculty at Calcutta University (Bengal Engineering College), where he was awarded the Premchand Roychand Scholarship and the Mouat Gold Medal for outstanding research contributions. In 1971, he joined Rensselaer Polytechnic Institute, Troy, NY, as a member of the faculty in the Electrical Engineering Department, where he was responsible for organizing the power electronics program for five years. From 1976 to 1987, he was a Research Engineer at the General Electric Research and Development Center, Schenectady, NY. In 1987, he joined the University of Tennessee, Knoxville, as Professor of Electrical Engineering (Condra Chair of Excellence in Power Electronics). He is also Distinguished Scientist in the EPRI-sponsored Power Electronics Applications Center in Knoxville, and a Senior Advisor to the Beijing Power Electronics Research and Development Center in China. He has served as a consultant in a number of industries, including the General Electric R&D Center, Bendix Corporation, Lutron Industries, PCI Ozone Corporation, and the Research Triangle Institute, and has visited a number of countries as a UN consultant. His research interests are power converters, ac drives, microcomputer control, and application of fuzzy logic and expert systems in power electronics. He has published over 90 papers and holds 16 U.S. patents (3 more pending). He is the author of the book *Power Electronics and AC Drives* (Prentice Hall, 1986), which has been translated into Japanese and Chinese. In addition, he edited the IEEE books *Adjustable Speed AC Drive Systems* (1981) (translated into Chinese) and *Microcomputer Control of Power Electronics and Drives* (1987). He also contributed the section on ''AC Drives'' in *Systems and Control Encyclopedia* (New York: Pergamon, 1987).

Dr. Bose is Chairman of the IEEE Industrial Power Converter Committee, Associate Editor of the *IEEE Transactions on Industrial Electronics*, and is Power Electronics Committee Chairman of the Industrial Electronics Society. He has been a keynote speaker at a number of national and international conferences and has served on the committees of a large number of professional organizations. He is listed in *Who's Who in Technology*, *International Who's Who in Engineering*, *Personalities in America*, *Biography International*, *Directory of World Researchers*, *Leading Consultants in Technology*, and *Who's Who in Electromagnetics*. The Institute of Electronics and Telecommunication Engineers, India, gives the Bimal Bose Award in Power Electronics annually to an Indian engineer for outstanding contributions in power electronics. Dr. Bose is also a recipient of the GE Publication Award and the Silver Patent Medal.